30TH EUROPEAN SYMPOSIUM ON COMPUTER AIDED PROCESS ENGINEERING

PART B

30TH EUROPEAN SYMPOSIUM ON COMPUTER AIDED PROCESS ENGINEERING

PART B

Edited by

Sauro Pierucci
AIDIC Servizi s.r.l.,
Milano, Italy,
sauro.pierucci@polimi.it

Flavio Manenti
SuPER Team, Sustainable Process Engineering Research
Dipartimento di Chimica, Materiali e Ingegneria Chimica,
Politecnico di Milano, Milano, Italy,
flavio.manenti@polimi.it

Giulia Luisa Bozzano
SuPER Team, Sustainable Process Engineering Research
Dipartimento di Chimica, Materiali e Ingegneria Chimica,
Politecnico di Milano, Milano, Italy,
giulia.bozzano@polimi.it

Davide Manca
PSE-Lab - Process Systems Engineering Laboratory,
Dipartimento di Chimica, Materiali e Ingegneria Chimica,
Politecnico di Milano, Italy,
davide.manca@polimi.it

ELSEVIER

Amsterdam – Boston – Heidelberg – London – New York – Oxford
Paris – San Diego – San Francisco – Singapore – Sydney – Tokyo

Elsevier
Radarweg 29, PO Box 211, 1000 AE Amsterdam, Netherlands
The Boulevard, Langford Lane, Kidlington, Oxford OX5 1GB, UK
50 Hampshire Street, 5th Floor, Cambridge, MA 02139, USA

Notices
Knowledge and best practice in this field are constantly changing. As new research and experience
broaden our understanding, changes in research methods, professional practices, or medical treatment
may become necessary.

Practitioners and researchers must always rely on their own experience and knowledge in evaluating
and using any information, methods, compounds, or experiments described herein. In using such
information or methods they should be mindful of their own safety and the safety of others, including
parties for whom they have a professional responsibility.

To the fullest extent of the law, neither the Publisher nor the authors, contributors, or editors, assume
any liability for any injury and/or damage to persons or property as a matter of products liability,
negligence or otherwise, or from any use or operation of any methods, products, instructions, or ideas
contained in the material herein.

British Library Cataloguing in Publication Data
A catalogue record for this book is available from the British Library

Library of Congress Cataloging-in-Publication Data
A catalog record for this book is available from the Library of Congress

ISBN (Part B): 978-0-12-823512-6
ISBN (Set) :   978-0-12-823377-1
ISSN: 1570-7946

For information on all Elsevier publications visit our
website at https://www.elsevier.com/

Working together
to grow libraries in
developing countries

www.elsevier.com • www.bookaid.org

Publisher: Susan Dennis
Acquisition Editor: Kostas Marinakis
Editorial Project Manager: Lena Sparks
Production Project Manager: Paul Prasad Chandramohan
Designer: Greg Harris

Typeset by SPi Global, India

Contents

Sauro Pierucci, Flavio Manenti, Giulia Bozzano, Davide Manca (Eds.)
Proceedings of the 30th European Symposium on Computer Aided Process Engineering
(ESCAPE30), May 24-27, 2020, Milano, Italy. © 2020 Elsevier B.V. All rights reserved.
http://dx.doi.org/10.1016/B978-0-12-823377-1.50115-4

A Two-stage Stochastic Programming Model to Determine the Optimal Screening Strategy for Colorectal Cancer

David Young, Selen Cremaschi[*]

Department of Chemical Engineering, Auburn University, Auburn, AL 36849, USA
Szc0113@Auburn.edu

Abstract

Screening for colorectal cancer (CRC) is an effective way to drastically reduce the impact of the disease or prevent it altogether. This paper presents a stochastic mathematical programming model to determine the optimal screening strategy for CRC of a given population. The objective of the model is to maximize the expected quality adjusted life years an individual would gain by following the optimum screening strategy. The model incorporates the uncertainty of CRC progression through the use of the time taken to progress to the various stages of the disease. The data to model the uncertainty of the progression of CRC within an individual was obtained from a continuous time simulation. The solution of the stochastic programming model for the average-risk male population yielded an expected gain of 0.2384 quality-adjusted life years with three colonoscopies.

Keywords: Colorectal cancer, stochastic programming, cancer screening

1. Introduction

According to the World Health Organization, colorectal cancer (CRC) was the 3rd most common, as well as the 2nd most deadly, form of cancer in the world in 2018 (World Health Organization, 2019). The lethality of CRC increases drastically as the disease spreads throughout the entire body, with the 5-years survival rate of the diagnosis at the most advanced cancer stage being 14 %, whereas diagnosis at the less advanced stages average to a 5-year survival rate of 80 % (National Cancer Institute, 2019). There is also a significant economic burden due to CRC. It has been estimated that CRC related costs will be 17 billion USD for the US alone in 2020 (Mariotto et al., 2011). Therefore, early detection of CRC can drastically reduce both the lethality and the economic burden of the disease. The process of testing asymptomatic individuals for the presence of CRC, or its precursor adenomas, is known as screening.

When screening for CRC, there are a number of possible test types to use, each with their own advantages and drawbacks. These tests can be placed into two main categories, visual and stool-based tests. The visual tests, e.g., colonoscopy, sigmoidoscopy or computed tomographic colonography, are generally more accurate than the stool based tests, but considered to be more of a burden on the patient (Issa and Noureddine, 2017). The stool based tests, e.g., FIT, gFOBT or MT-sDNA, are less accurate but less burdensome (Issa and Noureddine, 2017). Four components define a screening strategy: screening (1) starting age (2) test type(s), (3) frequency, and (4) ending age. The current screening strategy suggestions for the US are presented in a report by the US Preventative Services Task Force (USPSTF) and were determined through a combination of expert opinions and simulation evaluations (Bibbins-Domingo et al., 2016).

The ideal outcome for screening is to identify the precursors of CRC to prevent CRC from developing in the first place. The most common pathway for the development of CRC is known as the adenoma-carcinoma sequence (Loeve et al., 2004). This pathway, depicted in Figure 1, begins with a healthy individual developing a precancerous lesion known as an adenoma. As the adenoma grows, the likelihood of it transitioning into a cancerous state increases with the adenoma's size. However, it has been observed that some cases of CRC occur with no visible adenomas present (Soetikno et al., 2008), which is represented by the pathway from a flat adenoma to a cancerous state in Figure 1. It should also be noted that not all adenomas proceed to a cancerous state within an individual's life. Although the general progression of CRC is known, the exact transition rates are not known with certainty.

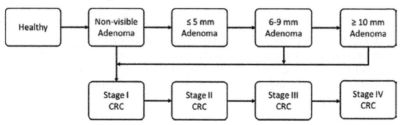

Figure 1 Adenoma-carcinoma sequence

Numerous studies have been conducted to evaluate various screening strategies for CRC. To account for the uncertain nature of CRC progression, researchers turn to the use of microsimulations. Microsimulations are models used to study the population level trends of an applied policy through the simulation of a large number of unique entities and applying the same policy across the population (Orcutt, 1957). When used for evaluating screening strategies for CRC, microsimulations treat the strategies as the policies applied to the population with each individual demonstrating a different progression of CRC. Cost-effectiveness metric is a common approach to compare screening strategies for a given population. The metric measures the total cost for gaining an additional quality adjusted life year for a population, where a quality adjusted life year (QALY) is a discounted measure of quality of life based on an individual's health state. For example, in a recent study, Haug *et al.* (2016) investigated the cost effectiveness of a hypothetical screening test and FOBT. The hypothetical test had a higher sensitivity for detecting CRC but could not detect adenomas. It was found that the hypothetical test was not cost effective compared to FOBT. The study concluded that new tests should be able to detect the presence of adenomas to be considered an effective screening test. However, it is computationally prohibitive to analyze all potential screening strategies using simulation-based what-if analysis. The most extensive of the cost-effectiveness studies (Knudsen et al., 2016) evaluated around only 11 % of the potential screening strategies defined by the range of starting and ending ages as well as the range of the screening frequency. Therefore, there is no guarantee that the strategies deemed the best are the optimal, or near optimal, screening strategies.

This paper introduces a mathematical programming model to determine the optimal screening strategy for CRC using a two-stage stochastic programming (TSSP) model. The goal of the TSSP is to determine a screening strategy that maximizes the expected QALY gained by a population. As a case study, we utilize data generated by a microsimulation model to construct our uncertain distributions for the TSSP, and evaluate the effect of number of screenings in an individual's lifetime on the optimal screening strategy.

2. Problem statement and formulation

The objective of the TSSP model is to maximize the expected value of the total quality adjusted life years (QALY) gained from screening, by identifying which screening test type and at what age a screening test should occur for a given population. The identified screening strategy, X, is the first-stage decisions of the model, with the resulting life span from screening, Y, representing the fixed recourse actions for the TSSP. The uncertain parameter sets of the model, θ and τ, represent the ages at which CRC progresses to the next state and the ages of death from both non-CRC and CRC sources. The different potential sources of death are described through set D. Health states are defined with set H, where each element corresponds to a health state in Figure 1. The scenarios in which the uncertainties are realized represent individuals within a population. The scenarios are generated through sampling from distributions that describe at what age the individual progresses to the next health state. These ages are then converted into a $|H|x|A|$ or $|D|x|A|$ matrix of binary values to describe the progression through the various health states or death states for that scenario, respectively.

The deterministic equivalent of the two-stage stochastic program, which is a mixed integer linear programming model, is given in Figure 2, along with the corresponding nomenclature. The value for expected QALY gained is calculated in Eqn. (1), in which the difference from the health states for the screened, Y, and unscreened, θ, lifetime of an individual are weighted according to the health state specific utility factor, C_h, with a disutility, $Dis_{h,t}$, of the screen tests performed on the individual. The effects of the screening decisions, X, are enforced through fixed recourse actions, Eqns. (2)-(18), modifying an individual's lifetime given the health state they are in at the time a screening action is taken. The state an individual is screened is determined through Eqns. (2)-(4). The screening result, ν, for the first test performed is enforced through the product of the screening decision and the unscreened lifetime health matrix, θ, in Eqn. (2). Subsequent screening results are enforced through Eqn. (3), with the additional term disallowing positive screens, $\nu=1$, for cases in which the first screening test returned a positive result for a health state other than healthy. Eqn. (4) allows the screening results to only identify one health state per screening of previously healthy individuals. The ages at or after which a positive result is obtained for a screening test are tracked through Eqns. (5)-(10). Eqns. (5) and (6) track the results from the first screening test, identifying if the individual has a screening test that detected a health state other than healthy at or prior to the specified age. Eqns. (7) and (8) provide a lower bound for the results of the subsequent screening tests with an additional term to disallow multiple positive screens, with an upper bound for the screening results enforced in Eqns. (9) and (10). The ages at which an individual is no longer living, ξ, is evaluated through Eqns. (11)-(13), where Eqns. (11) and (12) set the lower bounds for the ages of death from various sources, and Eqn. (13) sets the upper bound on ξ at a given age. Finally, the individuals' new lifetimes are constructed through Eqns. (14)-(18), where Eqn. (14) tracks the health state of healthy for the individual, allowing the individual to return to healthy state if a positive screening test occurs while the individual is within the adenoma health state. Eqn. (15) corresponds to the health states of adenoma and undetected CRC stages, in which once the state is detected via screening, the individual is no longer within that state and shifts to healthy or clinically detected CRC states, respectively. Eqn. (16) enforces the states associated with clinically detected CRC, where if an individual has a positive screening result within an undetected CRC stage, that individual then has the state set to clinical stages disallowing the further progression of CRC. The ages at which the health state is at death is tracked via Eqn. (17), and Eqn. (18) requires the individual to be at only one health state at each given age. Eqn. (19) allows only one screening test type per year. The ordering of the screening tests is enforced through Eqn. (20), requiring the second screening test to occur at an age after the first test, etc. Finally, Eqns. (21)-(29) are implemented to introduce variables, η, ω, and φ to linearize the nonlinear relationships of the "and" binary operator. The variable η introduced through Eqns. (21)–(23) are used to remove the multiplication of binary variables v and ψ through exact linearization. Similarly, ω and φ are introduced in Eqns. (24)-(26) and (27)-(29) to remove the multiplication of ξ by ψ and η by ξ via exact linearization respectively.

Figure 2 TSSP formulation of determining screening decisions for detecting CRC

3. Case study

We use the TSSP formulation of the CRC screening planning problem applied to data generated from a CRC microsimulation based on the CRC-SPIN model (Rutter and Savarino, 2010) from the US's Nation Institute of Health's cancer modeling consortium, CISNET. The uncertain distributions for constructing θ and τ were created by fitting distributions for the ages at which different health states were reached using the microsimulation to generate 40 million individuals. This case study aims to understand the effect of the maximum number of screens within an individual's lifetime when incorporating data from a microsimulation for uncertain parameters. For this study, we only consider a single test type, colonoscopy. Additionally, we assume that the accuracy of the test is 100%, and individuals are perfectly compliant. The screening window is set to ages 20 to 100. The model is constructed and solved within Pyomo 5.6.6.

3.1. Maximum screens within a lifetime

The TSSP model requires that the maximum number of screens within a lifetime, $|\mathbf{Z}|$, to be specified. The maximum allotted screens were raised from one to five screens to evaluate its impact on the optimum solution and the model's computational complexity. The same 100 scenarios were used for all five cases, and the model was solved using an Intel® Xeon® 20-core 2.30 GHz processor with CPLEX 12.6.3.0. Table 1 presents the optimal solution, the corresponding objective function value, model size and solution time based on the maximum number of possible screens, $|\mathbf{Z}|$. As the value of $|\mathbf{Z}|$ increases, the ages of screening expand to later years, as the largest gain in life years can be attributed to the individuals who develop CRC early on in life. This trend can be seen through the expected QALY gained, in which the incremental gain decreases as the value of $|\mathbf{Z}|$ increases. As can be seen from Table 1, the number of constraints and variables increases linearly with the increase in the maximum number of screens, which is expected. The solution time grows exponentially with the increase in the maximum number of screens.

Table 1 TSSP model results for an increasing number of total screening tests in a lifetime

$|\mathbf{Z}|$	Age(s) to screen	E(QALYG)	Variables	Constraints	Solution time (s)
1	48	0.1438	292,781	713,902	4.09
2	44,72	0.2384	488,362	1,290,284	15.20
3	44,72,91	0.2386	683,944	1,866,666	52.89
4	44,72,91	0.2386	879,524	2,443,048	111.45
5	44,72,91	0.2386	1,075,105	3,019,430	251.77

Given the 100 scenarios, we observe diminishing returns in the benefits of allowing additional screenings. There is a 66 % increase in the expected QALY gained when the maximum number of screens, $|\mathbf{Z}|$, is increased from one to two. However, when increasing the maximum number of screens from two to three there is a less than 0.1 % increase in QALY gained, with no gain for increasing the maximum number of allowable screens any further. With a single screening, the optimum age is 48. However, the age for the first screening is lower for more than one screening. With the ability to screen more times within a life, the optimal strategy can allow for an early screening to maximize the life gain for individuals that develop cancer early on in their life. With the inclusion of a third screening, the first two ages for screening remain the same for the case of two screens. This behavior explains the small increase in the expected QALY gained, allowing for the prevention of the cases of CRC for the older population, which only provides a marginal benefit from a quality of life standpoint.

4. Conclusions and future recommendations

This paper presented a TSSP model to determine the optimal screening strategy for colorectal cancer within a population. The uncertainty in the TSSP is the progression of CRC. The model was solved for a range of the maximum number of screens within an individual's lifetime. As the number of maximum screens increased, the model size only had a linear increase while the solution time encountered an exponential growth. The optimum solutions for each number of maximum allotted screens showed diminishing returns with the increase in the total number of maximum screens. This behaviour is expected to be seen, as for the majority of the population, who never develop colorectal cancer, screening is a burden on life rather than providing a benefit. Additionally, as more were allowed, screens late in life were recommended, though the gain in quality of life was minimal.

In the formulation of the model, many simplifying assumptions have been made which will lead to the determined screening strategies to not translate well to clinical settings. As future work, the model will rectify the assumptions of perfect compliance and perfect test accuracy through the incorporation of uncertainty for both screening test adherence and test accuracy. The result of a test will become uncertain and depend on the health state of the individual at the time of screening, the test type chosen, and the individual themselves, and the uncertainty for test adherence will depend both on the individual and the test type chosen.

References

Bibbins-Domingo, K., Grossman, D.C., Curry, S.J., Davidson, K.W., Epling, J.W., Garc\'\ia, F.A.R., Gillman, M.W., Harper, D.M., Kemper, A.R., Krist, A.H., others, 2016. Screening for colorectal cancer: US Preventive Services Task Force recommendation statement. Jama 315, 2564–2575.

Haug, U., Knudsen, A.B., Lansdorp-vogelaar, I., Kuntz, K.M., Baden-wuerttemberg, C.R., Cancer, G., Hospital, M.G., 2016. Development of new non-invasive tests for colorectal cancer screening: The relevance of information on adenoma detection 136, 2864–2874. https://doi.org/10.1002/ijc.29343.Development

Issa, I.A., Noureddine, M., 2017. Colorectal cancer screening/: An updated review of the available options 23, 5086–5096. https://doi.org/10.3748/wjg.v23.i28.5086

Knudsen, A.B., Zauber, A.G., Rutter, C.M., Naber, S.K., Doria-Rose, V.P., Pabiniak, C., Johanson, C., Fischer, S.E., Lansdorp-Vogelaar, I., Kuntz, K.M., 2016. Estimation of Benefits, Burden, and Harms of Colorectal Cancer Screening Strategies: Modeling Study for the US Preventive Services Task Force. JAMA 315, 2595–2609. https://doi.org/10.1001/jama.2016.6828

Loeve, F., Boer, R., Zauber, A.G., Van Ballegooijen, M., Van Oortmarssen, G.J., Winawer, S.J., Habbema, J.D.F., 2004. NATIONAL POLYP STUDY DATA/: EVIDENCE FOR REGRESSION OF, International Journal of Cancer. https://doi.org/10.1002/ijc.20277

Mariotto, A.B., Robin Yabroff, K., Shao, Y., Feuer, E.J., Brown, M.L., 2011. Projections of the cost of cancer care in the United States: 2010-2020. J. Natl. Cancer Inst. 103, 117–128. https://doi.org/10.1093/jnci/djq495

National Cancer Institute, 2019. Cancer Intervention and Surveillance Modeling Network (CISNET) [WWW Document]. URL https://cisnet.cancer.gov/ (accessed 2.27.19).

Orcutt, G.H., 1957. A new type of socio-economic system. Rev. Econ. Stat. 116–123.

Rutter, C.M., Savarino, J.E., 2010. An evidence-based microsimulation model for colorectal cancer: Validation and application. Cancer Epidemiol. Biomarkers Prev. 19, 1992–2002. https://doi.org/10.1158/1055-9965.EPI-09-0954

Soetikno, R.M., Kaltenbach, T., Rouse, R. V, Park, W., Maheshwari, A., Sato, T., Matsui, S., Friedland, S., 2008. Prevalence of Nonpolypoid (Flat and Depressed) Colorectal Neoplasms in Asymptomatic and Symptomatic Adults. JAMA 299, 1027–1035. https://doi.org/10.1001/jama.299.9.1027

World Heath Organization, 2019. Cancer [WWW Document]. URL https://www.who.int/news-room/fact-sheets/detail/cancer (accessed 2.27.19)

Sauro Pierucci, Flavio Manenti, Giulia Bozzano, Davide Manca (Eds.)
Proceedings of the 30th European Symposium on Computer Aided Process Engineering
(ESCAPE30), May 24-27, 2020, Milano, Italy. © 2020 Elsevier B.V. All rights reserved.
http://dx.doi.org/10.1016/B978-0-12-823377-1.50116-6

Beyond OPOSPM: A Corrected Maximum Entropy Weibull Distribution for Solving Population Balances

Menwer Attarakih[a], Hans-Joerg Bart[b]

[a]*The University of Jordan, School of Engineering, Department of Chemical Engineering, 11942 Amman, Jordan*
[b]*Chair of Separation Sciences and Technology, The University of Kaiserslautern, 67653 Kaiserslautern, Germany*
m.attarakih@ju.edu.jo

Abstract

The Population Balance Equation is a transport equation which accommodates the evolution of particle size distribution due to convection, nucleation, growth, breakage and coagulation in space-time with no general analytical solution. As a reduced model, OPOSPM is a two-moment model for solving this equation and finds its way in modelling real chemical engineering equipment ranging from pilot extraction columns to annular centrifugal extractors with no fundamental principle to predict the full-size distribution. To overcome this problem, we decoded the underlying distribution that is consistent with the two moments of OPOSPM by maximizing the Shannon entropy. The analytical form of this distribution is found to be a Weibull distribution. This distribution is evolved by the two moments of OPOSPM which may move faster or slower than the exact solution. To correct the prior Weibull distribution, we minimized the relative entropy as represented by the Kullback-Leibler divergence (KLD) with Weibull distribution as the most uncommitted prior probability distribution. The posterior distribution, viewed as a correction to the prior Weibull distribution, is found by expanding the minimum KLD solution using a set of orthogonal Legendre polynomials. This sequence of continuous approximations is found to converge exponentially to the exact solution in the sense of RMSE, KLD and mean properties.

Keywords: OPOSPM, Maximum Entropy, Kullback-Leibler Divergence, Weibull.

1. Introduction

Physical and engineering sciences which are discrete either at the micro or macroscopic levels are of great theoretical and practical applications. The evolution of these systems is governed by a Boltzmann-like equation which is coined as the population balance equation (Ramkrishna and Singh, 2014). The PBE is known to admit analytical solution only for a few cases with restricted forms of interaction kernels. As a special case of the discrete sectional quadrature method of moments (SQMOM) (Attarakih et al., 2009), the reduced two-equation model OPOSPM (One Primary and One Secondary Particle Method) for solving the PBE finds its way in modelling real chemical engineering equipment ranging from pilot extraction columns to annular centrifugal extractors used to recover spent nuclear fuels and online monitoring and analysis of the multiphase flow behaviour in industrial and chemical engineering equipment (Wardle, 2013, Mickler et al., 2014, Attarakih et al., 2019, Schaefer et al., 2019). In spite of this, OPOSPM like other moment methods, fails to predict the full-size distribution which is vital for online control purposes (Mickler et al., 2014) and to evaluate the particle fluxes at zero particle size in cases such as droplet evaporation. To overcome this problem, we used the Shannon maximum entropy method to decoded the underlying distribution, which is consistent with the two moments of OPOSPM, namely the total number and volume concentrations of the particulate system. The analytical form of this distribution is found to be the well-known Weibull distribution. Generally speaking, this distribution needs further corrections for complicated shapes of the evolving number concentration function in space and time. To accomplish this, the KLD is minimized to extract the OPOSPM corrected functional.

2. Solution of the PBE using the corrected Weibull distribution method

In one dimensional particle property space the PBE which takes into account particle growth (rate G), breakage (frequency Γ) and coagulation frequency (ω) is written as:

$$\frac{\partial f(x,\mathbf{r},t)}{\partial t} + \nabla \cdot (\langle u \rangle f(x,\mathbf{r},t)) + \frac{\partial (G(x,S)f(x,\mathbf{r},t))}{\partial x} = R\{f\} \tag{1}$$

$$R\{f\} = -\Gamma f(x,\mathbf{r},t) + \int_x^\infty \upsilon(x')\Gamma(x',S)\beta(x,x')f(x',\mathbf{r},t)dx'$$
$$- f(x,\mathbf{r},t)\int_0^\infty \omega(x,y)f(y,\mathbf{r},t)dy + \frac{1}{2}\int_0^\infty \omega(x,y)f(y,\mathbf{r},t)f(x-y,\mathbf{r},t)dy \tag{2}$$

where $f(x,\mathbf{r},t)$ is the number density concentration as function of particle size (x), physical space vector ($\mathbf{r}$), time (t) and $\langle u \rangle$ is the mean particle velocity vector in physical space which is function of particle size and other continuous environment variables S. During growth the particles undergo relatively slow process relative to the instantaneous breakage with daughter particle distribution $\beta(x,x')$ and mean particle number $\upsilon(x')$, while the binary coagulation frequency is $\omega(x,y, S)$ between particle of sizes x and y.

2.1. OPOSPM: A reduced population balance model

The OPOSPM transport model consists of two equations one for the dispersed particulate phase volume concentration (α) and the total number concentration (N). The transport equation for (α) is derived from Eqs(1) and (2) by mathematically representing the number density function by a single Dirac delta function centered at particle volume $v(d_{30})$: $f=N\delta(x-v(d_{30}))$, and by multiplying Eqs.(1) and (2) by x and integrating both sides with respect to x from 0 to ∞ one gets (Attarakih et al., 2013):

$$\frac{\partial \alpha}{\partial t} + \nabla \cdot (\langle u \rangle \alpha) = G(d_{30},S)N \tag{3}$$

On the other hand, the number concentration transport equation is derived by setting: $f = N\delta(x-v(d_{30}))$ and integrating both sides of Eqs.(5) and (6) with respect to x from 0 to ∞ to get:

$$\frac{\partial N}{\partial t} + \nabla \cdot (\langle u \rangle N) = (\upsilon(d_{30}) - 1)\Gamma(d_{30},S)N - \frac{1}{2}\omega(d_{30},d_{30},S)N^2 \tag{4}$$

The source term in Eq.(3) takes into account particle growth while that in Eq.(4) accounts for the net total number produced by particle breakage and coagulation. It is clear that the particle breakage is linear in N while particle coagulation is a second-order process in terms of N. Both breakage and coagulation frequencies are functions of d_{30}.

2.2. Derivation of OPOSPM-Weibull distribution using the MaxEnt Method

The OPOSPM loses the particle density concentration because of averaging (*f*) over the particle property space where the reconstruction of (*f*) in simple or complex physical space domains is by no means trivial (Gzyl and Tagliani, 2010). In theoretical physics literature, this problem is usually encountered and is known as the moment problem which is faced by the uniqueness of distribution reconstruction. To overcome the uniqueness problem, the maximum entropy method is used to reconstruct a continuous number concentration function constrained by the OPOSPM transported moments (α and N). By maximizing the Shannon entropy, one gets a distribution that is statistically most likely to occur (Gzyl and Tagliani, 2010). The result is a solution of constrained convex NLP which is given by the following optimal functional:

$$f(x,\mathbf{r},t) = p(x)\exp\!\left(\lambda_0(\mathbf{r},t) + \lambda_3(\mathbf{r},t)x^3\right) \tag{5}$$

In Eq.(5) λ is a vector of Lagrange multipliers that are derived by matching the moments of Eq.(5) to those found from OPOSPM model; namely, α and N. The preexponential $p(x)$ is particle property space coordinate transformation to satisfy left regulatory condition $f(0) = 0$. Based on the derived analytical forms of λ_0 and λ_3, we found that the normalized f^* is a Weibull distribution with shape parameter equals to 3 (due to conservation of mass), scale parameter d_{30} (mean mass particle diameter) and zero location parameter. The particle property space transformation $p(x)$ is found to be $p(x) = x^2$ which is related to the transformation of dimensionless particle volume to dimensionless particle diameter.

2.3. Correction of OPOSPM-Weibull distribution using the KLD

Following the standard nomenclature of entropy information theory, the OPOSPM-Weibull distribution is called prior distribution. To correct this distribution, we minimized the relative entropy as represented by the Kullback-Leibler divergence (KLD) (Tanaka and Toda, 2012) with Weibull distribution as the most uncommitted probability distribution with respect to the unknown information:

$$f(x,\mathbf{r},t) = f^*(x,\mathbf{r},t)\exp\!\left[\sum_{n=0}^{N-1}\gamma_n(\mathbf{r},t)\varphi_n(\zeta(x))\right] \tag{6}$$

In this equation φ_n is the nth degree Legendre polynomial and $\zeta(x)$ is a linear transformation to convert actual grid points to the domain of $\varphi_n \in (-1,1)$. The expansion coefficients (γ_n) are derived in closed analytical form following the same lines of Attarakih et al. (2019) that allowed us to derive the expansion coefficients in a closed form using the Gauss-Legendre integration quadrature to sample the number concentration function. This pointwise sampling using the orthogonal collocation method results in a set of N-PDEs when applied to the system of equations (1) and (2). In this way we provide a moment consistent solution to the PBE and minimize the lost information contained in the number density function due to the averaging process with respect to particle phase space.

3. Results and discussion

Since particle coagulation is the most complicated source term in the PBE, we concentrated on two coagulation mechanisms; namely, Brownian motion and turbulent diffusion. Therefore, the corrected OPOSPM-Weibull distribution method is validated through comparison to well-known analytical solutions. These solutions depend on the binary collision coagulation frequency (ω) which may occur through variety of mechanisms which include Brownian motion, turbulent diffusion and laminar shear. The Brownian motion and turbulent diffusion are the two popular mechanisms (Hidy and Brock, 1970) that are frequently used. In Brownian coagulation, ω depends on the volumes of the two colliding particles when one particle is in the continuum regime:

$$\omega(x, x') = \omega_0 (x + x')(x^{-1} + x'^{-1})\tag{7}$$

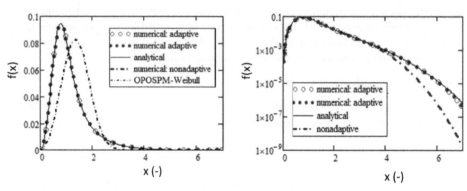

Figure (1): Comparison between the analytical solution (Gelbard and Seinfeld, 1978) and the predicted one by the OPOSPM-Weibull corrected method using 15 Gauss-Legendre nodes for the coagulation equation with Golovin kernel and first-order removal rate in a batch stirred vessels. $\tau = 2$, $\theta = 0.45$ (first order particle removal frequency), a = 0, b = 7 (limits of integration).

As an interesting case, we consider the Brownian coagulation with Knudsen number less than 0.1 where ω is approximately constant. If the initial population of the coagulating particles in a closed homogeneous space follows a Weibull distribution, then the maximized Shannon entropy constrained by OPOSPM moments is a Weibull distribution coinciding exactly with the analytical solution (Gelbard & Seinfeld) and spreading as a function of time with mean size and dispersion proportional to the mean mass particle diameter (d_{30}) and $(d_{30})^2$ respectively. In case of coagulation resulting from turbulent diffusion, the Golovin kernel is used which is proportional to the volumes of the colliding particles. The Weibull distribution for this case, with first order removal rate of particles, is evolved by the exact moments of OPOSPM which is found to move faster than the exact solution as shown in Figure (1) (Left). Therefore, a corrected Weibull distribution is used based on Eq.(6) in which the expansion coefficients were calculated based on the evolution of $f(x_i, t), i = 0, 1, ..N-1$ as function of time. The index of coagulation for this case is ≈ 90 percent which is defined as $I = 1 - m_0(t)/m_0(0)$. As time ODE solver, the AdamsBDF (Adams method with backward differentiation formulas) was used. It is clear that the corrected OPOSPM-Weibull distribution is artificially delayed by adding more exponential terms to recover the missed information due to using only two particle population moments (α and N) included in $f^*(x,t)$. For this case 15 sampling points, placed at the roots of Legendre polynomials, were found enough to predict the exact solution with root mean square error equals to 1.916×10^{-4}. (refer to Figure (2) (Right). The distribution of the expansion coefficients which appears in Eq.(6) (γ_n, n =1,2 ...N-1) was found concentrated in the interval $x \in (0, 2)$ near the sharp part of the exact distribution. On the right hand part of Figure (1), we zoomed in the tail of the distribution where particles of small concentration were underpredicted using 15 nodes of Gauss-Legendre fixed quadrature to integrate Eq.(2). This error is removed by using an independent adaptive integration quadrature (background grid) as shown in Figure (1) (Right) or by increasing the number of sampling points. The cost of computation in terms of the CPU time needed for integration of Eq.(2) using an adaptive quadrature is approximately 10 times that needed as compared to a nonadaptive Gauss-Legendre quadrature using 15 nodes.

Table (1): Comparison between adaptive and nonadaptive integration of Eq.(2) in the PBE to predict the first six low-order moments of the particle size distribution ($N = 15$ nodes, $\tau = 2$).

	Analytical	Integration	Integration	Relative error	
r	m_e	m_n: adaptive	m_n: nonadaptive	Adaptive	nonadaptive
0	0.108746	0.108938	0.110175	0.00176	0.01314
1	0.125471	0.125666	0.125854	0.00156	0.00305
2	0.196859	0.196924	0.192368	0.00033	0.02281
3	0.406493	0.405846	0.37809	0.00159	0.06988
4	1.051971	1.047919	0.9082	0.00385	0.13667
5	3.236571	3.215298	2.534925	0.00657	0.21679

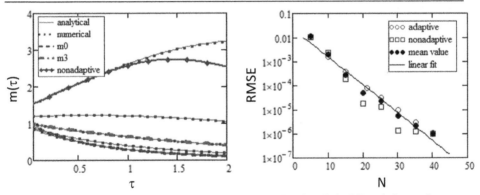

Figure (2): (Left) Comparison between predicted and calculated analytical first six low-order moments for the coagulation equation with first order removal. (Right): Effect of number of Gauss-Legendre nodes on the RMSE as compared with the analytical solution.

Concerning the calculated particle integral properties, and as shown in Figure (2) (Left), the predicted first low-order moments as compared to those calculated from the exact solution (Gelbard and Seinfeld, 1978) are indistinguishable. However, the 6th order moment deviates considerably from the exact one because of the error in the integration of the source term (Eq.(2)) due to using a nonadaptive integration quadrature. This effect of using nonadaptive and adaptive quadrature is shown in clearly in Table (1). This table compares the analytical and numerical moments for the PBE with coagulation source term using $N = 15$ and $\tau = 2$. Again, the error of integration is almost removed when switching to an adaptive integration quadrature with the same number of nodes (15 nodes). The convergence of the corrected OPOSPM-Weibull distribution method, as measured by the RMSE, is shown in Figure (2) (Right) based on fixed and adaptive integration quadrature. The regular convergence of the method based on the adaptive integration scheme of Eq.(2) for the coagulation part is due to fixing the source term integration error. On the other hand, the RMSE as function of number of integration nodes for the case of a nonadaptive scheme exhibits an irregular convergence behaviour. This is due to the combined effects of truncation error from the corrected OPOSPM-Weibull method and the nonadaptive integration schemes. The speed of convergence follows an exponential decay with a number constant $n_b \approx 4.0$. This means that the RMSE decreases to more than 99 percent of its initial value using $4n_b$ nodes.

4. Summary and Conclusions

It is proved that the MaxEnt distribution constrained by the OPOSPM moments is a Weibull distribution with shape parameter equals to three and scale parameter as d_{30}. This coincides with the exact solution for the case of Brownian coagulation with Knudsen number less than 0.1 and Weibull distribution as an initial condition. For general coagulation mechanism, OPOSPM-Weibull distribution needs to be corrected to account for lost information (shape) due to particle phase space averaging. To correct the prior OPOSPM-Weibull distribution, we minimized the relative entropy as represented by the Kullback-Leibler divergence with OPOSPM-Weibull distribution as the most uncommitted prior probability distribution. The posterior distribution, viewed as a correction to the prior OPOSPM-Weibull distribution, is found by expanding the KLD minimum solution using a set of orthogonal Legendre polynomials. As a test case with known analytical solution, the turbulent particle coagulation with first-order removal of particles is studied. The sequence of continuous approximations to the exact solution is found to converge exponentially in the sense of the RMSE, on the pointwise (in the sense of Kullback-Leibler divergence) and mean (weak convergence) levels. As a main conclusion, the OPOSPM-Weibull distribution as well as its corrected version are proved to be general methods to solve the PBE irrespective of the coagulation mechanism or any other active ones such as particle growth and breakage.

References

M.Attarakih, H.-J. Bart and M. Abu-Khader, 2019, On the solution of the population balance equation: From global to local constrained maximum entropy method. Chem. Eng. Sci., 2019, 115168.

M. Attarakih, M., Abu-Khader and H.-J. Bart, 2013, Modelling and Dynamic Analysis of an RDC Extraction Column using OPOSPM. Chem. Eng. Sci., 91, 180-196.

M. Attarakih, C. Drumm snd H.-J. Bart, 2009, Solution of the population balance equation using the sectional quadrature method of moments(SQMOM). Chem. Eng. Sci., 64, 742--752.

F. Gelbard and J. H. Seinfeld, 1978, Numerical solution of the dynamic equation for particulate systems. J. Comput. Phys., 28, 357-375.

H. Gzyl and A. Tagliani, 2010, Stieltjes moment problem and fractional moments, Applied Mathematics and Computation, 216, 3307–3318.

G. M. Hidy and J. R. Brock, 1970, The Dynamics of Aerocolloidal Systems, Pergamon Press, Oxford, England.

M. Mickler, H. B. Jildeh and H. J. Bart, 2014, Online monitoring, simulation and prediction of multiphase flows. Can. J. Chem. Eng., 92, 307–317.

D. Ramkrishna and M. R. Singh, 2014, Population Balance Modeling: Current Status and Future Prospects, Annu. Rev. Chem. Biomol. Eng., 5, 123-146.

J. Schaefer, M. W. Hlawitschka, M. Attarakih and H.-J. Bart, 2019, Experimental investigation of local bubble properties: Comparison to the sectional quadrature method of moments. AIChE J., e16694.

K. Tanaka and A. A. Toda, 2012, Discrete approximations of continuous distributions by maximum entropy. Economics Letters, 118, 445-450.

K. E. Wardle and H. G. Weller, 2013, Hybrid multiphase CFD Solver for coupled dispersed/segregated flows in liquid-liquid extraction. Int. J. Chem. Eng., 2013, 1-14.

Sauro Pierucci, Flavio Manenti, Giulia Bozzano, Davide Manca (Eds.)
Proceedings of the 30th European Symposium on Computer Aided Process Engineering
(ESCAPE30), May 24-27, 2020, Milano, Italy. © 2020 Elsevier B.V. All rights reserved.
http://dx.doi.org/10.1016/B978-0-12-823377-1.50117-8

The Effect of Age on the Delivery of Intravenous Anesthesia: a Physiologically-based Modeling Approach to Pediatric Patients

Daniel Salis, Adriana Savoca, Davide Manca

PSE-Lab, Process Systems Engineering Laboratory
Dipartimento di Chimica, Materiali e Ingegneria Chimica "Giulio Natta"
Politecnico di Milano
Piazza Leonardo da Vinci 32, 20133 Milano, Italy

Abstract

Selection of optimal dosing in anesthesia is a complex task because of the inter-individual variability in patients' response. In this context, computer-aided modelling can be a powerful tool to assess the impact of anatomical and physiological differences among patients and simulate different administration protocols. *In silico* simulations via pharmacokinetic (PK) and pharmacodynamic (PD) models allow investigating the concentration profiles and the resulting effects of drugs in patients. A physiologically-based (PB) approach to pharmacokinetic modeling is thus required to account for the influence of both anatomical and physiological features. We focus on the administration of propofol to patients from 1 to 19 years old and propose new correlations for the estimation of volumes of organs and tissues in these patients. The adapted PBPK model is then combined with a specific PD model, to predict the hypnotic effects of propofol in pediatric patients. The proposed model can thus be used for simulation, training, and control applications.

Keywords: physiologically-based pharmacokinetic model; anesthesia; propofol; bispectral index; pharmacodynamic model.

1. Introduction

From birth to adulthood, several anatomical, physiological, and biochemical changes occur in the human body. Most of them are simply related to its natural growth with increasing age while others to the progressive development and modification of the biochemical environment. These continuous changes affect drugs transport mechanisms in the body and thus, their pharmacodynamic effects on patients. For this reason, pediatric patients often require dosing modifications compared to adults. The changes that the body undergoes during child development make the physiological modeling of pediatric patients' rather challenging. However, a physiologically-based (PB) approach allows suitably describing the relation between the dose and the concentration of drugs, *i.e.* the pharmacokinetic (PK) profile, within the body of this patients' category. The PBPK model can then be combined to a pharmacodynamic (PD) model to simulate and predict the drug effect. This paper focuses on propofol, an intravenous (IV) anesthetic, whose administration is rather challenging because of its narrow therapeutic window. Although some general guidelines on propofol dosing exist, anesthesiologists rely heavily on their experience and habits to select the dose for induction (*i.e.* loss of consciousness produced with general anesthesia) in pediatric patients. The scientific literature proposes several basic three-compartment PK models for those patients. However, these models are neither anatomically- nor physiologically-based and, since they were identified from different groups of patients characterized by variable ages and body features, they show remarkable variability in predictions. This can easily generate confusion and ambiguity among clinicians. In this context, the introduction of a PBPK-PD model, specifically developed for pediatric patients in the 1-19 y age range, can help anesthesiologists. Indeed, computer-aided modeling and simulation is a suitable tool to identify ranges of optimal dosing and individualize clinical treatments, with the goal of making the whole procedure safer. In this work, we adapt a PBPK model previously developed for adult patients and combine it with a suitable PD model to predict the impact of age on propofol hypnotic effects.

2. Methods

2.1. Adaptation of the model to the anatomical differences of pediatric patients

The easiest and earliest change of the body with age that one can observe is related to its dimensions. Indeed, while growing up, a child increases the dimensions (weight) of their tissues, *e.g.*, bones, muscles, fat, and skin, but also of some organs *e.g.*, brain, heart, and liver. Other relevant changes are related to physiological aspects (*e.g.*, pH, immature enzymes, and membranes permeability) that influence the absorption, distribution, metabolism, and elimination of drugs in the body. To account for the differences among pediatric and adult patients, some parameters of the reference PBPK model of this work (Abbiati et al., 2016), *i.e.* the volume of organs and tissues and blood flowrates, were adapted. Specific correlations were identified with experimental data of cardiac output, blood volume, and organs and tissues weights of pediatric patients via either linear or nonlinear regressions. Gender-specific correlations were derived whenever gender-specific data were available.

To describe the cardiac output, we tested a set of correlations depending on total body weight (TBW) and age. Similarly, we tested the functional dependency of blood volume from age, TBW, and body surface area (BSA). The weights of organs and tissues were correlated either linearly or exponentially with age. An exception to this methodology was made for the adipose tissue weight. In this case, in agreement with the data trend, the age range was divided into subgroups, which allowed evaluating specific correlations.

2.2. Physiologically-based pharmacokinetic-pharmacodynamic modelling

The reference PBPK model presented by Abbiati et al. (2016) for IV drugs consists of five interconnected compartments (*i.e.* Plasma (P), Liver (L), Poorly perfused Tissues (PT), Highly perfused Organs (HO), and Gastro-Intestinal Circulatory System (GICS)) and was adapted to propofol by considering both hepatic (H) and extra-hepatic (K, kidneys and T, tissues) routes of metabolism and elimination. The dynamic profile of the drug concentration C_i within each compartment can be obtained by solving a system of five ordinary differential equations (ODEs) (Eqs. (1-5)) that consist of the drug material balances over those compartments, complemented by suitable initial conditions. In our model, compartment volumes V_i were estimated from the weights of organs and tissues as discussed in Section 2.1. Similarly, blood flowrates Q_{HA} (HA, hepatic artery), Q_{HV} (HV, hepatic vein), Q_{PV} (PV, portal vein), and Q_K (K, kidneys) were calculated as a fraction of cardiac output. Conversely, the fraction R of drug bound to plasma proteins was kept unchanged compared to adult patients (Brines et al., 1941). The remaining 7 parameters, *i.e.* drug transfer coefficients k and hepatic and renal efficiencies to calculate hepatic and renal clearances CL were identified by means of a nonlinear regression respect to experimental PK data of pediatric patients from Kataria et al. (1994) (age range 3-11 y). The prediction of the PBPK model was then validated with additional experimental PK data from the same study.

$$\frac{dC_P(t)}{dt} = -C_P(t)\left(k_{P-PT}(1-R) + k_{P-HO}(1-R) + \frac{Q_{HA}}{V_P} + \frac{Q_{PV}}{V_P} \right) + C_P(t)k_{PT-P}\frac{V_{PT}}{V_P} + C_L(t)\frac{Q_{HV}}{V_P} +$$

$$+C_{HO}(t)k_{HO-P}\frac{V_{HO}}{V_P} - C_P(t)(1-R)k_{E,P} - C_P(t)\frac{CL_K}{V_P} + \frac{IV(t)}{V_P} \tag{1}$$

$$\frac{dC_L(t)}{dt} = -C_L(t)\left(\frac{Q_{HV}}{V_L} + \frac{CL_H}{V_L} \right) + C_P(t)\frac{Q_{HA}}{V_L} + C_{GICS}(t)\frac{Q_{PV}}{V_L} \tag{2}$$

$$\frac{dC_{PT}(t)}{dt} = -C_{PT}(t)\left(k_{PT-P} + k_{E,T} \right) + C_P(t)k_{P-PT}(1-R)\frac{V_P}{V_{PT}} \tag{3}$$

$$\frac{dC_{HO}(t)}{dt} = -C_{HO}(t)k_{HO-P} + C_P(t)k_{P-HO}(1-R)\frac{V_P}{V_{HO}} \tag{4}$$

$$\frac{dC_{GICS}(t)}{dt} = -C_{GICS}(t)\frac{Q_{PV}}{V_{GICS}} + C_P(t)\frac{Q_{PV}}{V_{GICS}} \tag{5}$$

In order to model the pharmacological effect of propofol, the PBPK model was linked to a PD model by introducing an effect-site compartment. This extra compartment represents the propofol site of action, which embodies specific receptors located in the brain. Eq. (6) models the effect-site compartment by means of a first-order transport mechanism, governed by a kinetic constant k_{e0} (Sheiner et al., 1979). This approach allowed accounting for the delay between the time course of the pharmacological effect and the dynamics of plasma concentration. We adopted the modified sigmoid E_{max} equation (Eq. (7)) as PD model, in line with Rigouzzo et al. (2010) formulation. The drug PD effect consists in the bispectral index (BIS), a statistically-based empirically-derived parameter, which is obtained from the re-elaboration of electroencephalographic tracing (Kaul and Barthi, 2002). BIS baseline (*i.e.* E_0 in Eq. (7)) is usually around 95-100, while recommended BIS range for depth of anesthesia is 40-60 (Singh, 1999) also in pediatric patients.

$$\frac{dC_e}{dt} = k_{e0}C_P - k_{e0}C_e \tag{6}$$

$$E = E_0 - (E_0 - E_{max})\frac{C_e^{\gamma}}{(EC_{50}^{\gamma} + C_e^{\gamma})} \tag{7}$$

Parameter E_{max} in Eq. (7) was fixed at 0, as this is the minimum value that BIS can reach in clinical practice. The PD parameters γ (*aka* Hill parameter) and EC_{50} (concentration corresponding to 50% of E_{max}) were identified by means of a nonlinear regression procedure with BIS experimental data from Coppens et al. (2011). Additional data from the same study were used for validation of the combined PBPK-PD model.

3. Results and Discussion

3.1. Estimation of the individualized parameters

For the sake of space, we only show 4 representative correlations derived for the pediatric population. The rest of the proposed correlations are available in Salis (2019). Figure 1 reports the trends of cardiac output, blood volume, and brain and kidneys weights as a function of age, with the aim of showing the effect of growth stage on the anatomy of pediatric patients. While in some cases gender differences manifest from young age (see C panel), in other cases they are more evident after puberty (see A, B, D panels). When the trend of the data showed a constant increase across the age range, a linear correlation was implemented (*e.g.*, D panel). Differently, when adult values were reached around 11-12 y (*e.g.*, C panel) an exponential correlation was the preferred one. With respect to cardiac output, the correlation with age rather than TBW improved data fitting. Interestingly, no gender-differences were evident for patients younger than 7 y old. A correlation depending on BSA provided the highest R^2 value (0.97) to estimate the blood volume.

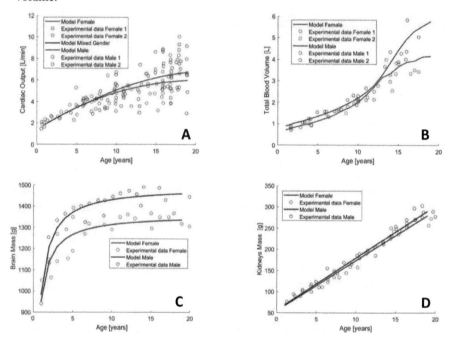

Figure 1 – Estimated (continuous line) vs measured (circles) values of cardiac output (A), blood volume (B), brain mass (C), and kidneys mass (D) of pediatric patients. Data from Valentin (2002), Brines et al., (1941), and Williams (1994). Blue refers to males, red to females.

3.2. Validation of the PBPK-PD model

Figure 2 (top panel) compares the predicted and measured concentration values of 3 representative patients studied by Kataria et al. (1994). The prediction capability of the model was acceptable in most patients, independently of the administration protocols. Despite the lack of experimental data on the very sharp peaks due to the quick re-distribution of propofol after the initial bolus, the simulated profile is consistent with the administered dose. The prediction capability of the model is quantified by evaluating the median absolute prediction error (MDAPE) between the model and the experimental data. The MDAPE for the three patients presented in Figure 2 (top panel) are respectively 16.78, 19.76, and 8.25%. Figure 2 (bottom panel) shows the predicted and observed BIS profiles for three patients (studied by Coppens et al., 2011). The combined PBPK-PD model shows a rather satisfactory prediction capability. It is worth mentioning that intra-operative BIS values are often affected by drug-independent disturbances that produce model deviations (*e.g.*, see the observed BIS increase in A panel after approximately 2 min). The model prediction capability is additionally assessed by evaluating MDAPE, which for the three patients is 17.94, 24.0, and 20.32% respectively.

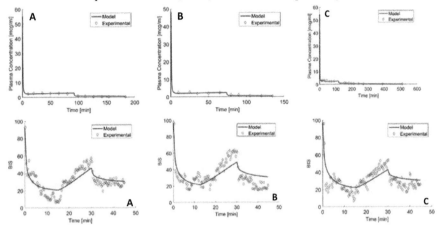

Figure 2 – (Top panel) Validation of the PBPK model with PK data of three patients administered with single (A and B) and double (C) propofol infusions. (Bottom panel) Validation of the PD response in terms of BIS simulated by the PBPK-PD model.

Figure 3 shows the comparison between the predicted concentration via PBPK and the classical three-compartment PK model of Kataria against data of two pediatric patients from a different study (Marsh et al., 1991). It is worth noticing that the early concentration dynamics is not well-described by the classical three-compartment model, as it does not display any concentration peaks.

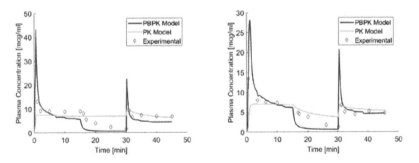

Figure 3 – Comparison of PBPK (blue continuous line) and classical PK (green continuous line) simulations with measured concentrations (red diamonds) of two pediatric patients from Marsh et al. (1991). As a result, in case of model-predictive control applications, the PBPK model can provide a more conservative control action. In addition, close plasma peaks prediction is particularly important to prevent adverse effects. In this dataset, the PBPK model overestimates the drug elimination, thus the metabolism and elimination description should be improved in future work.

4. Conclusions

The proposed PBPK model showed an acceptable predictive capability, with superior performance than the commonly used Kataria's PK model. We deem that the anatomical and physiological foundations are an important element to enhance the understanding and adoption by clinicians. The combined PBPK-PD model showed a satisfactory level of prediction of BIS data, with poor forecasts often caused by intra-operative disturbances. *In silico* simulations can enhance the understanding of patients' variability in the response to anesthetic drugs and improve clinical practice. Control applications of the developed PBPK-PD model are even more interesting. Specifically, the model can be implemented in target-controlled infusion (TCI) pumps (*i.e.* only the PBPK component) or closed-loop model predictive controllers of anesthesia (*i.e.* the full PBPK-PD model). In the first case, a target concentration is assigned by the anesthetist to the TCI device, and the model-based algorithm calculates the corresponding infusion rate. In the second case, a BIS setpoint is implemented and the model-predictive controller optimizes the propofol administration basing on actual BIS and the optimal predicted trajectory of patient's BIS, achieved by smooth and safe changes of propofol infusion rates, while maintaining the desired target value against external disturbances.

References

Abbiati RA, Lamberti G, Grassi M, Trotta F, Manca D, 2016, Definition and validation of a patient-individualized physiologically-based pharmacokinetic model. Comput. Chem .Eng. 84, 394-408.

Brines JK, Gibson JG, Kunkel P, 1941, The blood volume in normal infants and children. The J. Pediatrics 18, 447-57.

Coppens MJ, Eleveld DJ, Proost JH, et al., 2011, An evaluation of using population pharmacokinetic models to estimate pharmacodynamic parameters for propofol and bispectral index in children. JASA 115, 83-93.

Kataria B, Sudha A, Nicodemus HF, et al., 1994, The Pharmacokinetics of Propofol in Children Using Three Different Data Analysis Approaches. JASA 80 (1), 104-22.

Kaul H, Bharti N, 2002, Monitoring Depth of Anaesthesia. Indian J.Anaesth. 46, 323-32.

Marsh B, White M, Morton N, Kenny GNC, 1991, Pharmacokinetic model driven infusion of propofol in children. Br. J. Anaesth. 67, 41-48.

Rigouzzo A, Servin F, Constant I, 2010, Pharmacokinetic-Pharmacodynamic Modeling of Propofol in Children. JASA 113(2), 343-52.

Salis D, 2019,. Physiologically based pharmacokinetic-pharmacodynamic modelling for anesthesia in children (Master's thesis, Politecnico di Milano, Milan, Italy).

Sheiner LB, Stanski DR, Vozeh S, et al., 2019, Simultaneous modeling of pharmacokinetics and pharmacodynamics: Application to d-tubocurarine. Clin. Pharma. Therapeutics 25(3), 358-71.

Singh H, 1999, Bispectral index (BIS) monitoring during propofol-induced sedation and anaesthesia. Eur. J. Anaesthesiol. 16(1), 31-6.

Valentin J, 2002, Basic anatomical and physiological data for use in radiological protection: reference values: ICRP Publication 89. Annals of the ICRP, 32, 1-277.

Williams LR, 1994, Reference values for total blood volume and cardiac output in humans. In: Oak Ridge National Lab., TN (United States).

Sauro Pierucci, Flavio Manenti, Giulia Bozzano, Davide Manca (Eds.)
Proceedings of the 30th European Symposium on Computer Aided Process Engineering
(ESCAPE30), May 24-27, 2020, Milano, Italy. © 2020 Elsevier B.V. All rights reserved.
http://dx.doi.org/10.1016/B978-0-12-823377-1.50118-X

Physiologically-Based Pharmacokinetic and Pharmacodynamic Modeling of Unfractionated Heparin to Predict Activated Clotting Time

Filippo Regorda[a], Emiliano Vigoni[a], Giuseppe Pesenti[a], Marina Pieri[b],
Alessandro Belletti[b], Davide Manca[a,*]

*a*PSE-Lab, Process Systems Engineering Laboratory, Dipartimento di Chimica,
Materiali e Ingegneria Chimica "Giulio Natta", Politecnico di Milano, Piazza
Leonardo da Vinci 32, 20133 Milano, Italy
*b*Department of Anesthesia and Intensive Care, IRCCS San Raffaele Scientific Institute,
Via Olgettina 60, 20132 Milano, Italy
davide.manca@polimi.it

Abstract

Monitoring the coagulation time and regulating the administration of unfractionated heparin (UFH) during cardiopulmonary bypass (CPB) are challenging activities. The manuscript focuses on the development of a mathematical model to predict the activated clotting time (ACT) during CPB following an intravenous administration of heparin.

The overall mathematical tool features a physiologically-based pharmacokinetic (PBPK) model and a pharmacodynamic (PD) model. The PBPK model describes the human circulatory system and employs correlations from the literature to estimate its physiological parameters from individual characteristics (*i.e.* age, sex, race, weight, height, serum creatinine, and hematocrit) to yield a prediction of heparin plasma concentration as a function of time. The PD model predicts the ACT as a function of heparin concentration thanks to several differential equations that describe the coagulation cascade. The combined PBPK/PD model produces, for each patient, an individualized prediction of the resulting ACT dynamics, using either a population or an individualized approach. The model can be used to help monitoring the ACT trend during CPB and to optimize heparin administration in order to reach and maintain the therapeutic goal of 480 s.

Keywords: Heparin, ACT, Pharmacokinetics, Pharmacodynamics, Mathematical model.

1. Introduction

Heparin is the most widely used anticoagulant drug. Unfractionated heparin is administered intravenously for the prevention and treatment of thrombosis, especially in cardiac surgery. During this kind of operations, plasma concentration of heparin and the consequent effect on patient's body are difficult to control. The activated clotting time (ACT) is a widely used indicator capable of describing this anticoagulant effect during cardiopulmonary bypass (CPB) and involves the intrinsic coagulation cascade. It can be obtained through a quick bedside test that measures the time needed for the blood to clot after the addition of an activator. The established ACT clinical target during cardiac surgeries is 480 s. The present work considers as a case study the intravenous administration of UFH during CPB operations. During this type of surgical interventions, patients are connected to an external heart-lung machine, whose goal is to reproduce the vitals of heart and lungs. UFH is administered to patients to prevent the activation of the hemostatic process within the artificial circuit. Despite its widespread use, the pharmacokinetic and pharmacodynamic properties of heparin appear poorly understood. Consistently, only few models of heparin pharmacology are available in the literature. Most of these focus exclusively on the pharmacokinetics (PK), *e.g.*, (Jia *et al.*, 2015), or on the pharmacodynamics (Kogan *et al.*, 2001; Zhu, 2007). Furthermore, Delavenne (2017) developed a population-based PK/PD model, which adjusts the predicted ACT according to the measured anti-Xa activity, *i.e.* one of the enzymes of the coagulation cascade. However, these PK models are not physiologically-based and do not account for patients' characteristics such as the degree of renal function, whereas the PD models, with the exception of the one by Kogan *et al.* and Zhu, do not describe the complete coagulation cascade. We present a combined mathematical model featuring an individualized PBPK model and a PD one. The overall model is able to estimate heparin concentration in the human body to predict the ACT during CPB.

2. Methods

The experimental data used to validate the model were collected from San Raffaele hospital in Milan, after Ethical Committee approval and with patients' written consent. The data collection included sex (17 males and 6 females), age (36-77 y), height (160-190 cm), weight (46-115 kg), serum creatinine (0.63-1.46 mg/dL), hematocrit (31.9-54.9 %), antithrombin (ATIII, 65-109 %) and body surface area (BSA, 1.45-2.43 m^2) of a heterogeneous population of 23 *naïve* patients, *i.e.* without any clinical complications nor any kind of pre-operatory treatment. Furthermore, the data comprised the trend of ACT during CPB. Each patient received an initial bolus of heparin equal to 300 IU/kg. During the operation, they were connected to the extra-corporeal circuit (ECC), which contained a priming volume in the 750-1,600 mL range, containing 3,000-5,000 IU of heparin. Additional boluses in the 1,500-10,000 IU range were administered during the operation to maintain ACT at or above the 480 s target. UFH is a heterogeneous molecule with a wide range of molecular weights (5,000 to 30,000 Da, 20,000 Da on average). We describe heparin through its average molecular weight of 20,000 Da. Since the administered heparin remains confined within the intravascular area, the model takes into account the circulatory system as its distribution volume. Heparin is eliminated from the body through two pathways: (i) a metabolic process due to the aggregation of heparin to receptors of endothelial cells and macrophages, and (ii) an excretion one via renal filtration. The PBPK model features a total of three compartments, (i) RCS stands for the fraction of plasma contained within the kidneys, (ii) CS representing the human circulatory system (Pesenti *et al.*, 2019), and (iii) ECC that accounts for the extra-corporeal circuit.

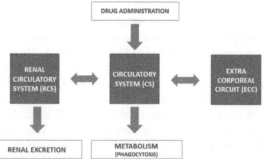

Figure 1 – Compartments of the PBPK model.

The model consists of three ordinary differential equations (ODEs), which describe the material balances of heparin in each compartment.

$$\frac{dC_{CS}}{dt} = \frac{\dot{m}_{bolus}}{V_{CS}} + \frac{(Q_{CS\leftrightarrow RCS}C_{RCS})}{V_{CS}} - \frac{(Q_{CS\leftrightarrow RCS}C_{CS})}{V_{CS}} + \frac{(Q_{CPB}C_{ECC})}{V_{CS}} - \frac{(Q_{CPB}C_{CS})}{V_{CS}} - K_{met}C_{CS} \quad (1)$$

$$\frac{dC_{RCS}}{dt} = \frac{(Q_{CS\leftrightarrow RCS}C_{CS})}{V_{RCS}} - \frac{(Q_{CS\leftrightarrow RCS}C_{RCS})}{V_{RCS}} - \frac{(GFRC_{RCS}(1-R))}{V_{RCS}} \quad (2)$$

$$\frac{dC_{ECC}}{dt} = \frac{(Q_{CPB}C_{CS})}{V_{ECC}} - \frac{(Q_{CPB}C_{ECC})}{V_{ECC}} \quad (3)$$

C_{CS}, C_{RCS}, and C_{ECC} are the concentrations of heparin (IU/mL) in the CS, RCS and ECC compartments. $\dot{m}_{bolus}$ is the flowrate of administered heparin (IU/min), R is the fraction of heparin bound to blood proteins (equal to 0.95), Q_{CPB} is the volumetric flow (mL/min) of the ECC priming volume. $Q_{CS\leftrightarrow RCS}$ and Q_{GFR} are the volumetric flowrates (mL/min) that represent, respectively, the plasma flow that reaches the kidneys and the glomerular filtration rate (GFR). They are estimated as a function of sex, age, serum creatinine, BSA, and hematocrit (Pesenti *et al.*, 2019). V_{CS}, V_{RCS}, and V_{ECC} are the volumes (mL) of plasma in the corresponding compartments. The CS and RCS volumes are evaluated as the 98% and 2% of the total blood volume, which is individualized according to patients' height and weight (Nadler *et al.*, 1962). Finally, the kinetic constant of the phagocytosis reaction rate, K_{met}, is evaluated through a nonlinear regression of PK data extracted from Olsson (1963). The initial concentration of heparin in each compartment is zero. The PD model implements the description of the intrinsic coagulation cascade published by Kogan *et al.* (2001) and Zhu (2007). Their models describe the whole reaction cascade with a Michaelis-Menten kinetics and employ second order kinetics for the inhibitory reactions, without considering the presence of heparin. UFH can reversibly bind to ATIII, which strengthens the coagulation cascade inhibitory activity. This reversible interaction causes an ACT increase. The heparin-antithrombin complex interacts with several coagulation factors. Since factors II_a and X_a are the most important during the hemostatic process, we consider only the interaction between the complex and these factors. Thus, the ODEs system developed by Kogan and Zhu is complemented with three additional reactions, which describe the interactions between heparin-antithrombin and factors II_a and X_a.

$$He + ATIII \rightarrow He\_ATIII \quad (4)$$

$$He\_ATIII + II_a \rightarrow II_a\_ATIII + He \quad (5)$$

$$He\_ATIII + X_a \rightarrow X_a\_ATIII + He \quad (6)$$

Assuming that during the incubation period (60 s) the reactions affecting the activation phase are negligible, the initial concentrations of the model are equal to the initial concentrations (μmol/L) of each factor and inhibitor taken from Kogan *et al.* (2001) and Zhu (2007). Because of the lack of data on the individual factor concentrations (but for ATIII), we assumed these values constant for all the patients. ACT is evaluated as the 30% of the conversion of fibrinogen (factor I_a) plus the incubation time (Eq. 7).

$$ACT = 60 + t|_{\chi=0.3} \quad (7)$$

The kinetic constant related to the interaction between the heparin-ATIII complex and factor II_a, due to the lack of experimental data, is evaluated through a nonlinear regression. In particular, it is evaluated both through an individualized approach, which minimizes the sum of squared errors between experimental values of ACT and the simulated ones of a single patient, and through a population approach that uses 8 patients for the identification procedure and 15 patients for the validation one.

$$\min_{K_5^{ind/pop}} SSE = \min_{K_5^{ind/pop}} \frac{1}{N_p} \sum_{i=1}^{N_p} \left(\frac{1}{N_i^{exp}} \sum_{j=1}^{N_i^{exp}} \left(\frac{ACT_{ij}^{exp} - ACT_{ij}^{sim}}{ACT_{ij}^{exp}} \right)^2 \right) \tag{8}$$

N_p is the number of patients, N_i^{exp} is the number of single patients' experimental values of ACT, ACT_{ij}^{exp} and ACT_{ij}^{sim} are, respectively, the experimental and simulated ACT values. The value of the population constant is 5.6 [μmol/L/min], while the individualized one is specific for each patient and covers a range of 2.4-33.5 [μmol/L/min].

The overall PBPK/PD model is completely individualized, since it grounds on the patients' clinical data. If one uses the individualized value of the kinetic constant related to Eq. 5, K_5, for the simulation, the ACT trend is obtained only *a posteriori* since it requires all the available experimental values of ACT during CPB. Vice versa, if one adopts the population value of K_5 for the simulation, it is possible to forecast the ACT trend *a priori*, although at the cost of reducing the prediction's precision. Therefore, we also proposed an adaptive model, which, starting from the population ACT model, can adapt its ACT prediction in real time by receiving as input the individualized experimental ACT measurements of patients undergoing CPB.

3. Results

For sake of space, we are presenting the results of the combined PBPK/PD model for only one patient, while the results of the adaptive algorithm refer to an outlier to show the progressive improvement of adapting the ACT predictions with the individualized on-line measurements during CPB. Figure 2 (panel a) shows the heparin plasma concentration in each compartment. The green line describes the heparin concentration in the circulatory system. Following the administration of the first heparin bolus (at 20 min), which depends on the weight of the patient, a first peak can be observed. The subsequent linear decrease is due to the metabolic and the excretion mechanisms. The most appreciable decrease in heparin concentration occurs when the patient is connected to ECC (at 44 min). Thus, the mixing of the priming volume within the CS and RCS compartments results in a significant dilution of blood, with a consequent decrease of heparin concentration. Finally, we observe again the linear decrease for the reasons previously cited.

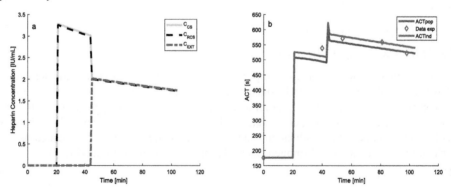

Figure 2 – (a) Heparin plasma concentration dynamics in each compartment. (b) Pharmacodynamic population/individual ACT dynamics during CPB.

The dashed blue line stands for heparin concentration in RCS. It is very close to the green line because the exchanged flow between RCS and CS is very high. Finally, the red line represents the heparin concentration trend in ECC. The initial concentration of heparin in this compartment is equal to 0 [IU/mL]. Afterwards, with the connection of ECC to the patient's plasma, the ECC heparin concentration increases due to the mixing and then linearly decreases according to the renal and hepatic elimination pathways. Figure 2 (panel b) shows the ACT dynamics adopting the population value of K_5 (blue line) and its individualized value (red line). It is worth observing that the two trends are similar, with SSE values equal to 0.0018 and 0.0008, respectively. Although both of them are completely individualized, since they are based on the patient's clinical data, the difference between the two curves is that the one obtained with the population approach is completely predictive and less precise. Conversely, the one obtained with the individualized approach simulates more precisely the patient's ACT trend, but it calls for the whole set of individual experimental data, which is available only at the end of the CPB procedure.

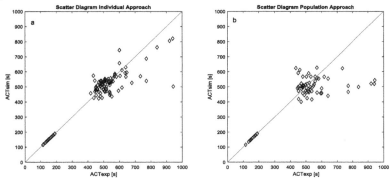

Figure 3 – Parity plots obtained with the (a) individual and (b) approach.

Figure 3 shows the model-simulated vs measured ACT values related to the individualized approach (panel a) and population approach (panel b). It is worth noticing that the individualized approach produces a significant improvement of the correlation between the experimental and simulated values of ACT. This is substantiated by the SSE values that are 0.0101 for the individualized approach and 0.0291 for the population one.

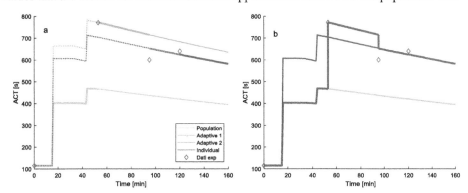

Figure 4 – Adaptive individualized approach to the PBPK-PD modeling.

Figure 4 (panel a) shows the dynamics of the ACT as a function of the different values of the kinetic constant K_5, which are obtained through different regressions carried out each time a new experimental value of ACT becomes available.

At the beginning (at 0 min), the basal value of ACT is known. Thus, we can simulate the *Population* curve using the population value of K_5. When a new experimental value of

ACT is available (at 53 min) we can simulate the ACT trend again taking into account the basal value and the new experimental value, obtaining a new prediction of ACT, *i.e.* *Adaptive 1* curve. This prediction replaces the former *Population* curve as the best current prediction, as it is based on a more individualized value of K_5, obtained via a nonlinear regression based on the two experimental ACT values. Then, the curve *Adaptive 2* is obtained by using the third experimental ACT value and the two previous measurements to regress the next adaptive value of K_5. Following this methodology, the curve *Individual* is obtained considering all the experimental ACT values available, yielding an individualized simulation of the ACT trend based on an individualized value of K_5. In Figure 4 (panel a), each curve is composed of (i) a continuous thick part, representing the best current prediction of ACT between two ACT measurements, (ii) a thin continuous part, which stands for the fragment of curve which is not considered once a new experimental ACT value is available, and (iii) a dotted part that represents the retrospective reconstruction of the past ACT trend. Despite the predictive uncertainty of each curve, the dynamic application of the model allows predicting the progress of the operation through the graphic display of the probable ACT trend. Figure 4 (panel b) shows the detail of the marching adaptive procedure of the ACT trend (red line), *i.e.* the connection between useful parts of each simulate curve, that moves from the population prediction (light blue line) to the individualized one (dark blue line).

4. Conclusions

Despite the existence in literature of a few models capable of describing heparin pharmacokinetics and pharmacodynamics, to our knowledge our model is the first one that combines the heparin concentration predictions from a PBPK model and a fully-mechanistic PD model of the intrinsic coagulation cascade. Indeed, it can be used as a fully individualized predictive tool. In fact, thanks to the patient's clinical data, it can describe the trend of the coagulation time. Using the population approach, we implemented a predictive model that achieves a rather acceptable precision. In addition, using the individualized approach, we obtained an even more precise model that can be used *a posteriori*. Finally, thanks to an adaptive identification algorithm, it is possible to predict the future ACT trends during CPB, and forecast, in real time, the ACT trend, according to the dynamic measurement of ACT experimental values.

References

Delavenne, X., et al., 2017. Pharmacokinetic/pharmacodynamic model for unfractionated heparin dosing during cardiopulmonary bypass. Br J Anaesth 118(5), 705-712.

Jia, Z., et al., 2015. Pharmacokinetic model of unfractionated heparin during and after cardiopulmonary bypass in cardiac surgery. J Transl Med 13, 45.

Kogan, A.E., Kardakov, D.V., Khanin, M.A., 2001. Analysis of the activated partial thromboplastin time test using mathematical modeling. Thromb Res 101(4), 299-310.

Nadler, S.B., Hidalgo, J.U., Bloch, T., 1962. Prediction of blood volume in normal human adults. Surgery 51(2), 224-232.

Olsson, P., Lagergren, H., Ek, S., 1963. The elimination from plasma of intravenous heparin. An experimental study on dogs and humans. Acta Med Scand 173, 619-630.

Pesenti, G., Savoca, A., Manca, D., 2019. Optimal dose administration of renally excreted drugs, Computer Aided Chemical Engineering. Elsevier, pp. 547-552.

Zhu, D., 2007. Mathematical modeling of blood coagulation cascade: kinetics of intrinsic and extrinsic pathways in normal and deficient conditions. Blood Coagul Fibrinolysis 18(7), 637-646.

Sauro Pierucci, Flavio Manenti, Giulia Bozzano, Davide Manca (Eds.)
Proceedings of the 30th European Symposium on Computer Aided Process Engineering
(ESCAPE30), May 24-27, 2020, Milano, Italy. © 2020 Elsevier B.V. All rights reserved.
http://dx.doi.org/10.1016/B978-0-12-823377-1.50119-1

Application of a Pharmacokinetic Model to Inform the Optimal Dose for Individualized Drug Administration

Giuseppe Pesenti[a], Marco Foppoli[b], Adriana Savoca[a], Davide Manca[a]*

[a]*PSE-Lab, Process Systems Engineering Laboratory, Dipartimento di Chimica, Materiali e Ingegneria Chimica "Giulio Natta", Politecnico di Milano, Piazza Leonardo da Vinci 32, 20133 Milano, Italy*
[b]*Unit of Lymphoid Malignancies, Division of Onco-Hematological Medicine, Department of Onco-Hematology, IRCCS San Raffaele Scientific Institute, Via Olgettina 60, 20132 Milano, Italy*
davide.manca@polimi.it

Abstract

Dose selection is critical in clinical settings and standard dosing protocols are not suitable for every patient, due to the significant degree of inter- and intra-individual variability of their pharmacokinetic response. Pharmacokinetic models can be used as clinical support tools to suggest individualized, optimal dosages according to each patient's characteristics. We consider the case study of high-dose methotrexate administration for the application of a physiologically-based pharmacokinetic model, with the goal of obtaining model-informed dosages that we also compare with the standard dosing protocol. The results demonstrate the feasibility of this approach, the potential benefits of improved individualized dosages, and the importance of establishing rational and well-defined administration targets.

Keywords: Optimal dosage, Personalized medicine, Model informed precision dosing, Pharmacokinetics, Methotrexate.

1. Introduction

Drug administration requires considering the individual characteristics of patients and dose selection becomes especially critical in clinical settings, as the pharmacokinetic response of hospitalized and ill patients presents a significant degree of inter- and intra-individual variability. Standard dosage guidelines and protocols are usually developed for average healthy subjects and therefore might be not suitable for clinical patients.

Pharmacokinetic models are mathematical tools that can be applied to suggest optimized dosages according to individual characteristics such as body weight, height, age, sex and degree of renal function (Pesenti et al., 2019a), within the context of personalized medicine and model-informed precision dosing.

This manuscript focuses on methotrexate (MTX) administration as a suitable case study to demonstrate the application of pharmacokinetic models. MTX is administered intravenously (IV) at high doses (HDMTX) to treat malignant tumors such as primary central nervous system lymphoma (PCNSL). HDMTX administration is characterized by a very large inter- and intra-individual variability of its pharmacokinetics, and dosages are usually administered as predetermined amounts per m^2 of body surface area (BSA), *i.e.* a function of body weight and height. They therefore exhibit a limited degree of dose adjustment, and appear to inadequately account for the individual degree of renal function. Furthermore, the literature reports that dose-finding studies in PCNSL are lacking and that there is no clear consensus regarding HDMTX optimal dosages (Joerger et al., 2012a). We therefore implemented and applied a physiologically-based pharmacokinetic model for HDMTX to this case study, to obtain model-informed optimal dosages for different targets and compare them with the clinical dosing protocols.

2. Methods

The minimal physiologically-based pharmacokinetic (PBPK) model for intravenous (IV) HDMTX developed in Pesenti et al. (2019b) was applied to this case study. This pharmacokinetic model was developed and validated using an experimental dataset of 89 Chinese patients with PCNSL (Mei et al., 2018).

The model explicitly accounts for the distribution, metabolism, and excretion of MTX within plasma, interstitial fluid (ISF), and intracellular fluid (ICF), as shown in Figure 1.

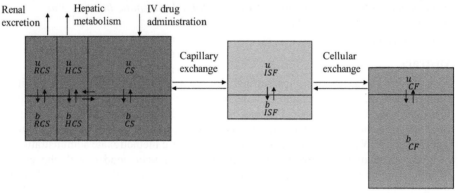

Figure 1 – Main processes and exchanges described by the minimal PBPK model (Pesenti et al., 2019b).

The model describes plasma with three compartments, *i.e.* the renal and hepatic circulatory systems (RCS and HCS), and the remaining overall circulatory system (CS), whereas the ISF and ICF compartments lump the interstitial and intracellular fluid of the entire human body. In each compartment, the concentration of the drug is considered homogeneous. The mathematical description is substantiated by five ordinary differential equations, describing the dynamics of the drug material balances within the five compartments (Eqs. 1-5).

$$\frac{dm_{CS}}{dt} = \dot{m}_{IV} - Q_{RCS}c_{CS} + Q_{RCS}c_{RCS} - Q_{HCS}c_{CS} + Q_{HCS}c_{HCS} + \tag{1}$$
$$-K_{CS \to ISF}c_{CS}^{u} + K_{ISF \to CS}c_{ISF}^{u}$$

$$\frac{dm_{RCS}}{dt} = Q_{RCS}c_{CS} - Q_{RCS}c_{RCS} - \dot{m}_{filtration}^{renal} - \dot{m}_{secretion}^{renal} + \dot{m}_{reabsorption}^{renal} \tag{2}$$

$$\frac{dm_{HCS}}{dt} = Q_{HCS}c_{CS} - Q_{HCS}c_{HCS} - \dot{m}_{elimination}^{hepatic} \tag{3}$$

$$\frac{dm_{ISF}}{dt} = K_{CS \to ISF}c_{CS}^{u} - K_{ISF \to CS}c_{ISF}^{u} - \dot{m}_{ISF \to ICF} + \dot{m}_{ICF \to ISF} \tag{4}$$

$$\frac{dm_{ICF}}{dt} = \dot{m}_{ISF \to ICF} - \dot{m}_{ICF \to ISF} \tag{5}$$

MTX is characterized by a reversible binding with plasma proteins both in plasma and in ISF compartments, and with cellular enzymes within ICF. The MTX bound fractions are estimated as $f_{plasma}^b = 0.42$, $f_{ISF}^b = 0.28$, $f_{ICF}^b = 0.90$ as in Pesenti et al. (2019b). In all model compartments, therefore, Eqs. (1-5) use the b and u superscripts to refer to bound and unbound concentrations respectively. Following its IV administration to the CS compartment ($\dot{m}_{IV}$, in mg/min), MTX is distributed via blood circulation to all body tissues and organs, where the unbound fraction is exchanged at the capillary level mainly by simple diffusion according to the capillary exchange parameters $K_{CS \to ISF}$ and $K_{ISF \to CS}$ (in mL/min). In addition, $\dot{m}_{ISF \to ICF}$ and $\dot{m}_{ICF \to ISF}$ (Eqs. (4-5), in mg/min) represent the active-transport MTX exchanges at the cellular level, that is modelled via a Michaelis-Menten kinetics as a function of c_{ISF}^u and c_{ICF}^u (Pesenti et al., 2019b).

Q_{RCS} and Q_{HCS} represent the plasma flows (in mL/min) that reach the kidneys, where MTX undergoes renal filtration, secretion and reabsorption, and the liver, where it is metabolized and secreted into the bile. While the model considers all these elimination pathways (for further details, see Pesenti et al. (2019b)), we focus on renal filtration (Eq. 6), which accounts for approximately 90% of elimination following IV HDMTX administration and is therefore the most important MTX elimination pathway.

$$\dot{m}_{filtration} = Q_{GFR} c_{RCS}^u \qquad (6)$$

Q_{GFR} is the glomerular filtration rate (GFR, in mL/min), *i.e.* the plasma flow that is filtered by the kidneys, and is individualized as a function of the patient's body weight, height, gender, age, and plasma creatinine (Ma et al., 2006). Similarly, the compartment volumes, the volumetric plasma flows, and the other model parameters are estimated considering the patient's characteristics such as body weight, height, gender, and hematocrit, as in Pesenti et al. (2019b). Four constants, related to the capillary and cellular exchanges, were identified with a population PK approach through a nonlinear regression against an experimental dataset (Mei et al., 2018).

3. Results and discussion

The minimal PBPK model was applied to investigate HDMTX pharmacokinetics by simulating MTX administration to virtual patients defined with average characteristics, *i.e.* male, 57 years old, 168 cm high, with 38.1 % hematocrit. Since body weight and GFR are key determinants of MTX pharmacokinetics, we investigated their effect by defining three/five different virtual patients and changing their body weight and GFR within the ranges found in the experimental dataset, *i.e.* 50-100 kg (for a fixed 120 mL/min GFR value) and 50-250 mL/min (for a fixed 68 kg weight). We considered the IV administration of a standard MTX dose for PCNSL, *i.e.* 500 mg/m² over 15 min followed by 3000 mg/m² over 3 h (Joerger et al., 2012a). Assuming an average 68 kg weight, the total 3500 mg/m² corresponds to 6203 mg.

Fig. 2 shows the simulated MTX plasma concentration profiles over 48 h with the fixed MTX 6203 mg dose and shows the effect of body weight (panels a-b) and GFR (panels c-d). MTX concentrations higher than 1 µmol/L after 48 h are widely considered a threshold for MTX toxicity (Joerger et al., 2012b) and the simulated profiles can also be evaluated to assess the associated toxicity.

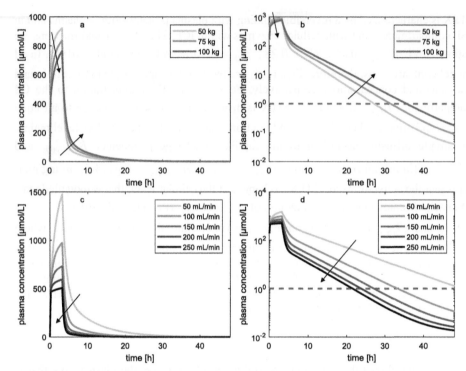

Figure 2 – Simulated MTX plasma concentrations for different virtual patients as a function of their body weight (top panels) and GFR (bottom panels), in both linear and logarithmic coordinates. In panels b and d, the dashed red line represents a toxicity threshold concentration after 48 h (Joerger et al., 2012b).

Higher body weights correspond to lower concentration peaks, which occur at the end of the infusion, since the same dose distributes in a larger volume. However, larger volumes would also require a higher volumetric clearance, whereas the fixed GFR determines a slower elimination following the peak. This can be seen as an inversion in the trend of the three lines after about 5 h from the infusion start.

According to model simulations, these two effects almost compensate each other, leading to values of the area under the curve (AUC) that only slightly increase with body weight in the 50-100 kg range, ranging from 3565 to 3578 µmol/L·h. The effect of GFR, which represents the degree of renal function, is more evident in panels 2c-d. Higher GFRs lead to both lower concentration peaks, and faster elimination dynamics. The AUC correspondingly decreases from 7929 µmol/L·h in case of 50 mL/min GFR, to 1926 µmol/L·h in case of 250 mL/min.

Our pharmacokinetic model was then applied to determine MTX optimal dosages that reach a given target. While the efficacy of MTX is mainly evaluated as the overall survival of the patients and MTX concentration targets are usually not defined, Joerger et al. (2012b) found that an MTX AUC of 1000-1100 µmol/L·h may be associated to improved clinical outcomes. They also reported a 24 h MTX concentration equal to 4-5 µmol/L as a suitable surrogate for the same AUC target. We simulated MTX infusions according to the standard PCNSL dosing protocol, *i.e.* up to 500 mg/m² during the first 15 min, and the remaining dose over 3 h. For each target, we identified the optimal dosage for the same virtual reference patient, at varying values of body weight and GFR, normalized over the patient's BSA/1.73 m².

Figure 3a shows the standard MTX dosing protocol for PCNSL (Joerger et al., 2012a),
i.e. a 3500 mg/m^2 dose as a function of the individual BSA, which is administered to
patients with a 60 mL/min minimum GFR. Figures 3b-c display the optimal dosages that,
according to the model, lead to an AUC of 1050 μmol/L·h and a 24 h concentration of
4.5 μmol/L, respectively.

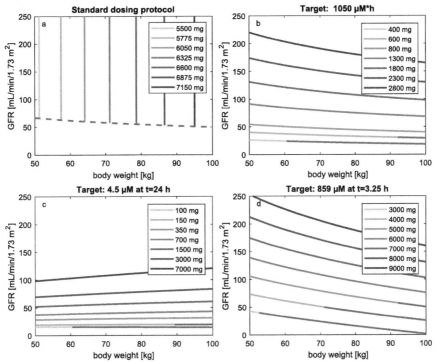

Figure 3 – MTX dosages as a function of body weight and BSA-weighted GFR. The standard
dosing protocol for PCNSL from Joerger et al. (2012a) (a) is compared with model-suggested
dosages corresponding to different targets (b-d). The bottom dashed red curve in panel a
represents the GFR minimum threshold for administration, equal to 60 mL/min. In panels b-d, the
red parts of the curves refer to dosages that lead to concentrations higher than 1 μmol/L after 48 h,
which are associated to MTX toxicity (Joerger et al., 2012b).

We investigated as an additional target a concentration of 859 μmol/L at the end of the
infusion (Fig. 3d), which corresponds to the model-simulated peak concentration
following the administration of the standard 3500 mg/m^2 to a reference virtual patient
with 68 kg body weight and 120 mL/min GFR.

As discussed earlier, the model describes a weak dependence of AUC from body weight,
and thus the optimal dosages to reach the target AUC present little changes with body
weight (Fig. 3b). In Figure 3d, suggested dosages show a weight-dependence similar to
the standard dosing protocol, *i.e.* for a given GFR both the administered and the model-
informed doses increase of about 2000 mg. Conversely, optimal dosages to reach the 24 h
concentration target (Fig. 3c) suggest an inverse relation with weight. In case of renal
function, all model-informed doses present a significant increase with GFR, consistently
with renal filtration being the most important MTX elimination pathway. Unlike these,
however, the standard protocol does not account for the individual degree of renal
function, since dosages are only adjusted according to BSA, if the GFR is above 60
mL/min.

The optimal dosages determined via our PK model differ from the standard protocol considering both the doses (especially in case of AUC target), and the trends as a function of individual body weight and GFR. While the reliability of the optimal dosages depends on the accuracy of the model simulations and should be subject to further studies and improvements, we believe that these results confirm that current MTX dosing protocols can be optimized in an individualized manner to achieve improved outcomes, in agreement with Abrey (2010).

4. Conclusions

Pharmacokinetic models are mathematical tools that can be applied as clinical support tools to suggest individualized, optimal drug dosages to reach desired targets. We applied a pharmacokinetic model of HDMTX for patients with PCNSL to demonstrate its usability, which allows comparing our model-informed dosages with the standard dosing protocol. The results prove the feasibility and potential benefits of this approach, and suggest, in agreement with the literature, that current MTX dosing protocols should be improved and optimized according to the patient's characteristics.

Finally, we believe that the difference among the obtained optimal dosages for different clinical targets underlines the importance of the administration targets, and shows again that pharmacokinetic models can guide their rational definition (Pesenti et al., 2019b), while simultaneously considering toxicity thresholds and other constraints.

References

Abrey, L. E. (2010). Hematology: Individualized methotrexate dosing in primary CNS lymphoma. Nature Reviews Clinical Oncology 7(6): 306.

Joerger, M., Ferreri, A. J. M., Krähenbühl, S., Schellens, J. H. M., Cerny, T., Zucca, E., Huitema, A. D. R. (2012a). Dosing algorithm to target a predefined AUC in patients with primary central nervous system lymphoma receiving high dose methotrexate. British Journal of Clinical Pharmacology 73(2): 240-247.

Joerger, M., Huitema, A. D. R., Illerhaus, G., Ferreri, A. J. M. (2012b). Rational administration schedule for high-dose methotrexate in patients with primary central nervous system lymphoma. Leukemia & Lymphoma 53(10): 1867-1875.

Ma, Y. C.., Zuo, L., Chen, J. H., Luo, Q., Yu, X. Q., Li, Y., Xu, J. S., Huang, S. M., Wang, L. N., Huang, W., Wang, M., Xu, G. B., Wang, H. Y. (2006). Modified Glomerular Filtration Rate Estimating Equation for Chinese Patients with Chronic Kidney Disease. Journal of the American Society of Nephrology. 17 (10):2937-2944.

Mei, S., Li, X., Jiang, X., Yu, K., Lin, S., Zhao, Z. (2018). Population Pharmacokinetics of High-Dose Methotrexate in Patients With Primary Central Nervous System Lymphoma. Journal of Pharmaceutical Sciences 107 (5):1454-1460.

Pesenti, G., Foppoli, M., Manca, D. (2019b). Development of a minimal physiologically-based pharmacokinetic model for high dose methotrexate. Submitted to Journal of Pharmacokinetics and Pharmacodynamics.

Pesenti, G., Savoca, A., Manca, D. (2019a). Optimal dose administration of renally excreted drugs. Computer Aided Chemical Engineering. 46: 547-552.

Sauro Pierucci, Flavio Manenti, Giulia Bozzano, Davide Manca (Eds.)
Proceedings of the 30th European Symposium on Computer Aided Process Engineering
(ESCAPE30), May 24-27, 2020, Milano, Italy. © 2020 Elsevier B.V. All rights reserved.
http://dx.doi.org/10.1016/B978-0-12-823377-1.50120-8

Energy-efficient Solvent Properties for the Post-combustion Carbon Dioxide Capture

He Jin, Pei Liu*, Zheng Li

State Key Lab of Power Systems, International Joint Laboratory on Low Carbon Clean Energy, Innovation, Department of Energy and Power Engineering, Tsinghua University, Beijing, 100084, China
liu_pei@tsinghua.edu.cn

Abstract

Heat consumption is a major concern for the development of the post-combustion CO_2 capture in thermal power plants. In this work, a mathematical model is implemented to minimize the heat duty for a conventional post-combustion CO_2 capture process. An explicit three-parameter vapor-liquid equilibrium (VLE) model is developed. In the VLE model, the solvent is characterized by the absorption heat, indexes for cyclic capacity and absorption capacity. The configuration of these properties is based on typical commercially available solvents. The minimal heat consumption of the optimal solvent is 2.44 MJ/kmol CO_2, which is 70 percent of the conventional MEA solvent. Besides, the match relationship between the absorption heat and lean solvent loading is investigated from the view of balance between absorption and regeneration processes.

Keywords: post-combustion CO_2 capture, modeling and simulation, solvent properties

1. Introduction

Post-combustion CO_2 capture is regarded as a most feasible approach to be configured with coal-fired power plants. However, the major limit for the technology is the high energy consumption for the conventional solvent regeneration, which leads to about ten percentage points penalty for net efficiency (Goto et al, 2013).

Improving solvent properties to be more energy-efficient in carbon capture process has become a focus in recent years. Li et al. proposed a simple VLE approach to optimize a conceptual solvent by using 2-amino-2-methyl-1-propanol (AMP) and N-methyl-diethanolamine (MDEA) aqueous solution (Li et al, 2016). The result showed that the conceptual solvent can reduce 34 percent of total equivalent work comparing to MEA solvent. Kim et al. pointed that the cyclic capacity, absorption performance and reaction heat should be considered simultaneously to minimize the energy demand (Kim et al, 2016). It was because that the impact of different properties on heat duty were interactive. The minimum achievable regeneration heat requirement in a typical process configuration was estimated to be 2.3~2.5 GJ/t CO_2 and the optimal reaction heat was in the range of 60~70 kJ/mol CO_2. Lee et al. developed a semi-empirical method to model CO_2 vapor-liquid equilibrium and absorption rate in a ternary amine solvent (Lee et al, 2019) and provided a new sight for identifying cost effective blended amine solvents in a traditional CO_2 capture process. Ahmad et al. took advantage of a computer aided molecular design technique for developing alternative solvents to replace conventional absorbents (Ahmad et al, 2018). By using the energy-efficient solvent, energy savings can be achieved up to 31.4% compared to the conventional MEA aqueous solvent.

This paper develops a simplified model to obtain an optimal conceptual solvent that owns a minimal heat consumption in a conventional post-combustion CO_2 capture process. An explicit three-parameter vapor-liquid equilibrium model is introduced. The solvent properties are characterized by the absorption heat, cyclic capacity and absorption capacity. The effect of the absorption heat on the heat duty is investigated. The match relationship between the absorption heat and lean solvent loading is also discussed from a view of balancing absorption and regeneration process.

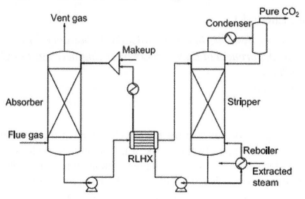

Figure 1. Configuration of a conventional post-combustion CO2 capture process

2. Model development

A typical configuration of a post-combustion CO_2 capture system applied in this study is shown in Figure 1. The flue gas is introduced to the bottom of the absorber and contacts with the countercurrent lean solvent. The CO_2 in the flue gas is absorbed and clean vent gas flows from the top of the column. Through the preheating process in the rich/lean heat exchanger (RLHX), the rich solvent enters the top of the stripper. The CO_2 in the rich solvent is desorbed by the steam generated from the bottom reboiler. The reboiler is heated by extracted steam from the stream cycle. The lean solvent flows from the reboiler to the RLHX to form a closed loop. The CO_2 stream in a high purity is obtained through a condenser. The key to describe the process is modeling the absorbing/striping process in the column, solvent vapor-liquid equilibrium (VLE) properties and heat consumptions.

2.1. Balance equations

The dominant control equations in the absorber and stripper column are balance equations, including mass, component and energy balances, which are listed as follows:

$$0 = \frac{\partial \dot{n}_{tot}^L}{\partial z} + \sum_i N_i \tag{1}$$

$$0 = -\frac{\partial \dot{n}_{tot}^V}{\partial z} - \sum_i N_i \tag{2}$$

$$0 = \frac{\partial \dot{n}_i^L}{\partial z} + N_i \tag{3}$$

$$0 = -\frac{\partial \dot{n}_i^V}{\partial z} - N_i \tag{4}$$

$$0 = C_p^L \dot{n}_{tot}^L \frac{\partial T}{\partial z} + N_{CO_2} \Delta H_{abs} + N_{H_2O} \Delta H_{vap} \tag{5}$$

where the subscripts i represents components H_2O and CO_2, L and V denote liquid and vapor phases respectively, $\dot{n}$ is the flow rate, N is mass transfer rate per unit height, T is temperature, C_p is the specific heat capacity, ΔH_{abs} and ΔH_{vap} stand for the absorption heat of CO_2 and vaporization heat of H_2O respectively.

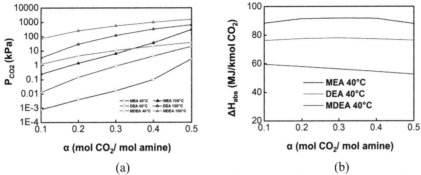

(a)   (b)

Figure 2. The vapor-liquid equilibrium (a) and heat absorption (b) of typical solvents

2.2. Vapor-liquid equilibrium (VLE) model for solvents

The vapor-liquid equilibrium is essential to present solvent properties that affect the performance of a CO_2 capture process. The VLE reflects the absorption heat, cyclic capacity and absorption capacity for an absorbent. The absorption heat can be obtained by Gibbs-Helmholtz equation as Eq. (6) shows, where $P^*_{CO_2}$ denotes equilibrium pressure of CO_2. A parameter $\Delta\alpha$ is defined in Eq. (7), referring the form of Eq. (6), which is the index to present the cyclic capacity in this work. The curves of VLE and absorption heat of typical amines are depicted in Figure 2. According to the data, the absorption heat ΔH_{abs} can be treated as a constant and $\ln P^*_{CO_2}$ is assumed as a linear function of carbon loading α. Then $\ln P^*_{CO_2}$ is integrated to $\Delta\alpha$ and $\frac{1}{T}$ and a three-parameter $(\Delta H_{abs}, \Delta\alpha, \alpha_0)$ model can be derived, as Eq. (8) shows. The parameter α_0 is an integral constant which stands for the absorption capacity of a solvent. Thus, the Eq. (8) is an explicit equation for the three main properties. The values of ΔH_{abs}, $\Delta\alpha$ and α_0 for typical commercially available solvents are listed in Table 1, including primary amine (MEA), secondary amine (DEA), tertiary amine (MDEA) and sterically hindered amine (AMP).

$$\Delta H_{abs} = -R \frac{\partial\left(\ln P^*_{CO_2}\right)}{\partial\left(\frac{1}{T}\right)} \tag{6}$$

$$\Delta\alpha = \frac{\partial\alpha}{\partial\left(\frac{1}{T}\right)} \tag{7}$$

$$\ln P^*_{CO_2} = \frac{\Delta H_{abs}}{R\Delta\alpha}(\alpha - \alpha_0) - \frac{\Delta H_{abs}}{RT} \tag{8}$$

Table 1. Values of ΔH_{abs}, $\Delta\alpha$ and α_0 for typical solvents

	Unit	MEA	DEA	MDEA	TEA	AMP
ΔH_{abs}	MJ/kmol CO_2	90.7	79.6	63.3	50.6	55.1
$\Delta\alpha$	(kmol CO_2*K)/mol amine	0.69	0.66	0.97	0.93	0.62
α_0	mol CO_2/mol amine	-1.68	-1.80	-3.10	-3.36	-1.75

2.3. Heat consumptions

In the carbon capture process, the total heat demand q contains three parts: the sensible heat q_{sen}, the vaporization heat q_{vap} and absorption heat q_{abs}.

$$q = q_{sen} + q_{vap} + q_{abs} \tag{9}$$

$$q_{sen} = C^L_p(T_{reb} - T_{RLHX})\dot{n}^L_{tot}/\Delta\dot{n}^V_{CO_2} \tag{10}$$

$$q_{vap} = \Delta\dot{n}^V_{H_2O} \cdot \Delta H_{vap}/\Delta\dot{n}^V_{CO_2} \tag{11}$$

$q_{abs} = \Delta H_{abs}$ (12) where $\Delta \dot{n}^V_{CO_2}$ is captured CO_2 flow rate, $\Delta \dot{n}^V_{H_2O}$ is stripped H_2O flow rate. In this work, a conceptual solvent with heat consumption minimum can be derived through solving an optimization problem. The structure of the optimization problem is presented in Table 2. In addition, the boundary conditions for ΔH_{abs}, $\Delta \alpha$ and α_0 refer to the data listed in Table 1.

Table 2. The structure of optimization problem for conceptual solvents

Objective function	Optimization variables	Main constraints for the process
Min q	ΔH_{abs}, $\Delta \alpha$ and α_0 α	$\Delta T = 5\ K$, $P_{ABS} = 100\ kPa$, $P_{RLHX} = P_{STR} = 200\ kPa$, $\eta = 90\%$

3. Results and discussions

The optimization results of conceptual solvents are listed in Table 3. The minimum for total heat demands in the typical carbon capture process is 2.44 MJ/kg CO_2. Comparing with 3.5 MJ/kg CO_2 for the conventional MEA solvent, the optimal solvent can reduce 30 percent of the heat consumption. Table 4 shows the impact of the increase of each property on absorption and regeneration. From this qualitative analysis, it can be noted that the raise of absorption heat ΔH_{abs} promotes the regeneration process but resists absorption process. The raise of cyclic capacity $\Delta \alpha$ and absorption capacity α_0 promotes the absorption process but resists regeneration process. Due to the opposite effect on absorption and regeneration, the values of properties may achieve to an optimal point that balances both the absorption and regeneration.

Table 3. The optimization results of conceptual solvents

	q	ΔH_{abs}	$\Delta \alpha$	α_0		α
Unit	MJ/kg CO_2	MJ/kmol CO_2	(kmol CO_2*K)/mol amine	mol amine	CO_2/mol	mol CO_2/mol amine
Values	2.44	61.1	0.97	-3.26		0

Table 4. Effect of the increase of each property on the absorption and regeneration

	ΔH_{abs}	$\Delta \alpha$	α_0
Absorption	-	+	+
Regeneration	+	-	-

where '+' stands for promotion, '-' stands for inhibition.

3.1. Impact of the absorption heat on the heat duty
Keeping the cyclic capacity, absorption capacity and lean solvent loading the same as the optimal solvent, the effect of heat absorption on the heat duty is displayed in Figure 3(a). The total heat reaches a minimum as the heat absorption increases, which is a balance result between sensible and vaporization heat. A higher heat absorption results in a higher CO_2 equilibrium pressure, so the absorption process is repressed. The adverse influence is characterized by the decrease of the cyclic loading as shown in Figure 3(b). Therefore, a higher lean solvent flow rate is required to capture the same amount of CO_2 as the heat absorption raises as shown in Figure 3(c). The increase in circulating rate leads to the increase of sensible heat. On the contrary, the higher CO_2 equilibrium pressure is, the easier for CO_2 to be stripped. As displayed in Figure 3(d), the temperature in reboiler decreases monotonically with the increase of absorption heat, which lowers the

vaporization heat. In addition, the temperature of hot rich solvent is higher than the bubble point so a part of CO_2 is pre-stripped in the RLHX.

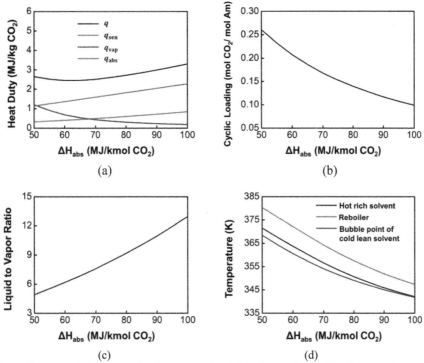

Figure 3. Effect of the absorption heat on the heat duty (a), cyclic loading (b), liquid to vapor ratio (c) and temperature in the regeneration side (d)

3.2. The match relationship between the absorption heat and lean solvent loading

In order to minimize the energy consumption, operational parameters should match the circulating solvents with different properties. In this study, the operational parameter is specifically lean solvent loading α. Keeping the cyclic capacity and absorption capacity the same, Figure 4 displays the effect of lean solvent loading on the heat requirement under different absorption heat. It is noteworthy that the total heat consumption is reduced at first then increased as lean carbon loading raises. The total heat consumption achieves to a minimum value as a result of mutual effect between the sensible heat and vaporization heat. The sensible heat raises with the lean solvent loading, as a higher lean loading results in a higher demand for the lean solvent flow rate to achieve the given CO_2 capture rate. Meanwhile, the vaporization heat decreases obviously with the lean solvent loading because a lower amount of stripping steam is required to reach a higher loading in the regeneration part. Comparing the solvents with different absorption heat, a lower absorption heat leads to a higher optimal lean solvent loading. The phenomenon can be explained by the opposite effect on absorption and regeneration. The increase of absorption heat and lean solvent both enhances absorption and inhibits regeneration. As the absorption heat raises, the increment of sensible heat is lower than the reduction of vaporization heat. In order to reach a new balance between absorption and regeneration, optimal lean solvent tend to move to an opposite direction to offset the effect.

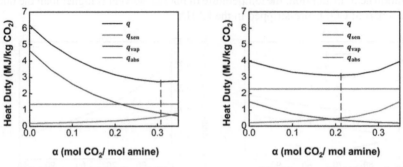

(a) $\Delta H_{abs} = 60 \; MJ/kmol \; CO_2$ (b) $\Delta H_{abs} = 90 \; MJ/kmol \; CO_2$

Figure 4. The effect of the lean solvent loading on the heat requirement for solvents with different absorption heat.

4. Conclusions

This paper develops a model for deriving a conceptual solvent with minimum of heat consumption in the post-combustion CO_2 capture process. A simplified three-parameter vapor-liquid equilibrium model is implemented. In the VLE model, solvent properties are characterized by the absorption heat, cyclic capacity and absorption capacity. The minimum of heat consumption is 2.44 MJ/kg CO_2, which is 70% of conventional MEA solvent. The increase of absorption heat raises sensible heat but reduces vaporization heat so the minimal heat consumption is a result of balancing between the absorption and regeneration process. In addition, to minimize heat duty, lean solvent loading is required to the match with the absorption heat. The optimal lean solvent loading is determined by offsetting the impact of changes in the absorption heat on the absorption and regeneration process.

Acknowledgments

The authors gratefully acknowledge the support by The National Key Research and Development of China (2016YFE0102500, 2018YFB0604301), Shanxi Key Research and Development Program (201603D312001), National Natural Science Foundation of China (71690245), and the Phase III Collaboration between BP and Tsinghua University.

References

Ahmad, M. Z., Hashim, H., Mustaffa, A. A., Maarof, H., & Yunus, N. A., 2018, Design of energy efficient reactive solvents for post combustion CO2 capture using computer aided approach. Journal of cleaner production, 176, 704-715.

Goto, K., Yogo, K., Higashii, T., 2013, A review of efficiency penalty in a coal-fired power plant with post-combustion CO2 capture. Applied Energy, 111, 710-720.

Kim, H., Lee, K. S., 2016, Design guidance for an energy-thrift absorption process for carbon capture: Analysis of thermal energy consumption for a conventional process configuration. International Journal of Greenhouse Gas Control, 47, 291-302.

Lee, J., Kim, J., Kim, H., 2019, A new modeling approach for a CO2 capture process based on a blended amine solvent. Journal of Natural Gas Science and Engineering, 61, 206-214.

Li, Z., Chen, S., Hopkinson, D., Luebke, D., 2016. Verification of a solvent optimization approach for postcombustion CO2 capture using commercial alkanolamines. International Journal of Greenhouse Gas Control, 44, 59-65.

Sauro Pierucci, Flavio Manenti, Giulia Bozzano, Davide Manca (Eds.)
Proceedings of the 30th European Symposium on Computer Aided Process Engineering
(ESCAPE30), May 24-27, 2020, Milano, Italy. © 2020 Elsevier B.V. All rights reserved.
http://dx.doi.org/10.1016/B978-0-12-823377-1.50121-X

The Role of Process Engineering in the Digital Transformation

Norbert Jung

AVEVA, Germany

Norbert.jung@aveva.com

Abstract

The process engineering discipline has been largely excluded from Digital Transformation trends. The objective of this presentation is to provide an overview of the obstacles to Digital Transformation for the process discipline and explain how these can be overcome. A special emphasis will be given on the role of the process simulation tool (white box modelling) as a catalyst for transformational change.

The presentation will examine several challenges specific to process engineering:

1) Process simulators are divided into single-purpose point solutions. Separate models may be created for process design, control strategy design, operator training simulation, performance monitoring and online optimization.

2) Process simulators are typically poorly integrated into engineering workflows beyond the process world, and if so, with a single directional information flow.

3) Legacy process simulators are overloaded with niche features and functions only usable by experts.

4) The potential benefits of Artificial Intelligence and Machine Learning for process engineering are not widely understood.

Industry stakeholders see the Digital Twin as the most important building block for Digital Transformation of the process industries. While legacy simulators are well-suited to accurately simulate processes, their decades-old architectures mean they are not ideal to serve the entire plant lifecycle and support the Digital Transformation. We will use the AVEVA SimCentral Simulation Platform[4] as an example of how the identified obstacles can be overcome with a next generation process simulator. Case examples from leading companies will be outlined.

Keywords: Process Simulation, Digital Transformation, Unified Engineering.

1. The Role of Process Engineering in the Digital Transformation

While Digital Transformation hits every corner of industry, the process engineering discipline has been largely excluded from this trend so far. PwC foresee that for process licensors / EPCs, data driven digital services can displace process technology as a differentiator[1].

2. An Industry in Need of Change

Never have the stakes been higher for companies when it comes to making improvements to their engineering work processes to maximize ROI on Capital Projects. Productivity has not developed in decades – the average Capital Project schedule lags by 20 months and goes over budget by 80%[5]. While the cost of engineering and design typically amounts to just 10% of the overall project cost, the work being carried out here heavily influences what happens in procurement and construction. The leading cause of rework in project execution is design errors and omissions, and according to research, they contribute to over 5.4% of the total construction cost[6]. Engineering errors alone make up 14.2% of the total contract value[7].

3. A New Approach for Unified Engineering

Companies' are beginning to make progress on their digitalization journey, finding the right applications for digital transformation and seeing increasingly better returns on their investment. While the age-old market environment challenges (such as supply and demand, cost and price) haven't gone away, competitive pressures are making the digital transformation opportunity more pressing than ever.

Many have already started to leverage the latest data-centric technology and work processes for their workforce to collaborate and take control of their data, reducing the risk for errors, delays and increased project cost throughout the asset lifecycle. This phase of the digitalization journey is what we call EPC 4.0.

To reduce the number of iterations in FEED, process engineers must work concurrently with other disciplines. All information must be stored and exchanged as data to ensure there is always clear visibility of progress across the entire project. Unified Engineering manages and drives positive change within an organization to ensure risk is minimized during the early project phase right up to the Digital Twin deliverable to the Owner.

Unified Engineering breaks down the silos between process and engineering design and ensures each discipline has ownership of their data and the reassurance that it is always correct. Early FEED is a highly iterative process but with Unified Engineering data is entered only once. The simulation data created in FEED is readily available for use in Detailed Design, increasing efficiency across projects. Procurement errors and delays are avoided, and rework caused by poor quality deliverables is eliminated.

Unified Engineering is not just about collecting simulation data into a database. It is about empowering people to take full control, to manage the data effectively. Even when big changes have been made, Unified Engineering ensures they can be easily validated.

4. Lifecycle Simulation Supports Unified Engineering

According to DECHEMA, one major obstacle for digital transformation is the division of process simulators into single-purpose point solutions. Today, separate models may be created – often in different tools – for process design, control strategy design, operator training simulation, performance monitoring and online optimization. This drives up the total cost of modelling to a degree than can become prohibitively expensive. One single model should be able to cover the entire plant lifecycle from idea to operations[2].

4.1 Problems with Legacy Simulators

Process simulators are irreplaceable tools for every process engineer. Since the nineteen seventies, process simulators have found widespread adoption within operating companies in oil & gas, refining and chemical industries, as well as the engineering companies and equipment manufacturers that service these industries. The tools available in the market today have incrementally improved over the years to provide more features and functionality. However, they trace their origins to legacy architectures, operating systems and aftermarket user interfaces, which create inherent limitations:

- They cannot support the full plant lifecycle as they are limited by their single-purpose architecture such as steady state process simulation, dynamic simulation, optimization, or flow network analysis for which they were originally designed.

- Extending their functionality can be performed by a very small number of software developers with chemical engineering knowledge, software programming skills, and/or knowledge of that particular specialized program.

- They are often based on decades old programming code that cannot leverage the more recent technological developments within the software industry.

The next generation of workers also expects a modern, scalable and easy to use solution with technology they now take for granted – high speed internet access, mobile devices, touch screens and virtual reality. New concepts like the Industrial Internet of Things (IIoT), Industry 4.0, and Artificial Intelligence have created greater opportunities with a new next generation platform that provides a "Digital Twin" of the plant through the process lifecycle that cannot be provided with today's tools.

4.2 Lifecycle Simulation

Lifecycle Simulation means that one process model is extended throughout the entire lifecycle of the plant, from concept through to operations. This requires a process design mode, a fluid flow/rating mode and a dynamic mode, in combination with the ability to toggle back and forth between modes. Optimization may be provided to any mode. Table 1 describes each phase of the project lifecycle, and how a maturing Digital Twin develops and provides benefits for each phase.

Lifecycle Phase	Model	Benefits
Conceptual Engineering	The Digital Twin of a process plant is "first born"	• Fast evaluation of design alternatives due to continuously solved and flexible specifications
		• A native Cloud application that protects IP to reduce IT costs • Open modeling for first-of-a-kind processes and equipment
Front End Engineering and Design (FEED)	The Digital Twin grows to represent all plant process equipment	• One product with one learning curve for multiple applications, such as process, process utilities, and relief and flare • Integrated Asset Modeling of interacting but separate systems, such as, an oil field gathering and topsides processing, or the process and its flare system • Automated population of the Unified Engineering database • Automated creation of FEED engineering deliverables • Multi-user collaboration of a single simulation
Detailed Engineering	Simulation-Driven Engineering: The Digital Twin grows to also represent the mechanical design and the control strategy	• Other disciplines, such as Controls, Mechanical, Piping, all contribute to the Unified Engineering database • Simulation takes information from the engineering database to test the Digital Twin continuously as it is designed • Process engineering trends towards new agile software engineering practices with a test-driven development now made possible because of the existence of the Digital Twin
Startup and Commissioning	The Digital Twin is used for Operator Training and Controls Checkout	• The actual DCS logic can be integrated to the Digital Twin • Operators are trained without a separate operator training simulator investment
Operations	The Digital Twin is a master simulation model for process improvement, equipment monitoring, optimization, and more	• One master Digital Twin model can be spawned to many applications, such as, training, equipment monitoring, and real-time optimization to reduce the sustainment costs associated with separate point solutions • No longer need to maintain several process simulation models for a plant—design model, operator training simulator (OTS) model, unit performance monitoring and real-time optimization (RTO)

4.3 Agile Process Design

In another engineering discipline, software engineering, work practices have changed significantly over the last 15 years. Previous software development followed a "waterfall" process of design specifications, component development, integration, in a sequential process with exit stage gates similar to the process engineering lifecycle stages. Now, software engineers embrace a new work process known as agile software development with test-driven development at its core.

Agile development plans small amounts of work with continuous integrated testing to reduce development cost while eliminating surprises at the end of the project. But, as plants are made of steel and concrete it is not easy to test a process design until it is procured, constructed, and started, at which time it is too late. Accordingly, engineering companies have numerous design reviews and use simulation as appropriate in dedicated studies to ensure design.

Next generation simulation software must allow process facilities engineering to move towards agile software development concepts using the Digital Twin during the design of the process plant. This First Born Digital Twin during design provides an opportunity to test new design and to continuously check inconsistencies at minimum cost.

For example, a process engineer of the future needs to design the emergency depressuring system for an offshore system. The engineer specifies a dynamic simulation from the engineering database. The valve Cv, and equipment volumes are taken from the engineering database. The engineer confirms the valve Cvs, that the depressuring time meets requirements, and that the temperatures are not too cold for the metallurgy. The emergency controls are integrated so that the volume between isolation valves is used for the calculation. Instead of doing this one time, the test is automated to confirm that the design continues to be adequate as the plant is further designed. Future changes to vessel size, control size, valve Cv will create a warning to the engineer. This depressuring test is one of hundreds of similar design tests necessary to prove the plant can start, operate, and shutdown properly given its feedstock, equipment design, and control design, as specified by the owner operator, and process, mechanical, and control engineers.

5. Conclusions

It used to be claimed that in order to cut cost and reduce project risks during the design and construction phase of major capital projects, you had to ensure that the plant design was completed 'right first time'. To eradicate iterations and rework in design and get it right from the outset, you would need to ensure that everyone in project execution was equipped with the latest and most accurate information. Although the 'right first time' approach is an attractive vision, the realities of a complex capital project present far too many obstacles. Reducing the risk of engineering and design errors is therefore an essential factor in lowering project cost and minimising the risk for overruns and delays.

To minimize the risk of cost overruns and delays, companies need an integrated, data-centric solution to manage all engineering information in one place. This enables engineers from all disciplines to collaborate effectively, detect and identify changes as soon as they occur and compare and update them efficiently. Organizations who rapidly and accurately communicate change in the FEED and detailed design phase will be the most effective during procurement and construction to capitalize on project execution.

Unified Engineering enables companies to leverage their EPC 4.0 strategy with data-centric collaboration on a global scale, digitally through one platform, so the entire process can be traced, tracked, and linked – from FEED engineering and detailed design, all the way up to day-to-day operations and maintenance of your asset.

Lifecycle process simulation has been a vision for process simulation providers and their customers for a long time. Today's simulators cannot leverage the rapid developments occurring in the software industry due to legacy architecture. The next generation Unified Lifecycle Simulation platform SimCentral Simulation Platform, by AVEVA is a brand new offering in the market. Being built from the ground up, it offers many advantages as this paper has outlined.

References

[1]Digital business models in plant engineering and construction in an international comparison, A benchmarking study of PwC and VDMA, May 2019 (link)

[2]DECHEMA Whitepaper Digitalisierung in der Chemieindustrie, September 2016 (link)

[3]DECHEMA Tutzingen Thesen 2018 (link in english)

[4]AVEVA SimCentral Simulation Platform (link)

[5]Optimise your engineering and design processes to boost collaboration and reduce project costs and delays; Sabharwal, A., Taylor, M.

[6]Unified Engineering: A new proposition to break down the silos between FEED and Detailed Design to minimize risk and maximize return on Capital Investment; Taylor, M.

[7]Building a Digital Twin of Your Process Plant with Unified Lifecycle Simulation; Jung, N., Depew, C.

Sauro Pierucci, Flavio Manenti, Giulia Bozzano, Davide Manca (Eds.)
Proceedings of the 30th European Symposium on Computer Aided Process Engineering
(ESCAPE30), May 24-27, 2020, Milano, Italy. © 2020 Elsevier B.V. All rights reserved.
http://dx.doi.org/10.1016/B978-0-12-823377-1.50122-1

A Mixed Integer Nonlinear Approach for the Automated Superstructure Generation Problem

Luca Mencarelli,* Alexandre Pagot

IFP Energies nouvelles, Rond-point de l'échangeur de Solaize, 69360 Solaize, France

luca.mencarelli.home@gmail.com

Abstract

We describe a new mixed integer nonlinear programming approach for the automated superstructure generation problem in process synthesis engineering, whose target consists in defining and optimizing the superstructure, i.e., the union of all the alternative structures, of a given chemical process cluster. We develop a mixed integer nonlinear formulation for the problem in order to define the links between the chemical units and we implement it with respect to the integrated process of catalytic reforming and light naphtha isomerization in petroleum refinery. The formulation is based on the definition of a graph, whose nodes are the chemical units and whose arcs represent the links between units. The chemical processes are then replaced by their corresponding surrogate models, which represent a systematic way to mathematically represent the input/output relationships of the given processes.

Keywords: Mixed Integer Nonlinear Programming, Superstructure, Surrogate modelling.

1. Introduction

Superstructure generation and optimization constitutes an emerging topic in Process System Engineering (PSE) (see Chen and Grossmann (2017)). The superstructure of a given chemical process is defined as the set of all possible alternative process structures. Generally, a superstructure is manually defined and then optimize, see, e.g., Duchêne et al. (2019) where a superstructure-based optimization methodology is proposed for the integrated process of catalytic reforming and light naphtha isomerization. However, when the superstructure is manually defined, several feasible or even optimal structures may be not encoded in superstructure representation: automated superstructure procedures can cope with this drawback. Automated superstructure approaches consider computational procedures in order to algorithmically define and optimize the superstructure. For a detailed survey about superstructure generation methodologies we refer the interested reader to Mencarelli et al. (2019).

2. Mixed integer nonlinear formulations

In this section, we introduce our mixed integer nonlinear programming (MINLP) formulations for the automated superstructure generation problem. A superstructure is represented by a graph $G(N,A)$ whose nodes represent units and edges represent links between units. We present two formulations: in the first one, nodes are splitters or process units, while, in the second one, there are no more nodes for splitters, which are substituted by cut-points.

2.1. With splitters nodes

Sets. Let L be the set of splitter branches and J be the set components in the superstructure. F and P represent the set of feed and products, respectively. We indicate with S the set of splitters. U is the set of process units and C is the set of process unit configuration.

Binary variables. Each arc is represented by a binary variable equal to 1 if the arc belongs to $G(N,A)$. a_{fu} indicate feed/unit arcs (f in F, u in U), a_{fn} feed/node arcs (f in F, n in N), a_{fnl} node/unit arcs (f in F, n in N, l in L), a_{n1n2l} node/node arcs (n_1,n_2 in N, l in L), a_{un} unit/node arcs (u in U, n in N), a_{upl} unit/product arcs (u in U, p in P, l in L), and a_{npl} node/product arcs (n in N, p in P, l in L),. Let v_{ns} and w_{uc} be two binary variables such that $v_{ns}=1$ if there is splitter s in S in node n in N and $w_{uc}=1$ if the process unit u in U is in configuration c in C, respectively.

Continuous variables. Each component flow is represented by a (non-negative) continuous variable Q_j. The superscripts *in* and *out* indicate inflow and outflow, respectively, while the subscripts have the same meaning as for the arc variables. Q_{uj} is the total inflow per component j in J per unit u in U, Q_{nj} is the total inflow per node n in N, and Q_{pj} is the total inflow per product p in P. V_{uc} indicates the vector of process variables per configuration c in C of process unit u in U.

Constraints. The total inflow for process unit, node, and product are given by:

$$Q_{nj}^{in} = \sum_{u \in U} Q_{unj} + \sum_{f \in F} Q_{fnj} + \sum_{n_1 \in N} \sum_{l \in L} Q_{n_1 nlj} \qquad \forall n \in N, \forall j \in J \qquad (1)$$

$$Q_{uj}^{in} = \sum_{f \in F} Q_{fuj} + \sum_{n \in N} \sum_{l \in L} Q_{nulj} \qquad \forall u \in U, \forall j \in J \qquad (2)$$

$$Q_{nj}^{in} = \sum_{u \in U} Q_{upj} + \sum_{n \in N} \sum_{l \in L} Q_{nplj} \qquad \forall p \in P, \forall j \in J \qquad (3)$$

Let i_{slj} be the outflow fraction per splitter s in S, branch l in L, and component j in J. The splitter outflow Q_{nlj}^{out} is such that the following big-M constraints hold:

$$Q_{nlj}^{out} \leq i_{slj} Q_{nj}^{in} + M(1 - v_{ns}) \qquad \forall n \in N, \forall j \in J, \forall l \in L \qquad (4)$$

$$Q_{nlj}^{out} \geq i_{slj} Q_{nj}^{in} - M(1 - v_{ns}) \qquad \forall n \in N, \forall j \in J, \forall l \in L \qquad (5)$$

$$Q^{out}_{nlj} \leq M \sum_{s \in S} v_{ns} \qquad \forall n \in N, \forall j \in J, \forall l \in L \qquad (6)$$

$$Q^{out}_{nj} = \sum_{u \in U} Q_{nulj} + \sum_{p \in P} Q_{nplj} + \sum_{n_1 \in N} Q_{n_1 plj} \qquad \forall n \in N, \forall j \in J, \forall l \in L \qquad (7)$$

Constraints (4)-(6) force splitter outflow to be equal to splitter inflow multiplied by the corresponding outflow fraction. Equation (7) is the material balance constraint between arc output and outflow. Let R_{ucj} be the surrogate model for all components but two of configuration c in C in process unit u in U.

$$Q^{out}_{uj} \leq R_{ucj}(Q^{in}_{ucj}, V_{uc}) + M(1 - w_{uc}) \qquad \forall u \in U, \forall j \in J \qquad (8)$$

$$Q^{out}_{uj} \geq R_{ucj}(Q^{in}_{ucj}, V_{uc}) - M(1 - w_{uc}) \qquad \forall u \in U, \forall j \in J \qquad (9)$$

$$Q^{out}_{uj} \leq M \sum_{c \in C} w_{uc} \qquad \forall u \in U, \forall j \in J \qquad (10)$$

$$Q^{out}_{uj} = \sum_{n \in N} Q_{unj} + \sum_{p \in P} Q_{upj} + \sum_{u_1 \in U} Q_{uu_1 j} \qquad \forall u \in U, \forall j \in J \qquad (11)$$

We retrieve the values of the two (not modelled) components by mean of carbon/hydrogen molar balance constraints (see Duchêne et al. (2019)). Moreover, we consider also the following arc constraints:

$$a_{nnl} = 0 \qquad \forall n \in N, \forall l \in L \qquad (12)$$

$$\sum_{p \in P} a_{up} + \sum_{n \in N} a_{un} \leq 1 \qquad \forall u \in U \qquad (13)$$

$$\sum_{u \in U} a_{nu} + \sum_{n_1 \in N} a_{nn_1 l} + \sum_{p \in P} a_{npl} \leq 1 \qquad \forall n \in N, \forall l \in L \qquad (14)$$

$$\sum_{n \in N} a_{fn} + \sum_{u \in U} a_{fu} = 1 \qquad \forall f \in F \qquad (15)$$

$$\sum_{u \in U} a_{up} + \sum_{n \in N} \sum_{l \in L} a_{npl} \leq 1 \qquad \forall p \in P \qquad (16)$$

$$\sum_{l \in L} (a_{n_2 n_1 l} + a_{n_1 n_2 l}) \leq 1 \qquad\qquad \forall n_1 n_2 \in N \qquad\qquad (17)$$

Constraint (12) prevents node loops in $G(N,A)$. Equations (13)-(14) constraint each arc from unit and node, respectively, to appear at most one time in $G(N,A)$, while constraints (15)-(16) force arcs from feed and product, respectively, to appear exactly one time in $G(N,A)$. Eq. (17) is the constraint selection for the node/node arcs.

Finally, we model splitter selection per node and configuration selection per process unit, respectively, as follows:

$$\sum_{s \in S} v_{ns} = 1 \qquad\qquad \forall n \in N \qquad\qquad (18)$$

$$\sum_{c \in C} w_{uc} = 1 \qquad\qquad \forall u \in U \qquad\qquad (19)$$

Several additional constraints can also be enforced for process output quality (see Duchêne et al. (2019)).

Objective function. We maximize the net (hourly) profit given by the difference between input naphtha costs and output earnings (see Duchêne et al. (2019)).

2.2. With cut-points

Instead of modelling explicitly the splitters, we define "common cuts" for splitter, feeds and products, by means of a binary matrix D_{lj} whose columns sum up to 1. The flows can be split in "common cuts" by applying the previous matrix to the flows. For instance, for unit/unit flows we have

$$Q_{u_1 u_2 l j} = D_{lj} Q_{u_1 u_2 j} \qquad\qquad \forall u_1, u_2 \in U, \forall l \in L, \forall j \in J \qquad\qquad (20)$$

Then, we select the routing of each common cut for each process, feed, and product by summing the previous common cut flows.

Moreover, several types of constraints are implemented:

- selection constraints: there should be at exactly one destination per feed split, one destination per nodes split:

$$\sum_{u \in U} a_{ful} + \sum_{p \in P} a_{fpl} = 1 \qquad\qquad \forall f \in F, \forall l \in L \qquad\qquad (21)$$

$$\sum_{u_2 \in U} a_{fuu_2 l} + \sum_{p \in P} a_{upl} \leq 1 \qquad \forall u \in U, \forall l \in L \qquad (22)$$

respectively, and at least one surrogate model configuration per process (see Eq. (19));

- arc rates constraints: the flow is equal to 0 if the corresponding arc does not belong to $G(N,A)$ (see Eq. (10));
- material balance constraints: flow conservation between process unit inlet and outlet flows (see Eq. (11));
- product quality constraints: minimum level of RON and maximum level of benzene for the gasoline (see Duchêne et al. (2019)).

Moreover, constraint (12) is removed. We introduce also the concept of "cut-point": there is a cut-point if the difference of consecutive values of the binary decision variables for arc activation/deactivation is equal to 1. We have as many types of cut-point as arc types. We can consider the splitter costs in the economic objective function by considering a penalty for the cut-point.

The next step consists in considering continuous splitters by introducing additional continuous variables:

- b_{u1u2l} for the flow ratio between process units u_1, u_2 in U per branch l in L,
- b_{ful} for the flow ratio between feed f in F and unit u in U per branch l in L, and
- b_{upl} for the flow ratio between units u in U and product p in P per branch l in L.

For each continuous variable, we add a bunch of constraints in order to guarantee the corresponding value is 0 if the arc is not activated. For instance, for process units we have

$$b_{u_1 u_2 l} \leq a_{u_1 u_2 l} \qquad \forall u_1, u_2 \in U, \forall l \in L \qquad (23)$$

Analogous constraints are considered for arcs between feeds and nodes, and nodes and products. Constraints (21)-(22) are replaced by

$$\sum_{u \in U} a_{ful} + \sum_{p \in P} a_{fpl} \leq \text{max\_arc} \qquad \forall f \in F, \forall l \in L \qquad (24)$$

$$\sum_{u_2 \in U} a_{uu_2 l} + \sum_{p \in P} a_{upl} \leq \text{max\_arc} \qquad \forall u \in U, \forall l \in L \qquad (25)$$

where max_*arc* is the maximum number of arcs among which a flow can be split.

Our superstructure generation methodology is hence articulated in two main steps: (i) find a first feasible solution with continuous splitter and high value for cut points penalty, and (ii) solve the problem by varying the number of cut point with low penalty.

3. Numerical Results

We consider the integrated process of catalytic reforming and light naphtha isomerization with aromatic extraction to obtain high octane gasoline with low level of benzene (for complete information about processes and instances, see Duchêne et al. (2019)). We set max_$arc := 2$ and $M := 600$.

The codes are implemented in GAMS 25.1.2 running BARON 18.5.8 on a Dell machine equipped with an Intel(R) Xeon(R) E5-1620 v3 CPU @ 3.50GHz with 16.00 GB RAM mounting Windows 7 Professional Operating System. For the Manual superstructure, allowed arc and splits have been bounded to represent the superstructure considered in previous works (see Duchêne et al. (2019)).

Table 1: Numerical results

Model type	Objective function	CPU time
Manual superstructure	42.41	1,060 seconds (*)
Formulation without cut-points variation	42.41	3,600 seconds (**)
Formulation with cut-points variation	42.21	2,581 seconds (***)

(*) optimality satisfied, optimal solution found after 19 seconds
(**) maximum time, optimal solution found after 17 seconds
(***) maximum time per iteration = 600 seconds

4. Conclusion

In this paper, we have proposed a novel automated superstructure methodology in order to (i) retrieve the best process structure, and (ii) determine the best operating conditions for the process. We have applied our method to the catalytic reforming and light naphtha isomerization integrated process. We obtain promising preliminary results: results obtained with our methodology based on cut-point variation provide similar results that direct optimization but provides objective function sensitivity to number of cut points.

References

Q. Chen, I. Grossmann, 2017, Recent developments and challenges in optimization-based process synthesis, Annual Review of Chemical and Biomolecular Engineering 8, 249–283.

P. Duchêne, L. Mencarelli, A. Pagot, 2019, Optimization approaches to the integrated system of catalytic reforming and isomerization processes in petroleum refinery, Tech. rep., IFP Energies nouvelles, Solaize, France.

L. Mencarelli, Q. Chen, A. Pagot, I. Grossmann, 2019, A review on superstructure optimization approaches in process system engineering, Tech. rep., IFP Energies nouvelles, Solaize, France, and Department of Chemical Engineering, Carnegie Mellon University, Pittsburgh.

Sauro Pierucci, Flavio Manenti, Giulia Bozzano, Davide Manca (Eds.)
Proceedings of the 30th European Symposium on Computer Aided Process Engineering
(ESCAPE30), May 24-27, 2020, Milano, Italy. © 2020 Elsevier B.V. All rights reserved.
http://dx.doi.org/10.1016/B978-0-12-823377-1.50123-3

Rational Design of Ion Exchange Simulated Moving Bed Processes

Marcus Fechtner[a,*], Achim Kienle[a,b]

[a]*Otto-von-Guericke-Universität Magdeburg, Chair for Automation and Modelling,
Universitätsplatz 2, 39106 Magdeburg, Germany*
[b]*Max Planck Institute for Dynamics of Complex Technical Systems,Process Synthesis
and Process Dynamics, Sandtorstraße 1, 39106 Magdeburg, Germany*
fechtner@ovgu.de

Abstract

Triangle theory, a powerful tool for the rational design of simulated moving bed processes, was developed by the group of Morbidelli, see (Migliorini et al., 1998) and references therein. In this paper, we extend this theory to classical ion exchange processes by applying the generalized approach of Migliorini et al. (2000). Results are verified by simulations of the related true moving bed process. For this purpose, our numerical approach for single column processes introduced in (Fechtner and Kienle, 2017) is extended to these types of processes while preserving all its advantages.

Keywords: triangle theory, ion exchange, true moving bed, simulated moving bed.

1. Introduction

Chromatographic ion exchange is an important class of separation processes applied in biotechnology and the pharmaceutical industry for the separation of amino acids and proteins, for example. Simulated moving bed (SMB) processes represent a powerful technology for continuous chromatographic separations. Triangle theory as introduced by Migliorini et al. (1998) can be used for the rational design of SMB processes. The theory is based on an idealized mathematical model that allows an analytical solution using the method of characteristics (MOC) for certain types of explicit adsorption isotherms including linear and Langmuir isotherms (Mazzotti et al., 1997). In the present contribution the theory is extended to stoichiometric ion exchange, which is also referred to as classical ion exchange (CIE) if a constant solution normality is assumed. Sorption is described by

Table 1: Process and simulation parameters.

parameter	value	description
$L[m]$	0.5	column length
$L_j[m]$	0.125	section length
$A[m^2]$	0.2	cross sectional area
$N_z[-]$	800	spatial grid points
$v_s[m/s]$	0.1	interstitial velocity
$\varepsilon[-]$	0.5	void fraction
$q_{tot}[mol/l]$	2.0	exchanger capacity
$c_{tot}[mol/l]$	1.0	solution normality
$K_{13}[-]$	8.0	equilibrium constant
$K_{23}[-]$	1.143	equilibrium constant
$\mu_1[-]$	2	stoichiometric factor
$\mu_2[-]$	1	stoichiometric factor
$\mu_3[-]$	1	stoichiometric factor
$c_1^{feed}[mol/l]$	0.3	feed of component 1
$c_1^{feed}[mol/l]$	0.4	feed of component 2

implicit isotherms resulting from the corresponding mass cation laws. Therefore, an analytical approach is not possible anymore. Using the theoretical results for a single column (Fechtner and Kienle, 2017, 2019) and following the ideas presented by by Migliorini et al. (2000), a corresponding semi-analytical approach is proposed. The approach allows to determine the total separation in the space of the design parameters. Results are validated by rigorous numerical solution of the full blown model. Further, they are shown to be superior to a simplified approach, where the ion exchange equilibrium is fitted with a Langmuir isotherm, and which is frequently applied in practice. Finally, use of the solution normality as additional design parameter is discussed.

2. Triangle theory

2.1. Ideal Model and CIE

The design procedure for the SMB first introduced by Migliorini et al. (1998) is based on the analytical solution of an ideal true moving bed (TMB) model

$$\frac{\partial}{\partial t}(c_{i,j} + Fq_{i,j}) + Fu_s \frac{\partial}{\partial z}(m_j c_{i,j} - q_{i,j}) = \mathbf{0} \tag{1}$$

using the MOC in case of Riemann problems, i.e. piece-wise constant initial conditions $c_j(0, z) = c_j^{init}$ and boundary conditions $c_j(t,0) = c_j^{feed}$ as well as $q_j(t,1) = q^{feed}$ (Rhee et al., 1989). Note, the process is initially equilibrated and the thermodynamic equilibrium between the fluid phase with c and the solid phase with q represented by some isotherm $q(\mathbf{c})$ holds, i.e. $\mathbf{q}_j(0, z) = \mathbf{q}_j(\mathbf{c}_j)$. Variable $t = t^* u_s / L$ and $z = z^* / L_j$ denote dimensionless time and space coordinates, respectively. The parameter F denotes the phase ratio and $m_j = u_j / Fu_s$

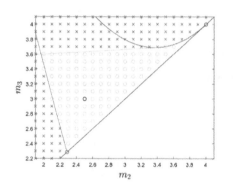

Figure 1: TMB triangle showing predicted region of complete separation. Circles indicate complete separation and crosses incomplete separation. Steady states obtained from dynamical simulation.

denotes the dimensionless flowrate ratio in section j. Eq. (1) is used to describe a true counter current continuous process divided into 4 sections for the separation of two components. A detailed representation of the process can be found in (Storti et al., 1993). The following conditions for a complete separation of components '1' and '2' have to be satisfied

$$\text{Section 1: } m_1 \geq \frac{q_{1,1}}{c_{1,1}}, \; m_1 \geq \frac{q_{2,1}}{c_{2,1}}, \quad \text{Section 2: } \frac{q_{2,2}}{c_{2,2}} \leq m_2 \leq \frac{q_{1,2}}{c_{1,2}},$$

$$\text{Section 3: } \frac{q_{2,3}}{c_{2,3}} \leq m_3 \leq \frac{q_{1,3}}{c_{1,3}}, \quad \text{Section 4: } m_4 \leq \frac{q_{1,4}}{c_{1,4}}, \; m_4 \leq \frac{q_{2,4}}{c_{2,4}}. \tag{2}$$

The quasi-linear PDE system in Eq. (1) in conjunction with the Riemann conditions can be solved apriori (Rhee et al., 1989) using the MOC. In short, a solution is composed of simple waves and shock waves for both components (Rhee et al., 1989; Smoller, 1994).

The velocities of these waves is related to the m_j values in Eq. (3) by (Migliorini et al., 2000)

$$\lambda_{k,j} = \frac{Fu_s(m_j - \lambda_k)}{1 + F\lambda_k}, \quad \tilde{s}_{k,j} = \frac{Fu_s(m_j - s_k)}{1 + Fs_k}, \quad k = 1, 2, \; j = 1, ..., 4, \tag{3}$$

where λ_k are the eigenvalues of the Jacobian $\partial \mathbf{q}/\partial \mathbf{c}$ and s_k follows from the jump conditions (Smoller, 1994) and is defined by $s_k = \Delta q_i / \Delta c_i$ for both components.

In this work, the CIE is used to define the thermodynamic equilibrium, thus the following implicit isotherm is used (Helfferich and Klein, 1970)

$$K_{i3} = \left(\frac{q_i}{c_i}\right)^{\mu_i} \left(\frac{c_3}{q_3}\right)^{\mu_3} = const, \; i = 1, 2,$$

$$c_3 = \mu_3 \left(c_{tot} - \frac{c_1}{\mu_1} - \frac{c_2}{\mu_2} \right), \quad q_3 = \mu_3 \left(q_{tot} - \frac{q_1}{\mu_1} - \frac{q_2}{\mu_2} \right). \tag{4}$$

Therein, μ_i denotes the reciprocal of the ionic charge and K_{i3} the equilibrium constant of component i. The index '3' refers to the component that is used to keep the solution normality constant. Using the general approach of Migliorini et al. (1998) described by Migliorini et al. (2000), Eqs. (4) can be used to obtain constraints on every m_j such that complete separation of components '1' and '2' can be achieved.

2.2. Results

Assuming complete regeneration in sections 1 and 4, we obtain for m_1 and m_4 the following bounds

$$m_1 \geq \left. \frac{dq_1(c_1)}{dc_1} \right|_{c_1 = 0} = \left(K_{13} \frac{q_{tot}}{c_{tot}} \right)^{\frac{\mu_3}{\mu_1}}, \quad -\frac{1}{F} \leq m_4 \leq \frac{q_2(c_2^{å})}{c_2^{å}}. \tag{5}$$

Note, any differential terms are obtained through implicit differentiation of Eq. (4). The required value of $c_2^{å}$ is obtained from an overall mass balance for component '2' and total regeneration in Section 4

$$(m_3 - m_2)c_2^{feed} = \left(m_3 - K_{23}^{\frac{1}{\mu_2}} \left(\frac{q_{tot} - q_2(c_2^{å})}{c_{tot} - c_2^{å}} \right)^{\frac{\mu_3}{\mu_2}} \right) c_2^{å} \tag{6}$$

for given values of m_2 and m_3. The value of $q_2(c_2^{å})$ is obtained by solving Eq. (4) for $c_1 = 0$. Assuming the variables m_1 and m_4 to satisfy Eq. (5), complete separation depends only on the choice of m_2 and m_3. Therefore, a corresponding region of complete separation can be projected into the m_2, m_3-plane, see the triangular shaped set in Fig. 1. The bounds of the triangular-like set are obtained by following Migliorini et al. (2000). The black line is simply defined by $m_3 = m_2$. The red and blue lines in Fig. 1 follow from

$$m_3 = \frac{q_1}{c_1^{feed}} + m_2 \left(1 - \frac{c_1}{c_1^{feed}}\right),$$

$$\text{red line: } m_2(c_1) = \left.\frac{\partial q_2}{\partial c_2}\right|_{c_2=0} = \left.\frac{q_2}{c_2}\right|_{c_2=0} = K_{23}^{\frac{1}{\mu_2}} \left(\frac{q_{tot} - q_1/\mu_1}{c_{tot} - c_1/\mu_1}\right)^{\frac{\mu_3}{\mu_2}},$$ (7)

$$\text{blue line: } m_2(c_1) = \left.\frac{\partial q_1}{\partial c_1}\right|_{c_2=0} = K_{13}^{\frac{1}{\mu_1}} \left(\frac{q_{tot} - q_1/\mu_1}{c_{tot} - c_1/\mu_1}\right)^{\frac{\mu_1+\mu_3}{\mu_1}} \left(\frac{c_{tot} - c_1/\mu_1^2}{q_{tot} - q_1/\mu_1^2}\right),$$

where c_1 is used for parametrization. Finally, calculation of the green line in Fig. 1 is required, which is more involved. The parameters of our example, see Tab. 1, are chosen such that they define a purely competitive adsorption without selectivity reversal and with favorable pure component isotherms. These assumptions allow to conclude that completely separated components define a solution in the concentration phase space that is composed of the four states $(0,0)$, $(c_1^0,0)$, (c_1^*,c_2^*), and $(0,c_2^0)$ (Storti et al., 1993; Migliorini et al., 2000). These states are connected by two shocks and two simple waves. In particular, $(c_1^0,0)$ and (c_1^*,c_2^*) are connected by a 1-simple wave, therefore

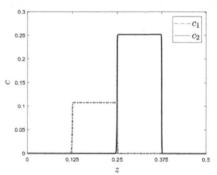

Figure 2: Steady state concentration profile for $m_2 = 2.5$ and $m_3 = 3.0$ (indicated by black circle) obtained through dynamical simulation.

they lie on the same integral curve Γ_1 corresponding to eigenvalue λ_1. In case of the green line, c_2^0 is the running parameter and the variables c_1^0, c_1^*, c_2^*, m_2, and m_3 are unknown. Their values are obtained by solving the following set of equations

$$m_2 = \frac{q_1^0/c_1^{feed}(c_2^{feed} - c_2^0) + q_2^0}{c_1^0/c_1^{feed}(c_2^{feed} - c_2^0) + c_2^0}, \quad m_3 = \frac{q_1^0 - m_2 c_1^0}{c_1^{feed}} + m_2,$$ (8a)

$$0 = \frac{q_1^*}{c_1^*} - m_3, \quad 0 = q_2^* - q_2^0 - m_3(c_2^* - c_2^0),$$ (8b)

$$\tilde{c}_1^0 = \int_{c_2^*}^{c_2^0} \frac{q_1}{q_2} \frac{\mu_2}{\mu_1} \frac{q_2/c_2 - \lambda_1}{q_1/c_1 - \lambda_1} dc_2 + c_1^*,$$ (8c)

where q_1^0 and q_2^0 are obtained by solving Eq. (4) for $c_2 = 0$ and $c_1 = 0$, respectively.

Similarly, $\mathbf{q}^*$ is obtained by solving Eq. (4) for $\mathbf{c}^*$. Note, equations in (8a) are easily solved for m_2 and m_3. However, they require some initial guess for c_1^0. Subsequently, equations in (8b) are solved for c_1^*, c_2^*. Finally, Eq. (8c) is used to obtain a $\tilde{c}_1^0$ that lies on the same integral curve Γ_1 as c_1^* does. Thus, the set of equations in Eq. (8) has to be solved iteratively until $|\tilde{c}_1^0 - c_1^0| < \varepsilon$ for some small $\varepsilon \ll 1$. The triangle-like set in Fig. 1 is verified by performing numerical simulations of the TMB (1) for different combinations (m_2, m_3). For this purpose, the numerical approach for a single column presented in (Fechtner and Kienle, 2017) was extended to solve also the continuous true counter-current model (1) without requiring a Jacobian. Since the same soprtion isotherm is applied as in (Fechtner and Kienle, 2017), the differential index (Unger et al., 1995) is one. Hence, standard solvers to efficiently solve the corresponding DAE system, for example trough method of lines (Schiesser, 1991), can be used providing the same advantages. Additionally, the Riemann set-up easily allows to obtain consistent initial conditions by solving Eq. (4) for piece-wise constant initial values just once. A particular simulation with $(m_2 = 2.5, m_3 = 3.0)$ is shown in Fig. 2. It clearly shows the complete separation of the target components as predicted by the Triangle-theory.

3. Simplified approach using Langmuir isotherms

One of the most popular sorption isotherms is the so-called Langmuir isotherm

$$q_i = \frac{a_i c_i}{1 + \sum_j b_j c_j} \qquad (9)$$

Beside the flexibility to reproduce many sorption mechanisms (Guiochon et al., 2006), it provides many mathematical features that simplify an analysis, in particular related to equilibrium theory (Rhee et al., 1989) and therefore also for the triangle theory (Mazzotti et al., 1997). If Eq. (9) is fitted to Eq. (4), the corresponding sets of complete separation

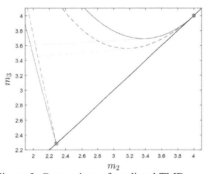

Figure 3: Comparison of predicted TMB triangles using CIE (solid lines) and Langmuir (dashed lines), respectively. Parameters: $a_1 = 4.0$, $b_1 = 0.413$, $a_2 = 2.286$, $b_2 = 0.095$

predicted by the two different models can be compared. Fig. 3 shows that the Langmuir-related triangular-like shape is a subset of one related to the CIE. There is a distinct difference particularly close to the optimal operating point, i.e. the intersection of the red and green lines. Hence, a design based on Langmuir isotherm can lead to suboptimal operating conditions. The results presented in Section 2, allow also an investigation of the effect of the solution normality c_{tot}, which can be used as a process design parameter. For this purpose, three scenarios with different but fixed solution normalities are considered. Further, the values of c_{tot} do not lie within a reversal zone (Fechtner and Kienle, 2019), i.e. $c_{tot} \notin [7, 8] / 49 \; mol / l$. The corresponding triangular-shaped sets can be seen in Fig. 4. From this figure it is clear that, at least in the range of these cases, c_{tot} differences have only a minor effect on the shape of the three sets. However, there is a significant change in the position of these sets in the m_2, m_3-plane. Thus, completely different regions for the sets of complete separation are available through variation of c_{tot}

4. Conclusion

In this paper, the triangle theory was applied to the classical ion exchange, which allows the rational design of ion exchange simulated moving bed processes. This can also be done also by using the Langmuir isotherm, which however is shown to lead to regions of suboptimal process conditions. In a first step, the potential of the solution normality as additional design parameter was investigated. It provides a greater flexibility for the choice of (m_2, m_3) values, which then can be used to accommodate other process aspects in order to increase the performance. Further, the efficient numerical approach for implicit adsorption isotherms presented in Fechtner and Kienle (2017) was successfully extended to TMB processes.

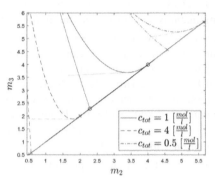

Figure 4: Effect of different but constant solution normality on the predicted TMB triangle. All three cases $c_{tot} = 1$ (solid lines), $c_{tot} = 4$ (dashed lines), and $c_{tot} = 0.5$ (dashdot lines) without selectivity reversal.

Acknowledgments

The financial support of the International Max Planck Research School for Advanced Methods in Process and Systems Engineering - IMPRS ProEng is greatly acknowledged. The research was also supported by the center of dynamic systems (CDS), funded by the EU-programme ERDF (European Regional Development Fund).

References

M. Fechtner, A. Kienle, 2017, Efficient simulation and equilibrium theory for adsorption processes with implicit adsorption isotherms – mass action equilibria, Chem. Eng. Sci., 171, 471-480

M. Fechtner, A. Kienle, 2019, Equilibrium theory of ion exchange chromatography with variable solution normality and steric hindrance, Chem. Eng. Sci., 199, 508-527

G. Guiochon, A. Felinger, D. G. Shirazi, A. M. Katti, 2006, Fundamentals of Preparative and Nonlinear Chromatography, Elsevier Academic Press, San Diego , 2

F. G. Helfferich, G. Klein, 1970, Multicomponent Chromatography Theory of Interference, M. Dekker, New York, 1

M. Mazzotti, G. Storti, M. Morbidelli, 1997, Optimal operation of simulated moving bed units for nonlinearchromatographic separations, J. Chrom. A, 769, 3-24

C. Migliorini, M. Mazzotti, M. Morbidelli, 1998, Continuous chromatographic separation through simulated moving beds under linear and nonlinear conditions, J. Chrom. A, 827, 161-173

C. Migliorini, M. Mazzotti, M. Morbidelli, 2000, Robust design of countercurrent adsorption separation processes: 5. nonconstant selectivity, AIChE J., 46, 1384-1399

H.-K. Rhee, R. Aris, N. R. Amundson, 1989, First-Order Partial Differential Equations: Volume II – Theory and Application of Hyperbolic Systems of Quasilinear Equations, Prentice Hall, New Jersey, 1

W. E. Schiesser, 1991, The Numerical Method of Lines Integration of Partial Differential Equations, Academic Press, San Diego, 1

J. Smoller, 1994, Shock Waves and Reaction–Diffusion Equations, Springer, New York, 2

G. Storti, M. Mazzotti, M. Morbidelli, 1993, Robust design of binary countercurrent adsorption separation processes, AIChE J., 39, 1825-1842

J. Unger, A. Kröner, W. Marquardt, 1995, Structural analysis of differential-algebraic equation systems: Theory and applications, Comp. & Chem. Eng., 19, 867-882

Sauro Pierucci, Flavio Manenti, Giulia Bozzano, Davide Manca (Eds.)
Proceedings of the 30th European Symposium on Computer Aided Process Engineering
(ESCAPE30), May 24-27, 2020, Milano, Italy. © 2020 Elsevier B.V. All rights reserved.
http://dx.doi.org/10.1016/B978-0-12-823377-1.50124-5

Optimal use of Process Streams as Working Fluids in Work and Heat Exchange Networks (WHENs)

Haoshui Yu[a,b], Chao Fu[c], Truls Gundersen[a*], Emre Gençer[b]

[a]*Department of Energy and Process Engineering, Norwegian University of Science and Technology, Kolbjoern Hejes v. 1A, NO-7491 Trondheim, Norway*
[b]*MIT Energy Initiative, Massachusetts Institute of Technology, 77 Massachusetts Avenue, Cambridge, MA 02139, United States*
[c]*SINTEF Energy Research, Kolbjoern Hejes vei 1.B, NO-7491 Trondheim, Norway*
truls.gundersen@ntnu.no

Abstract

Design of Heat Exchanger Networks (HENs) has been widely studied and applied since it can significantly reduce energy consumption in the process industries. However, pressure effects are ignored in HENs. To consider temperature and pressure simultaneously, Work and Heat Exchange Networks (WHENs) emerge as a new research topic in Process Systems Engineering. Even in cases where the supply and target pressures of the process streams are the same, the HENs problem can benefit from being expanded to a WHENs problem. In this paper, a methodology to extend the Heat Exchange Networks (HENs) problem to a Work and Heat Exchange Networks (WHENs) problem is proposed with the objective of improving energy/exergy efficiency of process plants. A case study illustrates the profitability of manipulating the pressure of streams that in the original problem definition are constant pressure streams. The exergy consumption is reduced by 29.92% in the case study.

Keywords: Heat Exchanger Network, Work and Heat Exchange Network, Working Fluids, Process Streams

1. Introduction

Heat Integration has been a successful field of Process Synthesis in reducing specific energy consumption in the process industries. Both Pinch Analysis pioneered in the 1970s and extended to a design methodology in the 1980s (Linnhoff and Hindmarsh, 1983), and Mathematical Programming formulations (Cerda and Westerberg, 1983), developed in the 1980s, have been used to design and optimize Heat Exchanger Networks (HENs). While significant savings have been achieved in thermal energy by using these methodologies, mechanical energy is also an important element in the energy system for most process industries. Similar to heat exchange for increasing or decreasing the temperature of process streams, compression and expansion are used to manipulate the pressure of process streams. As a result, the design task of Work Exchange Networks (WENs) was introduced (Huang and Fan, 1996) for savings in mechanical energy by work recovery. Both direct (flow work) and indirect (shaft work) exchange have been studied. Since pressure manipulations (compression/expansion) affect the temperatures of process streams, HENs and WENs should be designed simultaneously. Heating from compression and cooling from expansion may have a considerable impact on the heat recovery problem. Similarly, heat integration affects the temperatures of process streams and thus the work consumed/produced in pressure change. As a result, a new research field referred to as Work and Heat Exchange Networks (WHENs) has emerged during the last decade (Yu et al., 2019a). For this design problem, process streams have a specified supply and target state (temperature and pressure), and the objective is to develop a network of heat exchange equipment (heat exchangers, heaters and cooler) and pressure manipulators (compressors, pumps, expanders and valves) in such a way that a selected Key Performance Indicator (e.g. Energy/Exergy Efficiency or Total Annualized Cost) is optimized. Some early works (Fu and Gundersen, 2016b; Zhuang et al., 2018; Yu et al., 2019b) have demonstrated the potential of WHENs to significantly improve the energy situation in process plants beyond what can be obtained by HENs. Even in cases where the supply and target pressures of the process streams are the same, the HENs problem can benefit from being expanded to a WHENs problem. This is typically the case when the hot and cold composite curves do not match well and where pressure manipulations may bring the curves closer together to increase heat recovery. While this could be achieved by heat engines and heat pumps (Colmenares and Seider, 1987), a more direct and economic solution would be to manipulate the pressure of the process streams rather than using external working fluids. One example based on using the WHENs methodology is the novel sensible heat pump scheme (Fu and Gundersen, 2016c), where a stream with equal supply and target pressure is used as working fluid for a reversed Brayton cycle. Both compression and expansion are correctly placed above and below Pinch, respectively. In effect, process streams temporarily act as working fluids, i.e. they are compressed/expanded in such a way that their target pressures (equal to their supply pressures) are satisfied. The idea behind the sensible heat pump can also be applied to heat engines, where a process stream can be used as working fluid to generate power. One such power cycle is the open Organic Rankine Cycle (ORC) (Yu et al., 2017), where process streams act as working fluids. Thus, WHENs represent a generalization of industrial heat engines and heat pumps. For sub-ambient applications, pressure manipulation of process streams may replace external refrigeration cycles.

2. Problem statement and methodology

As stated above, it is quite common that composite curves do not match well, i.e. they open up considerably above and/or below Pinch. This means significant exergy losses from heat transfer. If, in addition, there is considerable heat surplus (below Pinch) or heat deficit (above Pinch), opportunities for work generation or heat pumping are lost. In such cases, regardless of the configuration of the heat exchanger network, the energy efficiency of the system is not satisfactory. To further improve the efficiency of the system, one can change the shape of the hot/cold composite curves, which means manipulation of the process streams beyond heat exchange. Pressure manipulation of process streams is an alternative scheme. As shown in Figure 1 (stream data in Table 1), the composite curves of the system do not match well. The temperature difference between the hot and cold composite curves below Pinch is very large. The exergy destruction is therefore large no matter how the heat exchanger network is designed.

Thus, to improve the energy efficiency of the system, one would like to extend the HEN synthesis problem to a corresponding WHEN problem. As shown in Figure 2, the pressure of process streams can be manipulated to enhance the match between the hot and the cold composite curves. In HENs, a process stream often passes through several heat exchangers to reach the target temperature. If the pressure of process streams is manipulated by a compressor, an expander, a pump, or a valve, as shown in Figure 2, the energy efficiency of the system can be improved. The maximum energy efficiency depends on the intermediate pressure level P_{int}, as indicated in Figure 2. In this study, we would like to determine the optimal pressure operator and the intermediate pressure to achieve the maximum energy/exergy efficiency of the system.

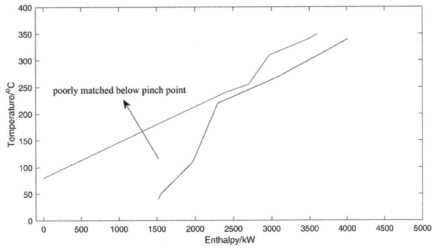

Figure 1. Example of poorly matched composite curves

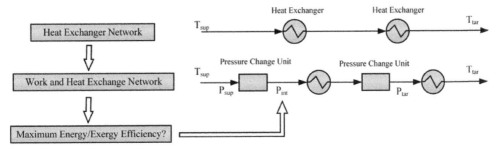

Figure 2. The HEN problem extended to a WHEN problem

Based on the shape of the composite curves, the pressure manipulator of one of the process streams should first be selected. If the first pressure changing unit is a turbine or a valve, the second pressure changing unit should be a compressor or a pump, and vice versa. In this study, to determine the near-optimal intermediate pressure, a simulation of the different intermediate pressures is performed in Aspen HYSYS. With different intermediate pressures, the hot and cold composite curves and the energy target of the system can be determined using heat integration methods. Finally, the optimal pressure changing units and the optimal intermediate pressure can be determined. Once the pressure manipulators and optimal intermediate pressure are determined, the final heat exchanger network can be synthesized based on conventional heat exchanger network synthesis technologies or models.

Since both work and heat are involved when pressure changing units are introduced to the system, exergy consumption of the system is chosen as the indicator of energy efficiency. Following Fu and Gundersen (2016a), the Carnot factor is adopted as the coefficient to calculate the exergy of thermal energy, however, this is an optimistic estimation assuming reversible operations. The coefficient can easily be changed depending on the process and the application.

3. Case study

In this section, an example is chosen to illustrate the advantage of extending HENs to WHENs. The process stream data are listed in Table 1 and the corresponding hot and cold composite curves are shown in Figure 1. It should be noticed that the composite curves are poorly matched below the Pinch, which indicates a large heat transfer irreversibility below the Pinch.

Table 1. Process stream data for the case study

Stream	Supply temperature (°C)	Target temperature (°C)	FCp (kW/°C)	Duty (kW)
H1	350	310	12	480
H2	340	240	5	500
H3	255	80	15	2625
C1	220	340	13	1560
C2	50	110	4	240
C3	40	270	3	690

When the problem is solved as a conventional heat integration problem, the corresponding minimum hot and cold utility loads are 405 kW and 1520 kW with a minimum heat recovery approach temperature of 10°C. The Pinch corresponds to 255°C for hot streams and 245°C for cold streams. In this case study, the hot and cold utilities are assumed to be supplied at 400°C and 15°C respectively. The reference temperature for exergy is chosen to be 15°C, which means the exergy content of cold utility is zero. As a result, the minimum exergy consumption of the system is 231.6 kW.

To improve the energy efficiency of the system, attention should be paid to the below Pinch part of the problem. If the pressure of a process stream below Pinch is changed, a better energy system could be expected. A process stream with appropriate thermodynamic properties should be chosen as the stream for pressure manipulation. In this case study, we assume that C2 is n-Hexane at the pressure of 3.13 bar (slightly above the saturation pressure at 110°C). The reason for this assumption is to guarantee C2 in liquid phase in the entire temperature range of 50°C to 110°C. The stream could have been other substances as long as they can act as working fluid for a heat engine in the relevant temperature range.

There is excess amount of heat below Pinch, thus the manipulation of a cold stream should be able to convert excess heat into power. Therefore, the first pressure manipulator should be a pump and the second one should be a turbine. Since the critical pressure of n-Hexane is 30.32 bar, the upper bound for the intermediate pressure is set to 30 bar in this study. The lower bound for the intermediate pressure is set to 8 bar.

The results under different intermediate pressures are illustrated in Figure 3, where the total exergy consumption, net power output and hot utility consumption are presented. It is clear that the net power output increases with the intermediate pressure. However, the variation in hot utility consumption is more complex. Hot utility consumption is constant when the intermediate pressure is less than 18 bar, which means that the pressure manipulation of C2 has no effect above the Pinch as long as the intermediate pressure is below 18 bar. When the intermediate pressure is larger than 18 bar, the hot utility consumption increases first and then decreases. With the increase in intermediate pressure, the evaporation temperature of C2 increases and the available heat above the evaporation temperature decreases. As a result, a new Pinch occurs in the system and the original Pinch is no longer a bottleneck of the system. More hot utility is required in such cases. However, when the intermediate pressure increases towards the critical pressure, hot utility consumption tends to decrease. This phenomenon can be explained as follows: With the increase of intermediate pressure, the evaporation heat decreases considerably, and C2 does not require as much heating load from hot process streams as in the low intermediate pressure situation. Therefore, the total exergy consumption of the system decreases at first, and it increases with the intermediate pressure in the range between 18 bar and 25 bar, while it finally decreases with intermediate pressure above 25 bar. The optimal intermediate pressure is thus 18 bar. When the intermediate pressure is less than 18 bar, the hot utility is 405 kW and pressure manipulation of process stream C2 has no effect on the heat integration above the original Pinch.

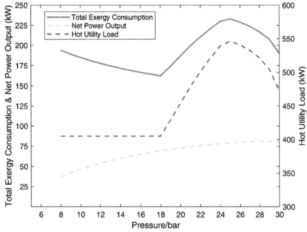

Figure 3. System performance with variation of the intermediate pressure

The optimal results indicate that C2 is pumped to 18 bar first, and then the hot streams in the system heat C2 to a saturated vapor state before entering a turbine. C2 is expanded to the original pressure 3.13 bar and generates 69.3 kW electricity (net power output). After expansion, C2 becomes a hot stream to be cooled to 110°C. In this process, the identity (hot/cold) of C2 changes.

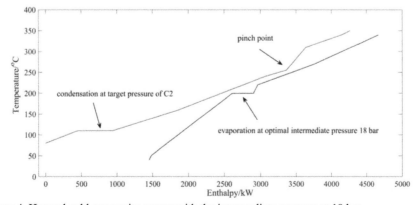

Figure 4. Hot and cold composite curves with the intermediate pressure at 18 bar

Figure 4 illustrates the composite curves under optimal conditions. Compared with the original composite curves shown in Figure1, a much better match between the curves is achieved. In the original HEN, the minimum exergy consumption is 231.6 kW, while the exergy consumption can reach 162.3 kW with one pressure changing stream. The exergy consumption is reduced by 29.92%. This case study shows the potential benefit of extending HENs to WHENs, even in cases where all the process streams are at constant pressure in the process.

4. Conclusions

In this paper, the Heat Exchanger Networks (HEN) problem is extended to a Work and Heat Exchange Network (WHEN) problem for cases where the hot and cold composite curves do not match well. Pressure manipulation of a process stream with the same supply and target pressure can improve the exergy efficiency of the whole system. The pressure changing units and the near-optimal intermediate pressure can be determined based on simulation and sensitivity analysis. A case study shows the potential advantage of extending the HEN to a WHEN problem. In this specific case study, the manipulation of a single process stream results in an open Organic Rankine Cycle (ORC). This also reveals that the integration of heat engines and heat pumps with HENs can be solved from the perspective of WHENs. A more systematic investigation on heat engines, heat pumps and refrigeration cycles will be performed in future work.

Acknowledgments

This publication has been funded by HighEFF—Centre for an Energy Efficient and Competitive Industry for the Future. The authors gratefully acknowledge the financial support from the Research Council of Norway and user partners of HighEFF, an 8-year Research Centre under the FME-scheme (Centre for Environment-friendly Energy Research, 257632).

References

J. Cerda, A. W. Westerberg, 1983, Synthesizing heat exchanger networks having restricted stream/stream matches using transportation problem formulations, Chemical Engineering Science, 38, 1723-1740.

T. R. Colmenares, W. D. Seider, 1987, Heat and power integration of chemical processes, AIChE Journal, 33, 898-915.

C. Fu, T. Gundersen, 2016a, Correct integration of compressors and expanders in above ambient heat exchanger networks, Energy, 116, Part 2, 1282-1293.

C. Fu, T. Gundersen, 2016b, Heat and work integration: Fundamental insights and applications to carbon dioxide capture processes, Energy Conversion and Management, 121, 36-48.

C. Fu, T. Gundersen, 2016c, A novel sensible heat pump scheme for industrial heat recovery, Industrial & Engineering Chemistry Research, 55, 967-977.

Y. L Huang, L. T. Fan, 1996, Analysis of a work exchanger network, Industrial & Engineering Chemistry Research, 35, 3528-3538.

B. Linnhoff, E. Hindmarsh, 1983, The pinch design method for heat exchanger networks, Chemical Engineering Science, 38, 745-763.

H. Yu, J.Eason, L. T. Biegler, X. Feng, 2017, Process integration and superstructure optimization of Organic Rankine Cycles (ORCs) with heat exchanger network synthesis, Computers & Chemical Engineering, 107, 257-270.

H. Yu, C. Fu, M. Vikse, T. Gundersen, 2019a, Work and heat integration – A new field in process synthesis and process systems engineering, AIChE Journal, 65(7):e16477.

H. Yu, C. Fu, M. Vikse, C. He, T. Gundersen, 2019b, Identifying optimal thermodynamic paths in work and heat exchange network synthesis, AIChE Journal, 65, 549-561.

Y. Zhuang, L. Zhang, L. Liu, Q. Meng, J. Du, 2018, Simultaneous Synthesis of WHEN based on Superstructure Modelling Considering Thermodynamic and Economic Factors, Computer Aided Chemical Engineering, 44, 1033-1038.

Sauro Pierucci, Flavio Manenti, Giulia Bozzano, Davide Manca (Eds.)
Proceedings of the 30th European Symposium on Computer Aided Process Engineering
(ESCAPE30), May 24-27, 2020, Milano, Italy. © 2020 Elsevier B.V. All rights reserved.
http://dx.doi.org/10.1016/B978-0-12-823377-1.50125-7

Computer Aided Molecular Design of Green Solvents for the Hydroformylation of Long-Chain Olefines

Tobias Keßler[a,*], Christian Kunde[a], Steffen Linke[b], Kevin McBride[c],
Kai Sundmacher[b,c] and Achim Kienle[a,d,*]

[a]*Otto-von-Guericke University Magdeburg, Chair for Automation/Modelling,
Universitätsplatz 2, 39106 Magdeburg*
[b]*Otto-von-Guericke University Magdeburg, Chair for Process Systems Engineering,
Universitätsplatz 2, 39106 Magdeburg*
[c]*Max-Planck-Institute for Dynamics of Complex Technical Systems, Process Systems
Engineering Group, Sandtorstr. 1, 39106 Magdeburg*
[d]*Max-Planck-Institute for Dynamics of Complex Technical Systems, Process Synthesis
and Dynamics Group, Sandtorstr. 1, 39106 Magdeburg*
tobias.kessler@ovgu.de; achim.kienle@ovgu.de

Abstract

A hydroformylation process of long-chain olefines is investigated. In an attempt to replace an established, toxic solvent used in this process, a computer aided molecular design approach based on group contribution methods is used to predict the solvent properties, as well as the liquid-liquid equilibrium of the mixture and environment, health and safety (EHS) criteria. Generating chemically feasible solvent candidates with the desired properties requires the solution of combinatorially complex mixed-integer nonlinear programs. First results of the approach are presented and discussed.

Keywords: MINLP, CAM(x)D, Green Chemistry, EHS Criteria, Group Contribution Methods

1. Introduction

The concept of "Green Chemistry" has gained an evergrowing interest over the last years. The focus of chemical engineers shifted from a mainly economical view on the process efficiency to a view on process efficiency with an awareness for the ecological impact. Solvents are a class of chemicals that are widely used in the chemical industry to dilute or extract other chemical species. Some well-established and frequently used solvents are toxic, for example dimethylformamide (DMF). Due to the many ways by which humans and the environment may be exposed to toxic solvents, they pose a potential health risk and should, therefore, be replaced by safer and ecologically benign alternatives.

The case study considered in this work is the hydroformylation of n-decene. For the economic efficiency of the process a high space-time yield of the catalyzed reaction needs to be achieved and the rhodium based catalyst needs to be recovered. To meet these requirements a thermomorphic multiphase system (TMS) (Schäfer et al., 2012) consisting of the polar solvent DMF and the non-polar solvent dodecane is employed. The TMS is homogeneous at reaction conditions to allow for good contact between the reactants and the catalyst, and biphasic at lower temperatures to allow for catalyst recycling.

In an attempt to replace the developmentally toxic solvent DMF by a safer and ecologically more benign alternative, a screening method was recently employed and two promising alternatives for DMF were identified (McBride et al., 2018). In a further study by the authors, a process optimization for those two alternatives was conducted and one of them delivered promising results (Keßler et al., 2019). Screening methods are, by design, only able to find alternatives already contained in the considered databases. In contrast to that, this work also aims at identifying new ecologically benign solvent candidates not yet included in the databases. To achieve this, a hierarchical computer aided molecular design approach based on group contribution methods is used.

2. Computer Aided Molecular Design

Computer Aided Molecular and Mixture Design problems are complex mixed-integer non-linear programs (MINLP) of the following form:

$$\min_{n,x} \quad J(n,p,q),$$

$$\text{s.t.} \quad s_1(n) \le 0,$$
$$s_2(n) = 0,$$
$$p = f(n),$$
$$q = g(x,n,p),$$
$$h_1(p,q,n) \le 0, \tag{1}$$
$$h_2(p,q,n) = 0,$$
$$p_k^L \le p_k \le p_k^U,$$
$$n_d^L \le n_d \le n_d^U,$$
$$q_j^L \le q_j \le q_j^U,$$
$$\sum_i x_i = 1,$$

where s are structural feasibility constraints, p and q are estimated molecule/mixture properties, and h are thermodynamic/physical property constraints. Upper and lower bounds are denoted by L and U, respectively. Each of the constraint types will be discussed in the following.

2.1. Structural Feasibility Constraints

Structural feasibility constraints are needed to ensure that the molecule obtained by a combination of predefined atom groups is chemically feasible. A list of the groups used in this work can be found in Table 1. The constraints used in this work are based on the works of Sahinidis et al. (2003) and Churi and Achenie (1996), namely:

The number of single and double bonds must be even. There must be a sufficient number of transition groups, having single and double bonds, to connect groups with only one bond type.

The number of bonds must at least equal the number of groups minus one and the number of bonds cannot exceed that of a complete graph in which all groups are connected.

The octet rule: Each groups valency is satisfied with a covalent bond. Note, that even if the valencies of the groups are satisfied, the bond types need to be checked in order to guarantee consistency.

Table 1: Groups in group set *i*. s denotes a free single bond valence, d denotes a free double bond valence, r denotes a free cyclic bond valence and AC denotes an aromatic C.

Main groups							
sCH3	ssCH2	dCH2	sssCH	sdCH	ssssC	ssdC	ddC
Aromatic groups							
rrACH	rrACs	rrACCH3	rrACCH2s	rrACCHss	rrACCHd	rrACNH2	
Functional groups							
sCH3CO	sCH2COs	CH=Os	sCH3COO	sCH2COOs	sOCH3	sOCH2s	sOCHss
sOCHd	sCH2NH2	ssCHNH2	dCHNH2	sCH2NHs	sCH2CN	sCOOH	sCH2NO2
ssCHNO2	dCHNO2						

Two adjacent groups may not be linked by more than one bond. This ensures that there are no double or triple bonds, which are formulated explicitly in the groups, i. e. C (valence: 4) can either be: ssCss, dCss, dCd, where s are single and d are double bonds. Each active group gets an index by consecutive numbering, allowing for a mapping of the connections of each group to other groups. Each group needs to be connected to at least one group with a lower index. Though the mapping may not be unique, this makes sure that only one connected molecule is obtained.

2.2. Property Estimation

Pure species properties: To estimate the properties of a structurally feasible molecule, so called group contribution methods are employed. In their simplest form, these methods assume that each of the groups in the molecule contributes a specific value to a specific property p,

$$p = \sum_i' n_i c_i, \tag{2}$$

Where n_i is the number of occurrences of group i and c_i is the contribution of group i to property p. There exist numerous group contribution methods for various molecule properties. In this work, the group contribution method by Marrero and Gani (2001) is used to estimate the boiling point T_b, as well as the heat of vaporization H_v of the generated molecule. Furthermore, to obtain a greener solvent candidate, the toxicity of the new molecule is measured by the oral rat LD_{50} and the permissible exposure limit PEL, calculated using the group contribution method by Hukkerikar et al. (2012). As an approximation of the thermodynamic properties of the solvent candidate, the Hansen solubility parameter (HSP) is determined using the group contribution method by Panayiotou (2008).

Mixture properties: The liquid-liquid equilibrium (LLE) of the mixture is defined as

$$\gamma^I x^I = \gamma^{II} x^{II}, \tag{3}$$

where γ is the activity coefficient and $\mathbf{x}$ is the composition of phases I and II. One of the most well known group contribution methods to model the non-ideal phase behavior in the activity coefficient is modified UNIFAC (Dortmund) (called UNIFAC in the remainder of this manuscript) (Weidlich and Gmehling, 1987). Group contribution methods are not able to sufficiently capture the behavior of large molecules (Struebing, 2011). In the hydroformylation process a rhodium-biphephos catalyst complex is used. Therefore, the catalyst distribution of the process during the phase separation cannot be modeled using UNIFAC. However, as the catalyst distribution has a high impact on the overall process cost (Keßler et al., 2019) the phase behavior of the mixture needs to be described during the generation of the new solvent candidate. To achieve this, COSMO-based methods are employed.

COSMO-RS is a quantum chemistry based method for the prediction of chemical potentials. The main idea is that each species has a characteristic charge density (the so-called σ-Profile). Those charge densities can be used to predict how the species will interact (Klamt et al., 2010). The σ-profiles can be calculated using commercial software packages. Additionally, there exists a group contribution method to calculate them (Liu et al., 2019). In our approach, the σ-profiles of the already known species of the mixture (decene, dodecane, undecanal, biphephos) are calculated a priori, while the σ-profile of the new molecule is estimated using the aforementioned group contribution method. Lin and Sandler (2002) proposed an activity coefficient model named COSMO-SAC (segment activity coefficients) based on σ-profiles,

$$\ln \gamma_{j/S} = \sum_m p_j(\sigma_m) \cdot \left\lfloor \ln \Gamma_S(\sigma_m) - \ln \Gamma_j(\sigma_m) \right\rfloor + \ln \gamma_{j/S}^{SG}, \tag{4}$$

where index j denotes the pure species and index S the mixture, $\gamma_{j/S}$ is the activity coefficient of species j in mixture S, $p_j(\sigma_m)$ is the charge density p of species j on segment σ_m, Γ are the segment activity coefficients and $\gamma_{j/S}^{SG}$ is the Stavermann-Guggenheim combinatorial term. The segment activity coefficients Γ are defined as

$$\ln \Gamma_k(\sigma_m) = -\ln\left(\sum_n p_k(\sigma_n)\Gamma_k(\sigma_n)\exp\left(\frac{-\Delta W(\sigma_m,\sigma_n)}{RT}\right)\right), k \in \{j,S\}, \tag{5}$$

where $R = 0.001987$ kcal/(mol $\cdot$ K) is the ideal gas constant and $\Delta W(\sigma_m, \sigma_n)$ is the energy required to obtain a (σ_m, σ_n) pair. This energy is called exchange energy, it is defined as

$$\Delta W(\sigma_m, \sigma_n) = \frac{\alpha}{2}(\sigma_m + \sigma_n)^2 + c_{hb} \max(0, \sigma_{acc} - \sigma_{hb}) \cdot \min(0, \sigma_{don} + \sigma_{hb}). \tag{6}$$

Here, σ_{don} is the smaller and σ_{acc} is the larger value of σ_m and σ_n, c_{hb} is a constant for hydrogen bonding interaction, σ_{hb} is a hydrogen bonding cutoff value and α is the misfit energy.

2.3. Constraints

The solvent we are looking for is meant for a specific process, therefore some specific property constraints are necessary. The boiling point is constrained to $T_b \in [350, 600]$ K, because the product of the process reacts to an unwanted side product at higher temperatures. Ideally, the new solvent has the same characteristics as DMF regarding the affinity to the catalyst and the reactant after the phase split. Therefore, as a pre-screening step to reduce the search space, the HSP is constrained to values close to the HSP value of DMF, $\delta_0 \in [24, 25.6]\sqrt{MPa}$.

Furthermore, to guarantee that the solver does not select the trivial solution of Eq. (3), the phase compositions are constrained to $x_1^I \in [0.7648, 0.9671]$, $x_2^{II} \geq 0.3$, following a prior optimization study (Keßler et al., 2019). Here, component 1 is the new polar solvent candidate and component 2 is the fixed non-polar solvent dodecane. In addition to the property constraints some complexity constraints are necessary, because GC methods only yield poor approximations if the molecules are too complex (Struebing, 2011). The number of groups is constrained to $\sum_i n_i \in [2,7]$, the number of main groups is constrained to 2 for cyclic molecules, the number of aromatic groups allowing side chains is constrained to 1, the number of chain-ending groups is constrained to 4 for acyclic and 1 for cyclic molecules, the number of non-chain-ending groups is constrained to 3 for acyclic and to 1 for monocyclic molecules.

2.4. Hierarchical Decomposition
The problem is decomposed into two relatively easy to solve subproblems. In the first step, the objective is to generate a molecule with a low boiling point, a high PEL and a high LD_{50},

$$\min_n J_1 = T_b - 20 PEL - 50 LD_{50}, \tag{7}$$

20 molecules are generated. Note, that the problem is a representative of a multi-objective optimization (MOO) problem. However, for this study we have chosen fixed weights.
In the second step, COSMO-SAC is solved for each of the 20 candidates with the objective to optimize the catalyst distribution between the phases,

$$\max_x J_2 = x_{cat}^I - x_{cat}^{II}, \tag{8}$$

where the existence of two phases is enforced through the constraint mentioned above. The optimizations are implemented as MINLPs and solved using the GAMS 26.1.0 framework with deterministic global optimization software BARON 18.11.12., Cplex 12.8.0 is used as an LP/MIP subsolver and CONOPT 4.09 is utilized as an NLP subsolver. The calculations are carried out on a Linux PC with 3.40 GHz Intel Core i7-6700 CPU and 16 GB memory. During the hierarchical optimization, the optimization time for the solution of COSMO-SAC is constrained to 9000 s.

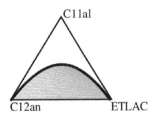

Figure 1: Phase equilibrium for ethyl lactate (ETLAC), calculated using COSMO-SAC.

2.5. Results
The solution of the first subproblem yields 20 solvent candidates. In the second subproblem, all except 6 candidates were eliminated based on the results of the COSMO-SAC calculations. For the eliminated candidates, the solver was not able to find feasible equilibrium compositions within the maximum allowable computation time. For all remaining solvent candidates, the applied models predict that the requirements on the boiling temperature, EHS criteria, and phase behavior are fulfilled. For one exemplary remaining candidate, ethyl lactate (ETLAC), the phase diagram calculated with COSMO-SAC is depicted in Figure 1.

3. Conclusion

In this work, we presented a systematic solvent and mixture design approach for identification of feasible solvent candidates for the hydroformylation of long-chain olefines. In our hierarchical approach, the molecule candidates are designed using group contribution methods. After suitable solvent candidates are chosen with a rough approximation of their thermodynamic behavior, a subsequent optimization with quantum chemical based methods is conducted to identify the best suitable candidates. The approach yields feasible green solvent candidates. Further investigation of the candidates is necessary to account for model prediction errors and additional process constraints. Future work will also account for process design to determine the green solvent with the best process performance. Furthermore, the MOO (Eq. (7)) will be investigated more thoroughly.

Acknowledgement: Gefördert durch die Deutsche Forschungsgemeinschaft (DFG) - TRR 63 "Integrierte chemische Prozesse in flüssigen Mehrphasensystemen" (Teilprojekt B9) - 56091768.

References

N. Churi, L. E. K. Achenie, 1996. Novel mathematical programming model for computer aided molecular design. Ind. Eng. Chem. Res. 35, 3788–3794.

A. S. Hukkerikar, S. Kalakul, B. Sarup, D. M. Young, G. Sin, R. Gani, 2012. Estimation of Environment-Related Properties of Chemicals for Design of Sustainable Processes: Development of Group-Contribution+ (GC+) Property Models and Uncertainty Analysis. J. Chem. Inf. Model 52, 2823-2839.

T. Keßler, C. Kunde, S. Linke, K. McBride, K. Sundmacher, A. Kienle, 2019. Systematic Selection of Green Solvents and Process Optimization for the Hydroformylation of Long-Chain Olefines. Processes, 7, 882.

A. Klamt, F. Eckert, W. Arlt, 2010. COSMO-RS: An alternative to simulation for calculating thermodynamic properties of liquid mixtures. Annu. Rev. Chem. Biomol. Eng. 1, 101–122.

S.-T. Lin, S. I. Sandler, 2002. A priori phase equilibrium prediction from a segment contribution solvation model. Ind. Eng. Chem. Res. 41 (5), 899-913.

Q. Liu, L. Zhang, L. Liu, J. Du, Q. Meng, R. Gani, 2019. Computer-aided reaction solvent design based on transition state theory and COSMO-SAC. Chemical Engineering Science 202, 300-317.

J. Marrero, R. Gani, 2001. Group-contribution based estimation of pure component properties. Fluid Ph. Equilibria, 183-208.

K. McBride, S. Linke, S. Xu, K. Sundmacher, 2018. PSE 2018, San Diego, USA. Ch. Computer Aided Design of Green Thermomorphic Solvent Systems for Homogeneous Catalyst Recovery, pp. 1783-1788.

N. V. Sahinidis, M. Tawarmalani, M. Yu, 2003. Design of alternative refrigerants via global optimization. AIChE J 49 (7), 1761–1775.

E. Schäfer, Y. Brunsch, G. Sadowski, A. Behr, 2012. Hydroformylation of 1-Dodecene in the Thermomorphic Solvent System Dimethylformamide/Decane. Phase Behavior-Reaction Performance-Catalyst Recycling. Ind. Eng. Chem. Res. 51, 10296-10306.

E. Stefanis, C. Panayiotou, 2008. Prediction of Hansen solubility parameters with a new group-contribution method. Int. J. Thermophys. 29 (2), 568-585.

H. Struebing, 2011. Identifying optimal solvents for reactions using quantum mechanics and computer-aided molecular design. Ph.D. thesis, Imperial College London.

U. Weidlich, J. Gmehling, 1987. A modified UNIFAC model. 1. Prediction of VLE, h^E and γ^∞. Ind. Eng. Chem. Res. 26 (7), 1372-1381.

Sauro Pierucci, Flavio Manenti, Giulia Bozzano, Davide Manca (Eds.)
Proceedings of the 30th European Symposium on Computer Aided Process Engineering
(ESCAPE30), May 24-27, 2020, Milano, Italy. © 2020 Elsevier B.V. All rights reserved.
http://dx.doi.org/10.1016/B978-0-12-823377-1.50126-9

Integration of Design and Operation Using Dynamic Perturbation and Chance Constraints with Unscented Transform

Christian Hoffmann, Joris Weigert, Erik Esche[a], Jens-Uwe Repke

Technische Universität Berlin, Process Dynamics and Operations Group, Straße des 17. Juni 135, 10623 Berlin, Germany
c.hoffmann@tu-berlin.de

Abstract

Process design is performed based on experience, heuristics, or simulation and optimization using mathematical models. However, many of these approaches focus on the steady-state design and only a few publications consider process operability under variability. In this contribution, we use a fully discretized dynamic model in combination with an optimal economic NMPC for process design. Fluctuations in the feed are modeled by an amplitude-modulated pseudo-random binary sequence to gain as much information as possible. Parametric uncertainty is accounted for by using the unscented transform approach for chance constraints. This framework enables simultaneous optimization under uncertainty. We successfully apply this framework to the process design of a simplified Williams-Otto process.

Keywords: Integration of Design and Operation, Economic NMPC, Unscented Transform, Optimization under Uncertainty, Chance-constrained Optimization

1. Introduction

Process design is a fundamental aspect of process systems engineering. An optimal design reduces both investment and operating costs and at best also increases separation efficiency and product purity. Conventionally, process design and control design are performed sequentially or as an iterative process (Seider et al., 2017) in which design decisions are made based on economic or other soft criteria for steady-state. Afterward, the design is fixed and the control structure is set up. However, this approach may lead to dynamic constraint violations, hinder robust performance, or simply reduce the controllability of a process during plant operation (Malcolm et al., 2007). Currently, there is a growing desire to perform these two subsequent tasks simultaneously (Seider et al., 2017).

Three approaches to solving optimization problems regarding the integration of design and operation (IDOP) have been suggested and their advantages and disadvantages have been discussed (Ricardez-Sandoval et al., 2009): (1) controllability index-based approaches, (2) robust approaches, and (3) dynamic optimization approaches.

In a previous contribution (Hoffmann et al., 2019), we suggested using the objective function of an economic nonlinear model-predictive controller (eNMPC) (Diehl et al., 2011), to account for the connection of economics and variability. In this work, we will extend our framework to incorporate parametric uncertainty. We will also elaborate on our strategy to account for dynamic disturbances.

In the next section, we describe our IDOP-eNMPC framework in more detail by discussing the methodology to account for dynamic fluctuations/variability and parametric uncertainty using amplitude-modulated pseudo-random binary sequences and the unscented transform of chance constraints. Afterward, we present a case study of a simplified Williams-Otto process to show the performance of the framework.

2. Theoretical Background

In the proposed framework, the dynamic optimization problem is turned into an NLP using orthogonal collocation on finite elements. Under these conditions, the optimization problem is

$$\min_{u,d} f$$

$$\text{s.t. } g(x,u,v,\theta,\xi,d) = 0 \tag{1}$$
$$h(x,u,v,\theta,\xi,d) \leq 0$$

where x is the state vector, u is the vector of manipulated variables, v represents dynamic disturbances, d represents the design vector, θ and ξ are the vectors of certain and uncertain model parameters. In addition, g are the algebraic constraints of the discretized dynamic process model and h are inequality constraints.

2.1. Dynamic disturbances

As we want to design a process, which is able to reject external disturbances, we have to represent these external disturbances by some method. In the past, several publications assumed sine signals whereas we use an amplitude-modulated pseudo-random binary sequence (APRBS) to generate our disturbance signal. These sequences are typically used for system identification (Nelles, 2001) and represent a signal that varies over the whole amplitude range. For this reason, they are more suitable for nonlinear systems compared to conventional pseudo-random binary sequences (PRBS). In this work, external disturbances in feed flows are represented by an APRBS (see Figure 5).

2.2. Introduction of uncertainty using chance constraints via the unscented transform

Another challenge in design is parametric uncertainty, e.g., in thermodynamic or kinetic models. Several approaches to consider uncertainty have been suggested, e.g., stochastic programming, probabilistic programming, and fuzzy mathematical programming (Sahinidis, 2004). In this contribution, we use chance-constrained optimization, i.e., we set a probability level α to which an inequality constraint must hold. The probability is computed by using the unscented transform (UT) of the inequality constraint, originally proposed by Julier and Uhlmann (2004). Here, the probability density function (PDF) of the prior variables, i.e., the uncertain parameters, is approximated via several sigma points (index sp). These sigma points propagate the prior distribution through the model to approximate the PDF of the inequality constraint. The idea of the UT is sketched below. Figure 1 shows the assumed prior PDF of an uncertain parameter. This prior PDF is approximated by sigma points whose number and location depend on the applied method. The equation system is formulated for all sigma points simultaneously. The expected value of the inequality constraint μ_h and its variance σ_h^2 are obtained by assuming a normal distribution and by weighting the specific realizations of the inequality constraints accordingly:

$$\mu_h = \sum_{sp} W_{sp} h_{sp} \tag{2}$$

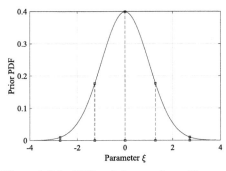

Figure 1: Prior PDF and sigma points with mean = 0 and standard deviation = 1.

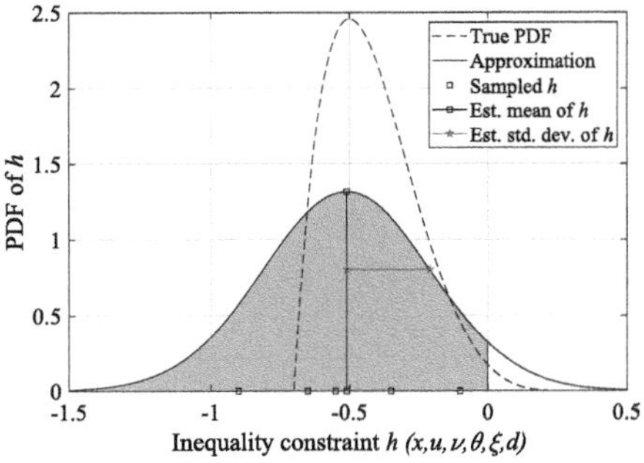

Figure 2: True and approximated PDF of an inequality constraint h.

$$\sigma_h^2 = \sum_{sp} W_{sp}\left(h_{sp} - \mu_h\right)^2 \tag{3}$$

This is illustrated in Figure 2, in which the gray area represents the probability that an inequality constraint holds. The true distribution, however, might be different, as shown in dashed lines in Figure 2. Hence, the assumption of a normal distribution does not necessarily have to hold and must be verified afterward.

Recently, Maußner and Freund (2018) compared several UT methods. They found the UT by Lévesque (2006) to yield a reasonable approximation and a weak dependence on the tuning parameters. Hence, we apply the Lévesque method in this framework and solve the following chance-constrained optimization problem in which we minimize the expected value of the objective function while ensuring that the inequality constraint holds to a probability level α:

$$\min_{u,d} E[f]$$

$$\text{s.t. } g\left(x, u, v, \theta, \xi_{sp}, d\right) = 0 \tag{4}$$
$$Pr\ \{h(x, u, v, \theta, \xi, d) \leq 0\} \geq \alpha$$

2.3. Stability
Stability is considered by a strict formulation of the terminal cost of the eNMPC problem. In this case, all differential states at the end of the horizon must be equal to their initial states, i.e. the process must be able to return to the initial state in spite of the disturbances:

$$x(t = t_{\text{end}}) = x(t = 0) \tag{5}$$

3. Algorithmic procedure and implementation

Based on the presented theoretic aspects, we develop an algorithmic framework presented in Figure 3. The dynamic model is initialized, preferably at steady-state. The process is then optimized based on steady-state assumptions by setting all derivatives of the Lagrange polynomials in the collocation approach to zero. Afterward, one may obtain an optimal steady-state design under uncertainty by using the UT method. In the next step, the derivatives of the Lagrange polynomials are assigned their non-zero values and dynamic disturbances are introduced via APRBS. This way, we obtain the design under variability with or without uncertainty. Finally, the results are verified by obtaining the true PDF of the inequality constraints via Monte-Carlo sampling. Note that the steady-

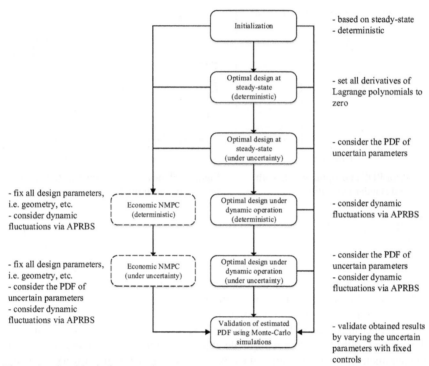

Figure 3: Algorithmic framework.

state optimizations are not necessary but optional. An advantageous side-effect of this model formulation is the ability to fix certain model parts to obtain a simpler problem, e.g. if design variables are fixed an optimal control problem is solved (dashed). This framework has been implemented in AMPL (Fourer et al., 2002), the optimization problems are solved with IPOPT (Wächter and Biegler, 2005). The process model is generated with MOSAICmodeling (Esche et al., 2017).

4. Case Study

The simplified Williams-Otto process (Williams and Otto, 1960) is shown schematically in Figure 4 and is chosen as a case study for the proposed method. The reactor is a continuously-stirred tank reactor (CSTR). Decanter, Distillation column, and recycle are expressed via component balances and splitting factors. Due to space limitations, we do not present the model here, but it can be found in (Hoffmann et al., 2019). Contrary to Hoffmann et al. (2019), we no longer assume the reactor level to remain constant to allow for more flexibility during operation. The manipulated variables of this process are the temperatures of streams 1, 2 and 3, and the reactor outlet. They are constant over a finite element and their change

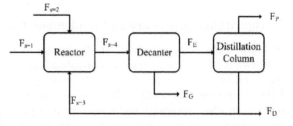

Figure 4: Scheme of the simplified Williams-Otto process.

from one finite element to the next is bounded. The design variables are the height and the diameter of the reactor and we maximize the net present value of the process. In addition, the reactor temperature shall remain below an upper bound:

$$h = T_R - T_R^{UB} \leq 0. \tag{6}$$

This inequality is transformed into a chance constraint (see Equation (4)). In our framework, we assume both feed streams 1 and 2 vary by ±5 % of their nominal values and introduce these fluctuations via APRBS as shown in Figure 5. The uncertain parameter is the activation energy of the first of three reactions, which is assumed to have a standard deviation of 3 %. We carried out process design for this system at steady-state (with and without uncertainty) and for dynamic (with and without uncertainty) but will limit ourselves to the comparison of the dynamic cases herein.

5. Results and Discussions

The IDOP is first solved deterministically. The inequality for the reactor temperature is considered as shown in Equation (6). This yields a reactor volume of 9.5 m³ and a net present value of 2.55 Mio. $. The results obtained under probabilistic conditions are shown in Figure 6. We see that (i) the net present value of the process has been decisively reduced in case uncertainty is introduced, and (ii) the reactor volume increases with an increasing probability level. In addition, contrary to the steady-state results for which every probability level was feasible, the process was not feasible for probability levels above 60 % under dynamic conditions. This demonstrates that dynamic fluctuations have a decisive impact on process design and that a pure steady-state analysis may not suffice to obtain sufficient disturbance rejection.

Referring to Figure 3, the last step of the framework is the validation of the actual probability distribution via Monte-Carlo sampling. In this case, 300 samples were taken for fixed manipulated variables. The results are shown in Figure 7 and demonstrate that the assumption of a normal distribution was justified in this case. However, this must always be validated and the results will depend on the nonlinearity of the process model, the magnitude of the standard deviations of the prior PDF, and presumably the number of uncertain parameters.

6. Conclusion and Outlook

In this contribution, our approach for integrating design and operation into a simultaneous optimization framework was extended to consider uncertain parameters by applying the unscented transform method. This makes it possible to approximate the probability density function of the inequality constraints and the expected value of the objective function without sequentially sampling over sigma points. Moreover, we

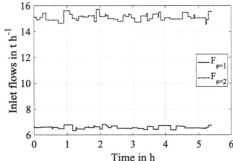

Figure 5: Feed fluctuations within ±5% of nominal feed flow using two APRBS.

elaborated on our methodology of introducing dynamic disturbances by using amplitude-modulated pseudo-random binary sequences. These cover a wider range of frequencies compared to a single sine signal. We successfully demonstrated this methodology for a case study: The design changes notably when considering dynamic fluctuations and

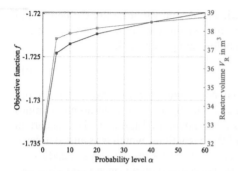
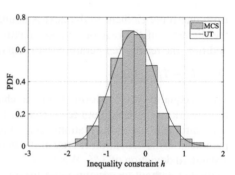

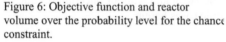

Figure 6: Objective function and reactor volume over the probability level for the chance constraint.

Figure 7: PDF of the inequality constraint obtained by 300 Monte-Carlo samples (MCS) and UT; probability level $\alpha = 60\%$.

uncertainty. For high probability levels, no feasible solution could be obtained, i.e. the process design would have to be changed, e.g. by adding additional units. In the future, we will combine this approach with a less restrictive formulation for stability and apply this framework to larger process models.

References

M. Diehl, R. Amrit, J.B. Rawlings, 2011, A Lyapunov Function for Economic Optimizing Model Predictive Control, IEEE Transactions on Automatic Control, 56, 3, 703–707.

E. Esche, C. Hoffmann, M. Illner, D. Müller, S. Fillinger, G. Tolksdorf, H. Bonart, G. Wozny, J.-U. Repke, 2017, MOSAIC - Enabling Large-Scale Equation-Based Flow Sheet Optimization, Chemie Ingenieur Technik, 89, 5, 620–635.

R. Fourer, D.M. Gay, B.W. Kernighan, 2002, Ampl: A Modeling Language for Mathematical Programming, Duxbury Thomson.

C. Hoffmann, E. Esche, J.-U. Repke, 2019, Integration of Design and Control Based on Large-Scale NLP Formulations and An Optimal Economic NMPCs, Proceedings of the 9th International Conference on Foundations of Computer-Aided Process Design, Computer Aided Chemical Engineering, Elsevier, 125–130.

S.J. Julier, J.K. Uhlmann, 2004, Unscented Filtering and Nonlinear Estimation, Proc. IEEE, 92, 3, 401–422.

J.-F. Lévesque, 2006, Second-Order Simplex Sigma Points for Nonlinear Estimation, AIAA Guidance, Navigation, and Control Conference and Exhibit, 6093.

A. Malcolm, J. Polan, L. Zhang, B.A. Ogunnaike, A.A. Linninger, 2007, Integrating systems design and control using dynamic flexibility analysis, AIChE Journal, 53, 8, 2048–2061.

J. Maußner, H. Freund, 2018, Optimization under uncertainty in chemical engineering: Comparative evaluation of unscented transformation methods and cubature rules, Chemical Engineering Science, 183, 329–345.

O. Nelles, 2001, Nonlinear system identification, Springer.

L.A. Ricardez-Sandoval, H.M. Budman, P.L. Douglas, 2009, Integration of design and control for chemical processes: A review of the literature and some recent results, Annual Reviews in Control, 33, 2, 158–171.

N.V. Sahinidis, 2004, Optimization under uncertainty: state-of-the-art and opportunities, Computers & Chemical Engineering, 28, 6-7, 971–983.

W.D. Seider, D.R. Lewin, J.D. Seader, S. Widagdo, R. Gani, K.M. Ng, 2017, Product and process design principles, Wiley.

A. Wächter, L.T. Biegler, 2005, On the implementation of an interior-point filter line-search algorithm for large-scale nonlinear programming, Mathematical Programming, 106, 1, 25–57.

T.J. Williams, R.E. Otto, 1960, A generalized chemical processing model for the investigation of computer control, Transactions of the American Institute of Electrical Engineers, Part I: Communication and Electronics, 79, 5, 458–473.

Sauro Pierucci, Flavio Manenti, Giulia Bozzano, Davide Manca (Eds.)
Proceedings of the 30th European Symposium on Computer Aided Process Engineering
(ESCAPE30), May 24-27, 2020, Milano, Italy. © 2020 Elsevier B.V. All rights reserved.
http://dx.doi.org/10.1016/B978-0-12-823377-1.50127-0

Modelling of Organophilic and Hydrophilic Pervaporations for Separation of Ethyl Acetate – water Mixture

Andras Jozsef Toth,[*,a] Eniko Haaz,[a] Reka Ladanyi,[a] Botond Szilagyi,[a] Daniel Fozer,[a] Asmaa Selim,[a,b] Tibor Nagy,[a] Peter Mizsey,[a,c]

[a]*Department of Chemical and Environmental Process Engineering, Műegyetem rkp. 3., Budapest, 1111, Hungary*
[b]*Chemical Engineering Department, National Research Centre, 33 El Buhouth Street, 12622 Cairo, Egypt*
[c]*Department of Fine Chemicals and Environmental Technology, Egyetemváros C/1 108., Miskolc, 3515, Hungary*
ajtoth@envproceng.eu

Abstract

Pervaporation is a separation method that is considered as green technology because of its low energy consumption. The mechanism of component separation in a liquid mixture by pervaporation is complex but it can be explained with the solution-diffusion mechanism. The work is motivated by an industrial separation problem, that is, ethyl acetate removal from aqueous mixture. To complete this goal hybrid organophilic/hydrophilic pervaporation of ethyl acetate/water mixture through commercially available Sulzer PERVAP™ 4060 and 1510 membranes are investigated to obtain information about the removal of ethyl acetate. Our experimental data are evaluated with the pervaporation model of our improvement (Valentínyi et al., 2013) and it is found that the model can be applied also for both cases. The hybrid separation process is rigorously modelled in professional flowsheet environment, and optimized with the dynamic programming optimization method. The objective function is product purity of 99.0, 99.5 m/m% in water and ethyl acetate content and the total annual cost is also determined. It can be determined, this hybrid separation should be become the alternative of distillation if the energy prices are too high.

Keywords: organophilic and hydrophilic pervaporation, flowsheet environment, model optimization, ethyl acetate removal

1. Introduction

Pervaporation (PV) is a chemical unit operation where the liquid mixture to be separated is vaporized at low pressure on the downstream/permeate side of the membranes and the separation of the mixtures takes place by preferential sorption and diffusion of the desired component through the membrane (Valentínyi et al., 2013). A solution to achieve the difference in the partial pressures is to maintain a low vapour pressure using a vacuum pump on the permeate side (Van Baelen et al., 2005). Pervaporation shows good features such as special separation effect, no-extra material addition and energy-saving which are difficult to obtain by other conventional methods (Szabados et al., 2018). Depending on the permeating component two main areas of pervaporation can be identified: hydrophilic (HPV) and organophilic pervaporation (OPV) (Heintz and Stephan, 1994a, b).

The aim of this work is to examine the ethyl acetate (EtAc) - water separation with pervaporation. The organophilic-hydrophilic pervaporation process is modelled and optimized for the separation of a binary mixture. EtAc forms heteroazeotrope with water (Gmehling et al., 1978), therefore this mixture cannot be separated with conventional distillation (Waltermann et al., 2017). Basically, the problem and the aims must be defined, that is, 5 m/m% ethyl acetate–water mixture with a feed flow of 1000 kg/h should be separated. The product purity of 99.0 and 99.5 m/m% should be achieved both for water and ethyl acetate.

2. Material and methods

Modelling of pervaporation has the following main steps (Toth et al., 2015):
1. System identification,
2. Model parameters estimation for pervaporation model,
3. Model verification/validation and
4. Optimization.

For the modelling of pervaporation, our model is selected and applied (Haaz and Toth, 2018). The parameters of the model are determined on the basis of experiments using the parameter estimation process (Valentínyi et al., 2013). The pervaporation model with the determined parameters is verified with the comparison of measured and modelled data (Toth, 2019). If the model is verified, which is, the model parameters are accurate, it can be applied for rigorous modelling in the professional flowsheeting environment (ChemCAD). In this step, the accuracy of calibrated model is checked with defined objective function (OF) that shows the sum of deviations of the modelled and measured data. (J means partial flux in Eq. (1)).

$$OF = \sum_{i=1}^{n} \left(\frac{J_{i,measured} - J_{i,modelled}}{J_{i,measured}} \right)^2$$

(1)

The validation of the pervaporation model takes also place in the flowsheeting environment. At first, the simulator program must be run with experimental data and if the results are suitable, the optimization process can be carried out. In this case, the membrane transfer area (A) is determined and changed for the sake of the minimum Total Annual Cost (TAC).

The composite PDMS (Sulzer PERVAP™ 4060) membrane is applied in organophilic experiments. The hydrophilic pervaporation is carried out with Sulzer PERVAP™ 1510 composite PVA membrane. The experimental set up is a P-28 membrane unit from CM-Celfa Membrantechnik AG (see Figure 1). The flat sheet membrane with 28 cm² effective area (A) is placed on a sintered disc separating the feed and the permeate sides. The volume of the feed tank is 500 ml. The concentration of the feed is considered to be constant. Cross-flow circulation velocity is kept at a permanent value of ~182 l/h.

The vacuum on the permeate side is maintained with a VACUUMBRAND PC2003 VARIO vacuum pump and kept at 6 Torr (8 mbar). The isotherm conditions are assured with a thermostat. The permeate is collected in two traps connected in series and cooled with liquid nitrogen to prevent loss of the permeate. The EtAc concentration of the feed (F), retentate (R) and permeate (P) are measured with Shimadzu GC2010Plus+AOC-20 autosampler gas chromatograph with a CP-SIL-5CB column connected to a flame ionization detector, EGB HS 600 headspace apparatus is used for sample preparation. The water content is measured with Hanna HI 904 coulometric Karl Fischer titrator (Haaz and Toth, 2018).

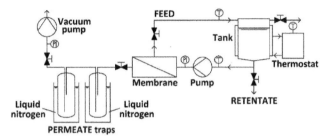

Figure 1. Schematic figure of CM-Celfa P-28 pervaporation unit (Haaz and Toth, 2018)

The pervaporation experiments are carried out at different temperatures (40; 50; 60°C) and feed ethyl acetate concentrations (OPV: 0.5; 1; 3 and 5 m/m% and HPV: 97; 98; 98.5; 99 m/m%) to investigate the temperature and concentration dependence of the pervaporation process.

In our modelling work, the methodology of Valentínyi et al. (2013) is selected. The model has been tested on several case studies and proved to be a good one for the description of pervaporation for engineering applications and design. The basic equation of the model introduces Eq. (2).

$$J_i = \frac{1}{1+\{[\bar{D}_i \cdot exp(B \cdot x_{i1})]/(Q_0 \cdot p_{i0} \cdot \bar{\gamma}_i)\}} \cdot \frac{[\bar{D}_i \cdot exp(B \cdot x_{i1})]}{\bar{\gamma}_i} \cdot \left(\frac{p_{i1}-p_{i3}}{p_{i0}}\right) \qquad i = (1, ..., k) \qquad (2)$$

The model is an improvement of Rautenbach's work (Rautenbach et al., 1990) and the improvements consider the concentration dependencies of the transport coefficient and the temperature dependencies of the pervaporation process. These improvements enable the accurate modelling of the pervaporation both for organophilic and hydrophilic ones (Lovasz et al., 2007).

The modelling of separation of binary ethyl acetate - water mixture consists of four main steps as follows in the simulator program (Toth et al., 2015):

1. Organophilic separation: this first step is to be designed that the permeate of the feed is enriched in the organic compound so that it enters the region where the hydrophilic pervaporation can be applied with success. The other design parameter is that in the retentate (water) there has to be practically no organic liquid since this flow will be discharged.

2. Liquid-liquid phase separator: the permeate of the organophilic pervaporation is separated into two phases: organic-rich and water-rich phases, if there is limited solubility. The aqueous phase is recycled to the feed of the first step. (If there were no limited solubility, this step can be omitted.)

3. Hydrophilic pervaporation: the organic-rich phase is fed into the hydrophilic pervaporation. The retentate of the hydrophilic unit is called the 'Ethyl acetate (organic) product', the concentrated ethyl acetate.

4. The retentate of the organophilic pervaporation and the permeate of the hydrophilic one are mixed with each other. This stream is the 'Water product' and this will be discharged.

Figure 2 shows the novel hybrid separation system.

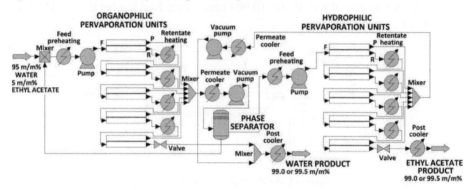

Figure 2. Flowsheet of ethyl acetate – water mixture separation with organophilic and hydrophilic pervaporation systems

3. Results and discussion

A comparison of the measured and calculated partial fluxes are presented in Figure 3 and Figure 4.

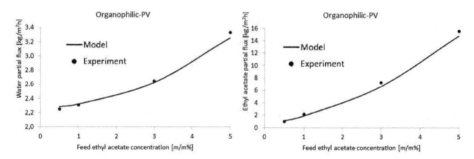

Figure 3. Measured partial fluxes of ethyl acetate and water compared to fluxes calculated with pervaporation model in a function of feed ethyl acetate concentration with PERVAP™ 4060 organophilic membrane at 60°C

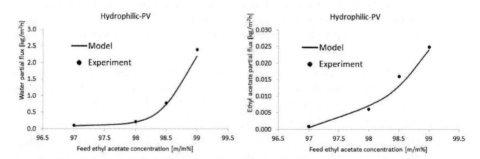

Figure 4. Measured partial fluxes of ethyl acetate and water compared to fluxes calculated with pervaporation model in a function of feed ethyl acetate concentration with PERVAP™ 1510 hydrophilic membrane at 60°C

The minimized objective functions are shown in Table 1.

Table 1 Objective functions resulted by pervaporation model

OF	Water	Ethyl acetate
Organophilic-PV	0.001	0.055
Hydrophilic-PV	0.021	0.245

Generally, it can be concluded that the pervaporation model with the concentration dependency of the transport coefficient fit for the pervaporation experiments in a wide concentration range of the feed flow, particularly in the case of water fluxes. Table 2 shows the necessary total membrane surface areas in the function of product purities.

Table 2 Effective membrane surface areas

Total A	EtAc product	Water product
	EtAc	Water
[m^2]	[m/m%]	[m/m%]
20	99.0	99.0
27	99.0	99.5
38	99.5	99.0
52	99.5	99.5

The conceptual design of an industrial process takes a small part of the project costs but offers a huge cost reduction opportunity for the whole project (Dimian, 2003). Investment costs are calculated according to the cost correlations of Douglas (1988) with the current M&S index. Heat exchangers and the low-temperature cooling apparatus for the permeates are also calculated (Toth et al., 2015). Membrane area-price function is determined on industrial data and used for the calculation of the capital costs of membrane modules (Koczka, 2009). Investment costs of the pervaporation depend on many parameters, e.g.: effective membrane area, the volume of the streams and purity of the products. 8000 annual continuous working hours are selected for the calculation of the operating cost. In this work, 2.5 years are taken as membrane depreciation time, because membranes should be generally replaced in approximately every 2-5 years (Haaz and Toth, 2018). 10-year amortization of capital cost is assumed for the total cost estimation. Table 3 shows the cost elements of hybrid organophilic-hydrophilic pervaporation system in the case of 52 m^2 membrane area.

Table 3 Main cost elements of hybrid ethyl acetate-water pervaporation system

10 years amortization	Investment cost	Operating cost	Total cost
	1000 USD/year	1000 USD/year	1000 USD/year
Phase separator	3	8	11
Permeate cooling	17	97	113
Heat exchangers	9	110	119
Membrane modules	197	41	238
Total	225	256	481

4. Conclusions

The experiments and simulations suggest that the pervaporation is able to remove the ethyl acetate from an aqueous mixture. Organophilic and hydrophilic pervaporations are modelled with our verified and adequate model in professional flowsheeting environment that enables verified rigorous modelling, optimization and cost estimation. The results show that the capital cost of the pervaporation unit is the highest part of the total annual cost.

Acknowledgments

This publication was supported by the János Bolyai Research Scholarship of the Hungarian Academy of Sciences, ÚNKP-19-4-BME-416 New National Excellence Program of the Ministry for Innovation and Technology, OTKA 112699, 128543 and 131586. This research was supported by the European Union and the Hungarian State, co-financed by the European Regional Development Fund in the framework of the GINOP-2.3.4-15-2016-00004 project, aimed to promote the cooperation between the higher education and the industry. The research reported in this paper has been supported by the National Research, Development and Innovation Fund (TUDFO/51757/2019-ITM, Thematic Excellence Program).

References

A. C. Dimian, 2003, Integrated Design and Simulation of Chemical Processes, Elsevier Science, Amsterdam, The Netherlands.

J. M. Douglas, 1988, Conceptual design of chemical processes, McGraw-Hill, New York.

J. Gmehling, U. Onken, J. R. Rarey-Nies, 1978, Vapor-liquid equilibrium data collection, Dechema, Virginia.

A. Heintz, W. Stephan, 1994a, A generalized solution-diffusion model of the pervaporation process through composite membranes Part I. Prediction of mixture solubilities in the dense active layer using the UNIQUAC model, J Membrane Sci 89, 1-2, 143-151.

A. Heintz, W. Stephan, 1994b, A generalized solution-diffusion model of the pervaporation process through composite membranes Part II. Concentration polarization, coupled diffusion and the influence of the porous support layer, J Membrane Sci 89, 1-2, 153-169.

E. Haaz, A. J. Toth, 2018, Methanol dehydration with pervaporation: Experiments and modelling, Sep Purif Technol 205, 121-129.

K. Koczka, 2009, Environmental conscious design and industrial application of separation processes, PhD Thesis, BME, Budapest.

A. Lovasz, P. Mizsey, Z. Fonyo, 2007, Methodology for parameter estimation of modelling of pervaporation in flowsheeting environment, Chem Eng J 133, 219-227.

R. Rautenbach, C. Herion, U. Meyer-Blumentoth, 1990, Pervaporation membrane separation processes, Membrane Science and Technology Series 1, 181-191.

E. Szabados, A. Jobbagy, A. J. Toth, P. Mizsey, G. Tardy, C. Pulgarin, S. Giannakis, E. Takacs, L. Wojnarovits, M. Mako, Z. Trocsanyi, A. Tungler, 2018, Complex Treatment for the Disposal and Utilization of Process Wastewaters of the Pharmaceutical Industry, Period Polytech Chem Eng 62, 76-90.

A. J. Toth, 2019, Comprehensive evaluation and comparison of advanced separation methods on the separation of ethyl acetate-ethanol-water highly non-ideal mixture, Sep Purif Technol 224, 490-508.

A. J. Toth, A. Andre, E. Haaz, P. Mizsey, 2015, New horizon for the membrane separation: Combination of organophilic and hydrophilic pervaporations, Sep Purif Technol, 156, 2, 432–443.

N. Valentínyi, E. Cséfalvay, P. Mizsey, 2013, Modelling of pervaporation: Parameter estimation and model development, Chem Eng Res Des 91, 1, 174-183.

D. Van Baelen, B. Van der Bruggen, K. Van den Dungen, J. Degreve, C. Vandecasteele, 2005, Pervaporation of water–alcohol mixtures and acetic acid–water mixtures, Chem Eng Sci 60, 1583-1590.

T. Waltermann, D. Münchrath, M. Skiborowski, 2017, Efficient optimization-based design of energy-intensified azeotropic distillation processes, Comput Aided Chem Eng 40, 1045-1050.

Sauro Pierucci, Flavio Manenti, Giulia Bozzano, Davide Manca (Eds.)
Proceedings of the 30th European Symposium on Computer Aided Process Engineering
(ESCAPE30), May 24-27, 2020, Milano, Italy. © 2020 Elsevier B.V. All rights reserved.
http://dx.doi.org/10.1016/B978-0-12-823377-1.50128-2

Superstructure Optimization for the Design of a Desalination Plant to Tackle the Water Scarcity in Texas (USA)

Marcello Di Martino[a,b,c], Styliani Avraamidou[b], Efstratios Pistikopoulos[a,b*]

[a]*Artie McFerrin Department of Chemical Engineering, Texas A&M University*
[b]*Texas A&M Energy Institute, Texas A&M University*
[c]*RWTH Aachen University*
stratos@tamu.edu

Abstract

Depleting water sources, as well as a growing population, together with the threats of climate change, emphasize the necessity of novel water sources for municipal use, as well as for energy generation. Desalination processes could play a key role in tackling these challenges since treating sea water, industrial wastewater or brackish water for reuse becomes possible. Consequently, this work focusses on the analysis and optimization of various reverse osmosis desalination systems through superstructure optimization for the development of optimal designs of desalination plants, to address the energy-water nexus.

The superstructure model and its optimization could be valuable for the evaluation of the best possible design and operation of a desalination system for a given input framework (energy and water) to meet set restrictions on output water specifications and energy or environmental goals. Additionally, the applicability of the developed superstructure model is illustrated through the case study of the design of a new desalination plant in South Central Texas.

Since the superstructure framework is formulated as a mixed-integer programming problem, the model can be optimized for varying scenarios, resulting in a plethora of optimal solutions for decision makers, including different desalination plant designs depending on the distinct input water characteristics, output restrictions and goals.

Keywords: Desalination, Optimization, Superstructure, Reverse Osmosis

1. Introduction

Water scarcity is a severe challenge, especially for arid and semi-arid regions such as Texas (USA), California (USA) and Baja California (Mexico) or the Middle Eastern Region. With a growing population, both water and energy demands are increasing. Since water is traditionally used as a coolant in energy production plants the water consumption further rises. Consequently, water and energy production are linked to each other, which in turn means that these challenges need to be solved by a Water-Energy Nexus approach (Allen et al. 2019, Gabriel et al. 2016).
Further, existing water supplies, like groundwater aquifer storage systems, are depleting globally (Y. Wada et al. 2010). Additionally, climate change is expected to make water shortages worse: The Inter-governmental Panel on Climate Change (IPCC) projected that up to two billion people worldwide could be facing water shortages by 2050 (R. C. Kundis, 2010). Therefore, to cope with these severe challenges, novel water sources are needed. Desalination processes could play a key role in tackling these challenges since

treating sea water, surface water, industrial wastewater or brackish water for reuse becomes possible.

So far, there have been a variety of distinct optimization analyses concerning reverse osmosis desalination systems addressing the energy-water nexus: Vakilifard et al. (2018) review optimization models concerning the energy-water nexus in water supply systems and identify knowledge gaps, as well as suggest future works. Among other things, a general lack of holistic water-energy nexus optimization approaches and a lack of optimization frameworks considering environmental impacts of solution strategies were identified. To address the energy-water nexus, Li (2018) minimizes the specific energy consumption of a hybrid membrane process consisting of reverse osmosis for desalination and pressure retarded osmosis for power generation. A systematic procedure for the optimization of the benefits of the water-energy nexus on the basis of a surplus on energy has been determined by Gabriel et al. (2016). Further, Tsolas et al. (2018) make use of water-energy nexus diagrams to identify a nexus for optimal resource generation and utilization.

These works focus on key parts and challenges of reverse osmosis desalination processes to address the interconnectivity of energy and water resources.

To our knowledge a holistic energy-water nexus approach optimizing the water and energy sources, as well as the membrane system, together with the operating conditions of the process, in an attempt to meet the local water demands for varying output water applications, has not yet been investigated.

Various desalination alternatives have been modeled and simulated permitting and facilitating superstructure optimization. The superstructure is formulated as a mathematical model, which has the form of a mixed-integer programming problem. The developed model can then be optimized for distinct scenarios resulting in a plethora of optimal solutions for decision makers, enabling a framework methodology, for the techno-economic and feasibility analysis of desalination plants. Hence, the elaborated approach can be used for reliable and fast screening of reverse osmosis plant designs prior to detailed plant modeling.

2. Reverse Osmosis Desalination Process Superstructure

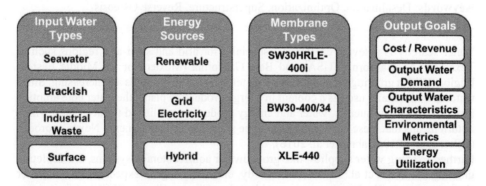

Figure 1: Overview of the reverse osmosis desalination process superstructure considerations.

The design of a reverse osmosis desalination process is addressed holistically in terms of the input water types, the energy sources (like grid electricity or renewable energies), the membrane types, as well as the process operation and parameters, for various output goals, not only maximizing revenue or minimizing cost, but also satisfying a given water demand for different output water characteristics (like municipal, irrigation, livestock or power plant usage), while environmental metrics can be considered. The framework is modifiable for any given region around the world, by adjusting restrictions concerning water and energy availability, emphasizing the framework methodology nature of the implemented approach. An overview of the general considerations for the superstructure can be found in Figure 1. The visualized framework is subsequently translated into a mathematical model, which has the form of a MINLP problem.

A schematic representation of a one-stage reverse osmosis process, together with the variables describing it are illustrated in Figure 2. A feed stream is pressurized so that a separation of the saline feed (Q_f, C_f, P_f) into a diluted permeate (Q_p, C_p, P_p) and a concentrated retentate (Q_r, C_r, P_r) can be achieved in the reverse osmosis membrane module.

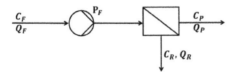

Figure 2: Schematic representation of the desalination separation step.

Membrane modeling is classically used to calculate the necessary pressurization of the feed streams, for a certain permeate concentration quality (or vice versa), since the pressurization is the main energy cost driver of the desalination system (A. Zhu et al. 2009).

To determine the properties of a desalination stage the following equations (1) to (5) are utilized:

$$SEC_{pump} = \frac{Q_f \cdot \Delta P}{\eta_{pump} \cdot Q_p} \tag{1}$$

$$\Delta P = P_f - P_p \tag{2}$$

$$Q_f = Q_p + Q_r \tag{3}$$

$$Q_f \cdot C_f = Q_p \cdot C_p + Q_r \cdot C_r \tag{4}$$

$$C_p = f(C_f, \Delta P, A, WR, Q_p) = x_1 \cdot \frac{Q_p}{A} + x_2 \cdot \frac{Q_p}{Q_f} + x_3 \cdot \Delta P \tag{5}$$

The energy consumption of the pump (see Equation 1) is mainly dependent on the transmembrane pressure (ΔP), as well as on the ratio of feed (Q_f) to permeate volume flow (Q_p). The transmembrane pressure (see Equation 2) is defined by the difference of the pressurized feed (P_f) and the permeate pressure (P_p). Further, a total mass balance, as well as a component mass balance are necessary to characterize the process stage (Equations 3 and 4).

The permeate concentration correlation (Equation 5) is based on a surrogate model, which in turn is a multivariate linear regression of normalized data. This data has been generated with the membrane supplier simulation tool WAVE from DOW Chemical for varying feed concentrations (C_f), membrane surface areas (A), output permeate flows and water recoveries ($WR = Q_p/Q_f$). To improve the accuracy of the surrogate model the parameters $x_i, \forall i = 1, \dots, 3$, change with the feed concentration, water recovery and water flux ($J_v = Q_p/A$). With the help of the multivariate-linear surrogate model, the high-fidelity membrane model is replaced, resulting in a model with reduced overall complexity, that requires reduced computational effort when embedded in an optimization problem.

Subsequently, either the permeate or the retentate flow (Q_r) can be redefined as the feed flow of a successive stage (dependent on the concentration). The optimization model has $DOF = w \cdot (4 \cdot n + 1)$ degrees of freedom, dependent on the number of stages n and available water sources w. The design variables include the feed flow ($Q_{f,1,j}$), the number of parallel flows ($m_{i,j}$), the surface area ($A_{i,j}$), the water recovery ($WR_{i,j}$), the transmembrane pressure ($\Delta P_{i,j}$), as well as the number of stages n_j, for stages $i = 1, \dots, n_j$ and for each water source $j = 1, \dots, w$.

3. Case Study

To illustrate the potential and functionality of the superstructure model the following case study is analysed. The design of a desalination plant which uses aquifer water ($C_f = 1500 mg/L$ and $Q_{f,1} \leq 35000 m^3/d$) and a minimal water utilization restriction of $WR \geq 57\%$, for South Central Texas, defined as region L by the Texas Water Development Board, is the focus of this scenario.

Firstly, the design of the desalination plant is determined, when only grid electricity is used. Secondly, the same optimization is performed, but now only solar and wind energy are available as energy supply sources. Then, the water utilization is maximized by maximizing the water recovery for a given feed flow restriction. With these solutions a Pareto Front for minimizing operational costs and maximizing the water recovery is determined.

In the first two optimization problems, the reverse osmosis operational process costs are minimized, which consist primarily of energy costs (A. Ghobeity, A. Mitsos 2014). Therefore, only energy costs together with concentrated brine disposal costs and membrane costs are considered as cost constituents of operational costs, to ensure that a membrane budget, as well as disposal limitations can be considered.

The energy costs are calculated based on the specific energy consumption of the pump, as well as an energy recovery device, which enables the usage of, for the separation not viable, high residual retentate pressures of respective stages to increase the overall process efficiency. Subsequently, the determined energy consumption is multiplied with an energy cost factor dependent on the energy source. The brine disposal costs are dependent on the feed concentration of the system, as well as the ratio of the retentate volume flow to the permeate volume flow. The disposal costs are scaled with a brine cost factor dependent on the water source. Further, the membrane costs summarize the purchase price of the selected membranes, as well as the pressure vessels with regard to an assumed membrane lifetime and the overall permeate water output. This results in operational costs in terms of $\$/m^3$ permeate.

The energy cost factor for grid electricity ($22.4\$/MWh$) is obtained from averaging the day-ahead market price from ERCOT (Electric Reliability Council of Texas). The price for using solar and wind energy results from an energy superstructure optimization for minimizing investment and operational costs of a set of renewable energy sources for constant power output. The power output is then varied over a specific range resulting in a constant slope of 29.84$/$MWh$ for solar and wind energy.

The results of the optimization are summarized in Table 1, as well as in Figure 4. In both cases, a three-stage process results in minimal operational costs. Although the energy price rises by 33%, the operational costs only increase by 11%. This is possible, because of lower pressures for each stage and a higher number of parallel flows for stages two and three. Consequently, the energy cost, as well as the membrane cost increase only slightly, to offset the higher energy price, resulting in a lower than expected operational cost increase.

Table 1: Top: Results of the design optimization with grid electricity; Bottom: Results of the design optimization with solar and wind energy (with batteries).

Grid Electricity, Cost: 22.4 $/MWh							
Stage	Q_f[m³/d]	C_f[mg/L]	P [mg/L]	WR [%]	C_p[mg/L]	C_r[mg/L]	m_i [-]
1	26961	1500	21.13	55.58	35.92	3332	5
2	11975	3332	20.93	60.98	45.84	9997	3
3	3954	9997	22.85	70.0	199.94	32858	2
Renewable Energy, Cost: 29.84 $/MWh							
Stage	Q_f[m³/d]	C_f[mg/L]	P [mg/L]	WR [%]	C_p[mg/L]	C_r[mg/L]	m_i [-]
1	25499	1500	18.11	50.63	39.81	2997	5
2	12589	2997	19.03	69.90	46.75	9848	4
3	3790	9848	18.39	69.99	192.78	32373	3

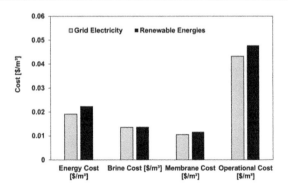

Figure 3: Comparison of operational cost constituents from the design optimization results, grid electricity and renewable energies.

Additionally, the energy consumption of the system using only renewable energies is minimized, for varying water recovery restrictions. This results in the Pareto Fronts summarized in Figure 4, for the operational costs (left), as well as cost constituents of these (right) versus the water recovery. Because of the nearly linear brine disposal cost decline $(-0.0034\$/(m^3 \cdot \%))$, $R^2 = 0.99$) and only marginally energy cost rise (for a water recovery of 88% to 98%, by 18%) with an increasing water recovery, decline the overall operational cost until a water recovery of 98%. If the water recovery needs to be further increased the energy cost increase significantly to offset the brine disposal savings. Consequently, the operational cost rise. In contrast, the membrane costs do not follow a specific trend as indicated by the dotted line in Figure 4.

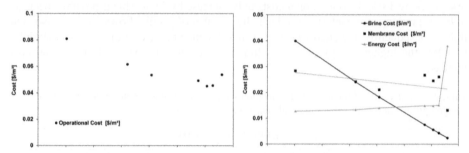

Figure 4: Pareto front minimizing energy and maximizing water recovery, Left: Operational cost dependent on water recovery; Right: Operational cost constituents dependent on water recovery.

4. Conclusion

With the newly developed framework methodology for the superstructure optimization of desalination plants, it is possible to assess desalination alternatives and analyse the impact of changing supply systems, e.g. like the energy source. Therefore, the analysis of various possible scenarios is enabled and facilitated. Further, the elaborated approach can be used for a reliable and fast screening of reverse osmosis plant designs, prior to detailed plant modelling, to advise decision makers, which desalination alternatives are worth further exploring and which not.

References

R. C. Allen, Y. Nie, S. Avraamidou, E. N. Pistikopoulos, 2019, Infrastructure Planning and Operational Scheduling for Power Generating Systems: An Energy-Water Nexus Approach, Computer Aided Chemical Engineering, 47, 233-238.

K. J. Gabriel, M. M. El-Halwagi, P. Linke, 2016, Optimization across water-energy nexus for integrating heat, power and water for industrial processes coupled with hybrid thermal-membrane desalination, Industrial & Engineering Chemistry Research, 55, 12, 3442–3466.

A. M. A. Ghobeity, A. Mitsos, 2014, Optimal design and operation of desalination systems: new challenges and recent advances, Current Opinion in Chemical Engineering, 6, 61-68.

R. C. Kundis, 2010, Water Supply, Desalination, Climate Change, and Energy Policy Symposium: Critical Intersections for Energy & Water Law: Exploring New Challenges and Opportunities, Pacific McGeorge Global Business & Development Law Journal 2, 2, 225–255.

M. Li, 2018, Optimization of multi-stage hybrid RO-PRO membrane processes at the water-energy nexus, Chemical Engineering Research and Design, 137, 1-9.

S. D. Tsolas, M.N. Karim, M. M. F. Hasan, 2018, Optimization of water-energy nexus: A network representation-based graphical approach, Applied Energy, 224, 230-250.

N. Vakilifard et al., 2018, The role of water-energy nexus in optimising water supply systems - Review of techniques and approaches, Renewable and Sustainable Energy Reviews, 82, Part1, 1424-1432.

Y. Wada et al., 2010, Global depletion of groundwater resources, Geophysical Research Letters, 37, 20.

A. Zhu, P. D. Christofides, Y. Cohen, 2009, Energy Consumption Optimization of RO Membrane Desalination Subject to Feed Salinity Fluctuation, Ind. Eng. Chem. Res., 48, 21, 9581–9589.

Sauro Pierucci, Flavio Manenti, Giulia Bozzano, Davide Manca (Eds.)
Proceedings of the 30th European Symposium on Computer Aided Process Engineering
(ESCAPE30), May 24-27, 2020, Milano, Italy. © 2020 Elsevier B.V. All rights reserved.
http://dx.doi.org/10.1016/B978-0-12-823377-1.50129-4

Optimal Design of a Multi-Product Polycrystalline Silicon Facility

César Ramírez-Márquez[a], Edgar Martín-Hernández[b], Mariano Martín[b], Juan Gabriel Segovia-Hernández[a]

[a]*Universidad de Guanajuato, Campus Guanajuato, División de Ciencias Naturales y Exactas, Departamento de Ingeniería Química, Noria Alta S/N, 20256, Guanajuato Gto., México*
[b]*University of Salamanca, Department of Chemical Engineering. Pza. Caídos 1-5, 37008 Salamanca, Spain.*

Abstract

The silicon industry is a source of different types of products, including materials for the implementation of renewable energy systems, with a comparatively lower environmental impact than conventional fossil energy sources, and high added value by-products. In this context, the exploitation of the different by-products generated in the production of polycrystalline silicon (polysilicon) offers opportunities to increase the economic efficiency of the polycrystalline silicon production processes. In this work, a silicon based refinery is conceptually designed, estimating the optimal operating conditions by using surrogate models for the major units involved. Although the main product is polysilicon, there are different products that could be generated in the process increasing its profitability, such as tetraethoxysilane (at different purities). Likewise, series of chlorosilanes with high added value, including SiH_4, SiH_2Cl_2, and SiH_3Cl, can also be produced. Additionally, an economic evaluation of the facility is carried out to determine its economic feasibility. The results show that the refinery produces tetraethoxysilane and chlorosilanes in addition to the production of polysilicon. The proposed design reduces the cost for polycrystalline silicon to 6.86 $/kg, below the commercial price estimated at 10 $/kg. Therefore, the refinery is not only capable to meet the market share requirements but that the generation of different high added value by-products increases the plant profit compared with the net income earned by a traditional polysilicon mono-product plants.

Keywords: Multi-Product, Polycrystalline Silicon, Economic Evaluation.

1. Introduction

In recent years, the polycrystalline silicon photovoltaic (PV) industry has grown vividly, developing a truly global supply chain. In the past 10 years, polycrystalline silicon based solar panels represent more than 90% of photovoltaic production, accounting more than 95% of production in 2018 (Mints, 2018). This development has been induced by the increase in the demand of photovoltaic (PV) energy, as well as by the technical progress in the performance of PV cells, and the improvement in the manufacturing processes of polycrystalline silicon, allowing drastic cost reductions in PV modules cost. However, the polysilicon production costs can be further improved valorizing the by-products generated in the process, which otherwise would be considered as waste.

In the case of the polycrystalline silicon industry, the main by-product of polycrystalline silicon manufacturing is tetrachlorosilane, which currently is fed back into the production cycle. Tetrachlorosilane can also be extracted and post-processed to obtain added value products. However, the processing tetrachlorosilane to obtain high added value by-products can be integrated with the main polycrystalline silicon production process, avoiding the need to dispose of waste streams and increasing the economic and environmental efficiencies of the process.

The statement above has been demonstrated by the polycrystalline silicon company Wacker™, who integrated the production of pyrogenic silica from tetrachlorosilane to the polycrystalline silicon process in different facilities, such as Charleston in the USA, and Burghausen and Nuenchritz in Germany (Rubber & Plastics News Report, 2016). Pyrogenic silica is a valuable product used as a filler in silicone elastomers and as an archeology control additive in paints, adhesives, and unsaturated polyester resins (Rubber & Plastics News Report, 2016). However, pyrogenic silica is not the only product that can be generated from tetrachlorosilane.

In the present work develops a superstructure for the selection of the portfolio of products from quartz including the production tetraethoxysilane (TEOS), which is the most prominent derivative of the family of silicon compounds. Tetraethoxysilane is mainly used in the manufacture of chemical and heat resistant coatings, organic silicon solvents, and precision casting adhesives. Additionally, the production of a series of chlorosilanes with high added value (silane, dichlorosilane and monochlorosilane) is also considered from trichlorosilane.

2. Methodology

To design a polycrystalline silicon process with an analogous production capacity to current polycrystalline silicon production companies as Wacker Co., an average production capacity of the plant of 15,000 annual metric tons of polycrystalline silicon is considered (Rubber & Plastics News Report, 2016). The polycrystalline silicon production process expand the one proposed by Ramírez-Márquez et al., (2019). In this work, the conceptual design of the process, named as Hybrid Process, is presented. The Hybrid Process is the result of a strategic combination of the stages of the Siemens and the Union Carbide process. The Hybrid Process is extended using a couple of reactive distillation columns for the production of high added value products such as: TEOS 98.5, TEOS 99.0, TEOS 99.5, silane, dichlorosilane and monochlorosilane. The process diagram for Multi-Product Polycrystalline Silicon Facility that was used in the present work is showed in Figure 1.

2.1 Modelling approach

The model for the superstructure is developed based on mass and energy balances, thermodynamics, experimental data and rules of thumb for basic units and surrogate models for major ones such as reactors and distillation columns. The process starts with the carboreduction process of quartz. The raw materials used are silica in form of quartz (SiO_2) and carbon (C). These raw materials are stored in storage tanks, to be further blended in a mixer, and fed into the carboreduction reactor. The storage tanks and mixers have been modeled through material balances. The model for the carboreduction reactor is based on the work reported by Wai and Hutchison (1989), computing the products distribution for a C/SiO_2 feeding molar ratio of 2:1, a total pressure of 1 atm, and a temperature range of 2500-3500 K. To achieve the production capacity of typical industrial plants, in the present work a feed of 150 kmol/h of SiO_2 and 300 kmol/h of C is considered. Based on that work, correlations are developed to estimate the distribution of the products obtained at the reactor (mol fraction) as a function of the reaction temperature (K).

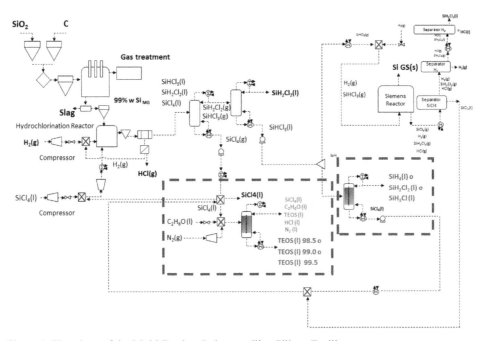

Figure 1. Flowsheet of the Multi-Product Polycrystalline Silicon Facility.

In the hydrochlorination reactor, $SiCl_4$ is hydrogenated in the presence of Si_{MG}. To model this equipment, the minimization for the Gibbs free energy for the system $SiCl_4$–H_2–Si_{MG} is used, based on the work by Ding, et al., (2014). For convenience, the reaction system $SiCl_4$–H_2–Si_{MG} was treated as ideal, and the following variables ranges were studied: temperature (T), 573–873 K; pressure (P), 1–20 atm; y molar feeding ratio (Rel) H_2/$SiCl_4$, 1-5 evaluating the yield to each product as a function of them. Then the surrogate models are developed to estimate the composition as a function of the operating conditions.

The condensation step was modelled based on material and energy balances considering complete separation of the effluent in a gas phase stream and the liquid phase stream. For the separation of the chlorosilanes two convectional distillation columns are used. The rigorous modeling and sizing of the columns was performed using the Aspen Plus software, based on a previous work (Ramírez-Márquez et al., 2019). By varying the feeding and the degrees of freedom as the reflux ratio, surfaces of response are obtained to estimate the energy involved in the reboiler, at the condense and their operating temperatures. The variables evaluated were the feeding molar ratio $SiCl_4$-(SiH_2Cl_2-$SiHCl_3$), within the range from 1 to 2.1698 for the first column; the SiH_2Cl_2-$SiHCl_3$ molar ratio, for a range from 2.99 to 7.5678 for the second column; and reflux ratio from 10 to 80 for the first column and from 60 to 90 for the second column.

For waste streams of $SiCl_4$, remnants of the first column at the bottom, process intensification adding a reactive distillation (RD) column is suggested to produce TEOS (at different purities 98.5-99.0 or 99.5). Sánchez-Ramírez et al. (2018) showed that the reactive distillation has a better performance than the conventional system regarding TAC values. The variables were evaluated in the following ranges: feeding molar ratio $SiCl_4$- C_2H_5OH values from 1 to 100 for the TEOS reactive column. Also, in the second distillation column at the bottom, a stream of pure trichlorosilane is obtained. That stream is divided into a splitter to feed the Siemens reactors or the reactive distillation columns for the disproportion of trichlorosilane to obtain silane, dichlorosilane or monochlorosilane (each one at 99.0 purity), as proposed by Ramírez Márquez et al. (2016). The trichlorosilane feed was varied in a range of 1 to 10 kmol/h.

The deposition of polycrystalline silicon was modeled according to the work presented by Del Coso and Luque, (2008). In this work, the kinetics of the deposition for polycrystalline silicon in the traditional Siemens reactor are provided. They present analytic solutions for the deposition process, based on the approach of splitting the second-order reaction rate into two systems of first-order reaction rate. The growth rate, deposition efficiency, and power-loss dependence on the gas velocity, the mixture of gas composition, the reactor pressure, and the surface temperature have been analyzed, providing information regarding the deposition velocity and the polycrystalline silicon production rate. The variables analyzed were the polysilicon growth rate, the deposition efficiency and the system temperature. The model defined was solved with the data reported by Del Coso and Luque, (2008) for a temperature range from 1372 to 1500 K.

2.2 Solution procedure

The process was formulated as a nonlinear programming (NLP) problem. The model consists of 3,014 equations and 3,716 variables, which are solved to optimize the operating conditions of the Multi-Product Polycrystalline Silicon facility, using a profit objective function, Eq. 1. Hence, the main variables of decision are: the temperature of the thermal carboreduction reactor; the temperature, pressure, and $H_2/SiCl_4$ feeding molar ratio of the hydrochlorination reactor, the feeding ratio and the reflux ratio of each distillation column, for the reactive columns the feeding ratio, and the operating temperature of the Siemens Reactor.

The objective function, Eq. 1, aims to maximize the process total profit, considering not only the production of the main product (polysilicon), but also the income from by-products (chlorosilanes), deducting the manufacturing cost.

$$\text{OF) } \max z = S_{polycrystalline\ silico} + p\,SP - b\,RM - c\,E \tag{1}$$

where, b is the unit cost of each raw material RM; c is the cost of each utility E; $d\,MO$ is the labour cost; p is the price of each by-product SP, and $S_{polycrystalline\ silicon}$ is profit from the sale of the polycrystalline silicon.

Also, a detailed economic evaluation based on the procedure proposed by Turton et al. (2012) has been carried out, estimating the equipment cost, production cost, maintenance, administration and manpower. The NLP problem was solved using a multistart initialization approach with CONOPT as the preferred solver.

3. Results

The results shown in Table 1 summarize the economic parameters of the process. It can be seen how with an adequate arrangement of the operation conditions of each unit, the production of tetraethoxysilane and chlorosilanes, the raw material consumption, and the services consumption, it is possible to reduce the cost for polycrystalline silicon to 6.86 \$/kg, below the commercial price estimated at 10 \$/kg. Besides, the comparison was made with the model without the addition of high value-added products, and the price of polycrystalline silicon in this context is 8.93 \$/kg (higher than the price by adding high value-added products). Also, the byproducts cost are: 1.5 \$/kg for TEOS 98.5; 2.5 \$/kg for TEOS 99.0; 3.75 \$/kg for TEOS 99.5; 88.44 \$/kg for SiH_4; 3.0 \$/kg for SiH_3Cl; and 3.67 \$/kg for SiH_2Cl_2. Despite being able to choose from a wide range of high value-added products such as: TEOS 98.5, TEOS 99.0, TEOS 99.5, silane, dichlorosilane and monochlorosilane, in the optimization it can be seen that solution choose the components of greater economic value for its production, as is the case of polycrystalline silicon, silane and TEOS 99.5. The objective function maximizes the profit of the Multi-Product Polycrystalline Silicon Facility, giving a maximum profit in the process of 113.57 M\$/y, and presents some particularities. For example, for a large production of silicon, the hydrochlorination reactor temperature is 573 K using a $H_2/SiCl_4$ molar ratio of 2.17. However, despite the low energy requirement of the reactor, high production costs of $SiHCl_3$ are obtained due to the use of considerable amounts of $SiCl_4$. It should be also noted that the process requires a high energy consumption in the distillation columns due to the high values of the reflux ratios. This guarantees a high polycrystalline silicon production capacity although the operating cost is high it also respects an adequate production of high value-added products such as TEOS and chlorosilanes, which makes the process of production of polycrystalline silicon much more profitable. The investment cost of the Multi-Product Polycrystalline Silicon Facility results in 85.93 \$M. It can be seen that the distillation columns (conventional or reactive) are the most expensive units, followed by the Siemens reactor and the thermal carboreduction reactor. Only these equipment represent more than 75% of the total cost of the process. Figure 2 shows the consumption of each one of the utilities and raw materials for the objective function evaluated, showing that the maximum profit in a Multi-Product Polycrystalline Silicon Facility.

Table 1. Profit [M\$/y], Operating costs [M\$/y], kg of polycrystalline silicon/h, kg of TEOS, and kg of silane of the objective function.

Profit [M\$/y]	113.57
Operating costs [M\$/y]	10.10
kg of polycrystalline silicon/h	1800.50
kg of TEOS (99.5 of purity)/h	632.84
kg of SiH_4/h	42.68
Price of Polycrystalline Silicon \$/kg	6.86
Price of TEOS 99.5 \$/kg	3.75
Price of SiH_4 \$/kg	88.44

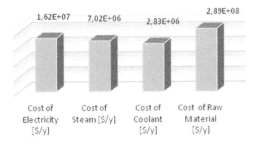

Figure 2. Utilities and raw materials for the Multi-Product Polycrystalline Silicon Facility.

4. Conclusions

In this work a superstructure optimization approach is used for the selection of the portfolio of products within a Multi-Product Polycrystalline Silicon Facility. Surrogate models for major units allow selecting the yield and operating conditions. The proposed process is able to meet the same production of polysilicon than current tradition polysilicon facilities at a lower production cost since the benefits obtained from selling the high added value by-products obtained increase the profit of the facility. The complete process, and therefore the operating conditions of each unit of the process were optimized under the objective of the maximization profit of the process. The optimal operating conditions of the facility that guarantee a lower energetic consumption, meeting with the required production of polycrystalline silicon require the production of high valuable by-products (TEOS 98.5, TEOS 99.0, TEOS 99.5, SiH_4, SiH_3Cl and SiH_2Cl_2), which aid in the economic sustainability of the process. The results after operating expenses, and considering the sale of polycrystalline silicon and the byproducts of the process, are an operational cost of 10 M\$/y. The investment for the process is 85.93M\$. Obtaining a competitive production cost for polycrystalline silicon of 6.86 \$/kg, below the commercial price estimated at 10 \$/kg, and the byproducts cost are: 1.5 \$/kg for TEOS 98.5; 2.5 \$/kg for TEOS 99.0; 3.75 \$/kg for TEOS 99.5; 88.44 \$/kg for SiH_4; 3.0 \$/kg for SiH_3Cl; and 3.67 \$/kg for SiH_2Cl_2.

References

E. Sánchez-Ramírez, C. Ramírez-Márquez, J. J. Quiroz-Ramírez, G. Contreras-Zarazúa, J. G. Segovia-Hernández, & J. A. Cervantes-Jauregui, 2018. Reactive Distillation Column Design for Tetraethoxysilane (TEOS) Production: Economic and Environmental Aspects. Industrial & Engineering Chemistry Research, 57(14), 5024-5034.

C. Ramírez-Márquez, E. Sánchez-Ramírez, J. J. Quiroz-Ramírez, F. I. Gómez-Castro, N. Ramírez-Corona, J. A. Cervantes-Jauregui, & J. G. Segovia-Hernández, 2016. Dynamic behavior of a multi-tasking reactive distillation column for production of silane, dichlorosilane and monochlorosilane. Chemical Engineering and Processing: Process Intensification, 108, 125-138.

Rubber & Plastics News Report, 2016. Wacker to build silica plant in Tenn. https://www.rubbernews.com/article/20161214/NEWS/161219980/wacker-to-build-silica-plant-intenn.

C. Ramírez-Márquez, G. Contreras-Zarazúa, M. Martín, & J. G. Segovia-Hernández, 2019. Safety, Economic, and Environmental Optimization Applied to Three Processes for the Production of Solar-Grade Silicon. ACS Sustainable Chemistry & Engineering, 7(5), 5355-5366.

G. Del Coso, C. Del Canizo, & A. Luque, 2008. Chemical vapor deposition model of polysilicon in a trichlorosilane and hydrogen system. Journal of the Electrochemical Society, 155(6).

W. J. Ding, J. M. Yan, & W. D. Xiao, 2014. Hydrogenation of silicon tetrachloride in the presence of silicon: thermodynamic and experimental investigation. Industrial & Engineering Chemistry Research, 53(27).

C. M. Wai & S. G. Hutchison, 1989. Free energy minimization calculation of complex chemical equilibria: Reduction of silicon dioxide with carbon at high temperature. Journal of Chemical Education, 66 (7), 546.

P. Mints, 2018. Photovoltaic Manufacturer Capacity, Shipments, Price & Revenues 2017/2018. SPV Market Research.

Sauro Pierucci, Flavio Manenti, Giulia Bozzano, Davide Manca (Eds.)
Proceedings of the 30th European Symposium on Computer Aided Process Engineering
(ESCAPE30), May 24-27, 2020, Milano, Italy. © 2020 Elsevier B.V. All rights reserved.
http://dx.doi.org/10.1016/B978-0-12-823377-1.50130-0

Synthesis and Optimization of a Furfural Production Process. A case Study of Mexico Considering Different Lignocellulosic Feedstocks

Gabriel Contreras-Zarazúa[a], Mariano Martin- Martin[b], Eduardo Sanchez-Ramirez[a], Juan Gabriel Segovia-Hernandez[a]

aDepartment of Chemical Engineering University of Guanajuato, Noria Alta S/N,36000, Guanajuato,Gto., Mexico.
bDepartment of Chemical Engineering, University of Salamanca, Plz. Caidos 1-5, 37008, Salamanca,Spain.
gsegovia@ugto.mx

Abstract

In this work the design, synthesis and optimization of a furfural production plant, considering the most abundant and common lignocellulosic wastes of Mexico is proposed. For the process, different pretreatment technologies and different purification process including intensified schemes are considered giving a total of 32 possible process alternatives. The pretreatment technologies are the dilute acid (DA) and ammonia fiber explosion (AFEX) respectively, for the separation zone we considered an azeotropic distillation process, a thermally coupled scheme distillation, a dividing wall column and one liquid- liquid extraction process. A two-stage procedure is used to determine the best process per biomass type. First, the processes are modelled in Aspen plus. Next, the best option per biomass is optimized using the differential evolution with tabu list in order to minimize the total annual cost and the environmental impact. The prescreening results indicate that the dilute acid pretreatment and the thermally coupled distillation provide the lowest cost and environmental impact for furfural production for all the raw materials. The optimization results indicate that a biorefinery with wheat straw as raw material is the best option to produce furfural due to its low cost and environmental impact which are 13 M\$/yr and 4,536,512 eco-points/year respectively.

Keywords: Furfural, Process Design, Multi-Objective Optimization, Process Intensification, Biorefinery

1. Introduction

Every year in Mexico the agricultural activities generate approximately 640 billion tons of lignocellulosic residues. However, only 5% of these wastes are used. This small percentage is used as food for livestock, compost or burned as fuel mainly, while the rest is incinerated at the harvest sites, which provokes several environmental problems. The lignocellulosic residues can be used to produce high-added value biochemicals. The use of waste has several advantages with respect to other biomasses. The two most important are that these residues do not compete with food avoiding ethical problems and the second reason is because these wastes are cheap. Furfural had been listed by The National Renewable Energy Laboratory (NREL) of the United States as one of the most important biochemicals produced from lignocellulosic residues due to its wide range of applications as fungicides, extractant for lubricant oils and its ability to compete with chemicals derived from petroleum (Marcotillio, 2011).

Traditionally Furfural has been synthesized by the acid hydrolysis and dehydration of hemicellulose fraction contained inside biomass. For this reason, raw materials with high content of hemicellulose are considered better raw materials. In this work is proposed the synthesis, design and optimization of furfural production processes considering the four most abundant agricultural residues of Mexico. The synthesis phase considers two different pretreatment options and four different process separation schemes including two intensified alternatives in order to generate the most energetic efficient process resulting in 32 possible designs. The best process scheme for each raw material was optimized using the differential evolution with tabu list. Two different indexes, which are the total annual cost (TAC) and eco-indicator 99 (EI99) have been used as performances criteria in order to determinate which are the best raw materials, and which is the best process structure for a furfural plant located at Mexico.

2. Methodology

The selection of raw materials is realized according to the four most abundant agricultural wastes generated in Mexico per year (SIAP, 2019), which are corn stover, wheat straw, sorghum bagasse and sugar cane bagasse. The furfural plants were designed considering a typical size production of 1000 kg/hr furfural (Marcotullio, 2011). We considered that the biomass is formed by cellulose, hemicellulose and lignin the most abundant fractions. An average for these three main fractions composition obtained from different works was used in order to consider the biomass variability.

The design and simulations of the processes were carried out using the software ASPEN PLUS®.The thermodynamic model used at the simulations is Non-random two-liquids coupled with the Hayden-O′Connell (NTRL-HOC) equation of state in order to predict the formation of two liquid phases characteristics of processes with organic compounds and water. The processes are divided in three sections, pretreatment, reaction and purification. For the pretreatment zone, to release of pentoses, two pretreatments have been considered. These pretreatments are the dilute acid with hot water (DA) and the ammonia fiber explosion (AFEX). During the DA pretreatment, the biomass is mixed with a dilute solution of acid in medium-high temperatures around 150-220°C and pressures of 4.75- 23.15 bar. One of the most common acid used is sulfuric acid. The main objective of this process is the solubilization of hemicellulose fractions and the reduction in the crystallinity of cellulose. During the AFEX pretreatment the biomass is exposed with ammonia at high pressure conditions (13.7-20.68 bar) and moderate temperatures (60-160°C) during residence times of 5 min in order to break the fibers inside biomass and release the sugars. Then the biomass is treated with enzymes to hydrolysate the chains of polysaccharides and convert them into monomers like glucose or xylose. Both pretreatments were simulated according with the methodology proposed by Conde-Mejia et al., (2012).

For reaction zone where the furfural is produced, the aqueous solution rich in pentoses produced during the pretreatment stage is introduced into a CSTR reactor with thermal conditions of 190°C and 13.14 atm. Sulfuric acid is fed to the catalyzed the reactor, the concentration of the acid inside the reactor needs to be 0.1M. Under these conditions the conversion of pentoses to furfural is 53%wt, which, represents an efficiency of 82.82% with respect to the theoretical value. A scheme of the reactor and a more detail about the conditions are reported by Zeitsch, (2000).

Different processes have been considered for the purification stage in order to reduce the energy consumption and determinate which is the best option to purify the furfural. The processes are Convectional azeotropic distillation (Quaker oats), which is the typical process used to purify the furfural. In order to reduce energy costs and consumption and improve the thermodynamic efficiency two intensified schemes have been considered: a thermally coupled scheme (TCC) and a divided wall column scheme (DWC). Finally, a liquid-liquid extraction coupled with distillation has also been considered (ED). The distillation schemes were designed in order to get a purity of furfural of 99.2% by mass, that is the minimum purity required to use the furfural in the production of fuels and polymers. The design parameters used for simulating were taken from the previous work,Contreras-Zarazúa et al., (2019). Figure 1 shows the superstructure diagram, which contains all the process alternatives considered in this work. Due to the magnitude of the problem a two-step procedure was used to solve the superstructure. In this case only the best process flowsheet with the less total annual cost and environmental impact for each raw material. These processes are selected to be optimized within Aspen Plus using the differential evolution algorithm with tabu list, which was programed in Visual basic inside EXCEL.

The Total annual cost (TAC) was chosen as a parameter to evaluate the processes economics and this metric was calculated using Guthrie method, the parameters for the equipment's were taken from Turton et al. (2008). We assume steel stainless steel as the construction material for all the equipment, and payback period of 10 years. The trays type sieve are selected with spacing between trays of 2 ft are considered. 8500 hours of yearly operation for each configuration were defined cooling water, heating and electricity are considered has operating cost. **The Eco-indicator** (EI99) was the index used to evaluate the environmental impact of biorefineries, it is a lifecycle method that evaluates different categories (steel, electricity, and vapor) where individual scores are assigned depending of amount of water used, emission produced during the operation of the plant among others.

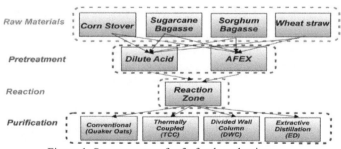

Figure 1. Superstructure for furfural production.

The Differential Evolution with Tabu List Algorithm proposed by Sharma and Rangaiah 2010 has been used at this work. The parameters required by DETL algorithm are the following: Population size (NP): 120 individuals, Generations Number (GenMax): 834, Tabu List size (TLS): 60 individuals, Tabu Radius (TR): 0.01, Crossover fractions (Cr): 0.8, Mutation fractions (F): 0.3. These values were determined through a previous tuning process of the algorithm. The implementation of the multi-objective optimization strategy involved a hybrid platform, which linked Aspen Plus[TM] and Microsoft Excel[TM] . The decision variables for each reactive distillation configuration are reported in Table 1. Finally, the multi-objective optimization problem can be expressed mathematically as in Eq. (1) and Eq. (2):

$$\min \quad Z = \{TAC; EI99\} \tag{1}$$

Subject to: $\quad y_{i,PC} \geq x_{i,PC}$
$$\tag{2}$$
$\qquad\qquad w_{i,FC} \geq u_{i,FC}$

The objective function is constraint to fulfill the purity and the mass flowrate vectors for the components in the mixture. For example, the values of the purities for the components obtained during the optimization process $y_{i,PC}$ must be either greater or equal to the specified values of purities for the component $x_{i,PC}$. Furthermore, the mass flowrates obtained $w_{i,PC}$ must also be either greater or equal to the specified values of the mass flowrate $u_{i,PC}$.

Table 1. Desion variables and optimization results for fufural production biorefineries.

Decision variables	Discrete variables	Continuous variables
Amount of raw material (kg/hr)	---	X
Number of stages extraction column, E1	X	---
Number of stages columns,	X	---
Feed stage, columns	X	---
Steam flowrate reaction zone (kg/hr)	---	X
Pressure steam in the reaction zone (atm)	---	X
Discharge pressure in AFEX pretreatment (atm)	---	X
Pressure reactor AFEX pretreatment (atm)	---	X
Entrainer mass flow (kg/hr)	---	X
Interlinking flow (kg/hr)	---	X
Reflux ratios	---	X
Heat duties equiments	---	X
Diameter columns	---	X

Finally, it is important to mention that this methodology is not exclusive for this process and it can be applied to different raw materials, chemical products and regions of Mexico and the world. Only data of conversion, pretreatment conditions or product specifications are required to apply this methodology to other raw materials and products.

3. Results

In this section are the prescreening results of 32 possible biorefineries are showed. Figure 2 shows a comparison of the TAC for all alternatives, the EI99 follows the same tendency that cost, due to the environmental impact depends strongly of utilities the electricity used for pumping cooling water, and the steam to provide energy to the process. The results indicate that biorefineries with AFEX pretreatment have higher energy consumption than biorefineries with DA. The AFEX pretreatment needs the compression and purification of ammonia which increases considerably the cost. The DA only requires the addition of sulfuric acid, which is a cheaper alternative, for this reason the AFEX alternatives are considerably more expensive. In the case of processes separations, the Extractive liquid -liquid processes are expensive compared with the Quaker Oats, TCC and DWC options. These results are due to the need for solvents since it involves additional energy consumption, environmental impact and solvent

Synthesis and Optimization of a Furfural Production Process. A case Study
of Mexico Considering Different Lignocellulosic Feedstocks.

779

recovery/separation units. In Figure 2 the TCC and DWC processes have similar cost with respect to the conventional Quaker Oats processes, because these alternatives does not have important energy savings, which is reflected on the total annual cost and eco-indicator. The large amounts of water inside the processes avoiding the elimination remixing phenomena, which is the main cause of inefficiency in distillation columns on DWC and TCC processes. However, the DA TCC has the lowest energy for all the raw materials. For this reason, DA pretreatment with the thermally coupled processes are considered as the best option because they show the lowest total annual cost and environmental impact.

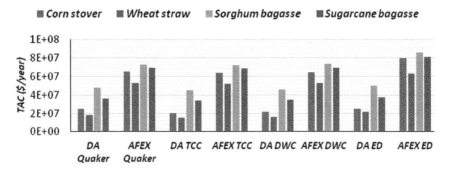

Figure 2. Total anal cost for all the alternatives.

In the Figure 3a the Pareto front of the DA using a thermally coupled column to process wheat straw is shown as a representative case, while in Figure 3 b are showed all the pareto fronts are presented. Note that in Figure 3 the designs obtained with the process optimization method converges to a single point, this point is called utopia point. This point represents the solution that has the best equilibrium for both objectives. Based on the results and considering only the total annual cost and the environmental impact as criteria, wheat straw is the best raw material to produce furfural. In contrast, sugarcane and corn stover are noticeably more abundant in Mexico, which can represent an advantage when supplying raw material to the process, however this process have higher TAC and EI99.

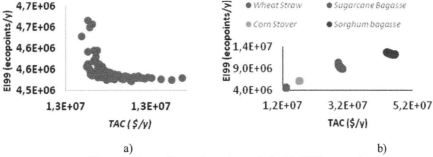

Figure 3. Pareto Fronts for DA coupled with TCC separation.

A scheme of the optimal process selected is presented in the Figure 4 that correspond DA pretreatment coped with a thermally coupled distillation. Some design parameter for wheat straw and corn stover processes as a representative case are showed in Table 2 using DA and TCC. Note, that the amount of biomass and water required in the wheat process is fewer than corn stover process which explain the lowest cost an environmental impact.

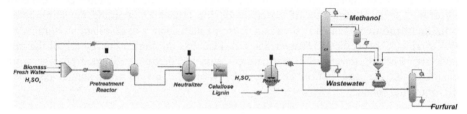

Figure 4. Scheme of the process selected.

Table 2.Representative parameter for bio refineries with wheat straw and corn stover.

Decision variables	Wheat straw	Corn Stover
Amount of raw material (kg/hr)	12213	15981
Amount of water (kg/hr)	10843.9	13680
Energy consumption (kW)	24,681	33,716
Total Annual cost ($/y)	13,092,504	17,122,917
Eco.indicator 99 (Eco-points/y)	4,536,512	6,130,272

4. Conclusions

This work has performed the synthesis, design and optimization of furfural production plants, considering different lignocellulosic wastes produced in Mexico. A two-stage procedure of synthesis and optimization is used to select the process alternative. Based on results of prescribing and optimization phases, we considered that a biorefinery to produce furfural with wheat straw as raw material is the best option based on lowest cost and eco indicators which correspond to values of 13M$/yr and 4,536,512 eco-points/year respectively.

Acknolwledgements

Authors acknowledge JCYL SA026G18 and CONACYT

References

Conde-Mejia, C., Jimenez-Gutierrez, A., & El-Halwagi, M., (2012). A comparison of pretreatment methods for bioethanol production from lignocellulosic materials. Process Safety and Environmental Protection, 90(3), 189-202.

Contreras-Zarazúa, G., Sánchez-Ramírez, E., Vázquez-Castillo, J. A., Ponce-Ortega, J. M., Errico, M., Kiss, A. A., & Segovia-Hernández, J. G. (2019). Inherently safer design and optimization of intensified separation processes for furfural production. Industrial & Engineering Chemistry Research, 58(15), 6105-6120.

http://infosiap.siap.gob.mx/gobmx/datosAbiertos.php accesed 10-June-2019

Marcotullio, G., (2011). The chemistry and technology of furfural production in modern lignocellulose-feedstock biorefineries.

Rangaiah, G. P. (2010). Stochastic global optimization: techniques and applications in chemical engineering. World Scientific.

Turton, R., Bailie, R. C., Whiting, W. B., & Shaeiwitz, J. A. (2008). Analysis, synthesis and design of chemical processes. Pearson Education.

Zeitsch, K. J. (2000). The chemistry and technology of furfural and its many by-products (Vol. 13). Elsevier.

Sauro Pierucci, Flavio Manenti, Giulia Bozzano, Davide Manca (Eds.)
Proceedings of the 30th European Symposium on Computer Aided Process Engineering
(ESCAPE30), May 24-27, 2020, Milano, Italy. © 2020 Elsevier B.V. All rights reserved.
http://dx.doi.org/10.1016/B978-0-12-823377-1.50131-2

Heat Exchanger Network Retrofit for Processes with Multiple Operating Cases: a Metaheuristic Approach

Jan A. Stampfli,[a,b,*] Donald G. Olsen,[a] Beat Wellig,[a] René Hofmann[b,c]

[a]*Lucerne University of Applied Sciences and Arts, Competence Center Thermal Energy Systems and Process Engineering, Technikumstrasse 21, 6048 Horw, Switzerland*
[b]*Vienna University of Technology, Institute for Energy Systems and Thermodynamics, Getreidemarkt 9/BA, 1060 Vienna, Austria*
[c]*AIT Austrian Institute of Technology GmbH, Center for Energy, Sustainable Thermal Energy Systems, Giefinggasse 2, 1210 Vienna, Austria*
jan.stampfli@hslu.ch

Abstract

An essential method to improve industrial energy efficiency is through the retrofitting of existing heat exchanger networks. This method presents a difficult challenge that is often compounded by the need to handle multiple operating cases behavior as well. Most research has been tackling retrofitting of such processes by deterministic mathematical approaches. With the increase in size and complexity, however, metaheuristic algorithms provide advantages in the search for the global optimum due to their exhaustive exploration of the search space. Hence, this research provides a two-level metaheuristic approach for the retrofit of processes with multiple operating cases. The retrofit problem is decomposed into a master and slave problem, whereby a genetic algorithm optimizes the network topology, and a differential evolution algorithm optimizes continuous variables such as the heat loads of heat exchangers. The developed algorithm has been successfully applied to a case study from literature with results showing that the incorporation of the suggested modifications can halve the total annual cost of the process.

Keywords: heat exchanger network (HEN), retrofit, multiple operating cases, genetic algorithm, differential evolution

1. Introduction

Energy optimization of industrial processes is an essential aspect of the general goal of improving energy efficiency worldwide. A key approach to help reach this goal is to use process integration techniques that focus on the network of heat exchangers (HEXs) used extensively in industry. A large portion of these process integration projects involves the retrofitting of existing industrial plants. However, industrial processes also exhibit multiple operating cases (MOCs) over time such as in the pharmaceutical, chemical, food, and beverage industries. Methods to help optimize MOCs design for the retrofit case are needed. To date, most research has focused on each challenge individually. Both are commonly solved as optimization problems using mathematical programming (MP). The MP approach can also be used to optimize for the retrofit case subject to MOCs behavior. The resulting mixed-integer nonlinear programming (MINLP) problem formulation can be solved using either deterministic or metaheuristic algorithms. Common deterministic methods that address retrofit MOCs design are the reverse matching approach (Kang and

Liu, 2014) and the reduced superstructure synthesis (Isafiade, 2018). However, the search for the global optimum is hampered by the increase in problem size and complexity, in particular by the implementation of mixers (bypassing and admixing). Metaheuristic algorithms are capable of a broader exploration of the search space owing to their ability to escape local optima by generating a random new solution. Aguitoni et al. (2018), in particular, showed the applicability of a metaheuristic for heat exchanger network (HEN) synthesis.

The specific contribution of this research to literature is to use a metaheuristic approach for the retrofit MOCs design. Thereby a two-level optimization approach is used based on a genetic algorithm (GA) for topology optimization and a differential evolution (DE) algorithm for continuous optimization.

2. Methodology

2.1. Heat Exchanger Network Retrofit of Processes with Multiple Operating Cases

In processes with multiple operating cases, the mass flows, specific heat capacity, supply, and target temperatures change over the course of the production period. To ensure a feasible HEN for each operating case, bypassing as well as admixing around key HEXs is often needed. There are basically five distinct operations to modify the existing HEN design which are often combined together: (1) re-piping of a HEX, (2) re-sequencing of a HEX, (3) modifying the area of a HEX, (4) adding bypasses or admixers to a HEX, and (5) incorporating a new HEX into the design. In practice, the cost to modify the area may differ between HEXs. Therefore, it is necessary to have different cost factors for each HEX. Fig. 1 shows the associated superstructure model of the retrofitting of MOCs design. In each enthalpy stage k, every hot process stream i can be matched with every cold process stream j and utility matches are possible (utility optimization). To ensure the energy balance of every process stream is balanced, utilities are also placed at the streams end. Each HEX can be bypassed (shown in stage 2) or admixed (shown in stage 1).

2.2. Metaheuristic approach

The metaheuristic approach uses an evolutionary concept of survival of the fittest. Thereby, a population of solutions (chromosomes) is initialized. In each generation, evolutionary operations (selection, crossover, and mutation) are applied. During the evolution, n best solutions are stored in a list, which is updated as soon as a better solution is found. As a result, several near-optimal solutions are determined, which can be compared in terms of practicability for detail engineering. The MINLP problem is decomposed into a master and slave problem (two-level optimization). To solve the master problem (modification of the HEN topology) a GA, and to solve the slave problem (modification of heat loads, bypassing, and admixing of fractions) a DE algorithm is used.

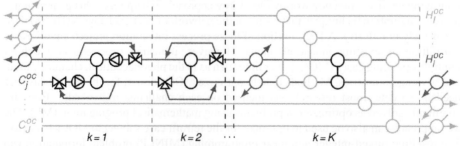

Figure 1: Superstructure for retrofit of MOCs design (*i*: hot process streams, *j*: cold process streams, *k*: enthalpy stages, *oc*: operating cases)

The algorithm is implemented in Python 3.7 using by using the Distributed Evolutionary Algorithms in Python (DEAP) library (Fortin et al. 2012). Experiments are run on a 2.8 GHz Intel i7 computer with 16 GB RAM.

2.2.1. Master Problem: Topology Optimization by Genetic Algorithm

A GA is used to optimize integer variables of the topology (HEX matches as well as the existence of bypassing or admixing). Thereby, the exchanger address matrix (EAM) represents individual solutions (chromosomes). Among others, Rezaei and Shafiei (2009) have used this approach. For the selection of a new chromosome, tournament selection is performed. Thereby, the fittest among *n* randomly chosen chromosome is selected. For evaluation of the fitness of each chromosome, the DE algorithm (described in section 2.2.2) solves the slave problem. With the probability of crossover P_C, selected parents mate to generate new children using the one-point crossover operation. By the probability of mutation P_M, genes (vector which, e.g., represents matches of a HEX to a process stream) in a chromosome are mutated based on a uniform distribution.

2.2.2. Slave Problem: Continuous Optimization by Differential Evolution

The DE algorithm initializes individuals consisting of continuous optimization variables (heat loads and split fractions for bypassing and admixing). The standard algorithm is configured as *DE/rand/1/bin*. This means that individuals for mutation are selected randomly, only one difference for perturbation (F_P: perturbation factor) is considered, and a binomial crossover is performed. Further, a stopping criterion is implemented, which terminates the DE evolution if no improvement in fitness after *n* generations is achieved.

2.2.3. Fitness Function and Constraints

For evaluation of the population, the fitness (maximization) is given by the inverse of the total annual cost (TAC) composed of yearly utility cost and annualized retrofit cost for area extensions, splits, re-piping, bypasses, admixers, and new HEXs:

$$fitness = \frac{1}{TAC} \tag{1}$$

In order to ensure thermodynamically feasible solutions, some constraints must be defined. First, the energy balance for all process streams *i, j* is fulfilled in each OC by:

$$\sum_k \sum_j \dot{Q}_{i,j,k}^{oc} \leq CP_i^{oc}(T_S^{oc} - T_T^{oc}) \qquad \forall i \tag{2}$$

$$\sum_k \sum_i \dot{Q}_{i,j,k}^{oc} \leq CP_j^{oc}(T_T^{oc} - T_S^{oc}) \qquad \forall j \tag{3}$$

Thereby, the sum of all heat loads matched with the actual process stream

Table 1: Stream data of OC 1 (4,664 h/y)

#	T_s (°C)	T_r (°C)	CP (kW/K)
H_1	280	50	50
H_2	210	100	70
C_1	30	190	40
C_2	150	280	60

For all streams: $h = 0.1$ kW/(m²K)

Table 2: Stream data of OC 2 (3,336 h/y)

#	T_s (°C)	T_r (°C)	CP (kW/K)
H_1	290	80	60
H_2	180	110	50
C_1	160	300	40
C_2	70	130	60

For all streams: $h = 0.1$ kW/(m²K)

In order to ensure practicality, the number of splits (corresponds to the sum of *Match*) per stage k and process stream is limited by

$$\sum_j Match^{oc}_{i,j,k} + 1 \leq MaxSplits \qquad \qquad \forall i,k,oc \qquad (6)$$

$$\sum_i Match^{oc}_{i,j,k} + 1 \leq MaxSplits \qquad \qquad \forall j,k,oc \qquad (7)$$

whereby *MaxSplit* is a user-defined parameter. All constraints are implemented using quadratic penalty functions described by

$$penalty = \Delta(X_{opt} - X_{viol})^2. \qquad (8)$$

This penalty function is applied to the fitness of each infeasible chromosome. X_{viol} describes the violation of the constraints (distance to the feasible region). X_{opt} describes the optimal value of X_{viol}. The weight " ensures that an infeasible solution is always larger than a feasible solution.

3. Illustrative Case Study

The introduced methodology is applied to a case study first introduced by Jones (1991). Stream data for the two operating cases (OCs) are shown in Tab. 1 and Tab. 2. Tab. 3 provides utility and cost data.

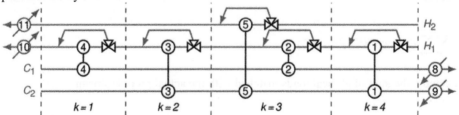

Figure 2: Existent HEN design

Table 3: Optimization parameters

Alg.	Pop. size	P_c	P_M	F_p	Max. iterations
GA	50	0.9	0.1	-	50
DE	100	0.9	-	0.5	200

Table. 4: Utility and cost data

Utility stream	T_s (°C)	T_r (°C)	h (kW/m²/K)	c_{UT} (CHF/MWh)
Steam (HU)	350	349	6	80
Cooling water (CU)	10	11	2	8

Cost for area extension of existing HEX (CHF): $1,474A_{ext}^{0.63}$; Cost for new HEX (CHF): $18,920+1,474A^{0.63}$; Split, bypassing, admixing, and re-piping cost per changed stream (CHF): 4,000; Plant lifetime: $n = 5$ y; Interest rate: $i = 10\%$

Tab. 4 includes optimization parameters of for the algorithm. Fig. 2 shows the actual MOCs design established by Pinch Analysis. The investment cost of the existent plant is depreciated, and thus resulting in TAC of 2,295,000 CHF/y.

4. Results and Discussion

Depending on the size of the EAM, it can be defined how many new HEX can be integrated during the retrofit process. For the actual case study, it was decided to have the possibility to integrate two new HEX (6 and 7). In Fig. 3, the resulting HENs for the best and the 2nd best solution are shown. Thereby, it can be seen that only existent HEXs are re-piped, re-sequenced, and extended but no new HEXs, splits, bypasses, or admixers are incorporated. A comparison of heat loads and corresponding areas of the retrofitted networks, as well as the existing design, is shown in Tab. 5. The TAC for the best solution amounts to 1,038,000 CHF/y, which is composed of 538,000 CHF investment cost and 896,000 CHF/y yearly operating cost. For the 2nd best solution, TAC accumulates to 1,046,000 CHF/y consisting of 555,000 CHF investment cost and 900,000 CHF/y yearly operating cost. It is imperative to notice that due to the assumption of constant re-piping cost, it cannot be clearly determined which of these solutions would be favorable to implement in practice. Nevertheless, compared to the existing design, a reduction of TAC of around 55 % can be achieved. For both solutions, substantial modifications to the HEN are needed.

Table 5: Comparison of heat loads and installed area of existent design with optimized solutions

HEX	Existing design			Best solution			2nd best solution		
	$\dot{Q}_{OC1}$ (kW)	$\dot{Q}_{OC2}$ (kW)	A (m²)	$\dot{Q}_{OC1}$ (kW)	$\dot{Q}_{OC2}$ (kW)	A (m²)	$\dot{Q}_{OC1}$ (kW)	$\dot{Q}_{OC2}$ (kW)	A (m²)
1	3,500	0	1,726	2,803	3,500	1,726	6,400	5,080	4,222
2	0	3,800	1,546	-	-	-	-	-	-
3	0	100	13	-	-	-	-	-	-
4	5,800	0	2,414	6,400	5,070	4,022	4,143	100	7,107
5	1,500	3,500	1,594	4,096	100	7,264	2,741	3,500	1,594
8	600	1,800	708	0	530	708	0	520	708
9	2,800	0	505	901	0	505	916	0	505
10	2,200	8,700	262	1,004	7,430	736	958	7,420	735
11	6,200	0	313	4,897	0	485	4,959	0	490

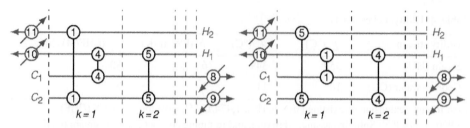

Figure 3: Optimized HEN design for the best solution (left) and 2nd best solution (right)

5. Conclusions

The presented approach introduces metaheuristic algorithms to the retrofitting of MOCs HEN designs. The method has been successfully applied to the case study. However, due to the assumption of fixed costs for splitting, re-piping, bypassing, and admixing, it cannot be clearly stated which solution is most beneficial to implement in practice. Therefore, these costs should be refined by making them dependent on plant layout, mass flow, and pressure drop. Using an evolutionary-based algorithm for topology optimization leads to substantially different solutions compared to the existing design. It should be investigated whether algorithms based on neighborhood structures (e.g., simulated annealing or variable neighborhood search) would be more appropriate to use. Such algorithms apply retrofit modifications such as re-piping and re-sequencing as neighborhood moves on the existing design.

Acknowledgments

This research project is financially supported by the Swiss Innovation Agency Innosuisse and is part of the Swiss Competence Center for Energy Research – Efficiency of Industrial Processes SCCER EIP. Further support is provided by the Lucerne University of Applied Sciences and Arts, Switzerland.

References

A.J. Isafiade, 2018, Retrofitting Multi-Period Heat Exchanger Networks using the Reduced Superstructure Synthesis Approach, Chemical Engineering Transactions, 70, 133-138.

E. Rezaei, S. Shafiei, 2009, Heat exchanger networks retrofit by coupling genetic algorithm with NLP and ILP methods, Computers and Chemical Engineering, 33, 1451-1459.

F.-A. Fortin, F.-M. De Rainville, M.-A. Gardner, M. Parizeau, C. Gagné, 2012, DEAP : Evolutionary algorithms made easy, Journal of Machine Learning Research, 13, 2171-2175.

L. Kang, Y. Liu, 2014, Retrofit of Heat Exchanger Networks for Multiperiod Operations by Matching Heat Transfer Areas in Reverse Order, Industrial & Engineering Chemistry Research, 53(12), 4792-4804.

M.C. Aguitoni, L.V. Pavão, P.H. Siqueira, L. Jiménez, M.A.S.S. Ravagnani, 2018, Heat exchanger network synthesis using genetic algorithm and differential evolution, Computers and Chemical Engineering, 117, 82-96.

P.S. Jones, 1991, Targeting and design for heat exchanger networks under multiple base case operation, PhD Thesis, University of Manchester Institute of Science and Technology, Manchester, United Kingdom of Great Britain and Northern Ireland.

Sauro Pierucci, Flavio Manenti, Giulia Bozzano, Davide Manca (Eds.)
Proceedings of the 30th European Symposium on Computer Aided Process Engineering
(ESCAPE30), May 24-27, 2020, Milano, Italy. © 2020 Elsevier B.V. All rights reserved.
http://dx.doi.org/10.1016/B978-0-12-823377-1.50132-4

Sustainable Process Synthesis, Design and Innovation of Bio-succinic Acid Production

Rofice Dickson[a,b], Enrico Mancini[a], Nipun Garg[a], Jay Liu[b], Manuel Pinelo[a], Seyed Soheil Mansouri[a,*]

[a]*Department of Chemical and Biochemical Engineering, Technical University of Denmark, Søltofts Plads, Building 229, DK- 2800 Kongens Lyngby, Denmark*

[b]*Department of Chemical Engineering, Pukyong National University, Busan, 48513, Korea*
seso@kt.dtu.dk

Abstract

Over the last decades, bio-succinic acid from renewable resources has gained significant attention as a precursor molecule for the synthesis of an array of other chemicals. The goal of this study is to obtain a novel process alternative for bio-succinic acid production, which is optimal and realistic in terms of process economics, implementation as well as environmental sustainability. Thereby, a hierarchical approach consisting of 3 stages: synthesis, design (& analysis) and innovation is used. In stage 1, a comprehensive superstructure is developed to systematically find the optimal processing route to produce bio-succinic acid. The proposed superstructure contains multiple process alternatives including different types of feedstock, pretreatment steps, fermentation technologies, and separation technologies all at acceptable technology readiness level (TRL). Based on the superstructure, a mixed-integer linear model was formulated. Once an optimal processing route is identified, then in stage 2, the selected process flowsheet is designed and analysed in detail. The primary goal at this stage is to identify process hotspots which enables to set design targets for further improvements. The identified process bottlenecks are then used in the 3rd stage where a phenomena-based synthesis methodology is applied, generating non-trade off and more sustainable process alternatives for producing bio-succinic acid.

Keywords: Process synthesis, Process intensification, Sustainable solutions, Succinic acid

1. Introduction

Succinic acid is an important precursor for producing more than 30 commercially valuable products in pharmaceutical, food, and agriculture industries. Succinic acid is largely produced from petroleum feedstock. However, technological advances in biorefinery have facilitated its production from renewable feedstock. Bio-succinic (bio-SA) acid is reported by both the European Commission (EC-DGE, 2015) and the U.S. Department of Energy (Werpy and Petersen, 2004) one of the top growing products within bio-based market, which is projected to reach 7 – 10 billion USD per year. Despite its numerous applications and growing market, bio-SA production is still at its fancy and not economically lucrative compared with that from petroleum.

It has been estimated that bio-SA leads to greenhouse gas saving of 4.5 – 5 kg per kg of succinic acid when compared to petrochemical based succinic acid (Hermann et al., 2007). However, bio-SA is not cost competitive with its petrochemical rival, mainly due to its high production cost. Purification of succinic acid from the fermentation broth is estimated to account 60 – 70% of the total production costs, while only 20 – 25% of the costs can be allocated to the upstream process including biomass pretreatment and fermentation process, and only 10 – 15% to the purchase of the feedstock itself (Morales et al., 2016). Therefore, bio-SA can only be a viable replacement for petroleum derived succinic acid if upstream and downstream technologies can lower the production cost by increasing the product yield and selectivity in former while lowering the purification cost in latter.

The necessity of major technological improvements to lower production cost makes the bio-SA process design, a complex combinatorial optimization problem. For instance, bio-SA can be produced from different feedstock including 1st (sugar/starch), 2nd (lignocellulose) and 3rd (aquatic biomass) generation. Different feedstock sources require different pretreatments, which in turn decides the formation of fermentation process inhibitors. To achieve high yield and selectivity of succinic acid, fermenter design and its operating condition, selection of appropriate microorganism and buffer are crucial decision variables that will decide the downstream purification. The potential technological decision variables in bio-SA purification include: centrifugation or microfiltration for cell separation, evaporation, solvent extraction, activated carbon, ultrafiltration, precipitation, ion exchange, reactive extraction, bipolar membrane, electrodialysis, direct crystallization and nanofiltration for succinic acid separation. Combining all process alternatives from feedstock selection to downstream processing makes the bio-SA production process very complicated in order to find best flowsheet for large-scale production taking into account technology readiness level (TRL) of these various technologies. Therefore, the goal of this study is to determine best (innovative and intensified) flowsheet for bio-SA production using 3 stage approach (Babi et al., 2015; Garg et al., 2019; Mansouri et al., 2013), as shown in Fig.1 with an aim that the resulting solution is the closest towards large scale implementation.

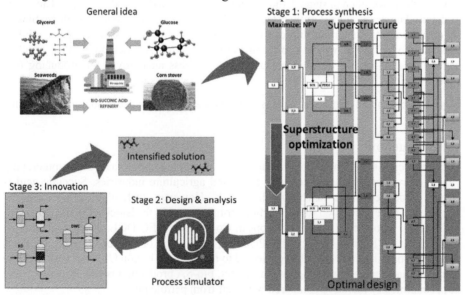

Figure 1. Methodology for determining innovative and intensified process design of bio-SA.

2. Methodology

The central theme of the proposed methodology is to increase the search space in stage 1 to find the base case flowsheet. Since the output from stage 1 comprises of single flowsheet, thus, search space is reduced in stage 2. The base case flowsheet is then rigorously simulated and analysed to determine improvement targets, leading to search space expansion using phenomena-based methodology in stage 3. Here feasibilities rules are used to reduce the search space to generate non-trade off solutions that are better than the base case as well as fulfils all desired improvement targets set in stage 2.

2.1. Stage 1: Synthesis

Objective: To identify an optimal processing route of bio-succinic acid among numerous process alternatives.

In stage 1, a superstructure is developed to systematically finding the optimal processing route to produce bio-SA, as shown in Fig.2. The proposed superstructure contains multiple process alternatives including different types of feedstock, different pretreatment steps, different fermentation technologies, and different separation technologies. The novelty of the proposed process synthesis superstructure features comprehensive network of 34 process alternatives with technology readiness level of 5–9 as the basis for optimal design identification. This is to ensure that the resulting solution from superstructure optimization is appealing from an implementation point of view. As indicated in Fig.2, bio-SA can be produced using glucose and glycerol (1st generation biomass), corn stover (2nd generation biomass), and *Saccharina japonica* (3rd generation biomass). It is assumed that glycerol is obtained from biodiesel and bioethanol industries, whereas glucose is obtained from 1st generation biomass. For effective utilization of biomass in fermentation, five pretreatment technologies are included in the superstructure: acid thermal hydrolysis of corn stover, deacetylation followed by acid thermal hydrolysis, alkaline (sodium hydroxide) hydrolysis, acid thermal hydrolysis of *Saccharina japonica*, and hot water wash hydrolysis. Once biomass is pretreated, it is processed using enzymatic hydrolysis in the presence of cellulase enzyme. The fermentation (production) of sugars can be carried out in batch or fed-batch fermenter in the presence of different microorganism and buffers. Nine fermentation technologies are included in the superstructure, which correspond to different titer (g/l), yield (g/g), and productivity (g/l/h) of succinic acid. After fermentation, cell mass can be removed using microfiltration or centrifuge. The broth can be then concentred either before or after isolation of succinic acid using evaporation or vacuum distillation. The colour impurities and protein can be removed from broth using activated carbon or nanofiltration. Isolation can be defined as recovering succinic acid from its salt. Since isolation is energy intensive, six processing alternatives namely electrodialysis, direct crystallization, reactive extraction, ion exchange column, reactive crystallization, and membrane technology (combination of ultra- and nano-filtration) are included in the superstructure. The isolated succinic acid is then purified using solvents, (such as methanol) or crystallization, and finally dried to remove moisture to desired purity.

To determine optimal flowsheet of bio-SA with purity of at least 99 wt.%, a techno-economic mixed-integer linear model (MILP) is formulated. The production target of succinic acid is set to 30 kt/y based on the capacity of main producers of bio-SA (Cavani et al., 2016). The objective function (*OBJ*) for the model is defined as

$$OBJ = S^{PROD} - C^{RAW} - C^C - C^U, \tag{1}$$

where S^{PROD} is revenue from the sales of succinic acid, C^{RAW} is raw material cost, C^C is chemical cost, and C^U is utilities cost.

2.2. Stage 2: Design and analysis

Objective: To conduct detailed design and analysis in order to identify process hotspots and set design targets.

Once an optimal route (base case) is identified, then in stage 2, the selected flowsheet is designed rigorously in PRO/II using the UNIQUAC thermodynamic method for modelling liquid–vapour and liquid–liquid equilibria of strongly non-ideal solution (Garg et al., 2019). The mass and energy balances are then utilized to carry out analysis in terms of process economics and environmental impact. The primary goal at this stage is to identify process hot-spots which enables to set new targets for further improvements to be achieved in innovation stage.

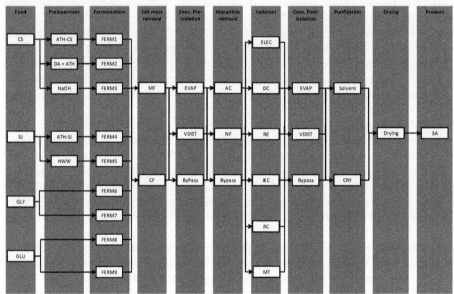

Nomenclature: CS = Corn stover; SJ = Saccharina japonica; GLY = Glycerol; GLU = Glucose; ATH-CS = Acid thermal hydrolysis of CS; DA + ATH = Deacetylation followed by ATH; ATH-SJ = Acid thermal hydrolysis of SJ; HWW = Hot water wash; FERM = Fermentation; MF = Microfiltration; CF = Centrifuge; AC = Activated carbon; NF = Nano-filtration; EVAP = Evaporation; VDIST = Vacuum distillation; ELEC = Electrodialysis; DC = Direct crystallization; RE = Reactive extraction; IEC = Ion exchange column (chromatography); RC = Reactive crystallization; MT = Membrane technology; CRY = Crystallization; SA = succinic acid

Figure 2. Superstructure for bio-SA production.

2.3. Stage 3: Innovation

Objective: To generate more sustainable and intensified (multi-functional) alternatives using phenomena-based synthesis method (Babi et al., 2015). In other words, flowsheets that meet both design specification of base case and improvement targets both economically and environmentally are considered non-trade off and more sustainable solutions.

In stage 3, the base case is translated into a task-based flowsheet; and later to phenomena-based flowsheet to identify an initial list of phenomena building blocks leading to increased search space. Since all the combination in phenomena building blocks are not feasible due to thermodynamic infeasibilities, the search space is then reduced by identifying feasible flowsheet alternatives that match the design specification of the base case as well as improvement targets determined in pervious stage.

3. Results and discussion

A hybrid approach consisting of 3 stages: synthesis, design (& analysis) and innovation is used to determine sustainable process design of bio-SA (Babi et al., 2015; Garg et al., 2019). As shown in Fig.3, the optimal flowsheet consists of a glucose as a feed, fermenter, centrifuge for broth clarification, distillation to concentrate the broth and remove unwanted organic acids and alcohols, followed by carbon treatment for removal of soluble solids causing colour and then finally crystallization and drying to get pure crystals of succinic acid. The solution is computed in 2.56 s and objective function value correspond to USD 48.61 million.

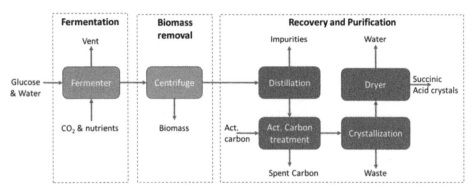

Figure 3. Optimal flowsheet in stage 1.

The optimal flowsheet is then simulated in PRO/II and process analysis is performed. Results indicate that the process requires heating and cooling loads of 20.3 and 19.1 MW, respectively, and yields 30 kt/y of succinic acid with purity greater than 99 wt.%. The sustainability analysis indicates loss of product and raw material in open path (in-out streams) containing crystallizer. The economic analysis shows high utility costs related to unit-op in open path i.e. reboiler of distillation column. As expected, the LCA analysis confirms with the high carbon footprint for reboiler of the distillation column.

Based on process analysis results, high energy consumption leading to high utility costs, loss of product and raw material, and high carbon footprint in distillation column are identified as process hotspots that are translated into design targets (reverse of hotspots). These design targets should be achieved in innovation stage to generate intensified sustainable flowsheet. Three intensified flowsheets are determined that satisfy base case constraints as well as design targets. In alternative 1, membrane bioreactor is considered as intensified flowsheet, in which reaction synthesis and separation take place simultaneously. In other words, the reaction product is removed continuously while cell remain in the fermenter, leading to increased cell concentration, thus, high product yield. In alternative 2, membrane crystallizer is considered as an intensified flowsheet, combining crystallization and separation of crystals from liquid phase. Whereas, alternative 3 is a combination of previous intensified flowsheet i.e., both membrane bioreactor and membrane crystallizer. Results of three alternative intensified flowsheets can be seen from radar plot depicted in Fig.4. The base case design is at the boundary while the more sustainable alternatives are all within the boundary, indicating that these intensified alternatives are non-trade off alternatives. It can be seen that process economics and environmental performance of alternative 3 is superior compared to base case and remaining intensified alternatives. Likewise, compared to base case, the number of required unit operation are decreased from 6 to 4 in alternative 3.

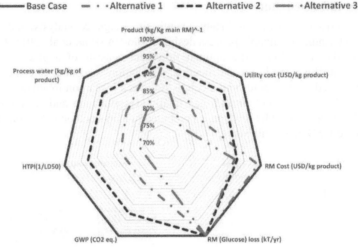

Figure 4. Economic, sustainability and LCA improvements relative to the base case design (HTPI: Human toxicity potential by ingestion, GWP: Global warming potential).

4. Conclusion

A hybrid approach comprising of 3 layers: synthesis, design (& analysis) and innovation is used to find non-trade off, more sustainable and intensified solutions to produce bio-SA. Results revealed that superstructure-based approach is useful to find novel processing route. However, if superstructure-based approach is combined with process intensification methodology remarkable improvement can be achieved. In this work, intensified flowsheet (alternative 3) compared to base case have achieved about 22% reduction in utility cost and 23% improvements in terms of environmental performance.

References

Babi, D.K., Holtbruegge, J., Lutze, P., Gorak, A., Woodley, J.M., Gani, R., 2015. Sustainable process synthesis-intensification. Comput. Chem. Eng. 81, 218–244. https://doi.org/10.1016/j.compchemeng.2015.04.030

Cavani, F., Albonetti, S., Basile, F., Gandini, A., 2016. Chemicals and Fuels from Bio-Based Building Blocks. John Wiley & Sons.

EC-DGE, 2015. From the Sugar Platform to biofuels and biochemicals, E4Tech, RE - CORD (Consorzio per la Ricerca e la Dimostrazione sulle Energie Rinnovabili), Wageningen University and Research Center. https://doi.org/contract No. ENER/C2/423-2012/SI2.673791

Garg, N., Woodley, J.M., Gani, R., Kontogeorgis, G.M., 2019. Sustainable solutions by integrating process synthesis-intensification. Comput. Chem. Eng. 126, 499–519. https://doi.org/10.1016/j.compchemeng.2019.04.030

Hermann, B.G., Blok, K., Patel, M.K., 2007. Producing Bio-Based Bulk Chemicals Using Industrial Biotechnology Saves Energy and Combats Climate Change. Environ. Sci. Technol. 7915–7921. https://doi.org/10.1021/es062559q

Mansouri, S.S., Ismail, M.I., Babi, D.K., Simasatitkul, L., Huusom, J.K., Gani, R., 2013. Systematic sustainable process design and analysis of biodiesel processes. Processes 1, 167–202. https://doi.org/10.3390/pr1020167

Morales, M., Ataman, M., Badr, S., Linster, S., Kourlimpinis, I., Papadokonstantakis, S., Hatzimanikatis, V., Hungerbühler, K., 2016. Sustainability assessment of succinic acid production technologies from biomass using metabolic engineering. Energy Environ. Sci. 9, 2794–2805. https://doi.org/10.1039/c6ee00634e

Werpy, T., Petersen, G., 2004. Top Value Added Chemicals from Biomass Volume I — Results of Screening for Potential Candidates from Sugars and Synthesis Gas Top Value Added Chemicals From Biomass Volume I : Results of Screening for Potential Candidates. https://doi.org/10.2172/15008859

Sauro Pierucci, Flavio Manenti, Giulia Bozzano, Davide Manca (Eds.)
Proceedings of the 30th European Symposium on Computer Aided Process Engineering
(ESCAPE30), May 24-27, 2020, Milano, Italy. © 2020 Elsevier B.V. All rights reserved.
http://dx.doi.org/10.1016/B978-0-12-823377-1.50133-6

Optimal Design of Macroalgae-based Integrated Biorefinery: Economic and Environmental Perspective

Rofice Dickson[a], Jun-Hyung Ryu[b], Jay Liu[a],*

[a]*Department of Chemical Engineering, Pukyong National University, Busan, 48513, Korea*

[b]*Department of Energy Engineering, Dongguk University, Gyeongju Campus, Gyeongju, 38066, Korea*
jaylie@pknu.ac.kr

Abstract

With the rapid depletion of fossil fuels and increasing environmental issues, viable alternatives are crucially needed to create a more sustainable and balanced energy infrastructure. Macroalgae have recently gained attention as a possible feedstock for biorefinery because of their high content of carbohydrates, proteins, and vitamins. To date, no commercial macroalgae-based biorefinery exists. Identifying efficient and environmentally friendly biorefining process is challenging due to many processing alternatives. Therefore, the aim of this study is to determine optimal design of macroalgae-based biorefinery employing a superstructure-based approach. Seventeen alternative processing technologies at acceptable technology readiness level are included in the superstructure to determine an optimal and realistic processing route by maximizing the net present value in the most environmentally beneficial manner. The results indicated that biofuel production from macroalgae is economically viable, at minimum ethanol selling price of USD 1.18/gal. Furthermore, the optimal design has achieved a 90% reduction in CO_2 emissions. Sensitivity analysis indicated that the purchasing price of macroalgae and selling price of heavier alcohols are the most sensitive parameters to process economics.

Keywords: Superstructure optimization, Process synthesis, Process integration, Macroalgae, Biofuel

1. Introduction

The current pace of utilizing petroleum resources is causing ecosystem damages. Global warming is a serious environmental issue, common to all mankind. Carbon dioxide emissions (CEs) from burning fossil fuel are thought of as one major contribution to global warming. To mitigate climate change impacts, highly efficient biorefineries utilizing sustainable biomass must be developed in order to replace fossil-based energy infrastructure.

Macroalgae (seaweed) have been considered as more sustainable biomass compared to agricultural crops since they do not compete for land and freshwater (Dickson and Liu, 2019). In particular, they are not quite used as food source on a global scale, which minimizes the impact on price related to the food versus fuel debate for terrestrial crops. Brown seaweed, *Saacharina japonica* (SJ) are fast-growing, high photosynthetically efficient aquatic plants (Brigljević et al., 2019). From an industrial point of view, numerous researchers have conducted techno-economic assessments of SJ and concluded that it is an excellent feedstock for producing biofuels owing to high carbohydrates contents, lack of lignin, and extensively available feedstock (Fasahati and Liu, 2015; Dickson et al., 2018). Therefore, the present study utilizes SJ as a feedstock for producing biofuels and value-added chemicals using the volatile fatty acid platform (VFAP).

In the VFAP, all non-lignin components of seaweed including carbohydrates, protein, and lipids are converted into volatile fatty acids (VFAs) consisting of acetic acid, propionic acid, and butyric acid through partial anaerobic digestion. VFAs can be then hydrogenated to produce mixed alcohols (MAs) consisting of ethanol, propanol, and butanol. Both VFAs and MAs have numerous applications in industries such as chemical, food, and pharmaceutical, and transportation sector, respectively. Pham et al. (2012) demonstrated that high product yields ranging from 0.31–0.41 g/g dry feed can be achieved through VFAP. Despite numerous application and promising yields, the effective and economically viable separation of VFAs is a key bottleneck to industrial scale application of VFAP owing to close boiling point of water and acetic acid (Dickson and Fasahati, 2019). Furthermore, determination of effective separation system for VFAs requires systematically evaluation of various alternative pathways, which make it complex combinatorial decision-making problem. Regarding environmental sustainability, anaerobic fermentation of biomass produces massive CO_2. It is reported that medium-sized biorefinery, processing 2–3.5 Mt/y sugarcane produces 110–193 kt/y of CEs during fermentation (Bonfim-Rocha et al., 2018), which requires process integration techniques to utilize CEs in order to improve environmental performance.

Based on the presented challenges, the aims of the present study are to determine the optimal pathway for the VFAP and to utilize all waste streams including CEs, wastewater, and undigested biomass from the processing to value-added chemicals through process integration techniques.

2. Methodology

To determine the optimal and sustainable processing route for the VFAP, superstructure-based approach is used. The major decision variables include technology selection for the VFAP and CO_2 utilization; the mass flow rate of each species in every stream; the heat and power consumption of each piece of equipment; the capital and the operating cost required for economic evaluation; and all emissions required for environmental evaluation.

2.1. Superstructure development

The superstructure is developed to systematically find the optimal processing route of VFAP, as shown in Fig.1. The proposed superstructure contains 7 processing intervals, each embedded with multiple process alternatives. The novelty of the superstructure features a comprehensive network of 17 process alternatives with technology readiness level of 5–9 as the basis for optimal design identification.

The biorefinery process starts with the anaerobic digestion of SJ. Anaerobic digestion consists of four stages; and in order to produce VFAs, partial anaerobic digestion is carried out using inhibitor such as iodoform, which eliminates methanogenesis step. The operating conditions for anaerobic digestion are 13 wt.% solid loading; a retention time of 120 h; an inhibitor loading of 30 ppm; a digestion temperature of 35 °C, and a yield of 0.35 g VFA/g of dry feed. After anaerobic fermentation, the outlet stream from the digester consists of solid, liquid, and gaseous products, which is sent to the purification section. In the purification section, gaseous- and solid- products are separated from the liquid products. Liquid products consisting of VFAs are sent to VFA extraction section, in which two alternative technologies are considered: classical dehydration and hybrid dehydration. The main equipment of the classical dehydration contains an extraction column, a rectification column, a stripping column, and a decanter. The hybrid process involves the combination of membranes and the classical dehydration process. The main goal in VFA extraction section is to concentrate VFAs from 5 wt.% to 95 wt.%. Once the VFAs are concentrated, they can be hydrogenated in the mixed alcohols synthesis section to produce mixed alcohols consisting of ethanol, propanol, and butanol.

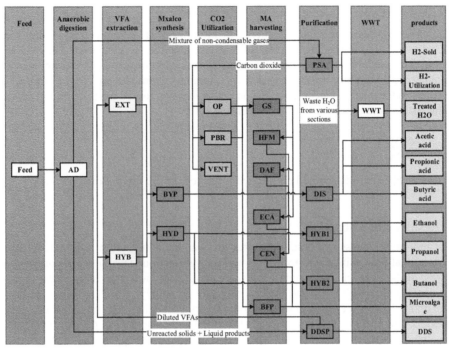

Nomenclature: AD = Anaerobic digestion; EXT = Extraction followed by distillation; HYB = Membranes followed by extraction and distillation; BYP = Bypass; HYD = Hydrogenation; OP = Microalgae cultivation in open ponds; PBR = Microalgae cultivation in photo-bioreactor; VENT = Venting CO_2 to atmosphere; GS = Gravity settler; HFM = Hollow filter membranes; DAF = Diffused air flocculation; ECA = Electrocoagulation; CEN = Centrifuge; BFP = Belt filter press; PSA = Pressure swing distillation; DIS = VFAs purification via distillation; HYB1 = MAs purification via pervaporation followed by distillation; HYB2 = MAs purification via molecular sieves followed by distillation; DDSP = Dry distillery solid purification;

Figure 1. The superstructure of biorefinery for producing biofuels and chemicals from *Saccharina Japonica*.

Alternative, hydrogenation can be bypassed and concentrated VFAs are separated into pure compounds. Mixed alcohols and mixed acids will be produced as the main products of biorefinery in the former (hydrogenation) and latter (bypass), respectively. If the latter is selected as an optimal decision, an upper limit of utilizing 30 wt.% of the VFAs is set for mixed acids production, because the main objective of the biorefinery is to produce biofuels. In CO_2 utilization section, the key objective is to convert CO_2 into microalgae either in open ponds or photobioreactor. If the production of microalgae is not economically favorable then the CO_2 is vented to the environment by paying a carbon tax of USD 20/t. For microalgae harvesting and dewatering, six process alternatives are included in microalgae harvesting section. The microalgae can be harvested in gravity settler, which can be dewatered either by hollow filter membranes, diffused air flocculation, or electrocoagulation followed by centrifugation. Alternatively, a belt filter press can be implemented at the outlet stream of gravity settler. The operating data and equipment costs considered for microalgae production are based on the work of (Davis et al., 2016). In purification section, separation of non-condensable gases, VFAs, MAs, and dry distillery solid (DDS) take place in pressure swing adsorption, distillation columns, pervaporation or molecular sieves followed by distillation, and centrifuge and dryer, respectively. A complete wastewater network consisting of anaerobic digestion, aerobic digestion, and reverse osmosis is included in the superstructure that treats polluted water from various processing stages back to the process.

2.2. Mathematical formulation and objective function

The optimal processing route of integrated biorefinery is determined by formulating mixed-integer non-linear model (MINLP), and its solution is computed using DICOPT solver. The model contained 7,476 continuous variables, in which 1,680 variables are nonlinear, 22 variables are binary, and the remaining variables are linear, and 6,517 equality and inequality constraints. The objective function for the model is the net present value that should be maximized and is defined as

$$NPV = \sum_{n=0}^{20} \frac{NCF_n}{(1+r)^n}, \tag{1}$$

where NCF_n is non-discounted cash flow for the year n, and r is the discount rate.

3. Results and discussion

The proposed process synthesis superstructure was implemented in GAMS (29.1.0) to find optimal processing route for VFAP and CEs utilization. The chemical composition (wt.%) of the SJ species reported by Roesijadi et al. (2010) was used in the present study. An upper limit of 400 kt/yr (dry basis) is set on the SJ supply.

The optimal flowsheet is an integrated biorefinery producing both mixed acids, mixed alcohols, and microalgae production, as shown in Fig.2. The optimal pathway consists of anaerobic digestion, extraction followed by distillation, partial bypass and hydrogenation, hydrogen purification via pressure swing adsorption, the distillation of mixed acids, the dehydration of mixed alcohols using molecular sieves followed by distillation, DDS purification, wastewater treatment. In the integrated design, 30 wt.% of the concentrated VFAs are utilized to produce mixed acids, whereas the remaining VFAs are utilized to produce mixed alcohols. For CO_2 utilization, the optimal pathway consists of cultivation in open ponds, harvesting by gravity settler, and dewatering by hollow filtration membranes followed by centrifuge.

Flowrate summary balance results indicate that the biorefinery utilizes 400 kt/y biomass. It produces 19 Mgal/yr mixed alcohols and 17 Mgal/yr mixed acids as main products and 0.98 kt/yr hydrogen, 111.8 kt/yr DDS, and 28.17 microalgae as byproducts. Integration of microalgae process with biorefinery utilized 90% of CO_2 emissions from processing.

Techno-economic results indicate that the minimum ethanol selling price and the net present value of optimal design are USD 1.18/gal and USD 44 million, respectively. The total capital investment of biorefinery is calculated to be USD 215 million, where 69% is consumed by the VFA section and the remaining 31% by microalgae section. The total cost of manufacturing is calculated to be USD 102.93 million/y, where VFA section accounts for 89% and reaming 11% to microalgae section.

The freshwater requirement of the VFA process is calculated to be 6.26 gal/gal of alcohols and acids. About 73% of the overall water makeup is due to water evaporation in the cooling tower. The water requirement of microalgae section is 157.7 t/h owing to the evaporation of water from the pond surfaces.

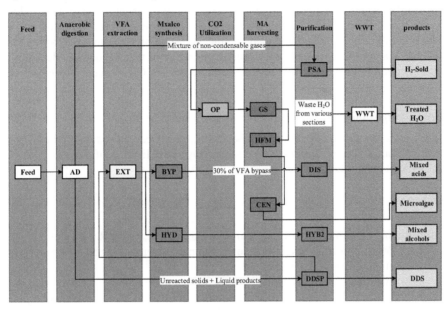

Figure 2. Optimal biorefinery structure.

3.1. Sensitivity analysis

The optimization model also performs sensitivity analysis to evaluate the major bottlenecks to the process economics. The results indicate that fixed capital investment, the seaweed price, and the internal rate of return (IRR) are the most important parameters for determining the economic viability of a biorefinery. Therefore, to ensure the economic viability of a seaweed-based biorefinery, efficient farming is necessary to increase the seaweed productivity.

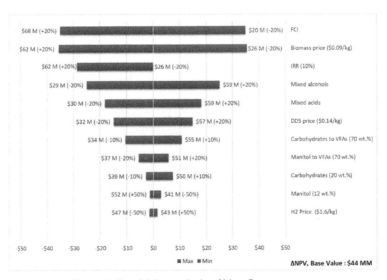

Figure 3. Sensitivity analysis of biorefinery parameter.

4. Conclusion

An optimization-based superstructure for macroalgae-based integrated biorefinery is proposed that determines optimal topology based on net present value as well reduces CO_2 emissions from the processing. A techno-economic assessment indicated that the production of biofuels and value-added chemicals results in a minimum ethanol selling price of \$1.18/gal. An environmental assessment indicated that the optimal design is an environmentally friendly process because it utilizes 90% of CEs produced by biorefinery processing.

Acknowledgement

This research was supported through the Basic Science Research Program of the National Research Foundation of Korea (NRF) funded by the Ministry of Science and ICT (2017R1A2B4004500).

Reference

Bonfim-Rocha, L., Gimenes, M.L., Bernardo de Faria, S.H., Silva, R.O., Esteller, L.J., 2018. Multi-objective design of a new sustainable scenario for bio-methanol production in Brazil. J. Clean. Prod. 187, 1043–1056. https://doi.org/10.1016/j.jclepro.2018.03.267

Brigljević, B., Liu, J.J., Lim, H., 2019. Comprehensive feasibility assessment of a poly-generation process integrating fast pyrolysis of S. japonica and the Rankine cycle. Appl. Energy 254, 113704. https://doi.org/10.1016/j.apenergy.2019.113704

Davis, R., Markham, J., Kinchin, C., Grundl, N., Tan, E.C.D., Humbird, D., 2016. Process Design and Economics for the Production of Algal Biomass: Algal Biomass Production in Open Pond Systems and Processing Through Dewatering for Downstream Conversion. Natl. Renew. Energy Lab. 128. https://doi.org/10.2172/1239893

Dickson, R., Fasahati, P., 2019. Optimal design for integrated macroalgae-based biorefinery via mixed alcohol synthesis, in: 29th European Symposium on Computer Aided Process Engineering. Elsevier Masson SAS, pp. 253–258. https://doi.org/10.1016/B978-0-12-818634-3.50043-6

Dickson, R., Liu, J., 2019. Optimization of seaweed-based biorefinery with zero carbon emissions potential, in: 29th European Symposium on Computer Aided Process Engineering. Elsevier Masson SAS, pp. 247–252. https://doi.org/10.1016/B978-0-12-818634-3.50042-4

Dickson, R., Ryu, J.-H., Liu, J.J., 2018. Optimal plant design for integrated biorefinery producing bioethanol and protein from Saccharina japonica: A superstructure-based approach. Energy 164. https://doi.org/10.1016/j.energy.2018.09.007

Fasahati, P., Liu, J.J., 2015. Impact of volatile fatty acid recovery on economics of ethanol production from brown algae via mixed alcohol synthesis. Chem. Eng. Res. Des. 98, 107–122. https://doi.org/10.1016/j.cherd.2015.04.013

Roesijadi, G., Jones, S.B., Zhu, Y., 2010. Macroalgae as a Biomass Feedstock: A Preliminary Analysis, Pacific Northwest National Lab.(PNNL). https://doi.org/10.2172/1006310

Sauro Pierucci, Flavio Manenti, Giulia Bozzano, Davide Manca (Eds.)
Proceedings of the 30th European Symposium on Computer Aided Process Engineering
(ESCAPE30), May 24-27, 2020, Milano, Italy. © 2020 Elsevier B.V. All rights reserved.
http://dx.doi.org/10.1016/B978-0-12-823377-1.50134-8

Integrating Superstructure Optimization under Uncertainty and Optimal Experimental Design in early Stage Process Development

Stefanie Kaiser, Sebastian Engell

TU Dortmund University, Chemical and Biochemical Engineering, Process Dynamics and Operations Group, Emil-Figge-Straße 70, 44227 Dortmund,
stefanie2.kaiser@tu-dortmund.de

Abstract

We present an iterative methodology that combines superstructure optimization, sensitivity analysis, and optimal design of experiments. In the early design phase, usually no accurate models for use in superstructure optimization are available, and the uncertainties of the models can influence the structure of the optimal design. The accuracy of the models is gradually increased by experimental investigations. In order to reduce the time and effort needed for process development, the experiments should focus on the most influencing parameters with respect to the design decisions. After one or few process structures have been fixed, further experiments will then lead to quantitatively accurate predictions. The methodology is applied to the case study of the hydroaminomethylation of decene.

Keywords: Early stage process design, superstructure optimization, model refinement, optimal experimental design

1. Introduction

Early stage process design is a crucial phase in the development of new processes in the chemical industry, because it largely determines the final investment and production costs. On the other hand, in this phase decisions have to be taken based on limited knowledge and uncertain data. Due to shorter product cycles, the pressure to reduce the development time is increasing. Therefore, fast, efficient, and risk aware process development strategies are needed. The known methodologies for process synthesis can be divided into two categories – hierarchical or knowledge-based methods (Douglas, 1985) and optimization-based methods (Grossmann et al., 1999). In the process industries, knowledge-based methods are still common. However, they generally fall short in terms of finding synergies between the different unit operations and innovative process layouts, because the choice of the process structure and the unit operations, laboratory experiments, and process optimization are performed consecutively. The work of different groups on different unit operations is combined at a very late stage of process development, which can lead to suboptimal decisions, avoidable cost, time delays, and re-work in later stages. Optimization-based methods have become popular in academia (Kuhlmann & Skiborowski, 2016) but they usually require good process models. Since the process models are uncertain in an early design phase, superstructure optimization under uncertainties has been proposed by Steimel & Engell (2015) and Steimel & Engell (2016). To overcome these issues, a holistic approach is proposed in this work that bridges between the planning and design of laboratory experiments and superstructure

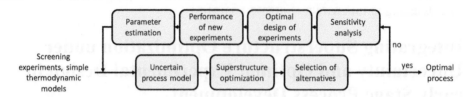

Figure 1: Schematic representation of the approach for integrated process development.

optimization under uncertainty. Promising process designs are optimized with respect to the production costs using superstructure optimization for early stage models with large uncertainties. The impact of the uncertain parameters is analyzed via a local sensitivity analysis. The computed sensitivities are then used as weights in an optimal design of experiments to perform experiments which provide most information. The methodology is applied to a case study from the Berlin-Dortmund-Magdeburg Collaborative Research Center InPROMT, a homogenously catalyzed hydroaminomethylation process.

2. Methodology

The starting point of the design process is that coarse models of all process units under consideration are available, typically based on screening experiments and simple thermodynamic models. Moreover, confidence intervals for the uncertain model parameters must be known. The subsequent iterative cycle of the choice of unit operations, laboratory experiments, and process optimization is depicted in Figure 1.

The models with uncertainties are used for a superstructure optimization under uncertainty, and thereafter a sensitivity analysis with respect to the uncertain parameters is performed. Optimal design of experiments is used to design experiments that target the most cost-influencing parameters. After performing the targeted experiments, improved models are fitted, and the procedure is repeated until one design is found to be superior over all other designs. This work focuses on the superstructure optimization, the sensitivity analysis, and the optimal design of experiments, which are explained in the following subsections.

2.1. Superstructure optimization under uncertainties

In superstructure optimization under uncertainties, first, a set of process alternatives is generated. Secondly, models of the process units in the superstructure are set up. The optimal configuration can then be determined by solving the following optimization problem (Steimel & Engell, 2015):

$$\min_{x_\omega, y} Z = G(y) + \sum_{\omega=1}^{\Omega} \pi_\omega F_\omega(x_\omega, y)$$

$$\text{s.t.} \quad h(x_\omega, y) = 0$$
$$g(x_\omega, y) \le 0 \tag{1}$$
$$x_\omega \in X_\omega, y \in \{0,1\}$$

Usually binary and continuous decisions are involved. Thus the optimization problems typically results in mixed integer nonlinear programs (MINLP (Chen & Grossmann, 2017)). The objective function is composed of a part $G(y)$ describing the costs taking the first-stage decision and a part $\sum_{\omega=1}^{\Omega} \pi_\omega F_\omega(x_\omega, y)$ describing the expected cost of the second stage decision via weighting and summation of the costs of Ω discrete scenarios F_ω. It is minimized subject to the equality constraints $h(x_\omega, y)$, given by physical relations such as mass and energy balances, kinetics, and thermodynamics. Process specifications and equipment limits are modeled by the inequality constraints $g(x_\omega, y)$. Nonlinearities introduced by e.g. the reaction kinetics often result in nonconvex problems and therefore global optimization techniques, such as evolutionary algorithms are required.

In this work, the superstructure optimization platform FSOpt is used, which was developed by (Steimel & Engell, 2015). In FSOpt, a two stage optimization is performed, where decisions that cannot be adapted to the realization of the uncertainty are fixed but operational parameters are assumed to be adapted to the future realization of the uncertainty and therefore act as recourse variables. Internally, a memetic algorithm is employed (Urselmann et al., 2011). Discrete decisions (e.g., binary decisions as selection or omission of a process unit), are optimized by an evolutionary algorithm while continuous variables are handled by a gradient-based solver.

2.2. Sensitivity analysis

A sensitivity analysis is used to identify the most cost-influencing parameters among the uncertain parameters. For sensitivity analysis a sampling is needed. Latin hypercube sampling (LHS) was chosen in this work, because it covers the complete space with a comparably small number of samples. A linear regression is performed that correlates the n uncertain parameters x_i to the regressed objective value $\hat{Z}_j$:

$$\hat{Z}_j = \beta_0 + \sum_{i=1}^{n} \beta_i x_i. \tag{2}$$

The intercept β_0 and the regression coefficients β_i are determined via least squares. In order to make the regression coefficients comparable they are standardized with zero mean and a standard deviation of one. The Standardized Regression Coefficients SRC are computed as:

$$SRC_j = \frac{\beta_j \hat{s}_i}{\hat{s}}, \qquad \text{with } \hat{s} = \left[\sum_j^N \frac{(z_j - \bar{z})^2}{N-1}\right]^{1/2} \text{ and } \hat{s}_i = \left[\sum_j^N \frac{(x_i - \bar{x})^2}{N-1}\right]^{1/2}, \tag{3}$$

where N is the number of samples. The SRCs are independent on the regressor x_j. Therefore, they can be used to compare the impact of the uncertain model parameters. A large SRC means that the corresponding parameter has a large impact on the objective.

2.3. Optimal design of experiments

New experiments are designed such that the most influencing parameters found by the sensitivity analysis can be estimated more precisely. The methodology described by Franceschini & Macchietto (2008) is applied and in addition to the standard approach, the parameters are weighted with the previously computed SRC. Improving the parameter precision is mathematically equivalent to decreasing a measure of the parameter variance-covariance matrix V, which is computed as

$$V(\hat{\theta}, \phi) = \left[\sum_r^{n_{resp}} \sum_s^{n_{resp}} \tilde{\sigma}_{rs} Q_r^T \cdot SRC \cdot Q_s\right]^{-1}, \tag{4}$$

with the number of responses n_{resp} and a diagonal matrix containing the previously computed SRCs SRC. Q_r is the dynamic sensitivity matrix that contains the sensitivities of the expected model outputs $\hat{y}$ with respect to the parameters θ at all sampling times. Here, a D-optimal design is chosen that minimizes the determinant of the variance-covariance matrix V by variation of the experimental conditions and the sampling times.

3. Case study – Hydroaminomethylation of 1-Dodecene

The proposed approach is applied to the homogeneous catalysed hydroaminomethylation of 1-decene. The catalyst is rhodium that has been preformed with a sulphoxantphos ligand. To recover the expensive catalyst, the usage of a thermomorphic solvent system (TMS) with the solvents methanol and dodecane as proposed by Huxoll et al. (2019) is used. The reaction medium is miscible at reaction temperature, and after cooling it splits

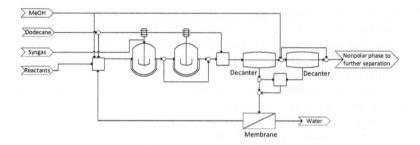

Figure 2: Superstrucure of the hydroaminomethylation process.

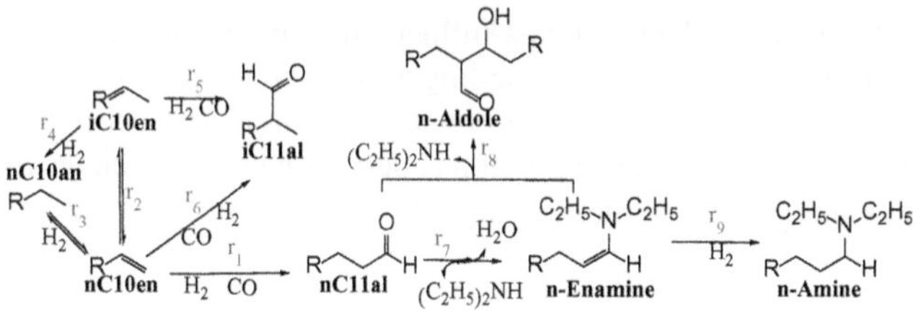

Figure 3: Reaction network of the hydroaminomethylation.

in two phases. The catalyst and the polar solvent methanol can be recycled and the unpolar solvent, the product, and the remaining reactants can be purified further. This purification stage is not considered in this work. The water that is formed during the reaction is separated via a membrane from the recycle stream. The process superstructure considering reactors, decanters, and a membrane is depicted in Figure 2.

3.1. Process model

For the modeling of the reactor the reaction kinetics are needed. The hydroaminomethylation is a combination of a hydroformulation step and a subsequent reductive amination. The reaction kinetics of the hydroformulation as described by Hentschel et al. (2015) and of the reductive amination as proposed by Kirschtowski et al. (2019) are combined. The reaction network is depicted in Figure 3. All parameters were fitted to experimental data of the hydroaminomethylation in a solvent system consisting of methanol and dodecane.

Thermodynamic models are needed to compute the gas solubilities in the reaction medium and the phase separation in the decanter. The solubilities of hydrogen (H_2) and carbon dioxide (CO_2) are approximated by the solubilities in pure solvent and calculated with the equation of state PC-SAFT. Since the PC-SAFT models are not suitable for optimization (Nentwich & Engell, 2019), neural networks were trained to the calculated H_2 and CO_2 concentrations with respect to the temperature, the partial pressures, and the solvent composition. The liquid-liquid equilibrium in the decanter is modeled with the g^E-Model UNIFAC-DO. A neural network was trained to fit the distribution coefficients $K_i = \frac{x_1}{x_{FEED}}$. The membrane is described by a constant retention for each component i, defined as $R_i = 1 - \frac{w_{i,Perm}}{w_{i,Feed}}$, with w_i as the weight fraction in the permeate and in the feed respectively, and a constant area specific permeate flow. The production cost per ton of product is the objective function. It is composed of the costs of the raw materials, the investment costs and the utility costs. The costs for the solvents are not considered, because it is assumed that the solvents can be recovered in the downstream processing.

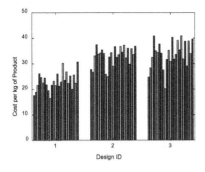

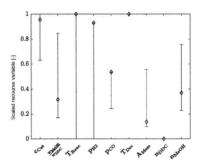

Figure 4: Costs for the three best designs.　　Figure 5: Recourse variables scaled with respect to their bounds.

3.2. Optimization results

In this work, we only consider the kinetic parameters as uncertain. Other parameters such as the distribution coefficients and the membrane retentions that are also uncertain and influence the production costs will be considered in future work. For 18 uncertain parameters (9 pre-exponential factors k_i and 9 activation energies E_A) discrete realizations were considered, giving rise to 25 different scenarios. In Figure 4, the costs for the three best designs that are structurally different are shown for these 25 scenarios. It can be seen that design one is superior to the others. However, the costs vary a lot and the equipment size still has to be chosen. Therefore, a model improvement is necessary. For the best design, two reactors and two decanters are used and the nonpolar solvent is fed between the reactors and the decanters. Depending on the realizations of the uncertainties, the operating conditions are adjusted as shown in Figure 5.

3.3. Sensitivity analysis and design of a new experiment

For the best design, the SRCs are computed and presented in Figure 6. It can be seen that the reaction rate constant k_3 has the largest impact on the production costs due to the large confidence interval, followed by the parameters k_1 and E_{A1}.

An optimal design of experiments, weighted by the SRCs, was performed as described in section 2.3. The decision variables were the sampling times, the temperature, the partial pressures of H_2 and CO, and the solvent composition. The optimal experimental conditions are shown in Table 1 and were found to be independent of the initial values. The optimal sampling times are after 40, 44, 62, 161 and 166 minutes. It is predicted that by performing this experiment the confidence intervals of the most influencing parameters k_3 and k_1 will be reduced by 35% and 14% respectively.

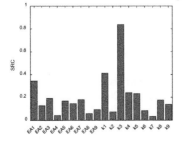

Figure 6: SRCs for the kinetic parameters.

Table 1: Optimized conditions for the next kinetic experiment.

	Temperature [K]	Pressure [bar]	Catalyst concentration [mol/mol]	Gas composition (CO: H_2) [mol/mol]	Solvent composition (MeOH:DDC) [kg/kg]
Optimal value	386	37.76	0.0001	0.2	7.19

4. Conclusion and Outlook

We presented a systematic methodology for early phase process development. By combining superstructure optimization under uncertainty, sensitivity analysis, and optimal design of experiments, the experimental work is focussed on determining the most influencing parameters and thus the time for process development can be reduced. The designed experiments will be conducted in the future to continue with the iterative cycle. The approach will also be applied to uncertainties in thermodynamic models and other models of other process units.

Acknowledgement

Gefördert durch die Deutsche Forschungsgemeinschaft (DFG) - TRR 63 "Integrierte chemische Prozesse in flüssigen Mehrphasensystemen" (Teilprojekt D1) – 56091768. Funded by the Deutsche Forschungsgemeinschaft (DFG) - TRR 63 "Integrated Chemical Processes in Liquid Multiphase Systems" (subproject D1) - 56091768.

References

Chen, Q., & Grossmann, I. E. (2017). Recent Developments and Challenges in Optimization-Based Process Synthesis. *Annu. Rev. Chem. Biomol. Eng.*, *8*(1), 249–283.

Douglas, J. M. (1985). A hierarchical decision procedure for process synthesis. *AIChE J.*, *31*(3), 353–362.

Franceschini, G., & Macchietto, S. (2008). Model-based design of experiments for parameter precision: State of the art. *Chem. Eng. Sci.*, *63*(19), 4846–4872.

Grossmann, I. E., Caballero, J. A., & Yeomans, H. (1999). Mathematical programming approaches to the synthesis of chemical process systems. *Korean J. Chem. Eng.*, *16*(4), 407–426.

Hentschel, B., Kiedorf, G., Gerlach, M., Hamel, C., Seidel-Morgenstern, A., Freund, H., & Sundmacher, K. (2015). Model-based identification and experimental validation of the optimal reaction route for the hydroformylation of 1-dodecene. *Ind. Eng. Chem. Res.*, *54*(6), 1755–1765.

Huxoll, F., Bianga, J., Vogt, D., & Sadowski, G. (2019). Model-based Solvent Screening for a Reductive Amination. *ECCE12*.

Kirschtowski, S., Kadar, C., Seidel-Morgenstern, A., & Hamel, C. (2019). Reductive amination in different solvent systems: reaction network analysis and kinetics. *ECCE12*.

Kuhlmann, H., & Skiborowski, M. (2016). *Synthesis of Intensified Processes from a Superstructure of Phenomena Building Blocks*.

Nentwich, C., & Engell, S. (2019). Surrogate modeling of phase equilibrium calculations using adaptive sampling. *Comput. Chem. Eng.*, 204–217.

Steimel, J., & Engell, S. (2015). Conceptual design and optimization of chemical processes under uncertainty by two-stage programming. *Comput. Chem. Eng.*, *81*, 200–217.

Steimel, J., & Engell, S. (2016). Optimization-based support for process design under uncertainty: A case study. *AIChE J.*, *62*(9), 3404–3419.

Urselmann, M., Barkmann, S., Sand, G., & Engell, S. (2011). Optimization-based design of reactive distillation columns using a memetic algorithm. *Comput. Chem. Eng.*, *35*(5), 787–805.

Sauro Pierucci, Flavio Manenti, Giulia Bozzano, Davide Manca (Eds.)
Proceedings of the 30ᵗʰ European Symposium on Computer Aided Process Engineering
(ESCAPE30), May 24-27, 2020, Milano, Italy. © 2020 Elsevier B.V. All rights reserved.
http://dx.doi.org/10.1016/B978-0-12-823377-1.50135-X

A Thermodynamic Approach for Simultaneous Solvent and Process Design of Continuous Reactive Crystallization with Recycling

Nethrue Pramuditha Mendis,[a] Jiayuan Wang,[b] Richard Lakerveld[a,*]

[a]*Department of Chemical and Biological Engineering, The Hong Kong University of Science and Technology, Clear Water Bay, Hong Kong S.A.R.*
[b]*School of Chemical Engineering, Zhejiang University of Technology, Hang Zhou 310014, China.*
r.lakerveld@ust.hk

Abstract

Solvent selection for continuous reactive crystallization processes with downstream separation of reactants and solvents for recycling is challenging due to the influence of the solvent type on various equilibria that occur within such process and their close interaction with operating conditions. Therefore, computational tools are needed to support decision making. In this work, a simultaneous solvent and process optimization framework for continuous reactive crystallization processes with recycling is presented. The PC-SAFT equation of state is used as the unified thermodynamic framework, which is combined with continuous mapping to make the resulting optimization problem computationally tractable. The approach is demonstrated for a continuous synthesis and purification process of the active pharmaceutical ingredient dalfampridine.

Keywords: reactive crystallization, pharmaceuticals, solvent design, process design, PC-SAFT

1. Introduction

Separation and purification of active pharmaceutical ingredients (APIs) are carried out extensively through solution crystallization in the pharmaceutical industry. Solvents are the medium for solution crystallization processes and have a substantial impact on the process performance and on aspects related to safety, health, and environment. However, solvent selection is generally complicated by the large number of available solvent types and their mixtures and different process performance criteria. Traditional methods based on heuristics may not lead to an optimal trade-off. Furthermore, important progress on the prediction of solvent properties from thermodynamic models has been achieved. Therefore, there is a need to replace solvent selection heuristics with mathematical optimization-based approaches. Due to the strong interconnection between the solvent choice and process operating conditions, those two design problems need to be solved simultaneously to identify the optimal solvent mixture. Such optimization-based solvent selection approaches have been developed for stand-alone crystallizers (Karunanithi et al., 2006). However, solvent recycling may be important for reducing the solvent waste and aligns well with the pharmaceutical industry's current trend towards continuous manufacturing. Therefore, solvent separation needs to be considered as well. Wang and Lakerveld (2018a, 2018b) developed a solvent selection framework for continuous antisolvent crystallization with solvent recycling based on the PC-SAFT equation of state (Gross and Sadowski, 2001), where solvent selection, crystallization and downstream separation were all treated in an integrated manner. Supersaturation is the driving force for crystallization, which can be generated through a reaction. Reactive crystallization is complicated by the necessity to consider reaction equilibria and the potential to form multiple solid phases. Recycling of reactants and solvents is likely to be important for optimal performance. However, optimization-based solvent selection methods for reactive crystallization processes (with or without recycle structures) have not been developed yet.

The objective of this work is to develop a simultaneous solvent and process optimization framework for continuous reactive crystallization processes with recycling. The PC-SAFT equation of state (Gross and Sadowski, 2001) is used as the unified thermodynamic model to predict reaction, solid-liquid, and, vapor-liquid equilibria. The continuous mapping method (Stavrou et al., 2014) is adopted to convert the original MINLP problem into a computationally tractable NLP problem.

2. Approach

The proposed approach involves a process model with a unified thermodynamic model and optimization. The synthesis and crystallization of dalfampridine, a potassium channel blocker API for treatment of multiple sclerosis, from isonicotinamide is used to illustrate the approach.

2.1. Synthesis Reaction

Dalfampridine can be synthesized via the Hofmann rearrangement of isonicotinamide (sub), where an isonicotinamide solution reacts with an alkaline aqueous solution of NaOCl at 45-80 °C (Rane and Sharma, 1994) as follows:

$$Sub + NaOCl(io_1) + 2NaOH(io_2) = API + NaCl(io_3) + Na_2CO_3(io_4) + H_2O(w) \tag{1}$$

The use of an inert organic co-solvent (sol), typically sulfolane (Rane and Sharma, 1994), is preferred to minimize side reactions and to dissolve the substrate.

2.2. Process Configuration

The process consists of a continuous crystallizer followed by a flash drum, which enables the recycling of reactants and solvents (see Figure 1). The substrate (in solid form), a pure make-up solvent stream, and the recycled solvent stream are mixed before being fed to the crystallizer. In the crystallizer, the fully dissolved substrate is mixed with an alkaline aqueous solution of NaOCl. The API is synthesized in the crystallizer and will crystallize immediately due to its low solubility in the reaction medium. Note that the solubility of the substrate in the reaction medium should be sufficiently high to avoid its crystallization. The API crystals are separated by a filter, and the mother liquor is sent to the flash drum, where the mother liquor (consisting of reactants) is concentrated and partially recycled. The flash drum is considered a single vapor-liquid equilibrium stage. The main purpose is to enable recycling of the reactant, but the possibility of solvent recycling is also included by considering an additional recycle from the top of the flash drum, which may contain a substantial amount of solvents that can be suitable for recycling.

2.3. Thermodynamic Modeling

The PC-SAFT equation of state describes the Helmholtz free energy of a mixture, which is the starting point to calculate all thermodynamic properties in this type of processes such as fugacity coefficients, activity coefficients, and residual enthalpies (Gross and Sadowski, 2001). In this work, a pure substance is characterized by five parameters described in detail by Gross and Sadowski (2002), which consider dispersive and associative interactions. Ionic interactions are not explicitly considered, and both the

A Thermodynamic Approach for the Simultaneous Solvent and Process Design for Continuous Reactive Crystallization with Recycling

807

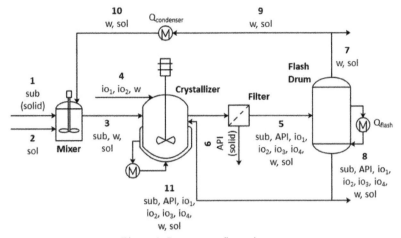

Figure 1: Process configuration

substrate and the API are assumed to be neutral due to the presence of a strong base (NaOH) in the reaction medium.

Solubility data are typically used for parameterization of compounds that are solid at room temperature, which includes many APIs. Due to insufficient solubility data, the PC-SAFT pure component parameters of isonicotinamide and dalfampridine (Table 1) are determined by fitting their activity coefficients in a selected set of solvents, which are calculated using the Pharma Mod. UNIFAC group contribution-based activity coefficient model (Diedrichs and Gmehling, 2011). The pure component parameters for water were obtained from the literature (Gross and Sadowski, 2002). The synthesis reaction is modeled as an equilibrium reaction using activities (*a*), according to:

$$\prod_i a_i^{v_i} = K_{eq} \tag{2}$$

where *i* and *v* stand for compounds and their stoichiometric coefficients in Eq. (1), respectively. The experimental system described in Rane and Sharma (1994) is used to determine the reaction equilibrium constant (K_{eq}=4.13×10^5 at 80 °C). Activities are approximated with mole fractions for the ionic compounds. Crystal formation in the crystallizer is modeled by assuming solid-liquid equilibrium, described by:

$$x^{sol}\gamma^{sol} = \exp\left|\frac{\Delta H_f^m}{R}\left(\frac{1}{T_m} - \frac{1}{T}\right)\right|, \tag{3}$$

where x^{sol} and γ^{sol} are the mole fraction solubility and the activity coefficient of the solute, respectively. ΔH_f^m and T_m are the enthalpy of fusion (22.6 kJ/mol for isonicotinamide (Li et al., 2016); 20.07 kJ/mol for dalfampridine (Chen et al., 2017)) and the solid melting temperature (428.5 K for isonicotinamide (Li et al., 2016); 432.2 K for dalfampridine (Chen et al., 2017)).

The downstream separation in the flash drum is modeled as a vapor-liquid equilibrium using fugacity coefficients in liquid and vapor phases.

Table 1: PC-SAFT parameters for the substrate and the API

Component	m	σ (Å)	ε/k (K)	ε^{AB}/k (K)	κ^{AB}	*Association Scheme*
Isonicotinamide	5.45	2.41	160.86	1807.86	0.010	2/2
Dalfampridine	6.30	2.87	131.29	2027.81	0.010	2/2

The total molar enthalpy of a given stream is determined as the sum of ideal and residual contributions, where the latter is directly calculated from PC-SAFT. The ideal contribution to the total enthalpy is linked with the PC-SAFT pure component parameters of the compounds of a mixture using a quantitative structure-property relationship (QSPR), which is described elsewhere in detail (Stavrou et al., 2014). The process model (assuming steady-state conditions) is completed by material balances (over the mixer, crystallizer and filter, and flash separator) and enthalpy balances (over the flash separator and the condenser), which are omitted here for brevity. Only the solvent and water are considered for enthalpy calculations.

Reaction equilibrium is assumed within the crystallizer, and the crystal formation is calculated by assuming solid-liquid equilibrium at the crystallizer outlet. The vapor-liquid equilibrium in the flash drum is modeled assuming that the vapor phase consists of solvent and water only. Several inequality constraints are imposed to enforce a practically feasible process. In particular, the substrate should be fully dissolved when entering and leaving the crystallizer, which leads to the following constraints:

$$x_{sub,3} \leq x_{sub,3}^{sol}, \quad x_{sub,5} \leq x_{sub,5}^{sol}, \quad x_{sub,11} \leq x_{sub,11}^{sol}. \tag{4}$$

Furthermore, it is assumed that all the ionic compounds are fully dissolved in all streams in which they are present. The following constraint is applied to avoid an impractically small liquid fraction of the material in the bottom of the flash drum:

$$x_{liquid,8} \geq 0.7. \tag{5}$$

The following constraint on the crystallizer size is applied to avoid that the reactant recycle stream would become excessively large:

$$(F_5 + F_6)\tau \leq V, \tag{6}$$

where F stands for stream flow rates, τ is the residence time (set as 1 h), and V is the reactor volume (set as 10 m^3). Finally, the solvent parameter space, y, was constrained to the PC-SAFT parameters from a solvent database, adopted from Wang and Lakerveld (2018a), using a convex hull.

2.4. Optimization Problem

The objective function represents the total production cost normalized by the product (i.e., API) flow rate, which is minimized to determine the optimal solvent parameters, y, and operating conditions, x, for the process, as follows:

$$\min_{x,y} J = \frac{c_{sol}F_2(x,y) + c_{cw}Q_{condenser}(x,y) + c_{steam}\dfrac{Q_{flash}(x,y)}{eff}}{F_6(x,y)} \tag{7}$$

s.t.   process model

      thermodynamic model

      Constraints (4)-(6) and convex hull constraint for y

where Q stands for heat flow rates. The parameters c_{sol} (7.94 USD/L), c_{cw} (2.07×10^{-7} USD/kJ), and, c_{steam} (2.24×10^{-5} USD/kJ) represent the costs for solvent, cooling water, and steam, respectively. The average solvent and utility costs are estimated from Lab Alley (www.laballey.com), and the U.S. Energy Information Administration (https://www.eia.gov), respectively. An efficiency factor (*eff*) of 0.8 was used to account for losses during steam generation and distribution. The substrate flow rate, F_1, is fixed at 1 mol/s, and NaOCl and NaOH are fed at stoichiometric ratios. The water flow rate in Stream 2 is fixed at 30 mol/s to ensure full dissolution of NaOCl and NaOH. The crystallizer and flash pressures are atmospheric and the mixer and crystallizer

A Thermodynamic Approach for the Simultaneous Solvent and Process
Design for Continuous Reactive Crystallization with Recycling
809

temperatures are set to room temperature (25 °C) and 70 °C (which falls within the temperature range reported in the literature for dalfampridine synthesis (Rane and Sharma, 1994)), respectively. The solvent type, make-up solvent flow rate, flash temperature, and two split fractions are the free variables. The resulting MINLP is solved with the continuous mapping method (Stavrou et al., 2014).

3. Results

The use of the continuous mapping method allowed for a tractable optimization problem, which is otherwise computationally prohibitive in its original MINLP form. By relaxing the PC-SAFT pure component parameters and solving the resulting NLP using the GAMS/CONOPT solver, a hypothetical optimal solvent had been identified before it was mapped on to the solvent database using Taylor expansion to identify a real solvent. The real solvent identified in this case was 2-propanol, which was verified for its miscibility with water. Miscibility with water is essential to avoid any liquid-liquid phase separation in the crystallizer, which is undesirable. The optimal operating conditions (see Table 2) were determined by solving an NLP with fixed solvent PC-SAFT parameters for 2-propanol, which correspond to an objective function value of 0.0582 USD/mol.

The solvent for a reactive crystallization process in general needs to have a higher solubility for the substrate and a lower solubility for the API to enable efficient crystallization-based separation of the API. Furthermore, the solvent should favor the forward reaction and allow for easy recovery in a flash drum from the mother liquor if reactant/solvent recycling is also desired. The identified optimal solvent (2-propanol) has a higher solubility compared to water for both the substrate and the API according to the model predictions. Even though a higher solubility for the substrate is favorable, the crystallization yield tends to be lower when the solubility of the API in the solvent is higher. Apparently, this adverse effect of 2-propanol on the crystallization yield was compensated by optimizing the crystallization medium composition, which contains both water and 2-propanol. In particular, the similarity between the values of the crystallization yield and the normalized reaction extent (see Table 2) suggest that the solubility of the API in the medium is sufficiently low to enable near-complete separation of the API. At the same time, the solvent medium affects the extent of the reaction as well, which is another factor that affects the final crystallization yield.

Split fraction 1 determines the fraction of reactants recycled. A higher reactant recycle stream is likely to allow for a larger reaction extent, but may also facilitate the reverse reaction due to the recycle flow of product into the crystallizer. A larger reactant recycle stream also results in a larger crystallizer volume to achieve a given residence time. The optimal value for split fraction 1 (0.56) shows the need to maintain a sufficiently large purge stream to avoid a strong impact of these negative effects on the objective function at the expense of more loss of reactant. Similarly, split fraction 2 determines the flow rate of the solvent recycle stream, where the solvent is mostly recovered due to its lower boiling point compared to water. This stream is closely related to the make-up solvent flow rate. The optimal value for split fraction 2 (1.00) indicates that it is more beneficial to minimize the make-up solvent flow rate (i.e., the solvent cost) compared to minimizing the energy penalty (for condensation) associated with a larger recycle stream. This case clearly shows how inherent trade-offs exist among the different solvent properties and the process operating conditions for continuous reactive crystallization processes with possible solvent and reactant recycle streams and why it is important to optimize the solvent type and operating conditions simultaneously.

Table 2: Optimal Operating Conditions

Yield (F_6/F_1)	0.9408
Normalized Reaction Extent (ξ/F_1)	0.9442
Make-Up Solvent Flow Rate (F_2/F_1)	0.0537
Flash Temperature (°C)	97.74
Split Fraction 1 (F_{11}/F_8)	0.56
Split Fraction 2 (F_9/F_7)	1.00

4. Conclusion

A thermodynamic approach is presented for the simultaneous optimization of solvent type and process operating conditions for continuous reactive crystallization processes including recycling of reactants and solvents with an economic objective function. The PC-SAFT equation of state can be used to construct a unified thermodynamic framework to model reaction, solid-liquid, and vapor-liquid equilibria within the overall process model. Continuous mapping method allows for the original MINLP to be converted into an NLP problem, which is computationally tractable at least for the investigated case in this work. The proposed approach has been successfully applied to the case of the API dalfampridine in which several inherent trade-offs between solvent properties and process conditions exist, which shows the potential of the proposed approach to improve continuous pharmaceutical processes that are industrially relevant.

Acknowledgment

This work was financially supported by the Research Grant Council of Hong Kong under Grant No. 16214418.

References

Chen C.-T., Lee C.-A., Tang M., Chen Y.-P., 2017, Experimental investigation for the solubility and micronization of pyridin-4-amine in supercritical carbon dioxide, Journal of CO2 Utilization, 18, 173–180.

Diedrichs, A., Gmehling, J., 2011, Solubility Calculation of Active Pharmaceutical Ingredients in Alkanes, Alcohols, Water and their Mixtures Using Various Activity Coefficient Models, Industrial & Engineering Chemistry Research, 50(3), 1757–1769.

Gross J., Sadowski G., 2001, Perturbed-Chain SAFT: An Equation of State Based on a Perturbation Theory for Chain Molecules, Industrial & Engineering Chemistry Research, 40(4), 1244–1260.

Gross J., Sadowski G., 2002, Application of the Perturbed-Chain SAFT Equation of State to Associating Systems, Industrial & Engineering Chemistry and Research, 41(22), 5510–5515.

Karunanithi A. T., Achenie L. E. K., Gani R., 2006, A computer-aided molecular design framework for crystallization solvent design, Chemical Engineering Science, 61(4), 1247–1260.

Li B., Wu Y., Zhu J., Chen K., Wu B., Ji L., 2016, Determination and correlation of solubility and mixing properties of isonicotinamide (form II) in some pure solvents, Thermochimica Acta, 627–629, 55–60.

Rane D. S., Sharma M. M., 1994, New strategies for the Hofmann reaction, Journal of Chemical Technology & Biotechnology, 59(3), 271–277.

Stavrou M., Lampe M., Bardow A., Gross J., 2014, Continuous Molecular Targeting–Computer-Aided Molecular Design (CoMT–CAMD) for Simultaneous Process and Solvent Design for CO 2 Capture, Industrial & Engineering Chemistry Research, 53(46), 18029–18041.

Wang J., Lakerveld R., 2018a, Integrated solvent and process design for continuous crystallization and solvent recycling using PC-SAFT, AIChE Journal, 64(4), 1205–1216.

Wang J., Lakerveld R., 2018b, Integrated Solvent and Process Optimization Using PC-SAFT for Continuous Crystallization with Energy-intensive Solvent Separation for Recycling, Computer Aided Chemical Engineering, 44, 1051–1056.

Sauro Pierucci, Flavio Manenti, Giulia Bozzano, Davide Manca (Eds.)
Proceedings of the 30th European Symposium on Computer Aided Process Engineering
(ESCAPE30), May 24-27, 2020, Milano, Italy. © 2020 Elsevier B.V. All rights reserved.
http://dx.doi.org/10.1016/B978-0-12-823377-1.50136-1

Synthesis of Complex Distillation Sequences with Multiple Feeds

José A. Caballero, Juan A. Labarta-Reyes, Juan A. Javaloyes-Anton

Institute of Chemical Process Engineering, University of Alicante. Carretera de San Vicente s.n. 03690, Alicante. Spain.

caballer@ua.es

Abstract

In this work, we address the problem of synthesizing sequences of distillation columns to sharply separate the components of multiple feeds of zeotropic mixtures in which each feed share at least one component with at least another feed.

We show that the space of feasible alternatives can be characterized by extending the concept of basic separation. The space of basic separations can be generated by combining the common sub-mixtures (or separation tasks) in the set of basic separations generated by each individual feed. However, the different composition and origin of repeated sub-mixtures can generate different arrangements in distillation columns with eventually very different performance even though the sequence of separations task be the same in some of them. We illustrate the procedure with an example involving two feeds and four components.

Keywords: Thermally coupled distillation, MINLP, separation sequences.

1. Introduction

The general separation problem was defined by Rudd and Watson (1968) as the transformation of several source mixtures into several product mixtures. In 1985 Westerberg (1985) claimed that this problem was essentially unsolved and after fifty years the general separation problem has not been completely solved and it is likely not to be solved in the near future. If we focus on the more specific problem of separation based on distillation, there is not a unified solution for the separation problem, instead, different researchers focused on specific problems based mainly on the physical characteristics of the mixture. Thus it is common to differentiate between mixtures containing azeotropes and mixtures that do not form azeotropes. While azeotropic mixtures are considerably more difficult to separate, the set of alternatives (sequences of columns) is considerably smaller (Górak and Sørensen 2014).

In the case of zeotropic separation we can differentiate two kinds of problems: when the product sets contain non-overlapping species with each other –referred to as sharp separations- and when there are overlapping species (non-sharp separations.) The nature of these problems requires different solution approaches. In the case of sharp separations, we can differentiate two cases. When a given separation task performs a separation between two key components consecutive in volatility (i.e. there is no other component with intermediate volatility between the selected key components) and when key components are not consecutive (Górak and Sørensen 2014).

Historically, sharp separation sequences were assumed to be performed by «conventional columns». A conventional column can be defined as columns having one feed, and producing two products and includes a condenser and a reboiler. Following this assumption, the problem of developing an algorithm to enumerate the feasible separation sequences is straightforward (Westerberg and Wahnschafft, 1996), but the selection of the best alternative in terms of energy consumption, total cost or any other criteria is no so easy due to potential large number of feasible alternatives. The earliest attempts were based on heuristics extracted from case studies (Lorenz Biegler et al. 1997). The first models based on mathematical programming were linear MILP models and from that point, models evolved to MINLP using from shortcut to rigorous column models. A comprehensive review can be found in (José A. Caballero and Grossmann 2014).

For a single feed, the characteristics of the search space for the general zeotropic sharp split separation problem –feasible sequences that could include the optimal one- were established by different authors in the last 10-15 years (Caballero and Grossmann 2006; Giridhar and Agrawal 2010). Shah and Agrawal (2010) defined a «regular configuration» as a sequence formed by exactly N-1 columns (where N is the number of key components to be separated). A regular configuration in which each column has a condenser and a reboiler is a «basic configuration». Basic configurations are important because they can be generated only by relations between separation tasks and it allows separating the structural considerations associated with the separation from the heat transfer needed in distillation. The extension from basic to regular configuration only requires to substitute internal heat exchangers (those associated with a sub-mixture that is not a final product) by thermal couples. Shah and Agrawal (2010), and Caballero and Grossmann (2006) established that the search space must be formed by the set of regular configurations.

In this work, we present a discussion on how to generalize the concept of basic/regular configuration when we deal with the separation of multiple feeds that share some components. In the next sections first we clearly state the problem, then we include a discussion on how to generalize the concept of regular/basic configurations depending on the components present in each feed. Finally, we include some conclusions.

2. Structural considerations for distillation sequences with multiple feeds.

The problem we are dealing with can be stated as follows. Given is a set of zeotropic mixtures (feed streams) in which each stream shares at least one component with at least another stream. The objective consists of synthesizing a sequence of distillation columns to separate N key components (N ≤ total number of components) with the best performance in a given index (e.g. cost).

The first stage is determining with is the space of feasible alternatives, or alternatively which is the space of regular configurations. However, taking into account that all the regular configurations can be generated by the set of basic configurations just by removing condensers and/or reboilers associated with sub-mixtures connecting two distillation columns, the problem is reduced to determine the space of basic sequences.

The extension to basic sequences when there are multiple feeds can be done based on the following observations:

a. As a general rule, it is possible to generate all the basic sequences of a system with multiple feeds, from the combination of common separations (or common sub-mixtures) of each one of the single feed basic configurations.

b. When two sub-mixtures formed by the same components, but different compositions (i.e. each sub-mixture comes from a different feed) are merged in a single column, then we must avoid mixing the feeds and a two-feed column must be used. In another case, we generate a point of inefficiency due to the mixture of streams. An extra decision is determining the relative positions of both feeds in the new column.

c. Given k feeds each one with n_k key components, for a total of N different key components, in which a given feed shares at least one component with another feed. If we sort the components by volatility and in each one of the feeds there is not any component missing between the lightest and heaviest in that feed, it is possible to generate basic/regular configurations with could range from max(n_k-1) to (N-1) columns.

d. If in some of the feeds there are missing components between the lightest and the heaviest one (e.g. The N components are A, B, C, D and we have a feed formed only by A and C), then we should consider the alternative of the general rule (separate A from C –A/C-) but also the possibility of adding the feed (or sub-mixture) AC as a second feed together with the sub-mixture ABC. While the first case will yield lower energy consumption, it also includes one more distillation column. Therefore, both situations must be considered.

3. Example

We will illustrate the generalization of basic sequences with multiple feeds with the following small example. We have two feed streams, the first formed by the components A, B and C (ABC) sorted by decreasing relative volatility and a second feed formed by a mixture of B, C, and D (BCD). The objective is generating the full space of basic alternatives for the sharp separation of the four components A, B, C and D. According to Giridhar and Agrawal (2010) for a three-component mixture, there are 3 basic configurations, shown in Figure 1 for the first feed.

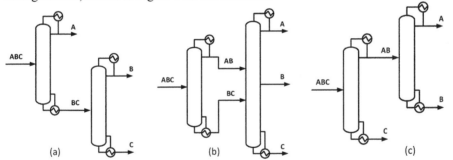

Figure 1. Basic sequences for a three component system. a) Direct; b) Pre-fractionator, c) Indirect.

The basic sequences for the second feed are the same simply changing the name of the components accordingly. The space of basic sequences can be generated by combining configurations (a), (b) and (c) in Figure 1 for Feed 1 and Feed 2. The simple combination produces initially 9 possible sequences. However, depending on the composition and the origin of the shared sub-mixtures new sequences arise. Figure 2 shows the alternatives for the example.

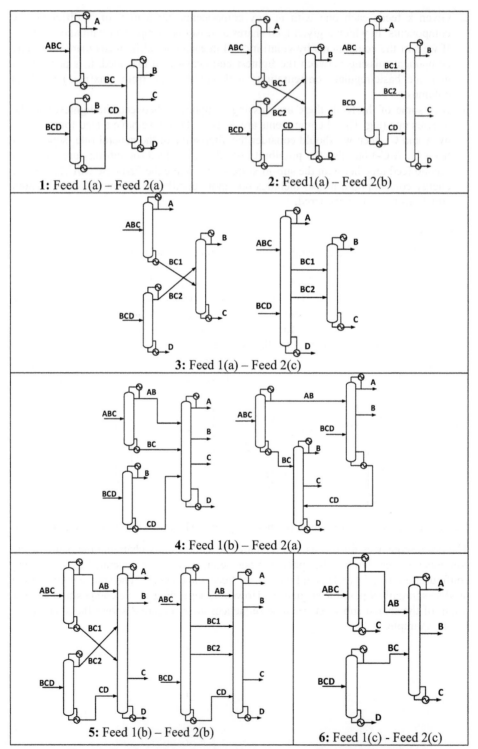

Figure 2. Basic sequences for the example. Feed 1 = ABC; Feed 2 = BCD.

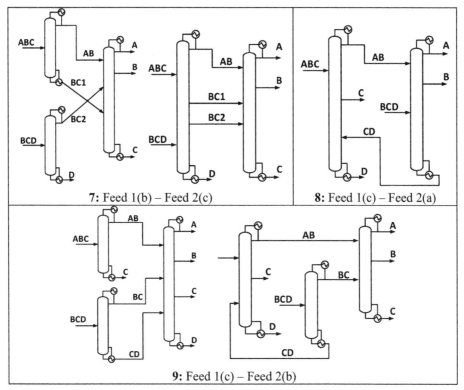

Figure 2. (cont) Basic sequences for the example. Feed 1 = ABC; Feed 2 = BCD.

In Figure (2), in the configuration 1, the Feed 1 and 2 share the final products B and C. (Feed 1 is performing the separation A/BC – B/C and Feed 2 B/CD – C/D). However, product B is produced by both sequences by a rectifying section, while product C is produced by a rectifying section (Feed 2) and a stripping section (Feed 1). Therefore it is possible to merge in a single column separations B/C and C/D. A similar situation occurs in configuration 6, but now the product C is produced by two stripping sections and product B by a rectifying section (Feed 2) and a stripping section (Feed 1). In configuration 8 again products B and C are shared by the two sequences, however, in this case, both B and C are produced by a rectifying and a stripping section and we can merge separation A/B with B/CD in a single column and AB/C with C/D in another column. The final result is that this configuration requires only two distillation columns.

Configuration 4 also share products B and C, however, Feed 1 produces product B simultaneously by a stripping and a rectifying section. And Feed 2 produced B just by a rectifying section. Product C is produced by a stripping section by Feed 1 and by a rectifying section by Feed 2. This situation gives a new degree of freedom because we can merge in a single column the separation that generates the stripping section of B: A/B with either B/C from Feed 1 or B/CD from Feed 2, while at the same time we merge in a single column the two contributions that form product C.

In configurations 2, 3, 5 and 7, sequences generated by Feed 1 and 2 share the sub-mixture BC. However at the difference of the previous cases in which the final products were pure components, now the compositions in both sub-mixtures (BC1 and BC2) can be very different. Therefore, depending on the relative compositions we can merge them in a single column or not. We have different alternatives: If the compositions are different but when added to a second column (that should be a two feed column) they maintain its relative positions we can use a single column just adding a new column section between both feeds. If this is not the case, then we have a trade-off between the cost due to the extra energy consumption if we mix those two streams to reduce the number of columns or maintain two separated columns but avoiding the inefficiency of mixing those streams. If we take into account all the possibilities we finish, for this small example, with 15 basic configurations, 10 of them require 3 distillation columns and 5 can perform the separation using just 2 distillation columns. In larger problems, the space of alternatives is too large to be exhaustively generated. In those cases, previous results can be used to extend the logical relationships presented by Caballero and Grossmann (2006) and formulate the problem as a Generalized Disjunctive Programming problem.

4. Conclusions

In this paper, we have shown how to generalize the concepts of basic and regular configurations in thermally coupled distillation of zeotropic mixtures with a single feed to multiple feeds. As a general rule it is possible to generate all the basic sequences from the union of the sequences generated by individual feeds by merging the common parts. This procedure will produce basic sequences with different number of columns depending on the sub-mixtures and final products shared by the different feeds. Sub-mixtures involving the same components with different compositions generate multiple-feed columns. The relative position of those feeds could have important effect on energy consumption.

Acknowledgments

The authors acknowledge financial support to the Spanish «Ministerio de Economía, Industria y Competitividad» under project CTQ2016-77968-C3-2-P (AEI/FEDER, UE).

References

Caballero, J A, and Ignacio E. Grossmann. 2006. "Structural Considerations and Modeling in the Synthesis of Heat-Integrated−Thermally Coupled Distillation Sequences." *Industrial & Engineering Chemistry Research* 45 (25): 84, 54–74.

Caballero, José A., and I. E. Grossmann. 2014. "Optimization of Distillation Processes." In *Distillation: Fundamentals and Principles.*, edited by Andrzej Gorak and Eva Sorensen, 437–96. London: Elsevier.

Giridhar, Arun, and Rakesh Agrawal. 2010. "Synthesis of Distillation Configurations: I. Characteristics of a Good Search Space." *Computers & Chemical Engineering* 34 (1): 73.

Górak, Andrzej., and Eva. Sørensen. 2014. *Distillation : Fundamentals and Principles*. London.

Lorenz Biegler; Ignacio Grossmann; Arthur Westerberg. 1997. *Systematic Methods of Chemical Process Design*. New Jersey: Prentice Hall PTR.

Rudd, D.F., and C.C. Watson. 1968. *Strategy of Process Engineering*. Edited by John Wiley & Sons Inc. New York.

Shah, Vishesh H, and Rakesh Agrawal. 2010. "A Matrix Method for Multicomponent Distillation Sequences." *AIChE Journal* 56 (7): 1759–75.

Westerberg, A. 1985. "The Synthesis of Distillation-Based Separation Systems." *Computers & Chemical Engineering* 9 (5): 421–29.

Westerberg, Arthur W., and Oliver Wahnschafft. 1996. "Synthesis of Distillation-Based Separation Systems." *Advances in Chemical Engineering* 23 (C): 63–170.

Sauro Pierucci, Flavio Manenti, Giulia Bozzano, Davide Manca (Eds.)
Proceedings of the 30th European Symposium on Computer Aided Process Engineering
(ESCAPE30), May 24-27, 2020, Milano, Italy. © 2020 Elsevier B.V. All rights reserved.
http://dx.doi.org/10.1016/B978-0-12-823377-1.50137-3

Integrating Suppliers into the Simultaneous Process and Product Design of Formulated Products

Manuel Taifouris [a], Mariano Martín [a], Alberto Martínez [b], Nats Esquejo [c].

[a] Department of Chemical Engineering, University of Salamanca. Plz. Caídos. 1-5. 37008. Spain

[b] Procter and Gamble. Brussels Innovation Center. Temselaan 100. 1853 Strombeek-Bever . Belgium

[c] Procter and Gamble. Newcastle Technical Center. Whitley Rd, Longbenton, Newcastle Upon Tyne, Tyne And Wear, NE12 9SR

Abstract

In this work, we present an extended pooling problem for the design of formulated detergents that includes process and product design and supplier's selection. It was a multiobjective, multiperiod and multiscale optimization product. The integrated problem presented was highly non-linear and non-convex. To address the problem, two different mathematical formulations have been compared. A traditional MINLP and a reformulation of the problem using a decision vector and the definition of penalties reducing the need for binary variables. To present the problem, a case study in Europe was formulated considering several ingredients, suppliers and price policies. The traditional formulation takes days to converge if it converges at all, while the reformulation, in spite of the larger problem size, achieves solution in 20 hours. Furthermore, it was demonstrated that when considering a multiobjective optimization (profit and environmental impact), the model can reduce the CO_2 emissions by 40% in the design of a set of detergents, maintaining the benefit within 1.39% of the maximum by selecting the detergent composition and the suppliers.

Keywords: Integrated process, product and supply chain, mutiobjective optimization, environmental friendly

1. Introduction

For a product to be competitive in a global market, it has to meet specific consumer needs and likes but also it has to be profitable and environmentally sustainable. In order to address all this issues simultaneously, the concept of process and product design (Ng and Gani, 2018) is gaining support. This integrated approach is particularly important in the design of formulated products, since, changes in the composition may result in difficulties in processing certain formulas, further limiting the feasible set of products and the selection of the ingredients also have marketing, logistics and environmental issues involved (Martín and Martínez, 2018). The manufacture of formulated products can be approached using an extended pooling problem. In the pooling problem, a series of ingredients, which can be supplied by different companies, are mixed to obtain a product with properties that meet the customers' expectations (Audet et al, 2004). The prices of these ingredients may have an associated uncertainty (Martín & Martínez, 2015) or be fixed by contracts depending on their variability during the year (Martín & Martínez, 2018). By further extending the pooling problem to integrate the product and process design and supply chain, the mathematical problem becomes a large non-linear, non complex problem that includes bilinear terms

In this work, a mathematical model is formulated to integrate suppliers selection, process and product design to determine the optimal formulation of three types of powdered detergents considering that the ingredients can come from different suppliers, each one at a distance from the manufacturer and with different prices depending on that distance. This distance affects the price of the ingredients, the cost of transport and the environmental impact.

2. Methodology

In this work, we develop a problem formulation for the integrated process and product design together with the supplier selection for the case of formulated products. The production process consists of 5 stages (Martín & Martínez, 2013): The homogeneous mixture of the ingredients, an atomization to avoid possible jams, a drying process in a spray drier, a cooling process and a finishing stage, where a series of additives are added to adjust the properties. The ingredients can be provided come from different suppliers. The distance affects the prices (the further away the supplier is, the cheaper the ingredients will be) and affects the environmental impact (the further away the supplier is, the higher the CO_2 emissions). In addition, some ingredients have their prices fixed by multiannual contracts while others will have associated market variability and average prices are computed using probability data. The model is multiobjective (profit and environmental impact) and multiperiod (three years). Two different formulations are developed to solve the extended pooling problem.

The first formulation is based on an extension to the work by (Martín and Martínez, 2015&2018) based on a mixed integer nonlinear programming (MINLP) formulation. We adapt that work to our problem. Our mathematical model is developed considering the mass balances, the process constraints, the final product's performance, the environmental impact of the ingredients and their transport, the pricing policies and the price of ingredients with associated uncertainty.

The ingredients of the current powder detergents can be classified into 7 groups (surfactant, builder, bleach, fillers, enzymes and polymers) and, following the open literature (European Ecaolabel, 2011), we consider the most typical ingredients of each group (2 o 3 ingredients per group) for a total of 17 ingredients. The work of Martín and Martínez (2015) is extended to include suppliers and this affects some variables such as ingredient cost, emissions of CO_2, etc. The amount purchased from any factory determines the cost and the CO_2 emissions due to transportation every year, for each ingredient and for each supplier. Supply capacity and process limits are included. In addition, all the variables depend on the temporal dimension because the model is multiperiod.

-Regarding product performance, we use the correlation from the work of Martín & Martínez (2013) but considering the 17 ingredients. We fix three types of detergents, Detergent A: High performance and high price, Detergent B: Medium performance and average price; Detergent C: Sufficient quality and low price.

- On the one hand, we consider four different types of price policies (1.-linear discount, 2.-logarithmic discount, 3.-constant elasticity and 4.-fixed discount) to calculate the final prices of the ingredients whose prices can be fixed using three-year contracts. The optimal selection of the price policies depends on the necessary amount to produce the optimal product. On the other hand, the probability values and the prices associated with that probability are used to calculate the average prices of the ingredients with associated uncertainty. Both of prices are calculated every year although the optimization chooses the best policy considering a temporal horizon of the three years. To evaluate the transportation cost, we use the distances between the factory and the suppliers, the diesel price and the consumption of the truck. Using the loading capacity, we calculate the cost of unit transport and, therefore, the final transport cost depends on the distance and the purchased amount of each ingredient.

-The environmental impact is computed using the carbon footprint of each ingredient and the transportation.

-The main objective function accounts for the income for the sale of the three different detergents, the raw material costs, the transport costs and the cost of the intermediate tanks (to do the intermediate mixtures). The model is multi-objective and, therefore, the second objective (environmental impact) is added using the ε-constraint method considering different values of emissions of CO_2.

However, to select the best policy, we use binary variables in the first formulation, therefore, the model is an MINLP. It is a problem because, the model cannot be solved in a rational time and we have to reformulate the whole model to remove all the binary variables and only use continuous variable to facilitate the resolution of the problem. To achieve this, the dimension of the amount of raw material purchased variable is increased, which also depends on the price discount policy, $ccp_{(ye,i,sup,po)}$. In this reformulation, this variable is responsible for selecting and indicating the best policy through its indexes, in a similar way as already did in the previous case with the suppliers. For each year and for each ingredient, the variable $ccp_{(ye, i, sup, po)}$ will be equal to 0 for all combinations of 'sup' and 'po' except for one, which will be the optimal supplier and policy selection. The information provided by $ccp_{(ye,i,sup,po)}$ will be the amount purchased from ingredient 'i' in the year 'ye' and to the supplier 'sup' using the policy 'po'. Its value tells us the amount purchased and, its indexes, the supplier and the optimal policies. Therefore, we transform the initial MINLP into a nonlinear programming (NLP), in the second formulation. We have to change some equations and add some penalties into the model to avoid that the model selects different policies in different years, since the contract with the suppliers lasts 3 years and therefore, although the optimization evaluate the model every year, if the best policy is selected, this have to fixed during the 3 years.

3. Case of study

To show the use of the formulations, a case study in Europe is considered. Surfactants, polymers and antifoam prices are assumed to be subjected to market variability and the rest of the ingredients were fixed by contracts. Three inorganic suppliers, three organic suppliers and six enzyme suppliers are considered. The factory is located in Frankfurt (Germany) and all the suppliers are in Europe and represent actual factories of the important chemical companies. The solution of the optimization should show the optimal selection of the suppliers, ingredients, policies and the amount produced. The MINLP formulation consists of 5195 equations and 4320 variables (780 binary variables) and the NLP one consists of 11971 equations and 14083 variables. Although the MINLP model is much smaller in terms of equations and variables, the presence of integer variables make it much more difficult to solve, so that a valid solution is not found in more than 20 hours. Therefore, we proceed to evaluate the performance of the NLP model giving feasible results in the 20 hours established as a limit with a tolerance lower than 6%. A commercial solver, BARON is used for an Intel Core i7-7700 with 3.6 GHz and 32 Gb of RAM.

First, the model is optimized without environmental constraints to compare the detergent composition as the environmental objective is implemented, see Table 1. The profit is 79.529 M€. Next, the profit and detergent composition are evaluated with different limits of carbon footprint. The pareto curve can be seen in Figure 1.

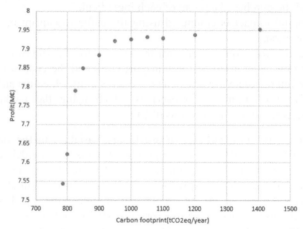

Figure 1.-Pareto curve for the profit as a function of the carbon footprint

When we add the environmental constraint, the model has to choose fewer polluting ingredients, however the system can still maintain a benefit close to the maximum. We can verify that between the value of 1400 tCO2eq/year and 850 tCO2eq/year (39% reduction of the emissions), the profit only decreased by 1.29%, However, from this point, the profit start to fall sharply. This is because the model lost the ability to compensate for environmental limitations with changes in the composition of the final product and changes in the selection of suppliers or in polities. The model have to select the less polluting ingredients and, in some cases (below 825 tCO2eq/year), the maximum demand cannot be met because combinations of ingredients that simultaneously meet the requirements of carbon footprint and yield cannot be found, so that by lowering the sold amount, the obtained profit fells. Therefore, the utopia point is 850 tCO2eq/year. For this point, the optimal selection of suppliers, ingredients, formulation and polities can be seen in the Table 1.

Most of the selected suppliers are the closest to the factory (the supplier 3 for inorganic ingredients and the supplier 4 for organic ingredients). Most of the ingredients that are purchased through contracts are very abundant, regarding their upper limits, so the linear and logarithmic policies are used. Regarding the composition, the requirement performance of each type of detergent is different and, therefore, their composition is different too. Each detergent tries to achieve the goals (performance, profit and environmental) with different set of possible compositions. As it can be seen in Table 1, the requirement of enzymes and polymers (the ingredients which more influent in the performance) is the highest in the case of A detergent and the lowest in the case of C detergent, since, the performance of the A detergent have to be higher than the performance of the C detergent, however in the intermediate case, the B detergent have a higher amount of polymers than the A detergent to compensate the lower amount of enzyme and achieve its performance requirement. The rest of the compositions are similar between the three detergents. However, in the case of the C detergent did not require the same amount of polymers, since its performance is expected to be lower than B detergent. The locations of the selected suppliers can be seen in the Figure 2 for both the economic (b) and multiobjective economic-environmental (a) solutions where a change in suppliers is shown.

Table 1.-Optimal detergent composition and selection of suppliers and policies

Without environmental constraints					
HC (tCO2e/year)	Ingredient	Amount(t/year)	Carbon FootPrint (t/ti)	Price policy	**Profit(M€)**
	LAS LINEAR ALKYL ARYL SULFONATES	120.00	4.20	-	
	ZEOLITE	427.00	1.76	Logarithmic	
	SODIUM PERBORATE TETRAHYDRATE	95.50	0.40	Logarithmic	
	SODIUM SULFATE	80.00	0.30	Constant elasticity	
	ANTIFOAM	0.80	1.76	-	
	CELLULOSE	12.67	3.69	Logarithmic	
	CARBOXYMETHYL CELLULOSE	0.80	2.22	-	
	WATER	63.37	0.00	-	
	Optimal formulation(ti/tp)				
	Type of detergent				
		A	**B**	**C**	
1404	LAS LINEAR ALKYL ARYL SULFONATES	15%	15%	15%	**7.95**
	ZEOLITE	56%	50%	60%	
	SODIUM PERBORATE TETRAHYDRATE	5%	19%	5%	
	SODIUM SULFATE	10%	10%	10%	
	ANTIFOAM	0%	0%	0%	
	CELLULOSE	3%	1%	1%	
	CARBOXYMETHYL CELLULOSE	0%	0%	0%	
	WATER	12%	5%	8%	
With environmental constraints					
HC (tCO2e/year)	Ingredient	Amount(t/year)	Carbon FootPrint (t/ti)	Price policy	**Profit(M€)**
	ALCOHOL ETHOXYLATE	120.00	3.70	-	
	POLYPHOSPHATES	240.69	1.02	Linear	
	SODIOUM PERBORATE	200.00	0.40	Logarithmic	
	XYLENE SULPHONATE	200.00	0.03	Logarithmic	
	ANTIFOAM	0.80	1.76	-	
	PROTEASE	104.13	3.69	Logarithmic	
	POLYMERS	145.20	0.17	-	
	WATER	135.82	0.00	-	
	Optimal formulation(ti/tp)				
	Type of detergent				
850		A	B	C	**7.85**
	ALCOHOL ETHOXYLATE	15.00%	15.00%	15.00%	
	POLYPHOSPHATES	31.07%	28.72%	32.58%	
	SODIOUM PERBORATE	25.00%	25.00%	25.00%	
	XYLENE SULPHONATE	25.10%	24.94%	24.92%	
	ANTIFOAM	0.10%	0.10%	0.10%	
	PROTEASE	1.99%	0.97%	0.54%	
	POLYMERS	0.10%	3.53%	0.10%	
	WATER	1.63%	1.74%	1.75%	

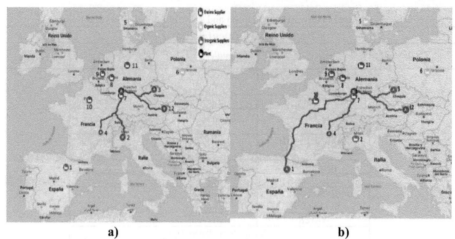

a)   b)

Figure 2.-Optimal solution for the design of powder detergents. a: Environmental friendly; b: Economic

4. Conclusion and future work

In this work, we have developed a mathematical formulation for the optimal design of formulated products. This framework can be applied to any formulated product present in the food industry, pharmaceutical and cosmetics among others. It has been shown that through the correct selection of ingredients and suppliers, the CO_2 emissions of the production process could be substantially reduced to more than 35% without significantly affecting the benefit. Being able to simultaneously select suppliers, ingredients and discount policies provides flexibility to adapt to different environmental limits. However, there is a limit value from which the profit starts to fall sharply since it is no longer possible to compensate for the environmental impact without reducing the production or having to use more expensive ingredients.

Acknowledgement:

P&G and PSEM3 USAL for funding the research

Reference

Audet, C., Brimberg, J., Hansen, P., Le Digabel, S., Mladenovi, N., 2004. Pooling Problem: Alternate Formulations and Solution Methods. Manag. Sci. 50, 761-776.

Calfa, B.A., Grossmann, I.E., 2015. Optimal procurement contract selection with price optimization under uncertainty for process networks. Comp. Chem Eng. 82, 330–343.

European Ecolabel, 2011 Revision of Ecolabel Criteria for Laundry Detergents 2008-2010 Background   report. http://ec.europa.eu/environment/ecolabel/documents/Laundry%20Detergents%20technical%20report.pdf (Accessed 07 October 2019)

Karuppiah, R., Martín, M., Grossmann, I.E., 2010. A simple heuristic for reducing the number of scenarios in two-stage stochastic programming. Comput. Chem. Eng. 2010, 34, 1246–1255.

Martín M., Martínez A., 2015. Addressing Uncertainty in Formulated Products and Process Design. Ind Eng Chem Res. 54 (22), 5990-6001.

Martín M., Martínez A., 2018. On the effect of price policies in the design of formulated products. Comput. Aided Chem. Eng. 109, 299-310.

Martín, M., Martínez, A., 2013. Methodology for simultaneous process and product design in the consumer products industry: The case study of the laundry business. Chem. Eng. Res. Des. 91 .795–809

Ng K.M., Gani R., 2018 . Chemical Product Design: Advances in Research and Teaching. Computer Aided Chemical Engineering. 40, 21-32.

Sauro Pierucci, Flavio Manenti, Giulia Bozzano, Davide Manca (Eds.)
Proceedings of the 30th European Symposium on Computer Aided Process Engineering
(ESCAPE30), May 24-27, 2020, Milano, Italy. © 2020 Elsevier B.V. All rights reserved.
http://dx.doi.org/10.1016/B978-0-12-823377-1.50138-5

Modeling Framework for Joint Product and Process Synthesis with Material Recovery Opportunities

Ana Somoza-Tornos[a], Qi Chen[b], Moisès Graells[a], Antonio Espuña[a], Ignacio E. Grossmann[b]*

*aDepartment of Chemical Engineering, Universitat Politècnica de Catalunya
Escola d'Enginyeria de Barcelona Est, C/ Eduard Maristany 16, 08019 Barcelona,
Spain*
*bCenter for Advanced Process Decision-making, Department of Chemical Engineering,
Carnegie Mellon University, Pittsburgh, PA 15213, USA*
grossmann@cmu.edu

Abstract

The circular economy paradigm requires process synthesis to be expanded beyond the consideration of production activities aimed at market needs and to integrate valorization processes upcycling waste from different sources (industrial and urban). With this aim, this contribution presents a modeling approach for the joint synthesis of production processes and products from a waste-to-resource perspective.

The system is modeled through a superstructure with features from state-task network (i.e. the activation/deactivation of units) and state-equipment network (i.e. multiple tasks in a unit) representations. The problem is formulated using a Generalized Disjunctive Programming approach (GDP).

The proposed approach is tested with a case study addressing the synthesis problem of polyethylene pyrolysis, as a central step required to address the need to close the associated material loops. Decisions are made on the separation and reuse of the pure or mixed light gases from the reactor outlet (material reuse vs. energy valorization).

Results demonstrate the ability of the proposed approach to represent alternatives that cannot be considered if only STN or SEN models were used.

Keywords: process modeling, synthesis, superstructure, optimization, generalized disjunctive programming, circular economy.

1. Introduction

State-task network (STN, (Kondili et al., 1993)) and state-equipment network (SEN, (Smith, 1996)) are two process representations commonly used as a base for the superstructure representation required to address the conventional problem of process synthesis. While the STN representation is easier to formulate, the SEN representation is more suitable for modeling equipment networks, as it reduces the number of process nodes and prevents zero-flow singularities (Chen and Grossmann, 2017).

However, both conceptual models generally rely on the premise that product specifications are narrowly bounded (i.e. final products are single-component with a defined purity), and fail to consider other decisions that would affect the final result (i.e.

solutions in which intermediate products or mixtures may be sold or recycled into the process). This problem becomes crucial in the synthesis of processes addressing the circular economy paradigm, where material recovery alternatives are numerous and diverse. Hence, this work presents a novel modeling approach for the optimal synthesis of processes with flexible product composition, including equipment activation/ deactivation, and the possibility of selling/recycling mixed streams.

This is particularly interesting for the application of circular economy principles to process design, which has been gaining importance in recent years (Avraamidou et al., 2020). Processes for the chemical upgrading and recycling of polymers, such as the pyrolysis of plastics, lead to hydrocarbon mixtures similar to those from crude oil cracking but with different compositions. The two main alternatives for these products include their use as fuels (i.e. waste-to-energy, Honus et al., 2016) and their separation to recover the monomers that can be used to produce new chemicals or polymers (Hong and Chen, 2017), which results in a more efficient use of valuable resources and may increase incentives for recycling and closing material loops.

2. Problem statement

The problem addressed in this paper can be stated as follows: given is a set of raw materials (usually subproducts/waste) and process alternatives (equipment and tasks), the objective is to find the path to convert these materials into the most valuable resources, taking into account current market requirements.

In order to achieve this objective, these elements have to be represented in a flexible superstructure that considers different alternatives for pure or mixed products (i.e. selling or recycling) and also different flowsheeting alternatives and equipment design.

3. General framework for joint process and product synthesis of

The proposed general framework for addressing the synthesis problem consists of a three-step approach based on the work by Yeomans and Grossmann (1999): superstructure representation, modeling (Generalized Disjunctive Programming - GDP), and model resolution.

3.1. Superstructure representation

Separation processes are generally modeled considering that the inlet is separated in all the products that integrate it. STN leads to easier problem formulations, whereas SEN is more easily solved since it prevents zero-flow singularities (Chen and Grossmann, 2017). However, the synthesis of waste-to-resource processes requires a more flexible superstructure representation of separation sequences, including the activation and deactivation of equipment (as in STN) and the flexible assignment of tasks to equipment (as in SEN). This is done through the implementation of the most general form of SEN network (Yeomans and Grossmann, 1999) which does not avoid zero-flow singularities. A generic example of superstructure representation of a process flowsheet including flexible product composition and material recovery is shown in Figure 1.

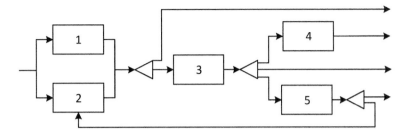

Figure 1. Example of superstructure for joint product and process synthesis.

3.2. GDP formulation

The superstructure defined in the previous step is now modeled and formulated using GDP (Raman and Grossmann, 1994). Let $j \in J$ define the set of equipment in the superstructure and $k \in I_j$ the set of tasks that can be performed in each equipment j. x_j and z_{jk} denote the continuous variables representing the operating conditions of the system, while the Boolean variables Y_j and W_{jk} represent whether equipment j is active and whether task k is assigned to it, respectively. The resulting formulation is as follows:

$$\min z = \sum_{j \in J} c_j + f(x_j, z_{jk}) \tag{1}$$

$$\text{s.t.} \quad f(x_j, z_{jk}) \leq 0 \tag{2}$$

$$\left[\begin{array}{c} Y_j \\ \bigvee_{k \in I_j} \left[\begin{array}{c} W_{jk} \\ f_{jk}(x_j, z_{jk}) \leq 0 \\ c_j = \gamma_{jk} \end{array} \right] \end{array} \right] \vee \left[\begin{array}{c} Y_j \\ x_j = z_{jk} = 0 \\ c_j = 0 \end{array} \right] \quad \forall j \in J \tag{3}$$

$$\Omega(W_{jk}) = True \tag{4}$$

$$Y_j \in \{True, False\} \quad \forall j \in J \tag{5}$$

$$W_{jk} \in \{True, False\} \quad \forall j \in J, k \in I_j \tag{6}$$

The objective function to be minimized (Eq. 1) includes the fixed cost associated to the active equipment units and a function of the continuous variables (i.e. variable costs and income from selling the products). Algebraic constraints in Eq. (2) are equalities and inequalities that must be satisfied for any realization of the discrete variables, typically including mass balances that define the connections among the nodes of the superstructure. On the other hand, constraints that are inherent to equipment activation and task assignments are modeled in nested disjunctions. The external ones are based on the existence of equipment j, while the internal ones define task selection. Thus, if equipment j is active ($Y_j = True$) and task k is selected ($W_{jk} = True$), constraints $f_{jk}(x_j, z_{jk}) \leq 0$ are applied and the related fix costs are considered in the objective function $c_j = \gamma_{jk}$. Conversely, if equipment j is not selected ($Y_j = False$) continuous variables and fix costs are set to 0. Finally, logical constraints among the nodes of the superstructure are given by $\Omega(W_{jk})$ (Eq. (4)). These include enforcements of consecutive tasks in order to meet recipe-based constraints.

3.3. Model resolution

The model is implemented in Pyomo and solved with DICOPT after its reformulation to a MINLP using the Big M method. The MINLP involves 36 binary variables, 2353 continuous variables and 4280 constraints and was solved in 34 CPUs on an Intel Xeon processor operating at 2.20GHz.

4. Case study

The proposed framework has been applied to the synthesis of the process of polyethylene pyrolysis for the recovery of hydrocarbons. Experimental data from the literature is used to model the outlet from the pyrolysis furnace. Kannan et al. (2014) reported high conversions (>99%) of the polymer to gas when operating at 1000°C, leading to outlet compositions of: 5% methane, 46% ethylene, 18% propylene, 3% propyne, 2% 1-butene, 13% 1,3-butadiene and 13% benzene. The main objective is to identify to which extent the gas resulting from the pyrolysis of polyethylene at such conditions should be separated into its compounds, according to the cost of separation and the market price for pure or mixed compounds. The model should also identify if any of the streams could be used as fuel to satisfy the energy requirements of the furnace used to maintain the operating conditions.

5. Results and discussion

In this section, the results for the synthesis of the case study are presented following the methodology described in section 3.

5.1. Superstructure representation

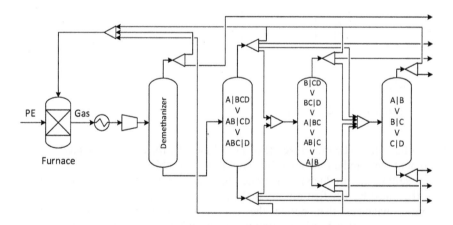

Figure 2. Superstructure representation of the process.

Figure 2 shows the superstructure for the proposed case study. The outlet of the pyrolysis reactor is cooled and compressed to enter the distillation sequence where the different hydrocarbons may be recovered. For the sake of simplicity and due to the different boiling point of methane compared to the rest, the stream is demethanized before entering the distillation sequence. After this step, a four component mixture distillation train is considered, in order to split the inlet into its fractions of ethylene (A), propylene (B), 1,3-butadiene (C) and benzene (D). Propyne and 1-butene are recovered with 1,3-butadiene since their low concentration would not justify two extra separation stages. The first column considers the three possible tasks for the first level separation of the four-component mixture. The second one includes the three-component separations of the streams resulting from the previous column, plus the separation A|B in case AB|CD is selected in column one. Finally, column 3 can perform the two-component separation of outlet streams from column two. All three distillation columns can be active or inactive, but the existence of one implies that the previous ones need to exist. All outlet streams can be introduced to the next separation level, sold as final product, or reused in the process as fuel for the furnace.

5.2. Model formulation

The model is formulated following the GDP described in section 3.2 with the following considerations:

- The objective function is the profit maximization taking into account: the income for product sales (proportional to its purity), fix and variable costs for the active distillation columns, and fresh fuel savings.
- $f(x_j, z_{jk}) \leq 0$ include the mass balances at the nodes of the superstructure (e.g. the distillate of column one can be sold as a product, used as fuel at the furnace or go to column two if AB or ABC mixes are produced).
- $f_{jk}(x_j, z_{jk}) \leq 0$ represent the equations that depend on the column activation and task selection (e.g. mass balance of the distillation columns or reflux ration calculation).
- $\Omega(W_{jk})$ denotes the logical constraints that should be enforced (e.g. column 3 can only be active if column 1 and 2 are also active).

5.3. Solution

Figure 3 depicts the optimal solution for the flowsheet design for the material recovery from polyethylene pyrolysis. In this particular case all units were selected, so zero-flow singularities are not present.

The methane from the gas demethanization is sold, and the bottoms are sent to column 1. Here, task A|BCD is active, leading to the production of ethylene. Likewise, propylene and 1,3-butadiene are recovered in the distillates of columns 2 and 3, respectively. Thus, direct distillation was found to be the optimal option. Ethylene, propylene and benzene are sold, while 1,3-butadiene is burned as fuel at the furnace due to its low purity.

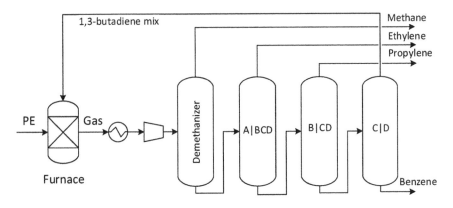

Figure 3. Optimal flowsheet design for the material recover from polyethylene pyrolysis.

6. Conclusions

This paper has introduced a general framework to represent, model and solve the joint product and process synthesis problems resulting from the consideration of waste-to-resource transformations. To achieve this objective, the work has followed the three-step method proposed by Yeomans and Grossmann (1999). First, the model is represented through the generalized version of a SEN, including task selection and equipment activation and deactivation to address the singularities of processes for material recovery. Second, we formulate the model as a GDP. Finally, the model is transformed into a MINLP through the Big M method and solved in Pyomo/DICOPT. The capabilities of the model have been tested through its application to the synthesis of a flowsheet for the recovery of hydrocarbons from the pyrolysis of polyethylene. The proposed methodology has been proven useful to identify the optimal extent of separation and the most economically profitable products in a systematic way. Future work will include the implementation of decomposition techniques to address the cases which present zero-flow singularities.

Acknowledgements

Financial support received from the Spanish "Ministerio de Economía, Industria y Competitividad" and the European Regional Development Fund, both funding the research Project AIMS (DPI2017-87435-R) is fully acknowledged.

Ana Somoza-Tornos thankfully acknowledges financial support received from the Spanish Ministry of Education, Culture and Sport (Ayuda para la Formación de Profesorado Universitario - FPU15/02932).

References

Avraamidou, S., Baratsas, S.G., Tian, Y., Pistikopoulos, E.N., 2020. Circular Economy - A challenge and an opportunity for Process Systems Engineering. Comput. Chem. Eng. 133, 106629. https://doi.org/10.1016/j.compchemeng.2019.106629

Chen, Q., Grossmann, I.E., 2017. Recent Developments and Challenges in Optimization-Based Process Synthesis. Annu. Rev. Chem. Biomol. Eng. 8, 249–283. https://doi.org/10.1146/annurev-chembioeng-080615-033546

Hong, M., Chen, E.Y.X., 2017. Chemically recyclable polymers: A circular economy approach to sustainability. Green Chem. https://doi.org/10.1039/c7gc01496a

Honus, S., Kumagai, S., Němček, O., Yoshioka, T., 2016. Replacing conventional fuels in USA, Europe, and UK with plastic pyrolysis gases – Part I: Experiments and graphical interchangeability methods. Energy Convers. Manag. 126, 1118–1127. https://doi.org/10.1016/j.enconman.2016.08.055

Kannan, P., Al Shoaibi, A., Srinivasakannan, C., 2014. Temperature effects on the yield of gaseous olefins from waste polyethylene via flash pyrolysis. Energy and Fuels. https://doi.org/10.1021/ef500516n

Kondili, E., Pantelides, C.C., Sargent, R.W.H., 1993. A general algorithm for short-term scheduling of batch operations—I. MILP formulation. Comput. Chem. Eng. 17, 211–227. https://doi.org/10.1016/0098-1354(93)80015-F

Raman, R., Grossmann, I.E., 1994. Modelling and computational techniques for logic based integer programming. Comput. Chem. Eng. 18, 563–578. https://doi.org/10.1016/0098-1354(93)E0010-7

Smith, E.M., 1996. On the optimal design of continuous processes, Ph.D. Dissertation, under supervision of C. Pantelides. Imperial College of Science, Technology and Medicine, London, UK.

Yeomans, H., Grossmann, I.E., 1999. A systematic modeling framework of superstructure optimization in process synthesis. Comput. Chem. Eng. 23, 709–731. https://doi.org/10.1016/S0098-1354(99)00003-4

Sauro Pierucci, Flavio Manenti, Giulia Bozzano, Davide Manca (Eds.)
Proceedings of the 30th European Symposium on Computer Aided Process Engineering
(ESCAPE30), May 24-27, 2020, Milano, Italy. © 2020 Elsevier B.V. All rights reserved.
http://dx.doi.org/10.1016/B978-0-12-823377-1.50139-7

Value Chain Synthesis in Algae Biorefineries under Uncertainty

Melina Psycha, Lorenzo-Andreas Mamos, Antonis Kokossis

School of Chemical Engineering, National Technical University of Athens, Zografou Campus, 9, Iroon Polytechniou Str., GR-15780 Athens, Greece
akokossis@mail.ntua.gr

Abstract

The work focuses on exploring the uncertainties concerning the prices of chemicals and the involved markets regarding algae biorefineries. A product-oriented approach is analyzed which directly links the customization of product portfolios with market needs and behaviors. For this purpose, the microalga Dunaliella is selected leading to four interested markets (pharmaceuticals, nutraceuticals, cosmetics and food). A number of scenarios are studied referring to different market behaviors and the Cauchy distribution is used for the uncertainty analysis. The combination of markets is taken into consideration focusing on the achievement of a potential investment with high profitability and low risk. The combination of the cosmetic and the food sector constitutes the most suitable field to steer future investments and the carotenoids group includes the target-products to be considered during the formulation of product portfolios.

1. Introduction

The merits of microalgae as an alternative source of biomass are well established over the years, especially because of their versatility in terms of products. This potential in addition to the utilization of carbon dioxide, which microalgae need for their growth, render the development of a large-scale application extremely promising either as a standalone venture or in integration with other plants (Galanopoulos et al., 2019). Specifically, the co-production of specialty chemicals from microalgae is gaining ground as the related markets expand and profit margins grow (García Prieto et al., 2017; Psycha and Kokossis, 2017). A plethora of microalgae has been studied and researched, especially for applications in the pharmaceutical, nutraceutical and cosmetic sector (Chua and Schenk, 2017; Panis and Rosales Carreon, 2016; Psycha et al., 2018).

The volatility of markets and prices regarding the specialty chemicals present in algae value chains constitutes a great challenge and adds to the uncertainty of the value chain synthesis (Psycha and Kokossis, 2016). Uncertainty analysis is imperative considering the high-value chemicals involved and the risk that concerned markets can show. Several studies have been conducted to address this issue based on performance measures of potential investments (Gong et al., 2016) as well as processing paths optimization (Rizwan et al., 2015). This paper deals with the alignment of the interested market sectors with the respective product portfolios and proposes a product-oriented approach in order to reach potential investments characterized as flexible, profitable and of low risk.

2. Product-oriented approach

The methodology follows a five-step course keeping in mind the challenges related to chemicals pricing, product synthesis and the evolution of markets according to Figure 1.

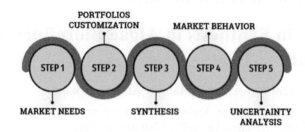

Figure 1. Step-by-step methodology of the product-oriented approach

2.1. Market needs

The first step refers to the identification of interested markets related to the specialty chemicals extracted from microalgae as products. Such products can find applications in the pharmaceutical sector (anti-inflammatories, antidepressants, anti-metastatic action etc.), the nutraceutical sector (antioxidants, food supplements etc.), the cosmetic sector (sunscreens, creams, scrubs etc.) and the food sector (natural colorants, functional ingredients such as emulsifiers etc.).

2.2. Portfolios customization

The second step relates to the customization of product portfolios based on the market needs of Step 1. The products are classified according to their possible applications on each market sector.

2.3. Synthesis

The synthesis step refers to a simultaneous screening of the processing paths instead of evaluating each path separately. The representation of all the available options is achieved by the development of a superstructure involving feedstocks, processes, intermediate mixtures or fractions and products. The synthesis model as well as the mathematical formulation of the problem follow the guidelines of Psycha and Kokossis (2016) and deal with profit maximization. The model is formulated into a MILP model, it is optimized by employing commercial software and is resolved with the use of integer cuts in order to provide multiple solutions to the problem.

2.4. Market behavior

Market behavior plays a significant role in order to address additional challenges related to prices fluctuations. On that note, three scenarios are established that depict patterns of future chemicals prices compared to current numbers (base-price):

- *Scenario 1:* Optimistic behavior. The prices are considered constant and no change is reported. As a result, the chemicals prices are assumed to be 100% of the base-price.
- *Scenarios 2 (a and b):* Realistic behavior. Prices are decreased by 20% and 40% in Scenario 2a and Scenario 2b respectively.
- *Scenarios 3 (a and b):* Pessimistic behavior. Prices are decreased by 50% and 60% in Scenario 3a and Scenario 3b respectively.

Table 1 summarizes behaviors and scenarios as well as the respective percentages of the base-price.

Table 1. Summary of price percentage in each scenario

	% of base-price				
Market behavior	Scenario 1	Scenario 2a	Scenario 2b	Scenario 3a	Scenario 3b
Optimistic	100%	-	-	-	-
Realistic	-	80%	60%	-	-
Pessimistic	-	-	-	50%	40%

2.5. Uncertainty analysis

The final step follows the Monte Carlo method and combines market needs with market behaviors. For the purposes of this paper, the Cauchy distribution is used for each scenario and for the different market sector described in Step 1. Random numbers are produced for the prices of the products with the initial numbers being those presented in Step 4 for each scenario.

3. Real-life case study

This study refers to the processing of the microalga Dunaliella for the production of high-value chemicals in a real-life biorefinery undertaken by the D-Factory, an FP7 collaborative project aiming at a commercial scale biorefinery process. Following the product-oriented approach, the abovementioned market sectors are taken into consideration, four different product portfolios are constructed considering the value chain of Dunaliella (Figure 2) and uncertainty analysis is applied following the scenarios of Step 5. According to the individual product portfolios, all sectors include 7 products except nutraceuticals, which includes 6.

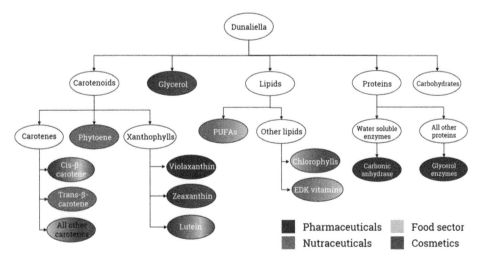

Figure 2. Value chain of the microalga Dunaliella indicating product portfolios for each market sector

4. Comparative results

Figure 3 depicts profits for each market sector following the market-behavior scenarios. For the purposes of this study, Scenarios 3 (a and b) are not listed due to the unsustainable solutions they produce. The larger margin of profit is observed in the cosmetic sector since all scenarios, including the ones following the realistic behavior, provide sustainable solutions. On the other hand, nutraceuticals offer a small profit margin but they stand with one product less in their portfolio.

According to the results, the markets could be arranged in order of decreasing profitability as follows: Cosmetics → Food sector → Pharmaceuticals → Nutraceuticals. Similarly, they could be arranged in order of decreasing risk: Pharmaceuticals → Food sector → Nutraceuticals → Cosmetics.

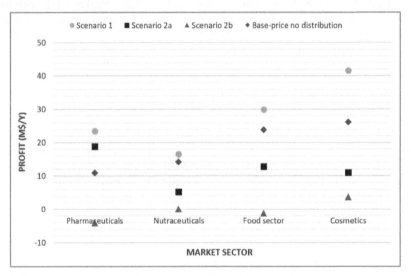

Figure 3. Profit chart for each market sector according to the scenarios

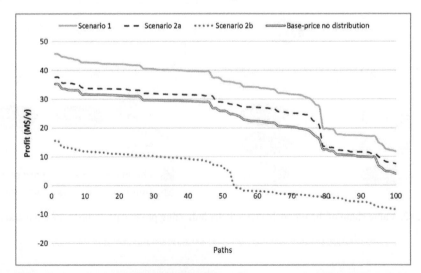

Figure 4. Profit chart for the entire value chain (13 products)

Taking into consideration the existence of common products in the different portfolios, the opportunity arises for combinations of markets to establish flexibility, profitability and less risky options. An additional incentive to explore this option emerges from the results depicted in Figure 4. According to the profit evolution in multiple solutions, one can draw the conclusion that for the entire value chain the potential biorefinery would be economically sustainable. Thus, more chemicals in the product portfolio yield to more sustainable options (even for Scenario 2b for the first fifty paths).

Considering the results of Figures 3 and 4, combinations of markets are proposed based on profitability and risk. Indications on profitability and risk for different combinations of markets are presented in Figure 5. More suitable combination yielding to more profitable and less risky options appears to be the cosmetic and the food sector, which have five common products and three of them belong to the carotenoid fraction (cis-β-carotene, lutein, carotenes as a mixture).

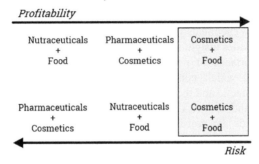

Figure 5. Profitability and risk indications on combinations of markets

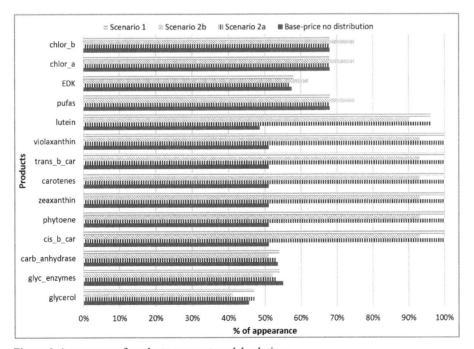

Figure 6. Appearance of products amongst model solutions

Following on the study of the total value chain of Dunaliella, Figure 6 presents the appearance of all products amongst the generated paths for each scenario. It is noteworthy that for the fraction of carotenoids (lutein, violaxanthin, trans-β-carotene, carotenes, zeaxanthin, phytoene and cis-β-carotene) a 50% increase in appearance is observed if one compares the base-price (no use of distribution) percentages with the ones of each scenario (with the use of the Cauchy distribution). This leads to the conclusion that carotenoids play the key role to the formulation of product portfolios and yield to higher profits. Moreover, markets with more carotenoids in their portfolios provide more profitable and less risky options, which confirms that the proposed combination of the cosmetic and the food sector as target-markets is the most suitable selection for future investment.

5. Conclusions and future work

The present work addresses challenges related to the uncertainty of markets and prices regarding the specialty chemicals present in algae value chains. The proposed product-oriented approach provides insight into the profitability and risk of a potential investment highlighting the importance of product selection and markets involved. Uncertainty analysis is conducted which combines market needs with market behaviors. The combination of the cosmetic and the food sector leads to the most suitable results in terms of high profitability and low risk and constitutes a fruitful field to steer a potential investment. Carotenoids are considered target-products and play the key role to the formulation of product portfolios. More research is required focusing on the use of more distributions customized for each individual market and on a more detailed investigation regarding the combination of markets.

References

C. Galanopoulos, P. Kenkel, E. Zondervan, 2019, Superstructure Optimization of an Integrated Algae Biorefinery, Computers and Chemical Engineering, 130, 106530

C.V. García Prieto, F.D. Ramos, V. Estrada, M.A. Villar, M.S. Diaz, 2017, Optimization of an Integrated Algae-based Biorefinery for the Production of Biodiesel, Astaxanthin and PHB, Energy, 139, 1159-1172

E.T.Chua, P.M. Schenk, 2017, A Biorefinery for Nannochloropsis: Induction, Harvesting, and Extraction of EPA-rich Oil and High-value Protein, Bioresource Technology, 244, 2, 1416-1424

G. Panis, J. Rosales Carreon, 2016, Commercial Astaxanthin Production Derived by Green Alga Haematococcus pluvialis: A Microalgae Process Model and a Techno-economic Assessment all through Production Line, Algal Research, 18, 175-190

J. Gong, F. You, 2016, Optimal Design and Synthesis of Algae Processing Network under Uncertainty based on Return on Investment, Computer Aided Chemical Engineering, 38, 2301-2306

M. Psycha, A.C. Kokossis, 2016, Synthesis and Optimization of Microalgae Biorefineries, Computer Aided Chemical Engineering, 38, 325-330

M. Psycha, A.C. Kokossis, 2017, Techno-economic Evaluation of an Integrated Microalga Biorefinery Targeting the Co-production of Specialty Chemicals, Computer Aided Chemical Engineering, 40, 1981-1986

M. Psycha, M. Kapnisi, A.C. Kokossis, 2018, Extended Value Cahin Synthesis towards the Design of Multi-Feedstock Algae Biorefineries, Computer Aided Chemical Engineering, 43, 645-650

M. Rizwan, M. Zaman, J.H. Lee, R. Gani, 2015, Optimal Processing Pathway Selection for Microalgae-based Biorefinery under Uncertainty, Computers and Chemical Engineering, 82, 362-373

Sauro Pierucci, Flavio Manenti, Giulia Bozzano, Davide Manca (Eds.)
Proceedings of the 30th European Symposium on Computer Aided Process Engineering
(ESCAPE30), May 24-27, 2020, Milano, Italy. © 2020 Elsevier B.V. All rights reserved.
http://dx.doi.org/10.1016/B978-0-12-823377-1.50140-3

Effect of Flue Gas Composition on the Design of a CO_2 Capture Plant

Ana Gabriela Romero-García,[a] Nelly Ramírez-Corona,[b*] Eduardo Sánchez-Ramírez,[a] Heriberto Alcocer-García,[a] Juan Gabriel Segovia-Hernández[a]

[a]*Departamento de Ingeniería Química, Universidad de Guanajuato, Noria Alta s/n,*
Guanajuato, Gto., 36050, México.
[b]*Departamento de Ingeniería Química, Alimentos y Ambiental, Universidad de las*
Américas Puebla. ExHda. Santa Catarina Mártir s/n, San Andrés Cholula, Puebla,
México, 72820
nelly.ramirez@udlap.mx

Abstract

According to studies conducted by the International Energy Agency, the energy sector is the biggest producer of greenhouse gas emissions (CO_2), having important environmental consequences. Various alternatives have been sought to reduce CO_2 emissions during electric production, highlighting as an alternative, the implementation of CO_2 capture and storage plants. In this work, it is shown the global optimization of a coupling CO_2 capture plant to an electric power plant, having as objective function minimize the energetic requirements of the process. For this study, it was considered four different fuels in the power plant; biogas, coal, non- associated natural gas, and associated natural gas. Two operating scenarios are considered: in the first, generate the same combustion gas flow for all the proposed fuels and in second, obtain the same energy demand with the 4 fuels. For the design and simulation, the software ASPEN Plus simulator was used.

Keywords: CO_2 Capture plant, biogas, coal, non- associated natural gas.

1. Introduction

In recent years demand for electricity has been rapidly increased, the International Energy Agency reported that 65% of the energy produced worldwide was obtained from the burning of fossil fuels, which are the main sources of CO_2 emissions, generating climate change as the main consequence (IEA, 2018). From 37.1 trillion tonnes of CO_2 produced in 2018, 35 trillion tonnes are related to the energy sector (EIA,2019), in that way, the production of energy by fossil fuels is considered unsustainable processes in accordance with the principles of green chemistry and circular economy. Considering the aforementioned, the production of greenhouse gases and their relationship with the energy sector is of significant importance. Understanding a thermoelectric generator (TEG) as an apparatus that produces electricity from waste heat. There are several ways to produce electricity, the first of them is by a conventional thermal power plant that works with a simple thermal cycle, with a yield of 33%, the rest of the energy is dissipated in the form of heat. On the other hand, there are combined cycle thermoelectric plants where electric and thermal energy is produced simultaneously from the same fuel. The advantage of these over conventional plants is that they take better advantage of the energy produced, thus achieving greater efficiencies and in turn have lower CO_2 emissions. Globally, several alternative solutions have been sought to reduce CO_2 emissions turning electricity production into cost-effective and sustainable processes. To achieve this goal, some authors propose different possibilities to reduce CO_2 emissions: 1) reduce the intensity of energy; 2) reduce the intensity of coal; for example, the use of carbon-free fuel; and 3) improve CO_2 capture. highlighting the implement of CO_2 Capture and Storage plants (CCS). Where post-combustion CO_2 capture is the most feasible technology than other alternatives; by reacting with alkanolamines as solvents, post-combustion capture technology is the best choice for CO_2 separation, because it has high efficiency, low cost, and facility to be adapted to existing power plants.

In order to have a positive environmental impact on CO_2 capture processes, it is necessary to highlight the technical challenges involved in the separation method of CO_2 due to the use of amine aqueous solutions, as well as consider using new ionic liquids solvents to CO_2 separation. To achieve high efficiency, low environmental impact and the best operating cost, it is important to consider two different aspects: first is needed to have a high concentration of CO_2 which depends on the type of fuel used in the power plant and second the election of the solvent used to CO_2 capture so as its proportions.

As discussed in Nagy and Mizey (2013), changing flue gases conditions significantly influence the optimal operation of the capture process, particularly the solvent and energy requiments. These authors evaluated the influence of type and flowrate of seven fuels (including 3 coals, 2 gasses, and one biomass) during capture process by means of a parametric study. Their findings indicate that different ratios absorbent/gas are required in order to operate the capture plant in optimum conditions. According to their results, the optimal L/G ratio shows a linear correlation with the CO_2 content of the flue gas.

In this work, we present a global optimization for the design of a CO_2 capture process coupled to a power generation plant (see Figure 1). The use of four different fuels in the power plant was considered; biogas, coal, non- associated natural gas, and associated natural gas. Two operating scenarios were considered; in the first, the same fuel flow was considered for all the plants and in the second, the same energy demand was specified. The design and simulation of the process plants were developed through the use of the ASPEN Plus simulator. Study Cases and Methodology: for the simulation of the power plant and the CO_2 capture plant, the ASPEN PLUS process simulator is used. In order to model the thermodynamic properties involved in the power generation plant, the Peng-Robinson method is used according to the reported by Hasan et al. (2012). For the combustion chamber, a RGibbs type reactor was selected, considering a molar ratio of air to the fuel of 30: 1 and a fuel flow of 1000kmol/h for all analyzed cases. Table 1 shows the mass percentages of the fuels used for the simulation. For the CO_2 capture process, it was considered a chemical absorption using as solvent an aqueous solution of monoethanolamine (MEA) with a weight of 30% in a RadFrac equilibrium stage block for the absorber and regenerator. The reactions involved in the CO_2 capture process are shown below from Eq. (1) to Eq. (5).

$$MEAH^+ + H_2O \leftrightarrow MEA + H_3O^+ \tag{1}$$

$$2H_2O \leftrightarrow OH^- + H_3O^+ \tag{2}$$

$$HCO_3^- + H_2O \leftrightarrow CO_3^{2-} + H_3O^+ \tag{3}$$

$$OH^- + CO_2 \xleftrightarrow{k1} HCO_3^- \tag{4}$$

$$MEA + CO_2 + H_2O \xleftrightarrow{k2} MEACOO^- + HCO_3^- \qquad (5)$$

Table 1. Fuel composition

	Natural Gas	Associated Gas	Biogas	Coal
CH_4	96.00	87.20	60.00	-
C_2H_6	1.80	4.50	-	-
C_3H_8	0.40	4.40	-	-
$i\text{-}C_4H_{10}$	0.15	1.20	-	-
N_2	0.70	2.70	2.00	-
CO_2	0.95	-	38.00	-
C	-	-	-	78.20
H	-	-	-	5.20
O	-	-	-	13.60
N	-	-	-	1.30
S	-	-	-	1.70

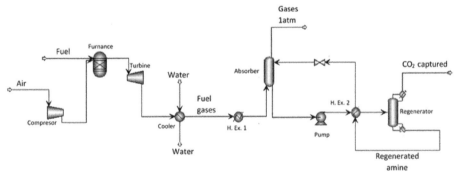

Figure 1. Representation of a thermoelectric power plant and the CO2 capture plant in post-combustion using chemical absorption with monoethanolamine

Because of the components present in the absorption are dissociate, it is necessary to achieve a CO_2 recovery in the gas output stream of the same equipment. In the case of the regenerator, the distillate flow and the reflux ratio were manipulated to capture the greatest amount of CO_2 from the flue gas stream from the thermoelectric plant and thus reduce CO_2 emissions into the atmosphere and the environmental impact that they generate For this reason, in all the cases analyzed, they were standardized to a purity of 99 mol% CO_2 and recovery of at least 95% of CO_2

2. Global Optimization

Once the Aspen Plus simulation is completed, a multi-objective optimization technique is employed having as objective function the minimization of energy requirement as reboiler heat duty. The minimization of this objective was subject to the required recoveries and purities in each product stream (Eq. 6).

$$Min(Q) = f(N_{tn}, N_{fn}, R_m, D_{rf}, F_{rn}) \tag{6}$$

Where N_{tn} is the total number of column stages, N_{fn} is the feed stage in the column, R_m is the reflux ratio, F_{rn} is the distillate/bottoms flux, and D_{cn} is the column diameter. This minimization considered 10 continuous and discrete variables.

To optimize the process route for CO_2 capture, a stochastic optimization method, Differential Evolution with Tabu List (DETL) was used, which has shown being robust to optimize intensified separation systems. This technique works as a combined system between the biological evolution from Differential Evolution technique and the random search method from the Tabu search technique. Sharma & Rangaiah, (2007) showed that the use of some concepts of the metaheuristic tabu could improve the performance of DE algorithm. The implementation of this optimization approach was made using a hybrid platform where the DETL method was coded using Microsoft Excel (ME). Initially, the method proposes a vector which is sent to Aspen Plus by means of dynamic data exchange (DDE). In there the separation process was rigorously simulated. For the optimization of process routes analyzed in this study, the following parameters for DETL method were used: 200 individuals, 500 generations, a tabu list of 50% of total individuals, a tabu radius of 0.0000025, 0.80 and 0.6 for crossover and mutation fractions, respectively.

3. Results

In this section, it is presented the results of the study cases where the operating conditions were varied for both constant fuel flow and energy demand. Both cases were analyzed for four different fuels. It is important to remark that the selection of fuel is very important because it has a direct impact not only on energy production but also on the fuel gas composition that is obtained (Nagy and Misey, 2013). Besides the concentration of the gases obtained will have a direct impact on the energy and solvent requirements used for the CO_2 capture plant. When it is presented the lower concentration of gases the capture efficiency will decrease, then the energy and solvent requirements for the capture will increase.

After the optimization process for reducing energy demand in the capture process, the optimum designs of absorber and desorber colums for Case 1 are presented in Table 2. For Case 2 the columns structure remains close to that obtained in Case 1, the operating parameters, however, shown important differences. The optimum operating parameters for both scenarios are shown in Table 3. For both cases, the CO_2 generated by GJ of energy produced in the power plant (CO_{2GEN}/E_{PP}) is larger when burning mineral coal and biogas than for the natural gasses. This is more noticeable for the scenario in which energy demand is specified, since it is necessary to adjust the feed flows of each fuel in order to reach the specified demand. It is important to highlight that CO_2 concentration in flue gases coming from burning mineral coal and biogas have lower values in the first scenario, but it significantly increases in the second case, which directly influences the capture effectiveness.

The optimum ratios of absorbent to flue gas (L/G), absorbent to CO_2 recovered (L/CO_2 REC) and the reboiler duty to CO_2 recovered (Q_R/CO_2 REC), are reported in Table 2. In Case 1, the largest value for L/CO_2 REC is obtained for the mineral coal, while for the other three fuels this ratio ranges between 13 and 15. The reboiler duty in the regenerator column (desorber) highly depends on the L/G ratio, so the largest requirement is also observed for this fuel. These results dramatically changed in Case 2, as the CO_2 concentration in the flue gas importantly increases, such that the absorbent and energy requirements during CO_2 capture diminishes.

Table 2. Optimal designs for constant fuel flow considering the best 3 fuels

Design Variables	Mineral coal	Biogas	Non associated gas	Associated gas*
Columns Topology				
Stages (Absorbed)	48	20	46	19
Stages (Desorbed)	25	39	37	17
Feed flue gas stage (Absorbed)	48	20	46	19
Feed solvent stage (Absorbed)	1	1	1	1
Feed stage (Desorbed)	3	3	3	3
Operation Specifications				
Top pressure (kPa)	88	88	88	88
Reflux ratio (Absorbed) Reflux	1.103	0.691	0.792	0.794
ratio (Desorbed) Heat duty	0.9006	0.809	0.839	0.796
(Desorbed) (GJ/h)	173.067	126.567	155.224	143.99
Streams mass flow				
Flue gas (kg s^{-1})	267.68	271.055	268.25	268.78
Feed solvent (kg s^{-1})	251	140.49	176.950	161.88

*Associated gas was taken as basis for the initial design

Table 3. Optimization results for all scenarios

Fuel type	CO_2 GEN/E_{PP} (Power plant)	L/G	L/CO_2 REC	Q_R/CO_2 REC
	kg/GJ	kg/kg	kg/kg	GJ/t CO2
Constan fuel in power plant				
Mineral coal	55.25	0.94	27.68	5.30
Biogas	60.13	0.58	13.93	3.09
Non associated gas	42.91	0.68	15.50	3.65
Associated gas	44.84	0.71	13.77	3.02
Constant energy in power plant				
Mineral coal	71.04	0.598	7.812	2.950
Biogas	71.23	1.023	13.524	3.694
Non associated gas	44.24	0.672	13.848	3.214
Associated gas	44.88	0.705	13.773	3.017

Nagy and Misey (2013) found optimum operating parameters for CO_2 capture plants by considering seven fuels and two operating cases (similar to those here considered).After a parametric searching, they reported L/G values ranging between 1 to 4, with Q_R/CO_2 REC close to 4. For the studied cases in this work, L/G ratio took values between 0.58 and 1.023. From the overall results, it is clear that the optimum designs obtained through a global optimization, wherein the column structures are considered, may significantly reduce not only the energy requirement but also the absorbent flowrate. Given the interest in CO_2 capture processes as an alternative to reduce the environmental impact during the generation of electricity, the implementation of this additional objective to the optimization problem may be considered in future works, in order to identify optimum solutions beyond the techno-economic point of view.

4. Conclusions

The implementation of the CO_2 capture process in power plants has been considered so far, the most mature technology to reduce the environmental impact associated with electricity production. Most research efforts in this field have been focused on performing techno-economic analysis and optimizing the energy efficiency of the capture process. There is a clear incentive to analyze the process from a holistic point of view, considering not only the CO_2 capture as a strategy to reduce the negative effects of the power plant but also by identifying new environmental effects due to the implementation of such capture process

References

EIA- U.S. Energy Information Administration - Independent Statistics and Analysis, 2019, "U.S. Energy-Related CO2 Emissions Expected to Rise Slightly in 2018", Remain Flat in 2019, U.S. Energy Information Administration (EIA). Taken from: www.eia.gov/todayinenergy/detail.php?id=34872.

International Energy Agency, 2018, "Electricity Information 2018 overview", International Energy Agency. Taken from: https://www.iea.org/statistics/electricity/

M. F. Hasan, R. C., Baliban, Elia, J. A. and C.A. Floudas, 2012, "Modeling, simulation, and optimization of postcombustion CO2 capture for variable feed concentration and flow rate. 1. Chemical absorption and membrane processes", Industrial & Engineering Chemistry Research, 51, 48, 15642-15664.

S., Sharma, and G.P. Rangaiah, 2013, "An improved multi-objective differential evolution with a termination criterion for optimizing chemical processes", Computers & Chemical Engineering 56, 155-173.

T. Nagy and P. Mizsey, 2013, "Effect of fossil fuels on the parameters of CO2 capture", Environmental science & technology,47, 15, 8948-8954.

Sauro Pierucci, Flavio Manenti, Giulia Bozzano, Davide Manca (Eds.)
Proceedings of the 30th European Symposium on Computer Aided Process Engineering
(ESCAPE30), May 24-27, 2020, Milano, Italy. © 2020 Elsevier B.V. All rights reserved.
http://dx.doi.org/10.1016/B978-0-12-823377-1.50141-5

Deterministic Global Optimization of Multistage Membrane Gas Separation Using Surrogate Models

Marius Hörnschemeyer[a]*, Christian Kunde[b]

[a]*Max Planck Institute for Dynamics of Complex Technical Systems, Sandtorstraße 1, 39106 Magdeburg, Germany*
[b]*Otto von Guericke University Magdeburg, Universitätsplatz 2, 39106 Magdeburg, Germany*
hoernschemeyer@mpi-magdeburg.mpg.de

Abstract

This paper deals with deterministic global optimization of multistage membrane gas separation processes that are described by spatially distributed models. The computational tractability of the optimization problem is improved by approximating the spatially distributed models with data-driven surrogates. The resulting problems are solved globally using BARON/GAMS. The binary separation of a mixture containing CO_2 and CH_4 is considered as a case study for multistage membrane gas separation processes. The influence of the feed composition on the globally optimal multistage configurations is studied.

Keywords: gas permeation, multistage, binary separation, deterministic global optimization, surrogate modeling.

1. Introduction

Selective membranes enable the separation of gas mixtures without energy-intensive phase changes. The product purity and recovery demands for gas separations are often beyond the limits of single stage systems. To overcome these limitations, configurations comprising multiple stages of membrane-based gas separation modules and recycles can be employed (Ismail et al., 2015).

The optimization of such processes typically leads to the solution of nonlinear problems with continuous and discrete variables. Utilizing deterministic global optimization to solve those mixed-integer nonlinear programs (MINLP) avoids suboptimal local solutions that may otherwise result in poor process design decisions. However, the large number of complex nonlinear expressions and the auxiliary variables make detailed models of spatially distributed processes, e. g. based on finite volume discretization, unfavorable for deterministic global optimization.

In this contribution, replacing a spatially distributed model of a membrane module by a data-driven surrogate is studied as an option to trade some model accuracy for better computational tractability of the global optimization. The required data for the surrogate generation is provided by simulation runs with a fully discretized model of the membrane-based separation process. The developed optimization method is demonstrated for the membrane-based removal of CO_2 from biogas. A parameter study is carried out to investigate the influence of the feed composition on the globally optimal configurations of membrane modules. This way, the findings on multistage binary separations in (Kunde and Kienle, 2018) are extended to membrane-based gas separation.

2. Model description

2.1. Spatially distributed model / Membrane module model

The membrane module model describes the purification of a binary gas mixture due to a selective flow through a membrane. A membrane module operating in countercurrent flow pattern is modeled. The feed flow $\dot{N}_\alpha^F$ enters the module and is transported along the membrane surface, while a part of it permeates through the membrane. The remaining gas on the retentate side leaves the module via the retentate flow $\dot{N}_{\alpha,out}^R$. The permeated gas is collected at the permeate side, transported in the opposing direction to the bulk flow at the retentate side and

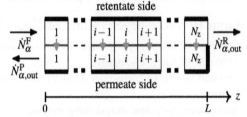

Figure 1: Finite volume discretization of the membrane module with $2N_z$ control volumes.

leaves via the permeate flow $\dot{N}_{\alpha,out}^P$. The permeating flux j_α^m is modeled according to the solution-diffusion-mechanism (Wijmans and Baker, 1995) assuming a constant permeance Q_α of the membrane. The fast permeating gas component A is enriched at the permeate side, while the slow permeating component B is enriched at the retentate side. Acting as a driving force for the flux

$$j_\alpha^m = Q_\alpha(x_\alpha^R P^R - x_\alpha^P P^P), \quad \alpha = A, B \tag{1}$$

the difference in partial pressure between both sides is determined using ideal gas behavior with mole fractions x_α and constant total pressures at retentate side P^R and permeate side P^P. The permeate flow is increased by increasing the membrane area A^m. The opposing bulk flows at retentate and permeate side are assumed to be driven only by advection and ideally mixed except in their flow direction. The bulk flows are modeled using mass balances coupled by the permeating flux j_α^m of Eq. (1).

$$\frac{\partial}{\partial z}\dot{N}_\alpha^R(z) = \frac{-A^m}{L}j_\alpha^m(z), \quad \dot{N}_\alpha^R(z=0) = \dot{N}_\alpha^F$$

$$\frac{\partial}{\partial z}\dot{N}_\alpha^P(z) = \frac{A^m}{L}j_\alpha^m(z), \quad \dot{N}_\alpha^P(z=L) = 0 \tag{2}$$

A numerical solution for the spatially distributed model is obtained by using the finite volume method as shown in Figure 1. Linear concentrations profiles are assumed in each control volume. The first-order upwind scheme is applied to the differential equation system, which is discretized by $N_z = 150$ control volumes for each flow channel, i. e. the retentate side and the permeate side.

2.2. Superstructure model

The superstructure model is adopted from Kunde and Kienle (2018) and allows to optimize cascades as well as a more complex superstructure called network (see Figure 2). Superstructures with membrane modules $s = 1, ..., N_{MO}$ are considered. Both superstructures have one overall feed $\dot{N}_\alpha^{FF}$, an overall retentate outlet $\dot{N}_\alpha^{RR}$, enriched in component B, and an overall permeate outlet $\dot{N}_\alpha^{PP}$, enriched in component A. Each module s has a feed flow $\dot{N}_{\alpha,s}^F$ and two product flows $\dot{N}_{\alpha,s}^R$ and $\dot{N}_{\alpha,s}^P$. No stream splitting is allowed. In the presented case study, minimum product purities x_B^{RR} and x_A^{RR} are required at the overall retentate and permeate outlet.

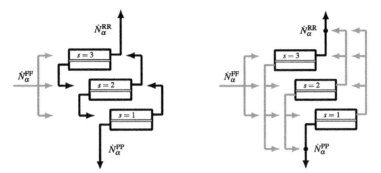

Figure 2: Superstructure models cascade (left) and network (right). Black arrows indicate locked connections and grey arrows potential connections, of which one has to be realized.

2.3. Objective function

As proposed by Kunde and Kienle (2018) a general performance indicator is chosen to serve as an objective function. The permeation effort

$$E_\mathrm{P} = \frac{\sum_{s=1}^{N_\mathrm{MO}} \sum_{\alpha=\mathrm{A,B}} \dot{N}_{\alpha,s}^\mathrm{P}}{\sum_{\alpha=\mathrm{A,B}} \dot{N}_\alpha^\mathrm{FF}} \tag{3}$$

is defined as the ratio of total amount of permeate to overall amount of feed. It is increased by repeated permeation, which requires larger membrane areas and additional gas compression. The permeation effort is therefore also an indicator for economic viability.

3. Surrogate modeling

Data-driven surrogate methods are applied here to obtain surrogates that accurately approximate the original model but require much less computational effort. The original model is treated as a black box with input and output data.

3.1. In- and outputs

In- and output variables are selected from the original model. This determines the properties of the input-output data and thereby affects accuracy and size of the surrogate. Here, we use the feed composition x_A^F and permeate yield Y^P as inputs.

$$x_\mathrm{A}^\mathrm{F} = \frac{\dot{N}_\mathrm{A}^\mathrm{F}}{\sum_{\alpha=\mathrm{A,B}} \dot{N}_\alpha^\mathrm{F}} \qquad\qquad Y^\mathrm{P} = \frac{\sum_{\alpha=\mathrm{A,B}} \dot{N}_\alpha^\mathrm{P}}{\sum_{\alpha=\mathrm{A,B}} \dot{N}_\alpha^\mathrm{F}} \tag{4}$$

At high retentate purities the flux j_α^m permeating through the membrane contains predominantly component B, thus reducing the permeate purity as well as the amount of retentate product. Therefore, combinations of x_A^F and Y^P that lead to a retentate purity well above product specifications are excluded from the data that is used to train the surrogate models. The corresponding input space Ω is defined as

$$\Omega = \left\{ x_\mathrm{A}^\mathrm{F} \in [0,1],\, Y^\mathrm{P} \in [0,1] \mid x_\mathrm{A}^\mathrm{F} \geq \kappa_1 Y^\mathrm{P} + \kappa_2,\, x_\mathrm{A}^\mathrm{F} \geq \kappa_3 Y^\mathrm{P} + \kappa_4 \right\} \tag{5}$$

with linear inequalities that remove most of the undesired input combinations.

The choice of the surrogate output is based on the authors previous evaluation of a number of alternative model formulations. Only the best performing model formulation from this evaluation is presented here. The model equations for each membrane module read

$$
\begin{aligned}
\dot{N}_{\mathrm{B}}^{\mathrm{R}} &= (1 - Y^{\mathrm{P}})^{f(x_{\mathrm{A}}^{\mathrm{F}}, Y^{\mathrm{P}})} \dot{N}_{\mathrm{B}}^{\mathrm{F}}, \\
\dot{N}_{\mathrm{A}}^{\mathrm{P}} &= Y^{\mathrm{P}} (\dot{N}_{\mathrm{A}}^{\mathrm{F}} + \dot{N}_{\mathrm{B}}^{\mathrm{F}}) - \dot{N}_{\mathrm{B}}^{\mathrm{P}}, \\
\dot{N}_{\mathrm{A}}^{\mathrm{F}} &= \dot{N}_{\mathrm{A}}^{\mathrm{R}} + \dot{N}_{\mathrm{B}}^{\mathrm{P}}, \quad \alpha = \mathrm{A}, \mathrm{B}
\end{aligned}
\tag{6}
$$

with values for f obtained from the spatially distributed membrane module model. The mapping f is considered to be the original model and approximated by a surrogate model $\tilde{f}$ that is parameterized with a set of sample points $S = \left\{ \left(\left(x_{\mathrm{A},k}^{\mathrm{F}}, Y_{k}^{\mathrm{P}} \right), f \left(x_{\mathrm{A},k}^{\mathrm{F}}, Y_{k}^{\mathrm{P}} \right) \right) \mid k = 1, ..., N_{\mathrm{S}} \right\}$ generated on a dense grid for the input space Ω.

3.2. Surrogate method

A broad range of data-driven surrogate methods is available in the literature. For noise-free data sets, such as generated by deterministic simulation models, Razavi et al. (2012) recommend interpolation methods. In the work at hand a radial basis function model is chosen. The radial basis function model $\tilde{f}(\mathbf{x})$, with $\mathbf{x} = (x_{\mathrm{A}}^{\mathrm{F}}, Y^{\mathrm{P}})^{\mathrm{T}}$, is constructed as a sum of a trend function $g(\mathbf{x})$ and a weighted sum of radial basis functions $\varphi(\mathbf{x}_{i}, \mathbf{x})$.

$$
\tilde{f}(\mathbf{x}) = g(\mathbf{x}) + \sum_{i=1}^{N_{\mathrm{R}}} w_{i} \varphi(\mathbf{x}_{i}, \mathbf{x})
\tag{7}
$$

The trend function $g(\mathbf{x})$ is calibrated on all sample points $(\mathbf{x}_{k}, f(\mathbf{x}_{k}))$ by least square fitting. The remaining difference between $g(\mathbf{x})$ and $f(\mathbf{x})$ is approximated by the radial basis functions. We choose a linear radial basis function $\varphi(\mathbf{x}_{1}, \mathbf{x}_{2}) = \|\mathbf{x}_{1} - \mathbf{x}_{2}\|$ with a weighted euclidean distance $\| \ \|$. The distance weights are empirically selected to reduce the maximum approximation error over all sample locations $\mathbf{x}_{k}$. The reference points $(\mathbf{x}_{i}, f(\mathbf{x}_{i})), i = 1, ..., N_{\mathrm{R}}$, of the radial basis function model are selected from the set of sample points S by an adaptive greedy sampling method that minimizes the maximum approximation error. In each step of the adaptive algorithm, the weights w_{i} are obtained by solving a linear equation system resulting from the interpolation conditions at the reference points $\tilde{f}(\mathbf{x}_{i}) = f(\mathbf{x}_{i})$.

3.3. Accuracy measures

The accuracy of the surrogate model is evaluated in terms of the errors between the original function f and the surrogate $\tilde{f}$ at all sample locations $\mathbf{x}_{k}$. The maximum approximation error $e_{\max}$ and the mean approximation error e_{mean} are defined as

$$
e_{\max} = \frac{\max\limits_{k} \left| f(\mathbf{x}_{k}) - \tilde{f}(\mathbf{x}_{k}) \right|}{\max\limits_{k} f(\mathbf{x}_{k}) - \min\limits_{k} f(\mathbf{x}_{k})}
\qquad
e_{\mathrm{mean}} = \frac{\frac{1}{N_{\mathrm{S}}} \sum_{k=1}^{N_{\mathrm{S}}} \left| f(\mathbf{x}_{k}) - \tilde{f}(\mathbf{x}_{k}) \right|}{\max\limits_{k} f(\mathbf{x}_{k}) - \min\limits_{k} f(\mathbf{x}_{k})}.
\tag{8}
$$

The error measures $e_{\max}$ and e_{mean} do not account for error propagation to other variables that are important for the overall process. Thus we define additional error measures $e_{\max}^{x_{\mathrm{B}}^{\mathrm{R}}}$, $e_{\max}^{x_{\mathrm{B}}^{\mathrm{P}}}$, $e_{\mathrm{mean}}^{x_{\mathrm{B}}^{\mathrm{R}}}$ and $e_{\mathrm{mean}}^{x_{\mathrm{A}}^{\mathrm{P}}}$ for the product purities by replacing f in Eq. (8) with $x_{\mathrm{B}}^{\mathrm{R}}$ and $x_{\mathrm{A}}^{\mathrm{P}}$, respectively.

4. Results

The present case study considers biogas upgrading as a separation of CO_2 (component A) from CH_4 (component B). Table 2 comprises all parameters and process requirements necessary to generate sample points and to carry out the superstructure optimization. The input space Ω contains 6262 equally spaced sample points, to which an empirically selected trend function is fitted. To keep the computational effort for parameter studies with many optimization runs feasible, we chose $N_R = 50$ reference points. The resulting approximation of the retentate outlet purity for a single module is shown in Figure 3. Table 1 presents the achieved approximation accuracy. Note that errors in process variables, such as the product purities, can be larger than the approximations errors of the surrogate due to error propagation.

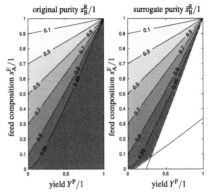

Figure 3: Retentate product purity obtained from the fully discretized model (left) and from the model formulation including $\tilde{f}$ (right). The straight lines indicate the input space restriction.

A parameter study is carried out to investigate the influence of the overall feed composition x_A^{FF} on the minimized permeation effort and corresponding optimal structures. The results are obtained using the solver BARON 15.9.22. (Tawarmalani and Sahinidis, 2005) and the subsolvers CPLEX and CONOPT in GAMS 24.2.1. Options are kept at default values except setting the relative termination tolerance to 1×10^{-3}. Optimizations of the cascade and network superstructure are performed at thirty values of x_A^{FF}. Each superstructure is optimized for 1, 2 and 3 modules. Solution times are in the order of minutes for each run. The lowest permeation efforts E_p achieved by these superstructures are depicted in Figure 4. There, the roman numerals indicate regions of x_A^{FF} that yield different optimal cascades. In region I, a two-staged cascade with a feed at stage $s = 2$ is optimal, whereas in region II, a two-staged cascade with a feed at stage $s = 1$ is optimal. The feed compositions in region III allow a single membrane module to be optimal. The permeation effort of optimal network configurations is significantly lower than that of optimal cascades at feed compositions close to the border between region I and II. These reductions are achieved by a single three-staged configuration, shown in Figure 4. At the feed composition $x_A^{FF} = 0.236$, a maximum relative reduction of 15.9 % between an optimal cascade with $E_p = 0.466$ and the optimal network configuration with $E_p = 0.392$ is observed.

Table 1: Accuracy of the model formulation that includes the surrogate.

error	e_{max}	$e_{max}^{x_B^R}$	$e_{max}^{x_A^P}$	e_{mean}	$e_{mean}^{x_B^R}$	$e_{mean}^{x_A^P}$
value	0.0119	0.0440	0.0105	0.0041	0.0014	0.0018

Table 2: Process parameters and requirements based on (Scholz et al., 2015).

parameter	permeance Q_A	permeance Q_B	retentate pressure P^R	permeate pressure P^P
value	$2.01 \times 10^{-8} \dfrac{mol}{s\,m^2\,Pa}$	$3.35 \times 10^{-10} \dfrac{mol}{s\,m^2\,Pa}$	$16 \times 10^5\,Pa$	$1 \times 10^5\,Pa$
variable	purity retentate x_B^{RR}	purity permeate x_A^{PP}		
domain	$[0.96, 1]$	$[0.96, 1]$		

5. Conclusion

In this contribution, the application of surrogate modeling allows for extensive parameter studies using deterministic global optimization, despite the high computational cost of the original spatially distributed process model. Results of the parameter study strongly suggests that the findings on multistage binary separation in (Kunde and Kienle, 2018) also extend to membrane-based gas separation: In certain parameter regions, countercurrent cascades are suboptimal compared to the alternative structure depicted in Figure 4. These parameter regions are located where the feed position of optimal cascades changes.

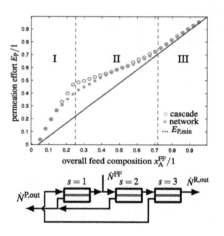

Figure 4: Minimized permeation effort of optimal structures and the theoretical minimum permeation effort $E_{P,min}$, i. e. for $Q_B = 0$, as functions of the feed composition (top). Alternative structure emerging from the network (bottom).

References

A. F. Ismail, K. C. Khulbe, T. Matsuura, 2015. Gas Separation Membranes : Polymeric and Inorganic. Springer International Publishing.

C. Kunde, A. Kienle, 2018. Global optimization of multistage binary separation networks. Chemical Engineering and Processing: Process Intensification 131, 164–177.

S. Razavi, B. A. Tolson, D. H. Burn, 2012. Review of surrogate modeling in water resources. Water Resources Research 48 (7).

M. Scholz, M. Alders, T. Lohaus, M. Wessling, 2015. Structural optimization of membrane-based biogas upgrading processes. Journal of Membrane Science 474 (Supplement C), 1–10.

M. Tawarmalani, N. V. Sahinidis, 2005. A polyhedral branch-and-cut approach to global optimization. Mathematical Programming 103, 225–249.

J. G. Wijmans, R. W. Baker, 1995. The solution-diffusion model: a review. Journal of Membrane Science 107, 1–21

Sauro Pierucci, Flavio Manenti, Giulia Bozzano, Davide Manca (Eds.)
Proceedings of the 30th European Symposium on Computer Aided Process Engineering
(ESCAPE30), May 24-27, 2020, Milano, Italy. © 2020 Elsevier B.V. All rights reserved.
http://dx.doi.org/10.1016/B978-0-12-823377-1.50142-7

An Innovative and Fully Automated System for Gel Electrophoresis

Konstantinos Theodoridis[(a,*)], Fotis Stergiopoulos,[a] Dimitrios Bechtsis,[a] Nikolaos Nikolaidis,[a] Dimitrios Triantafyllidis,[a] Apostolos Tsagaris,[a] Anastasios Filelis,[b] Asterios Papaikonomou,[b]

aInternational Hellenic University (IHU), Department of Industrial Engineering & Management, PO Box 141, Sindos, Thessaloniki, 57400, Greece

bEvresis S.A, DA 12a Block:39b Industrial Area, 57400, Sindos, Thessaloniki
kostastheod82@yahoo.gr

Abstract

Electrophoresis is a standard technique used in medical laboratories and research institutions worldwide, for DNA, RNA and protein analysis. Various methodologies and techniques have been developed over the past decades. The common ground used in all approaches is the separation of molecule particles based on their movement on a substrate under the existence of an electric field. Relevant research is assisted by the advancement of technology and focuses on the development of innovative and fully automated electrophoresis systems that use robotic systems and advanced programming techniques. To this extent, the proposed paper focuses on the presentation of an innovative fully automated electrophoresis system, currently being developed within the framework of a research project funded by the Greek National Programme for Competitiveness Entrepreneurship and Innovation. The system can process multiple protocols of gel electrophoresis, on a precast agarose film, utilizing a combination of hardware and software, with minimal intervention by humans. Healthcare professionals could significantly benefit from this system by obtaining fast and accurate results in a fully automated fashion, by eliminating human errors during the process.

Keywords: automated capillary gel electrophoresis, automated medical machine, prototype design, mechanical equipment

1. Introduction

Electrophoresis has been known for nearly a century, and various electrophoretic techniques have been developed over the decades. The basic principle is based on the separation of proteins, when an electrical field is applied across a compartment, filled with medium of different pH (Aslam et al., 2017). The first fundamental electrophoretic principle for the separation of acids and metals, was introduced as "isotachophoresis" (ITP) or "ion migration method" (Kendall et al., 1923). With the ITP method it was evident that when an electric field is applied, the charged protein components are separated according to the differences in their electrophoretic mobilities. A few years later, Tiselius constructed a U-tube system, that managed to separate two protein components, because of the thermal diffusion and convection phenomenon (Tiselius, 1937). Later on, several studies described ITP as "moving boundary electrophoresis" (Longsworth et al., 1939) or "displacement electrophoresis", and a successful separation of amino acids and proteins like asparate, glutamate, chloride and acetate, was conducted. A widely used type of electrophoresis is Gel Electrophoresis (GE), in which a compartment is filled with a gel medium, usually a natural anticonvective polymer like agarose or on polyacrylamide gel (PAGE). PAGE is used for complex protein analysis that is found in human tissues, cells, or other biological samples. The major advantage of this method is that it separates hundreds to thousands proteins located in a single gel (Magdeldin et al., 2014). Polyacrylamide gel is made up of chains of acrylamide monomers that are cross linked with N, also commonly known as "bis". The concentration of "bis" determines the pore size of the polyacrylamide gel (Holmes et al., 1991).

Another established electrophoresis method is Capillary Electrophoresis (CE), which usually takes place within a glass tube (Vesterberg, 1989), filled with a simple buffered aqueous electrolytes solution (FSCE) (Altria et al., 2006). It provides efficient separation analysis within a certain time window, low consumption of chemicals and limited operational and maintenance procedures (Jarvas et al., 2020). This method gained a lot of popularity especially in the pharmaceuticals industry. CE can be used for determining drug-related impurities, physicochemical measurements of drug molecules, counter-ion analysis for drug discovery and the separation of drug enantiomers.

Development of the CE led to more efficient systems, like the microchip electrophoresis (Durney et al., 2015; Jarvas, Guttman et al., 2020; Lacher et al., 2001; Masár et al., 2020). The microchip system provides a fast and effective analysis as it contains various microchannels that are made of glass and/or fused silica substrates with optimal thermal characteristics. The advantages of CE provided the opportunity to researchers to develop reliable, fast and economic fully automated systems (Bodnar et al., 2016) or semi-automated portable devices (Nguyen et al., 2014).

Nowadays, in the pharmaceutical industry, ongoing research focuses on the development of innovative and automated medical devices. Electrophoresis automated devices can execute analytical protocols with high precision, low operational costs and shorter delivery times. To this extend, our research team, has focused on fabricating an innovative and fully automated electrophoresis system, based on capillary gel electrophoresis. A user-friendly machine that efficiently carries out various kinds of electrophoresis (protein, haemoglobin, lipoprotein, immunoelectrohoresis, DNA/RNA) on precast agarose films has been successfully designed and manufactured as a prototype. The system uses state of the art information and automation technology methods together with ergonomic design characteristics.

2. Electrophoresis main components

The study of the prototype's design was based on commercial agarose precast films and commercial blood tubes, with standard dimensions. The agarose film's dimensions are 102x69 mm and can contain up to thirty blood deposits (samples), using a layout pattern of three columns by ten rows. Emphasis was given on designing quality moving mechanisms and smart automation systems for the final device. The overall assembly of the electrophoresis system is illustrated in figure 1, including the following subsystems, referred to thereafter as mechanical components: (i) tube drawer system, (ii) bar code scanner, (iii) wash tank, (iv) robotic arm/gripper, (v) sample carrier, (vi) electrophoresis chamber, (vii) frame/film manipulator, (viii) staining-unstaining chamber, (ix) drying chamber, (x) camera analysis chamber.

In addition, the proposed electrophoresis system will also include embedded computer systems, microcontrollers and microprocessors, a sophisticated software that can run multiple electrophoretic procedures, a user-friendly interface and a customized power-supply system. This manuscript is focusing on the product design characteristics and thus extensively discussing the mechanical components, their functionalities and the developed processes.

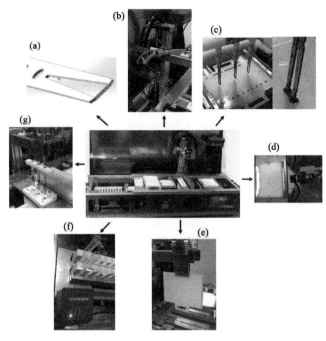

Figure 1, Automated Electrophoresis Machine layout. Design of the (a) V-shaped 316-SS finish, (b) screw drive mechanism of the robotic arm/gripper, (c) deposit of stained sample on the agarose film, (d) camera/analysis chamber, (e) gripper and film/frame manipulator, (f) sample tubes inside the drawer system and barcode scanner, (g) sample carrier and wash tank

2.1. Tube drawer system

The "tube drawer system" consists of three (3) drawers, each containing ten (10) positions for sample tubes. They were manufactured from polypropylene (PP) on a SLS 3D-printer (fig.1, f). These drawers are guided throughout aluminium profiles of shape type I and II, with specific tolerance-based dimensions. Each drawer has a hole underneath it, in order to allow a solenoid rod to engage and/or disengage automatically. The solenoids are mounted on a galvanized metal base and the whole base is fixed onto a rack which is driven by a belt drive system.

2.2. Electrophoresis chamber

The "electrophoresis chamber" subsystem was fabricated out of polypropylene (PP) by a CNC machine, and contains two opposite deeper compartments. On both compartments, two platinum electrodes were installed at the bottom edges, to apply the corresponding voltage. The internal design of the chamber has the appropriate shape dimensions allowing for a slight bending of the "frame/film manipulator". This task is accomplished by a cam-shaft mechanism that delivers a small force to the lid of the chamber which is fixed on coil springs. Furthermore, during electrophoretic processes, the film must have a steady state temperature of 20°C regardless of the outside ambient temperature. For this reason, a peltier sensor, two temperature sensors and a small fan were installed. The small fan was placed on the top surface of the lid, which has the appropriate openings for a straightforward airflow.

2.3. Main drive mechanism, robotic arm/gripper

The main drive system is the "robotic arm" and its guide rails were installed in parallel to the longitudinal X-axis of the system. The arm slides and moves by a belt drive system.

It also moves on the Z axis by a screw-drive system (fig.1, b). The gripping system, consists of two specially designed aluminium profiles that engage/disengage by a solenoid mechanism. The gripper is used to manipulate both the "frame/film manipulator" and the "sample carrier".

2.4. Chambers for the completion of the electrophoresis procedure

The "wash tank" with its lid was designed and fabricated with polypropylene (PP) material on a SLS 3D-printer. The lid consists of two rows by three holes each. This container is filled up with ethanol-based liquid and serves to wash the "sample carrier" and as a rest position for the "sample carrier", (fig.1, g).

Staining–unstaining chamber with its lid was also fabricated with polypropylene (PP) material on a SLS 3D-printer. Inside the chamber, an inner wall was built in, to separate it on two different compartments for staining and unstaining media.

The drying chamber was CNC machined out of aluminium. On the inner side of the chamber and along its perimeter, a thermal resistance was installed and covered with thermal isolation material. This system was built to work using the simple process of an oven.

The camera/analysis chamber and its lid were also designed and fabricated with polypropylene (PP) material on a SLS 3D-printer. A high-resolution camera is used to capture a clear photo of the film. For this reason, at the opposite side of the film's place, a 28mm diameter hole was opened to ensure that the camera can work properly. In addition, underneath the lid, two led tapes were installed for providing adequate light at the inner side of the chamber (fig.1, d).

3. System's operational principles

After designing the above described components and taking into consideration several dimension restrictions and requirements, it was decided to perform all movements along the "X" and "Z" axes. The machine operation starts over when the user places the agarose film into the "frame/film manipulator". Then it rotates 90° counter clockwise (CCW), by its vertical axis in to the horizontal position and stays still (standby position), as shown in figure 1, c.

The drawers of the "tube drawers' system, are exported instantaneously with the help of the solenoid mechanisms, and the operator/user places up to thirty (30) sample tubes. These tubes, have already a barcode tape on them which has been placed manually by the user, to distinguish each sample. Thereafter, each drawer is automatically inserted individually allowing for scanning and storing the data of the tubes, using a barcode scanner system.

The "sample carrier" has a custom designed V-shaped 316L-SS finish with a small opening and it is fixed on rods made of polypropylene PP (fig.1, a, c). Two sample carriers were fabricated and placed into the "wash tank" that is also used as a resting point. As soon as all the tubes are placed inside the drawer system, the "robotic arm/gripper" grabs the first of the two sample carriers, lifts it up and drags it to a predefined distance along the X axis and towards the first row of the tubes. Then it sinks inside the tubes, and a quantity of the stained medium (~1.2μl/rod) is entrapped inside the small opening. Simultaneously, the "sample carrier" moves backwards and stops above the agarose film. Then it moves downwards, until it touches the agarose film, and the stained medium is left on the film's surface, due to the surface tension (fig.1, c). After that the "robotic arm" returns the first "sample carrier" to its initial position ("wash tank") to be washed out, until it is ready to be used again. Immediately, the "robotic arm" grabs the second "sample carrier" and the same process is repeated until all the samples are safely deposited on the film.

After automatically depositing all samples (up to 30), the "robotic arm" grabs and pushes the "frame/film manipulator" inside the "electrophoresis chamber". The chamber is filled up with electrolyte buffer. The cam-shaft mechanism applies a small force to the lid which in turn compresses the edges of the "frame/film manipulator", and the film's edges are slightly immersed into the electrolyte buffer. Depending on time and voltage settings, the electrophoretic process starts until all the appropriate molecules are separated (fig.2, a). After the electrophoretic separation, the force described above is released, and the "robotic arm" returns the "frame/film manipulator" to its initial position.

The staining/unstaining, drying of the film and the analysis of the samples are procedures of major significance during an electrophoresis process. These procedures can be accomplished inside the shaped chambers described above. The robotic arm moves the "frame/film manipulator" towards X axis, from one box to the other, with the following order: to the "staining-unstaining" box and then to the "drying" box at specific time intervals. Afterwards, the "frame/film manipulator" ends up inside the camera/analysis box for a clear photo of the film by a CMOS camera and a CCTV lens. Eventually, the robotic arm returns the "frame/film manipulator" to its home position and the user pulls out the agarose film.

4. Results of the pilot testing

Based on the above operational process, our effort was to test the reliability of the sample carrier and the electrophoresis chamber. For this pilot experiment the tubes were filled with experimental stained medium (approximately of the same viscosity as of the blood). The "sample carrier" was successfully entrapped and deposited the appropriate quantity of the stained medium on the agarose film. The stained film inserted inside the electrophoresis chamber, where 100Volts were applied for a period of 15 minutes, resulting to the accomplishment of molecular separation of the stained medium. To analyze the results, a picture of the agarose film is captured from the high-resolution CMOS camera kit (fig.1, d), The final photo of the film, were further analysed, and a histogram plot with fraction analysis is illustrated in figure 2, b.

5. Conclusions

A prototype automated electrophoresis system, that can execute electrophoresis processes on precast gel agarose films, has been designed and manufactured. As a next step, the robustness of the machine has been evaluated by executing a full electrophoresis process involving a protein analysis. From the results acquired, the mechanical integrity of the main components of the system has been confirmed. In addition, the full automated electrophoretic process, provides accurate results and minimizes delivery times. The developed prototype system constitutes a major progress as regards to the development of state of the art fully automated electrophoresis systems. Further work in the future will

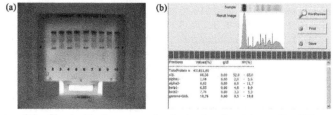

Figure 2, Photo of the film inside the camera/analysis chamber (a), results of the protein analysis (b)

focus on the optimisation of the design in terms of mechanical and electronic design.

Funding

This research has been co-financed by the European Regional Development Fund of the European Union and Greek national funds through the Operational Program Competitiveness, Entrepreneurship and Innovation, under the call RESEARCH–CREATE–INNOVATE (project code: T1EDK-02403)

References

Altria, K., Marsh, A., & Sänger-van de Griend, C. (2006). Capillary electrophoresis for the analysis of small-molecule pharmaceuticals. *ELECTROPHORESIS, 27*(12), 2263-2282. doi: 10.1002/elps.200600030

Aslam, B., Basit, M., Nisar, M. A., Khurshid, M., & Rasool, M. H. (2017). Proteomics: Technologies and Their Applications. *Journal of Chromatographic Science, 55*(2), 182-196. doi: 10.1093/chromsci/bmw167

Bodnar, J., Hajba, L., & Guttman, A. (2016). A fully automated linear polyacrylamide coating and regeneration method for capillary electrophoresis of proteins. *ELECTROPHORESIS, 37*(23-24), 3154-3159. doi: 10.1002/elps.201600405

Durney, B. C., Crihfield, C. L., & Holland, L. A. (2015). Capillary electrophoresis applied to DNA: determining and harnessing sequence and structure to advance bioanalyses (2009–2014). *Analytical and Bioanalytical Chemistry, 407*(23), 6923-6938. doi: 10.1007/s00216-015-8703-5

Holmes, D. L., & Stellwagen, N. C. (1991). Estimation of polyacrylamide gel pore size from Ferguson plots of normal and anomalously migrating DNA fragments. I. Gels containing 3 % N, N′-methylenebisacrylamide. *ELECTROPHORESIS, 12*(4), 253-263. doi: 10.1002/elps.1150120405

Jarvas, G., Guttman, A., Miękus, N., Bączek, T., Jeong, S., Chung, D. S., Pätoprstý, V., Masár, M., Hutta, M., Datinská, V., & Foret, F. (2020). Practical sample pretreatment techniques coupled with capillary electrophoresis for real samples in complex matrices. *TrAC Trends in Analytical Chemistry, 122*, 115702. doi: https://doi.org/10.1016/j.trac.2019.115702

Kendall, J., & Crittenden, E. D. (1923). The Separation of Isotopes. *Proc Natl Acad Sci U S A, 9*(3), 75-78. doi: 10.1073/pnas.9.3.75

Lacher, N. A., Garrison, K. E., Martin, R. S., & Lunte, S. M. (2001). Microchip capillary electrophoresis/ electrochemistry. *ELECTROPHORESIS, 22*(12), 2526-2536. doi: 10.1002/1522-2683(200107)22:12<2526::aid-elps2526>3.0.co;2-k

Longsworth, L. G., Shedlovsky, T., & MacInnes, D. A. (1939). ELECTROPHORETIC PATTERNS OF NORMAL AND PATHOLOGICAL HUMAN BLOOD SERUM AND PLASMA. *The Journal of Experimental Medicine, 70*(4), 399-413. doi: 10.1084/jem.70.4.399

Magdeldin, S., Enany, S., Yoshida, Y., Xu, B., Zhang, Y., Zureena, Z., Lokamani, I., Yaoita, E., & Yamamoto, T. (2014). Basics and recent advances of two dimensional- polyacrylamide gel electrophoresis. *Clinical Proteomics, 11*(1), 16. doi: 10.1186/1559-0275-11-16

Masár, M., Hradski, J., Nováková, M., Szucs, R., Sabo, M., & Matejčík, Š. (2020). Online coupling of microchip electrophoresis with ion mobility spectrometry for direct analysis of complex liquid samples. *Sensors and Actuators B: Chemical, 302*, 127183. doi: https://doi.org/10.1016/j.snb.2019.127183

Nguyen, T. A., Pham, T. N., Doan, T. T., Ta, T. T., Saiz, J., Nguyen, T. Q., Hauser, P. C., & Mai, T. D. (2014). Simple semi-automated portable capillary electrophoresis instrument with contactless conductivity detection for the determination of beta-agonists in pharmaceutical and pig-feed samples. *J Chromatogr A, 1360*, 305-311. doi: 10.1016/j.chroma.2014.07.074

Tiselius, A. (1937). A new apparatus for electrophoretic analysis of colloidal mixtures. *Transactions of the Faraday Society, 33*(0), 524-531. doi: 10.1039/TF9373300524

Vesterberg, O. (1989). History of electrophoretic methods. *Journal of Chromatography A, 480*, 3-19. doi: https://doi.org/10.1016/S0021-9673(01)84276-X

Sauro Pierucci, Flavio Manenti, Giulia Bozzano, Davide Manca (Eds.)
Proceedings of the 30th European Symposium on Computer Aided Process Engineering
(ESCAPE30), May 24-27, 2020, Milano, Italy. © 2020 Elsevier B.V. All rights reserved.
http://dx.doi.org/10.1016/B978-0-12-823377-1.50143-9

Integrated Design of Process Configuration and Scheduling for Hydrogen Peroxide Decontamination in Biopharmaceutical Injectable Manufacturing

Keisho Yabuta[a], Haruka Futamura[b], Koji Kawasaki[b], Hirokazu Sugiyama[a,*]

[a]*Department of Chemical System Engineering, The University of Tokyo, 7-3-1, Hongo, Bunkyo-ku, 113-8656, Tokyo, Japan*

[b]*Airex Co., Ltd., 14-13, Tsubaki-cho, Nakamura-ku, Nagoya-shi, 453-0015, Aichi, Japan*

sugiyama@chemsys.t.u-tokyo.ac.jp

Abstract

We present integrated process design and scheduling for hydrogen peroxide decontamination, a time-intensive change-over in biopharmaceutical injectable manufacturing. Models were developed that can (i) configure process parameters, e.g., loading amount of hydrogen peroxide in the isolator, and (ii) deal with the scheduling of filling and change-over of multiple batches/products under shift- and weekend-constraints. Sterility assurance level (SAL) of products and the required time for producing all batches were defined as the objective functions for quality and productivity, respectively. The models were applied to multiobjective optimization of process configuration and scheduling for producing 15 batches consisting of different product numbers, characteristics, and batch sizes. Pareto optimal solutions could be obtained that minimized both objectives. The trade-off became more significant when the product became more vulnerable to the residual hydrogen peroxide after decontamination and the product change-over became more frequent, which is the trend in the industry. Thus, the study motivates collaborative design of process and scheduling for the decontamination process in biopharmaceutical manufacturing.

Keywords: biopharmaceuticals, sterile manufacturing, multiobjective design, change-over, process performance

1. Introduction

In recent years, the number of approval for biopharmaceuticals, e.g., monoclonal antibodies, has increased drastically (Grilo and Mantalaris, 2019). Biopharmaceuticals are provided as injectables, and are produced batch-wise in a sterile environment such as isolator. Among various change-over operations between batches/products, decontamination of isolators is known as time-consuming. Because hydrogen peroxide (H_2O_2) is typically used as a decontaminant, the residual has a potential to oxidize the protein-based products. Figure 1 shows the typical H_2O_2 concentration profile. In the decontamination phase, the concentration increases up to 400 ppm by loading vaporized H_2O_2 into the isolator. In the aeration phase, the concentration is decreased down to a target concentration by ventilation. The process configuration, e.g., H_2O_2 loading amount, influences the level of the sterility assurance and the total time required.

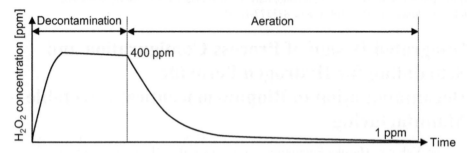

Figure 1. Typical concentration profile of vapor H2O2 in decontamination process (adapted from Yabuta et al., 2018b)

Radl et al. (2009, 2011) presented mechanistic models for describing distribution of H_2O_2 in the isolator considering condensation and absorption. Vuylsteke et al. (2019) developed a mechanistic model for predicting the concentration of H_2O_2 in the product filled after decontamination. We constructed a regression-based model, by progressively expanding the functionality to determine optimal configuration regarding rapidity and sterility (Yabuta et al., 2018a and 2018b). However, these previous studies have been focusing on one-time execution of the process, without considering the scheduling aspect. Thus in this work, we present a novel approach for designing H_2O_2 decontamination processes by integrating parameter configuration and scheduling. The work presents the model development and a case study on multiobjective optimization.

2. Method

2.1. Overview

Figure 2 shows task flow chart for sterile drug product manufacturing. Each task has a task ID j from one to seven. Production begins with the conditioning of temperature and humidity in the isolator. Decontamination and aeration are performed sequentially (see Figure 1), and then products are filled. If the next batch is not scheduled, the production ends. Otherwise, cleaning in place (CIP) is conducted for the manufacturing equipment, which is followed by format change if necessary, e.g., if the product of the next batch has a different vial size. If there is an interruption in the time line, e.g., weekend, the next batch is scheduled to a later time, e.g., Monday.

Two indicators are defined for evaluating the impact of the decision-making regarding process configuration and scheduling on productivity and product quality. One is the total time, T [h], required for producing the planned batches; the other is sterility assurance level, SAL [–]. SAL is the probability that a surviving microorganism exists in the product. Smaller values of SAL indicate lower probability, and thus are favorable for the product quality.

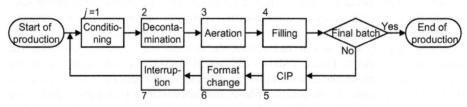

Figure 2. Task flow chart for sterile drug product manufacturing

2.2. Scheduling model

The scheduling model produces *T* as the objective function of productivity, by summing the durations of all tasks:

$$T = \sum_{n=1}^{nmax} \sum_{j=1}^{jmax} \tau_{n.j} \tag{1}$$

where *nmax*, *n*, *jmax*, *j*, and $\tau_{n.j}$ [h] are the total number of batches to be manufactured, the batch number, the total number of tasks, the task ID, and the duration of task *j* of batch *n*, respectively. The durations of decontamination and aeration ($\tau_{n,2}$ and $\tau_{n,3}$) are calculated by the decontamination process model explained in section 2.3. Constant values were used for the durations of conditioning, CIP, format change, and interruptions (defined as $\tau_{n,1}$, $\tau_{n,5}$, $\tau_{n,6}$, and $\tau_{n,7}$, respectively). The duration of filling, $\tau_{n,4}$, was converted from the batch size, q_n [vial batch^{-1}], as follows:

$$\tau_{n,4} = N \frac{q_n}{r_{\text{filling}}} \tag{2}$$

where *N* [–] and r_{filling} [vial h^{-1}] are the number of filling needles in the filling machine and filling rate, respectively.

Two types of input parameters are necessary for calculating *T*: product-related information and calendar information. Product-related information further consists of a set of batches and the target concentration of aeration. A set of batches is the list of batches to be manufactured, and is used for generating scheduling options by rearranging the production orders based on permutations with repetition. Each batch has information of product type, p_n [–], batch size, q_n, and target concentration, *c* [ppm]. Product type is used to judge the necessity of format change, i.e., format change is not conducted if p_{n+1} is equal to p_n. The target concentration represents the resistance of the product to oxidation by H_2O_2. While the current standard value is in the neighborhood of 1 ppm, a stricter value would be required for more sensitive products. As for calendar information, a set of days is used. Here, binary parameters distinguish the operation day and the non-operation day, i.e., interruption.

The basic tasks in Figure 2, namely, filling, CIP, format change, and interruption in scheduling, are defined with referring to Eberle et al. (2016). We newly added the durations of conditioning, decontamination, and aeration in this work to highlight more of the decontamination process.

2.3. Decontamination process model

Decontamination process model calculates the durations of decontamination, $\tau_{n,2}$, and aeration, $\tau_{n,3}$, as a part of the productivity objective *T*. Also, the model yields *SAL* as the product quality objective. The key variables of decontamination process are the injection rate of H_2O_2aq, x_i [g min^{-1} m^{-3}], and the target concentration, *c*, in aeration. Typically, the injection rate has stepwise values of x_1 and x_2 with the corresponding time spans of t_{d1} [min] and t_{d2} [min]. The models presented in our previous work (Yabuta et al., 2018b) have been modified to fit to the purpose of the current study:

$$SAL = 10^{6 - \frac{t_{d1} + t_{d2}}{3.71 - 1.72 x_1}} \tag{3}$$

$$\tau_{n,2} = \frac{t_{d1} + t_{d2}}{60} \tag{4}$$

$$\tau_{n,3} = \begin{cases} \dfrac{-24.2 + 1.39(x_1 t_{d1} + x_2 t_{d2}) + 0.765 H_0}{60} & \text{if } c = 1 \text{ ppm} \\ \dfrac{25.7 + 2.93(x_1 t_{d1} + x_2 t_{d2})}{60} & \text{if } c = 0.2 \text{ ppm} \end{cases} \tag{5}$$

where H_0 [%] is the relative humidity at the start of decontamination. These regression-based models were developed with experimental results using a medium-size isolator with the volume of 2.4 m³. Decontamination options can be generated by changing the value of the injection rate x_1.

3. Case study

The models were applied to two design cases where 15 batches consisting of different product characteristics are produced. The design problem is:

$$\begin{cases} \min_d SAL(d) \\ \min_{s,d} T(s,d) \end{cases} \tag{6}$$

where d and s are the options of decontamination and scheduling, respectively. Table 1 shows the summary of the input information in the two cases. Case 1 corresponds to small product variety with large scale production, and Case 2 to wide product variety with small scale production, i.e., the future industrial trend. The target concentration set as 1 ppm in Case 1 was reduced to 0.2 ppm in Case 2, to simulate future products that are more vulnerable to the residual H_2O_2. The numbers of the generated scheduling options for Cases 1 and 2 were 3,003 and 6,306,300, respectively. The durations of conditioning, CIP, format change, and interruption ($\tau_{n,1}$, $\tau_{n,5}$, $\tau_{n,6}$, and $\tau_{n,7}$) were set as 0.5, 3, 2, and 48 h, respectively. As for decontamination, 10 options were set by raising the value of x_1 from 1.1 to 1.4 linearly. The filling machine was assumed to have six filling needles with the filling rate of 3,000 vial h⁻¹ inside a 2.4 m³ isolator. Calendar information was defined as the iteration of five operation days and two non-operation days. The operation time in one week was from 0:00 a.m. on Monday (starting point of T) to 12:00 p.m. on Friday with three shifts.

Figure 3 shows the multiobjective evaluation result of Cases 1 and 2. Each marker shows one combination of the scheduling and decontamination options. The scattering of the markers in the horizontal direction is caused by the decontamination options, and that in the vertical direction is caused by the scheduling options. The maximum vertical range was ca. 40 h. The worst points were the options with many format changes.

Table 1. Summary of input information in Cases 1 and 2

	Case 1	Case 2
Total number of batches to be manufactured, $nmax$ [–]	15	15
Average batch size, $\overline{q_n}$ [vial]	20,667	14,933
Number of product types [–]	2	4
Target concentration in aeration, c [ppm]	1	0.2
Total number of scheduling options [–]	3,003	6,306,300

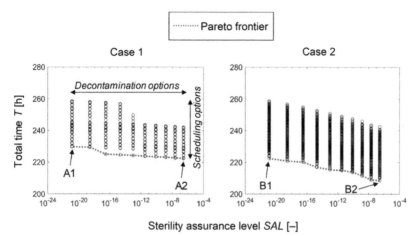

Figure 3. Multiobjective evaluation result

The Pareto frontier is indicated with the dotted line. In both results, the trade-off between SAL and T was observed, which became more significant in Case 2.

Figure 4 shows the breakdown of T at the points of A2 and B1 on the Pareto frontier in Figure 3. For simplification, conditioning, CIP, and format change were summarized as "other change-over". The values of T at A2 and B1 were almost the same (ca. 222.4 h) while the values of SAL were different (ca. 10^{-6} and 10^{-21}, respectively). The difference in the breakdown of A2 and B1 is in aeration and filling. The contribution of aeration drastically increased from 4.1 % to 16 % while that of filling decreased from 46 % to 34 %.

In order to assess the impact of the choice of the scheduling and decontamination options on the Pareto frontier, ratio r was defined as follows:

$$r = \frac{T_1 - T_2}{T_1} \tag{7}$$

where T_1 and T_2 are the leftmost and the shortest T (point A1 and B1 in Figure 3), and the rightmost and the shortest T (point A2 and B2), respectively. From Case 1 to Case 2, the ratio doubled from 3.2 % to 6.2 %. This result clearly indicates the increasing importance of decontamination in case of (i) strict target concentration, (ii) small batch sizes, and (iii) large number of products. These characteristics are exactly the trend in the biopharmaceutical manufacturing, and thus, integrated design approach of scheduling and decontamination will become more useful.

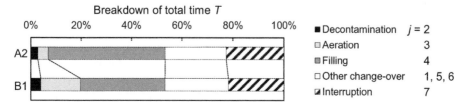

Figure 4. Breakdown of T at two points

The CPU time to obtain the results of Case 2, i.e., evaluating ca. 6 million generated options, was 343 s on Matlab® with parallel computing toolbox™ using 6 physical cores of Intel® Core™ i7-8700CPU@3.2GHz with 64.0 GB RAM.

4. Conclusions and outlook

We presented a novel approach for designing H_2O_2 decontamination processes by integrating parameter configuration and scheduling. Models were developed that can configure process parameters and deal with the scheduling of filling and change-over of multiple batches/products. SAL of products and the required time for producing all batches were defined as the objective functions for quality and productivity, respectively. Multiobjective evaluation was performed for two design cases with varying product numbers, characteristics, and batch sizes. Pareto optimal solutions could be obtained that minimized both objectives. The shift of the Pareto frontier was assessed, which indicated the increasing importance of decontamination in case of (i) strict target concentration, (ii) small batch sizes, and (iii) large number of products. This is exactly the trend in the biopharmaceutical industry, and thus, the work motivates collaborative design of process and scheduling for H_2O_2 decontamination in biopharmaceutical manufacturing. For future, more rigorous investigation of the decontamination process will be required, e.g., debottlenecking of aeration by effective removal of H_2O_2. Hybrid modelling would be effective to tackle complicated and dynamic phenomena during the entire process.

Acknowledgements

The authors would like to thank the experts from Airex Co., Ltd. for the contribution in the fruitful discussions. Financial supports by Grant-in-Aid for Young Scientists (A) No. 17H04964 as well as Grant-in-Aid for Research Fellow (DC2) No. 19J14085 from Japan Society for the Promotion of Science are also acknowledged.

References

L. Eberle, E. Capón-García, H. Sugiyama, A. Graser, R. Schmidt, K. Hungerbühler, 2016. Rigorous approach to scheduling of sterile drug product manufacturing, *Comput. Chem. Eng.*, 94, 221–234

A. Grilo and A. Mantalaris, 2019. The increasingly human and profitable monoclonal antibody market, *Trends Biotechnol.*, 37, 9–16

S. Radl, S. Ortner, R. Sungkorn, J. G. Khinast, 2009. The engineering of hydrogen peroxide decontamination systems, *J. Pharm. Innov.*, 4, 51–62

S. Radl, S. Larisegger, D. Suzzi, J. G. Khinast, 2011. Quantifying absorption effects during hydrogen peroxide decontamination, *J. Pharm. Innov.*, 6, 202–216

B. Vuylsteke, I. Luyckx, G. de Lannoy, 2019. The diffusion of hydrogen peroxide into the liquid product during filling operations inside vaporous hydrogen peroxide–sterilized isolators can be predicted by a mechanistic model, *J. Pharm. Sci.*, 108, 2527–2533

K. Yabuta, H. Futamura, K. Kawasaki, M. Hirao, H. Sugiyama, 2018a. Models for designing hydrogen peroxide decontamination processes in sterile drug product manufacturing, *Comput. Aided Chem. Eng.*, 43, 1613–1618

K. Yabuta, H. Futamura, K. Kawasaki, M. Hirao, H. Sugiyama, 2018b. Design-oriented regression models for H_2O_2 decontamination processes in sterile drug product manufacturing considering rapidity and sterility, *Int. J. Pharm.*, 548, 466–473

Sauro Pierucci, Flavio Manenti, Giulia Bozzano, Davide Manca (Eds.)
Proceedings of the 30th European Symposium on Computer Aided Process Engineering
(ESCAPE30), May 24-27, 2020, Milano, Italy. © 2020 Elsevier B.V. All rights reserved.
http://dx.doi.org/10.1016/B978-0-12-823377-1.50144-0

Social Life Cycle Assessment of Pulp and Paper Production – A Portuguese Case Study

Andreia Santos[a,*], Catherine Benoît Norris[b], Ana Barbosa-Póvoa[a],
Ana Carvalho[a]

[a]CEG-IST, Av. Rovisco Pais 1, Lisbon 1049-001, Portugal
[b]NewEarth B, Lois Ln, York, Maine 03909, United States of America
andreia.d.santos@tecnico.ulisboa.pt

Abstract

Due to its size and intense use of resources, the pulp and paper industry is responsible for many devastating environmental impacts such as carbon pollution and wildlife species' extinction. While these environmental impacts have been investigated in numerous studies through environmental life cycle assessment, little attention has been given to the equally devastating social impacts. For this reason, the main goal of this work is to carry out a social life cycle assessment (S-LCA) to quantify the social impacts that a Portuguese pulp and paper supply chain has on its stakeholders. These impacts are aggregated into five different social categories, including labor rights and decent work, community infrastructure, governance, health and safety, and human rights. In this work, data extracted from the Social Hotspots Database accessed through SimaPro will be used. The results of the S-LCA conducted will be discussed to identify which part of the pulp and paper supply chain is responsible for most of the social impacts and which of these impacts are more critical. Based on this discussion, recommendations for improving the social sustainability of the supply chain analyzed will be provided.

Keywords: Social life cycle assessment, Social Hotspot Database, Supply chain, Paper production, Social hotspots

1. Introduction

As one of the largest industrial sectors in the world, the pulp and paper industry is responsible for the intense use of resources, including the consumption of over 40 percent of all industrial wood traded globally. Furthermore, this industry is one of the world's most energy-intensive industries and the single largest consumer of water used in industrial activities in developed countries (WWF, 2019). This intense use of resources, along with unsustainable operations such as discharging pollutants in surrounding water bodies, makes the pulp and paper industry responsible for many devastating environmental impacts. These environmental impacts have been investigated in different studies using the environmental life cycle assessment (E-LCA) methodology including a study by Silva et al. where the environmental impacts associated with offset paper production in Brazil were estimated (Silva, et al., 2015); the work by Santos et al. where the environmental impacts associated with the life cycle of different products, such as tissue paper, produced in Portugal were assessed (Santos, et al., 2018); and the study by Corcelli et al. where an environmental assessment of papermaking from chemical pulp in Finland was conducted (Corcelli, et al., 2018). Besides the environmental impacts, the pulp and paper industry is also responsible for equally devastating social impacts (WWF, 2019). However, contrary to the environmental impacts, little attention has been given to the social impacts of this industry. Thus, the objective of this paper is to analyze the social impacts associated with the pulp and paper industry using the Portuguese printing and writing paper supply chain as an illustrative case study due to the relevance of this industrial sector in the Portuguese economy. In Portugal, the pulp and paper industry is responsible for 4 % of the gross value added generated by the manufacturing industry, 0.45 % of the gross domestic product, and 4.5 % of all exports (DGAE, 2017). The social impact will be analyzed using the social life cycle assessment (S-LCA) methodology to complement the existing E-LCA of the paper supply chain. The S-LCA will be implemented through the Social Hotspots Database (SHDB) in SimaPro. The remaining of this paper is organized into four sections. In Section 2, the S-LCA methodology and its application through the SHDB are described. In the following sections, the case study is presented (Section 3), and the results of applying the S-LCA methodology through the SHDB to the case study are discussed (Section 4). Finally, in Section 5, the main conclusions and some suggestions for future research are provided.

2. Methodology

Social life cycle assessment is a methodology mostly used to assess the potential social impacts of products along their life cycle from raw materials' extraction to final products' disposal (UNEP/SETAC, 2009). This methodology is similar to the environmental life cycle assessment methodology as both follow the ISO 14040 framework (ISO, 2006). Thus, S-LCA is comprised of four steps (Garrido, 2017):

<u>Goal and Scope Definition</u> – where the main objectives of the study, the functional unit, and the boundary of the product system are defined. The functional unit is a representative element of the system being study and provides a point of reference to quantify the magnitude of the social impacts associated with the product considered.

<u>Inventory Analysis</u> – consists of the collection of data using different indicators through questionnaires, literature review, and/or databases. The Social Hotspots Database is a database developed specifically for the purposes of supporting S-LCA. This database has generic social data for 160 indicators at country and sector levels based on statistics and information issued by governments and international organizations such as the World Health Organization.

<u>Impact Assessment</u> – the social data gathered in the previous step is converted into potential social impacts (named "impact subcategories"). Most S-LCA studies (Wu, et al., 2014) accomplished this by comparing the social data with performance reference points. In the SHDB, the social impacts are mostly determined by comparing the data obtained for each country-specific sector (e.g., data for "sector average wage" in "Wheat sector in China") involved in the product system under study with the worldwide distribution of data on this issue. Based on this comparison, a level of risk (low, medium, high, or very high risk) and a respective characterization factor (0.1, 1, 5, 10) (Benoît-Norris, et al., 2012) is attributed. The processes in a product system, which are more significant (i.e., where more hours of work are invested), will have a higher contribution to each impact subcategory. The labor intensity information is used together with the social risk levels, to express social impacts in terms of medium risk hours equivalent.

<u>Results Interpretation</u> – analysis of the results obtained in the previous step, which includes identifying the most critical social impacts (impact subcategories) and in which country-specific sector this social issue is most likely to arise (social hotspot).

In the next section, the application of the first three steps of the S- LCA methodology to this case study are presented. The last step is presented in Section 4.

3. Case Study

The first industrial process involved in the printing and writing paper production is pulping (i.e., pulp production). Pulp is mainly composed of cellulose fibers, which can be obtained from wood, fiber crops, or recycled paper. In this work, we focus on wood pulp production. After the trees are harvested, their trunks are bucked into logs that are delivered to mills where the logs are debarked and chipped. The next stage consists in separating the cellulose fibers from the other wood components such as lignin (the "glue" that cements the fibers together) and hemicelluloses. Several processes can be used in this stage, but the most common is the Kraft (sulfate) process where the wood chips are mixed and cooked with chemicals, caustic soda (NaOH) and sodium sulfate (Na_2S), and water under high pressure in a digester. The resulting raw pulp has a brown coloration caused by the presence of lignin that was not removed during cooking. The brown-colored raw pulp is then bleached to produce printing and writing paper. To improve the strength and optical properties of the paper, additives are added to the bleached pulp, which is then spread onto a traveling metal screen or plastic mesh (known as the "wire"). Water is drawn through the wire, leaving a web of fibers (paper sheet), which is passed through a series of rotating rolls to squeeze out water and air. The remaining water is removed by floating the sheet through a series of steam-heated rolls. After this stage, the paper sheet is usually wound onto jumbo reels, which can then be processed into smaller reels used for processing into various formats (The Navigator Company, 2019).

Following the methodology presented in the previous section:

Goal and Scope Definition – The main objective of this study is to assess the social impacts of Portuguese printing and writing paper supply chain to identify the critical hotspots. A cradle-to-gate boundary was considered, which includes the stages of the products' life cycle from growing and harvesting trees to paper production (including). The functional unit selected was 1 t of printing and writing paper produced from Kraft pulp.

Inventory Analysis – As mentioned in the previous section, the SHDB has social data for 160 indicators at the country and sector levels. For this reason, to conduct an S-LCA using this database, information on the country and sectors involved in the production of a product are required. The information needed is: 1) the materials used to produce a product, 2) which of the 57 GTAP (Global Trade Analysis Project) sectors the materials belong to, 3) in which country were the materials sourced from, and 4) what is the cost of the materials (Benoît-Norris, et al., 2018). Table 1 presents this information for the case study analyzed.

Table 1 - Main materials involved in the production of printing and writing paper

Materials	Costs (%)	GTAP Sector	Portugal	France	Germany	Spain	UK	USA	Algeria	Turkey
Wood	32 %	FRS	86.44 %	1.08 %	-	9.85 %	-	0.73 %	-	-
Chemicals	27 %	CHM	44.44 %	4.56 %	4.67 %	23.03 %	4.18 %	-	-	3.53 %
Water	18 %	WTR	100.0 %	-	-	-	-	-	-	-
Electricity	21 %	ELY	82.82 %	-	-	17.2 %	-	-	-	-
Fuels	3 %	GAS	0.0 %	-	-	77.84 %	-	-	22.16 %	-

The costs related to each one of the main materials identified in Table 1 were supplied by a Portuguese company operating in the printing and writing industrial sector. Due to the confidential nature of cost-related information, this data is shown in the table for each material as a percentage of the total production cost. The GTAP sectors involved in paper production are forestry (FRS), chemicals (CHM), water supply (WTR), electricity (ELY), and gas (GAS). To determine from which countries the main materials were sourced, the atlas of economic complexity was used considering a cut-off of 5% (i.e., countries that contributed less than 5% in the importation share were not included). From the countries identified in Table 1, the SHDB does not have data available for Algeria. For this reason, we use its neighboring country Morocco to approximate the social context of natural gas production.

Impact Assessment – The SHDB is used to conduct this step of the S-LCA. This database includes information on 146 indicators covering 24 impact subcategories aggregated into 5 impact categories: (1) Labor Rights & Decent Work, (2) Health & Safety, (3) Human Rights), (4) Governance), and (5) Community.

4. Results

From the application of the S-LCA methodology to the case study using the SHDB, different results were obtained for the different indicators, subcategories, and impact categories. Figure 2 presents, for each impact category, the percentage of social impacts that they are responsible for.

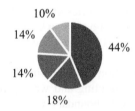

- Health & Safety
- Labor Rights & Decent Work
- Community
- Governance
- Human Rights

Figure 1 - Percentage of overall social impacts per impact category.

From the analysis of Figure 1, it can be concluded that the most critical social issues in the Portuguese printing and writing supply chain are related to health & safety, and labor rights & decent work. To analyze these issues in more detail, the contribution of each of the two impact subcategories that contribute to the health & safety and the contribution of each of the 11 impact subcategories that contribute to the labor rights & decent work is investigated (see Figure 2 and Figure 3).

- Injuries & Fatalities
- Toxics & Hazards

Figure 2 - Contribution of each of the two impact subcategories that contribute to the health & safety impact category.

From the analysis of Figure 2, it can be concluded that the most critical social issues in the Portuguese printing and writing supply chain related to health & safety belong to the Injuries and Fatalities impact subcategory. Each impact subcategory is categorized according to an indicator or a set of indicators that represent different social issues. The SHDB contains information for these indicators at a country and sector level. For the Injuries and Fatalities impact subcategory, the social issues addressed are the risk of having a fatal or non-fatal injury.

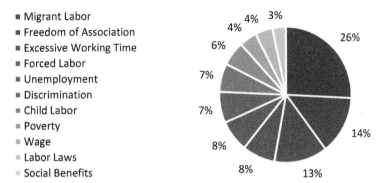

Figure 3 - Contribution of each of the 11 impact subcategories that contribute to the labor rights & decent work impact category.

From the analysis of Figure 3, it can be concluded that the most critical social issues in the Portuguese printing and writing supply chain related to labor rights & decent work belong to the Migrant Labor, Freedom of Association, and Excessive Working Time impact subcategories. The social issues addressed by these impact categories are the evidence of risk to migrant workers, the risk of not having the freedom of association, and the risk of having a high percentage of the population working more than 60 hours a week, respectively.

Figure 4 represents the contribution of each country and sector involved in the Portuguese printing and writing paper production to the four critical impact subcategories identified.

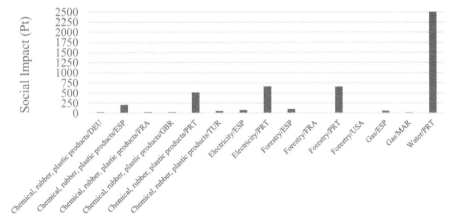

Figure 4 - Contribution of each country and sector involved in the Portuguese printing and writing paper production to the four critical impact subcategories.

From Figure 4, it is possible to conclude that the social impacts associated with the four most critical impact subcategories can be attributed to the Portuguese sectors since most of the materials used in the production of Portuguese printing and writing paper are produced in Portugal. Therefore, the social impacts associated with this region have a greater weight in the overall social impacts associated with the system under study in comparison with other countries included in the analysis, such as Spain, for example.

Consequently, the Portuguese printing and writing paper industrial sector can show rapid improvements if it addresses the social issues within the country, primarily in the arena of health and safety (the most critical impact category).

5. Conclusions

Although some research exists where E-LCA was applied to the paper industry, there was no literature found where the S-LCA was applied to the same industry. This work provided the first step in closing this gap by applying the S-LCA methodology through the SHDB to the Portuguese pulp and paper industry. Most social impacts identified were related to health & safety and labor rights & decent work issues mostly attributed to the Portuguese sectors. To improve its social impacts, the Portuguese printing and writing paper industrial sector should address the social issues within the country, including, among others, the risk of having a fatal or non-fatal injury.

This data could be used by different Portuguese companies that operate in the pulp and paper industry to benchmark the social impacts of their operations and determine whether they are performing better or worst them the national average. Future work should include the integration of environmental and social life cycle assessment to identify the impacts and hotspots of this industry from these two sustainability dimensions.

Acknowledgments

The authors gratefully acknowledge the project funding (PTDC/AGR-FOR/2178/2014_LISBOA-01-0145-FEDER-016733) and Ph.D. grant SFRH/BD/134479/2017.

References

Benoît-Norris, C., Bennema, M. & Norris, G., 2018. *The Social Hotspots Database,* Maine, USA: NewEarth B.

Benoît-Norris, C., Cavan, D. A. & Norris, G. A., 2012. Identifying Social Impacts in Product Supply Chains - Overview and Application of the Social Hotspot Database. *Sustainability,* 4(9), pp. 1946-1965.

Corcelli, F., Fiorentino, G., Vehmas, J. & Ulgiati, S., 2018. Energy efficiency and environmental assessment of papermaking from chemical pulp - A Finland case study. *Journal of Cleaner Production,* pp. 96-111.

DGAE, 2017. *Síntese de Indicadores Económicos.* [Online] Available at: https://www.dgae.gov.pt/documentacao/estatisticas/sintese-de-indicadores-economicos.aspx [Accessed 29 November 2019].

Garrido, S. R., 2017. Social Life-Cycle Assessment - An Introduction. *Encyclopedia of Sustainable Technologies,* pp. 253-265.

ISO, 2006. *Life Cycle Assessment – Principles and Framework,* Geneva, Switzerland: International Organization of Standardization.

Santos, A., Barbosa-Póvoa, A. & Carvalho, A., 2018. Life cycle assessment of pulp and paper production – A Portuguese case study. In: A. Friedl, et al. eds. *28th European Symposium on Computer Aided Process Engineering.* Graz, Austria: s.n., pp. 809-814.

Silva, D. A. L., Pavan, A. L. R., Oliveira, J. A. & Ometto, A. R., 2015. Life cycle assessment of offset paper production in Brazil - hotspots and cleaner production alternatives. *Journal of Cleaner Production,* 15 April, Volume 93, pp. 222-233.

The Navigator Company, 2019. *How paper is made.* [Online] Available at: http://en.thenavigatorcompany.com/Pulp-and-Paper/Paper/How-Paper-is-Made [Accessed 30 November 2019].

UNEP/SETAC, 2009. *Guidelines for Social Life Cycle Assessment of Products,* Paris, France: United Nations Environment Programme.

Wu, S., Yang, D. & Chen, J., 2014. Social life cycle assessment revisited. *Sustainability,* 6(7), p. 4200–4226.

WWF, 2019. *Pulp and Paper - Overview.* [Online] Available at: https://www.worldwildlife.org/industries/pulp-and-paper [Accessed 29 November 2019].

Sauro Pierucci, Flavio Manenti, Giulia Bozzano, Davide Manca (Eds.)
Proceedings of the 30th European Symposium on Computer Aided Process Engineering
(ESCAPE30), May 24-27, 2020, Milano, Italy. © 2020 Elsevier B.V. All rights reserved.
http://dx.doi.org/10.1016/B978-0-12-823377-1.50145-2

Determining the Design Parameters of Reactive Distillation Processes by a Quick Mapping Method

Rahma Muthia,[a] Megan Jobson,[a] Anton A. Kiss[a,b]

[a] Department of Chemical Engineering & Analytical Science, The University of Manchester, Sackville St, Manchester, M13 9PL, United Kingdom
[b] Sustainable Process Technology, Faculty of Science and Technology, University of Twente, PO Box 217, 7500 AE Enschede, The Netherlands
tony.kiss@manchester.ac.uk

Abstract

The application of reactive distillation in the chemical process industry promises significant benefits, such as boosting energy efficiency and reducing the overall cost. However, assessing and designing a reactive distillation process is still challenging as these tasks usually demand time-consuming procedures. To overcome this problem, the present work proposes a quick approach to determine the design parameters for a kinetically-controlled reactive distillation process according to the ratio between the Damköhler (Da) number and the chemical equilibrium constant (K_{eq}) – thus relating reaction kinetics and chemical equilibrium. This study employs a mapping method featuring an applicability graph that conveniently plots the reflux ratio vs. the number of theoretical stages and extends it to account for kinetically-controlled reactions. The method is demonstrated using the map for a generic quaternary reaction system, described as $A + B \rightleftharpoons C + D$, considering constant relative volatilities ($\alpha_{AB} = 2$ and $\alpha_{CD} = 6$) and various reaction equilibrium constants ($K_{eq} = 0.01, 0.1, 1$). For validation purposes, the applicability of reactive distillation is examined in two case studies – hydrolysis of methyl lactate and synthesis of methyl acetate. Modelling of both the generic and real systems suggests that, with a ratio Da/K_{eq} of 5 or more, the generic map can provide initial values for the design parameters of a reactive distillation column. Ultimately, the insights gained save time in effectively assessing the feasibility of reactive distillation at the conceptual design stage.

Keywords: reactive distillation, mapping method, Damköhler number, equilibrium constant, conceptual process design.

1. Introduction

Reactive distillation is an attractive and efficient process intensification method in the chemical industries. This technology combines reaction and separation functions in a single distillation column; the reaction converts feeds to products, while simultaneous separation enables removal of products. Reactive distillation has many advantages, such as reducing cost and energy consumption, enhancing conversion and selectivity, and overcoming unwanted azeotropes (Luyben and Yu, 2008). To gain these benefits, appropriate parameters for column design (e.g. number of stages, reflux ratio, liquid residence time and catalyst loading) must be determined. Over-design might result in an expensive and ineffective unit, while poor selection of the design parameters can lead to weak separation and reaction performance, or even an infeasible design. Therefore, a good understanding of the interplay between the design parameters of reactive distillation is crucial at the early phase of conceptual design.

The present work proposes a quick approach to determine the design parameters of reactive distillation using the simple ratio of the Damköhler (Da) number over the chemical equilibrium constant (K_{eq}), along with a mapping method for RD applicability. The work aims to find whether the generic maps can be applied for kinetically-controlled reactions, characterized in terms of the Da/K_{eq} ratio, to narrow the range of possible reactive distillation design parameters, namely liquid residence time, catalyst selection and catalyst loading. In this case, these inputs for reactive column design could expedite development of feasible designs.

2. Problem statement

For almost a century, reactive distillation columns have been designed and optimized, but reactive distillation design, simulation and evaluation remains time consuming (Li et al., 2016): obtaining a feasible reactive distillation column is not an easy or quick task, while column optimization is even more demanding. To overcome this problem, this work employs a mapping method to provide a rule of thumb for the ratio Da/K_{eq} that guides engineers to quickly determine the liquid residence time, catalyst selection (affecting kinetics) and catalyst loading for designing a reactive distillation column.

3. Overall approach to determine reactive distillation design parameters

3.1. Overview of the mapping method

The mapping method was originally introduced to visualize the applicability of equilibrium-controlled reactive distillation, using pre-defined applicability graphs of generic cases (Muthia et al., 2018a, 2018b). The method was then employed for preliminary economic ranking of RD designs and to investigate the feed locations of RD columns (Muthia et al., 2019). The mapping method utilizes a so-called applicability graph for RD, i.e., a plot of reflux ratio (RR) vs. the number of theoretical stages (NTS), depicted in Figure 1(a). A boundary line limits the applicability area of reactive distillation for products of specified purity (99 mol% in this study). The applicability graph, generated using Aspen Plus process simulator and displayed in Figure 1(a) for a quaternary system, A + B ⇌ C + D, approximates the region of feasible operation for a single reactive distillation column – see RD configuration in Figure 1(b).

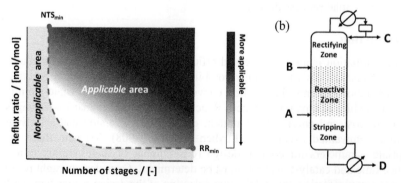

graph of reactive distillation used in the mapping method, and (b) a schematic reactive distillation column.

3.2. Use of mapping method to select the Da/K_{eq} ratio

The mapping method graphically correlates the performance of equilibrium-controlled reactive distillation processes, where each stage achieves the maximum possible conversion. This work extends the approach to consider kinetically-controlled reactions, where a smaller applicability area is observed (Muthia et al., 2018b). Finite reaction rates limit conversion on each stage, for example due to poor catalyst selection, poor catalyst performance, insufficient quantity of catalyst, or insufficient liquid residence time. The dimensionless Damköhler number, Da, captures these issues quantitatively:

$$Da = k_f \cdot M_r \cdot \beta \cdot \tau \qquad (1)$$

where k_f is the forward reaction rate constant (mol g_{cat}^{-1} min^{-1}), M_r the average molar mass of components ($g_{mixture}$ mol^{-1}), β the catalyst loading (g_{cat} $g_{mixture}^{-1}$) and τ the liquid residence time per stage (min). The Da number is defined in terms of average conditions in the column. A large Da value improves the performance of reactive distillation, increasing the applicability area, and *vice versa*. Moreover, when Da is large enough, the applicability area is similar to that of an equilibrium-controlled operation. Therefore, it is crucial to find a quick approach to estimate what Da number is 'large enough'. To do so, the sensitivity of the applicability area to the ratio Da/K_{eq} is explored.

In this work, two groups of generic quaternary systems with different volatility orders are chosen: group I_p ($T_{b,C} < T_{b,A} < T_{b,B} < T_{b,D}$) and group III_p ($T_{b,C} < T_{b,A} < T_{b,D} < T_{b,B}$). The classification follows the convention proposed by Luyben and Yu (2008). The two selected groups are beneficial in chemical industries because products can be easily collected at the top and bottom streams of a reactive distillation column. Here, constant relative volatilities ($\alpha_{AB} = 2$ and $\alpha_{CD} = 6$) and a range of fixed equilibrium constants ($K_{eq} = 0.01, 0.1, 1$) are assumed.

To validate the approach, two case studies are investigated – hydrolysis of methyl lactate and synthesis of methyl acetate by esterification; these represent typical non-ideal systems relevant to the chemical industries. As in Muthia et al. (2018b), the representative Damköhler number and chemical equilibrium constant in the case studies are calculated at the average boiling point of the reactants.

4. Results and discussion

4.1. Assessment of generic cases

Group I_p ($T_{b,C} < T_{b,A} < T_{b,B} < T_{b,D}$) is the predominant class of quaternary systems for the application of reactive distillation, as the products are the lightest and the heaviest compounds. Therefore, high purity products can be anticipated in the top and bottom outlets. In this assessment, relative volatilities α_{CA} and α_{BD} are set to 2.0 and 1.5, respectively, to be consistent with the specified volatilies $\alpha_{AB} = 2$, $\alpha_{CD} = 6$).

Figure 2 depicts the applicability graphs of group I_p in equilibrium-controlled and kinetically-controlled conditions, for values of the chemical equilibrium constants of 0.01, 0.1 and 1, respectively. For each graph, the equilibrium-limited case gives the largest applicability area (bounded by the solid line), as expected. Other lines indicate the applicability boundaries for kinetically-controlled reactive distillation processes. Clearly, the applicability area for RD decreases as the ratio Da/K_{eq} (i.e. the Damköhler number) is reduced.

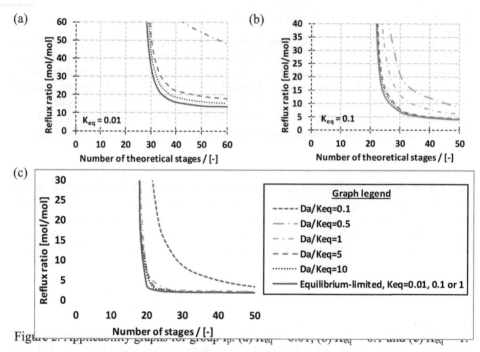

Figure 2. Applicability graphs for group I_p. (a) K_eq = 0.01, (b) K_eq = 0.1 and (c) K_eq = 1.

The applicability area is determined as the ratio Da/K_{eq} is varied from 0.1 to 10; Figure 2 shows that the high Da/K_{eq} ratios have a similar applicability area to that of equilibrium-controlled columns. The applicability bounds are almost equivalent when Da/K_{eq} is at least 5, except where the equilibrium constant is relatively low (e.g. K_{eq} = 0.01). In general, as K_{eq} increases, the kinetically-controlled and equilibrium-controlled boundaries become more similar. It is concluded that, in this case, Da/K_{eq} = 5 can be used as an initial criterion for determining reactive distillation design parameters.

Next, the assessment is performed for another group of quaternary systems – group III_p ($T_{b,C} < T_{b,A} < T_{b,D} < T_{b,B}$), with relative volatilities α_{CA} = 4, α_{AD} = 1.5 and α_{DB} = 1.4. That product D is an intermediate-boiling compound in the reactive distillation column potentially causes more reaction and separation challenges, relative to group I_p. Hence, the number of theoretical stages and reflux ratio of a reactive distillation column for this group are usually larger than those for group I_p (Muthia et al., 2018a, 2019).

Figure 3 depicts the applicability graphs of group III_p for chemical equilibrium constants of 0.01, 0.1 and 1. The application of reactive distillation is not beneficial for K_{eq} = 0.01 as the minimum reflux ratio is too high to be practical (RR_min > 50); therefore, this assessment only concerns chemical equilibrium constants of 0.1 and 1. As observed for group I_p, Da/K_{eq} values of 5 or greater have applicability areas that are only slightly smaller than those for equilibrium-limited reactive distillation. Again, for lower values of the equilibrium constant, the kinetically-controlled column under-performs more. An initial criterion for selecting reactive distillation design parameters is to design for $Da/K_{eq} \geq 5$; this finding is consistent with that for group I_p.

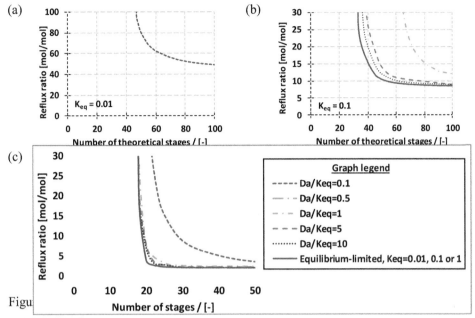

4.2. Case studies

Figure 2 and Figure 3 demonstrate the approach for generic cases, where relative volatilities and the equilibrium constant are assumed constant in the column. Two case studies aim to validate the findings for the generic cases: hydrolysis of methyl lactate (Eq. 2) and synthesis of methyl acetate by esterification (Eq. 3), representing groups I_p and III_p, respectively. Unlike ideal generic systems, the azeotropes present in these cases are expected to hinder the reactive distillation.

$$\text{Water (A) + methyl lactate (B)} \rightleftharpoons \text{methanol (C) + lactic acid (D)} \tag{2}$$

| T_b (°C) | 100 | 144.8 | 64.7 | 216.9 |

$$\text{Methanol (A) + acetic acid (B)} \rightleftharpoons \text{methyl acetate (C) + water (D)} \tag{3}$$

| T_b (°C) | 64.7 | 118 | 56.9 | 100 |

Sanz et al. (2004) present temperature-dependent K_{eq} and k_f (mol g_{cat}^{-1} min^{-1}) relationships for the hydrolysis of methyl lactate, where an azeotrope forms between water (97 mol%) and methyl lactate (3 mol%) at 99.8 °C.

$$\ln(K_{eq}) = 2.6 - 1954.2 / T \tag{4}$$

$$k_f = 1.65 \cdot 10^5 \cdot \exp(-50,910 / R \cdot T) \tag{5}$$

In the second case, two homogeneous azeotropes exist (methyl acetate (65.9 mol%)–methanol (34.1 mol%) at 53.7°C and methyl acetate (89 mol%)–water (11 mol%) at 56.4 °C. Pöpken et al. (2000) present correlations for K_{eq} and k_f (mol g_{cat}^{-1} min^{-1}) as:

$$\ln(K_{eq}) = -3.82 + 2408.65 / T \tag{6}$$

$$k_f = 4.94 \cdot 10^2 \cdot \exp(-49,190 / R \cdot T) \tag{7}$$

Figure 4 presents reactive distillation applicability graphs for both case studies generated via extensive simulation studies using Aspen Plus. It may be observed that the proposal to use $Da/K_{eq} \geq 5$ as an initial criterion for designing a reactive distillation

column applies very well: in both cases, the boundary line of the applicability region is
very close to that in equilibrium-controlled conditions.

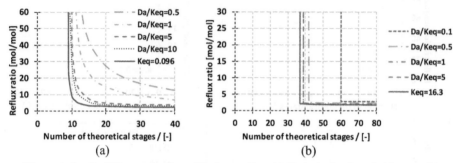

Figure 4. Applicability graphs for validation studies: (a) Hydrolysis of methyl lactate; (b)
Synthesis of methyl acetate

5. Conclusions

The mapping method has been successfully employed to visualize the performance of
reactive distillation in equilibrium-limited and kinetically-controlled reactions. This
work proposes $Da/K_{eq} \geq 5$ as a criterion to initialise reactive distillation design
parameters, namely liquid residence time, catalyst selection and catalyst loading, for
groups I_p and III_p. This approach should enable the range of design parameters selection
to be narrowed, to avoid time-consuming exploration of options at the conceptual
design stage. This heuristic may also be useful for other groups of quaternary systems.

Acknowledgements

RM gratefully acknowledges full fund support from LPDP (Indonesia Endowment Fund
for Education). AAK is thankful for the Royal Society Wolfson Research Merit Award.

References

H. Li, Y. Meng, X. Li, X. Gao, 2016, A fixed point methodology for the design of reactive
distillation, Chemical Engineering Research and Design, 111, 479-491.

W. L. Luyben and C.-C. Yu, 2008, Effects of Boiling Point Rankings on the Design of Reactive
Distillation, Reactive Distillation Design and Control, 487-518, USA, John Wiley & Sons Ltd.

R. Muthia, A. G. J. van der Ham, A. A. Kiss, 2018a, Preliminary economic ranking of reactive
distillation processes using a navigation method, Computer Aided Chemical Engineering, 43,
827-832.

R. Muthia, A. G. T. Reijneveld, A. G. J. van der Ham, A. J. B. ten Kate, G. Bargeman, S. R. A.
Kersten, A. A. Kiss, 2018b, Novel method for mapping the applicability of reactive
distillation, Chemical Engineering and Processing: Process Intensification, 128, 263-275.

R. Muthia, A. G. J. van der Ham, M. Jobson, A. A. Kiss, 2019, Effect of boiling point rankings
and feed locations on the applicability of reactive distillation to quaternary systems, Chemical
Engineering Research and Design, 145, 184-193.

T. Pöpken, L. Götze, J. Gmehling, 2000, Reaction kinetics and chemical equilibrium of
homogeneously and heterogeneously catalyzed acetic acid esterification with methanol and
methyl acetate hydrolysis, Industrial & Engineering Chemistry Research, 39, 2601-2611.

M. T. Sanz, R. Murga, S. Beltrán, J. L. Cabezas, J. Coca, 2004, Kinetic study for the reactive
system of lactic acid esterification with methanol: methyl lactate hydrolysis reaction,
Industrial & Engineering Chemistry Research, 43, 2049-2053.

Sauro Pierucci, Flavio Manenti, Giulia Bozzano, Davide Manca (Eds.)
Proceedings of the 30th European Symposium on Computer Aided Process Engineering
(ESCAPE30), May 24-27, 2020, Milano, Italy. © 2020 Elsevier B.V. All rights reserved.
http://dx.doi.org/10.1016/B978-0-12-823377-1.50146-4

Conceptual Design Based on Superstructure Optimization in GAMS with Accurate Thermodynamic Models

David Krone[a], Erik Esche[a], Norbert Asprion[b], Mirko Skiborowski[c], Jens-Uwe Repke[a]

[a]*Technische Universität Berlin, Process Dynamics and Operations Group, Straße des 17. Juni 135, 10623 Berlin, Germany*
[b]*BASF SE, Chemical Process Modeling, Carl-Bosch-Strasse 38, 67056 Ludwigshafen am Rhein, Germany*
[c]*TU Dortmund University, Department of Chemical and Biochemical Engineering, Laboratory of Fluid Separations, Emil-Figge-Straße 70, 44227 Dortmund, Germany*
david.krone@tu-berlin.de

Abstract

Conceptual design based on superstructure optimization is a complex task that neither commercial simulators nor dedicated modeling and optimization environments like GAMS, AMPL, and AIMMS are able to perform well by themselves: the first lack interfaces to state-of-the-art solvers, the latter do not provide accurate thermodynamic models. While previous research shows that GAMS can be interfaced with an external thermo engine, this interfacing requires additional C++ code, whose manual generation and consistent implementation is tedious, making the approach both error prone and impractical for larger design problems. By using MOSAICmodeling as a modeling environment, this shortcoming of the existing approach is eliminated by automatically generating all code needed for interfacing GAMS with an external CAPE-OPEN thermodynamic property package.

Keywords: conceptual design, automated code generation, CAPE-OPEN

1. Introduction

Conceptual design based on superstructure optimization involving nonlinear process models remains a challenging task. Commercial simulators do not allow for the formulation and optimization of large-scale superstructure models or do not have interfaces to suitable solvers, whereas dedicated modeling and optimization environments like GAMS, AMPL, and AIMMS do not provide accurate thermodynamic models, which are required to properly describe the behavior of a multicomponent system. Several authors have shown how to interface GAMS with accurate thermodynamic models, e.g., by using external equations (Skiborowski et al., 2015) or extrinsic functions (Manassaldi et al., 2019). Both approaches depend on additional C++ code which is compiled as a dynamic link library (DLL). However, a successful application of these approaches for the optimization of complex process models in GAMS, like the ones for conceptual design, is still hampered by the manual generation of the code for the DLL.

This shortcoming is addressed in this contribution as we demonstrate an enhancement of the approach by Skiborowski et al. (2015), in which the code necessary for interfacing GAMS with accurate thermodynamic models via CAPE-OPEN is generated automatically. This is achieved by a combination of a robust implementation of an equilibrium stage-based process model and the novel CAPE-OPEN Binary Interop Architecture (COBIA). The process model in GAMS and the additional C++ files for incorporating thermodynamics via COBIA are generated automatically by MOSAICmodeling (Technische Univerisät Berlin, 2019) via separate user-defined language specifications (UDLS). The concept of UDLS is described in detail in Tolksdorf et al. (2019). We demonstrate the ability of the automated code generation by presenting the results from a case study of the separation of the ternary mixture *n*-pentane, *n*-hexane and *n*-heptane by a sequence of vapor-liquid equilibrium-stage models, in which the resulting NLP is solved in GAMS using thermodynamic calculations in TEA (AmsterCHEM, 2019).

This work is an intermediate step towards a fully automated optimization-based approach for conceptual design, in which the MINLP describing the superstructure of a process network is solved in GAMS. Within this contribution, a superstructure formulation is employed, but optimization problems are reduced to NLP form by specifying the structural / binary variables within MOSAICmodeling prior to code export. Hence, the following sections focus on the development of the underlying robust superstructure that is used to create the NLP for the case study in hand.

2. Optimization Approach and Implementation

A state-space representation for the superstructure of a process network is chosen, originally introduced by Bagajewicz and Manousiouthakis (1992). Several equilibrium-stage-based vapor-liquid-separation-units (VL-U) are assembled into the superstructure by connecting their input and output streams to a distribution network that defines the interconnections between the separation units by a set of binary variables. Similar to the approach of Kuhlmann and Skiborowski (2017), inlet streams to the distribution network are allowed to be only split twice, in order to reduce the combinatoric complexity of the overall problem. The VL-U models are based on MESH equations, single phase enthalpies and distribution coefficients are implemented as external functions, which are formulated separately. A VL-U with an exemplary number of four equilibrium stages and a superstructure that connects six of those VL-Us for the separation of a ternary mixture of components A, B, and C is shown in Fig. 1.

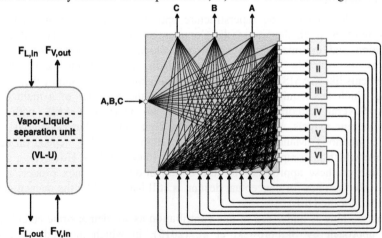

Figure 1: Vapor-liquid-separation unit (VL-U) and superstructure of six VL-Us

The figure shows all possible stream connections in the distribution network. The remainder of this section focuses on the three major features that are implemented in our approach to ensure both successful interfacing with the external thermodynamic property package and robust convergence of the superstructure during optimization in GAMS.

2.1. Robust superstructure formulation

By nature, superstructures for optimization-based conceptual design are highly complex systems. Applying the approach to complex distillation configurations, VLE models like the VL-U can frequently break down, i.e., in intermediate solutions there is no vapor or no liquid, or no phase at all present in some parts of the column. Model validity from "all liquid" to "all vapor" conditions is ensured in this approach by a robust formulation of the superstructure, relaxing all existing VLE by introducing additional complementary constraints (Gopal and Biegler, 1999), leading to the following model equations that describe the phase equilibrium on the ith stage of one VL-U

$$y_{i,j} = \beta_i \cdot K_{i,j} \cdot x_{i,j}, \tag{1}$$

$$\beta_i - 1 = s_i^V - s_i^L, \tag{2}$$

$$s_i^L \cdot F_i^L = 0, \tag{3}$$

$$s_i^V \cdot F_i^V = 0, \tag{4}$$

$$F_i^L, F_i^V, s_i^L, s_i^V \geq 0. \tag{5}$$

$$0 \leq x_{i,j}, y_{i,j} \leq 1 \tag{6}$$

The phase equilibrium (1) is updated by introducing the corrector β_i and adding complementarity constraints given by (3), (4), and (5). These constraints make sure that either the flow of a phase or its corresponding slack variable is at zero. Hence, if one phase disappears, the complementarity constraint ensures that the corresponding slack variable takes a positive value. Then, via Eq. (2), β_i has a value different from one and the VLE is relaxed.

For a consistently robust behavior at phase transitions, NCP functions (3) and (4) are themselves relaxed by an inexact smoothening technique, while (5) is removed (Kanzow and Schwartz, 2013), resulting in the following updated versions:

$$(s_i^L + t_i) \cdot (F_i^L + t_i) - (t_i)^2 \geq 0, \tag{7}$$

$$s_i^L \cdot F_i^L - (t_i)^2 \leq 0, \tag{8}$$

$$(s_i^V + t_i) \cdot (F_i^V + t_i) - (t_i)^2 \geq 0, \tag{9}$$

$$s_i^V \cdot F_i^V - (t_i)^2 \leq 0. \tag{10}$$

Hence, during optimization a sequence of the same problems is solved while parameter t_i is reduced until reaching a small tolerance of, e.g., 1e-7. By this formulation, we can ensure that any requests for thermodynamic calculations to the external thermo engine are both always feasible and do not lead to issues with problem convergence, while at the same time providing accurate derivatives to GAMS.

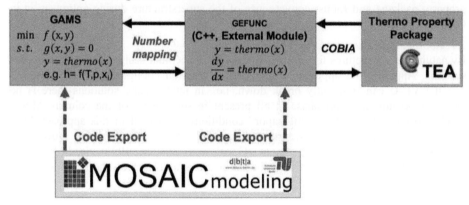

Figure 2: Interface between GAMS and a CAPE-OPEN property package

2.2. Interfacing GAMS with a CAPE-OPEN property package

Accurate thermodynamic property calculations are performed by a CAPE-OPEN thermo property package and provided to GAMS via the interface shown in Fig. 2. It consists of four parts: the external function calls in the program file of GAMS; a number mapping between this file and the C++ file of the external module; the function GEFUNC that is contained within the external module, where the actual calculations and thermo calls to the property package are performed (Skiborowski et al., 2015) and COBIA as the socket to the thermo package.

2.2.1. External function calls

In the GAMS model, all thermodynamic properties such as enthalpies, distribution coefficients, or dew / bubble point temperatures are defined in a separate block of external equations by specifying all input and output variables for each thermo call.

2.2.2. Number mapping

All external equations and variables defined within this block of external equations receive a unique number. These two sets of numbers ensure the implementation consistency of the external function calls made in GAMS and the calculations performed in the external module.

2.2.3. GEFUNC / External module (C++)

As described by Skiborowski et al. (2015), the function calculates the residual of every external equation and, in addition to that, calculates all first order derivatives with respect to all present output and input variables. For most property calls, input variables are temperature T, pressure p, and compositions x_j. All thermodynamic properties needed for these calculations are either provided by the property or flash routines of the property package or calculated implicitly. The latter is true for all first order derivatives of properties that are determined by flash routines, since the property package does not provide direct derivatives for these. Here, these missing values are computed by applying the implicit function theorem to the valid flash conditions and solving the resulting linear equation system by LU decomposition of the C++ library Eigen 3 (Guennebaud and Jacob, 2019).

2.2.4. COBIA

COBIA is relied upon to call the property package from GAMS' external module. All COBIA headers are added to the C++ project of the external module. The project is compiled as a DLL and added to the current GAMS workspace.

2.3. Implementation consistency

To facilitate the formulation of complex superstructure models and ensure implementation consistency across all program files, our own modeling environment MOSAICmodeling (Technische Universität Berlin, 2019) is applied and extended to allow for full COBIA support. The superstructure is fully formulated within MOSAICmodeling, wherein the calls for external computation of, e.g., enthalpies and separation coefficients are generically marked as "CAPE-OPEN" calls. Subsequently, as shown in Fig. 2, code is generated by two separate UDLS for both GAMS and the external module of GAMS, wherein the full COBIA calls and the generation of derivatives for GAMS is described depending on the exact structure of the GAMS model.

3. Case Study: Separation of a Ternary Mixture by a Dividing Wall Column

The capabilities of the approach are shown by generating an instance of the superstructure of six VL-Us introduced in Fig. 1, each VL-U consisting of 20 equilibrium stages, for the separation of a ternary mixture *n*-pentane, *n*-hexane, and *n*-heptane. The binary variables of the distribution network are specified so that the resulting instance of the superstructure serves as a surrogate model of a dividing wall column (DWC) as shown in Fig. 3.

The NLP problem is then solved in GAMS by CONOPT 3. All thermodynamic calculations are performed by a property package provided by TEA (AmsterCHEM, 2019). All variables are initialized arbitrarily within their bounds in order to test the robustness of the system. The reboiler duty is chosen as the objective function which is minimized in order to determine the most energy-efficient configuration of the DWC for the separation of the mixture. Extra inequality constraints ensure that the compositions of the desired products in each outlet stream remain above 0.9995. The saturated liquid feed stream of 20 kmol h^{-1} has the molar composition $x_1^F = 0.333$, $x_2^F = 0.333$ and $x_3^F = 0.334$ and the DWC operates at a pressure of 1 bar. The following five molar split ratios (cf. Fig. 3) are chosen as decision variables: reflux ratio v_R, boil up ratio v_{BU}, removal ratio of product stream B v_B, vapor split fraction v_V, and liquid split fraction v_L. The optimal ratios are determined by CONOPT 3 after 554 iterations and a CPU time of 4460 seconds at $v_R = 0.266$, $v_{BU} = 0.233$, $v_B = 0.528$, $v_V = 0.550$ and $v_L = 0.229$ with product purities of $x_1^A = 1.000$, $x_2^B = 0.9995$, and $x_3^C = 0.9995$ for a reboiler duty of 194.6 kW. The resulting temperature profiles of all column sections (I to VI) are presented in Fig. 3.

4. Conclusions and Outlook

This work presents the enhancement of an optimization approach in GAMS using accurate thermodynamic models via CAPE-OPEN by automated code generation. The results from a case study, in which the NLP resulting from a process model of six VL-Us is solved in GAMS, indicate that the automated code export works well for interfacing GAMS with the external thermo package and that the robust model formulation ensures convergence even for systems that are poorly initialized. The process model of the case study is an instance of the robust superstructure of the process network, which is already formulated in MOSAICmodeling, Hence, the next step towards optimization-based conceptual design is to export the entire superstructure to GAMS and investigate how the resulting MINLP can be solved effectively.

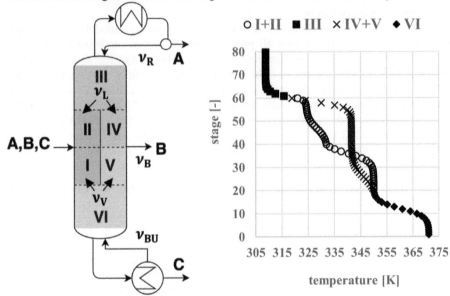

Figure 3: left: Combination of six VL-Us (I-VI) as a surrogate model of a DWC, right: Temperature profiles in the DWC for the optimized system

References

AmsterCHEM, 2019, COCO [WWW Document], URL https://www.amsterchem.com/coco.html (last accessed 25.11.19)

M. Bagajewicz, V. Manousiouthakis, 1992, AIChE Journal, Mass/heat-exchange networkd representation of distillation networks, 38, 11, 1769–1800

V. Gopal, L. T. Biegler, 1999, AIChE Journal, Smoothing methods for complementarity problems in process engineering, 45, 1535–1547

G. Guennebaud, B. Jacob, and others, 2019, Eigen v3 [WWW Document], URL http://eigen.tuxfamily.org (last accessed 25.11.19)

C. Kanzow, A. Schwartz, Comput. Optim. Appl. 2014, Convergence properties of the inexact Lin-Fukushima relaxation method for mathematical programs with complementary constraints, 59, 249–262

H. Kuhlmann, M. Skiborowski, 2017, Industrial & Engineering Chemistry Research, Optimization-Based Approach To Process Synthesis for Process Intensification: General Approach and Application to Ethanol Dehydration, 56, 45, 13461–13481

J. I. Manassaldi, M. C. Mussati, N. J. Scenna, S. G. Mussati, Computers & Chemical Engineering, 2019, Development of extrinsic functions for optimal synthesis and design – Application to distillation-based separation processes, 125, 532–544

M. Skiborowski, A. Harwardt, W. Marquart, 2015, Computers & Chemical Engineering, Efficient optimization-based design for the separation of heterogeneous azeotropic mixtures, 72, 34–51

Technische Universität Berlin, 2019, MOSAICmodeling [WWW Document], URL http://mosaic-modeling.de (last accessed 25.11.19)

G. Tolksdorf, E. Esche, G. Wozny, J.-U. Repke, 2019, Computers & Chemical Engineering, Customized code generation based on user specifications for simulation and optimization, 121, 670–684

Sauro Pierucci, Flavio Manenti, Giulia Bozzano, Davide Manca (Eds.)
Proceedings of the 30th European Symposium on Computer Aided Process Engineering
(ESCAPE30), May 24-27, 2020, Milano, Italy. © 2020 Elsevier B.V. All rights reserved.
http://dx.doi.org/10.1016/B978-0-12-823377-1.50147-6

A Multiperiod Approach for Flexible Work and Heat Integration

Leandro V. Pavão,* Mauro A. S. S. Ravagnani, Caliane B. B. Costa[a]

Department of Chemical Engineering, State University of Maringá
Av. Colombo, 5790, Bloco D90, CEP 87020900, Maringá, PR, Brazil
leandropavao@gmail.com

Abstract

Industrial plants are constantly subject to undergoing operating condition variations. Those may be due to, for instance, ambient temperature changes, altering feed temperatures or to reactants and raw material quality changes, which may lead to certain stream flow fluctuations. Those scenarios require that equipment involved in the process is sized accordingly for reaching target outlet parameters and maintain the process feasible. In heat integration, several works have proposed methodologies for synthesizing heat exchanger networks (HEN) with equipment that is able to operate properly regardless of changes in temperatures or flowrates. A methodology that achieved considerable success for designing flexible HEN is the multiperiod approach. In it, a finite number of extreme scenarios is considered and a HEN, feasible in all of them, is synthesized. In simultaneous work and heat integration, however, flexibility has not yet been explored in the literature. The solutions presented so far are obtained for nominal conditions, which may lead to equipment that is undersized when the process undergoes inlet pressure, temperature or flowrate variations. In that sense, the present work proposes an optimization-based methodology for automatically synthesizing work and heat exchange networks (WHEN) that are flexible for operating under a finite set of varying conditions, as proposed in multiperiod approaches. A work and heat integration case study is proposed with a finite number of scenarios. Then, a meta-heuristic solution approach is applied to the new proposed multiperiod model, and a single solution is obtained. The identified solution is able to perform feasibly under all the proposed extreme scenarios. Moreover, units were only slightly oversized in comparison to the nominal conditions, representing a relatively small additional capital investment.

Keywords: Optimization; Multiperiod; Work and Heat Integration; Work and Heat Exchange Networks; Meta-heuristics

1. Introduction

Material streams in industrial facilities typically face temporary alterations in nominal operating conditions. These changes may be due to variations in raw material quality, weather conditions, control system issues, fouling, among others. Consequently, some degree of flexibility is required when sizing the employed equipment.

Under the scope of industrial flexibility studies, much attention has been given to the design of flexible heat exchanger networks (HEN). These systems must be able to operate under variable temperature and heat capacity flowrate conditions. Note that heat exchanger areas are fixed, and it is required that these areas are able to handle different operating conditions. In general, this leads to some additional heat exchange surface requirement in the heat exchangers, which implies a greater capital investment than in a solution for the nominal state only. It is thus important to synthesize a network having this overdesign issue in mind in order to mitigate this additional capital investment.

A widely used approach for flexible HEN synthesis is the multiperiod concept. Under this consideration, a finite set of operating conditions is defined according to their duration probabilities throughout a year of operation. A pioneer mathematical programming approach for multiperiod HEN synthesis is the sequential framework of Floudas and Grossmann (1987). More recent contributions include the MINLP simultaneous models of Verheyen and Zhang (2006) and Pavão et al. (2018). The former employs deterministic methodologies as solution approach, while the latter uses hybrid meta-heuristic methods. Both models use as basis the stagewise superstructure (SWS) for HEN synthesis, developed by Yee and Grossmann (1990).

Another important field of energy integration regards the simultaneous integration of pressure and temperature change units, that is, work and heat integration. Although not as mature as heat integration literature, this new trend has shown in several recent studies that work and heat integration may lead to important energy savings in plants. The problem is similar to heat integration, but streams may also require compression or expansion. Work recovery may be performed, for instance, by means of single-shaft-compressor-turbine (SSTC) couplings or simply by power generation from turbines, which can be supplied to compression tasks.

Simultaneous optimization models have been proposed for designing networks with optimal placement and sizing of pressure manipulators (compressors, turbines, valves, SSTC units) as well as of temperature ones (heat exchangers and utility heaters and coolers). Onishi et al. (2014) proposed a WHEN synthesis MINLP model considering SSTC units. The model allowed a stream to pass multiple times through a heat recovery area, which was modelled with Yee and Grossmann's (1990) SWS. Nair and Karimi (2018) presented a model without streams pre-classification and assuming temperature-dependent properties. Based on the idea of multiple passes through a heat recovery area, Pavão et al. (2019) presented a matrix-based approach suitable for the use of a meta-heuristic solution method. The heat integration region was modelled with the enhanced SWS of Pavão et al. (2018).

Although efficient frameworks have been presented for work and heat integration, so far, the flexibility issue has not been approached, and remains an interesting opportunity (Yu et al., 2018). It is notable that stream pressure conditions may vary from the nominal ones, as well as temperatures and flowrates, due to the same factors mentioned previously. Hence, it is appropriate to design pressure manipulators having in mind some degree of flexibility. Hence, in this work, we propose a multiperiod WHEN synthesis framework able to perform pressure/temperature change tasks under multiple operating condition scenarios.

2. Problem statement

A set of process streams is given with supply and target temperature/pressure conditions, as well as heat capacity flowrates and heat transfer coefficients. Supply and target temperature and pressure, as well as heat capacity flowrates may vary. Therefore, a finite number of condition sets is known, and to each of these a duration time over a year is associated. A network of pressure manipulators (compressors, turbines, valves and SSTC units for work exchange among streams) and temperature manipulators (heaters, coolers and heat exchangers) must be designed so that all streams reach their target conditions in all periods. In case a SSTC unit requires additional power, an auxiliary motor is used.

Conversely, an auxiliary generator uses work surplus and produces electricity, which is sold to the grid.

Streams are assumed as ideal gases. Polytropic exponents, isentropic efficiencies and Joule-Thompson coefficients are known.

3. Mathematical model

The model proposed in this work is based on the master matrix concept of Pavão et al. (2019). That is, a matrix contains information of all stream passes through the heat exchange area, as presented in Figure 1.

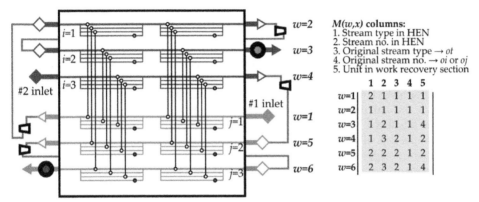

Figure 1. Master matrix-based structure for WHEN synthesis

Note that, in the superstructure, a given stream may have either hot or cold passes through the heat recovery region. The matrix contains information for correct stream identification and for the unit placed between passes through heat integration region (e.g., 1 for compressor, 2 for turbine, 3 for valves and 4 for final temperature correction heater/cooler). The algorithm reads the matrix data and is able to link the master superstructure to the heat integration superstructure in order to perform energy-related calculations and equipment sizing.

In order to consider multiple operating periods, several design-related variables must have individual values at each of these periods. For instance, heat exchanger areas, represented in the single period model as $A_{i,j,k}$, with indexes that represent hot and cold streams (i and j) and superstructure stage (k) must have an additional t index for periods. It is worth noting that associated with area calculations are all energy- and temperature-related variables, which also require the additional t index. Pressure manipulator variables require the index as well. In brief, illustrative equation forms for operating and capital costs (which are summed up as total annual costs to be minimized in the optimization model) are calculated as follows (a detailed single period model derivation can be found in Pavão et al. (2019)):

$$OC = \sum_{t \in NP} D_t (UC_t + WC_t) \tag{1}$$

where D_t is the period duration, UC_t are total utility costs for a given period and WC_t is the total electricity costs (which is negative if there is power surplus revenue) for a period. NP is the periods set.

$$CC = \sum_{i \in NH} \sum_{j \in NC} \sum_{k \in NS} Afun[\max_t(A_{i,j,k,t})] +$$

$$\sum_{m \in NHU} \sum_{j \in NC} \sum_{k \in NS} Afun[\max_t(Ahui_{m,j,k,t})] +$$

$$\sum_{i \in NH} \sum_{n \in NCU} \sum_{k \in NS} Afun[\max_t(Acui_{i,n,k,t})] + \qquad (2)$$

$$\sum_{oj \in NOC} Afun[\max_t(Ahu_{oj,t})] + \sum_{oi \in NOH} Afun[\max_t(Acu_{oi,t})] +$$

$$\sum_{w \in NW} Wfun[\max_t(Work_{w,t})] + MGfun[\max_t(MGWork_t)]$$

where *Afun* is the area capital costs function, *Wfun* is the pressure changer capital costs function, which automatically identifies the unit as compressor/expander (standalone or coupled via SSTC), or valve and uses the appropriate capital cost estimation formula and *MGfun* is the auxiliary motor/generator capital costs function, which automatically identifies whether a helper motor or generator is needed in the SSTC coupling and calculates its capital costs. *NH* and *NC* are hot and cold stream sets. *NS* is the HEN superstructure stages set. *NOH* and *NOC* are original hot and cold stream sets. *NW* is the general streams set. Input values in these functions are functions as well: max_t identifies the greater value within those with *t* index. That is, in order to feasibly operate in all periods, the unit must be sized according to the greatest period requirement. *A, Ahui* and *Acui* are areas for heat exchangers and inner stage utility units in Pavão et al.'s (2018) superstructure. *Ahu* and *Acu* are areas for final temperature correction heaters/coolers. Only one of these units can be placed at the end of a stream, regardless of how many times it passes through the heat recovery area. That is why these areas have *oi* and *oj* index, which regard the original stream index. *Work* is the shaft-work in compressors/turbines, or the energy relief in valves. These units have the generic stream index *w*, which is translated to/from the *i/j* notation for the heat integration region by the algorithm. *MGWork* is the total net power required/generated in the SSTC coupling. Power lack or surplus is automatically identified for sizing a helper motor/generator.

4. Case study

The case study tackled here has one hot, low-pressure stream, one cold, constant-pressure stream and one cold, high-pressure stream. Four operation periods with equal durations are considered. Stream data is presented in Table 1. Parameters that vary in each period are supply temperatures (Ts1-Ts4), heat capacity flowrates (F1-F4) and supply pressures (ps1-ps4). Temperatures are given in K, heat capacity flowrates in kW/K and pressures in bar. Heat transfer coefficients are of 0.1 kW/(m²K) for process streams and 1.0 kW/(m²K) for hot and cold utilities (HU and CU). Hot and cold utilities cost 337 $/(kWy) and 100 $/(kWy). Electricity cost is 455.04 $/(kWy) and its revenue price is 364.03 $/(kWy). The polytropic exponent is 1.352; isentropic efficiency is assumed as 1.0 for compressors and turbines and Joule-Thompson coefficient value is 1.961 K/MPa. The annualizing factor is 0.18. The exchanger minimal approach temperature (EMAT) is 1 K. The algorithm used for solving the multiperiod model for this case study is based on the SA-RFO implementation for WHEN synthesis (Pavão et al., 2019). The code was revamped so that the multiple periods were considered. The implementation was in C++

in Microsoft Visual Studio 2019. All optimization runs were carried out on a computer with an Intel® Core™ i7-8750H CPU @ 2.20 GHz and 8.00 GB of RAM.

Table 1. Case study stream data

St.	Ts1	Ts2	Ts3	Ts4	Tt	F1	F2	F3	F4	ps1	ps2	ps3	ps4	pt
1	288	274	274	302	123	3.0	3.2	2.9	3.2	1.0	0.9	0.9	1.1	4.0
2	213	224	202	224	288	2.0	2.1	2.1	1.9	-	-	-	-	-
3	113	119	107	119	288	1.7	1.8	1.8	1.6	4.0	4.2	3.8	4.2	1.0
HU	383	383	383	383	383	-	-	-	-	-	-	-	-	-
CU	93	93	93	93	93	-	-	-	-	-	-	-	-	-

$Afun(Area) = 71{,}337.07 + 747.9931\,(Area)$;
$Wfun(Work) = 51{,}104.85\,(Work)^{0.62}$ (standalone compressor);
$Wfun(Work) = 2585.47\,(Work)^{0.81}$ (standalone turbine);
$Wfun(Work) = 51{,}104.85\,(Work)^{0.62} - 985.47\,(Work)^{0.62}$ (SSTC compressor);
$Wfun(Work) = 2585.47\,(Work)^{0.81} - 985.47\,(Work)^{0.62}$ (SSTC turbine);
$MGfun(MGWork) = 985.47\,(MGWork)^{0.62}$ (for both aux. motor or generator);

A considerable problem in multiperiod solutions is overdesign. In that sense, an important parameter to measure a multiperiod HEN solution efficiency are "required to available" ratios. In heat integration, these ratios refer to heat exchange surface. That is, the ratio between the required area in a given heat exchanger at a period, versus the maximum area among all periods in that unit. Considering temperature manipulating units (heat exchangers, heaters and coolers), the methodology was able to find a solution with an average total required to total available area ratio of 97.4% (if only heat exchangers are considered, the ratio is of 99.1%). We can extend that idea to compressors and expanders. For the former, the average required to available compressing capacity ratio is of 88.0%. For the latter, the required to available expansion capacity is of 91.6%. The helper motor is designed with 105.5 kW power, leading to an average required to available power ratio of 84.4%. The multiperiod WHEN solution is presented in Figure 2.

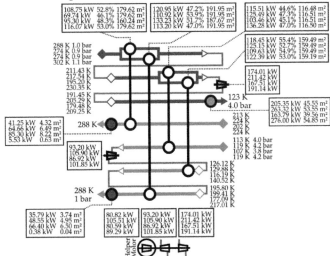

Figure 2. Multiperiod WHEN solution for the case study. For each unit, each row of values refers to calculated variables in a period of operation (heat duty/work in kW, stream split fraction in % and area in m²).

The multiperiod solution found has TAC of 753,083 $/y, with capital costs of 456,137 $/y and operating costs of 296,946 $/y. For comparison purposes, when the algorithm was run for the nominal case only (i.e., period 1), TAC was 689,892 $/y, with capital costs of 421,557 $/y and operating costs of 268,336 $/y. Hence, the implementation of a WHEN able to operate feasibly at multiple conditions in this case led to a small additional capital investment of 34,580 $/y (8.2 % increase). Moreover, the aforementioned ratio values are similar to those presented in multiperiod case studies comprising heat integration only (see Pavão et al. (2018)), which means the methodology extension to work and heat integration was satisfactory. The processing time was of 4,084 s.

5. Conclusions

A novel framework for multiperiod work and heat exchange network synthesis was proposed. The method is based on an extension of a matrix-based model and a meta-heuristic approach is used to solve such a model. Tests were conducted for a case study. The methodology was able to identify a solution with small additional investments in comparison to the nominal case solution. The algorithm was able to identify a single work and heat exchange network configuration able to operate feasible in all periods. The design also has good "required to available" ratios for all units. The method found a solution with little overdesign. That is, all units have similar requirements for area, compression/expansion capacity and auxiliary motor power in all periods.

Acknowledgements

The authors gratefully acknowledge the financial support from CAPES (88887.360812/2019-00 and 88881.171419/2018-01) and CNPq (305055/2017-8, 428650/2018-0 and 311807/2018-6).

References

Floudas, C.A., Grossmann, I.E., 1987. Automatic generation of multiperiod heat exchanger network configuration. Comput. Chem. Eng. 11, 123–142.

Nair, S.K., Karimi, I.A., 2018. Exploiting the Synergy between Work and Heat for Holistic Energy Integration, in: Computer Aided Chemical Engineering. Elsevier B.V., pp. 403–408.

Onishi, V.C., Ravagnani, M.A.S.S., Caballero, J.A., 2014. MINLP Model for the synthesis of heat exchanger networks with handling pressure of process streams. Comput. Aided Chem. Eng. 33, 163–168.

Pavão, L.V., Miranda, C.B., Costa, C.B.B., Ravagnani, M.A.S.S., 2018. Efficient multiperiod heat exchanger network synthesis using a meta-heuristic approach. Energy.

Pavão, L. V., Costa, C.B.B., Ravagnani, M.A.S.S., 2019. A new framework for work and heat exchange network synthesis and optimization. Energy Convers. Manag. 183, 617–632.

Pavão, L. V, Costa, C.B.B., Ravagnani, M.A.S.S., 2018. An enhanced stage-wise superstructure for heat exchanger networks synthesis with new options for heaters and coolers placement. Ind. Eng. Chem. Res. 57, 2560–2573.

Verheyen, W., Zhang, N., 2006. Design of flexible heat exchanger network for multi-period operation. Chem. Eng. Sci. 61, 7730–7753.

Yee, T.F., Grossmann, I.E., 1990. Simultaneous optimization models for heat integration—II. Heat exchanger network synthesis. Comput. Chem. Eng. 14, 1165–1184.

Yu, H., Fu, C., Gundersen, T., 2018. Work and Heat Exchange Networks – Opportunities and Challenges. Comput. Aided Chem. Eng. 44, 481–486.

Sauro Pierucci, Flavio Manenti, Giulia Bozzano, Davide Manca (Eds.)
Proceedings of the 30th European Symposium on Computer Aided Process Engineering
(ESCAPE30), May 24-27, 2020, Milano, Italy. © 2020 Elsevier B.V. All rights reserved.
http://dx.doi.org/10.1016/B978-0-12-823377-1.50148-8

Multi-Objective Evolutionary Algorithm based on Decomposition (MOEA/D) for Optimal Design of Hydrogen Supply Chains

Victor H. Cantú,[a,*] Catherine Azzaro-Pantel,[a] Antonin Ponsich[b]

[a]*Laboratoire de Génie Chimique, Université de Toulouse, CNRS, INPT, UPS, 4 allée Emile Monso, 31432 Toulouse Cedex 4, France*
[b]*Departamento de Sistemas, Universidad Autónoma Metropolitana Azcapotzalco, Av. San Pablo Xalpa 180, Ciudad de México, Mexico*
vcantume@inp-toulouse.fr

Abstract

This work introduces an efficient tool for the design of sustainable hydrogen supply chains (HSCs), considering both economic and environmental concerns, through an appropriate multi-objective strategy. Within this hybrid strategy, a multi-objective evolutionary algorithm deals with integer variables and Pareto front construction, which reduces the original mixed-integer linear programming (MILP) to multiple linear programming (LP) sub-problems. The proposed methodology is validated through the comparison of the true Pareto fronts given by CPLEX, for three increasing size instances. Numerical results prove that the hybrid approach reproduces accurately the optimal fronts while reducing drastically (up to 20 times) the CPU time with respect to the MILP solver.

Keywords: Hydrogen supply chain, Multi-objective optimization, Hybrid evolutionary algorithm.

1. Introduction

Hydrogen is expected to play a significant role in low-carbon energy landscape. According to the Hydrogen Council (2017), hydrogen will cover 18% of global energy demand by 2050. However, much of the future expansion of hydrogen utilization depends not only on technological developments and energy policies, but also on the hydrogen supply chain (HSC) deployment. In this way, designing a cost-efficient infrastructure, encompassing the wide spectrum of production and distribution options that may evolve over time with growing demand, is a significant challenge.

The HSC deployment has been studied from different perspectives. One of the most popular approaches found in the dedicated literature is that proposed in Almansoori and Shah (2006), in which the HSC design problem is tackled through a mathematical programming (MP) model considering production, storage and distribution echelons. The resulting mixed-integer linear programming (MILP) problem consists in minimizing the total daily cost (*TDC*), which includes infrastructural, operating and transportation costs. The optimization problem is then efficiently solved by MP techniques. Yet, comprehensive analysis is needed to evaluate and optimize the sustainability of hydrogen energy systems and, in particular, the environmental aspects through the potential impacts associated with hydrogen production, distribution and storage. In this vein, the minimization of the environmental impact of supply chains (SCs) through Global Warming Potential (*GWP*), has received much attention. This indicator has thus been proposed as a second objective in Almaraz et al. (2014a). The resulting bi-objective problem is solved by CPLEX by means of the ε-constraint method within GAMS environment. This methodology has now been used for different case studies in France (Almaraz et al., 2014b), Germany (Almansoori and Betancourt-Torcat, 2016) and Portugal (Câmara et al., 2019).

Even if the optimization problems derived from the above-cited works have been solved to optimality, it is worth mentioning that their computational complexity involves solution times that might rapidly rise with the instance size. In addition, for more than one objective, the construction of the Pareto front by MP techniques is usually a time-consuming task, since each Pareto solution requires at least one scalar optimization. An alternative to the solution of Process Engineering optimization problems is to use metaheuristics, and specifically, Multiobjective Evolutionary Algorithms (MOEAs). MOEAs are stochastic population-based nature-inspired algorithms, able of handling multiple objectives, continuous and discrete variables, nonlinear and multimodal functions. However, as these search algorithms are designed to work over unconstrained search spaces, they generally exhibit a poor performance when solving highly constrained problems, even if sophisticated constraint-handling techniques have been proposed.

The scientific objective of this work is thus to propose a hybrid methodology to solve the HSC problem, which decomposes the global problem in such a way that advantages can be taken of the strengths of each single approach, mitigating simultaneously their disadvantages: the construction of the Pareto front is carried out by the evolutionary algorithm, whereas the equality constraints are treated by the exact technique. Besides, the integer variables are handled by the MOEA, so that the original MILP problem is reduced to multiple LP sub-problems, which can be efficiently solved.

The remainder of this work is as follows: in the next section, a brief definition of the HSC problem is provided. Then, the proposed solution strategy is explained in section 3. Section 4 presents three case studies used for validation, while the computation experiments are described and discussed in section 5. Finally, some conclusions and perspectives for future work are proposed in section 6.

2. Problem definition

The mathematical model considered in this work is taken from Almansoori and Shah (2006) and from its adaptation proposed in Almaraz et al. (2014a). Accordingly, the total geographic area is divided into grids (nodes). Each grid has a total hydrogen demand that has to be satisfied. In addition, hydrogen can be transported between grids so that one grid cannot simultaneously import and export hydrogen. For instance, in the example shown in Figure 1, the geographic area is divided into 9 grids and grids 4, 6 and 7 cannot export hydrogen to other grids because they already import from grid 5. For each grid (g), a number of plants (N_{pig}) for each production type (p) and product physical form (i) must be determined, as well as the corresponding total production rates (P_{pig}) and the inlet/outlet hydrogen flows $Q_{ilgg'}$, where l accounts for the type of transportation mode. Three types of production plants (steam reforming, coal and biomass) and two storage types (liquid, gaseous) have been considered.

The two objectives to be minimized are (1) the total daily cost (*TDC*), which includes investment costs related to plant installation (*FCC*) and transportation (*TCC*), and operation costs for production (*FOC*), transportation (*TOC*) and storage (*FOC*); and (2) the *GWP*, formulated in Almaraz et al. (2014a) as indicated in Eq. (2). The *GWP* accounts

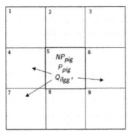

Figure 1. Example of grid discretization of geographic area.

for gas emission due to production (GW^{prod}), storage (GW^{stock}), and transportation (GW^{transp}). It is worth mentioning that the resulting problem is NP-hard. The complete formulation, particularly regarding constraints related to storage and transportation, the bounded production capacity of each plant and the satisfaction of hydrogen demand in each grid, can be found in Almansoori and Shah (2006) and Almaraz et al. (2014a).

$$TDC = \frac{FCC + TCC}{\alpha CCF} + FOC + TOC \tag{1}$$

$$GWP = \sum_{pg} P_{pg}\left(GW^{prod} + GW^{stock}\right) + \sum_{gg'}\left(\frac{2WL_{gg'}Q_{gg'}}{TCap}\right)GW^{transp} \tag{2}$$

3. Methodology

The complexity due to the combinatorial and multi-objective nature of the HSC problem deserves the development of an adapted solution strategy. The original MILP problem is decomposed into two parts (see Figure 2): the integer (master) sub-problem and the continuous (slave) sub-problem. The master sub-problem is treated by the multi-objective evolutionary algorithm, in which the integer variables (number of production units) are encoded in every individual in the population. For each individual, which is now a partial solution, a linear programming sub-problem is solved to determine the corresponding optimum production rates and transportation flows. This LP problem is constructed according to the values of the integer variables provided by the MOEA in such a way that it is almost a canonical transportation problem. The integer variables produced by the MOEA may be repaired to ensure that this problem is feasible. Subsequently, the MOEA recovers the continuous variables (P_{pig}, $Q_{ilgg'}$) from the LP solver, in order to compute the *TDC* and *GWP* objectives. Once evaluated, each individual has its fitness function value assigned by the MOEA, which evolves the population to the next generation. The proposed methodology is presented in an algorithmic scheme as follows:

1. Assign integer variables (NP_{pig}) using a stochastic operator.

2. Construct the transportation problem, identifying demand and source grids.

3. Solve the multi-objective transportation problem (LP).

4. Compute the TDC and GWP objectives for the current solution.

5. Evolve population according to MOEA.

6. If the termination criterion is not reached, go to step 1.

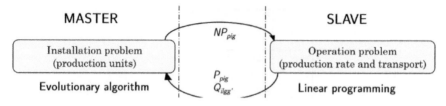

Figure 2. Hybrid (master - slave) approach.

The first key point of this methodology is the construction of a feasible transportation problem using the integer variables provided by the evolutionary module. The set of grids G is divided into importing (G^I) and exporting (G^E) grids according to the number of plants installed and their production capacity: if, for a given grid, the production capacity of all plants installed is lower than the grid demand, the grid is considered as a "source" (G^E). If the total production capacity (over all grids) does not meet the total demand, plant units are randomly added in order to ensure feasibility of the transportation problem.

Besides, to handle multiple objectives within the LP sub-problem, both criteria (*GWP* and *TDC*) are integrated in the objective function through a scalarizing function (such as the weighted sum or the Tchebycheff function). These functions involve weight vectors associated to each objective priority. In this way, the LP can be easily hybridized with the Multi-Objective Evolutionary Algorithm based on Decomposition (MOEA/D) (Zhang and Li, 2007). Indeed, this MOEA assigns a scalarization (like the LP formulated here) of the original multi-objective problem to every individual in the population, with a specific weight vector each. Then, each individual solves its respective scalar sub-problem through a collaboration with the neighbour solutions in the population. Consequently, each LP to be solved inherits its weight vector (used in the scalarizing function) from the individual, establishing a direct relationship between the objective space explored by the individual and by the LP.

In this work, the weighted Tchebycheff function (Coello et al., 2007) is used, so that the resulting LP sub-problem is formulated as follows:

$$
\begin{aligned}
\min \quad & \max_{k \in K}\left\{\lambda_k \left| f_k(x) - f_k^* \right|\right\} \\
\text{s.t.} \quad & \sum_p P_{pig} = \sum_{\lg'}\left(Q_{i\lg g'} - Q_{i\lg'g}\right) + D_{ig}^T && \forall i \in I, g \in G \\
& PCap_{pi}^{\min} NP_{pig} \leq P_{pig} \leq PCap_{pi}^{\max} NP_{pig} && \forall p \in P, i \in I, g \in G \\
& Q_{i\lg g'} \geq 0 && \forall i \in I, l \in L, g, g' \in G
\end{aligned}
\tag{3}
$$

where λ_k is the k-th weight vector ($k = 1,\ldots, K$), x represents the set of real decision variables (P_{pig}, $Q_{i\lg g'}$), $f_k(x)$ the objective functions and f_k^* is the reference point (composed of single-objective optima). NP_{pig} are considered as constants in Eq. (3). It is to note that the optimum for the original MILP problem and the new one remains the same.

4. Case study

In this work, three increasing size instances are considered that correspond to the data for the Great Britain case study (Almansoori et al., 2006). Instances 1 and 2 represent a part of the entire geographic area of Instance 3. Please note that the number of decision variables in Table 1 represents the actual decision variables of the hybrid methodology, although those for the original MILP formulation might be greater.

Table 1. Case study.

	Instance 1	Instance 2	Instance 3
Number of grids	6	12	34
Number of integer variables	18	36	102
Number of continuous variables	48	168	1224

5. Results

For the evolutionary algorithm, the population size and number of generations are 51 and 510, respectively. Likewise, 51 weight vectors are used for CPLEX using the Tchebycheff decomposition. The obtained Pareto fronts are presented in Fig. 3-5. As can be observed, the approximations of the Pareto front for both approaches are similar, as most solutions are overlaid. The stair shape of the Pareto front is due to the discrete nature of the problem, and precisely, to the constraint on maximum production capacity. Furthermore, Table 2 shows that, for the hypervolume indicator (which represents the hyper-space dominated by a Pareto front approximation, i.e., the higher, the better), both strategies perform similarly for all instances (results in accordance with Fig. 3-5). However, the computational time increases drastically for the deterministic algorithm, both because of the need for solving the problem multiple times and to the combinatorial aspect.

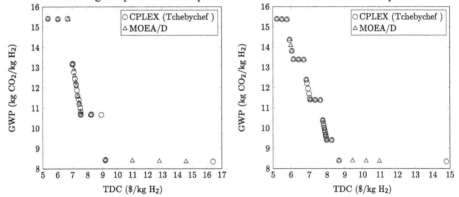

Figure 3. Obtained Pareto front for Instance 1.   Figure 4. Obtained Pareto front for Instance 2.

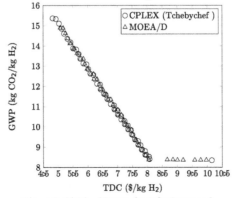

Figure 5. Obtained Pareto front for Instance 3.

Table 2. Numerical comparison of results for the hybrid and classical approaches.

	Instance 1		Instance 2		Instance 3	
	Hybrid	CPLEX	Hybrid	CPLEX	Hybrid	CPLEX
CPU time(s)[a]	164.65	**52.87**	**226.08**	4577.76	**1908.96**	45094.32
Hypervolume	**63.29**	63.04	**54.27**	54.26	14.80	14.80

[a] Computational experiments were carried out with a processor Intel Xeon E3-1505M v6 and 32 Go RAM.

The CPU time for the hybrid strategy remains yet acceptable even for the largest instance (lower than one hour), while the time required by the classical approach is prohibitive (more than 12 hours). In addition, note that the time proportion devoted to the solution of the LP sub-problems is practically the same in the three instances. To conclude, the solution strategy proposed in this work is able to accurately reproduce the optimal Pareto front, with CPU times up to 20 times lower than those required by the MILP approach.

6. Conclusions and perspectives

A hybrid approach combining MOEA and linear programming has been developed to overcome the main drawbacks that are present in MP techniques when solving multi-objective problems, and taking full advantage of MOEAs for the construction of the Pareto front for the solution of HSC design. The proposed methodology is capable to efficiently solve the multi-objective HSC problem as has been validated with the exact solutions given by CPLEX for three increasing size instances. Besides, the computational times for the proposed methodology are significantly inferior to that of the classical approach. This is promising for the solution of larger size instances and for a more realistic (nonlinear) model of the HSC to be considered.

References

The Hydrogen Council (2017) Hydrogen scaling up: A sustainable pathway for the global energy transition.

Almansoori, A., and Shah, N. (2006). Design and operation of a future hydrogen supply chain: snapshot model. *Chemical Engineering Research and Design, 84*(6), 423-438.

Almaraz, S. D. L., Azzaro-Pantel, C., Montastruc, L., and Domenech, S. (2014a). Hydrogen supply chain optimization for deployment scenarios in the Midi-Pyrénées region, France. *International Journal of Hydrogen Energy, 39*(23), 11831-11845.

Almaraz, S. D. L., Boix, M., Azzaro-Pantel, C., Montastruc, L., and Domenech, S. (2014b). Spatial-based approach of the hydrogen supply chain in the Midi-Pyrénées region, France. In *Computer Aided Chemical Engineering* (Vol. 33, pp. 307-312). Elsevier.

Almansoori, A., and Betancourt-Torcat, A. (2016). Design of optimization model for a hydrogen supply chain under emission constraints-A case study of Germany. *Energy*, 111, 414-429.

Câmara, D., Pinto-Varela, T., and Barbósa-Povoa, A. P. (2019). Multi-objective optimization approach to design and planning hydrogen supply chain under uncertainty: A Portugal study case. In *Computer Aided Chemical Engineering* (Vol. 46, pp. 1309-1314). Elsevier.

Zhang, Q., and Li, H. (2007). MOEA/D: A multiobjective evolutionary algorithm based on decomposition. *IEEE Transactions on Evolutionary Computation*, *11*(6), 712-731.

Coello, C. A. C., Lamont, G. B., & Van Veldhuizen, D. A. (2007). Evolutionary algorithms for solving multi-objective problems (Vol. 5, pp. 79-104). New York: Springer.

Sauro Pierucci, Flavio Manenti, Giulia Bozzano, Davide Manca (Eds.)
Proceedings of the 30th European Symposium on Computer Aided Process Engineering
(ESCAPE30), May 24-27, 2020, Milano, Italy. © 2020 Elsevier B.V. All rights reserved.
http://dx.doi.org/10.1016/B978-0-12-823377-1.50149-X

Integrated In Silico Design of Catalysts and Processes based on Quantum Chemistry

Christoph Gertig[a], Lorenz Fleitmann[a], Carl Hemprich[a], Janik Hense[a], André Bardow[a,b], Kai Leonhard[a,*]

[a]*Institute of Technical Thermodynamics, RWTH Aachen University, 52062 Aachen, Germany*
[b]*Institute of Energy and Climate Research (IEK-10), Forschungszentrum Jülich, 52425 Jülich, Germany*
Kai.Leonhard@ltt.rwth-aachen.de

Abstract

Most chemical processes rely on suitable catalysts. Thus, selecting the right catalyst for a process is an important task in chemical process design. However, searching new catalysts can be very tedious. Therefore, computer-aided molecular design (CAMD) methods are very desirable to identify promising candidate catalysts *in silico* and thereby minimize experimental effort. However, methods for computational catalyst design are still in their infancy and often focus on the catalyst turnover number and frequency only while the best catalyst is the one that maximizes the overall process performance. In this work, we therefore propose a method for computer-aided molecular and process design (CAMPD) of catalysts and the corresponding process. A key element is the efficient but accurate prediction of reaction kinetics with advanced quantum chemical methods. We demonstrate the design method for catalytic carbamate cleavage and show that only the integrated catalyst and process design identifies the catalysts that maximize process performance.

Keywords: catalysis, reactions, computer-aided molecular design, process design

1. Introduction

Catalysts are indispensable in the production of chemicals: More than 90 % of newly developed chemical processes require catalysts (Hagen, 2015). Therefore, finding a suitable catalyst is a very important task in chemical process design. Still, catalysts are usually found by experimental screenings or combinatorial chemistry. Such search methods are usually not target-oriented and often lead to huge experimental effort. In many fields of chemistry, experiments can already today (partly) be replaced by quantum chemical (QC) predictions. QC methods have even been combined with computer-aided molecular design (CAMD) methods e.g., for solvent design (Gertig et al., 2020).

However, the *in silico* design of catalyst molecules is still regarded as one of the "Holy Grails in Chemistry" (Poree and Schoenebeck, 2017). Only few approaches have been proposed for the *in silico* design of molecular catalysts. Some authors study catalytic effects in an abstract catalytic environment. The "Theozymes" approach (Tantillo et al.,1998) places functional groups representing the catalyst around reacting molecules. Subsequently, the spatial positions of the functional groups are optimized e.g., to decrease the activation energy of the reaction. Dittner and Hartke (2018) optimize an abstract environment of reacting molecules to study the effect of optimal catalysts. Such approaches are very valuable to understand the influence of catalysts, but do not design real catalyst molecules. Rarely, approaches have been proposed that optimize real catalyst structures *in silico*. Lin et al. (2005) design transition metal catalysts based on a set of functional groups as building blocks using a tabu search algorithm. Quantitative structure-property relationships (QSPR) are fitted to experimental data and used for performance prediction. The design is based on objectives like density and toxicity. Thus, an optimized catalytic effect is not directly predicted. Chang et al. (2018) design Ni catalyst complexes for catalytic CO/CO_2 conversion. Selected groups of the ligands are optimized to lower the activation energy of the rate-limiting reaction step. Semi-empirical QC methods are used to predict activation energies during design. Promising candidates are subsequently investigated using quantum mechanical density functional theory (DFT).

Despite these encouraging first approaches to *in silico* design of molecular catalysts, two important elements are still missing (Gertig et al., 2020): First, a reliable prediction is required for the acceleration of chemical reactions by candidate catalysts to ensure reliable design results. Thus, reaction rate constants should be predicted using advanced quantum chemical methods. Second, acceleration of chemical reactions is not the ultimate objective of catalyst design but maximum performance of the chemical process. Consequently, catalyst design should be integrated with process design.

In this work, we present the CAT-COSMO-CAMPD method for computer-aided molecular and process design that integrates the optimization of catalyst structures and processes. We calculate reaction rate constants for the designed catalysts based on transition state theory (TST) (Eyring, 1935) and advanced QC methods. A hybrid optimization scheme determines optimal catalyst structures and process conditions: Catalyst structures are designed and optimized using the genetic optimization algorithm LEA3D (ligand by evolutionary algorithm) (Douguet et al., 2005). Optimal process conditions are determined by deterministic process optimization, thus enabling a process-based assessment of all candidate catalysts. The proposed integrated design method is presented in Section 2. The method is demonstrated for the integrated catalyst and process design for a carbamate cleavage process (Section 3).

2. Computer-Aided Catalyst and Process Design

Based on the generic CAMD problem (Gani, 2004), we formulate the computer-aided catalyst and process design problem as optimization problem:

$$
\begin{aligned}
&\max_{x,y} f(x,y) && \text{process-based objective} \\
\text{s.t.} \quad & h_1(x,y) = 0 && \text{thermodynamics, kinetics and process} \\
& h_2(x,y) \leq 0 && \text{inequality constraints on properties and process} \\
& g(y) \leq 0 && \text{(in)equality constraints on molecular structure} \\
& x \in X \subset \mathbb{R}^n && \text{process degrees of freedom} \\
& y \in Y && \text{molecular structure}
\end{aligned}
\tag{1}
$$

In Problem (1), the process-based objective $f(x,y)$ depends on process degrees of freedom x and the molecular structure of the catalyst y. Equality constraints $h_1(x,y)$ model the reaction kinetics, equilibrium thermodynamics and processes. Inequality constraints $h_2(x,y)$ are used on thermodynamic and kinetic properties as well as process conditions. (In)equality constraints $g(y)$ ensure the design of chemically feasible structures and may also limit the explored molecular design space.

To solve the integrated catalyst and process design problem (Problem (1)), we propose the CAT-COSMO-CAMPD method. Following our integrated solvent and process design method COSMO-CAMPD (Gertig et al., 2019a), we solve the integrated design problem in a hybrid optimization scheme (Figure 1): Catalyst structures are designed and optimized using the genetic optimization algorithm LEA3D (Douguet et al., 2005) based on a given library of 3D molecule fragments as building blocks. Optimal process conditions are determined by deterministic process optimization.

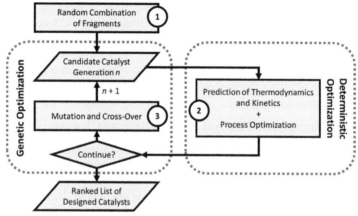

Figure 1: CAT-COSMO-CAMPD method for solution of the integrated catalyst and process design problem using a hybrid optimization scheme combining genetic optimization of molecular catalyst structures and deterministic process optimization.

In step 1 of CAT-COSMO-CAMPD (Figure 1), 3D molecule fragments from the fragment library are combined randomly to obtain an initial generation of candidate catalysts. It is important to ensure that all candidates contain a catalytically active group. In step 2, all candidates from the initial generation are evaluated. This evaluation requires the QC-based prediction of thermodynamic equilibrium properties as well as the prediction of reaction rate constants with transition state theory (TST) (Eyring, 1935). Geometry optimization and frequency analysis are performed for each candidate catalyst molecule as well as for transition states of the catalyzed reactions. The identification of transition states works reliably since the transition states are similar for all carboxylic acid-catalyzed reactions and the optimizations start from a general template. These calculations use the DFT method B3LYP with TZVP basis set and the software Gaussian 09 (Frisch et al., 2013). ORCA (Neese, 2018) is employed to calculate accurate electronic energies with DLPNO-CCSD(T) (Riplinger and Neese, 2013) and aug-cc-pVTZ basis set. We found that this combination of QC methods yields excellent results for different kinds of reactive systems (Gertig et al., 2019a; 2019b). Thermochemical calculations of ideal gas properties are performed with GoodVibes (Funes-Ardoiz and Paton, 2018) based on the rigid rotor harmonic oscillator (RRHO) approximation and quasi-harmonic treatment of low vibrational frequencies (Grimme, 2012). COSMO-RS (Eckert and Klamt, 2002) is used to account for solvation effects. This approach allows to predict both the required thermodynamic equilibrium properties as well as activation barriers between reactant states and transition states in gas and liquid phases. The predicted activation barriers are used in TST to calculate the rate constants of reactions catalyzed by the candidate catalysts.

All candidate catalysts are assessed based on their process performance. For this purpose, process models are formulated from balance and kinetic equations. These process models are used together with the property prediction methods described above in deterministic optimizations to optimize the process performance for each candidate catalysts. Process optimization employs the interior-point algorithm available in the MatLab (The MathWorks, Inc., 2015) function *fmincon*. The optimized process performance of the candidate catalysts is forwarded to the genetic algorithm. In step 3, the genetic algorithm performs mutations and crossovers for promising candidate catalysts to obtain a new generation of candidates. This new generation of candidate catalysts is again evaluated using QC methods and process optimization (step 2). Steps 2 and 3 are repeated for a predefined number of cycles. Subsequently, a ranking of designed catalysts is returned based on their process performance.

3. Case Study: Integrated Catalyst and Carbamate Cleavage Process Design

The proposed CAT-COSMO-CAMPD method is demonstrated for the design of catalyst and process for carbamate cleavage. Carbamate cleavage is part of a possible production route of industrially important isocyanates (Six and Richter, 2000). The reaction is slow and endothermic (Leitner et al., 2018) and continuous removal of the volatile by-product methanol is required to avoid instantaneous limitation by reaction equilibrium (Kaiser et al., 2018). As discussed in our previous work on solvent design for carbamate cleavage (Gertig et al., 2019a), this constant methanol removal can be achieved by a process comprising of a 2-phase batch reactor and a flash (Figure 2). The catalytic cleavage takes place in a liquid reaction phase that is flushed by inert N_2 to strip out the formed methanol. The flash is used to recycle stripped out solvent, isocyanate and catalyst. Here, we study the cleavage of methyl phenyl carbamate (MPC) to phenyl isocyanate and methanol.

As design objective $f(x, y)$, we choose the yield Y defined as the final amount of isocyanate divided by the initial amount of MPC in the reactor. The degrees of freedom x for process optimization are the flow of nitrogen $\dot{V}_{N_2}$, and the temperature T^F in the flash. The catalytically active group in the designed catalyst structures y is the carboxyl group as carboxylic acids are known to be catalytically active (Satchell and Satchell, 1975). It is important to note that the design method could also work with other catalytically active groups. As further building blocks for catalyst design, the fragment library contains various alkyl and aryl as well as keto, ether, ester, nitrile, amino, halide, sulfide and sulfene fragments. The constraints $h_1(x, y)$ include all equations for property prediction and the process model. Constraints $h_2(x, y)$ limit the flash temperature T^F between 280 and 380 K and the nitrogen flow $\dot{V}_{N_2}$ between 5×10^{-5} and 1.5×10^{-1} m³/s. Constant parameters are the reactor volume V^R of 1 m³, the reactor temperature T^R of 473.15 K and a reaction time of 12 h. The reactor is loaded with 15 m-% MPC and 5m-% catalyst. The solvent is diphenyl ether. LEA3D inherently ensures chemical feasibility of designed structures. Further constraints $g(y)$ limit the number of non-hydrogen

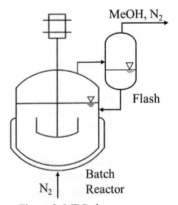

Figure 2: MPC cleavage process.

atoms in the catalysts to a maximum of 13 and ensure that each designed catalyst contains exactly one catalytically active group. The design is run for 6 generations of candidate catalysts after the random initial generation, with 12 candidate catalysts per generation.

The results of the integrated catalyst and process design are shown in Figure 3. 33 catalysts are designed that meet all constraints. The best designed catalyst (shown left in Figure 3) achieves an isocyanate yield of 21 % after 12 h. After few hours, complete conversion cannot be expected due to the slow nature of carbamate cleavage. The optimized process settings are: $\dot{V}_{N_2} = 5.4 \times 10^{-2}$, $T^F = 281.1$ K.

Besides the top catalyst, the design suggests several near-optimal candidates. Thus, the final choice could consider additional criteria like commercial availability and environmental properties.

Importantly, the top candidate from the integrated catalyst and process design differs from a simpler catalyst design with a high reaction rate constant as objective. The highest reaction rate is achieved by brominated formic acid. While brominated formic acid is expected to be unstable, it points here to the problem that a high reaction rate can still lead to poor performance in the MPC cleavage process (Figure 3). The reason is that besides the acceleration of the

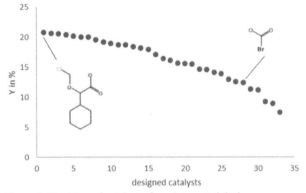

Figure 3: Ranking of catalysts from integrated design.

cleavage reaction, high process performance requires further criteria. Examples of such criteria are catalyst volatility leading to stripping by N_2 or the impact of the catalyst on the activity coefficient of methanol which influences the amount of methanol condensed and recycled in the flash. Only the integrated catalyst and process design accounts for the trade-offs between different properties and finds overall optimal solutions.

4. Conclusion

We propose the CAT-COSMO-CAMD method for computer-aided catalyst and process design. Equilibrium properties and kinetics are predicted based on advanced quantum chemical methods and transition state theory. A hybrid optimization scheme is employed to solve the integrated catalyst and process design problem: the genetic algorithm LEA3D is used to optimize catalyst structures and a deterministic algorithm is used for process optimization. The method is demonstrated for a catalytic carbamate cleavage process and identifies several promising catalyst molecules. The results show that catalyst design maximizing only the reaction rate may be misleading whereas the integrated catalyst and process design finds the catalysts that actually maximize process performance.

Acknowledgements

We thank the German Federal Ministry of Education and Research for funding of the project Carbon2Polymers (03EK30442C). Simulations were performed with computing resources granted by RWTH Aachen University under projects rwth0284 and rwth0478.

References

A. M. Chang, B. Rudshteyn, I. Warnke, V. S. Batista, 2018, Inverse Design of a Catalyst for Aqueous CO/CO$_2$ Conversion Informed by the NiII–Iminothiolate Complex, Inorganic Chemistry, 57(24), 15474-15480.

M. Dittner, B. Hartke, 2018, Globally Optimal Catalytic Fields–Inverse Design of Abstract Embeddings for Maximum Reaction Rate Acceleration, Journal of Chemical Theory and Computation, 14(7), 3547-3564.

D. Douguet, H. Munier-Lehmann, G. Labesse, S. Pochet, 2005, LEA3D: a Computer-Aided Ligand Design for Structure-Based Drug Design, J. Med. Chem., 48(7), 2457-2468.

F. Eckert, A. Klamt, 2002, Fast solvent screening via quantum chemistry: COSMO-RS approach, AIChE Journal, 48, 369–385.

H. Eyring, 1935, The activated complex in chemical reactions, J. Chem. Phys., 3(2), 107-115.

M. J. Frisch et al., 2013, Gaussian 09, Revision D.01.

I. Funes-Ardoiz, R. Paton, 2016, GoodVibes: GoodVibes v1.0.2, DOI: 10.5281/zenodo.595246.

R. Gani, 2004, Chemical product design: challenges and opportunities, Computers & Chemical Engineering, 28(12), 2441-2457.

C. Gertig, K. Leonhard, A. Bardow, 2020, Computer-Aided Molecular and Process Design based on Quantum Chemistry: Current Status and Future Prospects, Current Opinion in Chemical Engineering, 27, 89-97.

C. Gertig, K. Leonhard, A. Bardow, 2019a, Integrated Design of Solvents and Processes based on Reaction Kinetics from Quantum Chemical Prediction Methods, Computer Aided Chemical Engineering 46, 415-420.

C. Gertig, L. C. Kröger, L. Fleitmann, J. Scheffczyk, A. Bardow, K. Leonhard, 2019b, Rx-COSMO-CAMD: Computer-Aided Molecular Design of Reaction Solvents based on predictive Kinetics from Quantum Chemistry, Industrial & Engineering Chemistry Research, 58, 22835-22846.

S. Grimme, 2012, Supramolecular Binding Thermodynamics by Dispersion- Corrected Density Functional Theory, Chemistry–A European Journal, 18(32), 9955-9964.

J. Hagen, 2015, Industrial Catalysis, WILEY-VCH.

T. Kaiser, A. Rathgeb, C. Gertig, A. Bardow, K. Leonhard, A. Jupke, 2018, Carbon2Polymer–Conceptual Design of a CO$_2$- Based Process for the Production of Isocyanates. Chemie Ingenieur Technik, 90(10), 1497-1503.

W. Leitner, G. Franciò, M. Scott, C. Westhues, J. Langanke, M. Lansing, C. Hussong, E. Erdkamp, 2018, Carbon2Polymer–Chemical Utilization of CO$_2$ in the Production of Isocyanates, Chemie Ingenieur Technik 90 (10), 1504–1512.

B. Lin, S. Chavali, K. Camarda, D. C. Miller, 2005, Computer-aided molecular design using Tabu search, Computers & Chemical Engineering, 29(2), 337-347.

The MathWorks, Inc., 2015. MATLAB R2015b.

F. Neese, 2018, Software update: the ORCA program system, version 4.0, Wiley Interdisciplinary Reviews: Computational Molecular Science, 8, e1327.

C. Poree, F. Schoenebeck, 2017, A holy grail in chemistry: Computational catalyst design: Feasible or fiction?, Accounts of Chemical Research 50 (3), 605-608.

C. Riplinger, F. Neese, 2013, An efficient and near linear scaling pair natural orbital based local coupled cluster method,The Journal of Chemical Physics,138, 034106.

D. Satchell, R. Satchell, 1975, Acylation by ketens and isocyanates. A mechanistic comparison, Chemical Society Reviews, 4(2), 231-250.

C. Six, F. Richter, 2000. Isocyanates, organic. Ullmann's Encyclopedia of Industrial Chemistry.

D. J. Tantillo, C. Jiangang, K. N. Houk, 1998, Theozymes and compuzymes: theoretical models for biological catalysis, Current Opinion in Chemical Biology, 2(6), 743-750.

Sauro Pierucci, Flavio Manenti, Giulia Bozzano, Davide Manca (Eds.)
Proceedings of the 30th European Symposium on Computer Aided Process Engineering
(ESCAPE30), May 24-27, 2020, Milano, Italy. © 2020 Elsevier B.V. All rights reserved.
http://dx.doi.org/10.1016/B978-0-12-823377-1.50150-6

In silico Screening of Metal-organic Frameworks for Acetylene/ethylene Separation

Yageng Zhou[a], Teng Zhou[a,b,*], Kai Sundmacher[a,b]

[a] *Process Systems Engineering, Otto-von-Guericke University Magdeburg, Universitätsplatz 2, D-39106 Magdeburg, Germany*

[b] *Process Systems Engineering, Max Planck Institute for Dynamics of Complex Technical Systems, Sandtorstr. 1, D-39106 Magdeburg, Germany*

zhout@mpi-magdeburg.mpg.de

Abstract

Ethylene, used as feedstocks for producing polyethylene, is a valuable chemical in the petroleum industry. The separation of acetylene from ethylene in the ethane cracking process to produce high-purity ethylene is conventionally carried out by energy intensive partial hydrogenation or solvent absorption. Over the last decade, Metal-Organic Frameworks (MOFs) have emerged as a promising class of porous adsorbents. They are reported to have high performances in many gas separation applications thus could potentially lead to energy-efficient process alternatives (Li et al., 2012). In this work, a large-scale computational screening of 4764 different MOFs for the ethylene/acetylene separation is performed. As a result, 10 potential MOF candidates are identified as the best separation materials, which are targeted for further experimental synthesis and validation.

Keywords: metal-organic framework, acetylene/ethylene separation, GCMC simulation, adsorbent screening

1. Introduction

In the petrochemical industry, acetylene and ethylene are two important intermediate chemicals for producing consumer products. In the ethane cracking and biomass and coal pyrolysis processes, a mixture of C_2H_2 and C_2H_4 gases needs to be separated (Cui et al., 2016). Traditional separation methods, such as solvent absorption and partial hydrogenation, are quite energy-consuming (Studt et al., 2008).

Over the last few decades, metal-organic frameworks (MOFs), formed by inorganic centers and organic linking groups, have emerged as novel porous materials for gas storage and separation. It has been found that many MOFs exhibit high capacity and selectivity for the C_2H_2/C_2H_4 separation. Xiang et al. (2011) first reported a set of tunable mixed-metal-organic framework materials, among which M'MOF-3a showed the highest selectivities 25.5, 4.1 and 5.2 at 195 K, 273 K and 295 K, respectively. Bloch et al. (2012) demonstrated the high performance of FeMOF-74 with the C_2H_2 equilibrium uptake of 6.8 mmol/g and C_2H_2/C_2H_4 selectivity 2.08 at 318 K and 1 bar. Yang et al. (2014) reported that at 293 K and 1 bar the C_2H_2 uptake and C_2H_2/C_2H_4 selectivity of NOTT-300 are 6.34 mmol/g and 2.3, respectively. Hu et al. (2015) found that the suitable pores and opening windows of UTSA-100a can lead to a satisfying C_2H_2 uptake of 4.27 mmol/g and a high C_2H_2/C_2H_4 selectivity of 10.72 at 296 K and 1 bar. Cui et al. (2016) reported two new MOFs, SIFSIX-2-Cu-i (C_2H_2 uptake outperformed UTSA100a under 0.025 bar) and

SIFSIX-1-Cu (C_2H_2 uptake 8.5 mmol/g), and found their C_2H_2/C_2H_4 selectivities were in the ranges of 39.7 − 44.8 and 7.1 − 10.6, respectively, depending on the feed gas conditions. Recently, Wang et al. (2017) discovered BUT-11 that displayed a C_2H_2 uptake of 159.4 cm^3/g (≈ 7.12 mmol/g) at 298 K and 1 bar.

Given the structural diversities of MOFs, experimental synthesis and screening of MOFs for the separation of C_2H_2/C_2H_4 is costly and time-consuming. Fortunately, the significant progress of molecular simulation techniques makes it possible to utilize computational methods to discover promising MOFs for various gas separations, such as $CO_2/N_2/CH_4$ (Haldoupis et al., 2010; Wilmer et al., 2012a; Qiao et al., 2016), H_2/CH_4 (Wu et al., 2012; Altintas et al., 2018), C_2H_2/CH_4 and C_2H_2/CO_2 (Nemati Vesali Azar and Keskin, 2018), C_2H_6/C_2H_4 and C_2H_6/CH_4 (Altintas and Keskin, 2016), CO_2/H_2 (Avci et al., 2018), C_3H_8/C_3H_6 (Yeo et al., 2016), alkane isomers (Dubbeldam et al., 2012; Chung et al., 2017).

In this work, we perform a large-scale computational screening of 4764 experimentally synthesized MOFs for the separation of an equimolar C_2H_2/C_2H_4 gas mixture. First, we validate the accuracy of grand canonical Monte Carlo (GCMC) simulations by comparing the simulated and experimental adsorption uptakes of pure C_2H_2 and C_2H_4 gases. Next, the adsorption of the C_2H_2/C_2H_4 mixture in different MOFs is examined using GCMC simulations, based on which the working capacity and selectivity of each MOF are calculated. Finally, a separation performance index (SPI) is defined and determined for each material. Based on the ranking of SPI, the most promising MOFs are identified.

2. Materials and simulation details

2.1 MOF database
In this work, the computation-ready, experimental metal-organic framework (CoRE MOF) database developed by Chung et al. (2014) is utilized as the screening database due to the following considerations: first, the database consists of a variety of MOFs structures, which provide a rich search space for finding promising adsorbents; second, the structures in the database are immediately suitable for molecular simulation without any further modifications; third, all the MOFs have already been experimentally reported so that the screened materials can be synthesized and applied. There are totally 4764 MOFs in the CoRE MOF database.

2.2 Simulation details
Grand canonical Monte Carlo (GCMC) simulation is widely used for investigating gas adsorption in porous materials. In this study, we rely on GCMC for the simulation of C_2H_2/C_2H_4 adsorption in MOFs using RASPA software (Dubbeldam et al., 2016). Specifically, we consider equal probabilities for four types of Monte Carlo moves, which are translation, rotation, reinsertion, and swap. A cut-off radius of 12.0 Å is used and the simulation cell is expanded to at least 24.0 Å along each dimension where periodic boundary conditions are applied. Each simulation is carried out with first 30,000 cycles for equilibration and subsequent 20,000 cycles for production. More details of these simulations settings can be found in the literature (Dubbeldam et al., 2016).

Among the various C_2H_2 molecular models, the one proposed in Fischer et al. (2010) is used due to its validated accuracy. Similarly, the C_2H_4 molecular model is adopted from Liu et al. (2008). The model parameters of both molecules are listed in Table 1, including Lennard-Jones (LJ) potential parameters (σ and ε), partial charge (q), and bond length (l).

Table 1. Molecular model parameters of the C2H2 and C2H4 molecules

	Atoms	σ (Å)	ε (K)	q (e)	Bond length l (Å)
C_2H_2	C in C_2H_2	3.800	57.875	−0.278	1.2111 (C–C)
	H in C_2H_2	0	0	0.278	1.0712 (C–H)
C_2H_4	CH_2 (sp^2)	3.685	93.0	0	1.3300 (C–C)

Due to charged atoms in C_2H_2, Columbic forces cannot be omitted. Thus besides the LJ 12-6 potential for describing Van der Waals force, the force field function should also include the Columbic potential and be formulated as follows:

$$U = \sum 4\,\varepsilon_{ij}\left[\left(\frac{\sigma_{ij}}{r_{ij}}\right)^{12} - \left(\frac{\sigma_{ij}}{r_{ij}}\right)^{6}\right] + \sum \frac{q_i q_j}{4\pi\varepsilon_0 r_{ij}} \tag{1}$$

where ε_{ij} is well depth, σ_{ij} is collision diameter, r_{ij} is the distance between atoms i and j, q_i is the atomic charge of atom i, and ε_0 is 8.8542×10^{-12} ($C^2N^{-1}m^{-2}$). The employed LJ potential parameters are taken from the DREIDING force field (Mayo et al., 1990) with those of the missing atoms taken from the UFF force field (Rappe et al., 1992). The cross LJ parameters are computed using Lorentz-Berthelot combing rules (Maitland et al., 1981) except those between Cu and C of C_2H_2 that are modified according to Fischer et al. (2010) to account for the interactions with unsaturated metal sites. In order to calculate Columbic interactions, partial charges on every framework atoms are estimated using the EQeq method proposed by Wilmer et al. (2012b). Additionally, all MOFs are assumed to be rigid with the purpose of saving a large amount of computational time. Although this assumption is made at the cost of the sacrifice in simulation accuracy, it is a generally accepted practice in large-scale screening.

3. Evaluation metrics

It is well known that selectivity and working capacity are two key indicators for evaluating separation performance. Selectivity is defined as the ratio of equilibrium constant K. For the separation of component i from j, $S_{i/j}$ is determined as follows:

$$S_{i/j} = \frac{K_i}{K_j} = \frac{y_i}{x_i} \bigg/ \frac{y_j}{x_j}$$

where y and x are the gas and adsorbed phase compositions, respectively.

The working capacity of the adsorbent with respect to component i is defined as the difference between the equilibrium adsorption, $N_{i,ads}$, and desorption, $N_{i,des}$, loadings:

$$C_i = N_{i,ads} - N_{i,des}$$

Considering the significance of both selectivity and working capacity, we defined a separation performance index (SPI), the product of both criteria, to evaluate and rank the separation capabilities of MOFs:

$$SPI = S_{i/j} \times C_i$$

4. Results and discussion

Before large-scale MOF screening, it is necessary to first validate the accuracy of GCMC simulations. For this purpose, we collect reported, experimental C_2H_2 and C_2H_4 adsorption uptakes in different MOFs (Xiang et al., 2009; Bao et al., 2011; He et al., 2012) under 298 K and 1 bar. For these MOFs we perform GCMC simulations at the same condition to compute pure gas equilibrium adsorption uptakes. The detailed simulation settings are described in Section 2. As illustrated in Figure 1, a good agreement between experimental and simulated gas uptakes can be found. The average relative deviations of acetylene and ethylene uptakes are 0.147 and 0.138, respectively. The results confirm that our selection of molecular models and force field parameters is appropriate and the molecular simulation setup is reasonable for MOF screening.

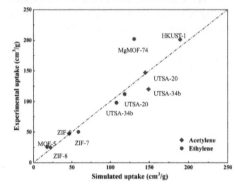

Figure 1: Comparison between experimental and GCMC simulated pure gas (C2H2 and C2H4) adsorption uptakes at 298 K and 1 bar

For the 4764 MOFs in the CoRE MOF database we conduct GCMC simulations and compute their selectivities and working capacities for C_2H_2 and C_2H_4 separation. In order to mimic the industrial adsorption process, the simulation temperature is fixed to 298 K and the adsorption and desorption pressures are set to 1 bar and 0.1 bar, respectively. The C_2H_2/C_2H_4 gas composition is specified to 50%/50% (mol/mol), a typical scenario in the biomass pyrolysis process (Cui et al., 2016). It is worth noting that for separating such an equimolar gas mixture, two different strategies can be employed. We can find either an adsorbent with a high $S_{C2H2/C2H4}$ and C_{C2H2} that selectively remove C_2H_2 from C_2H_4, or one preferentially adsorbs C_2H_4 with a high $S_{C2H4/C2H2}$ and C_{C2H4}. For better illustration, two separate plots corresponding to each strategy are presented in Figure 2.

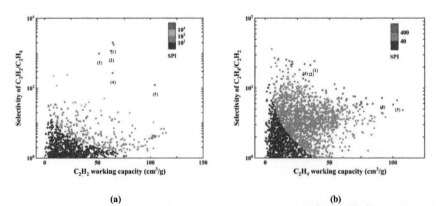

(a)   (b)

Figure 2: (a) GCMC simulated C2H2 working capacity and C2H2/C2H4 selectivity (b) GCMC simulated C2H4 working capacity and C2H4/C2H2 selectivity

As indicated in Figure 2(a), there are in total 975 C_2H_2-selective MOFs with $S_{C2H2/C2H4}$ ranging from 1.0 to 2005.6 and C_{C2H2} up to 114.8 cm^3/g. Among the 975 MOFs, 0.7% are found to have SPI value above 10^4, 1.7% between 10^3 and 10^4, 25.4% between 10^2 and 10^3, and 72.4% below 10^2. A trade-off between the selectivity and working capacity in the selection of MOFs can be observed. The top 5 MOFs with the highest SPI values are listed in Table 2, together with their important physical properties. The density ρ, pore limiting diameter (PLD), and porosity ϕ of the top 5 MOFs have been found to vary in limited ranges around 1.079 g/cm^3, 5.157 Å, and 0.561, respectively. Additionally, the Cu atom in MOF is found to be very favorable for the C_2H_2/C_2H_4 separation, mainly due to the strong interactions between C_2H_2 and the Cu open metal site. This finding agrees well with the experimental observations (Xiang et al. 2009).

Table 2. Top 5 MOFs for the separation of C2H2 from C2H4

Rank	CSD code	Metal	ρ (g/cm^3)	PLD (Å)	ϕ	C_{C2H2}	$S_{C2H2/C2H4}$
1	DOLXOR	Cu	1.087	5.360	0.559	64.2	2005.6
2	DOLXOR02	Cu	1.079	5.365	0.559	62.5	1177.1
3	KAHNOX	Cu	1.085	5.407	0.562	51.4	978.0
4	UBUROY	Cu, Zn	1.081	5.389	0.573	64.0	271.5
5	TANBOZ	Cu	1.061	4.265	0.550	104.2	121.8

As depicted in Figure 2(b), there are 2477 C_2H_4-selective MOFs with $S_{C2H4/C2H2}$ ranging from 1.0 to 36.1 and C_{C2H4} up to 107.9 cm^3/g. 1.7% of the MOFs are found to possess SPI value above 400, 66.3% between 40 and 400, and 32.0% below 40. Likewise, the top 5 MOFs with the highest C_2H_4 separation potentials are recognized and listed in Table 3. Large variations in the MOF's physical properties (0.774 g/cm^3 $\leq \rho \leq$ 1.511 g/cm^3, 2.593 Å $\leq$ PLD $\leq$ 4.441 Å, 0.432 $\leq \phi \leq$ 0.708) are observable and no strong evidence on the metal-dependence can be found among the top MOFs.

Table 3. Top 5 MOFs for the separation of C2H4 from C2H2

Rank	CSD code	Metal	ρ (g/cm^3)	PLD (Å)	ϕ	C_{C2H4}	$S_{C2H4/C2H2}$
1	SETFUT	Cd	1.511	2.593	0.444	38.4	24.3
2	BEXTUV	Mn	1.305	3.789	0.486	35.2	21.3
3	QUQPOI	Zn	0.774	4.340	0.667	103.3	6.7
4	ADIQEL	Co	1.238	3.914	0.432	30.7	22.1
5	DEYVUA	Zn	0.961	4.441	0.708	91.5	7.2

5. Conclusions

In order to address the challenge in the discovery of advanced materials for the energy-efficient acetylene/ethylene separation, we have systematically screened 4764 MOFs by use of GCMC simulations. Very promising MOFs are identified and the relevant physical properties of these materials are analyzed. In our future work, a detailed study on the adsorption kinetics will be carried out to identify adsorbents featuring high mass transfer rates. A rigorous evaluation of high-potential MOFs in a pressure or temperature-swing adsorption process will also be performed.

References

C. Altintas, I. Erucar, S. Keskin, 2018, ACS Appl Mater Interfaces, 10, 4, 3668-3679

C. Altintas, S. Keskin, 2016, Chem Eng Sci, 139, 49-60

G. Avci, S. Velioglu, S. Keskin, 2018, ACS Appl Mater Interfaces, 10, 39, 33693-33706

Z. Bao, S. Alnemrat, L. Yu, I. Vasiliev, Q. Ren, X. Lu, S. Deng, 2011, Langmuir, 27, 22,13554-13562

E.D. Bloch, W.L. Queen, R. Krishna, J.M. Zadrozny, C.M. Brown, J.R. Long, 2012, Science, 335, 6076, 1606-1610

Y.G. Chung, P. Bai, M. Haranczyk, K.T. Leperi, P. Li, H. Zhang, T.C. Wang, T. Duerinck, F. You, J.T. Hupp, O.K. Farha, J.I. Siepmann, R.Q. Snurr, 2017, Chem Mater, 29, 15, 6315-6328

Y.G. Chung, J. Camp, M. Haranczyk, B.J. Sikora, W. Bury, V. Krungleviciute, T. Yildirim, O.K. Farha, D.S. Sholl, R.Q. Snurr, 2014, Chem Mater, 26, 21, 6185-6192

X. Cui, K. Chen, H. Xing, Q. Yang, R. Krishna, Z. Bao, H. Wu, W. Zhou, X. Dong, Y. Han, B. Li, Q. Ren, M. J. Zaworotko, B. Chen, 2016, Science, 353, 6295, 141-144

D. Dubbeldam, S. Calero, D.E. Ellis, R.Q. Snurr, 2016, Mol Simul, 42, 2, 81-101

D. Dubbeldam, R. Krishna, S. Calero, A.Ö. Yazaydın, 2012, Angew Chem Int Ed, 51, 47, 11867-11871

M. Fischer, F. Hoffmann, M. Fröba, 2010, ChemPhysChem, 11, 10, 2220-2229

E. Haldoupis, S. Nair, D.S. Sholl, 2010, J Am Chem Soc, 132, 21, 7528-7539

Y. He, R. Krishna, B. Chen, 2012, Energy Environ Sci, 5, 10, 9107-9120

T.L. Hu, H. Wang, B. Li, R. Krishna, H. Wu, W. Zhou, Y. Zhao, Y. Han, X. Wang, W. Zhu, Z. Yao, S. Xiang, B. Chen, 2015, Nat Commun, 6, 7328

J.R. Li, J. Sculley, H.C. Zhou, 2012, Chem Rev, 112, 2, 869-932

B. Liu, B. Smit, F. Rey, S. Valencia, S. Calero, 2008, J Phys Chem C, 112, 7, 2492-2498

G.C. Maitland, M. Rigby, E.B. Smith, W.A. Wakeham, 1981, Oxford Clarendon Press

S.L. Mayo, B.D. Olafson, W.A. Goddard, 1990, J Phys Chem, 94, 26, 8897-8909

A. Nemati Vesali Azar, S. Keskin, 2018, Front Chem, 6, 36

Z. Qiao, C. Peng, J. Zhou, J. Jiang, 2016, J Mater Chem A, 4, 41, 15904-15912

A.K. Rappe, C.J. Casewit, K.S. Colwell, W.A. Goddard, W.M. Skiff, 1992, J Am Chem Soc, 114, 25, 10024-10035

F. Studt, F. Abild-Pedersen, T. Bligaard, R.Z. Sørensen, C.H. Christensen, J.K. Nørskov, 2008, Science 320, 1320-1322

X. Wang, L. Li, Y. Wang, J.R. Li, J. Li, 2017, CrystEngComm, 19, 13, 1729-1737

C.E. Wilmer, O.K. Farha, Y.S. Bae, J.T. Hupp, R.Q. Snurr, 2012a, Energy Environ Sci, 5, 12, 9849-9856

C.E. Wilmer, K.C. Kim, R.Q. Snurr, 2012b, J Phys Chem Lett, 3,17, 2506-2511

D. Wu, C. Wang, B. Liu, D. Liu, Q. Yang, C. Zhong, 2012, AIChE J, 58, 7, 2078-2084

S.C. Xiang, Z. Zhang, C.G. Zhao, K. Hong, X. Zhao, D.R. Ding, M.H. Xie, C.D. Wu, M.C. Das, R. Gill, K.M. Thomas, B. Chen, 2011, Nat Comm, 2, 204

S. Xiang, W. Zhou, J.M. Gallegos, Y. Liu, B. Chen, 2009, J Am Chem Soc, 131, 34, 12415-12419

S. Yang, A.J. Ramirez-Cuesta, R. Newby, V. Garcia-Sakai, P. Manuel, S.K. Callear, S.I. Campbell, C.C. Tang, M. Schröder, 2014, Nat Chem, 7, 121

B.C. Yeo, D. Kim, H. Kim, S.S. Han, 2016, J Phys Chem C, 120, 42, 24224-24230

Sauro Pierucci, Flavio Manenti, Giulia Bozzano, Davide Manca (Eds.)
Proceedings of the 30th European Symposium on Computer Aided Process Engineering
(ESCAPE30), May 24-27, 2020, Milano, Italy. © 2020 Elsevier B.V. All rights reserved.
http://dx.doi.org/10.1016/B978-0-12-823377-1.50151-8

Process Synthesis and Simultaneous Heat and Electricity Integration to Reduce Consumption of Primary Energy Sources

[a]Andreja Nemet[*], [b]Timothy Gordon Walmsley, [c]Elvis Ahmetović, [a]Zdravko Kravanja

[a]*Faculty of Chemistry and Chemical Engineering, University of Maribor, Smetanova ulica 17, Maribor 2000, Slovenia*
[b]*Sustainable Energy and Water Systems Group, School of Engineering, University of Waikato, New Zealand*
[c]*Faculty of Technology, University of Tuzla, Tuzla 75000, Bosnia and Herzegovina*
andreja.nemet@um.si

Abstract

A synthesis of an industrial utility system considering cogeneration options together with heat exchanger network synthesis has been developed. It consists of boilers at different temperature and pressure levels, steam turbines, condensers, cooling tower, deaerator and a heat exchanger network system, connecting the utility system with the process heat and electricity requirements. A mixed-integer nonlinear programming (MINLP) model was used for synthesis. A sensitivity analysis has been performed considering the price ratio of natural gas to electricity, while also estimating primary energy consumption and GHG emissions. The results indicate that the cogeneration is economically viable at different ratios of natural gas and electricity price. In addition, the sensitivity analysis shows the relationship between cogeneration and electricity purchase for obtaining the minimal primary energy consumption and consequently to reduce GHG emissions.

Keywords: cogeneration; utility system; heat exchanger network; primary energy source reduction; GHG emissions

1. Introduction

Process synthesis is usually performed sequentially, obtaining the optimal design for the reactors at first, followed by the design of the separation subsystem, and, finally, designing the heat recovery system and the utility system, according to an Onion diagram. On the other hand, there are existing examples using the simultaneous approach where processes are optimized or their flowsheets synthesized by performing simultaneous heat integration, for example, using the model by Duran and Grossmann (1986), or even synthesizing their heat exchanger networks (HENs) simultaneously, such as using the simultaneous HEN synthesis model by Yee et al. (1990). The solutions obtained are in many cases significantly superior to those obtained by the sequential approach, often featuring smaller consumption of utilities, lower capital investment, and reduced consumption of raw materials. However, simultaneous utility system synthesis has been studied to a rather limited extent so far, as follows.

Goh et al. (2016) developed an automated targeting model considering both the HEN and utility system utilizing a steam and power cascade as well as the heat and utility cascade. This approach presents a targeting method considering HEN and utility system simultaneously obtaining a "minimum" total operating cost, however, without synthesis of the utility system and HEN design. Luo et al. (2012) presented a hybrid targeting model, based on Pinch technology, and mathematical modeling. The study connected the utility system of a regenerative Rankine cycle based steam power plant with surplus heat from the process, presenting a way to include hot streams into the utility system. Lira-Barragán et al. (2014) presented a scheme for design optimization of process energy system integration considering a trigeneration system. In this study, the design of organic Rankine cycles, absorption refrigeration cycles and the heat exchanger network are considered. The streams of each utility system are considered in additional stages in a superstructure with fixed temperatures, in this way including the utility system into HEN synthesis. Luo et al. (2016) presented a model where the utility system, consisting of one boiler, a multi-stage turbine, a deaerator and a condenser, and the HEN synthesis were considered simultaneously. Elsido et al. (2019) performed a simultaneous heat integration and synthesis of steam and organic Rankine cycles, creating a connection between HEN and utility system synthesis. Martelli et al. (2017) considered HEN and utility synthesis in their work. A two-stage algorithm was developed, where in the first stage a targeting method was applied, while in the second stage the MINLP optimization occurred aided by the results from first stage. However, in their work, only a different presentation of utility streams is applied, not the trade-off between primary energy source and the utility and HEN system synthesis. Later a similar approach was used for heat recovery steam cycle optimization (Elsido et al., 2019). Liu et al. (2018) presented a HEN synthesis model accounting for a cooling water system. It should be noted that only Luo et al. (2016) considered the trade-off between the operating and investment costs and determined the primary energy sources actually bought by companies, e.g. natural gas and electricity, rather than steam, which is an intermediate energy carrier produced by a utility system. In this study, the system borders of HEN synthesis is widened to achieve more holistic and realistic trade-offs. Firstly, the HEN optimization is performed by simultaneously considering the synthesis of hot utility generation system. By this the trade-off between heat consumption "at-the-gate" of the company and the investment is established for the entire heat system. Secondly, the heat and electricity systems are considered simultaneously. This simultaneous handling of entire energy system leads to proper trade-off between energy utilization "at-the-gate" of the company and the investment. This wider scope of system borders enables achieving appropriate trade-offs between operating cost, considering primary energy source, and investment required for the utility system and HEN. In order to enable the evaluation of the mentioned trade-offs, the HEN superstructure is extended by: i) steam production system with boilers at different temperature ranges, ii) options with and without cogeneration, iii) hot and cold utility streams considered in each stage of the HEN superstructure, allowing better optimization of the entire HEN including heat exchangers between utility and process streams, and iv) both mass and energy flows and balances to appropriately track mass and heat losses in the (sub)systems. Note that temperatures and pressures of the steam headers (including superheated steam) are optimization variables, taking the advantages of interactions between steam production system, cogeneration system and steam utilization system (HEN).

2. Method

A superstructure approach applying MINLP model formulation has been formulated as represented in Figure 1. It consists of three boilers representing options for steam production at three different levels of superheated steam.

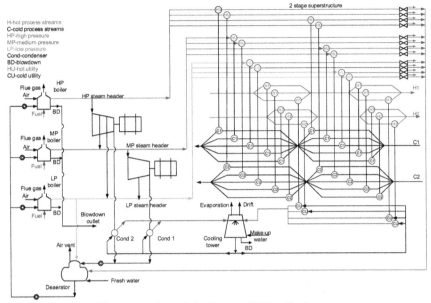

Figure 1: Superstructure of the cogeneration and simultaneous HEN synthesis.

It should be noted that the temperatures of steam headers are not fixed, and they are treated as optimization variables. Furthermore, the superstructure consists of two multi-stage turbines. The first is utilizing steam from the high pressure (HP) level, optionally releasing steam at medium pressure (MP), low pressure (LP), and/or condenser levels. The second turbine utilizes MP level steam, while releasing steam at LP level, if needed, before being sent to a condenser. The steam condensates released from condensers are directed to the deaerator. The superheated steam produced in the utility system is utilized in the process to heat cold process streams. The heat exchanger network (HEN) optimization is performed by the superstructure based on Yee and Grossmann (1990), while considering each utility stream in every stage of the superstructure as suggested by Isafiade and Fraser (2010). The condensate return is assumed to be returned in a vented pipeline at atmospheric pressure, causing both heat and mass loss from the system. Throttle valves are used to achieve atmospheric pressure in the pipelines. In this way, the loss due to flash steam is considered. The condensate is then returned to the utility system via the deaerator. Two cooling water cycles are presented in the superstructure in connection with a cooling tower: i) the first one supplies cooling water to the condensers after steam turbines and ii) the second one supplies cooling water to coolers in the HEN to cool hot process streams. The make-up water needs, as a result of evaporation, drift and blowdown water, are also considered. The water cycles of utility and process parts are closed via the deaerator. In the deaerator, the condensate from the condenser, condensate recovered from the process and fresh water inlet are considered as inlets. To operate the deaerator LP steam is used in the deaerator to operate the equipment and to preheat the water. The water from the deaerator is used in the selected boiler(s).

3. Case study

3.1. Input data
The process studied consisted of two hot and two cold streams with three different levels of intermediate utility available. The input data for streams are presented in Table 1. The

electricity requirement of the process was 1.5 MW. The fuel and utility prices are assumed as 40 €/MWh for natural gas, 8.75 €/MWh for cooling, and 80 €/MWh up to 140 €/MWh for electricity depending on the scenario. The fix charge for heat exchangers is 550 €, while the variable charges 15 €/m². The area exponent is set at 1. The fix charge for turbine is 18,200 €, and the variable charge is 2,173 €/MWh. For the boiler, the fixed charge is 28,400 € and the variable component is 2,220 € kg^{-1} s.

Table 1: Input data

Stream	T^{in}/ °C	T^{out}/ °C	FC/ MW °C^{-1}	h/ MW °C^{-1} m^{-2}
H1	377	40	0.5	0.00033
H2	317	97	0.4	0.0004
C1	137	277	17	0.00045
C2	77	127	16	0.00038
IU-saturated state	T_{lo}/°C	T_{up}/°C		h/MW °C^{-1} m^{-2}
LPS	120	148		10
MPS	148	208		10.5
HPS	208	252		11
IU-superheated state	T_{lo}/°C	T_{up}/°C		
LPS	130	497		
MPS	158	497		
HPS	218	497		

To determine the primary energy consumption of electricity bought from the grid network, the efficiency of the electricity production and transmission from natural gas is assumed to be 30.4 %. The GHG emission factor is taken as the LCA emission factors for the EU average. For natural gas, it is 0.237 t$_{CO2-eq}$/MWh and, for the electricity consumed, it is 0.578 t$_{CO2-eq}$/MWh$_e$ (EU, 2010).

3.2. Results

We compared a solution obtained by performing HEN optimization simultaneously with the synthesis of utility system excluding electricity generation and solution including electricity cogeneration. The first solution was obtained at electricity price of 80 €/MWh, while the second at 140 €/MWh. The selected heat exchangers are presented in Table 2. The heat consumptions in both cases were similar (1,904 MW no electricity generation vs. 1,929 MW in the case of cogeneration); however, lower temperature level of intermediate utility and larger areas of utility exchangers were selected when cogeneration was considered. As can be seen, the electricity price heavily effected the final HEN design, showing the significance of simultaneous consideration of the entire energy generation system with cogeneration and the HEN optimization.

Table 2: Area of heat exchangers in m² when considering HEN optimization and cogeneration

HE	H1-C1	H2-C1	H2-C2	H1-CW	H2-CW	IU-C1	IU-C2
No cogeneration	4,288	3,128	926	3,352	-	HPS 18,286	HPS 14,680
Cogeneration	3,910	2,444	-	3,455	573	MPS 24,023	MPS 20,329

Figure 2 presents the results of the sensitivity analysis, where the price of electricity was varied from 80 €/MWh up to 140 €/MWh. In Figure 2a, the cost distribution between annual investment, natural gas, electricity and cooling is presented, together with the TAC of utility system and HEN. As can be observed at lower price ratios, the TAC is lower, and the largest proportion of TAC is the electricity cost.

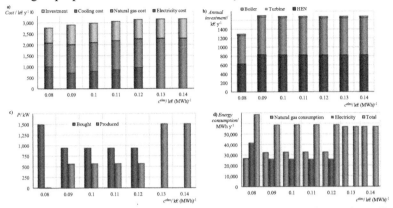

Figure 2: Results of the sensitivity analysis. a) Cost distribution between parts of TAC, b) cost distribution of annual investment, c) the amount of electricity produced via cogeneration and electricity bought from network, and d) "at-the-gate" energy consumption for various ratios between the electricity and natural gas prices

By increasing the electricity price, it becomes more economically viable to produce a larger amount of electricity compared to buying it. This is clearly visible in Figure 2c, where the electricity produced versus the one bought is presented. Figure 2b presents the further distribution of annual investment between HEN, turbines and boilers. As can be seen, the largest proportion of investment is in the HEN, and it is increasing with any increase of the electricity price. The boiler and turbine annual investment is also increasing with the increase of the price, which is a consequence of the basic trade-off between the operating cost and annual investment. Figure 2d presents the energy consumption within the company of the energy carriers supplied "at-the-gate". The trade-off between primary energy consumption and the investment is studied by determining the primary energy consumption and Greenhouse Gas (GHG) emission under various electricity prices. For the electricity bought from the network, it was assumed that the power plant operates at 30.4 % efficiency. As can be seen from Figure 3a, a minimum primary energy consumption occurred in the case with higher electricity prices. These results clearly show the reduction of primary energy consumption, when cogeneration of heat and electricity is used. This is a consequence of the shared heat and electricity production cycle that requires less primary energy. From a sustainability point of view, the optimal solutions should consider the transformations and distributions/transmissions of energy types from the primary energy source to minimize overall emissions. Figure 3b presents the GHG emission, which does lead to the conclusion that the lowest GHG emission matches the case with the lowest primary energy consumption.

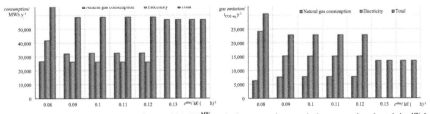

Figure 3: a) Primary energy consumption and b) GHG emission at various ratio between the electricity and natural gas prices

4. Conclusions

The study presents an attempt to simultaneously synthesize the utility system with HEN, taking advantage of the interactions among them. It is an important step in an appropriate evaluation of the optimal design considering the energy carriers "at-the-gate" of the company, rather than estimated prices of intermediate energy carriers (e.g. steam) within the company. In the case study presented, different HEN designs were obtained when considering only HEN optimization with utility system compared to the system with cogeneration. This result shows the significance of simultaneous consideration of energy generation system and HEN.

From a sustainability point of view, the trade-off should be widened to the overall primary energy source consumption of different alternatives. In the case study presented, it is shown that the lower primary energy consumption can be achieved, when the cogeneration is applied either partially of fully. The difference is even more significant in the case of GHG emission analysis of the cogeneration versus a separate heat and power generation.

References

E. Martelli, C. Elsido, A Mian, F. Marechal, 2017, MINLP model and two-stage algorithm for the simultanous synthesis of heat exchanger network, utility system and heat recovery cycles, Computers and Chemical Engineering, 106, 663-689.

W.S Goh., Y.K.Wan, C. K. Tay, R.T.L. Ng, D.K.S. Ng, 2016, Automated targeting model for synthesis of heat exchanger network with utility systems, Applied Energy, 162, 1272-1281.

C. Elsido, E. Martelli, T. Kreutz, 2019, Heat integration and heat recovery steam cycle optimization for a low-carbon lignite/biomass-to-jet fuel demonstration project, Applied Energy, 239, 1322-1342.

X. Luo, B. Zhang, Y. Chen, A. Mo, 2012, Heat integration of regenerative Rankine cycle and process surplus heat through graphical targeting and mathematical modeling technique, Energy, 556-569.

X. Luo, X. Huang, M.M. El-Halwagi, J.M. Ponce-Ortega, Y. Chen, 2016, Simultanous synthesis of utility system and heat exchanger network incroporating steam condensate and boiler feedwater, Energy, 875-893.

F. Liu, J. Ma, Y. Feng, Y. Wang, 2018, Simultanous integrated design for heat exchanger network and cooling water system, Applied Thermal Engineering, 128, 1510-1519.

C. Elsido, E. Martelli, I. E. Grossmann, 2019, A bilevel decomposition method for the simultanous heat integration and synthesis of steam/organic Rankine cycles, Computers and Chemical Engineering, 128, 228-245.

A.J. Isafiade, D.M. Fraser, 2010, Interval based MINLP superstructure synthesis of heat exchanger networks for multi-period operations, Chemical Engineering Research and Design. 88, 1329-1341.

M.A. Duran, I.E. Grossmann, 1986, Simultaneous optimization and heat integration of chemical processes. AIChE Journal, 32, 123-138.

T.F. Yee, I.E. Grossmann, Z. Kravanja,1990, Simultaneous optimization models for heat integration - III. Process and heat exchanger network optimization. Computers and Chemical Engineering, 14, 1185-1200.

L.F. Lira-Barragán, J.M. Ponce Ortega, M. Serna-González, M.M. El-Halwagi, 2014, Optimal desing of process energy systems integrating sustainable consideration, Energy, 76,139-160.

European Union, 2010, Covenant of Mayors, How to develop a Sustainable Energy Action Plan Part 2, https://conventiondesmaires.eu/support/funding-instruments_el.html, accessed 26.11.2019.

Sauro Pierucci, Flavio Manenti, Giulia Bozzano, Davide Manca (Eds.)
Proceedings of the 30th European Symposium on Computer Aided Process Engineering
(ESCAPE30), May 24-27, 2020, Milano, Italy. © 2020 Elsevier B.V. All rights reserved.
http://dx.doi.org/10.1016/B978-0-12-823377-1.50152-X

Coproduction of Ethylene and Propylene based on Ethane and Propane Feedstocks

H. Alejandro Pedrozo[a]; S. Belen Rodriguez Reartes[a,b]; Maria Soledad Diaz[a,b,*],
A. R. Vecchietti[c], Ignacio E. Grossmann[d]

[a] *Planta Piloto de Ingeniería Química (PLAPIQUI CONICET-UNS), Camino La Carrindanga km. 7, Bahía Blanca, Argentina*
[b] *Departamento de Ingeniería Química, Universidad Nacional del Sur (UNS), Bahía Blanca, Argentina*
[c] *Institute of Design and Development (INGAR CONICET-UTN), Avellaneda 3657, Santa Fe, Argentina*
[d] *Center for Advanced Process Decision Making, Carnegie Mellon University, 5000 Forbes Avenue, Pittsburgh, PA 15213, USA*
sdiaz@plapiqui.edu.ar

Abstract

In this work, we develop a mathematical model to make decisions about the optimal scheme and operating conditions of an olefin plant. We formulate a superstructure that includes ethane and propane steam cracking, propane dehydrogenation and olefins metathesis process for the co-production of ethylene and propylene. Furthermore, considering the relevance of the separation scheme, the state equipment network (SEN) representation is considered and rigorous equations to model distillation columns (MESH) are formulated. This model is implemented in GAMS to maximize the project net present value (NPV). Numerical results show that the combination of ethane steam cracking and olefin metathesis is the most profitable configuration under the price scenario considered in this work.

Keywords: olefin production, superstructure optimization, propane dehydrogenation, metathesis, steam cracking

1. Introduction

The shale gas revolution has led to a high availability of natural gas liquids (NGLs), which are excellent feedstocks for chemical industries. In particular, there are economic advantages of using NGLs for olefin production instead of naphtha feedstock (Siirola, 2014). Thus, there is a general trend to turn reactive furnaces to work with ethane for ethylene production, even in countries that do not have shale gas exploitation, since they can import ethane at competitive prices (U.S. Energy Information Administration, 2019). This feedstock switch has also promoted a propylene yield reduction since propylene selectivity from naphtha is higher than from ethane. In addition, propylene demand continues rising mainly due to polypropylene consumption (Baker, 2018). The combination of both facts encouraged the development of on purpose technologies for propylene production (Lavrenov, Saifulina, Buluchevskii, & Bogdanets, 2015).
There are numerous process alternatives to produce propylene from both, petrochemical raw material and chemical intermediates, such as methanol into olefins, methanol into propylene, olefin metathesis, propane dehydrogenation, and deep catalytic cracking. Among these alternatives, both propane dehydrogenation and olefin metathesis are

particularly interesting technologies since either could be used with ethane steam cracking to produce ethylene and propylene more efficiently.

To the best of our knowledge, an optimal design of a plant producing ethylene and propylene that includes propane dehydrogenation and metathesis of olefins as process alternatives has not been studied in the literature. In addition, numerous papers that address optimal plant designs use short-cut models in distillation columns (Chen & Grossmann, 2017). While these approaches allow simplifying the optimization model, unfortunately, they are much less accurate in comparison to rigorous mass balances, equilibrium, summation and heat (MESH) equations, and consequently, may provide only rough estimations that directly affect economic indicators.

In this work, we formulate a superstructure to determine the optimal scheme of an olefin plant. Raw materials include both ethane and propane, and the superstructure embeds steam cracking furnaces, propane dehydrogenation, and metathesis as potential technologies. Furthermore, taking into account the relevance of the separation scheme, the state equipment network (SEN) representation (Chen & Grossmann, 2017), and rigorous equations (MESH) to model distillation columns are formulated. Numerical results show that the optimal scheme includes a combination of ethane steam cracking and olefin metathesis.

2. Process description

The present work addresses the optimal design of a plant producing ethylene and propylene at a rate of 500 kt/year for each olefin. Figure 1 shows the plant sections, where the different alternatives for the reactive pathways are presented. The raw materials are ethane and propane, and the entire process can be represented through three different sections: alkane conversion, separation train, metathesis section.

2.1. Alkane conversion

2.1.1. Ethane conversion

The commercial technology to produce ethylene from ethane feedstock is steam cracking. We should note that the reactor capacity for ethylene production is not fixed. This olefin is required to satisfy market demand, but it could also be transformed into propylene in the plant. Thus, discrete decisions are related to the number of furnaces included in the optimal design.

2.1.2. Propane conversion

We consider three different reaction pathways for handling propane feedstock, which are: steam cracking of propane, Pt-based propane dehydrogenation (Pt-PDH), and Cr-based propane dehydrogenation (Cr-PDH).

Steam cracking of propane mainly produces ethylene. It employs complex furnaces operating at high temperatures, as in steam pyrolysis of ethane. There are also discrete decisions associated to propane production furnaces in the plant.

Pt-PDH is a commercial process, developed by UOP Oleflex, with a 36 % propane conversion per pass, and an 85 % propylene selectivity (Maddah, 2018).

Cr-PDH is another propane dehydrogenation technology, commercialized as Catofin Process, which has a 40 % propane conversion per pass, and its selectivity towards propylene is around 88 % (Maddah, 2018).

2.2. Separation train

Since the output streams from ethane and propane processing reactors have roughly the same chemical species, both streams can be mixed and processed through the same separation train to purify the olefin products. Thus, this strategy comprises process intensification.

The separation train consists of a quench tower to reduce the temperature reactor output stream, a series of compression stages, an acid gas removal unit to eliminate carbon dioxide and hydrogen sulfide, a dehydration process, a reactor for acetylene hydrogenation, a cold box for hydrogen separation, and a sequence of distillation columns to perform the final product purification.

In the representation of Fig. 1, the "main separation" block includes demethanizer, deethanizer, and depropanizer columns, and acetylene reactor; their interconnections are modeled with discrete variables. C2 and C3 splitters purify the main products, ethylene, and propylene, respectively, and the separated ethane and propane are recycled to "Alkane conversion" section. The debuthanizer column produces a butene stream that can be either sold or fed to the "Metathesis section". In addition, pyrolysis gasoline is obtained from debutanizer column bottom, but for the sake of clarity in Fig. 1, this product is omitted.

2.3. Metathesis section

An alternative process to produce propylene is the metathesis of ethylene and butenes. The propylene selectivity is about 95 %, and the butenes per-pass conversion is over 60 % (Ondrey, 2004). This technology employs a mixture of WO_3/SiO_2 and MgO as a catalyst for the metathesis and isomerization reactions.

A hydrogenation unit is used to eliminate diene and enyne compounds from the butene mixture. Then, the resulting stream is fed to an isomerization reactor to increase the composition of trans-2-butene. Next, ethylene and butene streams are fed to a fixed bed catalytic reactor where the metathesis reaction takes place. The output of this reactor is a mixture of ethylene, propylene, butenes and C_5^+ components. This mixture is treated in a series of distillation columns for propylene purification, which also involves discrete decisions regarding the separation scheme. From this set of columns, three output streams are obtained. First, the ethylene stream can be recycled or mixed with ethylene product stream. Second, the propylene stream is mixed with propylene product stream. Finally, the C_4^+ stream is sent to the debuthanizer column in the separation train section. Thus, in "Propylene purification" block (Fig. 1), there are also discrete decisions regarding the separation sequence.

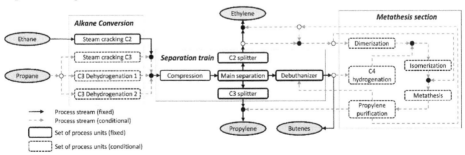

Figure 1: Plant sections for ethylene-propylene co-production

3. Mathematical modeling

We formulate process unit models within the superstructure representation and streams are defined by the connection between two units. The problem complexity of finding the optimal scheme increases with the number of units and tasks considered in the superstructure. In order to tackle this issue, Yeomans and Grossmann (Yeomans & Grossmann, 1999) have proposed the state equipment network (SEN) representation, which allows addressing the problem systematically. In addition, this representation allows presetting the number of columns, avoiding nonexistent process units in the superstructure. Consequently, the number of flow and size variables forced to be zero is reduced, as well as the potential issues regarding numerical singularities. In SEN, the fed and produced states of equipment units depend on potential tasks that can be performed in each unit. In this work, the tasks assignment is based on the location of the separation cut for the distillation column.

Figure 2a shows the state equipment network for the main separation block (see Fig. 1). In this work, states are characterized by their composition. After compression, the reactor output stream is sent to the main separation block which includes the columns: demethanizer, deethanizer and depropanizer separating the stream in component groups. The identified component groups are: H_2 (hydrogen), C_1 (methane); C_2 (ethane and ethylene); C_2^a (ethane, ethylene, and acetylene); C_3 (species with 3 carbon atoms), and C_4^+ (species with 4 or more carbon atoms). Therefore, the discrete decisions associated with the separation scheme focus on task assignments in the demethanizer, deethanizer and depropanizer (based on the separation cuts). In addition, the acetylene hydrogenation is an important process in this section that also has discrete tasks associated. In this work, only front-end configurations were considered for acetylene hydrogenation unit since they are more energy-efficient (Zimmermann & Walzl, 2009). Consequently, H_2, C_1 and C_2 species must be in the acetylene reactor feed stream. Propylene purification (in metathesis section) also includes discrete decisions associated with column separation tasks, as Fig. 2b shows. In this case, the mixture to be processed is composed of ethylene (Et), propylene (Pr), and species with 4 or more carbon atoms (C_4^+).

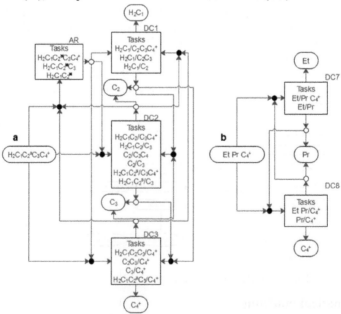

Figure 2: States equipment network. a) main separation train. b) propylene purification in the metathesis section. DC1: demethanizer. DC2: deethanizer. DC3: depropanizer. DC7: Deethylenizer. DC8: Depropylenizer. ●: mixer. ○: splitter

The corresponding disjunctions for the STN representation are as follows:

$$\bigvee_{t\in Ta_u}\begin{bmatrix} W_{u,t} \\ \left.\begin{array}{l} F_{s,u',c} = F_{u',u,c} \\ T_{s,u'} = T_{u,u'} \\ P_{s,u'} = T_{u,u'} \\ H_{s,u'} = T_{u,u'} \end{array}\right\} \begin{array}{l} c\in C \\ s\in SI_{u',u,t} \\ u'\in UI_u \end{array} \\ \left.\begin{array}{l} F_{u,s,c} = F_{u,u',c} \\ T_{u,s} = T_{u,u'} \\ P_{u,s} = P_{u,u'} \\ H_{u,s} = H_{u,u'} \end{array}\right\} \begin{array}{l} c\in C \\ s\in SO_{u,u',t} \\ u'\in UO_u \end{array} \end{bmatrix} u\in\{DC1,DC2,DC3,AR,DC7,DC8\}$$

where $W_{u,t}$ is the Boolean variable that is true if the task t is performed in unit u, and false otherwise; $F_{s,u',c}$ is the molar flow from state s to u' of the chemical compound c; $T_{s,u'}$, $P_{s,u'}$ and $H_{s,u'}$ are the temperature, pressure and enthalpy flow from state s to u', respectively; C is the set of chemical species; Ta_u is the set of tasks that can be performed in unit u; $SI_{u',u,t}$ is the state that is fed through mixer u' and processed in unit u when the task t is selected; $SO_{u,u',t}$ is the state that is delivered through splitter u and produced in unit u' when the task t is selected; UI_u and UO_u are the sets of input mixer and output splitter corresponding to unit u, respectively.

In the superstructure, we include different reactor types, heat exchangers, flash, pumps, compressors, mixers, splitters, and distillation columns. Each type of process unit has equations to describe its physical behavior and to calculate its costs when applicable. We formulate a Generalized Disjunctive Programming mode (Vecchietti & Grossmann, 2000); thus, the presence of each unit is associated with Boolean variables as follows

$$\begin{bmatrix} Y_u \\ h(x)\le 0 \\ Ax\le b \end{bmatrix} \vee \begin{bmatrix} \neg Y_u \\ Bx=0 \end{bmatrix}$$

where Y_u is the Boolean variable that is true if the unit u is present, and false otherwise; and the continuous variables x include material flows, operating temperature and pressure, enthalpy flows, unit internal variables, and unit capital cost. To solve the problem, we used the logic-based outer approximation algorithm (Turkay & Grossmann, 1996), in which the problem is decomposed into reduced NLP subproblems and the master MILP problem. In this way, NLP subproblems only include the nonlinear equations related to the disjunction active terms, avoiding potential issues regarding singularities. The master MILP is formulated based on the outer approximation with equality relaxation and augmented penalty approach (Viswanathan & Grossmann, 1990).

4. Case study

USA data prices reported in the literature (Boulamanti & Moya, 2017) were considered for the present case of study. Due to the active exploitation of shale gas resources in this country, ethane feedstock (146 EUR/t) is quite more economical than propane (394 EUR/t). When we solve the problem with the logic-based approach in GAMS 24.2.3, we found the optimal solution after solving three NLP subproblems and two Master problems, as Table 1 shows. The resulting Master MILP problems have 140 binary variables. Table 2 shows the most important economic indicators for the optimal scheme.

Numerical results indicate that the optimal scheme includes four steam cracking furnaces to produce ethylene from ethane in the alkane conversion section. Neither furnaces for propane steam cracking nor propane dehydrogenation technologies were selected. That means, propane feedstock was not employed in the optimal design. Instead, ethane feedstock is used to produce more ethylene for its further conversion in propylene through the metathesis process, whose section is included in the plant. Regarding the separation scheme, Table 3 shows the tasks assigned for each equipment unit. It is observed that a deethanizer first configuration was selected in the optimal solution scheme.

Table 1: Summary of iterations with the logic-based outer approximation algorithm

Iteration/subproblem	Objective	CPU time (s)	Constraints	Continuos vars.
NLP 1 (CONOPT)	1526	74	38847	38783
Master MILP 1 (Cplex)	2006	3921	71699	86919
NLP 2 (CONOPT)	2040	784	37681	37233
Master MILP 2 (Cplex)	1475	59075	115362	132362
NLP 3 (CONOPT)	2037	1104	37764	37316

Table 2: Economic indicators for the optimal solution

Net present value (MM$)	2040	Revenues (MM$/year)	1229
Investment (MM$)	1142	- Ethylene (MM$/year)	569
Net income (MM$/year)	564	- Propylene (MM$/year)	603
		- By-products (MM$/year)	57

Table 3: Selected tasks for equipment in the optimal scheme

Equipment	DC1	DC2	DC3	AR	DC7	DC8
Task	C_1/C_2	$C_1C_2^a/C_3 C_4$	C_3/C_4	$C_1C_2^x$	Et/Pr	Et Pr/C_4

5. Conclusions

This work addresses the optimal design of an olefin plant producing ethylene and propylene. The optimal plant design includes four ethane steam cracking furnaces, and no propane feedstock is employed. The selected reactive pathway to produce propylene was the metathesis of olefins and the optimal configuration includes the deethanizer column as the first separation step.

References

Baker, I. (2018). Polypropylene. In *Fifty Materials That Make the World* (pp. 169–173). Springer.
Boulamanti, A., Moya, J. A. (2017). *Renewable and Sustainable Energy Reviews*, *68*, 1205–1212.
Chen, Q., Grossmann, I. E. (2017). *Annu. Rev. Chem. Biomol. Eng.* 8 (1), 249–283.
Lavrenov, A., Saifulina, L., Buluchevskii, E. , Bogdanets, E. N. (2015). *Catal. Ind. 7*(3), 175–187.
Maddah, H. A. (2018). *ASRJETS*, *45*(1), 49–63.
Ondrey, G. (2004). *Chem. Eng.*, *111*(3), 20–24.
Siirola, J. J. (2014). *AIChE Journal*, *60*(3), 810–819
Turkay, M., Grossmann, I.E. (1996)," *Comp Chem Eng*, 20, 959-978.
U.S. EIA (2019). https://www.eia.gov/todayinenergy/detail.php?id=38232
Vecchietti, A., Grossmann, I.E. (2000). *Comput. Chem. Eng.* 24, 2143-2155.
Viswanathan, J., Grossmann, I. E. (1990). *Comput. Chem. Eng.* 14 (7) 769-782
Yeomans, H., Grossmann, I. E. (1999). *Comput. Chem. Eng.*, *23*(6), 709–731.
Zimmermann, H., Walzl, R. (2009). Ullmann's Encyclopedia of Industrial Chemistry, Ethylene. John Wiley & Sons, Inc., New York.

Sauro Pierucci, Flavio Manenti, Giulia Bozzano, Davide Manca (Eds.)
Proceedings of the 30th European Symposium on Computer Aided Process Engineering
(ESCAPE30), May 24-27, 2020, Milano, Italy. © 2020 Elsevier B.V. All rights reserved.
http://dx.doi.org/10.1016/B978-0-12-823377-1.50153-1

Circular Economy Analysis of Helium Recovery from Sales Gas Product

Ahmed AlNouss, Saad A. Al-Sobhi [*]

Chemical Engineering Department, College of Engineering, Qatar University. Doha,
Qatar

saad.al-sobhi@qu.edu.qa

Abstract

The helium presence in natural gas (NG) is usually low, thus it seems infeasible economically to recover it. However, the continuous increase in helium demand with a growing rate of about 5%, industrial projects are searching for economic approaches to recover helium from sales gas at the earlier stages of the liquefaction process. This work investigates the techno-economic and environmental benefits of recovering helium from sale gas product. Among the available recovery technologies, namely, cryogenic fraction, adsorption-based processes, and membrane-based processes, the cryogenic fractionation is considered for analysis due to its wide use in industry. The cryogenic fractionation represented by three different configurations; single column, double columns fractionation, and cold box are developed using Aspen HYSYS to perform the steady-state simulation with a basis of 1400 MMSCFD of natural gas. Aspen Process Economic Analyzer and Aspen Energy Analyzer, are then used to carry out the economic evaluation and utility optimization steps. The results for all alternatives are compared in terms of helium recovery, emissions reduction, energy savings, and economic profitability. An illustrative case study is presented for the assessment of helium recovery for different helium molar composition in the NG feedstock and various helium selling prices. The results demonstrate cold box as the optimal technology for 3.5 vol% helium recovery with approximately \$25.4 per kg of helium produced (PHP) compared to approximately \$24.2 and \$24.3 PHP for double column and single column options, respectively. Moreover, higher concentration of helium at around 7% indicates a profitability profile with lower overall net economic value of approximately \$11.7 PHP for cold box alternative. The results for all options indicate high purity for helium with more than 98% and a recovery of more than 99%.

Keywords: Sustainable design, Helium recovery, Sales gas, Process Simulation, liquefied natural gas (LNG)

1. Introduction

The importance of helium comes for its unique properties such as inertness, high thermal conductivity, low solubility, low density and low boiling point. In addition, it has irreplaceable industrial and research applications where helium is used in critical technologies such as nuclear facilities, fiber optics and electronics fabrication, leak detection systems, aircraft manufacturing, magnets production and MRI scanners (Hamedi et al., 2019). Cryogenic separation is used heavily in natural gas liquefaction (NGL) processes to separate hydrocarbons, nitrogen and helium. Majority of newly established NGL plants utilize cryogenic separation technology. It is considered as a conventional process to produce crude helium from natural gas (NG) stream (Mehrpooya and Shafaei, 2016). It can be divided into two main categories: high-pressure distillation processes and multi-stage flash systems (Ansarinasab et al., 2018).

Although helium is considered the second most common element in the universe, recoverable known helium reserves may get depleted within a few decades. Therefore, efficient processes should be implemented to recover this vital resource. In addition, the technical and economic performance along with environmental compliance must be enhanced to increase the benefits from the recovery process and decrease the environmental impacts. This research paper explores the techno-economic and environmental analysis of recovering helium from sale gas product for various concentration levels. The cryogenic fractionation represented by three different configurations; single column, double columns fractionation, and cold box are developed using Aspen HYSYS software to perform the steady-state simulation with a basis of 1400 MMSCFD of natural gas.

2. Model development

The extraction of helium from NG follows four main steps as highlighted in Figure 1. First, the gas feed is purified from acid gases, mercury and water. The heavier hydrocarbons are then extracted from the gas stream before entering nitrogen rejection unit (NRU) where most of the remaining methane gas is separated from nitrogen and helium mixture. Finally, helium is recovered from the nitrogen-rich stream in one or two steps to produce crude (50-70 mol%) or purified (99.99 mol%) helium (Hamedi et al., 2019).

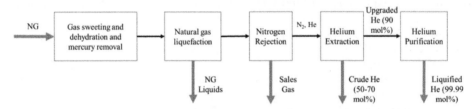

Figure 1: Block flow diagram of helium production for LNG with high nitrogen content

Given a typical LNG process, with desirable products as shown above, it is desired to investigate the economic and environmental benefits of recovering helium from the sale gas product. It is assumed in this paper that a 50% split of sales gas product is to be directed to liquefaction section. Aspen HYSYS software is used to simulate the three configurations; single column, double columns fractionation, and cold box with a basis of 1400 MMSCFD of natural gas (NG). The basic NGL configuration is based on Recycle split-vapor (RSV) technology, which has been described in an earlier study (AlNouss et al., 2018) and investigated more in (Al-Sobhi and AlNouss, 2018) using a sustainability metric. In the single column process, the purified NG product from the RSV unit is precooled to around -130 °C before being fed to a high-pressure distillation column operating at 20 bar. The overhead product of the column containing helium and nitrogen is further cooled to around -225 °C and enters a two-phase separator. The top stream from the separator is the helium product and the bottom is the nitrogen product. The bottom product from the column is considered as LNG stream. The simulated Aspen HYSYS model for single column process is illustrated in Figure 2.

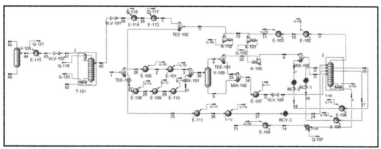

Figure 2: Simulation process flowsheet for single column helium recovery.

The double-column process starts with a heat exchanger to cool the NG product from the RSV NG recovery unit to around -130 °C. The stream then enters a two-phase separator to flash the gas from liquid and both enters the distillation column operating at 20 bar. The overhead stream is directed to a heat exchanger to cool the helium and nitrogen stream to around -225 °C before entering a second two-phase separator. The separator flash out helium from the top and leaves nitrogen in the bottom stream. Similar to the single-column, the bottom product from the column is considered as LNG stream. Figure 3 illustrates the simulated Aspen HYSYS model for double-column process.

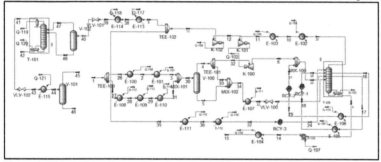

Figure 3: Simulation process flowsheet for double column helium recovery.

The last configuration is the cold box technology. NG product from the RSV NG recovery unit enters the cold box unit where it is first cooled to around -148 °C before entering a two-phase separator. The top stream from the separator is cooled to around -193 °C and enters a second two-phase vessel. The top stream is further cooled to around -220 °C and then flashed into helium top product and nitrogen bottom product. The bottom product form the second vessel is recycled back to the first vessel. Whereas the bottom product from the first vessel is cooled to around -193 °C and flashed to yield a bottom LNG product. Figure 4 illustrates the simulated model for the cold box technology.

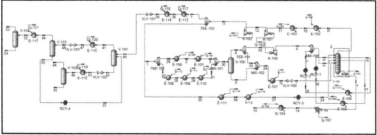

Figure 4: Simulation process flowsheet for cold box helium recovery.

After the simulation of the three cryogenic processes represented by single column, double columns fractionation, and cold box configurations, Aspen Process Economic Analyzer and Aspen Energy Analyzer, are used to carry out the economic evaluation and utility optimization steps with the prices of the main products and feeds as demonstrated in Table 1.

Table 1: Prices of main feeds and products.

Stream	Sales Gas	LNG	NGL	NG Feed	Helium
$/tonne	274.38	426.59	213.3	137.19	137.19

In order to perform a circular analysis, certain parameters have been varied. The percentage of helium in the feed has been varied between 1 and 7 mol%. The NG feed compositions of the three cases are illustrated in Table 1.

Table 2: NG feed composition for the three scenarios.

Component	Case a	Case b	Case c
Feed Composition (Vol%)			
Methane	85%	79%	82.3%
Ethane	5%	5%	5.4%
Propane	2%	2%	2.1%
i-Butane	1%	1%	0.7%
n-Butane	0%	0%	0.4%
i-Pentane	0%	0%	0.2%
n-Pentane	0%	0%	0.2%
n-Hexane	0%	0%	0.2%
Nitrogen	5%	5%	5.0%
Helium	1%	7%	3.5%

3. Results and discussion

The results for the single and double columns alternatives have demonstrated promising helium recovery with up to 99.9% compared to Sales gas product split and up to 49.9% compared to NG feed as illustrated in Figure 5. High percentages of energy savings and environmental emissions reduction approximated at 74% are observed for the single and double columns alternatives from the actual and target total utilities requirement and carbon emissions in Figures 6. In addition, with the increase of helium presence in sales gas, the cold box alternative demonstrated a constant and higher increase in the recovery of helium compared to the other two alternatives.

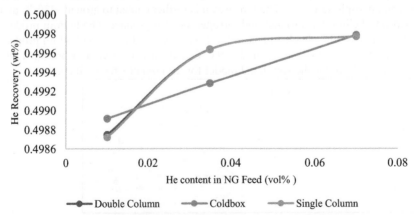

Figure 5: Helium recovery trend with the change in He content in NG feed.

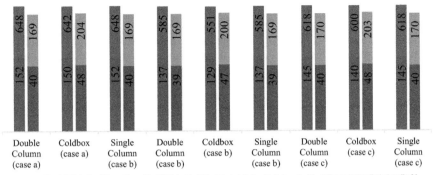

Figure 6: Actual and target total utilities requirement and carbon emissions for the three cases.

Nevertheless, the cold box alternative has shown higher net profit per kg of He product with around $25.4 at 3.5vol% helium content, compared to approximately $24.2 and $24.3 for double column and single column options, respectively. This profitability decreases with the increase in helium content in NG as indicated in Figure 7. These profitability figures are calculated from the different costs and revenues associated with the studied cases and technologies presented in Figure 8.

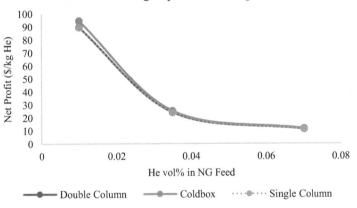

Figure 7: Helium recovery trend with the change in He content in NG feed.

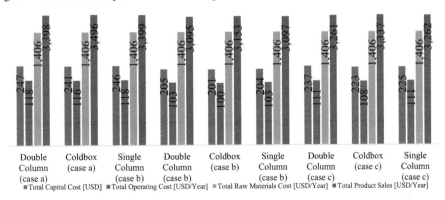

Figure 8: Revenue and costs associated with the different helium recovery cases and technologies.

These results indicate the potential of helium recovery as a key figure to enhance circular economy. More analysis can be done to find the optimal ratio of the Sales gas split that maximizes profit and minimizes environmental damages. Moreover, the investment in helium recovery can be investigated through sustainability metrics to ensure the long term profitability.

4. Conclusions

The global demand of helium reached approximately 5.9 billion cubic feet (Bcf) in 2016 with a global supply estimated at 6.0 Bcf. The major global reserves approximated at 8 million tons are located in US, Qatar, Algeria and Russia. These known helium reserves may get depleted within a few decades striking the need for efficient processes to be implemented to recover this vital resource. This work explores the techno-economic and environmental analysis of recovering helium from sale gas product for various concentration levels. The cryogenic fractionation represented by three different configurations; single column, double columns fractionation, and cold box are developed using Aspen HYSYS to perform the steady-state simulation with a basis of 1400 MMSCFD of natural gas (NG) and to perform profitability and environmental studies. The results demonstrate cold box as the optimal technology for 3.5 vol% helium recovery with approximately $25.4 per kg of helium produced (PHP) compared to approximately $24.2 and $24.3 PHP for double column and single column options, respectively. This profitability decreases with the increase in helium content in NG. These results demonstrate the potential of helium recovery as a key figure to enhance circular economy. However, more investment analysis needs be done through sustainability metrics to ensure the long term profitability of helium recovery.

References

S.A. Al-Sobhi, and A. AlNouss, 2018, Applying New Sustainability Metric in Different Natural Gas Liquid (NGL) Recovery Configurations to Extend Investment Decision and Incorporate Sustainability Analysis, Computer Aided Chemical Engineering, 43, 145-50.

A. AlNouss, M. Ibrahim, and S.A. Al-Sobhi, 2018, Potential energy savings and greenhouse gases (GHGs) emissions reduction strategy for natural gas liquid (NGL) recovery: Process simulation and economic evaluation, Journal of Cleaner Production, 194, 525-39.

H. Ansarinasab, M. Mehrpooya, and M. Pouriman, 2018, Advanced exergoeconomic evaluation of a new cryogenic helium recovery process from natural gas based on the flash separation – APCI modified process, Applied Thermal Engineering, 132, 368-80.

H. Hamedi, I.A. Karimi, and T. Gundersen, 2019, Optimization of helium extraction processes integrated with nitrogen removal units: A comparative study, Computers & Chemical Engineering, 121, 354-66.

M. Mehrpooya, and A. Shafaei, 2016, Advanced exergy analysis of novel flash based Helium recovery from natural gas processes, Energy, 114, 64-83.

Sauro Pierucci, Flavio Manenti, Giulia Bozzano, Davide Manca (Eds.)
Proceedings of the 30th European Symposium on Computer Aided Process Engineering
(ESCAPE30), May 24-27, 2020, Milano, Italy. © 2020 Elsevier B.V. All rights reserved.
http://dx.doi.org/10.1016/B978-0-12-823377-1.50154-3

Optimal Design and Operation of Flexible Polygeneration Systems using Decomposition Algorithms

Avinash S. R. Subramanian[a], Thomas A. Adams II[b], Truls Gundersen[a], Paul I. Barton[c],*

[a] *Department of Energy and Process Engineering, Norwegian University of Science and Technology (NTNU), NO-7491, Trondheim, Norway.*
[b] *Department of Chemical Engineering, McMaster University, Hamilton, ON, Canada.*
[c] *Process Systems Engineering Laboratory, Department of Chemical Engineering, Massachusetts Institute of Technology, Massachusetts 02139, United States.*
pib@mit.edu

Abstract

A flexible design solution for a polygeneration system that utilizes a hybrid waste tire and natural gas feedstock to produce a mix of electricity, fuels and chemicals is presented. The optimal design and operation under uncertainty problem is formulated as a scenario-based two-stage stochastic MINLP. The problem is modeled using the recently developed GOSSIP software framework and solved using two methods: ANTIGONE to solve the full-space problem or NGBD with a decomposition strategy. The scaling of solution times of these two methods with number of scenarios is compared. The results of the stochastic formulation are compared with the deterministic approach to demonstrate the improvement in economic performance as a result of taking uncertainty into consideration (the value of the stochastic solution).

Keywords: Polygeneration System, Decomposition Algorithms, Flexible Design, Stochastic Programming, Global Optimization.

1. Introduction

Polygeneration systems produce more than one kind of product, typically a mix of electricity, fuels and chemicals and as such offer several economic and environmental advantages over single product systems. Polygeneration processes that utilize multiple feedstocks may enable the exploitation of certain synergies, for instance, heat integration of exothermic and endothermic processing units or blending the different qualities of syngas generated to provide the correct H_2/CO ratio for downstream synthesis processes (Adams and Barton, 2011). Furthermore, implementing a flexible design may enable polygeneration systems to maintain competitiveness in the face of uncertainties (such as in product prices or environmental policies) (Chen et al., 2007). Flexible design involves oversizing process equipment in order to allow adjustment of operating conditions so as to produce the most valuable product mix for a given realization of uncertainty. Thus, the optimal design and operation problem involves determining the best trade-off between the increased capital cost associated with larger equipment capacities (modeled with `here-and-now' variables fixed before realization of uncertainty) and the expected increase in net present value (NPV) due to operational flexibility (modeled with `wait-and-see' variables after realization of uncertainty). Previous work by Chen et al. (2011) studied the optimal design and operation of a

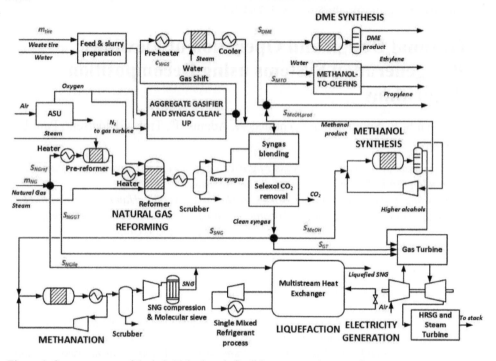

Figure 1: Superstructure of the hybrid feedstock flexible energy polygeneration process

flexible energy polygeneration process in which coal and biomass are co-gasified to produce a mix of naphtha, diesel, methanol or electricity. The flexible design problem was formulated first as a scenario-based two-stage stochastic NLP and solved with BARON and later as an MINLP and solved using the nonconvex generalized Benders decomposition algorithm enhanced with additional dual information (Chen et al., 2012).

In this work, a process that uses a hybrid of a waste tire and natural gas feedstock to produce electricity, liquefied (synthetic) natural gas (LNG), methanol, dimethyl ether (DME) or olefins is studied. 100% operational flexibility is assumed, thus no limits are imposed on the turndown ratios of the product trains. The two feedstocks produce syngas streams of different quality, thus syngas blending to achieve the correct H_2/CO ratio for downstream synthesis is considered. The optimization problem is formulated as a two-stage stochastic MINLP using the recently developed GOSSIP software framework that contains implementations of different decomposition algorithms such as NGBD (Li et al., 2014), Lagrangian Relaxation and Modified Lagrangian Relaxation, as well as a link to ANTIGONE (Misener and Floudas, 2014) to solve the deterministic equivalent problem and primal subproblems in NGBD (Kannan, 2018).

2. Process Description

Figure 1 presents a superstructure of the polygeneration system that utilizes a hybrid of waste tire and natural gas feedstocks to produce the following products: electricity, liquefied (synthetic) natural gas (LNG), sulfur, methanol, dimethyl ether (DME) or olefins. The key operational decision variables for the optimal design and operation problem are presented in Figure 1.

The overall plant scale is determined by two decision variables representing the tire and natural gas mass flow rates: m_{tire} and m_{NG}. The pulverized waste tire slurry is fed to an oxygen-blown entrained flow gasifier operating at 1250 °C and 56 bar to generate syngas which typically has a low H_2/CO ratio (~ 0.7). The syngas can be upgraded using a water gas shift (WGS) reactor in order to get the appropriate ratio for downstream synthesis sections. The conversion of CO (c_{WGS}) in the WGS reaction is a decision variable; high conversion results in hydrogen-rich syngas at the expense of higher steam consumption and lower energy efficiency. Sulfur-containing compounds are removed in a Selexol unit and converted to elemental sulfur in a Claus plant. The tire-derived syngas then heads to a blending section. The natural gas feedstock follows one of three routes. The first branch leads to an autothermal reforming section to generate (a higher quality of) syngas for blending and downstream synthesis, the second branch leads to a liquefaction section and leaves as LNG, while the third branch is fed to a gas turbine for electricity generation. The S_{NGref}, S_{NGliq} and S_{GT} decision variables determine the fraction of natural gas sent to the reforming, liquefaction or gas turbine sections. The optimal reformer operating conditions recommended by Adams and Barton (2011) are used resulting in an H_2/CO ratio of ~3.0.

After CO_2 removal using Selexol, the blended syngas heads to one of three downstream sections: Methanation, Methanol synthesis, or a gas turbine with the syngas split fractions given by S_{SNG}, S_{MeOH}, and S_{GT} respectively. The methanol produced could either be sold as a final product or be further converted to DME or olefins with the methanol split fractions given by $S_{MeOH,prod}$, S_{DME} and S_{MTO} respectively. Off-gases from methanol, DME synthesis and the methanol-to-olefins process are fed to the gas turbine. Heat from the gas turbine exhaust as well as from exothermic process units is used to generate steam for further electricity production in the steam turbine.

Mass and energy balances are first implemented using rigorous models in Aspen Plus v10 for most unit operations except for the Selexol-based H_2S and CO_2 removal sections which are modeled using Aspen HYSYS v10. The surrogate process model was then regressed using sample data points generated by the rigorous simulation in order to keep the optimization problem tractable for global optimization solvers. Further details of the polygeneration process and mathematical model are available in Subramanian et al. (2019 a,b).

3. Optimization problem formulation

The flexible design problem is formulated as a scenario-based two-stage stochastic nonconvex MINLP which takes the general form given below, where: y denotes discrete design decision variables (equipment capacities) which can take on values in Y, x_h are operational decision and state variables in scenario h which can take on values in X, $g^{(1)}$ and $h^{(1)}$ are constraints on the design variables (such as the capital cost model and budget constraints) while $g^{(2)}$ and $h^{(2)}$ are operational constraints such as process mass and energy balances, the operating cost model, scale and throughput constraints. The term ω_h denotes the realization of the uncertain parameters in scenario h, while p_h denotes the probability of occurrence of scenario h, where h can take on values in $\{1,..,N_{scen}\}$. The function $f^{(1)}$ denotes the part of the objective function dependent on design variables while $f^{(2)}$ denotes the part dependent on operational variables.

For the flexible design problem, the objective function is the NPV. The equipment capacities are discretized as detailed in (Chen et al., 2012) because the current version of NGBD is only guaranteed to converge to ε-optimality with binary first-stage variables. The prices of the different products are uncertain parameters and are assumed to belong to a normal distribution with mean and standard deviations calculated from historical data (Table 1).

$$\max_{y,x_h} \quad f^{(1)}(y) + \sum_{h=1}^{N_{scen}} p_h f^{(2)}(x_h, y, \omega_h)$$

s.t.: $\quad \mathbf{g}^{(1)}(y) \le \mathbf{0},$

$\quad\quad \mathbf{h}^{(1)}(y) = \mathbf{0},$

$\quad\quad y \in Y,$

$\quad\quad \left. \begin{array}{l} \mathbf{g}^{(2)}(x_h, y, \omega_h) \le \mathbf{0}, \\[2mm] \mathbf{h}^{(2)}(x_h, y, \omega_h) = \mathbf{0}, \\[2mm] x_h \in X. \end{array} \right\} \quad \forall h \in \{1,...,N_{scen}\},$

$\hfill (1)$

Two-stage stochastic MINLPs exhibit a decomposable structure and thus are amenable to solution using duality-based decomposition algorithms such as nonconvex generalized Benders decomposition (NGBD) as detailed by Li et al. (2014). Motivated by the need for versatile implementation of the NGBD algorithm to a general application, recent work involved the development of the GOSSIP software framework (Kannan, 2018). GOSSIP includes subroutines for reformulating user input, detecting special structure, automatic construction of the subproblems required by the NGBD algorithm, bounds tightening techniques, automatic scenario generation, as well as links to several state-of-the-art solvers for solution of the various sub-problems.

In this work, the flexible design problem is formulated using GOSSIP as a nonconvex MINLP problem with 90 binary 1st stage variables and $321 * N_{scen}$ continuous 2nd stage variables, and 18 1st stage constraints and $338 * N_{scen}$ 2nd stage constraints. The nonconvexities arise due to bilinear terms in the mass balance model. The problem formulation is augmented with reformulation-linearization technique (RLT) equations which yield tighter convex relaxations as detailed by Sherali (2002).

Two cases are studied with 32 scenarios (2 scenarios for each of the 5 uncertain parameters) and 72 scenarios (3 scenarios for P_{Elec} and P_{NG}, and 2 scenarios for the other uncertain parameters). The optimization problem is solved using two methods: ANTIGONE to solve the full-space problem or NGBD as a decomposition strategy. The scaling of solution times of these two methods with number of scenarios compared.

Table 1: Uncertain parameters and values. *The prices of propylene and ethylene are assumed to be linearly correlated.

Uncertain Parameter	Description	Units	Mean	Std. dev.
P_{NG}	Henry hub Natural gas price	$/MMBtu	5.5	3.0
P_{Elec}	Hourly Electricity price	$/MWh	96.1	22.1
P_{MeOH}	Methanol price	$/kg	0.5	0.2
P_{DME}	DME price	$/kg	0.8	0.2
$P_{Ethylene}$	Ethylene price	$/kg	1.05	0.37

Table 2: Results of the flexible design optimization problem. *ANTIGONE did not converge in 5000 seconds in either case.

	Mean Value Problem	Case 1	Case 2
N_{scen}	1	32	72
Capital Costs (M$):			
Aggregate tire gasifier	-	279.7	342.1
Air Separation Unit	-	178.7	178.7
Water Gas shift	-	10.4	10.4
Natural Gas reformer	-	45.1	-
Selexol for CO2 removal	-	24.2	39.3
Methanation	-	-	-
Methanol synthesis	-	57.0	57.0
DME synthesis	-	87.2	87.2
Methanol To Olefins	-	-	-
Electricity generation section	385.0	194.4	194.4
Liquefaction	-	-	-
Water systems & Miscellaneous	58.1	109.8	109.8
Total Capital investment (M$)	443.2	986.5	1018.9
Operation mode:			
Natural Gas to Electricity (%)	100.0	-	-
Tire to DME & Electricity (%)	-	6.3	47.2
Tire & NG to DME & Electricity (%)	-	43.8	2.8
Tire to Methanol & Electricity (%)	-	-	50.0
Tire and NG to Methanol & Electricity (%)	-	50.0	-
Mean Annual Net Profit (M$)	127.8	236.0	221.5
NPV (M$)	559.8	884.1	753.5
EEV (M$)		589.3	320.8
VSS (M$)	-	294.8	432.7
Total wall time (s) – ANTIGONE	3.0	*	*
Total wall time (s) – NGBD	106.83	241.7	260.4

4. Results and Discussion

Table 2 presents the results of the flexible design optimization problem. The NPV increases as a result of considering uncertainty since the increase in annual profit due to operational flexibility exceeds the higher capital investment required. The value of stochastic solution (VSS) increases as more scenarios are considered in Case 2 compared to Case 1 since the expectation of the expected value problem (EEV) is much lower in Case 2. Thus, the nominal design (corresponding to the solution of the mean value problem) performs much worse under the uncertainties characterized by Case 2 than Case 1. Solving the mean value problem results in building only a natural gas to power plant. However, considering the substantial variation in hourly electric prices (Case 1 and Case 2) results in also building tire gasification, natural gas reforming, methanol and DME synthesis sections. We note that, for the characterization of uncertainty considered, the production of liquefied (synthetic) natural gas or olefins is never preferred. In addition, representing the variability of natural gas prices with 3 scenarios in Case 2 results in a solution in which natural gas is only used a small percentage of the time. Figure 2 illustrates the favorable scaling of the NGBD algorithm compared with ANTIGONE as the number of scenarios is increased. However, the

NGBD algorithm performs worse than ANTIGONE for a small number of scenarios since the set of feasible candidate solutions of the 1st-stage variables is relatively large compared to cases in which several scenarios are considered. We also note that adding RLT cuts results in a substantial improvement in the convergence time of the NGBD algorithm.

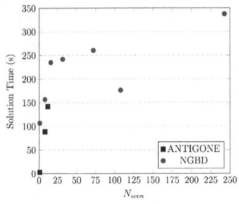

Figure 2: Scaling of solution times of NGBD and ANTIGONE with N_{scen}

5. Conclusions and Future Work

A flexible design solution for an energy polygeneration system that utilizes a hybrid waste tire and natural gas feedstock to produce a mix of products has been developed using a two-stage stochastic programming approach. The results suggest substantial value in taking uncertainty into account. In addition, the results show a favorable computational performance of using the NGBD decomposition algorithms over a state-of-the-art MINLP solver. Future work will involve adding complexity to the model by considering the gasifier and reformer operating conditions as decision variables.

References

T. A. Adams II, P. I. Barton, Combining coal gasification and natural gas reforming for efficient polygeneration, Fuel Processing Technology 92 (2011) 639-655.

Y. Chen, T. A. Adams II, P. I. Barton, Optimal design and operation of flexible energy polygeneration systems, Industrial & Engineering Chemistry Research 50 (2011) 4553-4566.

Y. Chen, X. Li, T. A. Adams II, P. I. Barton, Decomposition Strategy for the Global Optimization of Flexible Energy Polygeneration systems, AIChE Journal 58 (2012) 3080-3095.

X. Li, A. Sundaramoorthy, P. I. Barton, Nonconvex generalized benders decomposition, in: Optimization in Science and Engineering, Springer, 2014, pp. 307-331.

R. Misener, C. A. Floudas, ANTIGONE: Algorithms for Continuous/Integer Global Optimization of Nonlinear Equations, Journal of Global Optimization 59 (2014) 503-526.

R. Kannan, Algorithms, analysis and software for the global optimization of two-stage stochastic programs, Ph.D. thesis, Massachusetts Institute of Technology, 2017.

A. S. R. Subramanian, T. A. Adams II, T. Gundersen, Technoeconomic Analysis of a Waste Tire to Liquefied Synthetic Natural Gas (SNG) Energy System, Submitted (2019a).

A. S. R. Subramanian, T. A. Adams II, P. I. Barton, T. Gundersen, Optimal Design and Operation of a Hybrid Solid Waste and Natural Gas Feedstock Energy Polygeneration System, In Preparation (2019b).

H. D. Sherali, Tight Relaxations for Nonconvex Optimization Problems using the Reformulation-Linearization/Convexification Technique (RLT), in: Handbook of global optimization, Springer, 2002, pp. 1-63.

Sauro Pierucci, Flavio Manenti, Giulia Bozzano, Davide Manca (Eds.)
Proceedings of the 30th European Symposium on Computer Aided Process Engineering
(ESCAPE30), May 24-27, 2020, Milano, Italy. © 2020 Elsevier B.V. All rights reserved.
http://dx.doi.org/10.1016/B978-0-12-823377-1.50155-5

Computational Shape Optimization of Microreactors based on CFD Simulation and Surrogate Model driven Optimization

Runzhe Liang, Zhihong Yuan[*]

Department of Chemical Engineering, Tsinghua University, Beijing 100084, China

zhihongyuan@mail.tsinghua.edu.cn

Abstract

Pharmaceutical industry has become an emerging industry worldwide. However, the automation level and the production efficiency of pharmaceutical manufacturing are relatively low because of the large-scale utilization of batch mode. In the context of the rise of microdevices, this paper investigated the shape optimization of Y-shape microreactors for the production of the optically pure chiral product (S)-1-phenylethylamine. We established the computational fluid dynamics (CFD) based automatic simulation platform to obtain a large number of simulation data sets. We built the data-driven surrogate model based on support vector machine (SVM). Then, we formulated the optimization framework to obtain the optimal shape parameters. By shape optimization of microreactors, the yield of the main product can be increased to about 4.3 times as high as that of the initial microreactor.

Keywords: microreactor, shape optimization, data-driven model, CFD automatic simulation

1. Introduction

The traditional batch operation mode is widely adopted in the pharmaceutical industry. Although batch processes have a few advantages such as equipment flexibility, product recovery ability, practicality and so on, it often means the waste of resources and low operational asset efficiencies. To solve the problem, continuous processes can be utilized which means to feed and transform the input materials continuously, and to remove the processed output materials continuously from the system (U.S. Food and Drug Administration, 2019). In general, continuous processes can be considered to have great application potential in improving the flexibility, robustness and reducing operating cost of pharmaceutical manufacturing, which can realize the modernization of pharmaceutical manufacturing better.

The rise of microdevices provides a potential way of continuous pharmaceutical manufacturing. As one of the methods of process intensification, due to large specific surface area, microdevices usually have better mass transfer and heat transfer, which can significantly improve the selectivity and yield of the reaction (Tian et al., 2018). Consequently, operation under microfluidic conditions can be expected to greatly improve the operability and stability of the system (Plutschack et al., 2017). The development of additive manufacturing also provides conditions for precise processing of microdevices (Addison, 2018), however, the design and manufacturing of microdevices mainly follow the trial-and-error approach at present and usually require a large number of experiments and capital to seek the desirable candidate without any guarantee of optimum solutions. There are relatively few studies on systematic shape optimization of microreactors, most of which only focus on the simulation of single microreactor. Inspired by the aforementioned issues, the presented work combines the computational fluid dynamics (CFD) simulation and data-driven optimization methods to formulate the framework for the shape optimization of microreactors to obtain the highest yield of main products. In our work, the synthesis of S-1-phenylethylamine by the reaction of acetophenone and isopropylamine is used as an example. In detail, our investigations can be divided into three parts: the establishment of automatic CFD simulation platform, the establishment of the data-driven model and the model optimization. Via the CFD simulation platform, a large number of simulation results can be obtained automatically within a certain period of time. CFD simulation results then feed to the building of the data-driven surrogate model based on support vector machine (SVM) method. The surrogate model will replace the original partial differential equations of the microreactor to represent the relationship between main product yield and geometric and shape conditions. Hence, the optimization model can be built to obtain the optimal parameters.

2. Reaction Information

In this paper, an enzymatic reaction is carried out as an example, to produce the optically pure chiral product (S)-1-phenylethylamine (PEA) since this product is an important pharmaceutical intermediate from acetophenone (APH) and isopropylamine (IPA) catalyzed by amine transaminase (ATA), with acetone (ACE) as a by-product, as shown in Figure 1:

Figure 1. Reaction producing (S)-1-phenylethylamine from acetophenone

The reason why the reaction is chosen for study is that it is a typical and important reaction with unfavorable thermodynamic conditions. The reaction follows a ping pong bi-bi mechanism in which isopropylamine (IPA) binds to the enzyme first, and after acetone (ACE) is released acetophenone (APH) binds next, and finally the product (S)-1-phenylethylamine (PEA) is released from the enzyme (Al-Haque, 2012). As a transaminase-catalyzed reaction, the reaction is heavily influenced by inhibition of the substrate APH and the product PEA, with a small equilibrium constant. The kinetic model is described as Eq. (1):

$$r_{PEA} = \frac{d[PEA]}{dt}$$

$$= \frac{[E_0]k_{cat}^f k_{cat}^r ([APH][IPA] - \frac{[PEA][ACE]}{K_{eq}})}{\begin{aligned}&\{k_{cat}^r K_M^{APH}[IPA](1 + \frac{[PEA]}{K_{Si}^{PEA}} + \frac{[IPA]}{K_{Si}^{IPA}}) + k_{cat}^r K_M^{IPA}[APH](1 + \frac{[APH]}{K_{Si}^{APH}} + \frac{[ACE]}{K_{Si}^{ACE}}) + \\ &k_{cat}^f \frac{K_M^{PEA}[ACE]}{K_{eq}}(1 + \frac{[APH]}{K_{Si}^{APH}} + \frac{[ACE]}{K_{Si}^{ACE}}) + k_{cat}^f \frac{K_M^{ACE}[PEA]}{K_{eq}}(1 + \frac{[PEA]}{K_{Si}^{PEA}} + \frac{[IPA]}{K_{Si}^{IPA}}) \\ &+ k_{cat}^r[APH][IPA] + k_{cat}^f \frac{K_M^{PEA}[IPA][ACE]}{K_{eq}K_i^{IPA}} + \frac{k_{cat}^f[ACE][PEA]}{K_{eq}} + k_{cat}^r \frac{K_M^{IPA}[APH][PEA]}{K_i^{PEA}}\}\end{aligned}} \quad (1)$$

Al-Haque et al. (2012) determined the parameters of the reaction system in detail through a large number of experiments and data fitting. At the same time, the mass transfer coefficient is also the key to affect the mixing and reaction rate. In this case, two compounds involved in the reaction are regarded as slow diffusion compounds: ATA ($D = 1 \times 10^{-11}$ m²/s) and APH ($D = 1 \times 10^{-12}$ m²/s), while other compounds are regarded as fast diffusion compounds, with the same diffusion coefficient ($D = 1 \times 10^{-9}$ m²/s) (Grundtvig et al., 2017).

3. Method Description

3.1. Microreactor Information

The initial microreactor type studied is the Y-shape microreactor (Figure 2), where APH and IPA enter from one end of the microreactor, while the enzyme ATA enters from the other end of the microreactor, and they mix and react in the main reaction channel.

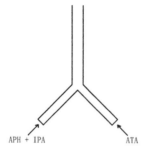

APH + IPA   ATA

Figure 2. Initial configuration of the microreactor

Because of the low flow velocity and the existence of two slow diffusion substances, APH and ATA, although there is an intersection in the microreactor, the overall mixing effect is still poor, and the characteristics of laminar flow pattern and slow diffusion also make the radial diffusion of reactants difficult, so it is difficult for APH and ATA to reach a relatively uniform distribution. The reaction can only take place at the interface between the two parallel flows, which greatly affects the overall reaction rate and the yield of PEA.

3.2. Research Method

The idea of this work is to improve the mixing situation by optimizing the shape of the microreactor, and to interfere with the original laminar flow pattern so that the slow diffusion substances can achieve better radial mixing effect. For example, a depression on the wall of the microreactor is designed in this paper, which can influence the flow condition to some extent. When there is a depression on the wall, there will be two main effects: on the one hand, the depression can disturb the original flow pattern, and it is equivalent to reducing the distance of radial diffusion needed in a certain length range, which contribute to the improvement of conversion greatly; on the other hand, the occurrence of the depression will reduce the cross-sectional area of the microreactor. According to the continuity principle, the flow rate will accelerate, so that the residence time will reduce, which is not conducive to the improvement of conversion. In order to get a higher yield, it is necessary to design relevant parameters of the depression, such as the location of the depression x, the length of the depression l, the depth of the depression h and so on (Figure 3).

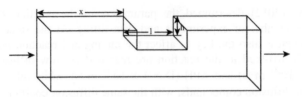

Figure 3. Determining parameters when introducing a depression

Due to existence of the grey box model of CFD simulation, a large number of data can be generated by CFD simulation, and then a surrogate model can be built based on SVM method, and the optimal solution with the highest product yield can be also obtained through optimization of related models. The flow chart is shown as Figure 4:

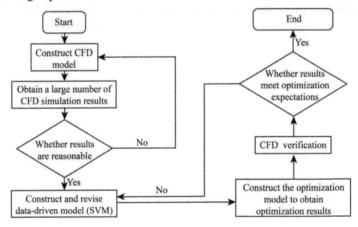

Figure 4. Research flow chart

4. Results and Discussion

The length, width and height of the main reaction channel of the initial microreactor are set as 10 mm, 0.3 mm and 1 mm respectively. The length and width of inlet passages are 3 mm and 0.15 mm respectively. The angle of the intersection is 90 °. The mass fractions of ATA, APH and IPA in the feed are 0.2 %, 0.3 % and 5 %, respectively, and the flow rate is 0.1 mm/s.

Considering the manufacturing difficulty, the distance between the beginning position of the depression and the intersection should not be less than 0.1 mm, the length of the depression should not be less than 0.1 mm, and the depth of the depression should not be more than 0.25 mm. According to the established surrogate model, we can get the objective function and constraints as Eq. (2):

$$\max y = f(x, l, h)$$
$$s.t.\ x \geq 0.1$$
$$l \geq 0.1 \tag{2}$$
$$x + l \leq 10$$
$$0 \leq h \leq 0.25$$

Where $y = f(l, x, h)$ is the regression model obtained by SVM.

In order to build the above optimization model, the first step is to build an automatic simulation platform to get a large number of simulation results. In this work, ANSYS is utilized as the computational fluid simulation software, and the structured mesh is used for mesh generation to ensure mesh quality. In order to balance simulation time and simulation accuracy, the number of volume meshes divided in each simulation is about 1,000,000, so as to ensure that each solution time is not too long (about one hour). In this study 670 simulations are included in total, 530 of which are used as training sets with 121 boundary conditions (for example, when the length of the depression is zero, the yield is the same as that of the initial microreactor) while the others are used as test sets.

The second step is to set up the SVM-based surrogate model. After all data are normalized, radial basis function is used as kernel function for nonlinear regression, and appropriate parameters such as values of λ and penalty factor C are selected to ensure the regression effect and avoid over fitting. The regression results are listed in Table 1:

Table 1. SVM regression results

Number of support vectors	Regression coefficient R^2 (for training sets)	Regression coefficient R^2 (for test sets)
193	0.957	0.938

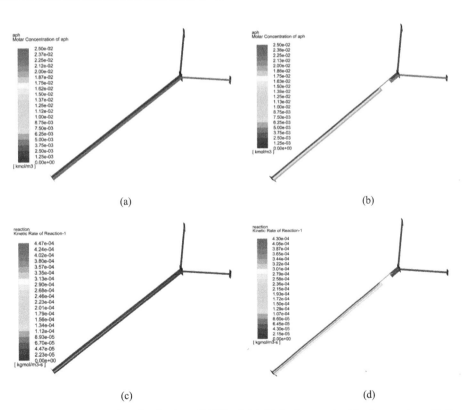

(a)   (b)

(c)   (d)

Figure 5. Concentration distribution of APH of a) initial microreactor b) microreactor with the optimal depression parameters and reaction zone distribution of c) initial microreactor d) microreactor with the optimal depression parameters

After the establishment of the data-driven surrogate model, the last step is to obtain the optimal parameters via optimization of Eq. (2), and then check the optimization result by CFD simulation. Because support vector theory is generally sensitive to missing data, if the simulation result is basically consistent with the optimization result, it is proved that the optimal parameters of depression have been obtained; if they are inconsistent, the simulation result is fed back to the training set and the model needs to be retrained, so as to obtain a new surrogate model and new optimal depression parameters, which will be checked again, until they are basically consistent.

To deal with this NLP problem, the software GAMS is utilized in this study to obtain the optimal solution, with CONOPT solver. After gaining several groups of inconsistent results and updating, the optimization result can be considered equal to the simulation result, where x, l and h are 0.72 mm, 0.77 mm and 0.25 mm, respectively, and the yield can be increased to 4.3 times of that of initial microreactor. Comparison figures are shown in Figure 5.

It can be observed from the figures above that there is almost no radial diffusion of APH in the initial microreactor, however in the optimized microreactor, diffusion effect has greatly improved after a short and deep depression. Things are the same for ATA. Because the radial diffusion effect of substances with small diffusion coefficient is improved, and the mixing condition of reactants is improved, the reaction zone is obviously expanded, resulting in a large increase in the yield.

5. Conclusion and Prospect

A systematic shape optimization method of microreactors based on CFD simulation and the surrogate model was proposed in this work. Through the establishment of the CFD based automatic simulation platform, a large number of simulation data can be obtained within a certain period of time, and a data-driven surrogate model can be also built by SVM regression, so as to determine the objective function and constraints, which can be solved by the reliable optimization algorithm to obtain the optimal parameters of geometry. The yield of the optimized microreactor has been greatly improved in the work, and in the future, the work will focus on the following two points: 1) to verify the results by a series of experiments; 2) to include more arguments to prove the general applicability of the optimization method.

References

U.S. Food and Drug Administration, 2019, Quality Considerations for Continuous Manufacturing.

Tian Y, Demirel S E, Hasan M M F, Pistikopoulos E N, 2018, An overview of process systems engineering approaches for process intensification: State of the art, Chemical Engineering and Processing - Process Intensification, 133:160-210.

Plutschack M B, Pieber B, Gilmore K, Seeberger P H, 2017, The Hitchhiker's Guide to Flow Chemistry, Chemical Reviews, 117(18):11796-11893.

Addison K, Stark, 2018, Manufactured Chemistry: Rethinking unit operation design in the age of additive manufacturing, AIChE Journal, 64: 1162-1173.

Al-Haque N, Santacoloma P A, Neto W, Tufvesson P, Gani R, Woodley J M, 2012, A robust methodology for kinetic model parameter estimation for biocatalytic reactions, Biotechnology Progress, 28(5):1186-1196.

Grundtvig I P R, Daugaard A E, Woodley J M, Gernaey K V, Krühne U, 2017, Shape optimization as a tool to design biocatalytic microreactors, Chemical Engineering Journal, 322:215-223.

Sauro Pierucci, Flavio Manenti, Giulia Bozzano, Davide Manca (Eds.)
Proceedings of the 30th European Symposium on Computer Aided Process Engineering
(ESCAPE30), May 24-27, 2020, Milano, Italy. © 2020 Elsevier B.V. All rights reserved.
http://dx.doi.org/10.1016/B978-0-12-823377-1.50156-7

High-purity DMC Production by Indirect Alcoholysis of Urea: Optimal Design and Control

Iulian Patraşcu,[a] Costin Sorin Bîldea,[a] Anton A. Kiss [b,c*]

[a] *University "Politehnica" of Bucharest, Polizu 1-7, 011061 Bucharest, Romania.*
[b] *The University of Manchester, Department of Chemical Engineering and Analytical Science, Sackville Street, The Mill, Manchester M13 9PL, United Kingdom.*
[c] *University of Twente, Sustainable Process Technology, PO Box 217, 7500 AE Enschede, The Netherlands.*

a.a.kiss@utwente.nl , tony.kiss@manchester.ak.uk

Abstract

This work shows that it is feasible to convert a greenhouse gas to a green solvent. Dimethyl carbonate (DMC) is an eco-friendly chemical compound which can be obtained by indirect alcoholysis of urea with propylene glycol, followed be the trans-esterification of propylene carbonate (PC) with a large excess of methanol. However, this process route requires the energy-intensive separation of the DMC-methanol azeotrope. Here, we propose a new process in which the transesterification reaction is performed with excess of PC, which allows obtaining high purity DMC (99.8%wt) in a less complex process. By optimizing the new process, the total annual cost is minimized to 4.71 M\$/year (for a production capacity of 32 ktpy DMC), and by heat integration the energy requirement is reduced to only 2.64 kWh/kg DMC. The dynamics and control of the process show that ±10% changes of the production are easily accommodated.

Keywords: Alkyl carbonate, Process design, Process optimization, Plantwide control

1. Introduction

Carbon dioxide, available from CCS activities, can be used as feedstock for producing various chemicals. Dimethyl carbonate (DMC) is an essential chemical used in the production of polycarbonates, batteries and fuel additive (Keller et al., 2010). In contrast to solvents such as dimethyl sulphate and phosgene, DMC has low toxicity and fast biodegradability (Santos et al., 2014). DMC can be produced by various methods: phosgenation, urea esterification, ethylene carbonate esterification, methanol oxy-carbonylation, and direct synthesis from CO_2 and methanol (Kongpanna et al., 2015; Kuenen et al., 2016; Tan et al., 2018). The best reported process is the indirect urea alcoholysis (Figure 1), in which urea (produced by the CO_2-ammonia reaction) is used for the carbonylation of propylene glycol (PG) to make propylene carbonate (PC), which is further used in the transesterification with methanol (MeOH) to yield DMC (Wang et al., 2016). Recently, this process was used to obtain DMC/MeOH azeotrope (14.07 %mole DMC) using excess methanol for the transesterification step (Shi et al. 2017). This process requires 1.75 kWh/kg DMC as azeotrope with MeOH, to which one should add 2.55 kWh/kg DMC needed to break this azeotrope by extractive distillation with methyl isobutyl ketone (MIBK) as solvent (Hu and Cheng, 2017).

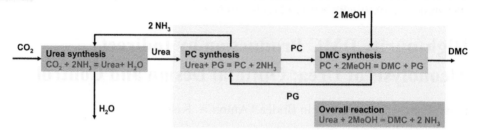

Figure 1. DMC synthesis by urea alcoholysis and transesterification of propylene carbonate

This study presents a new process that is specifically developed to produce high purity DMC (99.8 %wt). Process optimization is carried out to minimize the total annual cost, and heat integration is used to drastically reduce the energy usage, while an adequate process control structure is proposed to ensure controllability of the DMC plant.

2. Problem statement

The most important step of the DMC production by indirect alcoholysis of urea is the transesterification reaction of PC with methanol, followed by DMC purification by extractive distillation (Figure 2). A high PC conversion can be achieved if the reaction takes place with excess methanol (Figure 3 left). However, the composition of the reactor effluent is such that high purity methanol and DMC/MeOH azeotrope (Figure 3 right) can be obtained by conventional distillation. Thus, DMC purification and methanol recovery are achieved by extractive distillation (Figure 2), leading to high energy requirements. To solve this problem, this work proposes to carry out the transesterification reaction with excess PC instead of methanol, such that methanol is the limiting reactant and the DMC concentration in the reactor effluent exceeds the azeotropic value. Therefore, DMC can be obtained with high purity, while the azeotrope can be recycled to the process. Performing the reaction in this way, it is no longer necessary to use other costly separation techniques for breaking the azeotrope.

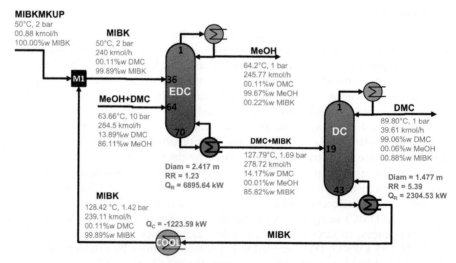

Figure 2. Process design for DMC purification by extractive distillation

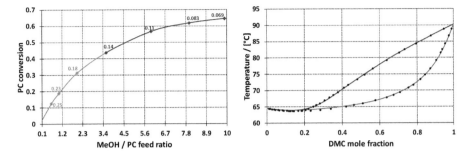

Figure 3. Dependence of the PC equilibrium conversion (40 °C) vs MeOH/PC feed ratio (left). VLE experimental data vs. values predicted by the NRTL model for MeOH / DMC (right).

3. Chemistry and kinetics

The process design developed in this work considers urea and methanol as raw materials. PC is obtained in the reaction of urea with PG, while DMC is obtained in the reaction of PC with methanol. The reaction rate for the PC synthesis step is given by (Shi et al. 2017):

$$r_{PC} = k \cdot c_{PG} \cdot c_{Urea}, \text{ with } k(T)/[m^3/(kmol/s)] = 0.02646 \cdot \exp(-562.6/T) \qquad (1)$$

For the DMC synthesis step, experimental data (Pyrlik et al. 2011) has been regressed to yield the following reaction rate:

$$r_{DMC} = k\left(x^2_{MeOH} x_{PC} - x_{PG} x_{DMC}/K_x\right), \text{ with } k_{(313\,K)} = 0.4166 \times 10^{-3} \text{ kmol/kg/s}, K_{x(313\,K)} = 0.2.$$

4. Results and discussion

Figure 4 presents the novel process design for DMC production, along with the mass balance and key design and operating parameters. Two stirred reactors are necessary to achieve a high conversion of urea. These reactors contain the MgO catalyst (2 %wt, about 400 kg), have 20 m³ each and operate at 180 °C and 10 bar. PG and urea are fed in stoichiometric ratio in the first stirred reactor (CSTR1). The ammonia produced here is removed as vapour by using a flash vessel (V-L). The second stirred reactor (CSTR2) achieves over 99.3% conversion of PG. The first distillation column (C1) removes completely the ammonia to avoid its accumulation in the DMC/MeOH recycle loop.

Note that the stoichiometric ratio of MeOH/PC for DMC synthesis is 2, but to obtain high purity of DMC this ratio is kept at 1 such that there is an excess of PC. The PC previously produced and the fresh MeOH are fed in a tubular reactor (RPLUG), containing 1270 kg of catalyst. The effluent of the reactor is separated in the second distillation column (C2) into a distillate containing DMC and MeOH, and a bottom product consisting of PG and PC. DMC is obtained as a high purity (99.8 %wt) bottom product of the third column (C3), while the distillate (MeOH/DMC azeotrope) is recycled to the transesterification reactor. The separation of PG from PC takes place in the fourth column (C4). The PC is recycled from its bottom to DMC synthesis, while PG with some PC is sent to the first reactor for PC synthesis.

The total number of stages (*NT*) and the feed tray location (*NF*) of each distillation column were determined by optimization, where the minimum of the total annual cost was the objective function. Figure 5 shows results concerning the distillation column C-3: optimal number of stages (left), temperature and concentration profiles (right).

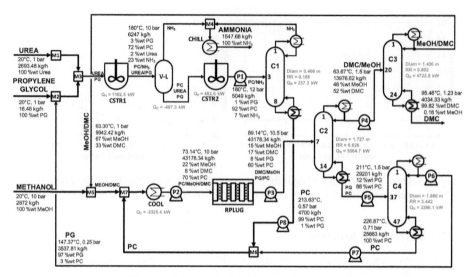

Figure 4. Process design for DMC production

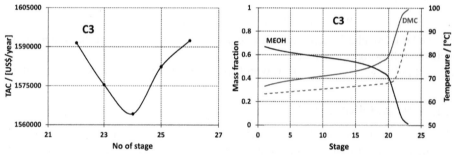

Figure 5. Column optimization (left). Temperature and mass composition profiles (right).

The dynamic simulation is built in Aspen Dynamic using a flow driven dynamic model. The basic control includes several pressure, liquid level, and temperatures control loops (for the stirred reactors, distillation columns, and various heat exchangers). More important, feeding the reactants in the correct amounts and avoiding their accumulation or depletion is the key to successful plantwide control. Thus, fresh urea sets the production rate. The ratio between reactants is kept constant at the inlet of the reactors, while fresh methanol and PG makeup flows are set by level control loops. Figure 6 shows the plantwide control structure of the heat integrated plant for DMC production, while the dynamic results are shown in Figure 7.

The performance of the plantwide control structure is tested by introducing feed flow rate disturbances. After two hours of steady state operation, the urea flow rate is increased in 1h ramp by 10%. The ratio controller increases the PG flow rate. As a result, more PC is produced. As the ratio MeOH/PC at the inlet of RPLUG is constant, more methanol is added to the process. Afterwards, the production of DMC is returned to initial value and the further decreased by 10%, by decreasing the fresh urea flow. During these changes, the PG flow rate is reduced, less PC is produced, and less MeOH is brought into the process. The control structure is clearly able achieve 10% production rate changes while maintaining high quality of the DMC product.

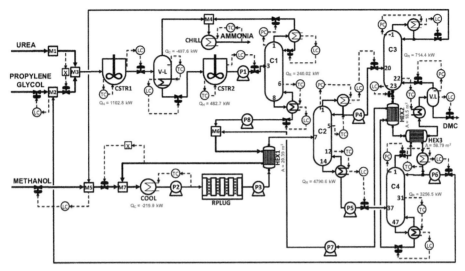

Figure 6. Control structure of heat integrated process design for DMC production

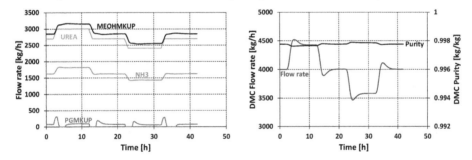

Figure 7. Dynamic results for production changes in the heat integrated DMC process

5. Process evaluation

The heat integration potential was analysed by Pinch Analysis, which revealed that up to 38% energy savings is possible. Using only a few process-process heat-exchangers, the energy requirement was reduced by 31%. Table 1 provides an overview of the economic evaluation, assuming a payback period of 3 years and 8000 hours/year operating time. The capital cost was evaluated according to Dimian (2003). The heating and cooling costs taken into account are: LP steam (6 bar, 160 °C, $7.78/GJ), HP steam (41 bar, 254 °C, $9.88 /GJ), and cooling water (1bar, 25 °C $0.72/GJ).

Table 1. Economic evaluation of the novel heat integrated DMC process

Item description *(unit)*	C1	C2	C3	C4	React	HEX	Cool	Mixer
Shell / [10³ $]	25.0	199.5	336.0	457.6	589.5	199.9	291.9	407.9
Trays / [10³ $]	1.1	16.4	35.0	55.6	–	–	–	–
Condenser / [10³ $]	82.3	553.8	123.3	580.4	–	–	–	–
Reboiler / [10³ $]	23.4	422.2	540.2	57.5	–	–	–	–
Heating / [10³ $/year]	53.8	1363.1	160.1	926.6	384.5	–	–	–
Cooling / [10³ $/year]	1.4	65.5	94.7	10.7	–	–	14.9	–
TAC / [10³ $/year]	99.1	1826.0	599.6	1321.0	581.0	66.6	112.1	136.0

The total investment cost (including heat exchangers, distillation columns, reactors, vapor-liquid vessels and coolers) is $4998.5 \cdot 10^3$ US\$, while the total operating cost is $3075.1 \cdot 10^3$ US\$/year, with a total annual cost of $4712.3 \cdot 10^3$ US\$/year. The total net carbon tax for 2506 kg/h CO2 emissions is evaluated at 13.81 \$/h. The specific energy requirement is reduced to only 2.64 kWh/kg DMC for the new heat integrated process.

6. Conclusions

High purity DMC can be effectively produced by indirect alcoholysis of urea in the new process proposed in this study, by performing the transesterification reaction with excess PC (instead of methanol – as in a conventional process). This avoids the energy intensive DMC purification from the DMC/MeOH azeotrope. Moreover, the energy requirement is significantly reduced (by heat integration) to only 2.64 kWh/kg DMC, minimizing also the total annual cost to $4712.3 \cdot 10^3$ US\$/year. The new process is easily controllable, $\pm 10\%$ changes of the production flow rate being easily achieved.

Acknowledgment

Financial support of the European Commission through the European Regional Development Fund and of the Romanian state budget, under the grant agreement 155/25.11.2016 Project POC P-37-449 (ASPiRE) is gratefully acknowledged. AAK gratefully acknowledges the Royal Society Wolfson Research Merit Award.

References

A. C. Dimian, 2003, Integrated design and simulation of chemical processes, Elsevier, Amsterdam.

C.-C. Hu, S.-H. Cheng, 2017, Development of alternative methanol/dimethyl carbonate separation systems by extractive distillation - A holistic approach, Chemical Engineering Research and Design, 127, 189-214.

N. Keller, G. Rebmann, V. Keller, 2010, Catalysts, mechanisms and industrial processes for the dimethylcarbonate synthesis, Journal of Molecular Catalysis a-Chemical, 317, 1-18.

P. Kongpanna, V. Pavarajarn, R. Gani, S. Assabumrungrat, 2015, Techno-economic evaluation of different CO2-based processes for dimethyl carbonate production, Chemical Engineering Research and Design, 93, 496-510.

H. J. Kuenen, H. J. Mengers, D. C. Nijmeijer, A. G. J. van der Ham, A. A. Kiss, 2016, Techno-economic evaluation of the direct conversion of CO_2 to dimethyl carbonate using catalytic membrane reactors, Computers & Chemical Engineering, 86, 136-147.

A. Pyrlik, W. Hoelderich, K. Müller, W. Arlt, J. Strautmann, D. Kruse, 2011, Dimethyl carbonate via transesterification of propylene carbonate with methanol over ion exchange resins, Applied Catalysis B: Environmental, 125, 486-491.

B. A. V. Santos, V. M. T. M. Silva, M. J. Loureiro, A. E. Rodrigues, 2014, Review for the direct synthesis of dimethyl carbonate, ChemBioEng Reviews, 1, 214-229.

L. Shi, S.-J. Wang, D.S.-H. Wong, K. Huang, 2017, Novel process design of synthesizing propylene carbonate for dimethyl carbonate production by indirect alcoholysis of urea, Industrial & Engineering Chemistry Research, 56, 11531-11544.

H-Z. Tan, Z-Q. Wang, Z-N. Xu, J. Sun, Y-P. Xu, Q-S. Chen, Y. Chen, G-C. Guo, 2018, Review on the synthesis of dimethyl carbonate, Catalysis Today, 316, 2-12.

M. Y. Wang, H. B. Wang, Q. H. Qu, L. N. He, 2016, Industrial production of dimethyl carbonate from CO_2 in China, in P. Tundo, L. N. He, E. Lokteva, C. Mota (Eds) Chemistry beyond chlorine, Springer, Cham.

Sauro Pierucci, Flavio Manenti, Giulia Bozzano, Davide Manca (Eds.)
Proceedings of the 30th European Symposium on Computer Aided Process Engineering
(ESCAPE30), May 24-27, 2020, Milano, Italy. © 2020 Elsevier B.V. All rights reserved.
http://dx.doi.org/10.1016/B978-0-12-823377-1.50157-9

Optimization of Shell and Tube Heat Exchangers Sizing with Heat Transfer Enhancement

Zekun Yang, Yingjie Ma, Nan Zhang,* Robin Smith
Centre for Process Integration, School of Chemical Engineering and Analytical Science, The University of Manchester, Manchester M13 9PL, UK
nan.zhang@manchester.ac.uk

Abstract

Heat transfer enhancement (HTE) is an efficient technology to improve the performance of shell and tube heat exchangers (STHEs). However, even though there are widely accepted commercial software packages being used in heat exchanger design combined with HTE, such as HTRI and Aspen EDR, the design procedure still requires extensive user manipulation and fine tuning, which not only is time-consuming but also leads to varied qualities due to human factors. Therefore, a systematic optimization methodology is required in order to achieve an efficient and accurate design solution. This paper presents a generalized disjunctive programming (GDP) model for the optimization of STHE design. The model is formulated as a mixed integer non-linear programming (MINLP) problem using GAMS (General Algebraic Modeling System), involving selection for 12 technology combinations (four tube-side techniques, three shell-side techniques) and all discrete decisions for each selection are modeled by disjunctions. The model is then applied to a case study to minimize the total capital cost. Both global optimization solver BARON, and general MINLP solver DICOPT are tested. The results show the developed HTE optimization method provides a better design solution compared with conventional STHE design procedure.

Keywords: Mathematical programming, heat transfer enhancement, shell and tube heat exchanger design

1. Introduction

Shell and tube heat exchanger (STHE) is a common heat transfer device widely used in oil, gas and chemical industries because of the simple structure and high capability of pressure drop. To increase the economic benefits, reducing the cost of STHE is always a challenge for industrial fields. Many conventional heat exchanger design methods, which are based on the plain tube and normal segmental baffle, have been developed for STHE sizing. These methods apply various algorithms and optimization approaches, which involve SA (simulated annealing) (Chaudhuri et al., 1997), MINLP (mixed integer nonlinear programming) (Mizutani et al., 2003), algorithm based on tube count table (Costa & Queiroz, 2008), GA (genetic algorithms) (Ponce-Ortega et al., 2009), MILP (Mixed-Integer Linear Programming) (Gonçalves et al., 2017). Nevertheless, a relatively high exchanger area under large heat duties is led, since a low utilization efficiency of exchanger geometries, followed by demanding a high capital investment.

To break geometry bottlenecks, heat transfer enhancement (HTE) techniques are developed to improve the performance of STHE through modifications of surface or structure. The main advantages of the HTE applications in different fields involve: (a) Reduce the required exchanger area for STHE design. (b) Avoid additional area, repiping work and installing new exchangers for heat exchanger network retrofit. (c) Increase the conversion from pressure drop to heat transfer coefficients to avoid exceeding the limitation of process pump capacity.

HTE techniques can be categorized into tube-side and shell-side enhancement. Tube-side enhancement techniques include tube inserts (coiled-wire, twisted-tape) and internal fins, which are respectively able to increase heat transfer performance and geometrical area of STHE. Helical baffles and external fins are generally used as the shell-side intensified techniques. Compared with segmental baffles, the conversion from pressure drop to heat transfer rate can be significantly increased by using helical baffles. For external fins, it is similar to internal fins and can extend the surface area to 2-4 times. Relevant correlations have been developed by numerous papers (Jiang et al., 2014; Pan et al., 2013; Smith, 2016; Wang et al., 2012).

In recent years, human factors normally lead to different qualities of design as using the existing STHE design methods, because different users have to carry out various operations to converge the software, such as the selection of baffle type and tube inserts, adjusting tube pitch, tube diameter and twisted pitch. These operations cause various degrees of deviations for different users, and further increase computation time. In order to overcome the existing drawbacks, this paper aims to extend the existing mathematical models that have been developed for STHE to achieve automated heat exchanger sizing with using HTE. GDP is introduced in this model to select all discrete decisions, which mainly include the number of tube passes, TEMA tube sizes, helical angle and tube configurations.

2. Mathematical Model

2.1. Assumption
The assumptions below are required for this mathematical model, as described:
1. Single phase heat transfer in STHEs.
2. Baffles with 20-45% cut.
3. Straight tube bundle.
4. Fluid properties are assumed constant.
5. Constant fouling resistance.

2.2. Design Variables
The main decision variables in the configuration of STHE involve: continuous variables (tube pinch PT, tube number N_t, , tube length L, tube inside and outside diameter D_i, D_O, tube inlet and outlet nozzle diameter $D_{TN,inlet}$, $D_{TN,outlet}$, shell inner diameter D_{SI}, tube outside bundle diameter D_{SB}, shell inlet and outlet nozzle diameter $D_{SN,inlet}$, $D_{SN,outlet}$, , baffle spacing B_S, baffle inlet and outlet spacing B_{in}, B_{out} and baffle cut B_c) and Integer variable (baffle number N_b, the number of tube passes N_{TP}). Additionally, Boolean variables are applied in expressing the disjunctions and transformed into equivalent numbers of binary variables. Cost is defined as a free variable to formulate the objective function.

2.3. Design Equations
Tube-side modeling involves plain tube (PT), coiled-wire (CW), twisted-tape (TT) and internal fins (IF). GDP is developed to select the discrete decisions, which include: tube outside diameter D_O, number of tube passes N_{TP}, tube-side velocity V_T and total tube-side pressure drop ΔP_T. The required Boolean variables and logic propositions for each disjunction are demonstrated in detail.

For the selection of the tube diameters, the general TEMA tube outside diameters of STHE are respectively 0.01905m and 0.02550m. The tube wall thickness of 0.002108m can be used for steel tube. The following disjunction D1 is used to select the tube sizes, as shown:

$$\begin{bmatrix} De_1 \\ D_O = 0.01905 \\ D_i = 0.01483 \end{bmatrix} \lor \begin{bmatrix} De_2 \\ D_O = 0.02550 \\ D_i = 0.02128 \end{bmatrix} \tag{D1}$$

Where De_1 and De_2 are Boolean variables, and corresponding to binary variables de_1 and de_2. If selection De_1 is true ($de_1 = 1$), D_O and D_i are respectively equal to 0.01905m and 0.01483m, otherwise ($de_1 = 0$) D_O and D_i are assigned 0.02550m and 0.02128m. Eqs. (1-2) are used to model D1:

$$D_O = 0.01905\, de_1 + 0.02550\, de_2 \tag{1}$$

$$D_i = 0.01483\, de_1 + 0.02128\, de_2 \tag{2}$$

In order to only select one type of tube sizes, logic equation Eq. (3) is presented:

$$de_1 + de_2 = 1 \tag{3}$$

Similarly, the number of tube passes can be arranged in 1, 2, 4 and 6 passes. Disjunction D2 is presented to select one type of tube pass:

$$\begin{bmatrix} N_1 \\ N_{TP} = 1 \\ V_T = V_{T1} \\ \Delta P_T = \Delta P_{T1} \end{bmatrix} \lor \begin{bmatrix} N_2 \\ N_{TP} = 2 \\ V_T = V_{T2} \\ \Delta P_T = \Delta P_{T2} \end{bmatrix} \lor \begin{bmatrix} N_3 \\ N_{TP} = 4 \\ V_T = V_{T3} \\ \Delta P_T = \Delta P_{T3} \end{bmatrix} \lor \begin{bmatrix} N_4 \\ N_{TP} = 6 \\ V_T = V_{T4} \\ \Delta P_T = \Delta P_{T4} \end{bmatrix} \tag{D2}$$

Where N_1, N_2, N_3 and N_4 are Boolean variables, and then are transformed to binary variables: n_1, n_2, n_3 and n_4. V_{T1}, V_{T2}, V_{T3} and V_{T4} respectively are the tube-side velocity under 1, 2, 4 and 6 tube passes. Similar to the selection of tube sizes, the disjunctions are able to be formulated by logic equations.

Additionally, the tube-side velocity V_T is affected by different tube passes. To avoid directly multiply the N_{TP} by the correlation of V_T, the big-M method is applied in determining the V_T based on D2. The value for M depends on the maximum value of variable which need to be selected in disjunction and is equal to 10 for V_T selection. The correlation of V_T can be found by Wang et al. (2012).

Next, the design models of PT, CW, TT and IF can be respectively found in the literatures (Wang et al., 2012; Jiang et al., 2014; Pan et al., 2013). The tube-side heat transfer coefficient h_T and pressure drop in straight section ΔP_{TS} can be respectively formulated through these models. Finally, total tube-side pressure drop ΔP_T can be obtained based on the sum of ΔP_{TS}, the pressure drop in the tube entrances, exists and reversals ΔP_{TR} and the pressure drop in tube-side nozzles ΔP_{TN}. Smith (2016) presented the correlations to calculate ΔP_{TR} and ΔP_{TN}. The big-M method is used to selectΔP_T. The values of M are equal to 200000 for (N_1 and N_2) and 150000 for (N_3 and N_4). Shell-side model covers three shell-side intensified techniques which are segmental baffles (SSB), helical baffles

(HB) and external fins (EF). Moreover, tube-layout angle T_A, helical angle β_{HB}, shell-side Nusselt number Nu_{HB} and friction factor f_{HB} for helical baffle are automatically selected through disjunction D3 and D4.

For the selection of tube layout angle, general tube configurations include square ($T_A = 90°$), rotated square pitch ($T_A = 45°$), triangular ($T_A = 30°$) and rotated triangular ($T_A = 60°$). Various tube arrangements tend to lead significant impacts for shell-side velocity V_S, shell-side diameter D_{SI}, heat transfer coefficient h_S and equivalent diameter D_{SE}. The following disjunction D3 demonstrates the selection for tube configurations.

$$
\begin{bmatrix}
TA_1 \\
T_A = 90 \\
F_P = 0.85 \\
P_{CF} = 1 \\
P_C = 1 \\
C_{De} = 4/\pi
\end{bmatrix}
V
\begin{bmatrix}
TA_2 \\
T_A = 45 \\
F_P = 1 \\
P_{CF} = \sqrt{2}/2 \\
P_C = 1 \\
C_{De} = 4/\pi
\end{bmatrix}
V
\begin{bmatrix}
TA_3 \\
T_A = 30 \\
F_P = 1 \\
P_{CF} = 1 \\
P_C = 0.866 \\
C_{De} = 2\sqrt{3}/\pi
\end{bmatrix}
V
\begin{bmatrix}
TA_4 \\
T_A = 60 \\
F_P = 1 \\
P_{CF} = \sqrt{3}/2 \\
P_C = 0.866 \\
C_{De} = 2\sqrt{3}/\pi
\end{bmatrix}
\quad \text{(D3)}
$$

Where F_P is the pitch factor and it is able to impact the correlations of h_S, P_{CF} is the pitch correction factor for flow direction and it directs different V_S, P_C is the pitch configuration factor which impacts D_{SI}. C_{De} is the pitch factor which leads different values for D_{SE}. Corresponding to Boolean variables, binary variables ta_1, ta_2, ta_3 and ta_4 direct the logic equations to achieve the selection of various layout angle.

Design model of SSB has been demonstrated by Wang et al. (2012) and Smith (2016), involving detailed equations which are able to calculate shell side heat transfer coefficient h_S and pressure drop ΔP_S. Pan et al. (2013) summarized the design method for the helical baffle to predict the shell-side heat transfer performance and friction factor. Based on Pan's (2013) approach, the correlations of shell-side Nusselt number Nu_{HB} and friction factor f_{HB} depend on the baffle configurations which are categorized as a various helical angle ($\beta_{HB} = 20°$, $30°$, $40°$ and $50°$). Disjunction D4 demonstrate the selection for β_{HB}.

$$
\begin{bmatrix}
HA_1 \\
\beta_{HB} = 20 \\
Nu_{HB} = Nu_{HB,HA1} \\
f_{HB} = f_{HB,HA1}
\end{bmatrix}
V
\begin{bmatrix}
HA_2 \\
\beta_{HB} = 30 \\
Nu_{HB} = Nu_{HB,HA2} \\
f_{HB} = f_{HB,HA2}
\end{bmatrix}
V
$$
$$
\begin{bmatrix}
HA_3 \\
\beta_{HB} = 40 \\
Nu_{HB} = Nu_{HB,HA3} \\
f_{HB} = f_{HB,HA3}
\end{bmatrix}
V
\begin{bmatrix}
HA_4 \\
\beta_{HB} = 50 \\
Nu_{HB} = Nu_{HB,HA4} \\
f_{HB} = f_{HB,HA4}
\end{bmatrix}
\quad \text{(D4)}
$$

Boolean variables (HA_1, HA_2, HA_3 and HA_4) respectively formulate the helical baffle model under different β_{HB}. Binary variables (ha_1, ha_2, ha_3 and ha_4) are transformed form Boolean variables and construct the logic equations through the big-M approach. The values of M are respectively equal to 200 for Nu_{HB} and 100 for f_{HB} formulation.

The relevant correlations of EF haven been demonstrated by Pan et al. (2013) to predict the performance of finned tube in STHE in which the shell-side coefficient and pressure drop at finned tube are tested, as related to fin geometries. The overall heat transfer coefficient U_O is the important criterion for evaluating the performance of STHXs and can be calculated based on h_T, h_S which are simultaneously optimized with considering heat transfer enhancement techniques.

2.4. Constraints and Objective Function

The design of STHEs must respect the relevant constraints to direct the feasible results. Smith (2016) proposed the required constraints, which involve the popular size, the limitations for pressure drops and velocities. Additionally, the actual geometrical area supplied by tubes is necessary to satisfy the required area obtained from the thermal performance of exchanger, as demonstrated:

$$A' \geq A \tag{4}$$

Where A' is the geometrical area based on design techniques of tube and shell. The objective of this optimisation model is to minimize the capital cost. Pan et al. (2013) proposed the correlation to calculate the capital cost, as shown:

$$\text{Cost} = \left(K_0 + \sum K_i\right) EA^{0.8} \tag{5}$$

Where K_0 is the economic coefficient of PT-SSB exchanger, K_i is the economic coefficient for various heat transfer enhancement techniques. EA is the exchanger area related to the number and types of tube.

3. Case Study

In this section, the fluid properties and geometrical details of required base case can be found by Pan et al. (2013). The applied model includes 1175 variables, 1532 equations and is then operated on PC i5-3570. The optimum results are used to evaluate the performance of proposed model with different heat transfer enhancement technologies, through comparison with the results reported by Pan et al. (2013). Figure 1 shows the comparison of results based on the percentage of capital cost reduction. The pressure drop constraint is set at the same value between optimization and simulation for each technique combination.

As expected, the diagram shows that the optimization models lead to a higher enhancement level than the results of Pan et al. (2013), and the differences between the two involve: PT-SSB (-2.2%), PT-EF (-3.2%), CW-SSB (-3.8%), CW-EF (-6.3%), TT-

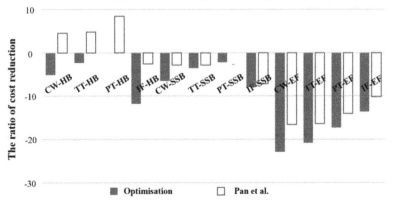

Figure 1. Reduced percentage of capital cost between Pen et al. and proposed model

SSB (-0.7%), TT-EF (-4.5%), IF-SSB (-0.8%) and IF-EF (-3.4%). It is obvious that there is an improvement using the proposed model. Compared with the results in case study-2, the helical baffle models are able to lead a dramatically decrease of capital cost (PT-HB -8.4%, TT-HB -7.1%, CW-HB -9.7% and IF-HB -9.2%), since a higher upper bound of shell-side pressure drop raises the space of optimization in this case. Moreover, an error that appeared in Pan et al. (2013) causes the wrong results for using helical baffles. In their work, helical baffle spacing should be equal to 0.252m, but Pan et al. used a special value 0.043 for baffle spacing, which is not practical. For the HB models in this paper, the baffle spacing is rigorously calculated and modified.

4. Conclusions

A disjunctive mathematical model for STHE optimization is proposed in this paper, which provides the selection for applying 5 types of heat transfer enhancement technique, and then applied in sizing an actual STHE under the given heat duty and streams properties. In GAMS, all variables are optimized simultaneously under detailed constraints and the objective: minimizing the total capital cost. The discrete decisions, which are formulated by disjunctions (D1-D4), are automatically selected to achieve the optimal solution.

Consequently, the optimization implemented by proposed model shows a better performance than that obtained from Pan et al. (2013). Furthermore, this model not only eliminates the influence by human factors, but also achieves the optimal solution under less time, which is possible to improve the performance of software packages through combining with the rigorous model.

References

Chaudhuri, P. D., Diwekar, U. M., & Logsdon, J. S. (1997). An automated approach for the optimal design of heat exchangers. *Industrial & engineering chemistry research*, *36*(9), 3685-3693.

Costa, A. L., & Queiroz, E. M. (2008). Design optimization of shell-and-tube heat exchangers. *Applied Thermal Engineering*, *28*(14-15), 1798-1805.

Gonçalves, C. D. O., Costa, A. L., & Bagajewicz, M. J. (2017). Alternative Mixed-integer linear programming formulations for shell and tube heat exchanger optimal design. *Industrial & Engineering Chemistry Research*, *56*(20), 5970-5979.

Jiang, N., Shelley, J. D., & Smith, R. (2014). New models for conventional and heat exchangers enhanced with tube inserts for heat exchanger network retrofit. *Applied Thermal Engineering*, *70*(1), 944-956.

Mizutani, F. T., Pessoa, F. L., Queiroz, E. M., Hauan, S., & Grossmann, I. E. (2003). Mathematical programming model for heat-exchanger network synthesis including detailed heat-exchanger designs. 1. Shell-and-tube heat-exchanger design. *Industrial & engineering chemistry research*, *42*(17), 4009-4018.

Ponce-Ortega, J. M., Serna-González, M., & Jiménez-Gutiérrez, A. (2009). Use of genetic algorithms for the optimal design of shell-and-tube heat exchangers. *Applied Thermal Engineering*, *29*(2-3), 203-209.

Pan, M., Jamaliniya, S., Smith, R., Bulatov, I., Gough, M., Higley, T., & Droegemueller, P. (2013). New insights to implement heat transfer intensification for shell and tube heat exchangers. *Energy*, *57*, 208-221.

Smith, R. (2016). *Chemical process design and integration*. Second edition ed.; John Wiley & Sons, Inc.: Chichester, West Sussex, United Kingdom.

Wang, Y., Pan, M., Bulatov, I., Smith, R., & Kim, J. K. (2012). Application of intensified heat transfer for the retrofit of heat exchanger network. *Applied Energy*, *89*(1), 45-59

Sauro Pierucci, Flavio Manenti, Giulia Bozzano, Davide Manca (Eds.)
Proceedings of the 30th European Symposium on Computer Aided Process Engineering
(ESCAPE30), May 24-27, 2020, Milano, Italy. © 2020 Elsevier B.V. All rights reserved.
http://dx.doi.org/10.1016/B978-0-12-823377-1.50158-0

The Evaluation of Combined Heat and Mass Exchanger Network Synthesis using Novel Stage-Wise Superstructure

Eleonora Amelia, Kitipat Siemanond

ªThe Petroleum and Petrochemical College, Chulalongkorn University, Soi Chulalongkorn 12, Phayathai road, Pathumwan, Bangkok 10330, Thailand
kitipat.s@chula.ac.th

Abstract

The Combined Heat and Mass Exchanger Network Synthesis (CHAMENS) comprising a win-win strategy for simultaneously diminishing the emission alongside maximizing the profits of the whole systems has been accomplished in this work. The novelty comes from the development of the original Stage-Wise Superstructure (SWS) to be able to overcome the CHAMENS problem by using more accurate formula to determine the exchanger configurations, initialisation strategies, favourable boundaries to solve the complexities, eradicate a number of the heat and mass exchangers, and decrease the Total Annualized Cost (TAC). The purpose of this work is to generate the new applicable method which is noticeable and flexible to be implemented with a better accuracy output for the small, moderate, and large chemical process plants using GAMS. The TAC, several units required, some advantages and limitations of each method have been compared and analysed. The result for the application of this work in CHAMENS achieves the significant TAC reduction € 2,591,720 compared to the current best result of the previous literature.

Keywords: CHAMENS, Novel Stage-Wise Superstructure, Total Annual Cost.

1. Introduction

Nowadays, a circular economy exists as a critical mission for any industries to afford the infeasibility of the conventional linear economy since the industries and population growth increase together with the expansion of the pollutants. It demonstrates that the energy and environmental problem are determined as the eminent parts in the distinctive industrial worldwide. Hence, a poor energy system alters the environmental destructions such as uncontrollable air pollution, high GHG emission, and global warming. According to the BP energy outlook, the primary energy consumption is expected to grow up about 18 billion toe in 2040. However, LCIB scenario cut down CO_2 emission of the industries and buildings to 15 % (3.9 Gt by 2040) associated by the expansion of circular economy activities (*BP Energy Outlook*, 2019). The current restrictions such as the conventional linear economy, inefficiency energy usage, energy crisis, costly energy price, and sustainability of the process plant needed lead to the advancement of optimum integration in both heat and mass exchanger network. Therefore, the circular economy should not only be a theoretical system but also an implementation of the circular economy's principles including the regeneration of all waste liabilities to become the assets which satisfy the standard setters i.e. the government regulations, customer demanding satisfaction regarding to minimize the cost, waste, and diminish the energy usage.

Figure 1. The Circular Economy of CHAMENS.

Based on Figure 1, CHAMENS contributes to the implementation of the circular economy. It has been applied to the Carbon Capture Storage (CCS), bioethanol production process, calcium looping systems, and COG sweetening (Yoro, Sekoai, Isafiade, & Daramola, 2019). The green and sustainable Heat Integration-Azeotropic Dividing Wall Column (HI-ADWC) in (Yang et al., 2019) has been generated to recycle solvent tert-butanol in ADWC separating binary azeotropic mixtures. However, the literature distributions about CHAMENS are still limited about 9 % (Yoro et al., 2019). The objective of this work is to invent a reliable optimization for CHAMENS with acceptable accuracy modeling of the novel Stage-Wise Superstructure (SWS) by developing the original SWS from (Yee T. F, 1990) to be able to solve the CHAMENS problems, to achieving the minimum material usage and competitive TAC compared to the other optimization methods.

2. Methodology

2.1. Mass Exchanger Network Synthesis (MENS)
After inputting all known data, deciding the variables and the boundaries is necessary to provide a good result. DICOPT is used to solve MINLP in this part.

2.2. Heat Exchanger Network Synthesis (HENS)
After completing the data extraction, CPLEX, MIP solver, is applied to avoid all nonlinearities and provide good initialization for the next step. Secondly, all accurate formularies and considerations are contemplated to avert the underestimation of the heat exchanger configurations, and the optimal solutions are produced by using DICOPT as MINLP solver. Then, the optimal solutions of this second step are taken to determine the types of the hot and cold utilities required at the minimum TAC.

2.3. Combined Heat Exchanger Network Synthesis (HENS)

In this part, MENS is solved firstly to get the flowrates at each hot and cold stream with the minimum mass exchanger matchings and costs of the external Mass Separating Agent (MSA), fresh source, and waste. The boundaries and constraints depend on the concentrations and the flowrate in each stream. Then, the HENS is applied in the same way as the HENS step above. In the end of this step, the results of MENS and HENS are combined and analyzed to validate their reliabilities before designing the network. All the methodologies in this work are resolved in GAMS 24.2.1 (General Algebraic Modeling System), and the platform server with 1.80 GHz Intel ® Core TM i7-8550 and 20 GB of RAM are operated.

2.4. Mass Exchanger Network Synthesis (MENS)

2.4.1. Case study 1. Ammonia removal using water based MSA in the packed column.

Based on the case study in PhD. Thesis (Jide, 2007), the process lean streams, L_1 and L_2, are used to remove contaminants from 5 gaseous rich streams. One external high-priced MSA L_3 is also allocated when using only two free process lean streams is not adequate. Our task is to provide the minimum TAC as it can be seen in Figure 2. The minimum composition difference is 0.0007. The IBMS method (Jide, 2007) provided the result of using external MSA 2.809 kg.s^{-1} impacting to their TAC $ 133,323 y^{-1}, and The Total Capital Cost (TCC) $ 196,358. This TAC was affected by the cost coefficient that they used was $ 14,670 s.kg^{-1} with the operational time 8150 hours per year and $ 0.0005 s.kg^{-1} for the cost coefficient of the external MSA. Moreover, FLM-SWS method (Jide, 2007) has the result TAC $ 134,000 y^{-1} and TCC $ 218,000 using external MSA 2.904 kg.s^{-1}. Using the same parameter to make equitable comparison, the result of MSA required by using our work is 2.595 kg. s^{-1}, with TCC $ 103,411 and TAC $ 49,160 y^{-1}. Our result has lower TAC than the IBMS method in (Jide, 2007) due to the target concentration of L3 is not counted at their objective function and our method has the lowest total height of the mass exchangers 743m. The FLM-SWS cited in (Jide, 2007) for the cost coefficient of the external MSA should be corrected to $ 0.0005 s.kg^{-1}. Moreover, our method still has the lowest TCC and TAC in comparison to both IBMS model and FLM-SWS because the number of its mass exchanger is only 7 units and the external MSA required is still the lowest. The flowrates of MSA$_1$ and MSA$_2$ are 1.46 kg. s^{-1}, and 1 kg. s^{-1}. The result using IBMS method has the larger TAC because heat exchange of HENS in IBMS method cannot occur freely, and it only depends on the hot streams at the supply and target temperature. Moreover, our work does not have the splitting at both the rich streams and the lean streams, so it is safe and reliable to be applied in the real industrial application.

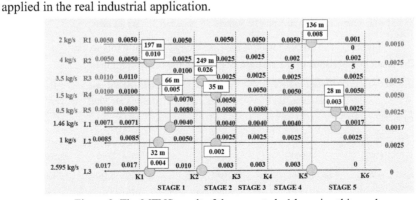

Figure 2. The MENS result of the case study 1 by using this work.

2.5. Heat Exchanger Network Synthesis

2.5.1. Case Study 2 HENS problem of a chemical cluster using three-plants.

In this case study (Hong et al., 2019), the three plants are possible to exchange heat across the plant. The distance among the plants is constant 0.25 km. EMAT is set at 10 °C. The 7 stages are used to get high degree of freedom in the stream matchings. The pressure drop is neglected. The optimal solution provided in this work is compared to the other literatures which used the advancement of SWS (Chang, Chen, Wang, & Feng, 2017) and Transshipment model (Hong et al., 2019) currently. The TAC of this work exhibited in Table 1 is 65 % lower than the current best of the advancement transshipment model in (Hong et al., 2019). Based on this result, several heat exchanger matchings, hot and cold utilities which are the lowest cause the TAC reduction. When the stream matchings are needed, the binary variable in this case equals to 1. Moreover, the binary variable is zero, if the stream matchings do not appear. To get the minimum number of heat exchanger, our program will force the binary variable to be zero until getting the minimum units required at the minimum TAC. The three perceived interplant heat exchangers facilitate the network to diminish the energy demand by utilizing the excess of energy in the plant becoming the additional heating/cooling source for the other plant. The number of heat exchanger units in this work is the fewest in contrast to the other literatures, and the heat exchanger cost of this work is still the lowest due to the fewest units required.

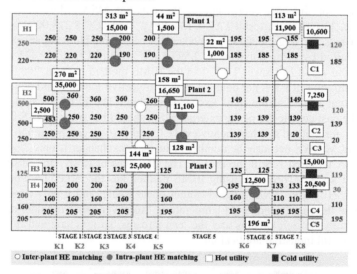

Figure 3. The HENS result of the case study 2 by using this work.

Table 1. The result comparisons of the case study 2 among the other literatures.

Parameters/ Methods	Modified SWS (Chang et al., 2017)	Modified SWS (Chang et al., 2017)	New Transhipment (Hong et al., 2019)	This Work
Heat exchanger units	20	14	14	9
Inter-plant heat exchangers	0	2	5	3
Hot utilities/HUC (kW/$)	15,500/-	6,250/-	2,776/427,620	2,500/500,000
Cold utilities/CUC (kW/$)	66,400/ 664,000	57,100/571,000	53,626/536,262	53,350/ 533,350
TAC, $/y	3,856,860	2,143,444	1,671,023	1,091,166

2.6. Combined Mass and Heat Exchanger Network Synthesis

2.6.1. Case study 3 CHAMENS problem of ammonia recovery.

This case study is obtained from PhD. thesis (Ghazouani, 2018). The ammonia waste from the calcium chloride plant is allocated. Noticing the distinctive of this work among the other previous works, the objective functions are minimizing the TAC. The Exchanger Minimum Approach Temperature (EMAT) is set at 35 °C. The TAC produced by our work is still the lowest because the cold utilities are not needed. The 4 heat exchanger matchings and 5 heating utilities satisfy the heating and cooling demand. The result in (Ghazouani, 2018) has higher heating and cooling demand because HENS is not resolved while the result in (Tan, Ng, Foo, El-Halwagi, & Samyudia, 2014) deals with HENS using EMAT 35 °C having the total area of the heat exchangers 8,544.2 m^2 with 8 heat exchanger matchings while the results of our work successfully defeat their results using the same conditions. The total area of the heat exchangers provided by our results 2,971 m^2 with 7 heat exchanger matchings. The novel SWS successfully provides the result of the CHAMENS with the fewest TAC and the energy demand required. After avoiding the non-linearities by using MIP, the results using MINLP tend to decrease the number of the heat exchangers and minimize their areas, and the energy demand for the heating and cooling utilities.

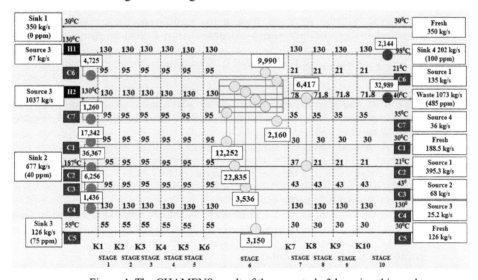

Figure 4. The CHAMENS result of the case study 3 by using this work.

Table 2. The result comparisons of the case study 3 among the other literatures.

Parameters/ Methods	Superimposed mass and energy curves, SMEC (Tan et al., 2014)	New Transhipment (Ghazouani, 2018)	This Work
Flowrate Fresh/ Waste (kGs-1)	654.9/ 1063.9	655/ 1063.9	664.5/ 1073
Total fresh cost (€)	327.5	327.5	332
Hot Utilities / HUC (kWs-1 / €)	132,927/ 4,785,372	131,883.5 / 4,747,806	67,386/2,425,896
Cold Utilities / CUC (kWs-1 / €)	79,228/ 713,052	78,184.5 / 703,660.5	35,133/ 316,197
TAC (€)	5,498,751	5,451,794	2,860,074

3. Conclusion

In this paper, the three case studies MENS, HENS, and CHAMENS have been accomplished due to validate the models contributing to the optimal solutions compared to the different methods FLM-SWS, IBMS, SMEC, and Transhipment model. The results shown are economically viable as the significant TAC reduction can be obtained. This novelty of SWS contains different solving strategy than the original SWS as the initialization step can help the model to get better local optimal solution. It takes the problems to MINLP optimization. This work has been accomplishing the CHAMENS problem with the significant TAC reduction € 2,591,720 compared to the current best result of the previous literature.

Acknowledgements

We would like to express our best gratitude to Chulalongkorn University's Rachadapisaek Sompote Fund (2017) for supporting this research, and The Petroleum and Petrochemical College (PPC) for partially funding support. Moreover, we would like to thank to Mr. Natchanon Angsutorn for his guidance.

References

BP Energy Outlook. (2019). Retrieved from https://www.bp.com/content/dam/bp/business-sites/en/global/corporate/pdfs/energy-economics/energy-outlook/bp-energy-outlook-2019.pdf

Chang, C., Chen, X., Wang, Y., & Feng, X. (2017). Simultaneous synthesis of multi-plant heat exchanger networks using process streams across plants. *Computers & Chemical Engineering, 101*, 95-109. doi:10.1016/j.compchemeng.2017.02.039

Ghazouani, S. (2018). *Linear optimization models for the simultaneous design of mass and heat networks of an eco-industrial park.* Université Paris Sciences et Lettres Paris, France. (HAL Id: tel-01699284)

Hong, X., Liao, Z., Sun, J., Jiang, B., Wang, J., & Yang, Y. (2019). Transshipment type heat exchanger network model for intra- and inter-plant heat integration using process streams. *Energy, 178*, 853-866. doi:10.1016/j.energy.2019.04.112

Jide, I. A. (2007). *Interval Based MINLP Superstructure Synthesis of Heat and Mass Exchange Networks.* Rondebosch, South Africa.

Tan, Y. L., Ng, D. K. S., Foo, D. C. Y., El-Halwagi, M. M., & Samyudia, Y. (2014). Heat integrated resource conservation networks without mixing prior to heat exchanger networks. *Journal of Cleaner Production, 71*, 128-138. doi:10.1016/j.jclepro.2014.01.014

Yang, A., Jin, S., Shen, W., Cui, P., Chien, I. L., & Ren, J. (2019). Investigation of energy-saving azeotropic dividing wall column to achieve cleaner production via heat exchanger network and heat pump technique. *Journal of Cleaner Production, 234*, 410-422. doi:10.1016/j.jclepro.2019.06.224

Yee T. F, G. I. (1990). Simultaneous Optimization Models for Heat Integration II. Heat Exchanger Network Synthesis. *Computers and Chemical Engineering, 14*(10), 1165-1184. doi:10.1016/0098-1354(90)85010-8

Yoro, K. O., Sekoai, P. T., Isafiade, A. J., & Daramola, M. O. (2019). A review on heat and mass integration techniques for energy and material minimization during CO2 capture. *International Journal of Energy and Environmental Engineering, 10*(3), 367-387. doi:10.1007/s40095-019-0304-1

Sauro Pierucci, Flavio Manenti, Giulia Bozzano, Davide Manca (Eds.)
Proceedings of the 30th European Symposium on Computer Aided Process Engineering
(ESCAPE30), May 24-27, 2020, Milano, Italy. © 2020 Elsevier B.V. All rights reserved.
http://dx.doi.org/10.1016/B978-0-12-823377-1.50159-2

An Improved Superstructure-Based Model for Integrating an Organic Rankine Cycle into Total Site

Zheng Chu, Nan Zhang*, Robin Smith

Centre for Process Integration,Department of Chemical Engineering and Analytical Science, the University of Manchester, M13 9PL,Manchester, United Kingdom

nan.zhang@manchester.ac.uk

Abstract

The organic rankine cycle (ORC) could be a promising technology for the further exploitation of the industrial low-grade waste heat. This paper aims to present an improved superstructure-based mixed integer non-linear program (MINLP) model for the integration of an ORC within a total site to recover low-grade waste heat. The model can consider energy-capital trade-off, which includes utility cost, ORC power output, relevant capital cost for ORC and heat exchangers. By using this model, the selection of matches between waste heat streams and the ORC and the operating conditions of ORC could be determined simultaneously. A case study is presented to illustrate the application of this method.

Keywords: Organic Rankine Cycle, Heat integration, MINLP model, Stage-wise superstructure

1. Introduction

The common problem featured in industrial operations is that large quantities of low-grade waste heat are rejected to environment even though, in some cases, the maximum heat recovery through utilisation of all process streams has been reached. With the improvement of low-grade heat exploitation technologies such as Compression Heat Pumps (CHP), Absorption Heat Transformers (AHT), Absorption Heat Pumps (AHP), Absorption Chillers (AbC) and Organic Rankine Cycles (ORC), further exploitation of low temperature waste heat could have economic potentials (Oluleye, 2016). Among these technologies, ORC is becoming a promising technology for commercial applications in industrial fields.

Desai and Bandyopadhyay (2009) proposed a sequential method to integrate an ORC with background processes. Waste heat streams are firstly identified by pinch analysis, and then an ORC is integrated in a heuristic way. Another sequential method was proposed by Chen et al. (2014). First, they synthesized a stand-alone heat exchanger network (HEN) for background processes. Then, an ORC is incorporated into the HEN by using a stage-wise superstructure-based model. Yu et al. (2017) integrated ORC with background processes in an indirect way. In their work, hot water is used as an intermediate between heat sources and an ORC. They presented a nonlinear program (NLP) model which could determine the integration strategy of hot water simultaneously with the techno-economic optimization of ORC. Yu et al. (2018) extended their work by considering different configurations of ORC architectures when integrate an ORC with background processes.

This paper aims to provide an improved superstructure-based MINLP model for the integration of an ORC with multiple waste heat streams. The superstructure is firstly proposed by Yee and Grossman (1990) and is improved by the authors for ORC integration. The annualized cost for ORC integration is considered as the objective to be minimized. By using this model, the selection of matches between waste heat streams and ORC with its corresponding operating conditions can be determined simultaneously.

2. Problem Statement

In the problem statement, waste heat streams are defined directly with the assumption that the background processes have already been integrated. Given a set I= {i|1, 2 ... I} of waste heat streams to be cooled from their supply temperatures $T_{i,in}$ to their target temperatures $T_{i,out}$. The heat capacity flow rates of waste heat streams are also given as CF_i. The cold utility is set as cooling water with its supply temperature $T_{cw,in}$ and outlet temperature $T_{cw,out}$. For the sake of simplicity, multiple choices of cold utilities are not considered. In this paper, waste heat streams are regarded as heat sources for evaporation of ORC working fluid, which is represented by the upper part of Figure 1. And as for condensation, cooling water is used, which is represented in the lower part of Figure 1.

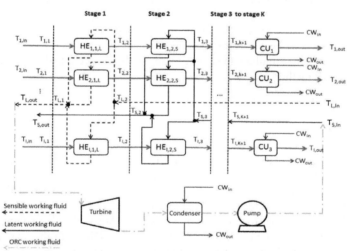

Figure 1. Schematic diagram of the superstructure

3. The Stage-wise Superstructure

Isothermal mixing is assumed for the outlet streams at each stage in this superstructure. To deal with the phase change, in this superstructure, the working fluid is divided into two sub-flows to carry the sensible heat and latent heat separately (shown in Figure 1). For the sake of simplicity, this superstructure matches these two heat flows sequentially, i.e. the latent flow is considered after the sensible heat requirement is fulfilled. In this case, from stage K to stage 2, the sensible heat flow is matched, and in stage 1 matched the latent heat flow. Using only one stage for latent heat transfer is reasonable due to the evaporation process is isothermal. In this way, the criss-cross matches for latent heat flow will be ignored. However, according to Linnhoff and Ahamd (1990), in the most cases, vertical heat transfer can obtain the minimum heat transfer area rather than criss-cross. The superstructure is then derived as follows:

1. Assume the suitable number of stages, normally:
$$K = 1 + I$$
   Where K is the number of stages, I is the number of waste heat streams.
2. From stages K to 2, represent all of the potential matches between the sensible heat flow and waste heat streams. At the outlet of one stage, streams are isothermally mixed which then defines the inlet for the next stage.
3. At stage 1, both of the outlet and inlet temperatures are equal to the saturated temperature at that pressure.

4. Model formulation

4.1. The superstructure-based network

In this section, the model formulation for the evaporation network (shown in the upper side of Figure 1 will be discussed. The network model is developed in the steps as follows:

1) Overall energy balance for each stream
2) Energy balance at each stage
3) Cold utility load
4) Temperature assignment for the network inlet/outlet
5) The feasibilities of the second law of thermodynamics at each stage
6) Set the binary variables to determine the existence of process match
7) The minimum approach temperature feasibilities
8) The calculation of heat exchanger area for each feasible match
9) Calculate the split ratio of the ORC working fluid for each feasible heat transfer at each stage
10) Determine the excess heat exchanger unit

The model formulation from step 1 to step 8 is adopted from Yee and Grossman (1990). In the superstructure, as we split the phase-change stream into two sub-streams, i.e. the sensible heat stream and the latent heat stream, excess heat exchanger units may be created. One instance is presented in Figure 2. It could be realised that the two heat exchangers in dashed box could have potential to be merged into one. The case showed in Figure 2 could also appear in the network. Therefore, steps 9 and 10 are developed to deal with excessive heat exchanger units. In step 9, the split ratio is calculated as:

$$R_{S,i,k} = \frac{q_{S,i,k}}{CF_S \cdot (T_{S,k} - T_{S,k+1})}, i \in WS, k \in [2, K] \tag{1}$$

$$R_{L,i,k} = \frac{q_{L,i,k}}{(H_{L,out} - H_{L,in}) \cdot m_L}, i \in WS, k = 1 \tag{2}$$

Where R represents the spilt ratio, the subscripts S and L mean sensible heat stream and latent heat stream separately, the subscripts i and k represent waste heat stream and stage separately, CF is heat capacity flow rate, T is temperature, H is enthalpy, m is mass flowrate, and q is heat transfer amount. Eq. 1 calculates the spilt ratio R for sensible heat stream matches with each waste heat stream i at each stage from 2 to k. Similar, Eq. 2 calculates the spilt ratio R for latent heat stream matches with waste heat stream i at stage 1. In step 10, the excess heat exchanger unit is identified as:

$$(1 - \xi) \cdot (R_{S,i,k} - R_{L,i,k-1}) + Z_{S,i,k} + Z_{L,i,k-1} - 2 \cdot Y_{i,k} \geq 0, i \in WS, k = 2 \tag{3}$$

Where ξ is a very small constant number which could be 10^{-3}, Z is a binary variable which represents the existence of heat exchanger, Y is a binary variable to determine if the excess heat exchanger unit exists and is incorporated in the objective function.

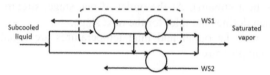

Figure 2. Excess heat exchanger units

4.2. ORC thermodynamic model

The ORC model is established by using Peng-Robinson equation of state (EoS) with the concept of state points (presented in Figure 3). The EOS can calculate the working fluid conditions (temperature, pressure, specific volume, enthalpy, entropy, etc.) at each point, so that the performance of each component (condenser, pump, evaporator and turbine) could be calculated. The specific formulations are omitted in this paper due to the limitation of pages. The ORC model used in this paper is also adopted by Yu et al. (2017). However, it should be mentioned that the evaporator is incorporated with the network, which has:

$$T_{S,in} = T_4 \tag{4}$$

$$T_{L,out} = T_1 \tag{5}$$

$$H_{S,in} = H_4 \tag{6}$$

$$H_{L,out} = H_1 \tag{7}$$

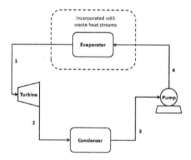

Figure 3. ORC schematic diagram with state points

4.3. Capital cost correlation

The capital cost of heat exchangers could be calculated by Equation (8) & (9), which are also adopted by Yu et al. (2017). Equation (8) calculates the heat exchanger manufacture cost CA_{he}; Equation (9) calculates the fixed charge FC_{he} for implementing heat exchangers.

$$CA_{he} = 190 + 310 \cdot A \tag{8}$$

$$FC_{he} = 5000 \cdot UN_{he} \tag{9}$$

The capital cost of the ORC pump C_{pump} is calculated by Equation (10), which is given by Hung et al. (2010).

$$C_{pump} = 900 \cdot (\frac{W_{pump}}{300})^{0.25} \tag{10}$$

The turbine cost C_{tur} is correlated with the turbine outlet volume V_2 in this paper. Equation (11) is taken from Quoilin et al. (2011).

$$C_{tur} = 1.5 \cdot (225 + 170 \cdot V_2) \tag{11}$$

4.4. Objective function

In this paper, the objective function OBJ includes utility cost, annualized capital cost, the fixed charge of heat exchangers and the profit from ORC operating.

$$\min : OBJ = C_{cu} + AF \cdot \sum C_{capital} - profit \tag{12}$$

Where C_{cu} is utility annual cost, AF is annualized factor, $C_{capital}$ is capital cost of each component.

5. Case study

In this case study, it is assumed that the background processes have been integrated, so that the waste heat stream data are given directly in Table 1.

Table 1. Waste heat stream candidates

Waste heat streams	Supply temperature (K)	Target temperature (K)	Heat capacity flow rate (kW/K)
stream 1	430.15	350.15	45
stream 2	410.15	300.15	35
stream 3	399.15	325.15	20

For this study, the following parameters are given as background data:
- Isentropic efficiency of the turbine and the pump is assumed as 75% and 90% separately.
- The heat transfer coefficients U between waste heat streams and ORC working fluid are set as $150\ W/(m^2 \cdot °C)$, and that between cooling water and ORC working fluid are set as $300\ W/(m^2 \cdot °C)$.
- The fixed charge FC of each heat exchanger is assumed as 5000 $/unit.

Rest of the fixed parameters which include the annualized factor AF, the annual operating hours OH, the electricity price, the cold utility cost are assumed as the same value as those used in Yu et al. (2017). The working fluid of ORC is set as R245ca. To solve the MINLP model, the General Algebraic Modeling System (GAMS) is used as our solution platform with DICOPT as the MINLP solver. The optimized results of the overall objective function are listed in Table 2, and the optimized operating conditions of ORC are presented in Table 3. The corresponding configuration of the network is shown in Figure 4.

Table 2. Overall optimal results

OBJ ($/year)	Cold utility (kW)	Network total area (m²)	Network unit number	Power output (kW)
-364829	1382.12	1911.44	4	774.12

Table 3. Optimal operating conditions of ORC

Variable	Optimal value	Variable	Optimal value
working fluid mass flow rate (kg/s)	30.23	turbine shaft work output (kW)	830.20
turbine inlet pressure (kPa)	741.33	pump work input (kW)	13.85
turbine inlet temperature (K)	363.65	condensation temperature (K)	300.00
turbine outlet pressure (kPa)	107.25	evaporation temperature (K)	363.65
turbine outlet temperature (K)	322.57	thermal efficiency	10.82%

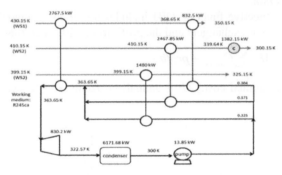

Figure 4. Configuration of the evaporation network

6. Conclusion

A superstructure-based MINLP model for the integration of an ORC with multiple waste heat sources is proposed in this paper. By using this model, the selection of matches between ORC working fluid and waste heat streams, the operating conditions of the ORC and the cold utility cost can be simultaneously determined with an optimal energy-capital trade-off. A simple case is given to illustrate the application of this model.

References

Chen, C., Chang, F., Chao, T., Chen, H. and Lee, J. (2014). Heat-Exchanger Network Synthesis Involving Organic Rankine Cycle for Waste Heat Recovery. *Industrial & Engineering Chemistry Research*, 53(44), pp.16924-16936.

Desai, N. and Bandyopadhyay, S. (2009). Process integration of organic Rankine cycle. *Energy*, 34(10), pp.1674-1686.

Hung, T., Wang, S., Kuo, C., Pei, B. and Tsai, K. (2010). A study of organic working fluids on system efficiency of an ORC using low-grade energy sources. *Energy*, 35(3), pp.1403-1411.

Linnhoff, B. and Ahmad, S. (1990). Cost optimum heat exchanger networks—1. Minimum energy and capital using simple models for capital cost. *Computers & Chemical Engineering*, 14(7), pp.729-750.

Quoilin, S., Declaye, S., Tchanche, B. and Lemort, V. (2011). Thermo-economic optimization of waste heat recovery Organic Rankine Cycles. *Applied Thermal Engineering*, 31(14-15), pp.2885-2893.

Yee, T. and Grossmann, I. (1990). Simultaneous optimization models for heat integration—II. Heat exchanger network synthesis. *Computers & Chemical Engineering*, 14(10), pp.1165-1184.

Yu, H., Eason, J., Biegler, L. and Feng, X. (2017). Simultaneous heat integration and techno-economic optimization of Organic Rankine Cycle (ORC) for multiple waste heat stream recovery. *Energy*, 119, pp.322-333.

Yu, H., Gundersen, T. and Feng, X. (2018). Process integration of organic Rankine cycle (ORC) and heat pump for low temperature waste heat recovery. *Energy*, 160, pp.330-340.

Sauro Pierucci, Flavio Manenti, Giulia Bozzano, Davide Manca (Eds.)
Proceedings of the 30th European Symposium on Computer Aided Process Engineering
(ESCAPE30), May 24-27, 2020, Milano, Italy. © 2020 Elsevier B.V. All rights reserved.
http://dx.doi.org/10.1016/B978-0-12-823377-1.50160-9

MINLP Synthesis of Flexible Process Flow Sheets under Variable Carbon Tax Rates

Klavdija Zirngast, Zdravko Kravanja, Zorka Novak Pintarič

University of Maribor, Faculty of Chemistry and Chemical Engineering, Smetanova 17, 2000 Maribor, Slovenia

zorka.novak@um.si

Abstract

This contribution presents methodology for inclusion of uncertain carbon tax rates into a mixed integer nonlinear programming (MINLP) process synthesis. Several approaches were developed and tested: two sequential deterministic methods with either fixed or increasing first-stage variables, and two stochastic approaches based on simultaneous Gaussian quadrature method for one- and multi-period process synthesis. Case study process flow sheet synthesis demonstrates that increased carbon tax rate leads to higher conversion, lower emission, lower raw material and utility consumptions, and improves process performance synergistically with process heat integration. Synthesis of optimal heat exchanger network shows that multi-period stochastic method produced around 5 % lower expected cost than sequential deterministic method which indicates a value of simultaneous stochastic process synthesis under uncertain carbon tax rate.
Keywords: MINLP synthesis, process flow sheet, carbon tax rate, stochastic two-stage with recourse

1. Introduction

European Union Emissions Trading System promotes reduction of greenhouse gas emissions in economically efficient manner (European Commission, 2019). Fossil fuels used for process heat and power are presently the largest contributors to global CO_2 emissions (Mahmoud and Sunarso, 2018). In order to curtail pollution, governments have created various policy mechanisms for pricing emissions, such as standards, carbon tax, energy tax, and emission trading systems (Lin and Li, 2011). Taxes on carbon emissions have proved useful for encouraging the emitters to reduce the emissions (OECD, 2018). Synthesis of efficient, optimal and flexible process flow sheets over the entire life cycle is important for reducing the emissions, however, long-term carbon tax rates are difficult to predict. A few recent works discuss design of process plants (Shahandeh and Li, 2017), production of syngas (Hernández and Martín, 2019) and supply chains (Alizadeh et al., 2019) under uncertain carbon tax rates. Novak Pintarič et al., 2019, developed an indicator for more detailed multi-objective analysis of Pareto process solutions with respect to variable carbon tax rates. They showed that increasing the carbon tax rate encourages the reduction of utility use and increases the savings and the net present value of heat exchanger network.

The effects of carbon tax rate are usually studied by parametric evaluations or optimizations of various process alternatives. This contribution, however, presents some novel insights into: a) impacts of carbon tax rates on topology, design, operation, economic and environmental efficiencies of optimal processes obtained during Mixed Integer Nonlinear Programming (MINLP) synthesis, and b) development of a systematic methodology which would generate optimal process flow sheets under variable carbon tax rates over longer time period.

2. Methodology for MINLP process synthesis under uncertain carbon tax

MINLP process synthesis problem with uncertain carbon tax rate can be described as a two-stage stochastic problem with recourse. First stage (topology and design) variables are equal for several future carbon tax rates and determined in advance, while second stage (operating and control) variables can be adjusted later after the uncertainty is resolved. Several approaches were developed and applied for solving such problems.

2.1. Deterministic approach

In deterministic approach, first stage variables are determined at an initial value of carbon tax rate (θ_d in MINLP model P1).

$$Z = \max\left(c^T y + f(d,x,\theta_d)\right)$$

s. t. $h(d,x,\theta_d) = 0$

$\qquad g(d,x,\theta_d) + By \leq 0 \qquad$ (P1)

$\qquad Ay \leq a$

$d,x \geq 0, \; y \in \{0,1\}$

Z scalar objective variable
c fixed costs
f variable cost function
y binary variables for process topology
d design variables for capacities and sizes of process units
x operating variables
θ uncertain carbon tax rate
h equality constraints
g inequality constraints
A, B and a matrices and vector of constants

The obtained values of binary and design variables (y and d) are then fixed, and one-scenario NLP problems are solved for operating and control variables at a finite number of discrete tax rate values (θ_t, $t \in T$). Objective values obtained (Z_t) are multiplied by the probability of each tax rate (pr_t) yielding a deterministic expected value of objective function, E(Z^{deter}), Eq. 1.

$$E(Z^{\text{deter}}) = \sum_{t \in T} pr_t \cdot Z_t \qquad (1)$$

2.2. Modified deterministic approach

The approach described in previous section assumed that first stage variables remain unchanged during the entire process lifetime. In practice, however, initial process design can be retrofitted to some extent at specific realization of uncertain parameters. Previous approach was therefore modified in a way that first-stage variables obtained at an initial value of carbon tax rate (d_d) can change by (Δd_t) at specific realization of uncertain tax rate (θ_t), and the increase can be limited by an upper bound (U) (model P2). The expected value is then calculated by Eq. 1.

$$Z_t = \max\left(c^T y + f(d_d + \Delta d_t, x_t, \theta_t)\right)$$

s. t. $h(d_d + \Delta d_t, x_t, \theta_t) = 0$

$\qquad g(d_d + \Delta d_t, x_t, \theta_t) + By \leq 0 \qquad$ (P2)

$\qquad Ay \leq a, \; \Delta d_t \leq U \qquad\qquad\qquad t \in T$

$\Delta d_t, x_t \geq 0, \; y \in \{0,1\}$

2.3. Stochastic approach – one-period Gaussian quadrature

In stochastic approach, a distribution function of carbon tax rate is assumed during a specific time period. MINLP synthesis is formulated as one-period multi-scenario problem in which carbon tax rates are assumed at Gaussian quadrature points, i.e. roots of the Legendre polynomials of specified order. The objective function of this model is an expected value in which the objectives derived at various tax rates are weighted by their probabilities, pr_t.

$$E(Z) = \max\left(c^T y + \sum_t pr_t \cdot f(d, x_t, \theta_t) \right)$$

$$\text{s. t.} \quad h(d, x_t, \theta_t) = 0$$

$$g(d, x_t, \theta_t) + By \leq 0 \qquad t \in T \qquad \text{(P3)}$$

$$Ay \leq a$$

$$d, x_t \geq 0, \; y \in \{0,1\}$$

2.4. Stochastic approach – multi-period Gaussian quadrature

In this method, a multi-period two-stage stochastic model with recourse is formulated in order to perform process synthesis simultaneously for multiple carbon tax rates over several time periods. A goal is to generate process configuration that would be optimal for a more extended time period during which carbon tax rate is expected to change. The problem (P3) is extended into a two-stage multi-period multi-scenario stochastic problem with recourse (P4).

$$E(Z) = \max\left(c^T y + \sum_t \sum_p pr_{t,p} \cdot f(d, x_{t,p}, \theta_{t,p}) \right)$$

$$\text{s. t.} \quad h(d, x_{t,p}, \theta_{t,p}) = 0 \qquad \text{(P4)}$$

$$g(d, x_{t,p}, \theta_{t,p}) + By \leq 0 \qquad t \in T, \; p \in P$$

$$Ay \leq a, \; d, x_{t,p} \geq 0, \; y \in \{0,1\}$$

3. Case studies

The aim of the first case study wass to demonstrate the effects of carbon tax rate on topology, design and operation of optimal process flow sheets obtained by MINLP synthesis. The heat exchanger network (HEN) case study demonstrates the applications of several methods described in Section 2.

3.1. Synthesis of optimal process flow sheet

First case study is a process for production of chemical B from reactant A (Figure 1). There are two alternative feed streams available: expensive Feed1 with lower content of impurity C and cheaper Feed2. The selected feed stream is mixed with the recycle stream, preheated and fed into the reactor. There are two alternative reactors in which reactant A is converted into product B: cheaper RCT1 with lower conversion and more expensive RCT2. Component C in purge stream is assumed to be a greenhouse gas (GHG). Consumptions of hot utility in heaters C1, C2 and C3 also contribute to total GHG emission of the process. The superstructure was modelled as an MINLP problem with maximization of profit at various carbon tax rates. Two synthesis options were considered for parametric analysis at various carbon tax rates: without and with heat integration using a model by (Duran and Grossmann, 1986).

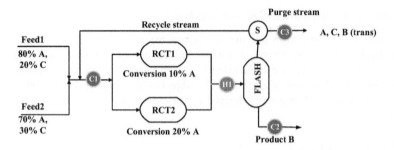

Figure 1: Process superstructure

Figures 2 to 5 demonstrate that increasing carbon tax rate leads to decreased GHG emission, increased overall conversion of reactant, reduced consumption of raw materials and decreased percentage of purge stream. Moreover, the synergies are established between the effects of carbon tax rate and heat integration as the effects are higher in heat integrated solutions. Higher carbon tax rates force the selection of more efficient process units, such as reactor RCT2 with higher conversion, and feed stream with lower content of impurities. In the heat integrated processes, cheaper feed stream Feed2 was selected only at low tax rates (up to 10 €/t), while at higher tax rates more expensive Feed1 with lower amount of impurity was selected.

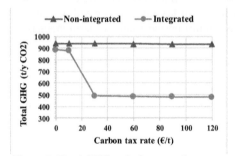

Figure 2: Total GHG emission vs carbon tax rate

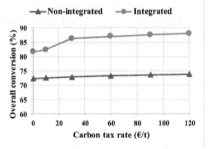

Figure 3: Overall conversion vs carbon tax rate

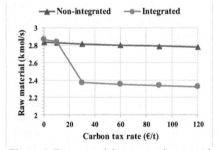

Figure 4: Raw material consumption vs carbon tax rates

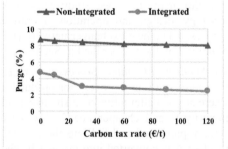

Figure 5: Purge stream percentage vs carbon tax rates

In the next step a MINLP synthesis of process flow sheet was performed under uncertain carbon tax rate by applying sequential one-scenario deterministic approach and simultaneous multi-scenario approach. Three carbon tax rates (10, 60 and 120) €/t with different probabilities within three periods were assumed. The expected profit of heat integrated the stochastic solution (110,972 k€/a) was slightly higher than the profit of deterministic solution (110,917 k€/a), indicating a value of simultaneous multi-scenario approach.

3.2. Synthesis of optimal Heat Exchanger Network

Heat exchanger network (HEN) consisted of 2 hot and 3 cold streams (Novak Pintarič et al., 2019). Supply and target temperatures, heat capacity flow rates (*CF*), and heat transfer coefficients (α) are shown in Figure 6. The network was modelled based on a multi-stage superstructure by (Yee and Grossmann, 1990). The objective function was minimum Total Annual Cost (TAC) composed of annualized investment cost, utility costs and carbon tax rate cost. The latter included emissions from hot utility production and construction of HEN which was proportional to HEN capital cost.

Future carbon tax rates were assumed within an interval from 10 €/t to 60 €/t during three time periods. Five quadrature points within this interval were (12.3, 21.5, 35.0, 48.5, 57.7) €/t CO_2. It was assumed that lower taxes would be more probable during the first period while in the last period probability would concentrate at higher values. Two shape parameters of Beta distribution (α, β) for periods 1, 2, and 3 were assumed as follows: (2, 6), (3, 3) and (7, 3). The numerical results obtained by applying four methods described in Section 2 are presented in Table 1.

Table 1: TAC and GHG emission of HENs obtained with different methods

| | Deterministic methods | | Stochastic methods | |
| | Fixed first-stage variables | Modified first-stage variables | One-period quadrature | Multi-period quadrature |
Period	TAC ($/y)	TAC ($/y)	TAC ($/y)	TAC ($/y)
1	1,471,251	1,471,243	1,396,198	
2	1,550,941	1,550,863	1,470,393	1,465,382
3	1,614,693	1,614,491	1,529,735	
Average	1,545,628	1,545,532	1,465,442	
GHG (t/y)	6375	6364	5936	5926

Optimal HEN obtained by deterministic method (Figure 6) had the total area 1,077 m², expected hot utility consumption 4,358 kW, and an average TAC over three periods 1,545,628 $/y. The network obtained by modified deterministic approach had the same topology while total HEN area increased by 6 %, i.e. for 63 m², which lead to slightly lower TAC. Optimal HEN obtained by simultaneous three-period Gaussian quadrature (Figure 7) had the total heat transfer area 946 m², expected hot utility consumption 4,040 kW, and the expected TAC 1,465,382 $/y. Its total GHG emission is by 7 % lower than GHG emission of HEN obtained by deterministic method.

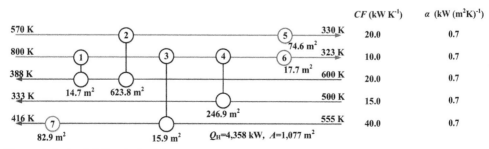

Figure 6: Optimal HEN obtained by deterministic method

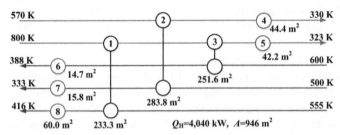

Figure 7: Optimal HEN obtained by three-period Gaussian quadrature

4. Conclusions

This study presented the effects of variable carbon tax rate on topology, design, operation, economics and environmental impacts of optimal processes obtained by MINLP synthesis. Several approaches were developed and tested for inclusion of uncertain carbon tax rate into process synthesis. Multi-period stochastic approach which considered various possible tax rates simultaneously yielded economically and environmentally better results than sequential deterministic approach, which indicates a value of stochastic solutions in process synthesis under uncertain carbon tax rate. The advantage of deterministic approach, however, is that the size of the model does not increase with the numbers of scenarios and periods.

Acknowledgment
The authors acknowledge financial support from the Slovenian Research Agency (PhD research fellowships MR-39209, program P2-0032, and project J7-1816).

References

Alizadeh, M., Ma, J., Marufuzzaman, M., Yu, F. 2019. Sustainable olefin supply chain network design under seasonal feedstock supplies and uncertain carbon tax rate. Journal of Cleaner Production, 222, 280-299.

Duran, M.A., Grossmann, I.E. 1986. Simultaneous optimization and heat integration of chemical processes. AIChE Journal, 32, 123-138.

European Commission. 2019. European Union Emissions Trading System (EU ETS). Available at: https://www.emissions-euets.com/carbon-market-glossary/872-european-union-emissions-trading-system-eu-ets. Accessed: 11.7.2019.

Hernández, B., Martín, M. 2019. Optimal production of syngas via super-dry reforming. Analysis for natural gas and biogas under different CO2 taxes. Chemical Engineering Research and Design, 148, 375-392.

Lin, B., Li, X. 2011. The effect of carbon tax on per capita CO2 emissions. Energy Policy, 39, 5137-5146.

Mahmoud, A., Sunarso, J. 2018. A new graphical method to target carbon dioxide emission reductions by simultaneously aligning fuel switching, energy saving, investment cost, carbon credit, and payback time. International Journal of Energy Research, 42, 1551-1562.

Novak Pintarič, Z., Varbanov, P.S., Klemeš, J.J., Kravanja, Z. 2019. Multi-Objective Multi-Period Synthesis of Energy Efficient Processes under Variable Environmental Taxes. Energy, 116182.

Shahandeh, H., Li, Z. 2017. Optimal design of bitumen upgrading facility with CO2 reduction. Computers & Chemical Engineering, 106, 106-121.

Yee, T.F., Grossmann, I.E. 1990. Simultaneous optimization models for heat integration II. Heat exchanger network synthesis. Computers and Chemical Engineering, 14, 1165 - 1184.

Sauro Pierucci, Flavio Manenti, Giulia Bozzano, Davide Manca (Eds.)
Proceedings of the 30th European Symposium on Computer Aided Process Engineering
(ESCAPE30), May 24-27, 2020, Milano, Italy. © 2020 Elsevier B.V. All rights reserved.
http://dx.doi.org/10.1016/B978-0-12-823377-1.50161-0

Design Space Investigation for Development of Continuous Flow Syntheses of Active Pharmaceutical Ingredients

Samir Diab, Dimitrios I. Gerogiorgis*

*Institute for Materials and Processes (IMP), School of Engineering, University of
Edinburgh, The Kings Buildings, Edinburgh, EH9 3FB, United Kingdom*
D.Gerogiorgis@ed.ac.uk

Abstract

Continuous flow chemistry and synthesis have received significant attention over the past
two decades for their potential for enhancing yields, selectivities, productivities, smaller
operation and implementation of otherwise difficult/dangerous reactions. Recent
demonstrations applied to a variety of different reaction types have highlighted the
potential for continuous manufacturing technologies for fine and speciality chemical
production, including many critical Active Pharmaceutical Ingredients (APIs) but also
many biopharmaceuticals and therapeutics. This study discusses recent demonstrations
from the literature on design space elucidation for continuous API production and further
highlights attainable regions of recoveries, material efficiencies, flowsheet complexity
and cost components for upstream (reaction + separation) via modelling, simulation and
nonlinear optimisation studies, providing insight into optimal regions of operation.

Keywords: Continuous flow synthesis; Active Pharmaceutical Ingredients (APIs);
pharmaceutical manufacturing; design space investigation; comparative evaluation.

1. Introduction

1.1 Continuous flow synthesis

The development of continuous flow technology and synthetic strategies by chemists and
engineers has been the focus of significant research attention over the past two decades
due to the wide variety of chemical processes whose performance can be improved or
intensified by switching from batch to continuous flow operation. Operating continuously
allows for smaller equipment dimensions, wherein mixing and heat transfer are
significantly enhanced and thus improving yields, selectivities, productivities and
allowing access to operating windows (e.g., high pressure/temperature, avoiding
prolonged presence of hazardous intermediates, circumventing requirements for
cryogenic conditions) that would be otherwise unsafe if implemented in batch mode.

1.2 Continuous manufacturing of active pharmaceutical ingredients

There has been significant research focus on continuous Active Pharmaceutical
Ingredient (API) production due to pressure on the pharmaceutical industry to reduce drug
development times, minimise product quality variation, process performance deviations,
overall costs and environmental impact via lower capital and operating expenditures that
are inherent of the smaller equipment and material usage reductions with continuous
operations. The chemistry, chemical engineering and process systems engineering

communities have approached both unit operation and plantwide Continuous Pharmaceutical Manufacturing (CPM) processes from both experimental (lab-based and pilot plants) and theoretical (mathematical modelling, simulation and optimisation) perspectives to elucidate promising designs for optimal continuous API synthesis.

1.3 This work: Integrated upstream continuous pharmaceutical manufacturing

The majority of design space investigation studies in the literature focus on the attainment of optimal unit operation performance or specified product quality attributes. Consideration of technoeconomic and environmental impacts of different designs are also important for the selection of feasible and viable process operating regions. Modelling and simulation aids design space elucidation without labour-intensive experiments. In this study, we discuss design space investigation efforts for various upstream continuous reaction + separation processes for different APIs, encompassing both technoeconomic and material efficiency considerations of upstream CPM plantwide design considerations.

2. Relevant Literature

2.1 Design space investigation of flow reactors

The demonstration of continuous flow chemistry of an API is the foundation of any CPM process; however, subsequent purification, separation (upstream) and drug product formulation (downstream) unit operations are often challenging and expensive processes that must be considered in the comparative evaluation of different designs. Establishing feasible operating regions to the meet desired product quality and process performance targets is an important stage of design that has been implemented in various CPM studies. Development of automated continuous flow systems for reaction optimisation has been a recent hot topic of research. Bédard et al. (2019) developed a continuous synthesis system composed of reagent/feedstocks and pumps and interchangeable reactor and separator modules with online analytics and a software interface for process control and reaction monitoring. The authors demonstrated a variety of pharmaceutically-relevant reactions in flow, elucidating optimal regions of operation regarding operating temperature, residence time, reagent ratios, catalyst and base loading. Wyvratt et al. (2019) characterised the design space of a Knoevenagel condensation by varying residence time and catalyst loading whilst minimising the number of experiments and material consumption required to adequately map the design space. Comparative evaluation of batch vs. continuous syntheses are also useful in quantifying technical and economic benefits of different production paradigms and flowsheet configurations. Ott et al. (2016) performed a Life Cycle Assessment (LCA) of different flowsheet configurations of batch vs. flow microreactor networks for rufinamide synthesis, considering various metrics related to plant material efficiencies and environmental impacts of different production options.

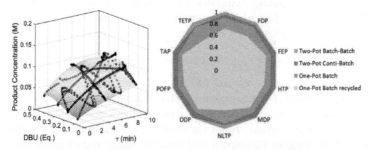

Figure 1: Flow synthesis design spaces: (a) Wyvratt et al., 2019, (b) Ott et al., 2016.

2.2 Design space investigation of separation processes

Design space investigation of separation options is also important when considering continuous API production. Gonzalez et al. (2019) used probabilistic modelling to establish the design space of a reaction and crystallisation to enhance process robustness and impurity control in the final product. The authors found a crystallisation combined with wet milling allowed greater robustness than a design without milling. Ridder et al. (2014) performed experiments and modelled the antisolvent crystallisation of flufenamic acid in a multisegment, multiaddition-plug flow crystalliser, where antisolvent feed rate to different tubular crystalliser segments was varied in order to either maximise the mean crystal size or minimise the product size distribution coefficient of variation. The authors presented Pareto fronts to show trade-offs between the two product quality attributes.

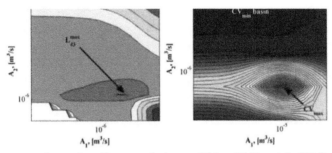

Figure 2: Design space of crystal quality vs. antisolvent addition (Ridder et al., 2014).

3. Plantwide design space investigation

In this study, we concentrate on upstream plantwide CPM studies we have previously done, encompassing both reaction (flow synthesis) and separation (continuous Liquid-Liquid Extraction (LLE) or antisolvent crystallisation) phenomena and unit operations as well as detailed Capital (CapEx) and Operating (OpEx) Expenditures cost components.

3.1 Upstream plantwide design case studies

Ibuprofen (analgaesic): three flow reactions followed by continuous Liquid-Liquid Extraction (LLE) with hexane (nHex) or toluene (PhMe) (Jolliffe and Gerogiorgis, 2016).

Artemisinin (antimalarial): two reactions and cooling-antisolvent crystallisation using ethanol (EtOH) or ethyl acetate (EtOAc) as antisolvents (Jolliffe and Gerogiorgis, 2016).

Diphenhydramine (antihistamine): one reaction followed by LLE with heptane (nHep), cyclohexane (CyHex) or methyl cyclohexane (MeCyHex) (Diab and Gerogiorgis, 2017).

Warfarin (anticoagulant): one reaction followed by continuous LLE with EtOAc, isopropyl acetate (iPrOAc) or isobutyl acetate (iBuOAc) (Diab and Gerogiorgis, 2018).

Atropine (nerve agent effects): three flow reactions followed by LLE utilising either diethyl ether (Et$_2$O), *n*-butyl acetate (nBuOAc) and PhMe (Diab and Gerogiorgis, 2019).

Nevirapine (HIV treatment): considers three flow reactions followed by crystallisation via pH change with different Solvent Recovery (SR) assumptions (Diab et al., 2019).

The extent of simulation/optimisation differs for each API case study. For ibuprofen, artemisinin and diphenhydramine, simulation studies are considered; for warfarin and nevirapine, nonlinear optimisation of the upstream plants have been implemented. Modelling, simulation and optimisation details are in the relevant literature references.

3.2 Technoeconomic analysis methodology

Process performance metrics encompassing technical performance, process intensity and costs are compared for different APIs and selected separation option. The process metrics considered are: plantwide API recovery, Mass Productivity (MP = 100 / E-factor, a measure of how efficiently material is used in a process), number of reaction and separation stages (a measure of process intensity) and CapEx and OpEx cost components per unit mass of API produced. Fig. 3 shows a radar plot of these metrics for each API.

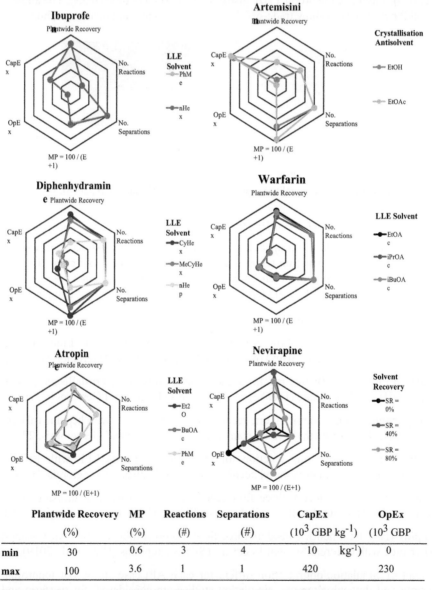

	Plantwide Recovery	MP	Reactions	Separations	CapEx	OpEx
	(%)	(%)	(#)	(#)	(10^3 GBP kg^{-1})	(10^3 GBP kg^{-1})
min	30	0.6	3	4	10	0
max	100	3.6	1	1	420	230

Figure 3: Performance metrics of various CPM processes for different APIs.

Each axis (process performance metric) in Fig. 3 bear different meaning depending on whether they have a high or low value. Clearly, high plantwide recoveries and MP but lower cost components are desirable. For the number of reaction and separation stages, reverse-ordered axes are used to illustrate that lower values are preferable (i.e., fewer unit operations equate to lower process complexity). The maximum and minimum values of each axis in these axes are also provided in Fig. 3. For each API, the number of reactions and separation stages have the same coordinates for each different separation option.

3.3 Separation process design option selection

For ibuprofen, the different separation options (LLE solvent = {nHex, PhMe}) give similar results and thus the LLE solvent with the lower environmental/EHS impact (i.e., PhMe) is preferable (Jolliffe and Gerogiorgis, 2016). Similarly, for warfarin and atropine, each considered LLE solvent performs similarly, however, each also have similar EHS characteristics; solvent selection should thus be informed by subsequent crystallisation process design (Diab and Gerogiorgis, 2018; 2019). For artemisinin and diphenhydramine, plantwide technoeconomic performance varies more drastically with separation solvent choice; for artemisinin, EtOH as antisolvent allows for lower costs and is more environmentally friendly that EtOAc (Jolliffe and Gerogiorgis, 2016), and for diphenhydramine, nHep has both poorer EHS characteristics than either CyHex or MeCyHex as well as incurring higher costs (Diab and Gerogiorgis, 2017). For nevirapine CPM, various values of solvent recovery are considered (SR); whilst high SR (= 80%) is attainable in lab-scale conditions, lower values are likely to be possible at larger scale operation. The assumed SR drastically affects OpEx, thus inducing the significant contribution of the latter towards total costs: here, OpEx >> CapEx (Diab et al., 2019).

3.4 Comparative evaluation and discussion

While comparing different APIs for their performance on a detailed level may not be considered so valuable given the widely varying process phenomena, highlighting typical regions of operation for different processes is useful. For example, the CPM designs for the considered APIs in this study have typical plantwide recoveries = 70–80%; although total cost components and material efficiencies vary, this highlights that beyond this API recovery, cost benefits are incremental at best and not worth the extra effort with respect to material consumption and increased equipment volumes required for higher flow rates. Quantification of dimensionless numbers for different continuous processes for different APIs may also provide valuable insight into the most promising regions of operation.

Total cost components (i.e., CapEx and OpEx) have been scaled per unit mass of API produced in the product streams of each upstream CPM plant for fair comparison where different plant capacities are considered. Each case study considered upstream plant total costs as the economic metric for comparative evaluation of different process designs. Comparison of optimal Net Present Values (NPVs) can also provide valuable insight and alternative process designs for different APIs, but are subject to API sales price variation, which may be quite significant for certain drugs (e.g., artemisinin). Ultimately, when choosing whether to switch to continuous operation, clear operational and economic benefits must be clear over traditional / current manufacturing methods for the API.

4. Conclusions

Demonstrated continuous flow synthesis of APIs pave the way for the design of CPM processes for lean and efficient production. Various demonstrations in the literature have elucidated operating regions and mapped design spaces on a technical basis at unit operation level. We have conducted technoeconomic plantwide analyses for upstream CPM (reaction + separation) for various APIs. Separation design is informed by technical, economic and EHS criteria. Currently, strategic pharma decisions on whether to design (or adopt) continuous operation are made on a case-by-case basis. Elucidating operating regions for demonstrated CPM for different APIs is an important step towards more systematic selection and screening of promising candidates for continuous production.

Acknowledgements

The authors acknowledge the support of the Engineering and Physical Sciences Research Council (EPSRC)/IAA, the Japan Society for the Promotion of Science, the Great Britain Sasakawa and Nagai Foundations and the Royal Academy of Engineering (RAEng).

References

A.-C. Bédard, A. Adamo, K.C. Aroh, M.G. Russell, A.A. Bedermann, J. Torosian, B. Yue, K.F. Jensen and T.F. Jamison, 2018, Reconfigurable system for automated optimization of diverse chemical reactions, *Science*, 361, 6408, 1220–1225.

S. Diab and D.I. Gerogiorgis, 2017, Process modeling, simulation, and technoeconomic evaluation of separation solvents for the continuous pharmaceutical manufacturing (CPM) of diphenhydramine, *Org. Process Res. Dev.*, 21, 7, 924–946.

S. Diab and D.I. Gerogiorgis, 2018, Process modelling, simulation and technoeconomic optimisation for continuous pharmaceutical manufacturing of (*S*)-warfarin, *Comput. Aided Chem. Eng.*, 43, 1643–1648.

S. Diab and D.I. Gerogiorgis, 2019, Technoeconomic mixed integer nonlinear programming (MINLP) optimization for design of liquid-liquid extraction (LLE) cascades in continuous pharmaceutical manufacturing of atropine, *AIChE J.*, 65, 11, e16738. DOI: 10.1002/aic.16738.

S. Diab, D.T. McQuade, B.F. Gupton and D.I. Gerogiorgis, 2019, Process design and optimization for the continuous manufacturing of nevirapine, an active pharmaceutical ingredient for HIV treatment, *Org. Process Res. Dev.*, 23, 3, 320–333.

F.L. Gonzalez, J.E. Tobora, B. Mack and E.C. Huang, 2019, Development and implementation of a quality control strategy for an atropisomer impurity grounded in a risk-based probabilistic design space, *Org. Process Res. Dev.*, 23, 2, 211–219.

H.G. Jolliffe and D.I. Gerogiorgis, 2016, Plantwide design and economic evaluation of two continuous pharmaceutical manufacturing (CPM) cases: ibuprofen and artemisinin, *Comput. Chem. Eng.*, 91, 269–288.

M.B. Plutschack, B. Pieber, K. Gilmore and P.H. Seeberger, 2017, The hitchhiker's guide to flow chemistry, *Chem. Rev.*, 117, 18, 11796–11893.

B.J. Ridder, A. Majumder and Z.K. Nagy, 2014, Population balance model-based multiobjective optimization of a multisegment multiaddition continuous plug-flow antisolvent crystallizer, *Ind. Eng. Chem. Res.*, 53, 11, 4387–4397.

B.M. Wyvratt, J.P. McMullen and S.T. Grosser, 2019, Multidimensional dynamic experiments for data-rich process development of reactions in flow, *React. Chem. Eng.*, 4, 1637–1645.

Sauro Pierucci, Flavio Manenti, Giulia Bozzano, Davide Manca (Eds.)
Proceedings of the 30th European Symposium on Computer Aided Process Engineering
(ESCAPE30), May 24-27, 2020, Milano, Italy. © 2020 Elsevier B.V. All rights reserved.
http://dx.doi.org/10.1016/B978-0-12-823377-1.50162-2

Optimization of Liquid Air Energy Storage (LAES) using a Genetic Algorithm (GA)

Zhongxuan Liu,[a] Haoshui Yu,[b] Truls Gundersen[a*]

[a]*Norwegian University of Science and Technology, Kolbjørn Hejes v1B, NO-7491 Trondheim, Norway*
[b]*Massachusetts Institute of Technology, 77 Massachusetts Ave, Cambridge, MA, 02139, USA*
truls.gundersen@ntnu.no

Abstract

Renewable energy sources have a growing share in the energy market due to the threat from climate change, which is caused by emissions from fossil fuels. A future energy scenario that is likely to be realized is distributed energy systems (DES), where renewable energy sources play an increasing role. Energy storage technologies must be adopted to achieve these two expectations. Liquid Air Energy Storage (LAES), is a cryogenic technology that is discussed in this paper. Two cases are considered in this work to represent different operating modes for the LAES process: with and without an extra amount of hot oil in the discharging process. The performance of the LAES system will be analyzed with different number of compression stages and expansion stages in each mode. A Genetic Algorithm (GA) is used to optimize the LAES process. The round-trip efficiency is 63.1 % after flowsheet improvement and optimization.

Keywords: Liquid air energy storage, round-trip efficiency, flowsheet improvement, genetic algorithm

1. Introduction

With the increasing focus on the environment, a lot of measures have been taken to reduce the emission of greenhouse gases. Renewable energy technologies are considered to replace traditional fossil fuels. However, once renewable energy is introduced in the energy market, the most important challenge is to keep the stability of energy supply due to the intermittent nature of renewable energy sources such as wind and solar.

Another likely trend for future energy systems is decentralization in the form of distributed energy hubs. These hubs are located close to available energy forms and specific energy demands. The advantages of distributed energy systems mainly include the flexibility to utilize various energy conversion technologies and the improved reliability of energy supply (or reduced vulnerability of the overall system) by operating these distributed energy systems in networks and integrating with local energy resources (Alanne and Saari, 2006).

Energy storage technologies must be adopted to smoothen variations in supply (typical for renewable energy sources) and demand (daily or seasonal variations) and to guarantee supply during energy deficit periods. Pumped hydroelectric energy storage (PHES) (Rehman et al., 2015), compressed air energy storage (CAES) (Bullough et al., 2004), and battery energy storage (BES) (Aneke and Wang, 2016) are mature energy storage technologies. However, because of the geographical constraints of PHES and CAES and capital considerations for BES, the application of these technologies is still limited.

Energy storage technologies that can overcome the drawbacks of the existing technologies are more likely to be adopted in future energy systems. Among the proposed energy storage technologies, liquid air energy storage (LAES) seems to be a promising option (Guizzi et al., 2015), since LAES can benefit from established technologies, such as gas liquefaction and air separation units, and it is not geographically constrained.

Until now, the largest reported LAES implementation is a plant with 15 MWh storage capacity that was built in the UK (Highview Power, 2019). The round-trip efficiency of the standalone process is around 60 %. Li et al. (2014) studied the integration of LAES and a nuclear power plant, and the round-trip efficiency was claimed to reach 70 %. An approach with a liquid air Rankine cycle was proposed by Ameel et al. (2013), and a round-trip efficiency of 43 % was achieved. A standalone LAES plant was simulated with a round-trip efficiency of 55 % (Guizzi et al., 2015). None of these studies have been applied in large scale. In addition, since the round-trip efficiency of a standalone LAES plant is lower than 60 %, there is still considerable need for improvement before the technology can be industrialized. However, very few papers are trying to optimize standalone LAES systems. Instead, the integration of LAES with external heat sources have been gaining more focus recently. A standalone LAES with optimal design integrated with external heat sources should be tested to further enhance the round-trip efficiency of the process. Thus, the LAES first needs investigation to increase overall efficiency, store hot and cold thermal energy efficiently, and obtain good response times, so that the technology with its potential advantages can be used in practical applications.

In this paper, two operating modes are studied for the LAES process: with or without introducing extra amounts of hot oil in the discharging process. A genetic algorithm (GA) is adopted to optimize the LAES process. GA is a search method used to find approximate solutions and is based on the concepts of "natural selection" and "genetic inheritance". The objective function is the round-trip efficiency (RTE, η_{RT}), which is the ratio of work output (W_{out}) in the discharging process and the work input (W_{in}) in the charging process. Results show that optimization with η_{RT} as objective function gives modest improvements compared with the original case.

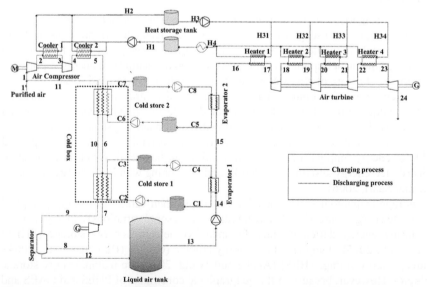

Figure 1: Flow diagram for the liquid air energy storage process

2. Design basis and optimization

The process in Figure 1 shows the liquid air energy storage process, having hot and cold thermal energy storages (Guizzi et al., 2015). The process is simulated in Aspen HYSYS V10.0 (Aspen HYSYS, 2017). The air, consisting of 78.82 % nitrogen, 21.14 % oxygen and 0.04 % argon, is assumed as the feed gas and is liquefied through this modified Claude process. The pre-purification unit (PPU) for the removal of CO_2, H_2O and other trace components is not included in the simulation. Other design conditions and assumptions used in this work are shown in Table 1.

The simulation model is optimized to maximize round-trip efficiency of the process. The pressures after the last-stage compressor and pump are set as variables. In addition, the operating temperatures and mass flow rates of hot oil, methanol and propane are defined as variables in order to manipulate the duty of heat exchangers during optimization. The inlet temperatures of compressors and turbines are also considered as variables, and this has direct effects on electricity consumption and generation in the process. The constraints applied in the optimization problem are the minimum temperature differences for heat exchangers, where 10 K for coolers and heaters and 3 K for evaporators and heat exchangers in the cold box have been assumed.

Table 1: Simulation conditions and assumptions

Parameter	Value	Unit
Ambient temperature	293	K
Ambient pressure	101.325	kPa
Cooling water temperature	288	K
ΔT_{min} of cooler	10	K
ΔT_{min} of heater	10	K
ΔT_{min} of cold box	3	K
ΔT_{min} of evaporator	3	K
Relative pressure drops of heat exchanger	1	%
Isentropic efficiency of compressor	85	%
Isentropic efficiency of turbine	90	%
Isentropic efficiency of cryo-turbine	75	%
Isentropic efficiency of pump	80	%

3. Results

3.1. Key performance indicators

In order to evaluate the performance of the different processes, two parameters will be introduced in this section: liquid yield and round-trip efficiency. Liquid yield η_{LA} is defined as the ratio between the mass flow rate of liquid air (m_{liq}) and the total mass flow rate of compressed air (m_{comp}) that includes the recycle of air:

$$\eta_{LA} = \frac{m_{liq}}{m_{comp}} \qquad (1)$$

The most important parameter is the round-trip efficiency η_{RT} that is defined as the work output (W_{out}) in discharge mode divided by the work input (W_{in}) in charge mode:

$$\eta_{RT} = \frac{W_{out}}{W_{in}} = \frac{m_{liq} w_T}{m_{comp} w_C} = \eta_{LA} \cdot \frac{w_T}{w_C} \tag{2}$$

where w_T and w_C represent the specific work [kJ/kg] of the expanders and the compressors, respectively.

3.2. Effects of different number of compression stages and expansion stages on the round-trip efficiency

Minimum compression work for a compressor is obtained by isothermal operation, thus multi-stage compression at low temperature with inter-stage cooling is used to minimize work consumption. Likewise, expansion at high temperature with inter-stage reheating maximizes work production. However, from an economic point of view, the number of compressors and expanders affects the capital cost, which increases with number of units and flowsheet complexity.

In the LAES process, when the number of compressor stages (with interstage cooling) is increased, the compression heat that can be recovered by hot oil and utilized in the discharging process decreases. The achieveable temperature of the hot oil is decreased, however, since cooling of air after compressor stages is repeated, the mass flow rate of hot oil increases. These two changes have opposite effects on the round-trip efficiency and power generation. Reduced temperature of hot oil has a negative effect, while increased mass flow rate of hot oil has a positive effect. The trade-off between the number of compressors, capital cost and compression heat (temperature and mass flow rate of the hot oil) should be balanced. In this section, two operating modes are discussed: with or without introducing extra amounts of hot oil in the discharging process. The performance of the LAES system will be analyzed with different number of compression stages and expansion stages in each mode. First, the case without extra amounts of hot oil is studied.

3.2.1. Without extra amounts of hot oil in the discharging process

Figure 2 demonstrates the effects of different number of compression stages and expansion stages on the RTE of the process without extra amounts of hot oil in the discharging process. As can be seen from the figure, the highest RTE (58.2 %) is obtained with 2-stage compressor and 3-stage expander. Common for all cases without extra hot oil, is the fact that the pinch points in the expansion heat exchangers are in the cold end. The reason why the combination of 2-stage compressor and 3-stage expander has the best performance with respect to RTE, is that the composite curves are closer to parallel than for other combinations. For 3-stage expansion, the RTE is reduced with increased number of compression stages. This is due to the fact that the reduction of hot oil temperature leads to a decreased temperature of inlet air to the expanders, even if the pinch points in the expansion heat exchangers are in the hot end when the number of compression stages is equal to or larger than 3. The decreasing temperature of hot oil has a decisive influence on the RTE in the case with 3-stage compressor and 3-stage expander.From the previous discussion, both temperature and mass flowrate of hot oil are affected by the number of compressor stages in the charging process. Since hot oil is used to transfer compression heat to the expansion section in the discharging process in order to increase work production, there is a strong link between the number of compression stages and the number of expansion stages. The location of the pinch points in the heat exchangers also plays an important role. As a result, for a given number of compressor stages, there exists an optimal number of expansion stages. This optimal matching can be found in Figure 2. Even though 4-stage expansion has a maximum RTE for 3-stage compression and similar for 5-stage expansion and 4-stage compression, these combinations have lower RTE than the simpler case with 3-stage expansion and 2-stage compression, which is the best combination overall.

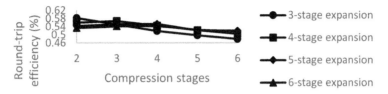

Figure 2: RTE of the LAES for combinations of compression and expansion stages

3.2.2. With extra amounts of hot oil in the discharging process

The pinch point analysis for the LAES process with 2-stage compression and 3-stage expansion indicates that the RTE can be further improved by shifting the pinch points to the hot end to reach a higher inlet temperature to the expanders. This can be achieved by providing enough hot oil in the discharging process. The effect of increasing the number of expansion stages on the RTE when the number of compression stages is fixed at 2, while other variables (such as pressure after the pump and inlet temperature to the expanders) are unchanged, is illustrated in Figure 3. There is a diminishing return on investment when increasing the number of expansion stages. When combining the economic considerations with the RTE, for 2-stage compression in the charging process, 4-stage expansion is recommended in the discharging process when sufficient amounts of hot oil is available. Key performance indicators are listed in Table 2. In this case, an extra amount of hot oil (731 kg/h) is added in the discharging process.

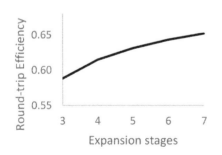

Figure 3: Analysis of the RTE when changing the number of expansion stages

Table 2: Key performance indicators for the LAES process with a 2-stage compressor and a 4-stage expander

Parameter	LAES	
	Charging	Discharging
Work (kW)	499.3	309.3
Liquid yield	0.865	
Round-trip efficiency	61.9 %	

Table 3: Genetic algorithm results

Parameter	LAES	
	Charging	Discharging
Work (kW)	498.9	314.8
Liquid yield	0.865	
Round-trip efficiency	63.1 %	

3.3. Optimization results

The work consumed in the charging process and produced in the discharging process, liquid yield, and the round-trip efficiency are shown in Table 3. Based on the results, the round-trip efficiency has been slightly improved from 61.9 % to 63.1 % by using GA.

4. Conclusions

Liquid air energy storage (LAES) is a viable option for grid-scale electrical energy storage, with the advantage that it is not geographically constrained. However, a low round-trip efficiency has limited the application of this technology. In this study, the cases without introducing extra hot oil in the discharging process is first studied, and the LAES process with a 2-stage compressor and 3-stage expander has the highest round-trip efficiency of 58.2 %. There is an optimal combination of number of compression stages and expansion stages. The combinations corresponding to 4 to 6 expansion stages are 3-stage, 4-stage and 4-stage compression, respectively. However, when introducing an extra amount of hot oil in the discharging process, the LAES process with a 2-stage compressor and 4-stage expander is recommended. An optimization method (Genetic Algorithm) is used to further improve the round-trip efficiency from 61.9 % to 63.1 %.

Acknowledgements

This publication has been funded by HighEFF - Centre for an Energy-Efficient and Competitive Industry for the Future. The authors gratefully acknowledge the financial support from the Research Council of Norway and user partners of HighEFF, an 8-years' Research Centre under the FME-scheme (Centre for Environment-friendly Energy Research, 257632).

References

K. Alanne and A. Saari, 2006, Distributed energy generation and sustainable development, Renewable and Sustainable Energy Reviews, 10(6): 539-558.

S. Rehman, L. M. Al-Hadhrami and M. M. Alam, 2015, Pumped hydro energy storage system: A technological review, Renewable and Sustainable Energy Reviews, 44: 586-598.

C. Bullough, C. Gatzen, C. Jakiel, M. Koller, A. Nowi and S. Zunft, 2004, Advanced adiabatic compressed air energy storage for the integration of wind energy. Conference Advanced Adiabatic Compressed Air Energy Storage For the Integration of Wind Energy, London, UK.

M. Aneke and M. Wang, 2016, Energy storage technologies and real life applications–A state of the art review, Applied Energy, 179: 350-377.

G. L. Guizzi, M. Manno, L. M. Tolomei and R. M. Vitali, 2015, Thermodynamic analysis of a liquid air energy storage system, Energy, 93: 1639-1647.

Highview Power, 2019, < https://www.highviewpower.com/technology/ >.

Y. Li, H. Cao, S. Wang, Y. Jin, D. Li, X. Wang and Y. Ding, 2014, Load shifting of nuclear power plants using cryogenic energy storage technology, Applied Energy, 113: 1710-1716.

B. Ameel, C. T'Joen, K. De Kerpel, P. De Jaeger, H. Huisseune, M. Van Belleghem and M. De Paepe, 2013, Thermodynamic analysis of energy storage with a liquid air Rankine cycle, Applied Thermal Engineering, 52(1): 130-140.

Aspen HYSYS, Version 10.0, 2017, Aspen Technology Inc., Burlington, MA.

Sauro Pierucci, Flavio Manenti, Giulia Bozzano, Davide Manca (Eds.)
Proceedings of the 30th European Symposium on Computer Aided Process Engineering
(ESCAPE30), May 24-27, 2020, Milano, Italy. © 2020 Elsevier B.V. All rights reserved.
http://dx.doi.org/10.1016/B978-0-12-823377-1.50163-4

Sensitivity Analysis of Desulfurization Costs for Small-Scale Natural Gas Sweetening Units

Yushi Deng[a], Shuang Xu[a], Kylie Webb[b], Harrison Wright[b], Paul S. Dimick[b], Selen Cremaschi[a]*, Mario R. Eden[a]

[a]*Department of Chemical Engineering, Auburn University, Auburn, AL 36849, USA*
[b]*IntraMicron, Inc., Auburn, AL 36832, USA*
selen-cremaschi@auburn.edu

Abstract

Natural gas from stranded sources are vented or flared rather than being utilized due to high gathering and processing costs. One of the hurdles that must be overcome for utilizing these stranded resources is the lack of scalable and easily deployable gas sweetening technologies. In this paper, three gas sweetening technologies, triazine-based absorption, a liquid redox process called LO-CAT®, and a newly developed process called SourCat™, that can be operated at smaller scales necessary for sweetening sour gas from stranded resources are compared in terms of their desulfurization costs. A sensitivity analysis using the Morris-One-At-a-Time (MOAT) method is performed to investigate the sensitivity of desulfurization cost to process and economical parameters. The results revealed that the desulfurization cost of triazine-based absorption is most sensitive to raw material costs. The parameters that determine the sulfur content inside the system have the strongest impact on the cost of the LO-CAT® process. The desulfurization cost of the SourCat™ process is most dependent on the parameters related to sulfur that needs to be removed and H_2S that needs to be adsorbed by the sorbent.

Keywords: Sensitivity analysis, Morris One-At-a-Time (MOAT), small-scale, desulfurization

1. Introduction

Natural gas, a colorless and odorless fossil fuel, is the second largest source of energy in the United States, which contributed 31% of the total primary energy consumption in the U.S. in 2018 (Dudley, 2018). Based on its hydrogen sulfide concentration, natural gas can be classified as sour gas (more than 4 ppm of H_2S) or sweet gas (no or a negligible amount of H_2S) (Faramawy et al., 2016). Hydrogen sulfide in sour gas has health and environmental effects, causes safety and corrosion issues, and should be eliminated below the sales gas specification limits (typically 4 ppm). Hence, removing hydrogen sulfide from natural gas, which is also called gas sweetening, is common practice.

Natural gas produced in small quantities or at remote locations is considered stranded gas. These natural gas resources are vented or flared because of high gathering and processing costs. The amount of stranded gas was over 200 Billion Cubic Feet (BCF) in 2017 (EIA, 2019). Processing stranded sour gas resources requires the development of scalable and easily deployable gas sweetening processes.

In this paper, we compare three gas sweetening processes that can potentially be deployed at capacities relevant for processing stranded gas resources. They are triazine-based absorption, a liquid redox process (modeled after the LO-CAT® process) and a new process called SourCat™. A process simulation model is developed for each technology, and desulfurization cost is calculated using an economic analysis software called ECON (Kalakul et al., 2014). A systematic sensitivity analysis (SA) is carried out using the Morris One-At-a-Time (MOAT) method to identify process and economic parameters for each technology that the desulfurization cost is most sensitive to.

2. Process Simulations and Desulfurization Cost Calculations

2.1. Triazine-based Absorption Process

Triazines are composed of three nitrogen and three carbon atoms in a six-membered ring, and 1,3,5-tris-(2-hydroxyethyl) hexahydro-s-triazine (also known as MEA triazine) is the triazine used most commonly for removing H_2S (Taylor et al., 2019).Triazine-based absorption is commercially used for sweetening sour gas when its H_2S concentration is below a few hundred ppm (Lozano, 2000). Here, we consider triazine-based absorption using flooded systems because they are designed to operate continuously and have lower capital expense (CAPEX) than batch systems (Lozano, 2000). A simplified process flow diagram (PFD) of the Aspen Plus simulation for the triazine-based absorption process is given in Figure 1. Sour gas is injected into an absorber with a triazine-based scavenger, and the liquid-gas mixture is separated in a tower where sweet gas is collected from the top and spent liquid scavenger from the bottom.

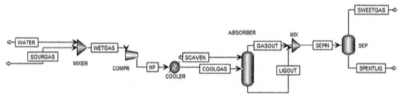

Figure 1: Process flow diagram of Aspen Plus simulation for triazine-based absorption process

2.2. Liquid Redox (LO-CAT®) Process

In the LO-CAT® process, H_2S is oxidized to elemental sulfur using a chelated iron solution. This process is primarily used for desulfurization at small scales (Speight, 2018). The PFD of the LO-CAT® process simulation is given in Figure 2. In the absorber vessel (T-1), H_2S from sour gas is absorbed by sodium ferric ethylenediaminetetraacetate (EDTA FeNa) solution. Ferric ion oxidizes H_2S to solid sulfur and is reduced to ferrous ion, which is oxidized back to ferric ion by oxygen in air in the oxidizer vessel (T-2). Ferric ion is then recycled back to the absorber. Sweet gas is the top product from the absorber. Fresh EDTA FeNa solution is added to the absorber to compensate for the solution loss with wet sulfur cake. To prevent iron precipitation and accelerate H_2S absorption, NaOH or KOH is used to control the solution pH between 8 and 9.

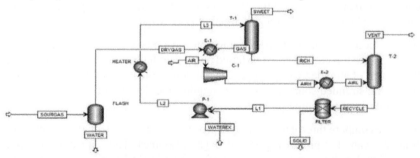

Figure 2: Process flow diagram of Aspen Plus simulation for LO-CAT® process

2.3. Chemical Oxidation (SourCat™) Process

The SourCat™ process is a new desulfurization process developed by IntraMicron, Inc., an Auburn University spin-off company. It utilizes a patented solid oxidative sulfur removal catalyst to convert H₂S to elemental sulfur. A simplified PDF of the process simulation is given in Figure 3. Sour gas and air are injected into the fixed-bed catalyst reactor, where H₂S is converted to solid sulfur and SO₂ with a selectivity to elemental sulfur over 90%. The reactor effluent is washed with water to remove solid elemental sulfur, which is collected by a filter. The small amount of SO₂ produced is carried by the gas steam (G and G2) and is separated from the sweet gas by an adsorption bed.

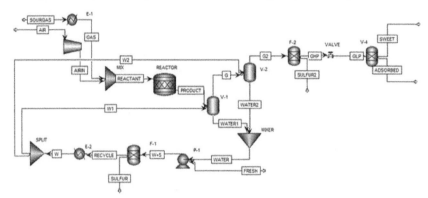

Figure 3: Process flow diagram of Aspen Plus simulation for SourCat™ process

2.4. Desulfurization Cost Calculations

Desulfurization cost (DC) is defined as the cost of sweetening one thousand standard cubic feet (MSCF) natural gas. Aspen Plus process simulations are used to calculate raw material and utility requirements, and equipment sizes for each process. Given these, the CAPEX and the operating expenses (OPEX) are estimated using ECON (Kalakul et al., 2014). Then, DC in \$/MSCF natural gas is calculated with (DF_{wp}) and without (DC_{wop}) payoff using Eqns. (1) and (2), respectively. In Eq. (1), the annual interest rate, r, is 10% and the payoff time, t, is 3 years. The variable *capacity* represents the sour gas flow rate in thousand standard cubic feet per day (MSCFD).

$$DC_{wp} = \frac{CAPEX \times \frac{r(1+r)^t}{(1+r)^t - 1} + OPEX}{Capacity} \tag{1}$$

$$DC_{wop} = \frac{OPEX}{Capacity} \tag{2}$$

3. Sensitivity Analysis of Desulfurization Cost

Sensitivity analysis (SA) is an approach for identifying important parameters that dominate model behaviour. A global SA method, Morris One-At-a-Time (MOAT) method, is chosen to study the sensitivity of desulfurization cost to process and economic parameters due to its efficiency and effectiveness (Gan et al., 2014). To apply the MOAT method, only one parameter is changed to a new value at each model evaluation. For an n-dimensional p-level orthogonal parameter space, the elementary effect, d_i, of the ith parameter, X_i, is defined by Eq. (3),

$$d_i = \frac{f\left(X_1,...,X_{i-1},X_i + \Delta,X_{i+1},...,X_n\right) - f(X)}{\Delta} \tag{3}$$

where Δ is a predetermined multiple of $\frac{1}{[p-1]}$. When p is even, $\Delta = \frac{p}{[2(p-1)]}$. The final Morris measures for the ith parameter are the mean (μ_i) and the standard deviation (σ_i) of d_i, and are calculated using Eqns. (4) and (5),

$$\mu_i = \sum_{j=1}^{k} \frac{d_i(j)}{k} \tag{4}$$

$$\sigma_i = \sqrt{\sum_{j=1}^{k} \frac{(d_j(j) - \mu_i)^2}{k}} \tag{5}$$

where k is the iteration number, which varies from 5 to 20. The higher the value of μ_i, the more sensitive the model response is to changes in parameter X_i. The higher the value of σ_i, the more interaction parameter X_i has with other parameters. The number of model evaluations for applying MOAT method is $k(n+1)$.

Process and economic parameters considered for SA of the desulfurization cost are summarized in Tables 1, 2, and 3. For SA, p is set to 4, and k was equal to 20 which required 160, 160, 200 desulfurization cost calculations for triazine-based absorption, LO-CAT®, and SourCat™ processes, respectively.

Table 1: Potential sensitive parameters for triazine-based absorption process

Parameters	Nominal Value	Range
Temperature	80°F	50-160°F
Pressure	300 psi	300-600 psi
Water Fraction	100 %	0 – 100 %
Gas flow rate	100 MSCFD	100 – 100000 MSCFD
H_2S Concentration	500 ppm	500-2000 ppm
Triazine Concentration	52 wt%	20 wt%-80 wt%
80wt% Triazine Scavenger Price	$2/kg	$1/kg – $2.3/kg

Table 2: Potential sensitive parameters for LO-CAT® process

Parameters	Nominal Value	Range
Pressure	14.7 psi	14.7-600 psi
Temperature	80°F	60-110°F
EDTA-FeNa Concentration	250ppm	250-3000 ppm
Sulfur Cake Water Fraction	50wt%	50-90 wt%
EDTA-FeNa Price	$2.15	$1.6 - $2.36/kg
Gas Flow Rate	100MSCFD	100-100000 MSCFD
H_2S Concentration	500 ppm	500-2000 ppm

Table 3: Potential sensitive parameters for SourCat™ process

Parameters	Nominal Value	Range
Gas Flow Rate	100 MSCFD	100 - 100000 MSCFD
H_2S Concentration	500 ppm	500 – 2000 ppm
Conversion of SO_2	1.96%	0 – 20%
Conversion of Sulfur	96%	80 - 98%
V-3 Split Fraction	99%	80 - 100%
F-2 Split Fraction	100%	90 - 100%
Sorbent Price	$2 /lb	$2 - $5/lb
Sorbent Capacity	0.03 g H_2S/g Sorbent	0.03 - 0.1 g H_2S/g Sorbent
Catalyst Price	$26/lb	$20 - $30/lb

3.1. Sensitivity of Desulfurization Cost for Triazine-based Absorption Process

The values of mean and standard deviation for all potential sensitive parameters are plotted in Figure 4 for the triazine-based absorption process. The gas flow rate and triazine concentration are the most significant parameters for this process' desulfurization cost. Gas flow rate determines the consumption rate of triazine solution, and triazine concentration determines the solution flow rate. For the triazine-based absorption process, 90% of desulfurization cost is raw materials, i.e., triazine solution cost. The SA results for desulfurization costs with and without payoff are very close (Figure 4) because CAPEX only contributes 1% to desulfurization cost for this process.

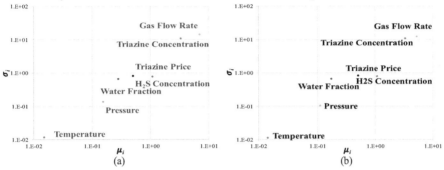

Figure 4: SA results for triazine-based absorption process. Mean and standard deviation values for potential sensitive parameters for desulfurization cost (a) with 3-year payoff and (b) after payoff.

3.2. Sensitivity of Desulfurization Cost for LO-CAT® Process

Similar plots to Figure 4 are provided for SA results of the LO-CAT® process in Figure 5. The gas flow rate, sulfur cake water fraction and H_2S concentration, which determine the sulfur amount inside the system, are the most sensitive parameters for desulfurization costs with and without payoff. This is because the sulfur amount influences the EDTA FeNa solution usage and air flow rate, which determine the size and utility of heat exchanger and compressor.

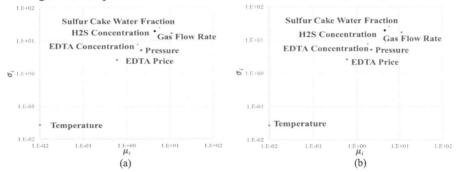

Figure 5: SA results for LO-CAT® process. Mean and standard deviation values for potential sensitive parameters for desulfurization cost (a) with 3-year payoff and (b) after payoff.

3.3. Sensitivity of Desulfurization Cost for SourCat^{TM} Process

The sensitivity analysis results for SourCat^{TM} process are compiled in Figure 6. The gas flow rate and H_2S concentration are the most sensitive parameters. Sulfur conversion, sorbent price, sorbent capacity and SO_2 conversion, which determine the total sorbent cost, also impact the desulfurization cost. This is because these parameters affect how much H$_2$S is left in the reactor effluent. Adsorption of the left H$_2$S is much more expensive compared to converting it to solid elemental sulfur in the reactor.

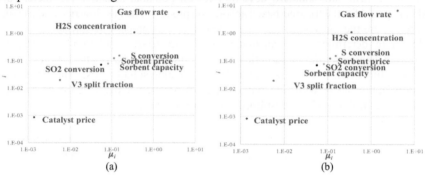

(a)   (b)

Figure 6 SA results for SourCat^{TM} process. Mean and standard deviation values for potential sensitive parameters for desulfurization cost (a) with 3-year payoff and (b) after payoff.

4. Conclusions

A systematic sensitivity analysis using MOAT method is performed to investigate which parameters have the most significant impact on desulfurization costs of three small-scale desulfurization processes. For triazine-based absorption, gas flow rate, triazine concentration and H$_2$S concentration that determine the raw material cost are the most sensitive ones because raw material makes up 90% of the desulfurization cost. For LO-CAT® process, parameters that determine the sulfur amount inside the system are the most sensitive ones, such as gas flow rate and H$_2$S concentration. For this process, parameters that are related to EDTA FeNa cost also have an impact on desulfurization cost. For SourCat^{TM} process, parameters controlling the sulfur content and H$_2$S amount that needs to be adsorbed by sorbent are the most sensitive ones. Gas flow rate and H$_2$S concentration are sensitive parameters for all three small-scale desulfurization processes.

Acknowledgements

The authors are grateful for the financial support provided by the DOE-RAPID Process Intensification Institute under contract DE-EE0007888-10-6.

References

Dudley, B. (2018). BP statistical review of world energy. *BP Statistical Review of World Energy*, 1–56.

EIA. (2019). U.S. Natural Gas Vented and Flared. Retrieved November 27, 2019, from https://www.eia.gov/dnav/ng/hist/n9040us2a.htm

Faramawy, S., Zaki, T., & Sakr, A. A.-E. (2016). Natural gas origin, composition, and processing: A review. *Journal of Natural Gas Science and Engineering*, *34*, 34–54.

Gan, Y., Duan, Q., Gong, W., Tong, C., Sun, Y., Chu, W., … Di, Z. (2014). A comprehensive evaluation of various sensitivity analysis methods: A case study with a hydrological model. *Environmental Modelling and Software*, *51*, 269–285.

Hugo Lozano, E. A. T. (2000). Re-generable H$_2$S Scavenger. *Laurance Reid Gas Conditioning Conference*.

Kalakul, S., Malakul, P., Siemanond, K., & Gani, R. (2014). Integration of life cycle assessment software with tools for economic and sustainability analyses and process simulation for sustainable process design. *Journal of Cleaner Production*, *71*, 98–109.

Speight, J. G. (2018). Gas cleaning processes. In *Natural Gas*. https://doi.org/10.1016/b978-0-12-809570-6.00008-4

Taylor, G., Smith-Gonzalez, M., Wylde, J., & Oliveira, A. P. (2019). *HS Scavenger Development During the Oil and Gas Industry Search for an MEA Triazine Replacement in Hydrogen Sulfide Mitigation and Enhanced Monitoring Techniques Employed During Their Evaluation*. https://doi.org/10.2118/193536-ms

Sauro Pierucci, Flavio Manenti, Giulia Bozzano, Davide Manca (Eds.)
Proceedings of the 30th European Symposium on Computer Aided Process Engineering
(ESCAPE30), May 24-27, 2020, Milano, Italy. © 2020 Elsevier B.V. All rights reserved.
http://dx.doi.org/10.1016/B978-0-12-823377-1.50164-6

Synthesis of Heat Pump Enhanced Solar Thermal for Low and Medium Temperature Operations

Ben Abikoye,[a,*] Lidija Čuček,[b,*] Danijela Urbancl,[b] Adeniyi Jide Isafiade,[a]
Zdravko Kravanja[b]

[a]*Department of Chemical Engineering, University of Cape Town, Private Bag X3, Rondebosch 7701, Cape Town, South Africa*
[b]*Faculty of Chemistry and Chemical Engineering, University of Maribor, 2000 Maribor, Slovenia*
abksem001@myuct.ac.za, lidija.cucek@um.si

Abstract

This study presents a multi-period mathematical programming approach for the design and optimization of heat pump-enhanced solar thermal for low and medium temperature applications in industrial, residential and other sectors. Mathematical models which capture the dynamic operating properties and thermodynamic features of combined solar thermal and multi-stage vapour compression heat pump cycle have been developed. The multi-period optimization context of the model accounts for the intermittent variability of relevant meteorological conditions and their effects on heat output from the heat pump. The design and optimization of the integrated system is implemented and solved in GAMS and analysis of the system shows good prospect for enhanced thermal energy from solar. The results obtained show significant increase in the amount of heat recovered from the heat pump as solar collector area increases up to 6,511 m^2 with average heat duty of about 1,615 kW and coefficient of performance of 1.81 obtained for that same collector size.

Keywords: Solar thermal, Heat pump, Solar-driven heat pump synthesis, Low and medium temperature level applications, Design and optimization.

1. Introduction

Due to the urgent need to reduce energy-related emissions as well as increasing supports for stringent environmental regulations, energy system designs that showcase the synergy between energy efficiency measures and renewable energy technologies have received global interests and considerable research attention (IRENA, 2017). One of such technologies is integrated design of solar thermal and heat pump system which has been widely described to be a relatively preferred sustainable source of heat (Allouhi et al. 2017) especially for low and medium temperature operations. One of the captivating features of solar thermal is its natural availability at diverse ambient temperature levels without any mechanical work input (Abikoye et al. 2019a). Heat pump on the other hand is an energy efficient technology that is used to upgrade heat from a relatively low temperature heat source and eventually deliver more heat than the total work input (Carbonell et al. 2014). These attributes provide the platform for using the combined technology to circumvent the low energy output limitation of solar thermal systems (especially in periods with low solar irradiation and ambient temperature). It also provides a sustainable means to overcome the start-up problem in most heat pump applications thereby enhancing the performance of heat pumping cycle.

While numerous studies have been carried out on heat pump technologies, less information is available in literature on the synthesis of solar-driven heat pump and on the application of combined solar thermal and heat pump for low and medium temperature level applications (Grubbauer et al. 2018). This is especially the case for studies that include optimization of the integrated systems. Most previous research contributions combining solar thermal and heat pump designs have been largely applied to residential buildings, while few other available cases of industrial heat pump design and optimization are based on industrial waste heat recovery through thermoelectric devices and organic Rankine cycles (Mateu-Royo et al. 2019).

Utilization of solar thermal in any form is a task that is highly challenging due to considerable intermittent supply and multi-period variability features of its energy output. Even with modern synthesis techniques, the general requirements for achieving optimal design solution is still a challenge. More so, if a moderately-sized solar design with simple technology is considered, not much higher temperature level can be reached for typical industrial streams (Abikoye et al. 2019a). However, integrating heat pump with such simple design could enhance the thermal output of the system, but combination of the two technologies is not trivial considering the transient nature of solar resource and its influence on the heat output from the combined technology. This is in addition to the complexities at the heat pump side of the integrated network when a high temperature lift is desired. Such intricacies are generally unavoidable due to the wide difference between evaporator and condensing temperatures while trying to maximize the heat load recoverable from condensing vapour in the heat pump.

To the best of authors' knowledge, study on combined heat pump/solar thermal utility system that incorporate the aforementioned features using a simultaneous design and optimization approach is still lacking. Hence, this study presents a comprehensive synthesis method for the utilization of combined solar thermal and heat pump technologies for low and medium temperature level heat generation.

2. Methodology

2.1. System description

The integrated system presented in this paper consists of solar thermal system (which supplies heat to the evaporator side of the heat pump) and the heat pump cycle (having multi-stage vapor compression features with successive condensation and sub-cooling for maximum heat recovery) and low/medium temperature heat production for potential integration with the industrial or residential heat network.

Figure 1 presents the structure of the combined solar thermal and heat pump technology. The integrated design comprises three loops: i) closed loop solar collector – heat pump – solar collector; ii) closed loop of heat pump alone; and iii) open loop heat pump – industrial process – heat pump. The heat transfer fluid (HTF) that runs through solar collector – evaporator – solar collector loop (first loop) is a mixture of water and ethylene glycol. In the second loop (closed loop of heat pump cycle), R-245CA refrigerant is used as the working media, while circulating pressurized water is used to recover heat from the hot refrigerant gas which is then further used in the industrial process loop (third loop). In Figure 1 the third loop is presented with a dashed line, as it is modelled as an open loop.

Having increased in temperature, the HTF from solar collector is used to vaporize the low-pressure refrigerant within the sealed compartment of the evaporator. Thereafter, the vaporized refrigerant goes through multi-stage vapor compression which further increases the pressure and temperature of the gas. The hot refrigerant gas is then finally used to raise the temperature of the circulating HTF on the heat recovery side of the heat pump cycle (i.e. condenser and sub-cooler). The advantage derived from an efficient heat pumping system is that more heat is delivered to the system than the total work input. In the conceptual framework of the design, the recovered heat can be used directly in the plant or stored in the tank to be used at a later time within the industrial heat network as shown in the integrated system (Figure 2) or for other potential uses such as space and water heating as demonstrated by Abikoye et al. (2019b). However, it should be noted that only the multiperiod integration between solar thermal and heat pump components of the integration is discussed in this paper.

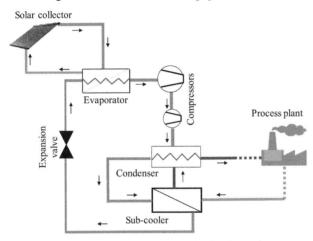

Figure 1: Integrated heat pump-enhanced solar thermal system

2.2 Model approach

The objective of the presented study is to maximize the total heat recovered from the vaporized refrigerant at the heat recovery side of the heat pump. The objective function is developed as shown in Eq. (1), where $\dot{Q}_{mp,dp,hp}^{gen}$ represents the total heat generated from the sub-cooler and condenser and delivered to the HTF in the process plant – heat pump – process plant loop. Sets *mp, dp* and *hp* represent monthly, daily and hourly periods, while *DPM* represents set of pairs of days and months as in Egieya et al. (2018).

$$\max \left(\sum_{mp \in MP} \sum_{dp \in DP} \sum_{hp \in hP} \bigwedge_{(mp,dp) \in DPM} \dot{Q}_{mp,dp,hp}^{gen} \right) \tag{1}$$

The main variables considered in the model include temperatures, flowrates and energy flows of streams across the system, mass enthalpies across the heat pump loop, the area of solar collector and efficiencies (for both solar collector and compressors). An important factor in modelling of combined solar thermal and heat pump system is the intermittent changes in ambient conditions and its effects on the heat output from the system. Hence, the mathematical model is formulated as a multi-period model. The model accounts for the dynamic behavior of the operating and thermodynamic features of the combined solar thermal-heat pump systems. The multi-periodicity framework of the model captures the time-dependency disposition of all the integration features. These characteristics are accounted for on hourly, daily and monthly time periods in the model.

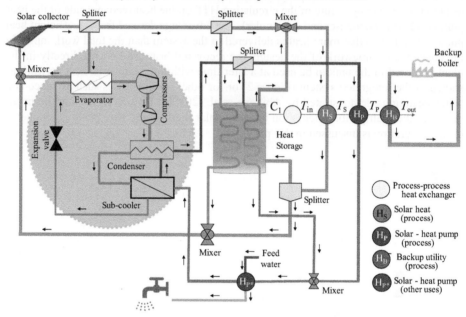

Figure 2: Industrial integration of combined solar thermal and heat pump system incorporated with periodic heat storage

To evaluate the periodic features on the heat pump side, correlations are developed for the changes in mass enthalpy with changes in temperature and pressure across the two-phase region of the refrigerant as shown in Figure 3 for R245CA. Thermodynamic data for the refrigerant are obtained from Aspen Plus V10 using REFPROP property method (Aspen Technology, 2019).

The periodic heat duty ($\dot{Q}$) and work ($\dot{W}$) required across units t such as evaporator (*evap*), compressors (*comp*), condenser (*cond*), sub-cooler (*cool*) and expander, are obtained by multiplying the flowrate (F) and the difference in mass enthalpy ($h^{out} - h^{in}$):

$$Q_{t,mp,dp,hp}, \ W_{t,mp,dp,hp} = F_{t,mp,dp,hp} \cdot \left(h^{out}_{t,mp,dp,hp} - h^{in}_{t,mp,dp,hp} \right),$$
$$\forall \ mp \in MP, dp \in DP, hp \in HP, \tag{2}$$
$$t \in \{\text{evaporator, compressor, condenser, sub cooler, expander}\}$$

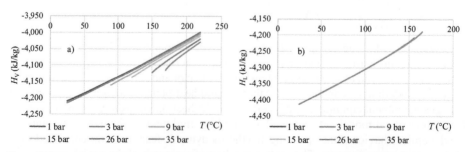

Figure 3: Mass enthalpy changing with temperature and pressure for a) vapor and b) liquid phase

3. Case Study and Results

The developed model is implemented based on the previous design of industrial integration of solar thermal by Abikoye et al. (2019a). The integrated solar thermal design is now modified by including the heat pump enhanced solar loop. The design is then simultaneously optimized for the maximum amount of heat energy that can be obtained from heat pump. Most integration parameters (such as flowrates, temperatures, pressures, energy flows, work required, mass enthalpies, mass fractions of liquid and vapor, efficiencies, collector area, heat capacities and cp/cv ratio) are variables which are then optimized to satisfy the objective of the design.

A reference location in Maribor, Slovenia, is used as the case study. Meteorological data (hourly solar irradiation and ambient temperature) of the location for the year 2016 are obtained from EC JRC PVGIS project (2017). To reduce the complexity of the model and computational time, the discretization of hourly, daily and monthly time periods follows the same techniques as used by Abikoye et al. (2019a). Readers are referred to the study for more details on solar thermal utilization in industrial process stream without heat pump. The resulting model consists of 9,971 single equations and 11,186 single variables. Solutions to the model was obtained in 60 minutes using SBB solver in GAMS (GAMS Development Corporation, 2019) with 0.1 % optimality gap on a personal computer with an Intel® Core™ i7-8700K CPU @ 3.70 GHz processor with 64 GB of RAM.

Figures 4 and 5 and Table 1 present summary of the results obtained. An example of the variability in the properties of streams in specific time period and collector area is shown in Figure 4 (e.g. when $A_{collector} = 5,000$ m^2 and period is M8, D1, H2 i.e. August 8-10 am). Figure 5 shows the relationship between the average $\dot{Q}^{gen}$ obtained and solar collector sizes ($A_{collector}$). From Figure 5, a steady increase in the amount of heat recovered from the heat pump can be observed up to $A_{collector} \approx 6,510.6$ m^2. A summary of the results showing this relationship is presented in Table 1 for different variables such as heat duty, power required, heat generated, and coefficient of performance (COP).

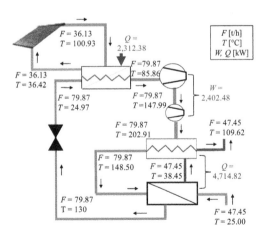

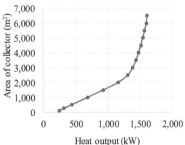

Figure 4: Values of variables in selected period and collector area ($A = 5,000$ m^2, M8, 8-10 am)

Figure 5: Average heat output with different sizes of solar collector

4. Conclusions and Recommendations

In this study, an integrated design and optimization framework that combined solar thermal and heat pump technologies has been proposed for enhanced thermal performance. The framework and method is based on a multi-period model formulation where the dynamic features of solar integration and heat output from the system are evaluated and accounted for on hourly, daily and monthly time periods. The obtained results show that combining heat pump with solar thermal can enhance the thermal performance and reliability of the solar system. Future work will include integration of the proposed design with industrial and residential heat network for maximum heat delivery, and economic and sustainability objectives for the integrated design.

Table 1: Average values of some integration variables for different collector areas

$A_{collector}$ (m²)	$\dot{Q}_{evap}$(kW)	$\dot{Q}_{cond}$(kW)	$\dot{Q}_{cool}$(kW)	$\dot{W}_{comp}$(kW)	$\dot{Q}^{gen}$(kW)	COP
100	11.94	-40.12	-8.85	37.04	237.20	1.32
500	59.67	-200.61	-44.26	185.20	433.10	1.32
1,000	119.35	-401.22	-88.52	370.40	677.99	1.32
2,000	236.94	-792.23	-175.18	730.46	1,155.44	1.33
4,000	440.49	-1,090.49	-239.24	889.24	1,480.20	1.50
6,000	629.90	-1,263.52	-245.33	878.95	1,601.92	1.78
6,510.6	672.60	-1,328.97	-256.08	912.46	1,614.58	1.81

Acknowledgements

The authors wish to acknowledge the supports received from the Erasmus+ programme of the European Union, Postgraduate Research Office and Faculty of Engineering and the Built Environment at the University of Cape Town, South Africa, and the Slovenian Research Agency (research core funding No. P2-0412 and P2-0032).

References

B. Abikoye, L. Čuček, A. Isafiade, Z. Kravanja, 2019a, Integrated design for direct and indirect solar thermal utilization in low temperature industrial operations, Energy, 182, 381-396

B. Abikoye, L. Čuček, A. Isafiade, Z. Kravanja, 2019b, Synthesis of Solar Thermal Network for Domestic Heat Utilization, Chem Eng Trans, 76, 1015-1020

A. Allouhi, Y. Agrouaz, M. Benzakour Amine, S. Rehman, M.S. Buker, T. Kousksou, A. Benbassou, 2017, Design optimization of a multi-temperature solar thermal heating system for an industrial process, Appl Energy, 206, 382–392

Aspen Technology, 2019, Aspen Plus, The Chemical Industry's Leading Process Simulation Software. <www.aspentech.com/en/products/engineering/aspen-plus> Accessed: 29.11.2019

D. Carbonell, M.Y. Haller, D. Philippen, E. Frank, 2014, Simulations of combined solar thermal and heat pump systems for domestic hot water and space heating, Energy Procedia, 48, 524–534

J.M. Egieya, L. Čuček, K. Zirngast, A.J. Isafiade, B. Pahor, Z. Kravanja, 2018, Biogas supply chain optimization considering different multi-period scenarios, Chem Eng Trans, 70, 985-990

GAMS Development Corporation, 2019, GAMS – Documentation, <gams.com/latest/docs/gams.pdf> Accessed: 29.11.2019

A. Grubbauer, J. Fluch, C. Brunner, T. Ramschak, V. Wilk, T. Fleckl, 2018, Renewable and highly efficient energy systems through innovative combination of solar thermal and heat pump systems, Chem Eng Trans, 70, 745-750

IRENA, 2017, Synergies between renewable energy and energy efficiency, <irena.org/-/media/Files/IRENA/Agency/Publication/2017/Aug/IRENA_REmap_Synergies_REEE_2017.pdf> Accessed 8.6.2019

C. Mateu-Royo, A. Mota-Babiloni, J. Navarro-Esbrí, J. Peris, F. Molés, M. Amat-Albuixech, 2019, Multi-objective optimization of a novel reversible High-Temperature Heat Pump-Organic Rankine Cycle (HTHP-ORC) for industrial low-grade waste heat recovery, Energy Conversion and Management, 197, 111908

Sauro Pierucci, Flavio Manenti, Giulia Bozzano, Davide Manca (Eds.)
Proceedings of the 30th European Symposium on Computer Aided Process Engineering
(ESCAPE30), May 24-27, 2020, Milano, Italy. © 2020 Elsevier B.V. All rights reserved.
http://dx.doi.org/10.1016/B978-0-12-823377-1.50165-8

Protein from Renewable Resources: Mycoprotein Production from Agricultural Residues

Thomas Upcraft[a], Rob Johnson[a], Tim Finnigan[a], Jason Hallett[a], Miao Guo[a,b]

[a] *Department of Chemical Engineering, Imperial College London, London, SW7 2AZ*
[b] *Department of Engineering, King's College London, Strand campus*
J.hallett@imperial.ac.uk, miao.guo@kcl.ac.uk

Abstract

As concerns intensify over the increasing impact of human activities on the environment, efforts are underway in several areas in order to mitigate the worst effects. In recent years agricultural systems have received intense public scrutiny and if the global population increases, then the risk to food security is of real concern. Food-grade Single Cell Proteins (SCPs), produced through microbial fermentation, are an alternative to traditional livestock protein sources. This study presents a conceptual design and economic evaluation of SCP production from cellulosic-derived sugars from agricultural wastes. We modelled an SCP biorefinery, with ionic liquid pretreatment, enzymatic hydrolysis and fermentation to convert rice straw to food-grade protein. A Techno-Economic Analysis (TEA) was performed to assess the feasibility and compare the minimum selling price (MSP) to meat protein sources. Technical constraints were evaluated, in addition to evaluating the impact of reagent prices to the commercial success of the process.

Keywords: Biorefinery, single cell protein, process design, techno-economic analysis

1. Introduction

Globally, 113 million people still exist in a state of 'crisis' over food security, with 109 million of those requiring humanitarian intervention, in part due to climate-related events (FAO et al., 2019). Agriculture accounts for 29% of global GHG emissions(Vermeulen et al., 2012) with livestock responsible for a significant proportion of emissions and land-water resource scarcity. There is now growing interest in meat-alternative protein sources with minimal environmental damage, such as food-grade single cell proteins (SCPs).

SCPs refer to edible unicellular microorganisms that can be used as a protein supplement for human consumption or animal feeds. Mycoprotein, an SCP success story, is derived from the fungus *Fusarium venenatum* and has been produced by Marlow Foods Ltd under the name Quorn™ since 1985, with current annual sales of over £200m(Quorn, 2018).

Mycoprotein is produced through the aerobic fermentation of glucose syrup with *F. venenatum*(Wiebe, 2002). Replacement of starch-derived glucose as a feedstock with cellulose-derived glucose offers potential reduced land-use through agro-residue waste utilisation coupled with partial carbon emission mitigation. One such agricultural residue is rice straw. Rice feeds over 45% of the world and is the staple food in Asia representing between 30-70% of the average person's caloric intake(IRRI, 2019). Much of the rice straw is burned causing air, land, and water pollution, severe health problems and decreased soil quality. Several pretreatment technologies are currently under investigation in tandem with hydrolysis and fermentation to convert rice straw to bioproducts, amongst which, the use of ionic liquids (ILs) is one of the most promising due to its high sugar release, low production of saccharification inhibitors and prevention of toxins accumulating. Furthermore, the use of promising low-cost food-grade ILs may eliminate many hurdles relating to food safety, thereby enabling lignocellulosic-SCP.

Biorefinery models for biochemicals have been widely studied at both the conceptual and detailed design phases, such as for bioethanol production (Humbird et al., 2011) and Acetone-Butanol-Ethanol. However, biorefinery models with IL pretreatment are a scarcity. Baral and Shah (2016) investigated IL pretreatment for ethanol production and concluded that IL recovery and cost were significant economic factors. Similarly, SCP production models are uncommon. Strong et al. (2016), highlighted a potential process pathway, whilst Molitor et al. (2019) developed a two-stage power-to-protein process economic model, fixing CO_2 as the carbon source. However, a research gap remains on modelling of lignocellulosic derived protein.

In this paper, a conceptual biorefinery model was developed to investigate the feasibility of the lignocellulose-to-SCP process based on in-house experimental data on lignocellulosic sugar extraction with food-grade ionic liquid choline hydrogen sulphate [Ch][HSO₄] and enzyme. Sensitivity analyses were conducted to highlight the performance-limiting factors to inform the process design and optimisation.

2. Methodology

2.1. Process Synthesis

2.1.1. Process Design

A hypothetical lignocellulosic SCP biorefinery was modelled in Aspen Plus V9 for 40,000t/a production of SCP paste, where IL pretreatment, enzymatic hydrolysis and fermentation processes were simulated based on our experimental results and publicly available information. Table 1 defines the process areas and their design basis/targets.

2.1.2. Modelling framework for performance evaluation

A framework was developed to integrate Aspen Plus with MATLAB for economic performance evaluation and sensitivity analysis (Figure 1). MATLAB was used to initialise the simulation, equipment sizing and costing and subsequent economic analysis.

Table 1. The overall goals and design basis of each process hierarchy

Area	Goal	Basis
Feed Handling	Fresh ionic liquid (IL) is mixed with recycled IL and water to specified composition. Biomass feed processed through solid handling infrastructure.	(Humbird et al., 2011)
Pretreatment	Biomass delignification, pulp washing and recovery, lignin precipitation.	(Brandt-Talbot et al., 2017), experiments
Enzymatic Hydrolysis	Saccharification of pulp to recover glucose-rich hydrolysate stream.	(Humbird et al., 2011), experiments
Fermentation	SCP fermentation, RNA reduction and centrifugation to achieve SCP paste product.	(Wiebe, 2002)
Separation	Flashing of volatiles and water from IL mixture to recover IL. Separation and recovery of furfural.	(Brandt-Talbot et al., 2017) + >98.5% furfural purity
Combustor	Combustion of recovered lignin, and other 'waste' streams for energy recovery in boiler.	(Humbird et al., 2011)
WWT	Wastewater treatment producing purified water.	(Humbird et al., 2011)
Utilities	Tracks utility demands around the plant: process water, cooling water, chilled water and electricity.	

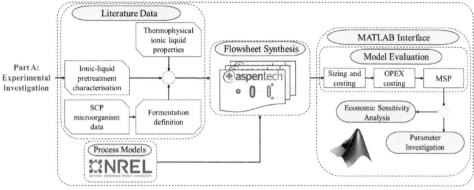

Figure 1. Modelling methodology highlighting the integration of MATLAB with the process simulator Aspen Plus.

2.1.3. Process Costing

The equipment sizing and costing were performed using two methods. For original design, factorial-based costing equations defined in Seider et al. (2017) were used. For the process design based on NREL hierarchy models (Combustor, WWT, (partial) Feed Handling), the cost was scaled based on a scaling variable as shown in Eq. (1).

$$Cost_2 = Cost_1 \left(\frac{Capacity_2}{Capacity_1} \right)^{0.6} \tag{1}$$

Utility costs were estimated via the procedure defined by Ulrich and Vasudevan (2006) in which a two-factor cost equation accounts for both inflation and energy costs.

2.2. Economic Evaluation

A Minimum Selling Price (MSP) was used for economic comparison, which is defined as the selling price of the SCP paste for which the Net Present Value is 0.

2.3. Scenario Evaluation

Experimental data was fed into the model for the evaluation of four different scenarios. The input parameters and scenarios are given in Table 2 and Table 3 respectively.

Table 2. Universal model input parameters across the scenarios based upon experimental work

Parameter	Value	Composition	%	Reactant	Cost ($/kg)
Temperature (K)	423	Cellulose	40.07	Rice straw	0.049
Biomass/IL (%)	10	Xylan	18.21	IL	1.24
Water loading of IL (%)	20	Lignin	23.37	Cellulase	6.27
Cellulase/cellulose (mg/g)	20	Mannan	0.68	Ammonia	0.61
Glucan recovery (%)	100	Arabinan	4.04	Nutrient	0.74
		Galactan	1.92		
		Acetate	1.7		
		Ash	10.00		

* IL = Ionic liquid; Composition = dry biomass feedstock composition, 20% moisture added

Table 3. Comparison between 4 experimental scenarios summarising the main differences for model input.

Scenario	1	2	3	4
Ionic Liquid	[Ch][HSO₄]	[Ch][HSO₄]	[TEA][HSO₄]	[TEA][HSO₄]
Novozymes® Enzyme	Food grade	CTEC 2	Food grade	CTEC 2
Pulp Yield (%)	70.9	70.9	50.8	50.8
Saccharification Yield (%)	45.2	59.1	93.0	97.0

3. Results

3.1. Food-grade Scenario

Evaluation of the process area investment costs as a share of the Fixed Capital Investment (FCI), reactant and utility costs, water demand and heat duty for scenario 1 are presented in Figure 2. Fermentation dominates over half of total FCI. Second and third main contributors are wastewater treatment (WWT) and combustion. Figure 2.b shows the weighting of reagent and utility costs. The nutrient, electricity, cellulase and feedstock are the most significant cost contributors. Process water contribution is marginal (0.03% of manufacturing costs). Heat duty demands are dominated by heating of the pretreatment feed and IL recovery (Figure 2.d), due to the large quantity of water in the system. Implementation of a multi-effect evaporation system for recovering the IL reduced the

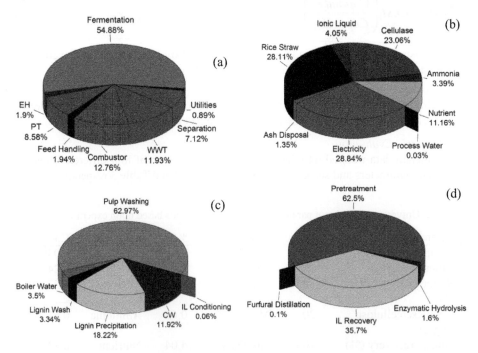

Figure 2. Scenario assessment showing (a) the proportion of fixed capital investment of process areas; (b) reagent and utility costs as a percentage of overall operating expenses; (c) water consumption in certain process tasks and (d) hot utility demand percentage between process tasks. EH = Enzymatic hydrolysis; PT = Pretreatment; CW = Cooling water

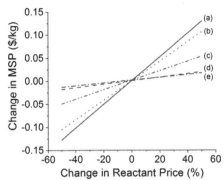

Figure 3. The % change in Net Present Value (NPV) as the % price of reactants changes. (a) rice straw; (b) cellulase; (c) nutrient; (d) [Ch][HSO₄]; (e) ammonia

heat burden significantly. Focus should be placed on reducing water usage throughout the process, through increasing biomass loading (biomass/IL) and reduction of water used in lignin precipitation.

Sensitivity analysis of the NPV to reactant prices is given in Figure 3. Feedstock costs are the most sensitive factor, followed by cellulase and nutrient. This highlights the improvement space in nutrient formulation and the importance to screen resilient feedstock, whose yield and price are less sensitive to environmental variation. Another sensitive factor is cellulase. Typical cellulase dosages range from 10-50+ mg cellulase/g cellulose, with higher rates achieving greater saccharification, therefore, scope for improvement exists through dosage optimisation. Interestingly, for a reasonable [Ch][HSO₄] price ($1.24/kg), IL price has a low impact on overall economics. Often, in stand-alone pretreatment processes, IL costs have a significant impact on economic performance, in this integrated biorefinery process, their significance is reduced. Production capacity also impacts MSP, as significant reductions in the MSP can be achieved for larger production volumes (Figure 4). The current Quorn production capacity is greater than 40,000 t/a.

3.2. Scenario Comparison

The evaluation of the MSP of the four scenarios is summarised in Table 4. The MSP is significantly reduced for scenarios 3 and 4 in which triethylamine hydrogen sulphate ([TEA][HSO₄]) was used. This is due to the higher saccharification yield which increased SCP production for similar production costs. Our experimental results suggest cellulase activity affects saccharification yield, where Cellic® CTEC 2 performed better for both ILs than food-grade enzyme, however, the most significant factor was IL performance. A lower pulp yield was obtained for [TEA][HSO₄] pretreatment, indicating greater delignification and hemicellulose removal, increasing cellulose accessibility to enzymes during saccharification.

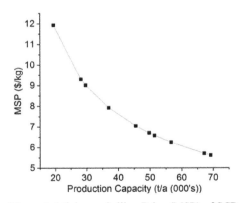

Figure 4. Minimum Selling Price (MSP) of SCP as a function of annual capacity production capacity for scenario 1.

3.3. Can we meet the meat-free protein supply with agro-residues?

The MSP was used as an indicator to compare to other protein sources, and Quorn™ mince based on retail market price. Table 5. Shows the price per kg of

Table 4. Minimum Selling Price (MSP) of the four scenarios at 40,000 t/a production capacity

Scenario	1	2	3	4
MSP $/kg	7.47	7.01	6.30	6.25

Table 5. Cost of products per kg of protein adjusted through Net Protein Utilisation ($/kgP)

Product	Egg	Beef[a]	Tofu	Chicken	Quorn[TM, b]	SCP[c]
Cost ($/kgP)	15.37	39.06	109.14	41.67	55.71	54.35

[a] Beef mince 10-15% fat; [b] Quorn mince; [c] Mycoprotein paste (wet-basis) MSP of $6.25/kg

protein (adjusted through Net Protein Utilisation, NPU) which shows that, for a current supermarket selling price of Quorn™ mince ($6.5/kg), protein costs are comparable with beef and chicken. It must be noted that the Mycoprotein (SCP) paste represents the crude protein product that is expected to undergo further texturisation. However, it is positive that the protein cost of the paste is comparable to other protein sources. Scenario 1 yields an SCP protein cost of $64.96/kgP and is the only one which uses both food-certified IL and cellulase, therefore, the adoption of this process technology may depend on food-certification of the reagents. However, this suggests a promising outlook on the economics of lignocellulosic mycoprotein.

4. Conclusions

Overall this study highlights the significant factors in lignocellulosic mycoprotein production. Fermentation dominates capital costs (over 50%). Feedstock, cellulase, and nutrient contribute significantly to operating costs, but ILs show low impact on overall economics. Large heating duties for the pretreatment reactor and IL recovery place a burden on economics through large steam demands, but process optimisation offers scope for improvement. Scenarios 2, 3 and 4 gave an MSP less than scenario 1, in which both food-certified cellulase and IL were used, but would require food-certification of the IL and/or cellulase for technology adoption. All MSPs were comparable to meat protein sources and scenarios 3 and 4 produce a mycoprotein paste for less than the supermarket price for select Quorn™ products, leaving room for further processing to the final consumer product. Our results demonstrate the economic feasibility of lignocellulosic mycoprotein and highlight the performance-limiting steps for future research efforts.

References

Baral, N.R., Shah, A. (2016) Techno-economic analysis of cellulose dissolving ionic liquid pretreatment of lignocellulosic biomass for fermentable sugars production. Biofuels, Bioproducts and Biorefining 10, 70-88.

Brandt-Talbot, A., Gschwend, F.J.V., Fennell, P.S., Lammens, T.M., Tan, B., Weale, J., Hallett, J.P. (2017) An economically viable ionic liquid for the fractionation of lignocellulosic biomass. Green Chemistry 19, 3078-3102.

FAO, IFAD, UNICEF, WFP, WHO, (2019) The State of Food Security and Nutrition in the World 2019, Safeguarding against economic slowdowns and downturns. FAO, Rome.

Humbird, D., Davis, R., Tao, L., Kinchin, C., Hsu, D., Aden, A., Schoen, P., Lukas, J., Olthof, B., Worley, M., Sexton, D., Dudgeon, D., (2011) Process Design and Economics for Biochemical Conversion of Lignocellulosic Biomass to Ethanol: Dilute-Acid Pretreatment and Enzymatic Hydrolysis of Corn Stover. National Renewable Energy Laboratory

IRRI, (2019) Our Work. International Rice Research Institute.

Molitor, B., Mishra, A., Angenent, L.T. (2019) Power-to-protein: converting renewable electric power and carbon dioxide into single cell protein with a two-stage bioprocess. Energy & Environmental Science.

Quorn, (2018) Quorn Foods sees 16% Global Growth in 2017.

Seider, W.D., Lewin, D.R., Seader, J.D., Widagdo, S., Gani, R., Ng, K.M. (2017) Product and process design principles : synthesis, analysis, and evaluation.

Strong, P.J., Kalyuzhnaya, M., Silverman, J., Clarke, W.P. (2016) A methanotroph-based biorefinery: Potential scenarios for generating multiple products from a single fermentation. Bioresour Technol 215, 314-323.

Ulrich, G., Vasudevan, P. (2006) How to estimate utility costs. Chem. Eng. 113, 66-69.

Vermeulen, S.J., Campbell, B.M., Ingram, J.S.I. (2012) Climate Change and Food Systems. Annual Review of Environment and Resources 37, 195-222.

Wiebe, M.G. (2002) Myco-protein from Fusarium venenatum: a well-established product for human consumption. Appl Microbiol Biotechnol 58, 421-427.

Sauro Pierucci, Flavio Manenti, Giulia Bozzano, Davide Manca (Eds.)
Proceedings of the 30th European Symposium on Computer Aided Process Engineering
(ESCAPE30), May 24-27, 2020, Milano, Italy. © 2020 Elsevier B.V. All rights reserved.
http://dx.doi.org/10.1016/B978-0-12-823377-1.50166-X

Energy Efficient Distillation by Combination of Thermal Coupling and Heat Integration

Mirko Skiborowski

TU Dortmund University, Department of Biochemical and Chemical Engineering,
Laboratory of Fluid Separations, Emil-Figge-Strasse 70, 44227 Dortmund, Germany

mirko.skiborowski@tu-dortmund.de

Abstract

Conventional heat-integration between adjacent columns, as well as thermal coupling and the equipment-integrated implementation in a dividing wall column are successful concepts for the improvement of the energy efficiency of distillation processes. While especially dividing wall columns have made a considerable impact in industrial application, further heat integration is prevented by the bidirectional transfer of liquid and vapor streams that impede a necessary pressure variation for modification of the boiling temperatures. This limitation can however be overcome by the modification of thermal couplings to one-directed liquid only transfer. While this concept has been proposed almost 20 years ago, it has received limited attention so far. In order to evaluate the prospect of this combination, the current article exploits a combination of a shortcut-based screening and a rigorous economic optimization, in order to evaluate a heat-integrated side-rectifier with liquid only transfer modification in comparison with a range of alternative options. The application to an exemplary case study highlights the huge potential of this combination, showcasing the possibility to save half of the energy required for a non-integrated configuration and even more than 30% compared to fully thermally coupled configurations, depending on the feed composition.

Keywords: distillation, thermal coupling, heat integration, rectification body method

1. Introduction

Despite serious concerns about the low thermodynamic efficiency, distillation processes remain the working horse for fluid separations, especially in case of large scale continuous production processes. Besides the exploitation of hybrid separation processes, combining distillation with other technologies such as extraction and membrane separations, a number of options for improving the energy efficiency in distillation processes have been established. These include e.g. direct heat integration and multi effect distillation, thermal coupling and the equipment integrated dividing wall columns (DWC), mechanical vapor recompression (MVR) and internally heat integrated columns, so called HiDiC (Kiss et al., 2012). The individual concepts allow for energy savings of up to 50% compared to the non-integrated distillation processes. Yet, choosing the right option requires a case specific evaluation of the different process concepts, which can be performed by means of shortcut methods (Skiborowski, 2018), as well as rigorous economic optimization of MESH based superstructure models (Waltermann and Skiborowski, 2019).

While some combinations of these concepts have recently been considered in case-specific evaluations, such as the combination of MVR and DWC (Jana, 2019; Patraşcu et al., 2018) or the extension of a HIDiC with further MVR through intermediate heat exchangers (Kiran and Jana, 2016), such evaluations are still scarce. An interesting combination of thermal coupling and heat integration has been proposed by Agrawal (2000a) almost two decades ago. However, despite the indicated prospect of these so-called double-effect thermally coupled configurations, which were evaluated based on very approximate calculation for theoretical mixtures with constant relative volatility, the concept has received little attention so far. While thermal coupling itself and DWC in specific are considered as one of the most prominent examples of process intensification in fluid separations, with more than 130 industrial-scale DWC implementations (Staak et al., 2014), a direct extension of these configurations to the aforementioned combination is infeasible, due the standard bidirectional transfer of liquid and vapor streams between thermally coupled column sections that impedes the necessary pressure variation. This variation only becomes feasible in case of a transformation of the thermal coupling to a one-directed liquid only transfer (LOT), as introduced by Agrawal (2000b) and more recently considered in a systematic generation of DWC configurations with LOT modifications that allow for an independent control of the vapor flow rate in each partitioned zone of the DWC (Madenoor Ramapriya et al., 2014). Apart from the improved operability, Jiang and Agrawal (2019) conclude that the possibility to combine heat-integration with thermal couplings is another major opportunity offered by the LOT modification, since even double-effect systems for basic configurations can oftentimes outperform the best DWC configurations.

In order to evaluate this potential, the current study performs an optimization-based evaluation of a heat-integrated side-rectifier with LOT modification with various competing process concepts. The evaluation is based on a combination of pinch-based shortcut models, as well as rigorous equilibrium-stage models for an economic process optimization. The results obtained for a representative case study on the separation of a benzene, toluene, ethylbenzene mixture illustrates the significant potential for process intensification by showcasing energy savings of more than 30% in comparison to the fully thermally coupled DWC and the superiority for a wide range of feed compositions.

2. Improved side-rectifier configuration with heat integration

Following the initial idea of (Agrawal, 2000a, 2000b) an improved side-rectifier configuration with heat integration is derived in a sequence of steps, starting from the direct split configuration, as illustrated in Figure 1.

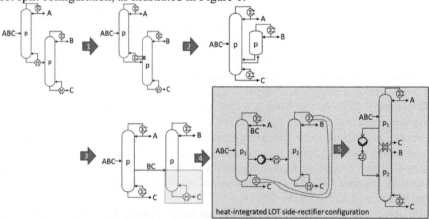

Figure 1: Transformation from direct split sequence over the thermally-coupled side rectifier to a heat-integrated LOT side-rectifier (HI-LOT-SR) configuration.

First, the direct split is converted to a thermally coupled side-rectifier, by an initial heat transfer of the reboiler of the first column (step 1) and a consecutive replacement of the reboiler by means of the bidirectional transfer of liquid and vapor (step 2). Subsequently the side-rectifier is modified to a LOT configuration, by exchanging the bidirectional transfer with a one-sided liquid transfer from the first to the second column, while extending the second column with an additional stripping section (step 3). Finally, a pump and heat exchanger are introduced into the liquid side stream in order to modify the operating pressure (p_2) of the second column (step 4). Pressure p_2 is determined such that the boiling temperature of the intermediate boiling product B is raised sufficiently above the boiling temperature of the heavy boiling product C at the operating pressure of the first column (p_1), enabling direct heat integration between both columns. According to Agrawal (2000a), this heat-integrated LOT side-rectifier (HI-LOT-SR) configuration could also be implemented in a consecutive column shell, when locating the second column on top of the first one (step 5).

3. Shortcut-based screening of alternative process configurations

In order to evaluate the potential benefits of the introduced HI-LOT-SR configuration, its performance has to be compared with alternative process configurations. For this purpose a shortcut-based screening method, developed in previous work (Skiborowski, 2018), is applied and extended, in order to include the HI-LOT-SR configuration. The initially developed algorithmic framework enables the evaluation of the minimum energy requirement (MED) of the simple column configurations (direct, indirect and intermediate split), six thermally coupled versions of these simple configurations, a heat integrated alternative for each of the simple configurations, as well as six configurations that consider MVR for either one or both columns in the direct and indirect split. Together with the LOT-SR and HI-LOT-SR a total number of 20 process configurations are evaluated by means of the Rectification Body Method (Bausa et al., 1998), while additional flash calculations and parametric optimizations are performed to evaluate the optimal distribution of the medium boiling product in the prefractionator, the distribution of heat loads in the LOT design, as well as the pressure levels in the heat-integrated and MVR designs (Skiborowski, 2018).

4. Economical optimization through MESH-based superstructure models

In order to evaluate the economic performance a MESH-based superstructure model is implemented and solved in GAMS, based on the previously developed superstructure models for simple and energy-integrated distillation processes (Waltermann and Skiborowski, 2019). The resulting mixed-integer nonlinear programming problem is solved in terms of a polylithic solution approach by means of a series of continuously relaxed nonlinear programming problems with the aid of additional nonlinear complementary constraints. The superstructure model for the HI-LOT-SR is a direct extension of the heat-integrated direct split configuration presented by (Waltermann and Skiborowski, 2019), for which an additional side stream is introduced for the first column, which is further connected to the second column, passing through the intermediate pump and heat exchanger, instead of the bottoms product. The latter is supposed to provide the heavy boiling product with the required purity specifications, as illustrated in Figure 1. The respective equation-oriented model for the superstructure and the economic model are described in further detail by (Waltermann et al., 2019; Waltermann and Skiborowski, 2019).

5. Case study

In the scope of the current study the separation of a zeotropic mixture of benzene, toluene and ethylbenzene is investigated. The thermodynamic properties are determined based on the Wilson model, the extended Antoine equation, as well as DIPPR correlations for the specific heat capacities and heat of vaporization. While the separation of this mixture, with a feed composition of 70 mol% benzene, 20 mol%, toluene and 10 mol% ethylbenzene was considered in the previous development of the shortcut screening approach (Skiborowski, 2018), the extended algorithmic framework is now used to evaluate potential feed compositions, for which the HI-LOT-SR provides potential MED savings in respect to all considered process configurations. Furthermore, an economic evaluation of the HI-LOT-SR is performed for the feed composition for which the largest MED savings are determined.

5.1. Shortcut-based screening

The MED of the 20 considered process configurations is evaluated for 171 feed compositions, resulting from an equidistant scattering of the composition space with variations in single component compositions of 5 mol%. Despite an energy conversion factor of 2 and isentropic and mechanical efficiencies of 80% and 90%, the MVR configurations provides generally the lowest MED. However, when considering the depreciation of the necessary compressor in the calculation of an estimate of the annual operating costs (AOC), MVR configurations are not the favorable choice for any of the feed compositions. Therefore, the following evaluation of the MED is first limited to the 14 configurations, excluding the MVR configurations. The results of this evaluation are illustrated in Figure 2, which indicates by means of different symbols, which process configuration provides the lowest MED for a specific feed composition.

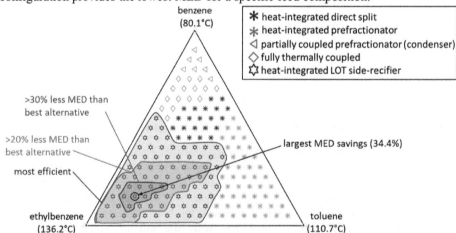

Figure 2: Illustration of favorable process configurations in terms of MED for different feed compositions (symbols indicate favorable process configuration at the specific feed composition).

While partially and fully thermally coupled configurations are preferred for high concentrations of benzene and low concentrations of toluene, heat-integrated direct split and prefractionator configurations are preferred for medium to high concentrations of toluene and low concentrations of ethylbenzene. The HI-LOT-SR provides the lowest MED for all feed compositions with medium to high concentrations of ethylbenzene. It has the lowest MED for 47% of the evaluated feed compositions, allowing for a reduction of more than 20%(30%) in respect to the best alternative configuration for 38(8) of the considered feed composition, with 34.4% saving potential for a feed composition of 15 mol% benzene, 15 mol%, toluene and 70 mol% ethylbenzene.

For the separation of a feed stream of 10 mol/sec and this feed composition, the required MED and the according AOC estimates of all 20 considered process configurations are illustrated in Figure 3. As highlighted, the fully thermally coupled DWC is the next best configuration in terms of MED, apart from the MVR configurations. Yet, it requires 52% more energy, which translates into similar savings in AOC, assuming that both processes are heated with the same high pressure steam.

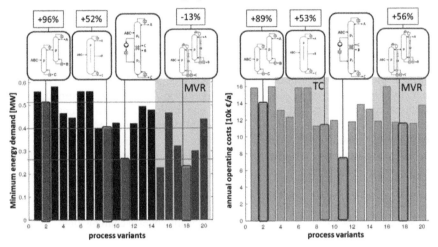

Figure 3: Illustration of single process performance for the selected feed composition in terms of MED (left) and estimated AOC (right)

5.2. Economic optimization

For further comparison the HI-LOT-SR configuration and the fully thermally coupled DWC are evaluated on the basis of an economically optimized design, making use of the aforementioned superstructure optimization approach (Waltermann and Skiborowski, 2019, 2017). The results are illustrated in Figure 4, considering a depreciation period of 5 years, an interest rate of 6% and an annual operating time of 8000h.

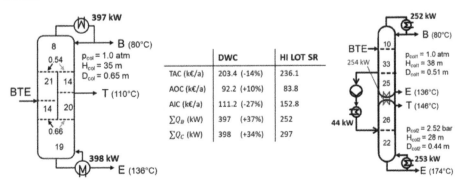

	DWC	HI LOT SR
TAC (k€/a)	203.4 (-14%)	236.1
AOC (k€/a)	92.2 (+10%)	83.8
AIC (k€/a)	111.2 (-27%)	152.8
$\sum Q_B$ (kW)	397 (+37%)	252
$\sum Q_C$ (kW)	398 (+34%)	297

Figure 4: Illustration of the results of the economic process optimization.

All products are required to be of 99.9 mol% purity. Given these assumptions, the DWC is still the most economic process, with a significantly lower investment. Yet, the rigorous design optimization confirms the potential energy savings determined by means of the shortcut screening, which however do not directly translate to AOC savings, since 20 bar steam is required for the reboiler of the second column in the HI-LOT-SR configuration, while 10 bar steam suffices for the DWC. Although the DWC is deemed economically superior under the current assumptions, the HI-LOT-SR configuration becomes more attractive in case of higher depreciation and utility costs.

6. Conclusions

The combination of thermal coupling and heat integration, enabled by the LOT modification, provides a promising option for further improvement of the energy efficiency of distillation processes. The comparative evaluation of multiple energy integrated process configurations highlights the significant improvement potential offered by the considered HI-LOT-SR configuration. The outlined combination of a shortcut-based screening and a subsequent economic optimization enables a time-efficient and case-specific evaluation of possible applications as well as a detailed economic comparison of the most promising options. As illustrated in the current case study such evaluation is of significant importance in order to determine the most effective process configuration for a specific application and economic scenario.

References

R. Agrawal, R., 2000a. Multieffect distillation for thermally coupled configurations. AIChE J 46 (11), 2211–2224.

R. Agrawal, 2000b. Thermally coupled distillation with reduced number of intercolumn vapor transfers. AIChE J 46 (11), 2198–2210.

J. Bausa, R.V. Watzdorf, W. Marquardt, 1998. Shortcut methods for nonideal multicomponent distillation: 1. Simple columns. AIChE Journal 44 (10), 2181–2198.

A.K. Jana, 2019. Performance analysis of a heat integrated column with heat pumping. Separation and Purification Technology 209, 18–25.

B. Kiran, A.K. Jana, 2016. Thermal integration of vapor recompression in a heat-integrated distillation: Impact of multiple intermediate reboilers. Chem. Eng. Res. Des. 114, 171–179.

A.A. Kiss, S.J. Flores Landaeta, C.A. Infante Ferreira, 2012. Towards energy efficient distillation technologies – Making the right choice. Energy 47 (1), 531–542.

G. Madenoor Ramapriya, M. Tawarmalani, R. Agrawal, 2014. Thermal coupling links to liquid-only transfer streams: A path for new dividing wall columns. AIChE J 60 (8), 2949–2961.

I. Patraşcu, C.S. Bîldea, A.A. Kiss, 2018. Heat pump assisted azeotropic DWC for enhanced biobutanol separation, in: Friedl, A., Klemeš, J.J., Radl, S., Varbanov, P.S., Wallek, T. (Eds.), 28th European Symposium on Computer Aided Process Engineering, vol. 43. Elsevier, Amsterdam, pp. 791–796.

M. Skiborowski, 2018. Fast screening of energy and cost efficient intensified distillation processes. Chemical Engineering Transactions 69, 199–204.

D. Staak, T. Grützner, B. Schwegler, D. Roederer, 2014. Dividing wall column for industrial multi purpose use. Chemical Engineering and Processing: Process Intensification 75, 48–57.

T. Waltermann, S. Sibbing, M. Skiborowski, 2019. Optimization-based design of dividing wall columns with extended and multiple dividing walls for three- and four-product separations. Chem. Eng. Process. 146, 107688.

T. Waltermann, M. Skiborowski, 2017. Conceptual Design of Highly Integrated Processes - Optimization of Dividing Wall Columns. Chemie Ingenieur Technik 89 (5), 562–581.

T. Waltermann, M. Skiborowski, 2019. Efficient optimization-based design of energy-integrated distillation processes. Comp. Chem. Eng. 129, 106520.

Sauro Pierucci, Flavio Manenti, Giulia Bozzano, Davide Manca (Eds.)
Proceedings of the 30th European Symposium on Computer Aided Process Engineering
(ESCAPE30), May 24-27, 2020, Milano, Italy. © 2020 Elsevier B.V. All rights reserved.
http://dx.doi.org/10.1016/B978-0-12-823377-1.50167-1

Optimization-Based Design of Rotating Packed Beds with Zickzack Packings

Kai Fabian Kruber, Hina Qammar, Mirko Skiborowski[*]

TU Dortmund University, Department of Biochemical and Chemical Engineering, Laboratory of Fluid Separations, Emil-Figge-Straße 70, 44227 Dortmund, Germany
mirko.skiborowski@tu-dortmund.de

Abstract

Due to the fast development of the market in the chemical industry, more flexible and efficient equipment is obligatory. High-gravity contactors in form of Rotating Packed Beds (RPBs) have the potential to meet these needs since they offer an enhanced mixing by imposing centrifugal forces resulting in an intensified mass and energy transport. With the rotational speed as an additional degree of freedom, RPBs offer faster start-up times and an enlarged operating window. Despite the increasing scientific work in the areas of experimental investigations and modeling, industrial applications are still limited due to a lack of reliable methods for scale-up and design. In respect to the latter, this work presents a nested superstructure approach for the optimization-based design of RPBs with zickzack packings that is further demonstrated for the dehydration of methanol.

Keywords: optimization, process intensification, rotating packed bed, zickzack packing

1. Introduction

During the last decades, the chemical industry started to face a transition to more flexible production plants motivated by a constant change in feedstock towards sustainable resources, as well as a more fluctuating market caused by globalization and steady cultural development. In the same period, high-gravity contactors, like Rotating Packed Beds (RPBs), have gained increasing attention to meet these challenges via process intensification (Neumann et al., 2018). RPBs enable intense mixing, as well as heat and mass transfer intensification between the contacted phases through the application of centrifugal forces, several times larger than earth's gravity. Besides shorter residence time and reduced equipment size, RPBs have considerably shorter start-up times compared to gravity-based static contactors. The rotational speed in an RPB offers an additional degree of freedom that enlarges the operating window and aids flexibility during operation.

While substantial research on RPBs is conducted with particular emphasis on feasibility studies, general process development and operation in absorption, stripping, and distillation, with a steadily increasing number of publications, most studies focus on experimental evaluation (Cortes Garcia et al., 2017) Only a few articles address general design guidelines (Agarwal et al., 2010; Sudhoff et al., 2015), while so far, only a single optimization-based design approach for RPBs was introduced by Qian et al. (2017). The presented method focused on the design of a single-stage rotor equipped with a wire-mesh packing for H2S-removal by absorption. However, especially for complex separation problems, the necessary rotor sizes may result in impractical designs and high uncertainty related to the varying loadings along the radial distance in the annular-shaped packing.

Especially for distillation, an alternative rotor design termed Rotating Zigzag Bed (RZB) has been promoted by Wang et al. (2008), which contrary to the single block packing, implements a tray-like structure of alternating baffles mounted on a rotating and a stationary disc. For the RZB, several hundred industrial applications for distillation have been reported primarily in Asia (Xu et al., 2012). The possibility of adjusting the distance between the baffles as well as the baffle size allows for the establishment of more uniform hydrodynamic conditions. However, the alternation of static and rotating baffles results in an increased pressure drop and power consumption. To overcome the latter limitations, Qammar et al. (2019) have recently introduced a single block Zickzack (ZZ) packing, which employs the same tray-like structure as in an RZB but can be implemented in a single-block RPB (see Figure 1), allowing for a reduced pressure drop and approximately constant F-Factors along the radial length. It was shown that the pressure drop for a 3D-printed ZZ packing was reduced by ten times compared to the equivalent RZB setup, also resulting in a considerable decrease in the electrical power consumption.

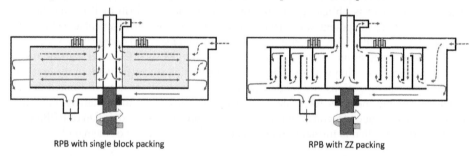

RPB with single block packing   RPB with ZZ packing

Figure 1: Schematic depiction of an RPB with a single block packing and an RPB with a ZZ packing including vapor (dashed lines) and liquid (solid lines) flows

Unlike the superstructure model of Qian et al. (2017), which evaluates the performance of a single stage RPB based on an HTU-NTU approach without further discretization along the radial length, the current work introduces an optimization-based approach for the conceptual design of a multi-stage RPB with ZZ packing, building on an efficiency-based equilibrium stage approach to represent the tray-like contacting in the ZZ packing. Therefore, a nested superstructure is developed, which enables the sizing of an RPB with a variable number of rotors and a variable diameter of each rotor, based on a rigorous equilibrium-tray model in combination with classical Murphree efficiencies. Additionally, the model is further complemented by general sizing constraints (Agarwal et al., 2010; Sudhoff et al., 2015) as well as an economic model, which allows for the minimization of the total annualized costs (TAC). The developed approach is further demonstrated for the dehydration of methanol.

2. Methodology

The optimization-based design approach for the RPB with ZZ packing builds on four elementary parts. First, a superstructure needs to be defined, which allows for a flexible sizing of the RPB in terms of the number and size of rotors, while the number of iterating baffles in the ZZ packing has to be matched to the number of equilibrium stages via an efficiency model and the specific hydrodynamic. Furthermore, a cost model and a strategy for initialization and optimization need to be specified.

2.1. Superstructure Model

The ZZ structure of the considered packing allows for a modeling approach based on equilibrium trays where two baffles are termed as a baffle pair represented by one equilibrium tray with a certain efficiency. Figure 2 illustrates the respective nested superstructure, showing only a radial intersection through the axisymmetrical RPB. While vapor streams are indicated by dotted lines, liquid streams are depicted by solid lines. There is an outer superstructure representing the number of rotors and an inner superstructure accounting for the number of baffle pairs in each rotor. This leads to the possibility of bypassing single stages in a rotor and bypassing

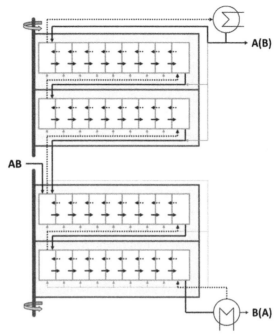

Figure 2: Superstructure representation of a Rotating Packed Bed (RPB) with Zickzack (ZZ) packings

of complete rotors resulting in different rotor diameters and different overall rotor setups, respectively. Analogously to the superstructure of a conventional column (CC) (see e.g. Kraemer et al., 2009), the reflux and the reboil stream can enter each rotor in the rectifying and stripping section, respectively, which is modeled by additional binary decision variables. The size of each rotor is determined by a decision variable for the location of the vapor stream coming from the rotor below. Since the rotor diameter can vary significantly, the current design assumes that the rectifying and stripping sections are implemented in separate housings, which however requires additional motor and shaft work. For the RPB design, the feed is always introduced at the eye of the rotor since the rotor is in constant rotational movement, while in an RZB, the upper plate is stationary, such that an intermediate feed position would be feasible.

2.2. Murphree Efficiency

Referring to Qammar et al. (2019), the efficiency of a baffle pair in a ZZ packing with 25 baffles is assumed to be about 15% - 30%. Therefore, the concept of Murphree stage efficiencies (ME) is utilized (Murphree, 1925), in order to account for the respective mass transfer limitation by a departure of the vapor composition from the equilibrium composition for each baffle pair. As a result, the vapor composition y leaving a baffle pair is determined from the equilibrium composition y^* and the ME η, cf. Equation (1).

$$y_{n,i} = y_{n+1,i} + \eta\left(y_{n,i}^* - y_{n+1,i}\right) \tag{1}$$

The ME is specific for the considered equipment and the investigated mixture, but also the considered rotational speed. For the explicit packing design, investigated system and specified hydrodynamics it is assumed to be constant. Aside from the mass transfer inside the packing, each existing rotor provides additional mass transfer in the casing, for which a ME of 90% is assumed, based on the experimental results by Qammar et al. (2019).

2.3. Sizing and costing

In order to appropriately design the multi-stage RPB, different aspects of the equipment have to be considered apart from the external heat exchangers and heat duties, which are common to the design of a distillation column, i.e., the rotors and casing, as well as the motor and the respective electrical power consumption.

Initially, the rotor geometry is determined based on the inner diameter at the eye of the rotor as well as the desired F-Factor within the rotor, which are required as model inputs. Based on the F-Factor and approximated vapor flowrates, the spacing between the baffles and the height of the rotor are calculated. The outer radius of the rotor is determined by the sum of the baffle radii depending on the superstructure decision variables. A correlation between the rotor and casing heights and diameters links the two geometries. With these geometric constraints, the cost for the RPB body is calculated based on an adjusted form of the cost correlations for a pressure vessel according to Biegler et al. (1997). The rotor costs are currently based on lab-scale equipment due to a lack of reliable data for industrial-scale applications. The costs for the motor and the drive are calculated by correlations from Woods (2007), as suggested by Sudhoff (2015).

2.4. Optimization approach

The initialization and optimization of the superstructure model is conducted similarly to the design of distillation columns, according to the approach presented by Skiborowski et al. (2015). The model was implemented in the optimization software GAMS and solved as a sequence of successively relaxed nonlinear programming problems with additional nonlinear complementary constraints, in order to solve the mixed-integer nonlinear programming problem. The thermodynamic models, including flash and enthalpy computations, are integrated via the use of external functions, as described in Skiborowski et al. (2015).

3. Results

The proposed optimization-based design approach is used to investigate the well-known case study of methanol dehydration with an equimolar feed flow of about 6.7 mol·s^{-1} (600 kg·h^{-1}) introduced as boiling liquid. A purity of 99 mol-% methanol for the distillate and 99 mol-% water for the bottom product are set as constraints. For the calculations, a depreciation time of five years with an interest rate of 6% is assumed. The necessary utilities are cooling water at 288 K (0.05 €·t^{-1}), 3 bar steam with a temperature of about 406 K (12 €·t^{-1}), and electricity (0.076 €·(kWh)$^{-1}$). For the RPB, a ME within the rotor of 30% is assumed, while the casing has an efficiency of 90%. As an initial setup for the RPB, four rotors for the rectifying section, two rotors for the stripping section, a maximum diameter of 1.2 m, and maximum F-factors within the rotors of up to 6 Pa$^{0.5}$ (Wang et al., 2019) are chosen, resulting in 15 baffle pairs per rotor based on approximated vapor flowrates. In contrast, the initial column setup consists of 30 trays per section and an ME of 70% per tray (Bausa and Steimel, 2018).

The optimization results for the RPB with ZZ packing are presented in Figure 3 with an additional comparison of the TAC of both RPB and CC. The structural depiction of the RPB indicates the bypassed regions (grey) and the used rotors and baffle pairs (white). For this case study, the rectifying section consists of three rotors with 15 baffle pairs each, and the stripping section comprises two rotors with 7 baffle pairs. Note that an additional constraint enforces equal sizes for the

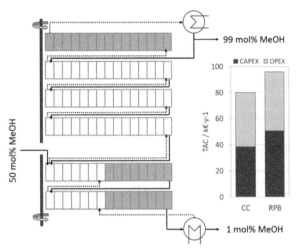

Figure 3: Optimized RPB structure and corresponding TAC compared to the CC

rotors in one section, in order to avoid empty casing volume. Besides the depicted structural decisions, the optimization also considers continuous operational degrees of freedom, i.e. the reboiler and the condenser duty. Based on the current cost correlations, the RPB is evaluated as the more expensive option in terms of operational and capital expenditures (CAPEX, OPEX). The increase in OPEX is about 8.9% compared to the CC related to the additional electricity input for the motor, while the necessary reboiler and condenser duties are comparable. The increase in CAPEX for the RPB compared to the CC is about 31.5% and almost entirely related to the rotors within the RPB. They account for an increase of 45.4% of the CAPEX, while the smaller casing saves about 18.6% of the costs. It should be noted that the cost increase for motor, drive and electricity is further enlarged by the consideration of two separate RPBs for rectifying and stripping section.

Despite the cost deficiency, a significant reduction in the apparatus height and volume can be achieved by the RPB. The height was reduced by approximately 91.6% considering a combined height for both RPBs (rectifying; stripping), while the overall equipment volume of the column shell is reduced by 13.4% through the RPBs.

4. Conclusion

The current work presents for the first time an equilibrium-stage based superstructure optimization approach for the design of RPBs with ZZ packings, which may also be used for the design of an RZB. The approach considers multiple rotors in individual RPBs for rectifying and stripping section. Furthermore, the model was extended by Murphree efficiencies in order to consider the characteristics of RPBs with ZZ packings. Applying a reliable polylithic modeling and solution approach similar to that of classical distillation columns, the approach effectively determines locally optimal solutions to an intricate multi-stage RPB design for the dehydration of methanol. The results indicate a potential for size reductions by means of the RPB, however, the applied cost model for the RPB needs further refinement since it is based on a currently available limited data set for sizing and costing of lab-scale equipment. Therefore, it is suggested that not too much emphasis is placed on the economic comparison. Besides the refinement of the cost model, additional pressure drop correlations, as well as an extended ME model should be considered in future improvements of the model for deriving a more general and reliable model for RPB design. Apart from these modifications, the superstructure model already presents a suitable platform that can further be exploited in the development of RPB-based processes.

Acknowledgment

Dr.-Ing. Mirko Skiborowski gratefully acknowledges financial support from the Max-Buchner Research Foundation.

References

Agarwal, L., Pavani, V., Rao, D. P., Kaistha, N., 2010, Process Intensification in HiGee Absorption and Distillation: Design Procedure and Applications, Ind. Eng. Chem. Res., 49, 20, 10046-10058

Bausa, J., Steimel, J., 2018, Extending Murphree Tray Efficiency from Mass to Heat Transfer in Distillation, Chem. Eng. Trans., 69, 451-456

Biegler, L. T., Grossmann, I. E., Westerberg, A. W., 1997, Systematic methods for chemical process design, Prentice Hall, Old Tappan, New Jersey, United States

Cortes Garcia, G. E., van der Schaaf, J., Kiss., A. A., 2017, A review on process intensification in HiGee distillation, J. Chem. Technol. Biotechnol., 92, 6, 1136-1156

Mondal, A., Paramanik, A., Bhowal, A.,Datta, S., 2012, Distillation studies in rotating packed bed with split packing, Chem. Eng. Res. Des., 90, 4, 453-457

Murphree, E. V., 1925, Rectifying Column Calculations, J. Ind. Eng. Chem., 17, 7, 747-750

Neumann, K., Gładyszewski, K., Groß, K., Qammar, H., Wenzel, D., Górak, A., Skiborowski, M., 2018, A guide on the industrial application of rotating packed beds, Chem. Eng. Res. Des., 134, 443-462

Qammar, H., Gładyszewski, K., Górak, A., Skiborowski, M., 2019, Towards the Development of Advanced Packing Design for Distillation in Rotating Packed Beds, 91, 11, 1663-1673

Qian, Z., Chen, Q., Grossmann, I. E., 2017, Optimal synthesis of rotating packed bed reactor, Comput. Chem. Eng., 105, 152-160

Skiborowski, M., Harwardt, A., Marquardt, W., 2015, Efficient optimization-based design for the separation of heterogeneous azeotropic mixtures, Comput. Chem. Eng., 72, 34-51

Sudhoff, D., Leimbrink, M., Schleinitz, M., Górak, A., Lutze, P., 2015, Modelling, design and flexibility analysis of rotating packed beds for distillation, Chem. Eng. Res. Des., 94, 72-89

Wang, G. Q., Xu, Z. C., Yu, Y. L., Ji, J. B., 2008, Performance of a rotating zigzag bed - A new HIGEE, Chem. Emg. Process, 47, 2131-2139

Wang, G. Q., Zhou, Z. J., Li, Y. M., Ji, J. B., 2019, Qualitative relationships between structure and performance of rotating zigzag bed distillation, Chem. Eng. Process., 135, 141-147

Woods, D. R., 2007, Rules of Thumb in Engineering Practice, Wiley-VCH Verlag, Weinheim, Germany

Xu, Z. C., Ji, J. B., Wang, G., Li, X. H., Li, Y., 2012, Rotating Zigzag Bed Application in Extractive Distillation Process of THF-Methanol-Water System, AIChE Spring Meeting & Global Congress on Process Safety

Sauro Pierucci, Flavio Manenti, Giulia Bozzano, Davide Manca (Eds.)
Proceedings of the 30th European Symposium on Computer Aided Process Engineering
(ESCAPE30), May 24-27, 2020, Milano, Italy. © 2020 Elsevier B.V. All rights reserved.
http://dx.doi.org/10.1016/B978-0-12-823377-1.50168-3

Design Concepts for Pressurized LNG Storage Tanks

Marian Krol

Linde AG, Engineering Division, Dr.-Carl-von-Linde-Straße 6-14, D-82049 Pullach, Germany

Abstract

The containment philosophy has been well defined by European and North American regulations e.g. EN 1473, NFPA 59A for the flat bottom LNG storage tanks. However, such established definition is missing for the pressurized storage tanks. An outlook will be given to the latest development of the prEN 1473 regarding the containment philosophy and the related safety design of the pressurized LNG storage tanks. The definition of the possible tank leakage will be discussed based on fracture mechanics and event probabilities for both atmospheric and pressurized storage tanks.

1. Main Text

The current version of EN 1473 is valid for plants with LNG storage at pressure lower than 0.5 bar(g) and a capacity above 200 t. The plants with storage inventories ranging from 50 t up to 200 t and a pressure higher than 0.5 bar(g) are covered by EN 13645.

Due to the lack of safety concept definitions for pressurized LNG vessels having storage capacities exceeding 200 tons and 0.5 barg and the failed integration of these tanks into EN 13645, it was required to trump up a new guideline for the more and more increasing demand of large pressurized storage capacities over 200 tons.

At the beginning a finding process for the definition of safety concepts and related selection criteria was required.

In the publication "Comparative Risk Assessment for Different LNG-Storage Tank Concepts" (Stefan Rath, Marian Krol, both from Linde AG) presented on the 14th International Symposium on Loss Prevention and Safety Promotion in the Process Industry in Florence 2013 it was proposed to replace the existing containment definition of atmospheric storage tanks in favor of a new definition based on integrity safety levels and to use it for atmospheric as well as for pressurized storage tanks:

"LNG can be stored either in flat bottom storage tanks or pressurized storage tanks such as bullets or spheres. Safety levels of atmospheric storage tanks are classified by codes as "single containment", "double containment" and "full containment". For spherical and bullet tanks an analogical definition by codes is missing and containment philosophies for atmospheric storage cannot be applied to pressurized storage. Therefore, a new definition is proposed to describe the safety levels of pressurized tank types and flat-bottom tank types consistently.

It is supposed to use the definitions single, double and full integrity instead of single, double and full containment in order not to mix up definitions. The integrity level a storage tank has been assigned to give a direct link to the consequences that would have to be taken into account in case the primary container fails totally. The advantage of these new containment definitions is having available a normalized basis for the comparison of different tanks fulfilling similar requirements on safety design."

This publication demonstrates that *"in general the risk to external population is the higher the lower the integrity level of the LNG storage"*.

After many presentations of the new concept authors received both positive and negative feedback, but the idea to classify atmospheric and pressurized tanks in a comparable manner was found mostly interesting.

Unfortunately, many discussions in the TC 282 WG 5 responsible for EN 1473 ("Installation and equipment for liquified natural gas - Design of onshore installations"), the TC 265 WG10 responsible for EN 14620 ("Design and manufacture of site built, vertical, cylindrical, flat-bottomed steel tanks for the storage of refrigerated, liquefied gases with operating temperatures between 0 °C and -165 °C") and the NFPA 59A ("Standard for the Production, Storage, and Handling of Liquified Natural Gas") showed that this integrity level classification of storage tanks was not supported by the majority of specialists involved in the standardization process. However, after a certain time it was astounding to notice a mind change within the TC 282 committee responsible for the EN 1473 Standard towards the preference of the well-known "containment" term instead of "integrity level". Now the proposed idea was suddenly accepted having changed the wording.

A further development of the idea took place after studying the fracture mechanics behaviour of atmospheric and pressurized cryogenic vessels and comparing probabilities of leak scenarios for both storage types. Several internationally recognized publications in equipment probability approaches area were compared.

The "Handbook of Scenarios for Assessing Major Chemical Accident Risks" issued in 2017 by Joint Research Centre (JRC) gives recommendations on possible major accident scenarios in the form of scenario trees. It is expected that the scenario recommendations will be useful to EU Member States and third countries to assess the Land-Use Planning cases, in complying with the requirements of the Seveso Directive. Unfortunately, there is no scenario for LNG pressurized tank, but due to the circumstance that the K_{IC} values for materials used in LPG service are generally comparable to those of the materials for LNG service the following conclusion may follow: "the leak in the tank shall be considered for both atmospheric and pressurized vessels".
The "Handbook" specifies for pressure vessel an annual probability of catastrophic failure as instantaneous release with 5E-7and a 10 mm diameter hole with 1E-5.

The "Failure Rate and Event Data for use within Risk Assessments" published on 02.02.2019 by HSE (Health and Safety Executive) presents the annular failure rates for LNG atmospheric and LPG pressurized vessel. According to this publication a catastrophic annular failure probability for the atmospheric LNG vessel is assumed to be

5E-8and a minor failure 3E-6. But this source inappropriately defines the minor leak as a 300 mm diameter hole for tanks bigger 12,000 m³. This is not probable since a crack having this rate would be much bigger than the critical one and at the end a zipping of tank would happen. The 13 mm diameter hole for pressurized LPG vessel shows the probability of 1E-5 what confirms previous JRC data.

The "Guidelines for quantitative risk assessment" 'Purple book' CPR 18E (2005 edition) Publication Series on Dangerous Substances (PGS 3) confirms the above rates for pressure vessel, i.e. annual probability of catastrophic failure as instantaneous release with 5E-7 and a 10 mm diameter hole with 1E-5. In contrast atmospheric cryogenic tanks possess the following annular failure probability of instantaneous release to the atmosphere:

- single containment: 5E-6
- double containment: 1.25E-8
- full containment 1E-8

The 10 mm diameter hole with release to the atmosphere for a single containment tank and release to the secondary container for a double containment has a probability of 1E-4.

It may be understood this value is also valid for full containment tank for the release

to the outer container due to the materials and equivalent stress level for double and full containment tank systems.

The "Risk Assessment Data Directory" Report No. 434 – 3 of March 2010 issued by International Association of Oil & Gas Producers OGP (Storage incident frequencies) describes the annular probability of primary containment catastrophic rapture for cryogenic atmospheric tanks with:

- 2.3E-6 – single containment
- 1E-7 – double and full containment.

The general annual leak frequency without definition for all containments tanks is 1E-5. Pressurized vessels with the hole of 10 mm diameter have an annular leak frequency of 3,5E-5 and for the catastrophic rupture the failure rate is 4.7E-5 per year.

The last 2019 edition of NFPA 59A "Standard for the Production, Storage, and Handling of Liquified Natural Gas (LNG)" in the chapter Release Probabilities and Conditional Probabilities also describes failure rates for different equipment. The annular probability of catastrophic rupture for cryogenic atmospheric tanks is:

- 1E-6 – single containment,
- 1.25E-8 – double containment, and
- 1E-8 - full containment.

The annual leak frequency for cryogenic tanks is not defined. Pressurized vessels leaking from a hole with 10 mm diameter have an annular probability of 1E-5 and for a catastrophic rupture it is 5E-7.

In contrast to the probabilistic approach, the German's deterministic approach to safety design of chemical plants discusses a few selected sources especially for possible leak area of pressurized vessels as basis for the consequence study. The mentioned extent of leak ranges from 20 mm² up to 100 mm², corresponding to an approximate hole diameter of 10 mm (refer to „Auswirkungsbetrachtungen bei störungsbedingten Stoff- und Energiefreisetzungen in der Prozessindustrie", Januar 2017).

From a fracture mechanics point of view it reveals that some possible leak scenarios require refinement. After analyzing the magnitudes of critical cracks, it can be said that the design requirement for atmospheric storage tanks in particular the dimensioning of Safety Valves should be done for a 20 mm diameter hole in the lower part of shell as specified in EN14620. This value corresponds very well to the fracture toughness properties of low alloyed Ni steels and the applied stress levels in the above-mentioned standard.

In the same it can be argued on the pressure vessels and the suggested hole diameter of 10 mm as leak source.

After a careful check of above publications on determining accident probabilities it came out that the likelihood of such an event like loss of containments is indeed comparable for atmospheric and pressurized tanks. The general tendency may be understood as the result of defining the possible leak for an atmospheric tank with diameter of 20 mm in the shell and for a pressurized tank with hole of 10 mm diameter.

This awareness has been taken as the basis for the new definition of "containment" in the prEN 1473 currently under revision. Both types of LNG storage, i.e. atmospheric and pressurized tanks, now possess a common definition as shown in the following excerpts from prEN 1473:

7.8.4.2 Single Containment
A single containment storage system is designed not to preclude the possibility of product spillage within the defined impounding area (see 7.2.2) in case of leakage.

7.8.4.3 Double Containment
A double containment storage system is designed to preclude the possibility of product spillage over the surrounding area in case of leakage from its primary container. Thus, a liquid tight secondary liquid container which is an integral part of the storage system is required to retain the full liquid inventory of LNG if drained from the primary container; while not intended to prevent the escape of product vapours resulting from that internal upset.

7.8.4.4 Full Containment
A full containment tank system is designed to both containing the full liquid inventory and controlling the vapour release in the event of product leakage from the primary liquid container. Transient product losses in case of product leakage from the primary liquid container due to outer container permeability are acceptable and subject to consistent limitations after consequence analysis.

The difference between the two storage concepts then turns out in the performance behavior, which is described in the following excerpts of prEN 1473:

7.8.5 Performance of atmospheric storage concepts
7.8.5.1 Gradual loss of containment
Leakage rates of equipment shall be established by the risk assessment based on the storage concept. For storage tanks, as a minimum, the scenario of a gradual loss of containment shall be considered:

- leak of 20 mm diameter as defined by EN 14620 for steel-steel or steel-concrete flat-bottom tank of atmospheric storage concepts;

7.8.5.4 Impounding
In case of single containment flat-bottom tanks, the impounding basin is required with a capacity of at least 110% of the largest tank.

7.8.6 Performance of pressurized storage concepts
7.8.6.1 Gradual loss of containment
Leakage rates of equipment shall be established by the risk assessment based on the storage concept. For pressure vessels, as a minimum, the scenario of a gradual loss of containment shall be considered:
- leak of a 8 mm diameter hole, unless demonstrated otherwise e.g. by the risk assessment. A broken instrument connection is considered a credible scenario.

7.8.6.4 Impounding
In case of single containment design, the spill from a liquid leak from the tank shall be handled by having a paved area with slope toward a safe location to avoid flammable liquid accumulation below the tank. The remote impounding basin shall have a capacity of minimum 20 % of the largest storage tank capacity and in addition shall observe requirements from Table 1 (below).

Table 1 — Pool fire sizing as function of tank types

	Atmospheric storage		Pressurized storage
Type of tank containment [a]	Metallic or with metallic roof only	Prestressed concrete with concrete roof	
Single containment	Impounding area	n/a	Remote impounding [b, c]
Double containment	Secondary container	n/a	Secondary container
Full containment	Secondary container	No pool fire	Remote impounding [c]

Remarks:
[a] For definition, see 7.8.4.
[b] For definition, see 7.8.6.4
[c] Sized for full line break prior to closure of the internal or integrated shut-off valve.

Considering that for pressurized LNG tanks the discharge connection is arranged below the liquid level in contrast to atmospheric tanks, the pipe break must be considered in the impounding basin design. The API Standard 625 ("Tank Systems for Refrigerated Liquified Gas Storage") serves as a good solution for this accidental scenario. The prEN 1473 asks for an additional requirement to size the remote impounding pit for a full line break before the internal or integrated shut-off valve will be closed.

In the following figure, examples of pressurized single and full containment vessels above 200 tons are presented. Note that the double containment requirements are still under discussion and the finalized draft of the new EN 1473 is planned to be published before end of 2020.

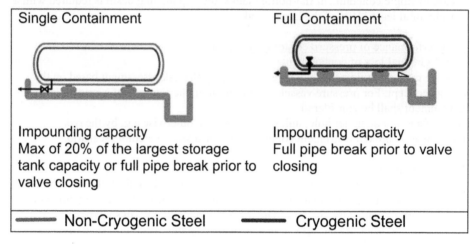

Figure 1 - Examples for pressurized vessels above 200 tons

References

Stefan Rath, Marian Krol, Comparative Risk Assessment for Different LNG-Storage Tank Concepts, CHEMICAL ENGINEERING TRANSACTIONS, VOL. 31, 2013

EN 1473:2016

prEN 1473:2019

NFPA 59A:2019

Handbook of Scenarios for Assessing Major Chemical Accident Risks, 2017, Joint Research Centre

Failure Rate and Event Data for use within Risk Assessments, 2019, HSE

Guidelines for quantitative risk assessment 'Purple book', CPR 18E, 2005

Risk Assessment Data Directory" Report No. 434 – 3 of March 2010, OGP

Auswirkungsbetrachtungen bei störungsbedingten Stoff- und Energiefreisetzungen in der Prozessindustrie", Januar 2017, VDI DECHEMA

Sauro Pierucci, Flavio Manenti, Giulia Bozzano, Davide Manca (Eds.)
Proceedings of the 30th European Symposium on Computer Aided Process Engineering
(ESCAPE30), May 24-27, 2020, Milano, Italy. © 2020 Elsevier B.V. All rights reserved.
http://dx.doi.org/10.1016/B978-0-12-823377-1.50169-5

Automatic Synthesis of Distillation Processes for the Separation of Heterogeneous Azeotropic Multi-component Mixtures

Thulasi Sasi, Kai Kruber, Moreno Ascani, Mirko Skiborowski*

TU Dortmund University, Department of Chemical and Biochemical Engineering, Laboratory for Fluid Separations, Emil-Figge-Strasse 70, Dortmund 44227, Germany

Abstract

The separation of azeotropic mixtures is a complex task that is frequently addressed by means of graphical analysis of residue curve maps and trial-and-error flowsheet simulations. While miscibility gaps in heterogeneous mixtures result in considerably more complex phase behaviour, the possible exploitation of a combination of decantation and distillation bears the potential for efficient separation processes. In order to enable an automatic generation of alternative separation sequences with closed recycle loops the current article presents an extension of a previously developed algorithmic framework for process synthesis of homogeneous distillation processes. This extension includes the computation and characterization of heterogeneous azeotropes and the analysis of the topology of the system, as well as an extended split feasibility algorithm, which also accounts for decantation at different temperature levels. The approach is fully algorithmic and includes a shortcut-based computation of the energy demand of the generated flowsheet variants.

Keywords: conceptual design, flowsheet optimization, heteroazeotropic distillation.

1. Introduction

Distillation is one of the most applied fluid separation process and contributes significantly to the energy requirement of the chemical industry. While energy efficiency and corresponding operational cost of separation processes are largely fixed during conceptual design, the prevailing method for process synthesis is based on expert knowledge in combination with graphical analysis and flowsheet simulation. In order to accelerate and simplify process synthesis a systematic and at best automatic identification of separation processes is required, which so far is not offered by any commercial flowsheet simulation software.

However, quite a few studies have addressed this synthesis problem in the past. Yet, the graphical analysis is still most popular, while being restricted to ternary mixtures. The first systematic methods for separation process synthesis were so-called expert systems, such as the blackboard system SPLIT (Wahnschafft et al. 1991). While the separation of multi-component mixtures was addressed, flowsheet generation was performed based on the evaluation of binary sub-systems, confirming split feasibility only in subsequent rigorous flowsheet simulation. Unlike SPLIT, the knowledge-based expert system PROSYN® (Schembecker and Simmrock 1997) is still available. The combined heuristic-numeric approach implements a concept of collaborating distributed expert systems that combines a variety of heuristic rules and physical property computations, including multi-component azeotrope computations (Schembecker and Simmrock

1995), with artificial intelligence. An algorithmic approach towards process synthesis based on the analysis of the mixture topology was first proposed at the end of the 1990s by Poellmann and Blass (1994) and Rooks et al. (1998), who proposed a matrix method to determine the topological distillation regions. This concept was further exploited by Tao et al. (2003) and Wasylkiewicz and Castillo (2001). Wasylkiewicz et al. (2003, 2006) implemented the matrix method in the software DISTIL, evaluating possible recycle structures based on the concept of preferred distillation regions, while checking the feasibility of heteroazeotropic distillation based on the boundary value method (BVM) (Pham et al. 1989). The BVM was also used by Prayoonyong and Jobson (2011) for more complex configurations of heterogeneous azeotropic distillation, while being limited to ternary mixtures due to the graphical analysis. Tao et al. (2003) developed a direct extension of the matrix method for the analysis of recycle structures, based on a different form of reachability matrix and a set of reachability rules, considering decantation alongside distillation. Yet, the approach focusses primarily on feasibility of distillation at total reflux, evaluating only residue curves.

Consequently, despite the reported efforts towards the synthesis of process alternatives for heteroazeotropic mixtures, there is still a need for an efficient algorithmic approach, which can be applied to arbitrary azeotropic multi-component mixtures and which considers split feasibility in a more general form. This paper combines proven methods with novel features to algorithmically generate process variants based on rigorous thermodynamic models, and include feasibility of distillation at total reflux and reversible distillation.

2. Methodology

The present work is an extension to the synthesis method for homogeneous azeotropic mixtures (Sasi et al. 2019). It builds solely on mathematical models for thermodynamic equilibrium computations, on which basis first a topological analysis of the mixture is performed and furthermore algorithms for split feasibility are exploited to generate and store flowsheet variants in terms of a tree structure.

2.1. Topological analysis

The topological structure of the mixture is defined based on the set of singular points and their allocation to distillation regions (DR) and compartments, which also results in the definition of distillation boundaries (DB). While the matrix method described by Rooks et al. (1998) can directly be applied to heterogeneous mixtures, it is important to first determine all relevant azeotropes and classify them in respect to their stability. The latter is accomplished by means of a dedicated homotopy continuation approach (Skiborowski et al. (2016)), which includes an efficient phase stability test (Bausa and Marquardt, 2000).

2.2. Split feasibility of separation

In order to generate possible flowsheets possible splits are evaluated algorithmically for a separation by either distillation or decantation. Split feasibility for distillation is determined based on the information of topological DR, residue curve and pinch line computations are used to determine the maximum recovery of potential sharp splits (Sasi et al. 2019). Thereby an explicit representation of DB is avoided, while split feasibility at total reflux and reversible distillation are considered. Further application of the rectification body method (RBM), checks for an intersection of rectifying and stripping profiles, while additionally providing an estimate of the minimum energy demand (MED) (Bausa et al. 1998). Feasible decanter splits are evaluated based on the phase stability test of Bausa and Marquardt (2000), while temperature sensitivity of the miscibility gap is evaluated as well. Potential cooling considers available utilities, while subsequent heating to saturation temperatures for downstream columns is added to the MED computation.

2.3. Generation of tree structure

Starting from the initial feed composition, potential splits are evaluated by the aforementioned split feasibility criteria. Each split is introduced as new branch in a tree structure, for which the two product compositions result in subsequent nodes of the branch. Each node is considered as new feed stream for split generation, unless the products are either the desired products or pure component, or no further separation is feasible. During the generation of the tree structure additional nodes are introduced by consideration of mixing with potential recycle streams. These are either SP, in case of homogeneous azeotropes or pure components, or the equilibrium liquid phases of heterogeneous azeotropes. Unlike the recycle of homogeneous SP, the recycle ratio for equilibrium liquid phases is determined geometrically. This mixing point is the point of intersection of the line joining the desired product and the heteroazeotrope, and the line joining the feed and the recycled liquid phase. Consequently, the recycle of a liquid phase

results in a configuration of a distillation column followed by a decanter, which indicates the possibility of replacing it with a heteroazeotropic distillation column. The possible substitution is illustrated in Figure 1. While the integrated heteroazeotropic distillation column can offer a lower MED,

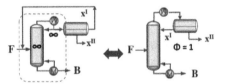

Figure 1: Standalone and integrated decanter

the current synthesis approach is for now restricted to the identification of the variant with standalone decanter, for which the distillation column and decanter are evaluated individually in terms of split feasibility and MED. After the generation of the tree structure is finished, a post-processing step is performed, which evaluates for each branch, if suitable destinations for end streams that do not correspond to desired products can be determined using the recycle reachability method developed by Tao et al. (2003). This involves the evaluation of adjacency and reachability matrices, similar for each stream in a flowsheet instead of SP. Using these matrices, it is determined if there is an exit point for each component, such that the mass balance is not violated while recycling streams within a flowsheet. Since this rule cannot be applied to processes involving entrainers that are regenerated within the flowsheet, the initial feed is considered as the recycle destination for such cases. Figure 2 illustrates the tree structure and an example process for the separation of a mixture of ethanol and water using toluene as an entrainer that introduces heterogeneity in the system at saturation conditions. Starting from a binary ethanol-water feed, two possible splits using distillation are determined. Split 1 recovers water, while split 2 recovers ethanol by initial mixing of the feed with the organic phase (OP) of the ternary heteroazeotrope. The necessary recycle ratio of the OP is determined geometrically such that the separation of ethanol and the ternary heteroazeotrope is established. The process obtained from the shaded branch of the tree successfully separates ethanol and water, but also generates a potential waste stream corresponding to the aqueous phase (AP). To maximize the recovery of the products, AP is recycled to the initial feed and the flowsheet is converged iteratively during post-processing. Similarly, another process alternative can be obtained from the second branch (Split 2) by recovering water from AP, and subsequently recycling the product on the DB to the initial feed.

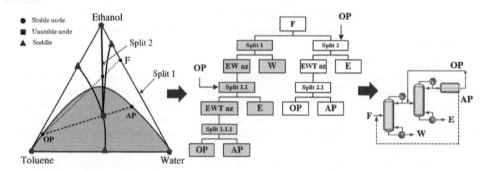

Figure 2: Illustration of tree structure with addition of decanter and a resulting process variant

3. Case Studies

The application of the approach is further illustrated for two case studies. The first case considers the separation of a ternary mixture of tetrahydrofuran (THF), methanol and hexane. Figure 3 illustrates the topology of the mixture, which is completely homogeneous at saturation conditions at atmospheric pressure, showing 3 binary azeotropes and 3 DR. However, at sub-cooled condition a miscibility gap originates from the binary

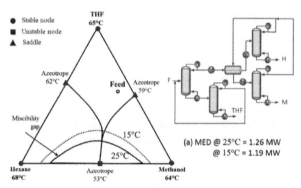

Figure 3: Topology and process alternative for the separation of the THF, methanol, hexane mixture at 1 bar.

methanol-hexane mixture, which is also indicated for 25°C and 15°C in Figure 3. For a feed consisting of 55 mol% THF, 35 mol% methanol and 10 mol% hexane, the current methodology generates two feasible flowsheets. The one with lower MED, shown in Figure 3, first performs a direct split of the feed for the separation of THF, followed by a decanter and the recovery of methanol and hexane from the subsequent liquid phases. The THF-methanol azeotrope is recycled to the initial feed based on the recycle reachability rule, and the methanol-hexane azeotrope is recycled to the decanter in the post-processing step. By reducing the decanter temperature from 25 to 15°C, the MED reduces by 5.6% due to the reduced recycle stream of the hexane-methanol azeotrope. Anyhow, the operating temperature of the decanter should be further optimized in an economic optimization of the feasible flowsheet, which is the main result of the presented synthesis approach.

The developed methodology is further applied to the separation of a quaternary mixture of methanol, ethanol, butanol and water, which was also investigated by Wahnschafft et al. (1992). Butanol and water are partly immiscible at saturation conditions, as illustrated in Figure 4.

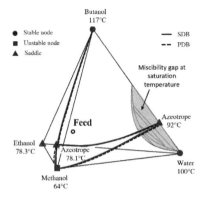

Figure 4: Topology of the methanol, ethanol, butanol, water mixture at 1 bar.

While the illustrated miscibility gap represents saturation conditions at 1 bar pressure, it is hardly affected by temperature modifications, according to the employed NRTL model. The mixture exhibits one homogeneous and one heterogeneous binary azeotropes that result in the separation of the composition space into two DR. Considering the same feed composition as investigated by Wahnschafft et al. (1992), i.e. 60 mol% methanol, 20 mol% ethanol and 10 mol% each of water and butanol, a total of 11 flowsheet variants are generated. The five variants that are able to retrieve all four pure components are further illustrated in Figure 5 together with their computed MED. The first three flowsheet variants involve the separation of the feed into two binary mixtures in the first column, followed by the separation of pure methanol and ethanol in a subsequent column. While flowsheet variant (c) resembles the only flowsheet proposed by Wahnschafft et al. (1992), the MED estimates of the generated flowsheets (a) and (b) are presumably offering a little over 10% energy savings with the same number of unit operations. Unlike variants (a)-(c), variants (d) and (e) start with the indirect split, where pure benzene is recovered first. In variant (d) the binary homogeneous ethanol-water azeotrope is recycled to the initial feed based on the recycle reachability algorithm during post-processing step, while pure methanol is recycled to the ternary feed of the second column to enable the complete recovery of water by exploiting the feasibility at finite reflux, since the PDB intersects the ethanol-methanol binary edge. While both variants operate without a decanter, they are evaluated with considerably larger MED.

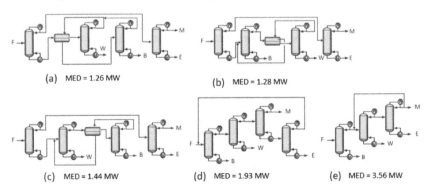

(a) MED = 1.26 MW   (b) MED = 1.28 MW

(c) MED = 1.44 MW   (d) MED = 1.93 MW   (e) MED = 3.56 MW

Figure 5: Process variants generated for the separation of the methanol, ethanol, butanol and water mixture.

4. Conclusion and outlook

The current article extends the previously developed algorithmic approach for the synthesis of distillation processes to the separation of heterogeneous azeotropic mixtures. The method is not restricted with respect to the number of components and incorporates general feasibility tests, which examine both limiting operational modes for distillation, total reflux as well as reversible distillation and decantation.

Although the current implementation only identifies combinations of simple columns and decanters, integrated heteroazeotropic distillation columns can be considered in a subsequent design study of promising flowsheet variants. Besides the connection to such a design optimization, future work will focus on the extension of the method towards alternative and more complex recycle options, pressure variations, as well as other process options, like extractive distillation.

References

J. Bausa, R. Watzdorf, W. Marquardt (1998): Shortcut methods for nonideal multicomponent distillation: I. Simple columns. In AIChE J 44 (10), pp. 2181–2198.

J. Bausa, W. Marquardt (2000): Quick and reliable phase stability test in VLLE flash calculations by homotopy continuation. In Computers & chemical engineering 24 (11), pp. 2447–2456.

P. Poellmann, E. Blass (1994): Best products of homogeneous azeotropic distillations. In Gas Sep. Purif. 8 (4), pp. 194–228.

P. Prayoonyong, M. Jobson (2011): Flowsheet synthesis and complex distillation column design for separating ternary heterogeneous azeotropic mixtures. In Chemical Engineering Research and Design 89 (8), pp. 1362–1376.

R. Rooks, V. Julka, M.F. Doherty, M.F. Malone (1998): Structure of Distillation Regions for Multicomponent Azeotropic Mixtures. In AIChE J 44 (6), pp. 1382–1391.

T. Sasi, J. Wesselmann, H. Kuhlmann, M. Skiborowski (2019): Automatic synthesis of distillation processes for the separation of azeotropic multi-component systems. In : Computer Aided Chemical Engineering, vol. 46: Elsevier, pp. 49–54.

G. Schembecker, K.H. Simmrock (1995): Azeopert-a heuristic-numeric system for the prediction of azeotrope formation. In Computers & chemical engineering 19, pp. 253–258.

G. Schembecker, K.H. Simmrock (1997): Heuristic-numeric design of separation processes for azeotropic mixtures. In Computers & chemical engineering 21, S231- S236.

M. Skiborowski, J. Bausa, W. Marquardt (2016): A Unifying Approach for the Calculation of Azeotropes and Pinch Points in Homogeneous and Heterogeneous Mixtures. In Industrial & Engineering Chemistry Research 55 (24), pp. 6815–6834.

L. Tao, M.F. Malone, M.F. Doherty (2003): Synthesis of Azeotropic Distillation Systems with Recycles. In Industrial & Engineering Chemistry Research 42 (8), pp. 1783–1794.

O.M. Wahnschafft, J.P. Le Rudulier, P. Blania, A.W. Westerberg (1992): Split: II. Automated synthesis of hybrid liquid separation systems. In Computers & chemical engineering 16, S305- S312.

O.M. Wahnschafft, T.P. Jurain, A.W. Westerberg (1991): SPLIT: a separation process designer. In Computers & chemical engineering 15 (8), pp. 565–581.

S.K. Wasylkiewicz (2006): Synthesis of separation systems for azeotropic mixtures: Preferred distillation region. In Comput.-Aided Chem. Eng. 21, pp. 1033–1038.

S.K. Wasylkiewicz, F.J.L. Castillo (2001): Automatic synthesis of complex separation sequences with recycles. In : Computer Aided Chemical Engineering, vol. 9: Elsevier, pp. 591–596.

S.K. Wasylkiewicz, L.C. Kobylka, F.J.L.Castillo (2003): Synthesis and design of heterogeneous separation systems with recycle streams. In Chemical Engineering Journal 92 (1-3), pp. 201–208.

Sauro Pierucci, Flavio Manenti, Giulia Bozzano, Davide Manca (Eds.)
Proceedings of the 30th European Symposium on Computer Aided Process Engineering
(ESCAPE30), May 24-27, 2020, Milano, Italy. © 2020 Elsevier B.V. All rights reserved.
http://dx.doi.org/10.1016/B978-0-12-823377-1.50170-1

Technical and Economic Feasibility of Direct Methane Conversion for Hydrocarbon Production: Process Design and Techno-economic Analysis

Thai Ngan Do[a], Yong Tae Kim[b], Jiyong Kim[a]

[a]*Department of Energy and Chemical Engineering, Incheon National University, 119 Academy-ro, Yeonsu-gu, Incheon, 22012, South Korea*
[b]*C1 gas Separation and Conversion Research Center, Carbon Resources Institute, Korea Research Institute of Chemical Technology, Daejeon 34114, Republic of Korea*
jykim77@inu.ac.kr

Abstract

In this study, we have developed a modelling and evaluation framework of a direct conversion of methane (CH_4) to value-added chemicals including light hydrocarbons, FT fuels, and aromatics. As novel catalysts for a direct CH_4 conversion are targeted to adapt to industrial applications, it is important to access the technological and economic feasibility. Various techniques in process systems engineering play a crucial role here in the application of the current or extended methodologies to support R&D targets and planning: identification of major cost- and energy-drivers, preliminary process scheme and debottleneck strategies. In this framework, we developed a conceptual conversion process, which consists of a reaction section of directly converting CH_4 into hydrocarbons, and a separation section of sequentially integrated technologies for recycles of CH_4, purifying ethylene, other C_{2+} hydrocarbon, and aromatics production. Then, the technical and economic feasibility of the process was evaluated, included a sensitivity analysis for identifying the bottleneck factors. Outstandingly, the direct methane conversion process achieves high energy efficiency (58.9 %), consumed a large amount of utility but still overcomes the intensive-energy penalty as in other petrochemical processes that are primarily due to the contribution of hydrogen as a by-product. The ethylene as one of main products was produced at 0.97 $/kg that can be reduced and competitive to the market in promised scenarios. Otherwise, the study provides the perspective on improving catalyst performance (e.g. higher yield of ethylene), which is critical to achieve high technical performance and economic benefits.

Keywords: process design, direct methane conversion, ethylene production, techno-economic evaluation.

1. Introduction

Ethylene is one of the important building blocks in petrochemical industries for a variety of derivatives such as polyethylene, ethylene glycol, ethyl-benzene, and styrene. As predicted, the global market demand has significantly grown, increases approximately 3.6 %/y to reach 184 MMt by 2022 (Rentech, 2018). To meet the growing demand of ethylene, ethylene production facilities are being on the increase, and alternative ethylene production routes has been developed. Typically, ethylene is produced by steam cracking of gas hydrocarbon (e.g. ethane, propane, butane) and liquid hydrocarbon (e.g. naphtha, gasoil, condensate), which is an intensive-energy penalty route (Amghizar et al., 2017). Many alternative routes are considered such as methanol-to-olefin or coal-to-olefin.

Interestingly, the direct methane conversion is a promising route to produce ethylene from natural gas (Oh et al, 2019), along with other high-value chemicals such as acetylene, benzene, naphthalene, and hydrogen as by-products. As novel catalysts for the direct methane conversion have been developed, it is important to examine and evaluate the technical and economic feasibility for real industrial applications. Herein, techniques in process systems engineering, such as process synthesis and techno-economic analysis, play an important role to identify the major cost- and energy-drivers, preliminary process scheme and debottleneck strategies that supports R&D and planning (Vooradi et al., 2018).

In this work, we developed the direct methane conversion process which converts a natural gas into ethylene and other high-value chemicals, and evaluated the techno-economic performance. Therein, the novel catalyst of Fe-based, which presents the outstanding performance (e.g. yield) in the laboratory-scale experiment was used. The data of the methane conversion and the selectivity to each hydrocarbon were obtained and input in the catalytic conversion model in the process. In the separation section, several technologies were integrated to separate and purify ethylene, other C_{2+} hydrocarbon and H_2 product, and recycle CH_4. The techno-economic evaluation for the process was performed via the carbon efficiency, process energy efficiency, and minimum selling price of ethylene. Most of natural gas was converted into ethylene and acetylene besides the small amount of aromatics (e.g. naphthalene and benzene). Interestingly, hydrogen as a by-product positively contributes on in both energy efficiency and economic benefit due to its high heating value and high selling price. Besides, the sensitivity analysis of the ethylene minimum selling price (MSP) on major economic parameters was examined to identify the debottleneck solutions for the improvements of economic feasibility.

2. Methodology

2.1. Process simulation

The process models of the direct methane conversion for the hydrocarbon production, included catalytic conversion and separation sections, was developed using Aspen Plus V10.0. The property method of Peng Robinson-Boston Martin (PR-BM) was applied, which is recommended for the hydrocarbon processing (Huang et al., 2018). In the catalytic conversion section, the reactor is simulated using a black-box model for simplify performing the convergences of the novel catalyst performance. The reactions were operated at the atmosphere pressure and at very high temperature (over 1200°C) that required a large amount of fuel gas for heating, beside the heat recovery from heat exchanger network and burning the formed coke among the reactions (de-coking). In the separation section, the reaction outlet stream was compressed, then and separate naphthalene and benzene before entering to the very low temperature separation for purification of ethylene, hydrogen and other light hydrocarbon (i.e. acetylene, ethane). Therein, the heat exchanger network was installed to enhance the energy efficiency. Finally, the methane-rich gas emitted from the column was recycled back to reactor.

2.2. Techno-economic analysis

The proposed process was evaluated in various criteria such as carbon and energy efficiency, and minimum selling price (MSP). In the technical performance of the direct methane conversion to hydrocarbon, the terms of carbon element efficiency (η_C) and energy efficiency (η_E) presents how efficiently fed carbon source (e.g. CH_4) and supplied energy (i.e., utilities such as electricity, heat, and refrigeration) was utilized and captured in the products (Do et al., 2019) as expressed in Eqns. (1) and (2).

$$\eta_C = \frac{Total\,carbon\,element\,in\,products}{Fed\,CH_4} \times 100\% \tag{1}$$

$$\eta_E = \frac{Heat\,flow\,of\,products + Consumed\,utilities}{Heat\,flow\,of\,fed\,CH_4} \times 100\% \tag{2}$$

In the economic evaluation, the production cost considered the capital expenditures (*CAPEX*), operating expenses (*OPEX*), and tax. The return on investment (*ROI*) was estimated based on the interest rate at 8 %, and tax rate at 35 % within 30 years of economic plant life. Thereby, the minimum selling price (MSP) of ethylene was indicated after excluding the sale credits from other products (e.g. hydrogen, acetylene, crude naphthalene, benzene) as shown in Eqn. (3). Notably, the price of hydrogen and other hydrocarbons were indicated in the correlation with the price of natural gas and ethylene (Huang et al., 2018).

$$MSP_{ethylene} = \frac{(ROI + OPEX + Tax) - \sum Sale\,credit\,of\,other\,products}{Amount\,of\,ethylene}, [\$/kg] \tag{3}$$

3. Results and discussion

3.1. Process simulation

The process simulation of the direct methane conversion resulted that 0.33 million cubic m³/h of natural gas was converted to the main product of ethylene at 0.49 Mt/y, and various hydrocarbon of raw acetylene, naphthalene, and benzene at 0.57, 0.03 and 0.09 Mt/y respectively. Hydrogen, which is one of the high-value heating components, was also produced at 0.35 Mt/y.

3.2. Techno-economic analysis

3.2.1. Technical performance

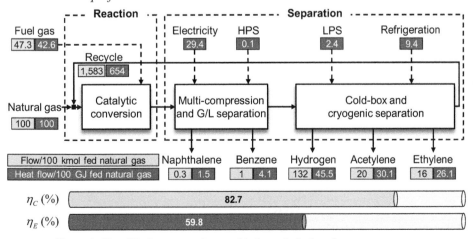

Figure 1. Simplified process scheme with the technical performance

Figure 1 presents the carbon element efficiency and energy efficiency together with the mass and energy balance among the process sections, presented on the basis of fed natural gas. Therein, 82.7 % of natural gas was converted into hydrocarbon products with 59.8 % in the energy conversion. As shown in Figure 1, 16 units of ethylene, 20 of acetylene, and the small volumes of naphthalene and benzene are produced from 100 units of natural gas material. On the energy basis, the process consumes 83.9 units in utilities to convert 100 units in fed natural gas into 107.2 units in products. Several types of heating utility such as fuel gas, high- and low-pressure steam (HPS and LPS), and cryogenic utilization are used in the process. However, the direct methane conversion process performs high energy efficiency compared to the typical petrochemical process (Salaheldin et al., 2017). It is primarily due to the large energy contribution of high heating value hydrogen product.

3.2.2. Minimum selling price

For the economic evaluation, this study examined the total production cost and the minimum selling price of ethylene besides other hydrocarbon products and hydrogen. Therein, the major component costs (e.g. capital cost and operating cost) were estimated using Aspen Process Economic Analyzer. The assumptions of material and utility prices are shown in Table 1. Consequently, the total production cost was around 1,408 MM$ that included *ROI*, *OPEX*, and tax is shown in Table 2.

Table 1. Raw materials and utilities price

Parameter	Value
CH_4 ($/MMBTU)	3.27
O_2 ($/ton)	40
Refrigeration ($/GJ)	8.85
Electricity ($/kWh)	0.07
Cooling water ($/m^3)	0.03
High pressure steam ($/ton)	14.5
Low pressure steam ($/ton)	10.5

Table 2. Total production cost

	Value
(a) *CAPEX* (MM$)	1,128
Direct plant cost	806
Indirect plant cost	322
(b) *ROI* (MM$/y)	100.2
(c) *OPEX* (MM$/y)	1,274
Raw materials	303.1
Utilities	937
(d) Tax (MM$/y)	33.7
(e) Total production cost [=(b)+(c)+(d)] (MM$/y)	1,407.9

Table 3. Minimum selling price and sale credits of products

	Price ($/kg)	Sale credit (MM$)
Ethylene	0.97	474.6
Hydrogen	1.42	499.0
Raw acetylene	0.63	358.8
Crude naphthalene	0.49	17.0
Benzene	0.64	58.5

Figure 2 presents the breakdown of total production cost and revenue from the sale of products. In the total production cost, the utility cost is a dominant component, accounts for 66.6 %, followed by raw material cost (21.5 %). It can be explained by the large consumptions of heating utility in the catalytic conversion section, and electricity and cryogenic utility in the separation section. The *ROI* budgets only 7.1 % while tax income and fixed-operating cost (*OPEX - FOC*) account for the same value at 2.4 %. In a revenue breakdown, the ethylene and hydrogen sale credits are the large portions with relatively similar value, at 33.7 % and 35.5 %, in accordance with the selling production cost at 474.6 MM$/y and 499.0 MM$/y as present in Table 3. Followed, the raw acetylene credit at 25.5 % and benzene credit at 4.2 %.

The hydrogen and hydrocarbon products are sold at relatively low prices, as shown in Table 3, while the minimum selling price of ethylene is 0.97 $/kg, which is relatively higher than the market price (around 0.84 $/kg). The MSP of ethylene can be reduced in case of higher selling price of by-product. Another critical insight is to improve catalyst performance as increasing the yield of ethylene from methane. If the strategy could obtain, it significantly improved not only technical performance but also the economic benefits. However, at the moment of the novel catalyst performance, the MSP of ethylene can be reduced as other products are sold at higher prices, or reduce material or utility cost.

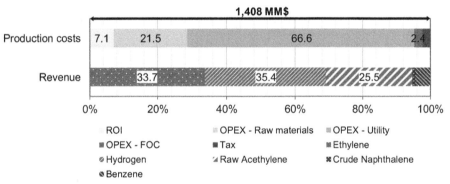

Figure 2. The breakdown of Production cost and Revenue

3.2.3. Sensitivity analysis

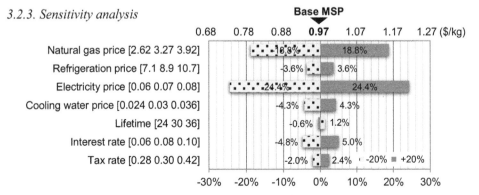

Figure 3. Sensitivity analysis of major economic parameter on Production cost

The sensitivity analysis of the ethylene MSP on the 20% changes of major economic parameters, in the case of other product prices are remained as in Table 3, is presented in Figure 3. It indicates that electricity price is the largest impact factor on MSP, which reduces by 24.4 % resulting in 0.74 $/kg of ethylene with a 20% reduction in electricity price. Natural gas price is the second sensitive parameter, which results in the MSP is from 0.79 to 1.12 $/kg within the examined range. Other factors are little effect on MSP, below 5%. As a result, the ethylene can be very competitive to the current market as reducing the price of natural gas or utility cost (e.g. electricity).

4. Conclusions

In this study, we developed the process of direct methane conversion to ethylene, C_{2+} hydrocarbon and aromatics production and conducted the techno-economic evaluation that identifies the major cost- and energy-drivers, and debottleneck strategies to improve the economic feasibility. The major findings and contributions of this study are as follows:

- The process performed carbon conversion at 82.7 % and energy efficiency at 59.8 %. Therein, H_2 has a large contribution on the energy efficiency besides the main product of ethylene and other hydrocarbon products due to its high heating value.

- Ethylene can be very competitive to the market as MSP is feasible to reduce with a lower price of electricity or natural gas (20% reduction), at 0.74-0.79 $/kg.

- The study also provides insight or targets for future research on catalyst development. In a scenario of higher ethylene yield, means achieved more ethylene production, the technical performance and economic feasibility significantly improve.

Acknowledgment

This work was supported by "Next Generation Carbon Upcycling Project" (Project No. 2017M1A2A2043137) through the National Research Foundation (NRF) funded by the Ministry of Science and ICT, Republic of Korea.

References

Rentech, 2019, Hydrocarbon processing: Petrochemical Technology - April 2018, 97, 4, https://www.hydrocarbonprocessing.com/magazine/2018/april-2018

I. Amghizar, L.A. Vandewalle, K. M. Van Geem, G. B. Marin, 2017, New Trends in Olefin Production, Engineering, 3, 171-178

S. C. Oh, E. Schulman, J. Zhang, J. Fan, Y. Pan, J. Meng, and D. Liu, 2049, Direct Non-Oxidative Methane Conversion in aMillisecond Catalytic Wall Reactor, Angew. Chem., 131, 7157-7160

R. Vooradi, M.O. Bertran, R. Frauzem, S.B. Anne, R. Gani, 2018, Sustainable chemical processing and energy-carbon dioxide management: Review of challenges and opportunities, Chem. Eng. Res. Des., 131, 440-464

K. Huang, J. B. Miller, G. W. Huber, J. A. Dumesic, and C. T. Maravelias , 2018, A General Framework for the Evaluation of Direct Nonoxidative Methane Conversion Strategies, Joule, 2, 2, 349-365

T. N. Do, J. Kim, 2019, Process development and techno-economic evaluation of methanol production by direct CO_2 hydrogenation using solar-thermal energy, J CO2 Util, 33, 461-472

M. Salaheldin, A.F. Abdul Moneim, M. Nashat Fors, 2017, Energy efficiency evaluation in petrochemicals industry, Proc. Int. Conf. Ind. Eng. Oper. Manag.,1058–1069.

Sauro Pierucci, Flavio Manenti, Giulia Bozzano, Davide Manca (Eds.)
Proceedings of the 30th European Symposium on Computer Aided Process Engineering
(ESCAPE30), May 24-27, 2020, Milano, Italy. © 2020 Elsevier B.V. All rights reserved.
http://dx.doi.org/10.1016/B978-0-12-823377-1.50171-3

Optimization Study of H2/CO Ratio in the Steam Gasification of PKS using Coal Bottom ash for fuel Production through Response Surface Methodology

Muhammad Shahbaz[a,b*], Tareq Al- Ansari[a], Gordon Mckay[a], Suzana Yusup[b], Muddasser Inayat[c]

[a]Division of Sustainable Development, College of Science and Engineering, Hamad Bin Khalifa University (HBKU), Qatar Foundation, P.O. Box 5825, Doha, Qatar
[b]Institute of Sustainable living, Centre of biomass and biochemical Center, Department of Chemical Engineering, Universiti Teknologi PETRONAS, Bandar Seri Iskandar 32610, Perak Darul Ridzuan, Malaysia
[c]Department of Mechanical Engineering, Universiti Teknologi PETRONAS, Bandar Seri Iskandar 32610, Perak Darul Ridzuan, Malaysia
mshahbaz@hbku.edu.qa

Abstract

H_2 and CO are the most critical components within the product gas obtained from the gasification of biomass. The composition of H_2 and CO is of significant importance as their ratio defines the utilization of the syngas. Application of syngas can include power generation, chemical products such as methanol, NH_3, and FT diesel. The objective of this study to optimize the parametric conditions for H_2/CO ratio in the gasification of PKS in TGA-MS set up using coal bottom ash as a catalyst and CaO as adsorbent. The experiments were designed using RSM and the effect of parameters such as temperature from (650-750 °C), particle size (0.5-1.0 mm), CaO/biomass ratio (0.5-2.0), and CBA wt % (0.02-0.10). The study demonstrates that the H_2/CO ratio is mostly influenced factor followed by the temperature and particle size, whereas the CaO/biomass ratio and CBA wt% are third and fourth influencing factors on H_2/CO ratio. The maximum H_2/CO ratio of 1.47 at optimum temperature of 715 °C, Particle size of 0.65 mm, CaO/biomass ratio of 1.45, and CBA wt % of 0.09%. H_2/CO ratio is important for its conversion into many products, such as methane, methanol, and FT diesel.

Keywords: H_2/CO ratio, gasification, RSM, optimization, TGA-MS.

1. Introduction

Energy is the backbone of modern human life. Fossil fuels are the primary source of the existing energy mix that contributed 81.7% of total energy needs (Inayat et al., 2020b). The progress of any country is highly dependent on reliable, affordable, and sustainable energy sources (Inayat et al., 2020b). It is forecasted by International Energy Agency that global energy consumption will increase by 53% in 2030 (Pang et al., 2010). Ever-increasing energy demand and limited fossil fuels motivate researchers to find alternative source of energy which are cheap and reliable to fulfill the future deficiency of fossils fuels. In this context biomass appears as cheap environmental friendly option of energy through thermal and biological conversion processes(Zeng et al., 2016). Among many, gasification is efficient and fast process that converts the biomass into gaseous fuel, which is sophisticated form of energy factor. The gasification process converts into syngas by partial oxidation of biomass at high temperatures. Syngas is consists of H_2, CO, CH_4, and CO_2 (Inayat et al., 2020a). Syngas can be utilized for different purposes such as liquid fuel production (Fisher Tropsch) or used as alternative fuel (Ma et al., 2015).

The quality and utilization of syngas depend on its H_2/CO ratio. Zeng et al. (Zeng et al., 2016) reported the production of high H_2/CO ratio from steam gasification of sawdust and achieved 0.279 Nm^3 kg^{-1} of the H_2 yield in the steam reactor by chemical looping gasification. (Ma et al., 2015) used hybrid catalyst to synthesized the hydrocarbons and Ft diesel from syngas using having H_2/CO ratio less than 1 and 2 respectively. (Saad and Williams 2017) investigated two-stage pyrolysis-catalytic reforming of plastics for producing good quality syngas comprised of H_2 and CO. (Inayat et al., 2019) reported the H_2/CO under the effect of temperature, biomass ratio, ER, and catalyst loading in catalytic and non-catalytic co-gasification. The utilization of PKS for the steam gasification have been reported in our previous study (Herman et al.,.2016).Literature shows that reported studies focus only a normal investigation of H_2/CO ratio under catalytic and nan-catalytic gasification. However, there is lacking systematic investigation of the H_2/CO ratio in catalytic steam biomass gasification using RSM.

In this present work, catalytic steam gasification of PKS was performed using coal bottom ash as a catalyst for maximum H_2/CO ratio. The aim of this investigation to optimize and study the systematic combined effect of gasification parameters such as temperature range of 650-750 °C, CaO/biomass ratio of 0.5-2.0, CBA wt% of 0.02-0.10, and Particle size of 0.5-1.0 mm , on H_2/CO ratio. This study will be a contribution towards utilization of waste biomass PKS for energy production to replace fossil fuel.

2. Methodology

PKS used as a feedstock in this study was collected from Kilang Sawit Nasarudin Sdn. Bhd PKS was dried in the oven to remove excess moisture content (Shahbaz et al., 2017). The dried PKS was grounded in size range of 20.5 to 1.0 mm. The thermochemical properties of PKS are presented in Table.1. The CBA is the residue of boiler of power plant located in Selangor Malaysia used as a catalyst, and CaO used as adsorbent was acquired from Kinetic Chemical Sdn Bhd.(Shahbaz et al., 2016) Table 1 presented the XRF analysis of CBA that detected Fe, Ca, Mg, and Al oxides, which makes CBA good candidate as catalyst for gasification. A multivariate design of experiment approach, Response Surface Methodology (RSM) with Central Composite Design (CCD) was applied by using Design-Expert Version 8.® software for the TGA-MS experiment design matrix (Inayat et al., 2020a). ANOVA analysis helps to quantify individual and interactive effect of process parameters on the response with the help of response surface (Shahbaz et al., 2017). Moreover, the process could be optimized with the help of tool present inside it (Shahbaz et al., 2016). In current study, the effect of four operating was chosen to see their effect on H_2/CO ratio. The range of process parameters is selected on the basis of trial runs and literature as follows, temperature (650-750 °C), particle size (0.1-1 mm), CaO/biomass ratio (0.5-2) and coal bottom ash wt% (0.02-0.10) (Shahbaz et al., 2017). Total twenty-one experiments were designed, which include five central runs, eight axial runs, and seven factorial runs.

A thermogravimetric analyzer EXSTAR TG/DTA 3200 attached a mass spectrometer (Pfeiffer Vacuum Thermostar) incorporated with setup of steam generation system was used for the gasification of PKS (Shahbaz et al., 2016). 20 mg of sample was used for each run, and all other materials (CBA and CaO) added according to the experiment design matrix. The experiments were repeated thrice in order to reduce the experimental error. The sample was heated up to 150 °C using N_2 rate of 100 ml/min. The sample was heated at heating rate of 25 °C/min in inert condition. The N_2 was replaced with the steam when temperature reached at 110 °C. The sample was heated up to the desired temperature according to designed matrix (Shahbaz et al., 2017). The biomass to steam ratio was 0.5 for each experiment.

Table.1 Proximate and ultimate analysis of PKS and XRF of CBA (Shahbaz et al., 2017)

Proximate analysis				Ultimate analysis	
Volatile matter (%)	80.81			C (%)	48.78
Fixed carbon (%)	14.25			H (%)	5.70
Ash content (%)	4.94			N (%)	1.01
				S (%)	0.21
HHV MJ/kg	18.82			O (%) (by a difference)	44.3
Compound	SiO	Fe₂O₃	CaO	Al₂O₃	MgO	K₂O₃
Coal Bottom Ash	44.1	24.3	13	9.21	1.88	1.25

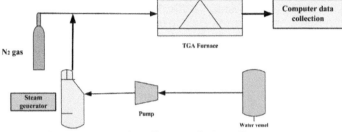

Figure1: Process Flow diagram of TGA-MS set up

Table.2: Experimental design and response results

Run	Temperature °C	Particle Size mm	CaO/Biomass ratio	CBA wt %	H₂/CO Ratio
1	700	0.75	1.25	0.003	1.431
2	700	0.75	1.25	0.06	1.470
3	650	0.50	2.00	0.02	1.218
4	700	0.75	2.30	0.06	1.334
5	650	1.00	2.00	0.10	1.237
6	700	0.75	0.18	0.06	1.407
7	700	0.75	1.25	0.06	1.468
8	700	0.75	1.25	0.06	1.477
9	700	0.75	1.25	0.06	1.470
10	750	1.00	2.00	0.02	1.252
11	700	0.75	1.25	0.06	1.470
12	650	0.50	0.50	0.02	1.295
13	700	1.10	1.25	0.06	1.253
14	700	0.39	1.25	0.06	1.356
15	630	0.75	1.25	0.06	1.182
16	650	1.00	0.50	0.10	1.254
17	750	0.50	0.50	0.10	1.355
18	700	0.75	1.25	0.12	1.450
19	750	0.50	2.00	0.10	1.430
20	770	0.75	1.25	0.06	1.315
21	750	1.00	0.50	0.02	1.294

3. Result and discussion

3.1. Statistical analysis

The functional relationship has been developed between process parameters and response (H_2/CO ratio) using RSM in catalytic steam gasification of PKS. The second-order quadratic model is found best for experimental data and a regression equation is developed in terms of coded factor, as shown in Table 3. From the ANOVA analysis it shows that model is significant as P–values are less than 0.05, and regression coefficient is 0.95 that shows the model fitted the data very well. Figure 2 shows that the predicted and experimental values are in close agreement. From ANOVA analysis it can be seen that temperature (A) and particle size (B) are more influencing variables towards H_2/CO ratio is due to having higher F-value and lower P-values as shown in Table 3. Whereas the CaO/biomass ratio and CBA show less effective as compared to it.

Table. 3 ANOVA for H2/CO in steam gasification of PKS

Source	F-value	P-value	Source	F-value	P-value
Model	9.026	0.006	AB	0.115	0.745
A-Temperature °C	6.072	0.048	AC	0.767	0.414
B-Particle size mm	3.665	0.104	AD	1.373	0.285
C-CaO/biomass ratio	1.546	0.259	BC	0.029	0.869
D-CBA wt%	0.115	0.745	BD	0.286	0.612
Pure error	4.3E-05	0.767	CD	0.073	0.795
Lack of Fit	0.008	R^2	0.95	Adj-R^2	0.85

Regression equation using coded factor:
H_2/CO ratio = $1.45 + 0.047A - 0.036B - 0.013C + 0.006D - 0.020AB + 0.016AC - 0.004AD - 0.007BC + 0.006BD + 0.022CD - 0.089A^2 - 0.061B^2 - 0.0281C^2 + 0.006D^2$

3.2. Parametric analysis

The ANOVA analysis and 3-Dimensional response surface are generated to describe the effect of the individual and interactive impact of parameters on H_2/CO ratio. As temperature and particle size shows more influence on response. From Figure.2 it can be seen that H_2/CO ratio is increased from 1.1 to 1.467 by increased in temperature from 650 to 715 °C and then dropped to 1.4 at smaller particle size. A similar trend shows a larger particle size with larger dropped at higher temperatures. The increase in H_2/CO ratio is due to increase in H_2 content, which enhances the activation of endothermic reactions such as water gas shift reaction methane reforming reaction (Shahbaz et al., 2016). The H_2/CO ratio varied in a similar pattern n when it investigated with CaO/biomass ratio and CBA wt %. The increase in ratio with the increase in CaO/biomass ratio and temperature is due to activation of endothermic reaction, and reduction of CO_2 is due to carbonation reaction (Shahbaz et al., 2017). The dropped in H_2 at elevated temperature is due to the reverse carbonation that observed by many researchers (Shahbaz et al., 2017). From figure 2 it can be seen that H_2/CO ratios are increased from 1.2 to 1.3 at small and higher particle size with the increased in CBA wt%. CBA also shows a similar effect when it is investigated with temperature. High H_2 yield causes increase in H_2/CO ratio that is due to the catalytic activity of Fe, Al, Ca, and Mg oxides of CBA, which have been used as a conventional catalyst in gasification (Inayat et al., 2020a).

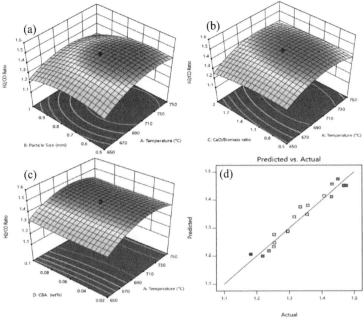

Figure 2: (a-c) 3-Dimension surface for the combined effect of process parameters H2/CO ratio for maxim and (d) Predicted vs Actual values from model

3.3. Optimization study

The obtained experimental results were utilized to optimize the parameters using the tool inside RSM for the maximize H_2/CO ratio yield (Shahbaz al., 2017). The predicted optimum parameters were summarized in Table 4. The predicted optimum parameters were performed thrice for the confirmation of predicted parameters. The standard deviation was found 0.005 shows the predicted and actual values are in close agreement.

Table 4. Optimization and predicted and experimental validation

Number	Temperature °C	Particle Size mm	CaO/Biomass ratio wt%	CBA wt%	H₂/CO Ratio
Predicted	715	0.66	1.45	0.09	1.4766
Exp. Run1	715	0.66	1.45	0.09	1.4650
Exp. Run 2	715	0.66	1.45	0.09	1.4699
Exp. Run 3	715	0.66	1.45	0.09	1.4799
Standard deviation					0.005

4. Conclusion

The catalytic steam gasification of PKS has been instituted in TGA-MS set up using CBA and CaO as a catalyst and adsorbent to investigate the H_2/CO ratio. The effect of four process parameters and interaction was studied by using RSM. The temperature and particle size have more influence on H_2/CO ratio as the ratio are increased from 1.1 to 1.4 by increasing the temperature from 650 to 710 °C and increased from 1.1 to 1.21 by increasing the particle size from 0.5 to 0.7 mm. Whereas, the CaO/biomass ratio and CBA wt% also shows a marginal effect on H_2/CO ratio.02-0.10. The optimum parameters were determined using tool inside RSM are temperature of 715 °C, CaO/biomass ratio of 1.45, particle size of 0.66mm, and CBA wt% of 0.9 for the maximum H_2/Co ratio of 1.47. The variation in H_2/CO ratio with the increase of CBA shows the catalytic activity of Al, Fe, Mg, and Ca oxides as detected in CAB using XRF analysis.

Acknowledgment

The authors are grateful to Universiti Teknologi PETRONAS, Malaysia, and Hamad Bin Khalifa University, Doha, Qatar, for providing financial and technical assistance.

References

A. Inayat, M. Inayat, M. Shahbaz, S. A. Sulaiman, M. Raza and S. Yusup, 2020a, Parametric Analysis and Optimization for the Catalytic Air Gasification of Palm Kernel Shell ssing Coal Bottom Ash as Catalyst, Renewable Energy, 145, 671-681.

A. P. Herman, S. Yusup, M. Shahbaz, 2016, Utilization of Bottom Ash as Catalyst in Biomass Steam Gasification for Hydrogen and Syngas Production, Chemical Engineering Transactions, 52, 1249-1254.

M. Inayat, S. A. Sulaiman, J. C. Kurnia, and M. Y. Naz, 2019, Catalytic and Noncatalytic Gasification of Wood–Coconut Shell Blend under Different Operating Conditions, Environmental Progress & Sustainable Energy, 38, 688-698.

M. Inayat, S. A. Sulaiman, M. Shahbaz, and B. A. Bhayo, 2020b,. Application of Response Surface Methodology in Catalytic Co-Gasification of Palm Wastes for Bioenergy Conversion using Mineral Catalysts, Biomass and Bioenergy, 132, 105418.

T. Ma, H. Imai, T. Shige, T. Sugio, and X. Li, 2015, Synthesis of Hydrocarbons from H 2-Deficient Syngas in Fischer-Tropsch Synthesis over Co-Based Catalyst Coupled with Fe-Based Catalyst as Water-Gas Shift Reaction. Journal of Nanomaterials, 2015, 2.

T. Oh, S. Y. Pang, and S. C. Chua, 2010, Energy Policy and Alternative Energy in Malaysia: Issues and Challenges for Sustainable Growth, Renewable and Sustainable Energy Reviews, 14(4), 1241-1252.

J. Saad, and P. T. Williams, 2017, Manipulating the H_2/CO Ratio from Dry Reforming of Simulated Mixed Waste Plastics by the addition of Steam, Fuel Processing Technology, 156, 331-338.

M. Shahbaz, S. Yusup, A. Inayat, D. O. Patrick, and A. Pratama, 2016, Application of Response Surface Methodology to Investigate the Effect of Different Variables on Conversion of Palm Kernel Shell in Steam Gasification using Coal bottom Ash, Applied Energy, 18, 1306-1315.

M. Shahbaz, S. Yusup, A. Inayat, D. O. Patrick, A. Pratama, and M. Ammar, 2017, Optimization of Hydrogen and Syngas Production from PKS Gasification by using Coal Bottom Ash, Bioresource Technology, 241, 284-295.

J. Zeng, R. Xiao, D. Zeng, Y. Zhao, H. Zhang, and D. Shen, 2016, High H_2/CO Ratio Syngas Production from Chemical Looping Gasification of Sawdust in a Dual Fluidized Bed Gasifier.Energy & fuels 30(3), 1764-1770.

Sauro Pierucci, Flavio Manenti, Giulia Bozzano, Davide Manca (Eds.)
Proceedings of the 30th European Symposium on Computer Aided Process Engineering
(ESCAPE30), May 24-27, 2020, Milano, Italy. © 2020 Elsevier B.V. All rights reserved.
http://dx.doi.org/10.1016/B978-0-12-823377-1.50172-5

CO2-based Acetic Acid Production Assessment

Kelvin A. Pacheco[*], Antonio E. Bresciani, Claudio A. O. Nascimento,
Rita M.B. Alves

Departamento de Engenharia Química, Escola Politécnica, Universidade de São Paulo, São Paulo, Brazil
kelvinpac@usp.br

Abstract

New synthetic routes to acetic acid production using CO_2 have been studied, such as methanol hydrocarboxylation, reaction of methane with CO_2, lignin with CO_2 and CO_2 hydrogenation. They represent a significant progress in synthetic chemistry, with the novel approach to acetic acid production and CO_2 transformation. These innovative routes can replace fossil raw materials by CO_2, additionally promote CO_2.abatement. This study presents an assessment of acetic acid production from CO_2 and identification of the most promising route by a multicriteria decision analysis, including process demand and characteristics, and a shortcut exergy criterion. Methanol hydrocarboxylation has demonstrated to be the best one. The process was designed based on hierarchical approach process synthesis in Aspen Plus simulator to verify its technical feasibility. An exergetic analysis was carried out in the proposed process design to evaluate thermodynamic inefficiencies. The gas recompression and the gas separation system presented the highest exergy destruction, in which possible process intensification or enhancements potentially improve the process.

Keywords: CO_2 routes to acetic acid, methanol hydrocarboxylation, process design, chemical reaction stoichiometry, exergetic analysis.

1. Introduction

Acetic acid is an important industrial chemical. According to the Mordor Intelligence Report (Intelligence, 2017), the global market was 14.2 Mt in 2017 and is expected to reach 18.2 Mt by 2023. The preferential route for glacial acetic acid production is methanol carbonylation which accounts for over 65% of the global capacity. New synthetic routes to acetic acid production using CO_2 have been studied, namely the reaction of methane with CO_2 (Wilcox et al., 2003), methanol hydrocarboxylation (Qian et al., 2016), lignin with CO_2 (Wang et al., 2019) and the hydrogenation of CO_2 (Jia et al., 2016). However, manufacturing C_{2+} carboxylic acids from CO_2 poses a commercial and innovative challenge: to reduce the production impact, lower cost raw materials and industrial design and engineering (Li et al., 2018).

The conversion of methane and CO_2 into acetic acid has received much attention recently, due to the improvement potential (100% atom economy, *i.e.* the total conversion of reactants to the desired product and avoiding the CO production step), but it presents thermodynamic restrictions. Wilcox, Roberts and Spivey (2003) synthesized acetic acid using a heterogeneous catalyst (Pd/carbon and Pt/alumina). So far, however, there has not been an efficient catalyst for acetic acid production from methane and CO_2 (Montejo-Valencia et al., 2017).

The second route is the methanol hydrocarboxylation. Qian *et al.* (2016) proposed the reaction of methanol, CO_2 and H_2 over bimetallic Ru-Rh homogeneous catalyst, the ligand was imidazole, the promoter was LiI and 1,3 dimethyl-2-imidazolidinoe as solvent. The reported yield was 77%, the TON exceeded 1000.

Within the context of biomass conversion and to valorize lignin as a renewable source of aromatics, Wang *et al.* (2019) proposed a synthesis of acetic acid from lignin, CO_2 and H_2 over ionic liquid (**e.g.**, [BMIm][Cl])-based catalytic system containing Ru–Rh bimetal catalyst and LiI. The yield achieved was 94%.

The hydrogenation of CO_2 was studied by Jia et al. (2016), who evaluated the thermodynamics, which results showed a favorable production of higher-carbon acids (acetic acid, propionic acid) over formic acid, nonetheless kinetic constraints in C-C coupling is difficult in practice. In order to design and synthesize a process, a multicriteria analysis was performed and the most promising route was selected. A process synthesis by hierarchical approach leads to a detailed flowsheet and an exergy analysis reveals the exergy inefficiencies locations.

2. Methods

2.1. Multi-Criteria Analysis for Route Selection

Multiple criteria decision analysis (MCDA) refers to making preference decisions (*e.g.* evaluation and selection) over the alternatives available characterized by multiple attributes. The four different routes were compared through a MCDA using the Technique for Order Preference by Similarity to Ideal Solution method The elicitation of weights was obtained by the Shannon Entropy method (Shannon, 1948) and a sensitivity analysis was carried out using Monte Carlo Simulation (10% variability in weights with 100,000 runs).

Three criteria were used: (**i**) the procedure proposed by Audus and Oonk (1997) (Table 1); (**ii**) short-cut exergy demand of the chemical reaction proposed by Müller and Arlt (2014); and (**iii**) Gibbs energy of reaction.

Table 1 – Process Characteristics and their values.

Characteristic	Value	
	1	2
Number of Processes	Reaction/Sep	React/H2/Sep
Operating Conditions	Mild	Mild/Medium
Discontinuities in the process	No	Yes
Change of phase	No	Yes
possibility for process integration	Yes	No
Catalytic System	Adequate	Limited

2.2. Process Synthesis by Hierarchical Approach

Chemical process synthesis is a complex scheme, which comprises process modeling and design; it can be solved in a sequential scheme, by decomposing the hierarchy of elements (reactor, separation, heat recovery and utility). Dimian and Bildea (2008) proposed an improved hierarchical approach, reducing interactions between levels leading to a more efficient design, and it was used in this study.

2.3. Exergy Analysis

An exergy analysis based on the simulation results was carried out. Exergy refers to the maximum capacity of a system to produce useful work when balanced with its surroundings (Szargut et al., 1987). The standard chemical exergy table defined by Szargut, Morris and Steward (1987) was used; for non-reference components, the method proposed by Haghbakhsh and Raeissi (2019) was used to estimate. The methodology described in Szargut, Morris and Steward (1987) was used to calculate the chemical exergy, work and heat for a given unit operation.

3. Results and Discussions

3.1. MCDA Results

Table 2 shows the performance of each alternative for a specific criterion and its relative weight. The criterion Gibbs energy of reaction exhibited negative values for three out of four of the production process alternatives evaluated. The same behavior was observed for exergy demand; only the production process using methane and CO_2 displayed a positive value. The process characteristics criterion demonstrated similar values for all the production processes evaluated (note the smaller the value, the better).

Table 2 – Decision matrix for the acetic acid production.

Production Process	$\Delta_r G$ (kJ/mol)	Exergy Demand (kJ/mol)	Process Characteristics[a]
Relative weight[b]	*0.149*	*0.148*	*0.704*
CO_2 and Methane	70.19	10.77	8
Methanol Hidrocarboxylation	-46.54	-28.31	9
Lignin Oxidation	-35.92	-23.43	9
CO_2 Hydrogenation	-21.54	-30.53	9

a – The process characteristics are present in Table 1, the summation of a specific characteristic yielded the stated value in this table.
b - The relative weights were calculated using the Shannon Entropy method (Shannon, 1948).

The most promising route is methanol hydrocarboxylation (score = 0.843, std deviation = 0.007), followed by lignin oxidation (score = 0.802, std deviation = 0.008), CO_2 hydrogenation (score = 0.772, std deviation = 0.009) and lastly CO_2 and methane (score = 0.153, std deviation = 0.009). The selected route is used throughout the study.

3.2. Process Synthesis

3.2.1. Basis of Design

Considering the chemical plants in operation, the proposed plant is 200 kton/year as a target production. The methanol hydrocarboxylation route was studied in terms of catalyst availability and literature data. Two studies reported experimental data. Qian *et al.* (2016), employed a Ru–Rh bimetallic catalyst, while the second Cui *et al.* (2017) used a Rh-based catalyst. The catalyst system reported in the latter was selected because the amount of corrosive LiI used was reduced by 1/3 and effectively yield acetic acid under relative mild conditions was achieved.

3.2.2. Chemical Reaction Analysis

Chemical Reaction Stoichiometry deals with constraints placed on changes in compositions of a closed system. It can be expressed as a set of linear equations, taking the conservation of atom types into account. The algorithm proposed by Smith and Missen (1982) was used to simultaneously determine the number of independent equations and a complete set of chemical equations. The system is represented by CH_3OH, CO_2, H_2, H_2O, CH_3COOH, CH_4, C_2H_5OH, $C_3H_6O_2$, $C_4H_8O_2$. An additional restriction was imposed, CO_2 and H_2 do react, under certain conditions, in an equal amount (Cui et al., 2017). This restriction was incorporated into the general description explicitly. A complete stoichiometric matrix in canonical form is presented in Eq. (1)-(5).

$$CH_3OH + CO_2 + H_2 \rightarrow CH_3COOH + H_2O \tag{1}$$
$$3CH_3OH \rightarrow 2CH_4 + CO_2 + H_2 + H_2O \tag{2}$$
$$2CH_3OH \rightarrow C_2H_5OH + H_2O \tag{3}$$
$$2CH_3OH + CO_2 + H_2 \rightarrow C_3H_6O_2 + 2H_2O \tag{4}$$
$$3CH_3OH + CO_2 + H_2 \rightarrow C_4H_8O_2 + 3H_2O \tag{5}$$

3.2.3. Reactor/Separator/Recycle

The reactor was simulated in Aspen Plus (RStoic module), the reactions in Eq (1) – (5) were used (180°C and 100 bar). The conversion for Eq (1) and (2) were adjusted according to the logistic fit of experimental data (Cui et al., 2017) as a function of temperature. For the conversion of Eq (3) – (5) a thermodynamic analysis was performed, and the maximum values were assumed. The solvent 1,3-dimethyl-2-imidazolidinone (DMI) (Cui et al., 2017) was also included in the simulations. The recycling of solvent and the catalyst and unreacted gases is considered.

3.2.4. Separation System

The first separation step permits the decomposition of the complex separation system into subsystems of separations, taking only monophasic streams into account. After examining the phase condition at the reactor outlet, a heterogeneous gas/liquid stream is present. The outlet stream of the reactor was cooled, goes pass through a valve to reduce the pressure and enters the flash. The temperature and pressure are optimized to recover at least 94% of CO_2 and more than 99% of hydrogen in the vapor stream and 97% of acetic acid in the liquid stream of the flash tank.

Gas Separation System

For generating separation sequences inside the subsystems (gas separation or liquid separation), the formalism of the task-oriented approach proposed by (Barnicki and Fair, 1992, 1990) was used.

An enrichment was coupled with purification to obtain a recycle stream with CO_2 and H_2 from the outlet of vapor split. The first part of the gas separation system is the removal of condensables, which are send to the liquid separation system, while the non-condensable stream enters the membrane module to remove methane. To simulate the membrane module, a model proposed by Pettersen and Lien (1994) was employed; it uses an analogy with the fundamental equation of heat exchangers. The permeability and selectivity values for the polyimide membrane were obtained from Abetz et al. (2006). The outlet stream from the membrane module is recompressed and feeds the reactor.

Liquid Separation System

A shortcut distillation column model was firstly used to estimate the parameters for a rigorous distillation column (RadFrac), in which the parameters were optimized to meet the purity requirement for acetic acid.

3.2.5. Process Analysis

In the proposed flowsheet design (Figure 1) methanol (16.3 t/h), carbon dioxide (28.9 t/h) and hydrogen (0.8 t/h) react in a solvent media yielding acetic acid (25.1 t/h). The gas separation system removes condensables using compressors (6.5 MW), coolers (7.4 MW) and a membrane module (pressure drop of 23.9 bar) yielding a stream of 57.5 %mol of hydrogen and 42.4 %mol of carbon dioxide, requiring 14.8 MW of power for the recompression system. In the liquid separation system, the solvent recovery column (17 stages and the reflux ratio of 0.09) is followed by the second column (10 stages with a reflux ratio of 2.46) to remove the lights. The dehydration column has 40 stages and reflux ratio of 5.71. Similar results were found by Feyzi and Beheshti (2017).

3.2.6. Exergy Analysis Results

An exergetic balance was performed for each subsystem of the flowsheet (Feed conditioning and recompression, reaction system, liquid-vapor split, gas separation system and liquid separation system) for identifying the magnitude and location of the inefficiencies (Figure 2). The thermodynamic inefficiencies occur mainly within the gas separation system and the gas recompression, indicating the units to be optimized.

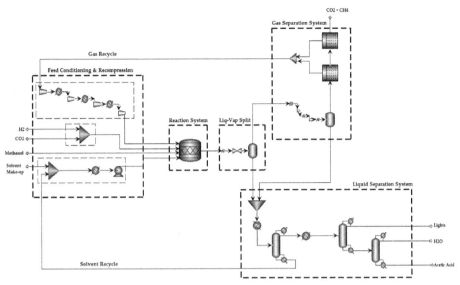

Figure 1 – Acetic acid from CO_2 flowsheet implemented in Aspen Plus.

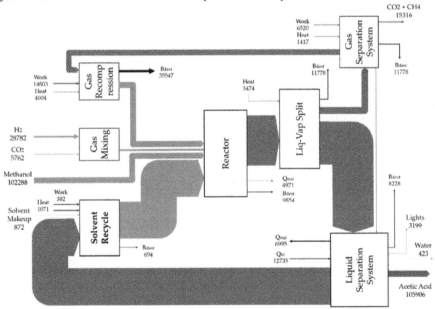

Figure 2 - True to scale exergy flow diagram (*Grassmann* chart) for acetic acid production. The main flows are shown.

4. Conclusions

This study presented an assessment of acetic acid production routes from CO_2 and a multicriteria analysis was used to select the most advantageous route in terms of process characteristic and energy demand. The methanol hydrocarboxylation route demonstrated to be the most promising and it was deeper studied. To the best of our knowledge there are no literature data regarding the process design of acetic acid production from CO_2. So, this work contributes to the field of process synthesis of CO_2 conversion to high added value products. The flowsheet of the production process was designed based on process synthesis and demonstrated to be feasible. The exergy analysis pointed out the locations and magnitude of thermodynamic inefficiencies that can be improved for better design.

Acknowledgment

The authors gratefully acknowledge the support from FAPESP and SHELL Brasil through the Research Centre for Gas Innovation (FAPESP Proc. 2014/50279-4), hosted by the University of São Paulo, and the support given by ANP (Brazil's National Oil, Natural Gas and Biofuels Agency) through the R&D levy regulation. This study was financed in part by the Coordenação de Aperfeiçoamento de Pessoal de Nível Superior - Brasil (CAPES) - Finance Code 001. The authors acknowledge FAPESP for a PhD scholarship grant (FAPESP Proc. 2017/26683-8).

References

V. Abetz, T. Brinkmann, M. Dijkstra, K. Ebert, D. Fritsch, K. Ohlrogge, D. Paul, K. Peinemann, S. Nunes, N. Scharnagl, M. Schossig, M., 2006. Developments in membrane research: From material via process design to industrial application. Adv. Eng. Mater. 8, 328–358.

H. Audus, H. Oonk, 1997. An assessment procedure for chemical utilisation schemes intended to reduce CO2 emissions to atmosphere. Energy Convers. Mgmt 38, S409–S414.

S.D. Barnicki, J.R. Fair, 1992. Separation system synthesis: a knowledge-based approach. 2. Gas/vapor mixtures. Ind. Eng. Chem. Res. 31, 1679–1694.

S.D. Barnicki, J.R. Fair, 1990. Separation system synthesis: a knowledge-based approach. 1. Liquid mixture separations. Ind. Eng. Chem. Res. 29, 421–432.

M. Cui, Q. Qian, J. Zhang, C. Chen, B. Han, 2017. Efficient synthesis of acetic acid via Rh catalyzed methanol hydrocarboxylation with CO2 and H2 under milder conditions. Green Chem. 3558–3565.

A.C. Dimian, C.S. Bildea, 2008. Chemical process design: Computer-aided case studies. John Wiley

V. Feyzi and M. Beheshti, 2017. Exergy analysis and optimization of reactive distillation column in acetic acid production process. Chem. Eng. Process. Process Intensif. 120, 161–172.

R. Haghbakhsh and S. Raeissi, 2019. A novel atomic contribution model for the standard chemical exergies of organic compounds. Fluid Phase Equilib. 112397.

Intelligence, M., 2017. Acetic Acid Market - Segmented by Application, and Geography https://www.mordorintelligence.com/industry-reports/global-acetic-acid-market-industry (accessed 4.2.18).

C. Jia, J. Gao, Y. Dai, J. Zhang, Y. Yang, 2016. The thermodynamics analysis and experimental validation for complicated systems in CO2 hydrogenation process, J. Energy Chem., 25, 1027–1037.

J. Li, L. Wang, Y. Cao, C. Zhang, P. He, and H. Li, 2018. Recent advances on the reduction of CO2 to important C2 + oxygenated chemicals and fuels. Chinese J. Chem. Eng. 26, 2266–2279.

B. D. Montejo-Valencia, Y. J. Pagán-Torres, M. M. Martínez-Iñesta, and M. C. Curet-Arana, 2017. Density functional theory (DFT) study to unravel the catalytic properties of M-exchanged MFI for the conversion of methane and carbon dioxide to acetic acid. ACS Catal. 7, 6719–6728.

K. Müller and W. Arlt, 2014. Shortcut evaluation of chemical carbon dioxide utilization processes. Chem. Eng. Technol. 37, 1612–1615.

T. Pettersen and K. M. Lien, K.M., 1994. A new robust design model for gas separating membrane modules, based on analogy with counter-current heat exchangers. Comput. Chem. Eng. 18, 427–439.

Q. Qian, J. Zhang, M. Cui, and B. Han, 2016. Synthesis of acetic acid via methanol hydrocarboxylation with CO2 and H2. Nat. Commun. 7, 11481.

C.E. Shannon, 1948. A mathematical theory of communication. Bell Syst. Tech. J. 27, 379–423.

W.R. Smith, R.W. Missen, 1982. Chemical reaction equilibrium analysis: theory and algorithms. Wiley New York.

J. Szargut, D. R. Morris, and F. R. Steward, 1987. Exergy analysis of thermal, chemical, and metallurgical processes. Hemisphere, New York.

H. Wang, Y. Zhao, Z. Ke, B. Yu, R. Li, Y. Wu, Z. Wang, J. Han, Z. Liu, 2019. Synthesis of renewable acetic acid from CO2 and lignin over an ionic liquid-based catalytic system. Chem. Commun. 55, 3069–3072.

E. M. Wilcox, G. W. Roberts, and J. J. Spivey, 2003. Direct catalytic formation of acetic acid from CO2 and methane. Catal. Today 88, 83–90.

Sauro Pierucci, Flavio Manenti, Giulia Bozzano, Davide Manca (Eds.)
Proceedings of the 30th European Symposium on Computer Aided Process Engineering
(ESCAPE30), May 24-27, 2020, Milano, Italy. © 2020 Elsevier B.V. All rights reserved.
http://dx.doi.org/10.1016/B978-0-12-823377-1.50173-7

CO$_2$ Conversion into Formates/Carbamates in an Electrolyte System

Maria C. M. Silva,[a]* Alessandra de C. Reis,[a] Antonio E. Bresciani,[a] Newton L. Ferreira,[b] Rita M. de B. Alves[a]

[a]Universidade de São Paulo, Escola Politécnica, Depart.de Engenharia Química
Professor Luciano Gualberto, travessa 3, 380 - São Paulo-SP 05508-010, Brazil.
[b]Centro Universitário FEI, Department of Chemical Engineering, Av. Humberto
Alencar Castelo Branco, 3972-B - Assunção, São Bernardo do Campo - SP,
09850-901, Brazil
mclaramendes@usp.br

Abstract

This paper explores the production of two intermediate chemicals with wide uses in industrial scale. The CO$_2$ hydrogenation using ammonia as an alkyl base produces ammonium formate and carbamate suitable for formic acid and urea synthesis. For this, an investigative simulation study was carried out to explore the possible operating conditions for each product. The given results pointed out that 50 °C and 1 bar favour the production of carbamate, obtaining 99% of yield and decrease formate one to less than 1%. However, low temperature (10 °C) and high pressure (50 bar) promote the formate yield to 81% and smaller quantities of carbamate, around 8%. CO$_2$ conversion is around 99% at 50 °C and 1 bar, when H$_2$O/ NH$_3$ ratio is 2.

Keywords: CO$_2$ hydrogenation, ammonia, ammonium formate, ammonium carbamate.

1. Introduction

Notably, climate change and the increase in temperature is directly caused by the increase in CO$_2$ emission, due to the greenhouse effect. To minimize this pollutant (CO$_2$) can be converted into valuable chemical products such as, methanol, acetic acid, dimethyl ether, formic acid and urea (Alper and Yuksel Orhan, 2017). To produce formic acid and urea, formates and carbamates are usually produced, as intermediates of the reaction. Methyl Formate is an intermediary in formic acid conventional production, which is mainly obtained by reacting carbon monoxide with methanol (Eq. 1 and 2) (Hietala et al., 2016).

$$CH_3OH + CO \rightarrow HCOOCH_3 \qquad (1)$$

$$CH_3OOCH + H_2O \leftrightarrow CH_3OH + HCOOH \qquad (2)$$

Carbamates are part of the urea synthesis, normally obtained from CO$_2$ and ammonia reaction (Eq. 3 and 4) (Morgan, 2013).

$$2NH_3 + CO_2 \leftrightarrow H_2NCOONH_4 \qquad (3)$$

$$H_2NCOONH_4 \leftrightarrow (NH_2)_2CO + H_2O \tag{4}$$

Jessop et al. have suggested that the addition of ammonia (NH_3) in the CO_2 hydrogenation improves the production of formate and carbamate (Jessop et al., 1995). In this work, the ammonia reacts with CO_2 and H_2 to produce ammonium formate and carbamate. This route will be modeled in aqueous solution, characterized as an electrolyte system. In general, an electrolyte system is made of chemical species that can dissociate partially or totally into ions in a polar liquid medium (i.e., solvent). The presence of ions in the liquid phase requires non-ideal solution thermodynamics.

2. Modeling

The set of independent reactions of the electrolyte system was defined by applying the Chemical Reaction Stoichiometry (CRS) method developed by Smith and Missen (1998). This method is able to identify the number of independent chemical reactions associated with each reaction step in the manufacture of the desired product, including intermediates that can be separated and recycled. This method defined the reactions that occur, the intermediates and the products of the reactions. After that, the thermodynamic analysis was performed to convert CO_2 into formate and carbamate. This step was simulated by an equilibrium reactor model (*RGibbs*) in Aspen Plus V9® process simulator, considering all the species involved in the reactions, being three gaseous species (H_2, CO_2, NH_3), liquid water (H_2O) and aqueous species (CO_3^{-2}, NH_4^+, OH^-, H_3O^+, $HCOO^-$, HCO_3^-, NH_2COO^-).

The inlet reactor was at 25 °C temperature and 1 bar. The thermodynamic behavior was predicted by the ElecNRTL model, which is proper to treat electrolyte species in the simulator and the activity coefficients of the ions are based on infinite dilution in pure water. The Gibbs energy of a system at a given temperature and pressure is minimum for the state of equilibrium. Thus, the equilibrium composition can be estimated by minimizing the Gibbs energy subject to constraints of the conservation elements. The choice of species present is an important consideration in the non-stoichiometric approach. All possible major products must be included for a realistic composition profile of a process. A sensitivity analysis was carried out conducted to evaluate the influence of temperature, pressure and ratio of the reactants on the system to convert the CO_2 into formate and carbamates. All the results are reported in terms of CO_2 and H_2 conversion and product yield. Table 1 provides the parameter definitions for the process.

Table 1. Definition of conversion and yield parameters

Parameter	Definition
CO_2 conversion	$\left(\dfrac{F_{CO_2,out} - F_{CO_2,in}}{F_{CO_2,in}} \right) x100$
H_2 conversion	$\left(\dfrac{F_{H_2,out} - F_{H_2,in}}{F_{H_2,in}} \right) x100$
$HCOO^-$ yield	$\left(\dfrac{F_{HCOO^-_{out}}}{F_{CO_2,in}} \right) x100$
NH_2COO^- yield	$\left(\dfrac{F_{NH_2COO^-_{out}}}{F_{CO_2,in}} \right) x100$

The effect of three variables was evaluated: temperature, pressure and reactants ($NH_3/H_2O/H_2/CO_2$) ratio. Initially, all the reactants were in the ($NH_3/H_2O/H_2/CO_2 = 1$) ratio at 1 bar and 25 °C. The temperature and pressure of the reactor were varied from 10 to 100 °C and from 1 to 50 bar, with 10 units of increment.

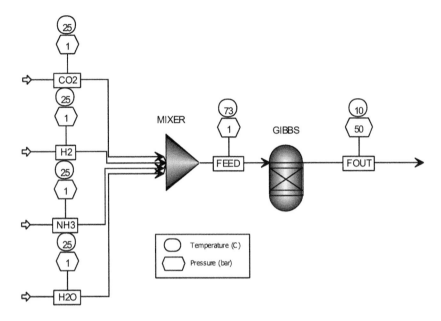

Figure 1. Simplified scheme of the process, initially at 25 °C, 1 bar and (NH3/H2O/H2/CO2 =1).

3. Results and Discussion

The procedure implemented by the Chemical Reaction Stoichiometry method resulted in 6 independent chemical reactions, which represent the electrolyte system of this study. Table 2 indicates all the reactions with their enthalpy and Gibbs energy of reaction and their remarks, respectively.

Table 2. Set of independent reactions for the electrolyte system

	Reaction	ΔH_R°	ΔG_R°	Remark
1	$CO_{2g} + 2NH_{3g} + H_2O_l$ $\leftrightarrow 2NH_{4aq}^+ + CO_{3aq}^{-2}$	170.67	-22.14	Endothermic, reversible, favored by high temperature
2	$H_2O_l + CO_{3aq}^{-2} \leftrightarrow 2OH_{aq}^- + CO_{2g}$	109.46	56.14	Endothermic, reversible, favored by high temperature
3	$3H_2O_l + CO_{2g} \leftrightarrow CO_{3aq}^{-2} + 2H_3O_{aq}^+$	2.58	104.10	Endothermic, reversible, favored by high temperature
4	$2H_{2g} + CO_{2g} + CO_{3aq}^{-2}$ $\leftrightarrow 2HCOO_{aq}^- + 2H_2O_l$	-66.32	-17.00	Exothermic, reversible, favored by low temperature
5	$CO_{2g} + H_2O_l + CO_{3aq}^{-2} \leftrightarrow 2HCO_{3aq}^-$	-27.51	-14.27	Exothermic, reversible, favored by low temperature
6	$CO_{2g} + 2NH_{3g} + CO_{3aq}^{-2}$ $\leftrightarrow 2NH_2COO_{aq}^- + H_2O_l$	115.29	-93.88	Endothermic, reversible, favored by high temperature

3.1. Sensitivity Analysis

In this process, CO_2 conversion is affected by the temperature and pressure applied to the system. Figure 2 a-b shows how these two variables influence the conversion of the reactants and products yields, respectively. The equilibrium conversion for both CO_2 and H_2 is high at lower temperature and higher pressure and decreases for higher temperature.

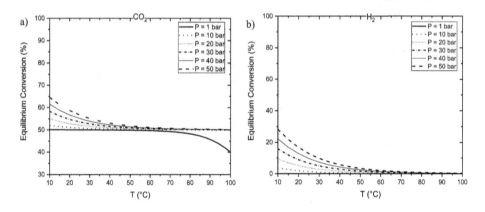

Figure 2. Effect of temperature and pressure on: a) CO2 conversion, b) H2 conversion at CO2/H2/NH3/H2O ratio = 1.

The highest CO_2 conversion (Fig. 2a) is 64% at 10 °C and 50 bar and ($NH_3/H_2O/H_2/CO_2$ =1) ratio. However, H_2 is less consumed at the same conditions, almost 30% conversion (Fig 2b). This difference is due to the numbers of reactions that CO_2 and H_2 participate in. CO_2 is consumed to produce ammonium formate and carbamate, while H_2 only reacts with ammonia and CO_2 to produce formate. Figure 3a-b are relative to the products yields.

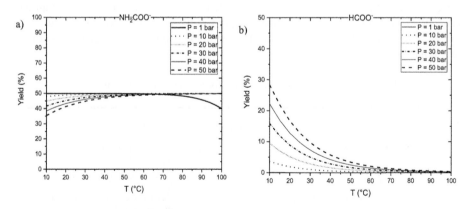

Figure 3. Effect of temperature and pressure on: a) Ammonium carbamate yield, b) Ammonium Formate yield at CO2/H2/NH3/H2O ratio = 1.

The ammonium formate yield increases at lower temperatures (10 °C) and higher pressure (50 bar), whereas ammonium carbamate yield is favoured at temperatures starting with 50 °C and room pressure (1 bar), according to Le Chatelier's Principle the formate reaction is exothermic, while, carbamate reaction is endothermic as shown in Table 3.

From all the reactants variation relatively to water, ammonium carbamates concentrations in solution is higher when H_2O/NH_3 ratio is 2. Figure 4 shows that the highest yield is obtained by fixing temperature and pressure at 50 °C and 1 bar, respectively, and varying H_2O/NH_3 ratio.

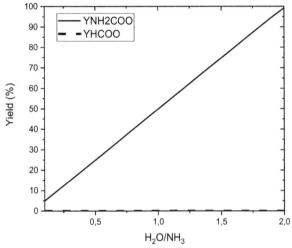

Figure 4. Effect of H2O/NH3 ratio on ammonium carbamate and ammonium formate yield at 50 °C and 1 bar.

Almost 99% of ammonium formate is obtained by fixing temperature and pressure at 10 °C and 50 bar, respectively, and increasing the H_2O/NH_3 ratio to 2. Figure 5 shows the conditions that the highest ammonium formate yield is reached.

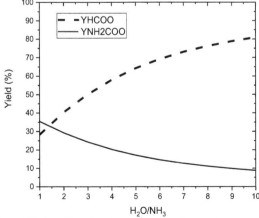

Figure 5. Effect of H2O/NH3 ratio of 10 on ammonium carbamate and ammonium formate yield at 10 °C and 50 bar.

This phenomenon occurs because a large quantity of water in the system enables the dissolution of the gases in the solution, which can increase the concentration of its ions. When there is less amount of ammonia in the solution, H_2 is free to reacts with CO_2, and produce more ammonium formate. As shown in Table 2, the reaction of ammonium formate production is exothermic.

4. Conclusions

The addition of ammonia makes the reaction thermodynamically viable for both ammonium formate and carbamate products. To detail the study on thermodynamic equilibrium on CO_2 and H_2 conversion into the products, the set of independent reactions was calculated through the Chemical Reaction Stoichiometry method. The influence of the variables studied, temperature, pressure and H_2O/NH_3 ratio were observed into both products yield. The results indicate that ammonium carbamate is favoured when temperatures are above 50 °C, low pressures, such as 1 bar, and H_2O/NH_3 ratio of 2 are applied. However, to shift the equilibrium to ammonium formate, lower temperature (10 °C), higher pressure and a H_2O/NH_3 ratio of 10 are required, reaching almost 81% of formates in the solution.

Acknowledgements: The authors would like to thank the sponsorship of Shell and FAPESP through the "Research Centre for Gas Innovation – RCGI" (FAPESP Proc. 2014/50279-4), hosted by the University of São Paulo, and the strategic importance of the support given by ANP (Brazilian National Oil, Natural Gas and Biofuels Agency) through the R&D levy regulation.

This study was financed in part by the Coordenação de Aperfeiçoamento de Pessoal de Nível Superior - Brasil (CAPES) - Finance Code 001.

References

Alper, E., Yuksel Orhan, O., 2017. CO2utilization: Developments in conversion processes. Petroleum 3, 109–126. https://doi.org/10.1016/j.petlm.2016.11.003

Hietala, J., Vuori, A., Johnsson, P., Pollari, I., Reutemann, W., Kieczka, H., 2016. Formic acid. Encycl. Ind. Chem. ULLMANN'S. https://doi.org/10.1002/14356007.a12_013.pub3

Jessop, P.G., Ikariya, T., Noyori, R., 1995. Homogeneous Hydrogenation of Carbon Dioxide. Chem. Rev. 95, 259–272. https://doi.org/10.1021/cr00034a001

Missen, R.W., Smith, W.R., 1998. Chemical Reaction Stoichiometry (CRS):

Morgan, E.R., 2013. Techno-Economic Feasibility Study of Ammonia Plants Powered by Offshore Wind. Univ. Massachusetts - Amherst, PhD Diss. 432.

Sauro Pierucci, Flavio Manenti, Giulia Bozzano, Davide Manca (Eds.)
Proceedings of the 30th European Symposium on Computer Aided Process Engineering
(ESCAPE30), May 24-27, 2020, Milano, Italy. © 2020 Elsevier B.V. All rights reserved.
http://dx.doi.org/10.1016/B978-0-12-823377-1.50174-9

Process Systems Design Framework for Resource Recovery from Wastewater

Alex Durkin[a], Marcos Millan-Agorio[a], Miao Guo[a,b,*]

[a] *Department of Chemical Engineering, Imperial College London, SW7 2AZ, UK*
[b] *Department of Engineering, Strand Campus, King's College London, WC2R 2LS, UK*
miao.guo@imperial.ac.uk

Abstract

A surrogate-based superstructure optimisation framework is presented and applied to the design of optimal flowsheets for the recovery of resources from wastewater. The process systems design framework involves training artificial neural networks (ANNs) using data sampled from commercial simulation software, where the sampling strategy incorporates Sobol sequences and support vector machines, ensuring good feasible design space coverage. A mixed integer linear programming (MILP) problem is formulated to solve the design problem for a set of optimal flowsheets highlighting the trade-offs between economic and environmentally focussed objective functions. However, despite the formulation of the MILP problem guaranteeing globally optimal solutions, this assurance comes at the expense of errors in the ANNs. These errors could become considerable for large design spaces, so exploration of the trade-off between optimality and accuracy is highlighted as a direction for future work.

Keywords: superstructure optimisation, resource recovery, surrogate modelling

1. Introduction

1.1. Background

Despite an explosion in process technology innovation, the successful deployment of these technologies is constrained by a lack of decision-making tools addressing the integration of technologies within optimal flowsheets. This process synthesis problem can be addressed by computer-aided process design, whereby evaluation of different flowsheets is achieved without the time and capital investments required for experimental or pilot scale studies. Specifically, superstructure optimisation can be used to rigorously search the design space for an optimal flowsheet, given a set of modular process units and possible interconnections (Yeomans and Grossmann, 1999).

Superstructure optimisation is a mathematical method whereby a flowsheet-wide performance indicator is optimised by determining the selection of process units, the design of these process units, and the interconnections between them. Binary variables are used for the selection of process units and interconnections, resulting in mixed integer programming (MIP) problems. However, there are many degrees of freedom in how to formulate and solve these MIP problems, including the choice of rigorous versus surrogate models. The former refers to complex models based on fundamental equations, whilst the latter addresses simpler reformulations to represent the complex underlying models in a more tractable form. Inherent in this decision is a trade-off between model complexity and tractability, where the use of accurate yet complex models lends to more computationally expensive optimisation problems, while more tractable surrogate models often come at the expense of solution accuracy.

Rigorous models are often embedded within black-box simulation software, allowing the user to observe input-output data but not the underlying model formulations. In these cases, computer experiments can be used to sample input-output data, providing training data for surrogate model formulations (Caballero and Grossmann, 2008). However, challenges associated with this approach include: choosing which variables to sample; assigning bounds to design variables; selecting a sampling strategy; and choosing surrogate model formulations which are accurate yet tractable. Further challenges with the superstructure optimisation methodology include: postulating the design space within a mathematical optimisation problem; formulating a tractable MIP problem; and solving the optimisation problem for the globally optimal flowsheet design. It is therefore beneficial to have methodological frameworks in place to assist in superstructure optimisation of process flowsheets.

1.2. Research Objectives

This research addressed the research objectives: develop a process systems design framework for the multi-criteria optimisation of process flowsheets; and application of the framework to resource recovery from wastewater, requiring tractable surrogate model formulations to represent complex process unit models. By addressing these objectives, this study provided a decision-making tool to assess process viability within integrated flowsheets, thereby assisting in resource recovery technology deployment.

Section 2 presents the methodology framework developed in this study. Section 3 applies the methodology to systems design for recovery of resources from a fermentation process wastewater. Finally, Section 4 presents some concluding remarks.

2. Methodology

Figure 1 shows the methodological framework developed in this study. The framework consists of 3 stages: an initialisation phase in which the flowsheet design space is posed; a surrogate modelling stage to generate the reduced-order surrogate models used to represent individual process units within the MIP problem; and the superstructure optimisation which solves the MIP problem for the optimum flowsheet.

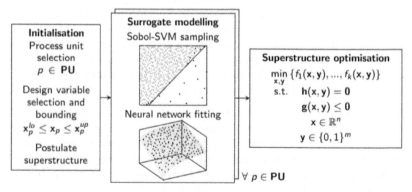

Figure 1. Process systems design framework.

2.1. Initialisation

In the initialisation phase, a set of process units were selected for consideration in the flowsheet optimisation. For each process unit within this set, design variables were chosen and bounds selected, thereby defining a hypercube representing the process unit design spaces. Connectivity between process units was then facilitated by connectivity constraints, thereby formulating the superstructure within the mathematical optimisation problem. Together, the individual process unit design hypercubes and superstructure connectivity constraints defined the entire flowsheet design space, within which the flowsheet configuration and active process unit designs were optimised.

2.2. Surrogate modelling

For each process unit, surrogate models were formulated to calculate output variables given different combinations of input variables. Output variables include process unit output stream flows and compositions as well as economic and environmental performance indicators. Input variables refer to the process unit design variables and the flows and compositions of influent streams. The surrogate models therefore facilitate the superstructure optimisation by relating different flowsheet designs to performance variables appearing in the objective function being optimised. Surrogate models can also be of a reduced order, relative to their rigorous counterparts, which is particularly useful when the rigorous models are highly dimensional and the input-output variables of interest are relatively few.

2.2.1. Sampling

The surrogate modelling phase begins with sampling input-output data from commercial process simulators embedding state-of-the-art rigorous models and costing functions. Sobol sequences were used to generate samples with good design space coverage with a minimum number of samples (Munoz Zuniga et al., 2013). Additionally, by ensuring information was sampled at the vertices of the design space, the surrogate model accuracy for these critical designs was increased. This is important due to the tendency for optimal solutions to exist at the bounds of the design space hypercube.

The modularity of the superstructure required not only design variables to be sampled, but also interdependent influent stream variables. The interdependencies were represented by calculating the covariance matrix for effluent variables from upstream process units. Then, by generating Sobol samples from an assumed underlying normal distribution, influent variable samples were extrapolated using the covariance matrix. This allowed influent variable interdependencies to be mapped between process units, ensuring meaningful influent compositions were being sampled.

2.2.2. Support vector machines (SVMs)

SVMs were integrated within the sampling strategy to simultaneously increase feasible design space coverage, and construct feasibility constraints. Feasibility of a given process unit design was determined by the successful or failed convergence of the black-box simulator, giving rise to a binary classification problem to which SVMs could be applied to determine the optimum separating hyperplane. By activating the SVMs after a few initial samples, subsequent infeasible design samples were substituted by samples at feasible designs. Specifically, SVMs with linear classification functions were used to generate linear feasibility constraints for use in the optimisation.

2.2.3. Surrogate models

The input-output data sampled from computer experiments was used to train surrogate models which represent the underlying complex black-box functions in a more tractable formulation for use in optimisation. Artificial neural networks (ANNs) were used as surrogate models due to their ability to model multiple input-output relations with good accuracy. Specifically, two-layer feed-forward ANNs were exploited due to their layered structure being representable by a set of linear constraints directly implemented in the mathematical optimisation. Additionally, formulation as a mixed integer linear programming (MILP) problem was facilitated using symmetric saturating linear functions and linear functions as activation functions in the hidden and output layer, respectively (Figure 2). The resulting ANN surrogate model constraints were therefore able to capture complex non-linearities from the rigorous models with a set of layered linear functions. ANN training and evaluation was performed in Python using Neurolab.

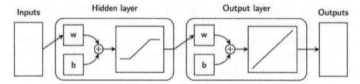

Figure 2. Two-layer feed-forward ANN configurations. Activation functions in the hidden and output layer are: symmetric linear saturating functions and linear functions, respectively.

2.3. Superstructure optimisation

The resulting MILP problem has the general formulation shown by Eq. (1) to Eq. (5),

$$\min_{x,y} z \tag{1}$$

$$s.t. \quad h(x, y) = 0 \tag{2}$$

$$g(x, y) \leq 0 \tag{3}$$

$$x \in \Re^{n} \tag{4}$$

$$y \in \{0,1\}^{m} \tag{5}$$

where z denotes the objective function optimising flowsheet-wide performance indicators dependent on the flowsheet configuration and active process unit designs. x and y are continuous design variables and binary selection variables, respectively. Both x and y are bounded by equality constraints, h, and inequality constraints, g, that enforce flowsheet connectivity and process unit surrogate models. The superstructure optimisation was formulated as a MILP problem in Pyomo and solved to global optimality using Gurobi (Hart et al., 2011; Gurobi Optimization, LLC, 2019).

3. Application

The methodology presented in Section 2 was applied to the design of an optimal process system to recover resources from wastewater. Specifically, the wastewater being considered comes from an industrial-scale fermentation process and is high in chemical oxygen demand (COD) and nutrients. The mathematical optimisation problem was posed to solve for a set of flowsheets representing the trade-off between economic and environmental objective criteria. Constraints implemented within the MIP problem also ensured that final effluent concentrations of total COD, total nitrogen (TN), and total suspended solids (TSS) were below environmental regulation limits. The application presented herein therefore explored: the trade-offs between recovering energy and/or nutrients; trade-offs between different flowsheets for recovering these resources; and the economic-environmental trade-offs between different flowsheet design focuses.

3.1. Process unit selection

Anaerobic reactors were considered for the recovery of biogas via decomposition of the wastewater COD. Specifically, two different reactor configurations were included in the superstructure, namely an upflow anaerobic sludge blanket (UASB) reactor and an anaerobic membrane bioreactor (AnMBR). For these reactors, the volumes and design of subsequent settling processes (surface area and waste sludge pumping rate) were optimised simultaneously within the flowsheet.

To ensure that final effluent constraints were met by the designed flowsheets, further processes units were considered to remove TN and TSS from the wastewater, namely: nitrification-denitrification (ND), anammox (AX), and secondary clarifiers (SC). Design variables for these process units included: volumes (ND, AX, SC), aeration rates (ND, AX), COD dosing rate (ND), and waste sludge pumping rate (SC).

The superstructure resulting from the initialisation phase is shown by Figure 3. Input-output data were sampled from GPS-X and CapdetWorks, which are state-of-the-art commercial simulators embedding rigorous wastewater treatment models and costing functions, respectively (Hydromantis, 2019).

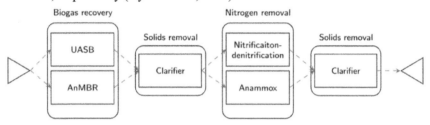

Figure 3. Superstructure of process units considered in application. Each functional stage (biogas recovery, solids removal, nitrogen removal) can also be bypassed.

3.2. Surrogate models

The input-output data was split into a training set, used to train the ANNs, and a test set used to validate the ANN performances (Table 1).

Table 1. Mean absolute error (MAE) and mean relative error (MRE) in ANN predictions.

Process unit	MAE	MRE / %
UASB	1.4	5.8
AnMBR	0.07	1.0
ND	7.7	19.9
AX	3.2	19.7

Some errors were accepted in the ANNs to avoid overfitting and maintain smooth input-output relations that well represented the underlying rigorous model trends. ANNs exhibited good performance for UASB and AnMBR models; AnMBR MAEs were particularly small due to the membrane resulting in small output concentrations. ND and AX models were less well represented by the ANNs due to the introduction of influent stream variables as inputs, thereby increasing the dimensionality of the design space.

3.3. Superstructure optimisation

The resulting MILP problem, containing connectivity constraints, process unit surrogate models, design variable bounds, and binary selection variables, consisted of 247 continuous variables, 195 binary variables, and 1060 linear constraints. Using Pyomo and Gurobi, the problem was solved to global optimality in 23.6 seconds, on a computer running 64-bit Linux on Dual 12-Core Intel Xeon 2.2 GHz processors with 96 GB RAM.

3.4. Solutions

The set of Pareto optimal flowsheets representing the tradeoff between economic and environmental objectives are shown in Figure 4a. The economic objective function was to minimise annual cost, incorporating fixed and operating costs (data obtained from CapdetWorks) as well as revenues from selling recovered biogas. The environmental objective function was to minimise annual greenhouse gas (GHG) emissions, with any produced biogas modelled as substituting natural gas production. The embedded GHGs, expressed as CO_2-eq per material, were obtained as life cycle impact factors from the ecoinvent database, using the ReCiPe Midpoint characterisation method. The optimum flowsheet designs for the economic and environmental objective function are shown in Figure 4b and 4c, respectively.

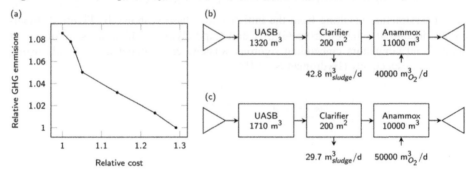

Figure 4. (a) Set of Pareto-optimal solutions representing the economic-environmental trade-off where data is shown relative to the optimum designs; (b) economic optimal flowsheet design; (c) environmental optimal flowsheet design.

Figure 4a depicts the trade-off between the different design criteria: the environmental optimum design is almost 30 % more expensive than the economic optimum; yet the cost optimal flowsheet emits more than 8 % CO_2-eq. Figure 4b and 4c only differ in the comprising process unit designs as a result of the limited feasible design space that meets final effluent constraints.

4. Conclusions

The presented design framework allows for MILP formulations for the optimisation of process systems, allowing for globally optimal flowsheets to be highlighted despite the incorporation of complex process units. However, as demonstrated, this guarantee of global optimality comes at the expense of some accuracy in the surrogate models. For larger superstructure postulations with many process units in series, the errors in the surrogate models propagate through the process train and become significant. Future work will aim to increase accuracy by: integrating the framework within an iterative approach; or exploring other surrogate models and their accuracy-tractability trade-off.

References

J. Caballero, I. Grossmann, 2008, An algorithm for the use of surrogate models in modular flowsheet optimization, AICHE Journal, 54, 10, 2633-2650

Gurobi Optimization, LLC, 2019, http://www.gurobi.com

W. E. Hart, J. P. Watson, D. L. Woodruff, 2011, Pyomo: modeling and solving mathemtical programs in Python, Mathematical Programming Computation, 3, 3, 219-260

Hydromantis Environmental Software Solutions, Inc., 2019, http://www.hydromantis.com

M. Munoz Zuniga, S. Kucherenko, N. Shah, 2013, Metamodelling with independent and dependent inputs, Computer Physics Communications, 184, 6, 1570-1580

H. Yeomans, I. E. Grossmann, 1999, A systematic modeling framework of superstructure optimization in process synthesis, Computers and Chemical Engineering, 23, 6, 709-731

Sauro Pierucci, Flavio Manenti, Giulia Bozzano, Davide Manca (Eds.)
Proceedings of the 30th European Symposium on Computer Aided Process Engineering
(ESCAPE30), May 24-27, 2020, Milano, Italy. © 2020 Elsevier B.V. All rights reserved.
http://dx.doi.org/10.1016/B978-0-12-823377-1.50175-0

Intensified green process for synthesizing non-phosgene hexamethylene-1,6-dicarbamate

San-Jang Wang,[a,*] David Shan-Hill Wong,[b] Yu-Zhang Chen,[b] En-Ko Lee[a]

[a]Center for Energy and Environmental Research, National Tsing Hua University, Hsinchu 30013, Taiwan
[b]Department of Chemical Engineering, National Tsing Hua University, Hsinchu 30013, Taiwan
wangsj@mx.nthu.edu.tw

Abstract

Hexamethylene diisocyanate (HDI) is an important chemical building block in the production of high value-added polyurethane because of its some excellent properties. Traditionally, the HDI synthesis route involves extremely toxic phosgene as an industrial scale reagent. Recently, thermal decomposition of hexamethylene-1,6-dicarbamate (HDC) has been considered as the most attractive non-phosgene process for the HDI synthesis because HDC can be synthesized by reacting 1,6-hexamethylene diamine (HDA) with a green compound, dimethyl carbonate (DMC), instead of toxic phosgene. Therefore, the intermediate HDC synthesis is crucial to the whole process. In the study, design of two plant-wide processes is explored for green HDC synthesis. In the first process, HDC is produced in two reactive distillation (RD) columns in series. Complete conversion of HDA is designed and excess DMC reactant is used to increase the reaction conversion. The mixture of un-reacted DMC and by-product methanol from RD column tops is separated by a series of conventional distillation columns containing a pre-concentrator column and an extractive distillation system comprising an extractive distillation column and a solvent recovery column. In the second process, RD is enhanced by vapor recompression (VR) to reduce energy consumption. The key cost saving from VR is attributed to fully take advantage of small temperature difference between RD column bottom and top, and higher RD column top temperature rendering condenser duty totally utilized by RD column bottom. Furthermore, additional latent heat of RD overhead vapor is released to the extractive distillation system by external heat integration, which can then achieve significant saving in the operation cost of this system. Compared to the RD intensified process, total annual cost of the RD+VR intensified process can be reduced by 35%.

Keywords: process intensification, reactive distillation, vapor recompression, green process.

1. Introduction

Hexamethylene diisocyanate (HDI) is an important chemical building block in the production of high value-added polyurethane products because of its excellent properties. HDI is traditionally synthesized by the phosgenation of 1,6-hexanediamine (HDA). Recently, a non-phosgene method, comprising two steps, has attracted much attention. The first step is the synthesis of hexamethylene-1,6-dicarbamate (HDC) and the second one is the decomposition of HDC to HDI. In this method, HDC is an intermediate and its synthesis is critical in the whole HDI production process. There are some routes to synthesize HDC. However, these routes suffer from strict reaction conditions, use of expensive catalysts, and production of some byproducts. In recent years, the reaction of HDA with dimethyl carbonate (DMC) under mild operation conditions has become an attractive and popular route to synthesize HDC. DMC is a green compound and used as an important building block for various organic synthesis. The HDC synthesis from DMC is considered as a promising means because DMC can replace phosgene for the methoxycarbonylation of HDA.

Recent research of producing HDC by reacting HDA with DMC mostly concentrated on catalyst screening (Li et al., 2014; Ammar et al., 2017). However, very few literatures investigated the process design of non-phosgene HDC synthesis. In this study, we present the plant-wide process design of non-phosgene HDC synthesis by the reaction of HDA with DMC. Reactive distillation (RD) and vapor recompression (VR), two promising technologies of process intensification, are employed here in the green HDC synthesis process. The stoichiometric molar ratio of two reactants, DMC and HDA, is equal to 2. In most experimental studies, the molar ratio of DMC to HDA is mainly in the range of 4 to 8. Excess DMC reactant is used in our study to increase reaction conversion and complete HDA reaction conversion is achieved by two tandem RD columns. Un-reacted DMC and by-product MeOH can form a minimum-boiling homogeneous azeotrope with temperature of 63.8 °C and DMC composition of 13.3 mol% at atmospheric pressure. This azeotrope is separated by a pre-concentrator column and an extractive distillation system (EDS) using aniline as the solvent. In addition, the RD column is enhanced by VR to reduce energy consumption by fully taking advantage of a narrow temperature difference between bottom and top streams of HDC synthesis RD column. Finally, the VR effect on the economic performance of RD process is evaluated.

2. Design of RD intensified process for HDC synthesis

The HDC synthesis by HDA and DMC consists of two reactions given below.

$$HDA + DMC \rightarrow HMC + MeOH \tag{1}$$

$$HMC + DMC \rightarrow HDC + MeOH \tag{2}$$

The overall reaction is

$$HDA + 2DMC \rightarrow HDC + 2MeOH \tag{3}$$

DMC is first reacted with HDA to form an intermediate HMC (dimethylhexane-1,6-monocarbamate). Then DMC is reacted with HMC to produce the main product HDC. Recently, Cao et al. (2018) screened several catalysts in the reaction of HDA with DMC, concluded that $Mn(OAc)_2$ was the most effective catalyst, and gave a kinetic model using $Mn(OAc)_2$ as a catalyst.

In the design of HDC synthesis process, the economic objective is to minimize the total annual cost (TAC) by adjusting design variables. TAC comprises annual capital cost and operation cost. Annual capital cost takes into account the annual costs of column, condenser, reboiler, compressor, and heat exchanger. Payback period is assumed to be eight years in this calculation. An annual operating time is assumed to be 8322 hours. The operation cost contains the costs of cooling water, steam, and electricity. The unit costs of these utilities are adopted from the formulas given by Turton et al. (2012).

In this study, a commercial simulator, ChemCad, is used to execute the process simulation of non-phosgene HDC synthesis. The pure components sorted in the order of increasing normal boiling temperature are as follows: MeOH (64.7 ℃) < DMC (90.3 ℃) < aniline (184.4 ℃) < HDA (201.9 ℃) < HMC (290.2 ℃) < HDC (371.8 ℃). Two reactants, HDA and DMC, are two intermediate boilers while the main product HDC and by-product MeOH are the heaviest and lightest boilers, respectively. This boiling point arrangement is the most favorable case for RD. Reactants can be easily kept within the RD column to proceed reaction while HDC and MeOH can be simply withdrawn from bottom and top, respectively, of the RD column. In the studied system, vapor-liquid equilibrium relationships for three pairs of binary components in a DMC-MeOH-aniline mixture can be described by UNIQUAC model (Hsu et al., 2010). The modified UNIFAC model is utilized to determine the phase equilibrium relationships of other pairs not built in the ChemCad database.

The optimal configuration of RD intensified HDC synthesis process cab be achieved by sequential iterative steps to minimize TAC. There are two RD columns and three conventional distillation (CD) columns in this configuration. Reflux ratio and reboiler duty are two operation variables in every column. However, there are many design variables in this process. Due to the scope limit, the optimization steps for different configurations are omitted. In the optimal RD intensified process, two reactants, HDA with 50 kmol/h and DMC with 235 kmol/h, are fed into the first RD (RD1) column at stages 8 and 9, respectively. This column has a rectification zone of 8 stages and a reaction zone of 39 stages. The RD1 column is chosen to be operated at 1 atm, the same value as that in the kinetic study of Cao et al. (2018). Because the boiling point of DMC is 90.3 ℃, the temperature for liquid-phase reaction of HDA with DMC is limited in our study to be not greater than 90 ℃. The maximum reaction conversion can be obtained when reaction temperature is set at 90 ℃. Thus, the RD column base is designed to be operated at 90 ℃. The catalyst is fed together with DMC into the RD1 column because of the consideration of reaction temperature constraint.

The bottom product of RD1 column contains by-product, intermediate, and main products (MeOH, HMC, and HDC) together with un-reacted HDA and DMC. In the patent of Wang et al. (2006), HDC can be separated from the reaction mixture by crystallization. Thus, in our study, HDC is assumed to be completely separated from the bottom product by crystallization. HDC with 29.9 kmol/h can be crystallized from the bottom stream of RD1 column. The mixture other than HDC is next fed into the second RD column (RD2) at stage 7 for further reaction. The RD2 column, operated at 1.09 atm, contains a rectification zone of 6 stages and a reaction zone of 43 stages. RD2 column base is also operated at 90 ℃. HDA is completely reacted and HDC of 50 kmol/h is achieved by RD1 and RD2. The reboiler duties of RD1 and RD2 are 3.48 GJ/h and 1.11 GJ/h, respectively.

The overhead products of the RD1 and RD2 columns, with top HDA composition set to be 10^{-5} mol%, are almost the mixture of DMC and MeOH and sent into the first distillation column (CD1) at stage 9. This column contains 17 stages and is operated at 0.65 atm. Because the MeOH composition (42.5 mol%) of this mixture is much lower than that (86.7 mol%) of the DMC-MeOH azeotrope, CD1 is designed to achieve high-purity DMC (99.9 mol%) from column bottom and concentrate the MeOH composition of column top. A DMC-MeOH mixture with a MEOH composition (76 mol%) closer to that of DMC-MeOH azeotrope is distilled from CD1 column top and then entered into an EDS involving an extractive distillation column (CD2) and a solvent recovery column (CD3).

CD2 and CD3 columns have 36 and 25 stages, respectively. DMC-MeOH mixture from the top of CD1 column is entered into the CD2 column at stage 27. Aniline, employed as a solvent to improve the relative volatility of DMC and MeOH, is fed into the 4th stage and takes DMC towards CD2 column bottom. MeOH with purity 99.9 mol% is obtained from CD2 column top. The ratio of MeOH to the sum of DMC and MeOH from CD2 column bottom is set to be 9.5×10^{-4} for ensuring 99.9 mol% DMC separated from CD3 column top. The bottom product of CD2 column is sent into the 8th stage of CD3 column. Aniline with purity 99.99 mol% is removed from CD3 column bottom and recycled back to the aniline feed location in the CD2 column. To reduce the energy consumption of these CD columns, aniline stream releases sensible heat first to the feed stream of CD1 column through the heat exchanger 1 (HX1), then to the feed stream of CD2 column through the heat exchanger 2 (HX2), and finally to be cooled down at 54.5 °C (Hsu et al., 2010) through the heat exchanger 3 (HX3). A makeup stream of aniline is added to compensate for solvent loss in the EDS. The high-purity DMC products from CD1 column bottom and CD3 column top are recycled back to DMC feed location of RD1. The reboiler duties of CD1, CD2, and CD3 columns are 5.23, 5.67, and 1.70 GJ/h, respectively. Heat duties released by the CD3 bottom stream to HX1, HX2, and HX3 are 0.95, 0.11, and 0.07 GJ/h, respectively. Total annual capital cost, total operation cost, and TAC are 458.0×10^3, 1966.1×10^3, and 2424.1×10^3 US$/year, respectively. The total operation cost accounts for the major part (81%) of the TAC.

3. Design of RD+VR intensified process for HDC synthesis

VR is an intensification technology to reduce energy consumption by increasing thermodynamic efficiency. It is particularly effective when the temperature difference between column bottom and top is small. In the studied RD1 and RD2 columns given in the HDC synthesis process intensified by RD, column bottoms are operated at 90 °C while the top temperature of RD1 and RD2 columns are about 72 °C and 69 °C, respectively. This small temperature difference between column bottom and top makes VR a practical method to reduce energy consumption of RD1 and RD2 columns. Similar optimization steps for HDC synthesis process intensified by RD are employed to the one intensified by RD and VR. Figure 1 shows the optimal configuration of HDC synthesis process intensified by RD and VR. RD1 and RD2 columns are divided into top and bottom sections. In the RD1 column, top section has the stages above HDA feed. In the RD2 column, top section has the stages above this column feed. Bottom section is operated at low pressure while top section is operated at high pressure. The vapor from the bottom section is compressed by a compressor into the vapor with high temperature and pressure and then entered into the top section. The overhead vapor from top section can be used as a heating medium and release latent heat to the reboiler of bottom section. Blue dotted line represents the path of latent heat released. In this study, a temperature difference between two outlet streams leaving a reboiler is limited to be 10 °C. The pressure of compressor outlet is adjusted to satisfy this requirement of 10 °C temperature difference. Because DMC composition of DMC-MeOH azeotrope decreases when pressure increases, some amount of un-reacted DMC in top section is more easily moved downwards the reaction zone to increase reaction conversion when top section is operated at high pressure. The latent heat of overhead vapor from top section of RD1 column is totally released to the reboiler of RD1 column. The latent heat of overhead vapor from top section of RD2 column can be released to not only the reboiler of RD2 column but also the auxiliary reboiler of RD1 column and the HX4 for feed preheating of CD2 column. Aniline stream also releases sensible heat first to the feed stream of CD1 column through the HX1, then to the feed stream of CD2 column through the HX2, and finally to be cooled down at 54.5 °C through the HX3. This heat integration path from the CD3 bottom to the aniline feed is denoted by cyan dotted line shown in Figure 1.

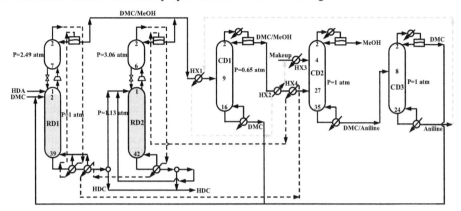

Figure 1. Configuration of HDC synthesis process intensified by RD and VR.

In the optimal configuration of HDC synthesis process intensified by RD and VR, top sections of RD1 and RD2 columns are operated at 2.49 atm and 3.06 atm, respectively. The optimal numbers of stages in the top sections of RD1 and RD2 columns are 7 and 6, respectively. The minimum TAC is achieved when the numbers of stages in the bottom sections of RD1 and RD2 columns are 40 and 43, respectively. The corresponding pressure at bottom section of RD2 column is 1.13 atm. The configuration of these designed CD columns is similar to that in the RD intensified process. CD1 column is operated at 0.65 atm. The number of total stages and number of feed stage are equal to 17 and 9, respectively. Overhead MeOH composition is set to be 76 mol%. Aniline (40 kmol/h) and the product distilled from CD1 column top are entered into stages 4 and 27, respectively, of CD2 column with 36 stages. In the CD3 column, the optimal feed location is the 8th stage under the number of total stage equal to 25 stages.

In comparison with the RD intensified process, the reboiler duties of RD1 and RD2 columns can be completely saved for the RD+VR intensified process. Furthermore, the reboiler duty of CD2 column can be substantially reduced from 5.67 GJ/h to 2.01 GJ/h because of the large latent heat released to the feed of CD2 column through HX4. The reboiler duty of CD1 column is also reduced from 5.23 GJ/h to 4.60 GJ/h because of the feed of CD1 column, from the overhead products of RD1 and RD2 columns, with higher temperature and pressure in the RD+VR intensified process. Only 49.9% of the steam cost in the RD intensified process is required in the RD+VR intensified process. The capital cost for compressor and electricity cost are the extraneous expenses under VR. All the costs except capital cost of HX are decreased by VR effect in the HDC synthesis process. Total annual capital cost, total operation cost, and TAC are 456.4×10^3, 1128.0×10^3, and 1584.4×10^3 US$/year, respectively. Compared with the process designed by RD, total operation cost and TAC can be reduced by 43% and 35%, respectively, for the process designed by RD+VR.

4. Conclusions

Some routes were used to synthesize HDC, an intermediate to manufacture HDI. Green HDC synthesis by reacting HDA with DMC has attracted much attention recently because of DMC usage to substitute toxic phosgene. In the study, we concentrate on the green HDC synthesis route by the reaction of HDC with DMC. Two plant-wide processes are proposed to produce HDC and separate the azeotrope of DMC and MeOH. In the optimal RD intensified process, two tandem RD columns are designed to achieve 100% HDA conversion by using excess DMC reactant. Because of small temperature difference between RD column bottom and top, an optimal reactive VR distillation process is designed to reduce energy consumption. Each RD column is divided into high pressure and low pressure sections by installing a compressor between these two sections. The latent heat of overhead vapor products from RD column tops can not only totally supply the heat duties of two RD column bottoms but also reduce substantial energy demand of CD columns. Simulation results demonstrate that the total operation cost and TAC of the RD intensified process can be substantially reduced by the effect of reactive VR.

References

M. Ammar, Y. Cao, L. Wang, P. He, H. Li, 2017, Synthesis of hexamethylene-1,6-dicarbamate by methoxycarbonylation of 1,6-hexamethylene diamine with dimethyl carbonate over bulk and hybrid heteropoly acid catalyst, Res. Chem. Intermed., 43, 6951-6972.

Y. Cao, L. Zhao, G. Zhu, L. Wang, P. He, H. Li, 2018, Kinetic study of methoxycarbonylation of 1,6-hexanediamine with dimethyl carbonate using Mn(OAc)$_2$ catalyst, Int. J. Chem. Kinet., 50, 767-774.

K. Y. Hsu, Y. C. Hsiao, I. L. Chien, 2010, Design and control of dimethyl carbonate-methanol separation via extractive distillation in the dimethyl carbonate reactive-distillation process, Ind. Eng. Chem. Res., 49, 735-749.

H. Q. Li, Y. Cao, X. T. Li, L. G. Wang, F. J. Li, G. Y. Zhu, 2014, Heterogeneous catalytic methoxycarbonylation of 1,6-hexanediamine by dimethyl carbonate to dimethylhexane-1,6-dicarbamate, Ind. Eng. Chem. Res., 53, 626-634.

R. Turton, R. C. Bailie, W. B. Whiting, J. A. Shaeiwitz, 2012, Analysis, Synthesis, and Design of Chemical Processes, Pearson Education, Boston.

G. Wang, J. Cheng, J. Yao, 2006, Method for Synthesizing Hexamethylene 1,6-Diamino Methyl Formate, China Patent CN1727330A.

Sauro Pierucci. Flavio Manenti, Giulia Bozzano, Davide Manca (Eds.)
Proceedings of the 30ʰ European Symposium on Computer Aided Process Engineering
(ESCAPE30), May 24-27, 2020, Milano, Italy. © 2020 Elsevier B.V. All rights reserved.
http://dx.doi.org/10.1016/B978-0-12-823377-1.50176-2

Heat Exchanger Network Optimization including Detailed Heat Exchanger Models using Trust Region Method

Saif R. Kazi[a], Michael Short[a,b], Lorenz T. Biegler[a,*]

[a]*Department of Chemical Engineering, Carnegie Mellon University, Pittsburgh, PA 15213, USA*
[b]*Department of Chemical and Process Engineering, University of Surrey, Guildford, GU2 7XH, UK*
lb@andrew.cmu.edu

Abstract

A trust region framework is presented to synthesize heat exchanger network with detailed exchanger designs. The heat exchanger network (HEN) is first synthesized using the stage wise superstructure (SWS) formulation of Yee and Grossmann (1990). After a topology is found in this step the heat exchangers and the connections, flows and intermediate temperatures are designed, using the first principles based differential algebraic (DAE) model presented in our previous work. These detailed DAEs for heat exchanger design are incorporated within a nonlinear programming (NLP) model using reduced order models and solved using NLP solver IPOPT with a trust region method. The results show that the new method is faster than the previous approaches while providing comparable results.

Keywords: Heat Exchanger Network, Trust Region, Mathematical Programming

1. Introduction

Optimization of HENs has been an archetypal problem in the process system engineering community for many years. The problem has been researched for more than 50 years with more than 400 research articles until 2002 (Furman and Sahinidis (2002)). Advances in mathematical programming have enabled solving large scale heat exchangers in reasonable time. Most recently-developed HENs models are derived from the formulation presented in Yee and Grossmann (1990) with many extensions proposed for stream splitting, non-isothermal mixing, and stream bypass.

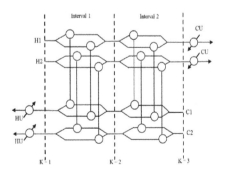

Figure 1: Superstructure formulation by Yee and Grossmann (1990)

Solutions obtained using these models are difficult to implement for real cases as the exchangers inside these networks are designed using shortcut models which are physically inaccurate.

Recent studies have addressed this issue by attempting to incorporate detailed design of exchangers within the MINLP HEN model. Liporace et al. (1999, 2000) derived the HEN using pinch analysis and removed exchangers which were very small or had many shells from subsequent iterations. Their study concluded that it is vital to include aspects of detailed design in designing the HEN. Mizutani et al. (2003b) developed an MINLP model for heat exchanger design using Bell-Delaware method. They subsequently used their MINLP model to design heat exchangers in the network and updating the individual stream heat transfer coefficients in the SWS model (Mizutani et al. (2003a)). Results indicated that the heat transfer coefficients for the converged solution were very different from their initial guesses. The MINLP models for exchanger design are nonconvex in nature and thus tend to suffer from convergence issues.

For this reason, Ponce-Ortega et al. (2009) used a genetic algorithm with a fitness function to filter out networks with detailed exchanger designs. Their approach used the sum of total annual cost (TAC) and temperature constraint violations as the fitness function. They used binary variables in the HEN model and the heat duties in the detailed exchanger model to verify convergence. As no information was passed between the detailed model and the networking model, the method cannot guarantee feasible designs. Ravagnani and Caballero (2007) improved upon the MINLP model of Mizutani et al. (2003a) by including TEMA standard values for number of tubes, tube lengths and diameters along with other constraints. This makes the model more nonlinear, nonconvex and difficult to converge with deterministic optimization algorithms. Although they were able to solve two example HEN problems in their follow-up paper, it required custom initialization to solve the highly nonconvex MINLPs for exchanger design.

Short et al. (2016a,b) devised a two-step strategy, where correction factors are used to update the number of shells, pressure drops and heat transfer coefficients in the MINLP HEN model. Individual heat exchangers are designed using the Bell-Delaware method manually after solving the SWS model. The method ensures that the TAC is the same for both the network design step and the detailed model, and also guarantees that the final network design is feasible with detailed models. The method, however suffers from lack of automation in the detailed design step, making it impractical for large-scale HEN problems. In addition, the Bell-Delaware method for multiple shells includes calculation of F_T correction factor and log mean temperature difference (LMTD) which are numerically unstable for optimization purposes and are based on empirical correlations.

Our previous work (Kazi et al. (submitted, 2019a)) addressed these shortcomings by introducing a novel method of exchanger design using first principles without F_T correction and LMTD terms. Subsequently, this method was combined with the two step strategy and with a more stable LMTD approximation to design network with detailed exchanger designs based on first principles discrete model (Kazi et al. (submitted, 2019b)). However, it was found that the method is computationally expensive as many iterations obtain the same solution. Additionally, the individual unit designs were solved for fixed heat and mass balances, thus neglecting the optimization of unit mass and heat balances.

In this study, we present a trust region based framework to simultaneously design HENs with detailed designs of individual exchangers. This method is inspired from previous work by Agarwal and Biegler (2013) and Eason and Biegler (2018), which use a filter-based strategy and reduced order models to create the trust region framework.

2. Methodology

In our method we first use the SWS model of Yee and Grossmann (1990) to obtain a HEN topology and initializations for the mass and energy balances of the network. Note that parameters in the MINLP for heat transfer coefficients are chosen such that the solution will underestimate the objective function and that an isothermal mixing assumption is used to avoid bilinearity in this step. After obtaining this network structure, we formulate an NLP representation that includes bilinear stream splitting and mixing equations that were excluded in the original MINLP.

To represent the heat exchangers in this NLP formulation we use reduced order models that are obtained via a trust region approach. In trust region optimization we can utilize external, black box or glass box models within a larger optimization problem. In our approach, the detailed exchanger models are obtained using the method presented by Kazi et al. (submitted, 2019a) whereby the heat and mass balances of the unit are given from the NLP suboptimization layer and a Bell-Delaware method is first used to enumerate designs in order to find the best configuration for the discrete decisions.

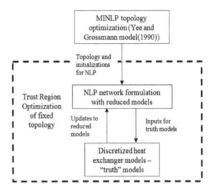

Figure 2 : Proposed algorithm for incorporating detailed designs into HEN synthesis

Following this, first principles equations are used to derive a set of DAEs based on the number of shell passes, number of tube passes, and number of baffles obtained in the Bell-Delaware optimization/enumeration. From this detailed discretized model we can easily obtain derivative information from the solution and use this to generate reduced order models that can be embedded within the network-level NLP.

2.1. Network-level NLP

The stream splitting and non-isothermal mixing constraints are added along with fixing the binary variables to the SWS solution to obtain the network level NLP. The NLP is formulated with reduced order models for detailed exchanger designs with trust region. After solving the NLP represented by Eq.(1), the solution is passed through the trust region filter to obtain the new trust region radius (Δ) for the next iteration. This is done until the infeasibility $\theta = \|y-d(x)\|$ and the trust region radius (Δ) are below threshold.

$$\min_{x,y} f(x,y)$$
$$s.t. \ c(x,y) = 0$$
$$g(x,y) \le 0 \tag{1}$$
$$y = r_k(x)$$
$$\| x - x_k \| \le \Delta_k$$

2.2. Reduced Order Model(ROM)

The reduced order modelsin the network-level NLP are generated by using the solution of the detailed DAE models and its sensitivity with the inputs from the NLP. The reduced order models are of the following form:

$$r_k(x) = \tilde{r}(x) + (d(x_k) - \tilde{r}(x_k)) + (\nabla_x d(x_k) - \nabla_x \tilde{r}(x_k))^T (x - x_k) \qquad (2)$$

where r - reduced order model, $\tilde{r}$ -low fidelity model, d - detailed model and x – reduced order variables

The models are updated at each iteration with the solution $(d(x_k))$ and sensitivity $(\nabla_x d(x_k))$ from the detailed models. The reduced order model satisfies a useful property of exactly matching function and gradient values with the detailed model at xk $(r_k(x_k) = d(x_k)$ and $\nabla_x r(x_k) = \nabla_x d(x_k))$.

2.3. Filter

A trust-region filter is used to determine the trust region radius (Δ) by comparing the descent in the objective value (f) and infeasibility (θ) in each iteration step. A step (s_k) is considered acceptable to the filter if for all $(\theta_j, f_j) \in F_k$

$$\theta(x_k + s_k) \leq (1 - \gamma_\theta)\theta_j \quad or \quad f(x_k + s_k) \leq f_j - \gamma_j \theta_j \qquad (3)$$

where γ_θ, $\gamma_j \in (0,1)$ are fixed parameters. The update is done by first calculating the ratio of reduction in infeasibility $(\rho_k = 1 - \theta(x_k + s_k)/\theta(x_k))$. The trust region radius is determined by following rule:

$$\Delta_{k+1} = \begin{cases} \gamma_c \Delta_k & if \ \rho_k < \eta_1, \\ \Delta_k & if \ \eta_1 \leq \rho_k < \eta_2, \\ \gamma_e \Delta_k & if \ \rho_k \geq \eta_2, \end{cases} \qquad (4)$$

where $0 < \eta_1 \leq \eta_2 < 1$ and $0 < \gamma_c < 1 < \gamma_e$

3. Results

Table 1: Example data, from Mizutani (2003a)

	m (kg/s)	T_{in} (K)	T_{out} (K)
H1	8.15	368	348
H2	81.5	353	348
C1	16.3	303	363
C2	20.4	333	343
HU		500	500
CU		300	320

where ΔT_{min} is 10 K, Area cost = $1000(NS) + 60(Area/NS)^{0.6}$$/year. Pumping cost = $0.7(\Delta P_t m_t/\rho_t + \Delta P_s m_s/\rho_s)$, where ΔP = Pa, m = kg/s, and $\rho = kg/m^3$. CU cost = 6 $/kW year and HU costs = 60 $/kW year. Overall heat-transfer coefficients of process stream with utility matches = $444 \ W/m^2 K$.

To demonstrate the proposed optimization approach we solve a simple HENS problem from Mizutani et al. (2003a). The stream data is shown in Table 1, with stream properties like viscosity, density, specific heat capacity and conductivity equal to [2.4e-04 Pa.s, 634 kg/m3, 2454 J/(kg.K), 0.114 W/(m.K)]. The dirt resistance factor r_d on both sides of the exchanger is assumed to be 1.7e-04 m2.K/W. The problem is modeled in the python based environment Pyomo and solved with NLP solver IPOPT 3.12. DICOPT and BARON are used as MINLP solvers

Table 2: Summary of solutions obtained for Example in comp arison with other studies

	This Study	Kazi et al.(submitted)	Short et al.(2016a)
Total Annual Cost ($/a)	96,596.17	97,360.94	97,159.3
Utility Costs ($/a)	90,000	90,000	90,036
Area Costs ($/a)	1,301.17	1,604.67	1,631.68
Pumping Costs ($/a)	1,295	1,756.26	1,491.63
Fixed Costs ($/a)	4,000	4,000	4,000
Number of matches	2	2	2
Number of exchangers	4	4	4

The results obtained from this strategy are reported in Table 2 along with the results from previous studies. The optimal network is presented in Figure 3. The total annual cost (TAC) and pumping costs obtained by the proposed strategy is less than reported in Kazi et al. (submitted, 2019b) and Short et al. (2016a). The optimal network in Figure 3 shows that two process and two hot utility heat exchangers are required to obtain desired outlet temperatures. The optimal network obtained is different from the network reported in our previous study.

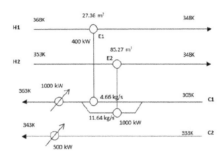

Figure 3: Proposed algorithm for incorporating detailed designs into HEN synthesis

In this network, the cold stream C1 undergoes splitting into two streams of flow rate 4.66 and 11.64 kg/s respectively. The total heat duty and area of process heat exchangers in the network are (400 kW, 27.36 m^2) and (1000 kW, 85.27 m^2) respectively.

Table 3 : Detailed heat exchanger results

	Exchanger 1	Exchanger 2
Area(m^2)	27.36	85.27
Duty(kW)	400	1000
Tube flowrate (kg/s)	8.15	81.5
Shell flowrate (kg/s)	4.66	11.64
Tube Pass	2	2
Baffles	11	6
Shell Dia(m)	0.32	0.81
Tube Count	150	438
Tube Length(m)	3.66	2.438
Overall Heat Transfer($W/m^2.K$)	478.9	439.9
$\Delta P_t(kPa)$	11.98	12.18
$\Delta P_s(kPa)$	5.85	5.12
Hot fluid	Tube	Tube

The detailed exchanger designs are reported in Table 3 along with allocation of hot and cold streams. Results show that both exchangers are designed with one shell and two tube passes heat exchanger. The pressure drops on tubeside and shellside streams are (11.98kPa, 12.18kPa) and (5.85kPa, 5.12kPa) respectively.

Future work will be aimed towards accelerating the convergence of the trust region algorithm. This will be aided by adding a compatibility check (see Eason and Biegler (2018)) such that the trust region NLP will always be feasible.

4. Conclusions

We present a new methodology for HEN synthesis which includes detailed heat exchanger design models. The new formulation uses the MINLP stagewise superstructure model to obtain a topology based on simplified exchanger models. This topology is then used as the basis of the NLP suboptimization with detailed heat exchanger models incorporated with a trust-region framework. The suboptimization provides optimal flow splits and detailed exchanger designs for the HENS based on detailed unit models. The heat exchanger design models are obtained through a rigorous optimization procedure whereby a DAE model is solved based upon a small enumeration of potential topologies based on Bell-Delaware equations. The new method is demonstrated on a small example and is shown to obtain excellent results in shorter times than other techniques while still providing guarantees on optimality. Future work is planned for application to larger problems and more advanced trust region strategies to decrease iterations.

References

A. Agarwal, L. T. Biegler, 2013. A trust-region framework for constrained optimization using reduced order modeling. Optimization and Engineering 14 (1), 3-35.

J. P. Eason, L. T. Biegler, 2018. Advanced trust region optimization strategies for glass box/black box models. AIChE Journal 64 (11), 3934–3943.

K. C. Furman, N. V. Sahinidis, 2002. A critical review and annotated bibliography for heat exchanger network synthesis in the 20th century. Ind. Eng. Chem. Res. 41 (10), 2335-2370.

S. R. Kazi, M. Short, L. T. Biegler, submitted, 2019a. Heat Exchanger Network Synthesis with Detailed Exchanger Designs - 1. A Discretized Differential Algebraic Equation (DAE) Model for Shell and Tube Heat Exchanger Design.

S. R. Kazi, M. Short, A. J. Isafiade, L. T. Biegler, submitted, 2019b. Heat Exchanger Network Synthesis with Detailed Exchanger Designs - 2. Hybrid Strategy for Optimal Synthesis of Heat Exchanger Networks with Detailed Individual Heat Exchanger Designs.

F. S. Liporace, F. L. P. Pessoa, E. M. Queiroz, 1999. Automatic Evolution of Heat Exchanger Networks with Simultaneous Heat Exchanger Design. Brazilian Journal of Chemical Engineering 16, 25–40.

F. S. Liporace, F. L. P. Pessoa, E. M. Queiroz, 2000. The influence of heat exchanger design on the synthesis of heat exchanger networks. Brazilian Journal of Chemical Engineering 17, 735–750.

F. T. Mizutani, F. L. Pessoa, E. M. Queiroz, S. Hauan, I. E. Grossmann, 2003a. Mathematical programming model for heat-exchanger network synthesis including detailed heat-exchanger designs. 2. Network synthesis. Ind. Eng. Chem. Res. 42 (17), 4019–4027.

F. T. Mizutani, F. L. P. Pessoa, E. M. Queiroz, S. Hauan, I. E. Grossmann, 2003b. Mathematical Programming Model for Heat–Exchanger Network Synthesis Including Detailed Heat–Exchanger Designs. 1.{Shell}–and–tube Heat–Exchanger Design. Ind. Eng. Chem. Res. 42 (17), 4009–4018.

J. M. Ponce-Ortega, M. Serna-González, A. Jiménez-Gutiérrez, 2009. Use of genetic algorithms for the optimal design of shell-and-tube heat exchangers. Applied Thermal Engineering 29 (2), 203 - 209.

M. A. S. S. Ravagnani, J. A. Caballero, 2007. Optimal heat exchanger network synthesis with the detailed heat transfer equipment design. Comp and Chem Eng 31 (11), 1432 -1448.

M. Short, A. Isafiade, D. Fraser, Z. Kravanja, 2016a. Two-step hybrid approach for the synthesis of multi-period heat exchanger networks with detailed exchanger design. Applied Thermal Engineering 105, 807-821.

M. Short, A. J. Isafiade, D. M. Fraser, Z. Kravanja, 2016b. Synthesis of heat exchanger networks using mathematical programming and heuristics in a two-step optimisation procedure with detailed exchanger design. Chemical Engineering Science 144, 372-385.

T. F. Yee, I. E. Grossmann, 1990. Simultaneous optimization models for heat integration—II. Heat exchanger network synthesis. Computers & Chemical Engineering 14, 1165–1184.

Sauro Pierucci, Flavio Manenti, Giulia Bozzano, Davide Manca (Eds.)
Proceedings of the 30th European Symposium on Computer Aided Process Engineering
(ESCAPE30), May 24-27, 2020, Milano, Italy. © 2020 Elsevier B.V. All rights reserved.
http://dx.doi.org/10.1016/B978-0-12-823377-1.50177-4

MINLP Model for Reliability Optimization of System Design and Maintenance Based on Markov Chain Representation

Yixin Ye[a], Ignacio E. Grossmann[a,*], Jose M. Pinto[b], Sivaraman Ramaswamy[b]

[a]*Department of Chemical Engineering, Carnegie Mellon University, Pittsburgh, PA 15213*
[b]*Business and Supply Chain Optimization, Linde.digital, Linde plc, Danbury, CT 06810*
grossmann@cmu.edu

Abstract

This paper proposes an MINLP model that represents the stochastic process of system failures and repairs as a continuous-time Markov chain, based on which it optimizes the selection of redundancy and the frequency of inspection and maintenance tasks for maximum profit. The model explicitly accounts for every possible state of the system. A decomposition method and a scenario reduction method are applied to this example to drastically reduce the computational effort. We show by an example that the proposed model and algorithms are capable of solving a practical problem based on the air separation process example that motivated our work, which features multiple stages, potential units and failure modes.

Keywords: reliability design, maintenance, optimization, Markov Chain, MINLP

1. Introduction

Plant availability has been a critical consideration for the design and operation of chemical processes as it represents the expected fraction of normal operating time, which directly impacts the ability of making profits. In practice, discrete-event simulation tools are used to examine the availability of a few selected designs of different redundancy levels under various maintenance and spare parts inventory policies (Sharda and Bury, 2008). However, the best plan selected through simulation is usually suboptimal because the list of design alternatives is often not exhaustive. Thus, there is a strong motivation for systematic optimization tools of redundancy design considering operational factors.

Several works have been reported regarding reliability considerations at the design phase (Kuo and Wan (2007)). In order to obtain a more comprehensive optimal design, it is important to consider the impact of operational factors such as maintenance on plant availability and their costs (Ding and Kamaruddin (2015)). Alaswad and Xiang (2017) provide a review for condition-based maintenance optimization models for stochastically deteriorating system with either discrete or continuous states. Pistikopoulos et al. (2001) and Goel et al. (2003) formulate MILP models for the selection of units with different reliability and the corresponding production and maintenance planning for a fixed system configuration.

Markov chain is a powerful mathematical tool that is extensively used to capture the stochastic process of systems transitioning among different states. Shin and Lee (2016) formulate the planning level problem of a procurement system as an Markov Decision Process to account for exogenous uncertainties coming from lead time and demand. Lin et al. (2012) model a utility system using Markov chain and carry out RAM (reliability, availability & maintainability) analysis iteratively to decide the optimal reliability design.

Terrazas-Moreno et al. (2010) use Markov chain as an uncertainty modeling tool for the optimal design of production site network considering reliability and flexibility. Kim (2017) presents a reliability model for k-out-of-n systems using a structured continuous-time Markov chain, which is solved with a parallel genetic algorithm.

Given the aforementioned research gaps and knowledge basis, this work extends our recent mixed-integer framework (Ye et al., 2017) and introduces a systematic approach to model the stochastic failure and repair process of the superstructure system as a continuous-time Markov chain. The new framework explicitly accounts for the long term property of each possible reliability scenario. Therefore, it is able to incorporate various kinds of decision making processes. Especially, comparing to Terrazas-Moreno et al. (2010) and Kim (2017), corrective maintenance and condition-based maintenance are incorporated in order to find the overall optimal selection of parallel units.

2. Motivating Example and Problem Statement

Consider an air separation unit (ASU) shown in Figure 1 as a motivating example. Critical processing units include the main air compressor, the pre-purifier, the booster air compressor, and the liquid O_2 pump.

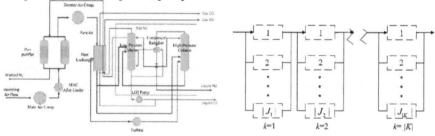

Figure 1. Typical flowsheet of an ASU   Figure 2. System topology and notations

The failure of any one of these processing stages can result in the failure of the entire system, which will compromise its ability to meet customer demands. In order to effectively increase the system availability, two strategies are considered.

2.1. Redundancy selection

The first strategy is to install parallel units for the critical stages. In Figure 2, the availability superstructure is formulated as a serial system of sequential stages, where each stage k has several potential design alternatives. The number and selection of parallel units have impacts on system reliability as well as capital costs.

2.2. Inspection Interval and Condition-based Maintenance

The second strategy is to carry out condition-based maintenance (CBM). Specifically, the units go through periodic inspections, and follow-up maintenance if the inspection result indicates that the equipment is going to fail shortly. The intervals between the periodic inspections impact individual unit failure rates and operational costs.

The ultimate goal is to achieve the optimal overall net present value for the system.

3. Mathematical Formulation

3.1. Markov Chain Representation

As mentioned in section 2.1, for each processing stage k, there is a set of potential units indexed by j. It is assumed that the time to failure and time to repair of each potential unit j follow exponential distributions with respective rate parameters $\lambda_{k,j}^0$ and $\mu_{k,j}$, which constitutes the transition matrix Q_k of the continuous-time Markov Chain of stage k. The system transition matrix W is then calculated as follows.

$$W = I_{(n_{|K|}n_{|K|-1}\cdots n_2)} \otimes Q_1 + I_{(n_{|K|}n_{|K|-1}\cdots n_3)} \otimes Q_2 \otimes I_{n_1} + \cdots + Q_{|K|} \otimes I_{(n_{|K|-1}n_{|K|-2}\cdots n_1)} \tag{1}$$

Element $W(\bar{s}, \bar{r})$ of matrix W is the transition rate from state $\bar{s}$ to state $\bar{r}$, which belongs to the system state space $\bar{S}$.

3.2. Logical constraints

Binary variable $y_{k,j}$ indicates whether unit j in stage k is selected.

$$\sum_{j \in J_k} y_{k,j} \geq N_k \tag{2}$$

Each possible combination of the potential units of one stage is called a stage design alternative indexed by h. Binary variable $z_{k,h}$ indicates the selection of stage design h for stage k. Set D contains the tuples of (j, k, h) where unit j is selected in design h of stage k, based on which $z_{k,h}$ and $y_{k,j}$ are connected as shown in (3), (4) and (5).

$$z_{k,h} \leq y_{k,j}, (j, k, h) \in D \tag{3}$$

$$z_{k,h} \leq 1 - y_{k,j}, (j, k, h) \notin D \tag{4}$$

$$z_{k,h} \geq \sum_{(j,k,h) \in D} y_{k,j} + \sum_{(j,k,h) \notin D} (1 - y_{k,j}) - |J_k| + 1, k \in K, h \in H_k \tag{5}$$

Equation (6) requires that one and only one design is selected for each stage.

$$\sum_{h \in H_k} z_{k,h} = 1, \forall k \in K \tag{6}$$

The combination of certain stage designs of each stage k is called a system design, which is indexed with $\bar{h}$. Set HC contains the tuples of $(k, h, \bar{h})$ where system design $\bar{h}$ contains stage design h of stage k. Binary variable $\bar{z}_{\bar{h}}$ indicates the existence of system design $\bar{h}$, and is related to the values of $z_{k,h}$.

$$\bar{z}_{\bar{h}} \leq z_{k,h}, \forall (k, h, \bar{h}) \in HC \tag{7}$$

$$\bar{z}_{\bar{h}} \geq \sum_{k \in K} \sum_{h \in H_k, (k,h,\bar{h}) \in HC} z_{k,h} - |K| + 1, \forall \bar{h} \in \overline{H} \tag{8}$$

Binary variable $\overline{zz}_{\bar{s}}$ indicates the existence of system state $\bar{s}$, which is required to be equal to $\bar{z}_{\bar{h}}$, if $\bar{s} \in \overline{T}_{\bar{h}}$, the subspace supported by system design $\bar{h}$.

$$\overline{zz}_{\bar{s}} = \bar{z}_{\bar{h}}, \forall \bar{s} \in \overline{T}_{\bar{h}} \tag{9}$$

$\pi_{\bar{s}}$ is the stationary probability of state $\bar{s}$, which has an upper bound of 1, and equals zero if state $\bar{s}$ does not exist.

$$\pi_{\bar{s}} \leq \overline{zz}_{\bar{s}}, \forall \bar{s} \in \overline{S} \tag{10}$$

The stationary probability distribution satisfies (11) and (12), which are based on the system transition matrix W and the existence of each system state.

$$\sum_{\bar{s} \in \overline{S}} \pi_{\bar{s}} \mathbf{W}(\bar{s}, \bar{r}) \leq M(1 - \overline{zz}_{\bar{r}}), \forall \bar{r} \in \overline{S} \tag{11}$$

$$\sum_{\bar{s} \in \overline{S}} \pi_{\bar{s}} \mathbf{W}(\bar{s}, \bar{r}) \geq M(\overline{zz}_{\bar{r}} - 1), \forall \bar{r} \in \overline{S} \tag{12}$$

Finally, the availability of the system is one minus the sum of the stationary probability of all failed states:

$$A = 1 - \sum_{\bar{s} \in \overline{S}^f} \pi_{\bar{s}} \tag{13}$$

3.3. Consideration of Inspections

The range of possible inspection intervals t_k^{insp} is discretized into a finite set of choices, T_l^{insp}. The selection of inspection intervals for each stage k is represented with binary variables $x_{k,l}$, where $x_{k,l} = 1$ when time length T_l^{insp} is selected for stage k.

$$\sum_{l \in L} x_{k,l} = 1, \forall k \in K \tag{14}$$

$$t_k^{insp} = \sum_{l \in L} x_{k,l} T_l^{insp}, \forall k \in K \tag{15}$$

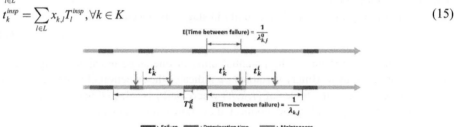

Figure 3. The impacts of inspections and maintenance

The equivalent failure rate $\lambda_{k,j}$ with inspections and maintenance is calculated in (16). Figure 3 shows a sketch of how $\lambda_{k,j}$ can be different from $\lambda_{k,j}^0$.

$$\lambda_{k,j}^0 - \lambda_{k,j} = \sum_{l \in L} x_{k,l} (e^{-\lambda_{k,j}^0 T_l^{insp}} - e^{-\lambda_{k,j}^0 (T_l^{insp} + T_k^d)}) / T_l^{insp}, \forall k \in K, j \in J_k \tag{16}$$

Each stage k has a inspection cost c_insp_k. Equation (17) enforces that the inspection cost for stage k is proportional to its inspection frequency and cost rate.

$$inspCost = \sum_{k \in K} c\_insp_k \sum_{l \in L} x_{k,l} \frac{T}{T_l^{insp}} \tag{17}$$

The repair cost is calculated according to the failure states. The repair cost in each state $\bar{s} \in \bar{S}$ is equal to the frequency of $\bar{s}$: $-W(\bar{s}, \bar{s})\pi_{\bar{s}}$, times the summation of the repair costs of all the units that are failed in state $\bar{s}$.

$$repaCost = -T \sum_{\bar{s} \in \bar{S}} W(\bar{s}, \bar{s})\pi_{\bar{s}} \sum_{(k,j) \in KJ_{\bar{s}}^f} c\_repa_k \tag{18}$$

The number of times for follow-up maintenance to take place in a single unit relative to its number of repairs is calculated by the relative difference between the equivalent failure rate and the original failure rate.

$$mainRatio_k \geq y_{k,j}(\lambda_{k,j}^0 - \lambda_{k,j})/\lambda_{k,j}, \forall j \in J_k \tag{19}$$

Equation (20) follows the same logic as in (18) to calculate costs according to failure states. Here, c_repa_k is replaced by c_main_k times $mainRatio_k$, which is the number of follow-up maintenance relative to the number of repairs.

$$mainCost = -T \sum_{\bar{s} \in \bar{S}} W(\bar{s}, \bar{s})\pi_{\bar{s}} \sum_{k \in K_{\bar{s}}^f} mainRatio_k c\_main_k \tag{20}$$

In addition to the costs, maintenance also causes downtime, which will result in the decrease of availability. Equation (21) calculates the downtime caused by maintenance in terms of the failure states $\bar{s} \in \bar{S}^f$ and those stages that fail in $\bar{s}$. The net system availability A is calculated as A minus the ratio of downtime caused by maintenance to the entire time horizon T.

$$mainTime = -T \sum_{\bar{s} \in \bar{S}^f} W(\bar{s}, \bar{s})\pi_{\bar{s}} \sum_{k \in K_{\bar{s}}^f} mainRatio_k T\_main_k \tag{21}$$

$$A^{net} = A - \frac{mainTime}{T} \tag{22}$$

3.4. Objective Function

The objective to be maximized is the Net Present Value NPV, the present value of net cash flow minus the investment costs. The yearly net cash flow is equal to revenue RV minus all the operational costs, and divided by number of years T. It is discounted by $\sum_{i=1}^{T} \frac{1}{(1+r)^i}$, where r is the rate of return (RoR) of cash flow. $instCost$ is the investment cost for installing the units depending on binary variables $y_{k,j}$. The revenue RV is proportional to system availability.

$$\max NPV = \frac{1}{T} \left(\frac{1-(1+r)^{-T}}{r} \right)(RV - repaCost - inspCost - mainCost) - instCost \tag{23}$$

$$inst\,Cost = \sum_{k \in K} \sum_{j \in J_k} y_{k,j} c\_inst_{k,j} \tag{24}$$

$$RV = A^{net} \cdot rv \tag{25}$$

4. Example

The model is applied to the motivating example of ASU (air separation unit) introduced in section 2, where the compressors have six failure modes and at least 2 units are needed for the pre-purifier. A time horizon of 10 years is considered. The exact numbers of relevant cost and reliability parameters of the units are proprietary information. Mean time between failures (MTBF) range from 5-25 years. Mean time to repair (MTTR) range from 8 - 1080hours. Capital cost of each unit range from \$85k - \$800k. Repair costs range from \$2k - \$20k per time. Inspection costs range from \$0.05k - \$0.5k per time. Maintenance costs range from \$1k -\$10k per time. Maintenance times range between 1 and 2 days. Inspection window lengths range between 5 and 6 day.

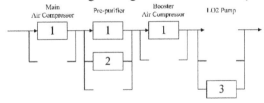

Figure 4. The optimal design

We propose an algorithm (Ye et al., 2019) that solves upper bounding MILPs and lower bounding MINLPs iteratively until the gap is closed. The algorithm converges in 7 rounds (ϵ= 1.7%) to the flowsheet shown in Figure 4. Only the least number of units are selected for each stage. For the main air compressor and the booster air compressor, more reliable and expensive units are selected, while for the LO2 pump, the solution selects the cheapest one. The expected system availability is 0.9866. The expected net present value is \$15,649.4k, with a revenue of \$29,597.8k and a penalty of \$421.9k. \$2,083k is spent on unit investment, \$262.7k is spent on inspections, \$7.4k is spent on maintenance, and \$48.9k on repair. Qualitatively speaking, this solution tends to spend more effort on reducing the failure rates for those failure modes with longer repair time.

The MILP models are solved with Xpress 29.01(748.8 CPUs), and the MINLP models are solved with SBB 25.1.1(492.0 CPUs).

5. Conclusions

In this paper, the stochastic process of system failures and repairs is modeled as a continuous-time Markov chain. Moreover, the impact of maintenance is incorporated.

With a general air separation unit as the motivating example, two strategies are considered to increase the availability of the system. The first strategy is to install parallel units for certain processing stages. The second strategy is to carry out periodic inspections, and condition-based maintenance if the inspection results indicate that the equipment will fail shortly. A non-convex MINLP model is proposed accordingly.

The non-convex MINLP model does not scale well, and has a large number of bilinear and multilinear terms. A decomposition scheme was proposed to reduce the size of the model and the computational time (Ye et al., 2019). The motivating example of the air separation unit is solved with the proposed specialized solution method.

References

Alaswad, S. and Xiang, Y. (2017). A review on condition-based maintenance optimization models for stochasticallydeteriorating system.Reliability Engineering & System Safety, 157:54–63.

Ding, S.-H. and Kamaruddin, S. (2015). Maintenance policy optimizationliterature review and directions.TheInternational Journal of Advanced Manufacturing Technology, 76(5-8):1263–1283.

Goel, H. D., Grievink, J., and Weijnen, M. P. (2003). Integrated optimal reliable design, production, and maintenanceplanning for multipurpose process plants.Computers & Chemical Engineering, 27(11):1543–1555.

Grossmann, I. E. and Trespalacios, F. (2013). Systematic modeling of discrete-continuous optimization modelsthrough generalized disjunctive programming.AIChE Journal, 59(9):3276–3295.

Kim, H. (2017). Optimal reliability design of a system with k-out-of-n subsystems considering redundancy strategies.Reliability Engineering & System Safety, 167:572 – 582.

Kuo, W. and Wan, R. (2007). Recent advances in optimal reliability allocation. InComputational intelligence inreliability engineering, pages 1–36. Springer.

Lin, Z., Zheng, Z., Smith, R., and Yin, Q. (2012). Reliability issues in the design and optimization of process utilitysystems.Theoretical Foundations of Chemical Engineering, 46(6):747–754.

Moubray, J. (1997).Reliability-centered maintenance. New York : Industrial Press, 2nd ed edition. "RCM II"–Cover.

Neuts, M. F. (1981).Matrix-geometric solutions in stochastic models: an algorithmic approach. Courier Corporation.

Pistikopoulos, E. N., Vassiliadis, C. G., Arvela, J., and Papageorgiou, L. G. (2001). Interactions of maintenance andproduction planning for multipurpose process plants a system effectiveness approach.Industrial & engineeringchemistry research, 40(14):3195–3207.

Sericola, B. (2013).Markov Chains: Theory and Applications. John Wiley & Sons.

Sharda, B. and Bury, S. J. (2008). A discrete event simulation model for reliability modeling of a chemical plant. InProceedings of the 40th Conference on Winter Simulation, pages 1736–1740. Winter Simulation Conference.

Shin, J. and Lee, J. H. (2016). Multi-time scale procurement planning considering multiple suppliers and uncertaintyin supply and demand.Computers & Chemical Engineering, 91:114–126.

Terrazas-Moreno, S., Grossmann, I. E., Wassick, J. M., and Bury, S. J. (2010). Optimal design of reliable integratedchemical production sites.Computers & Chemical Engineering, 34(12):1919–1936.

Weibull, W. et al. (1951). A statistical distribution function of wide applicability.Journal of applied mechanics,18(3):293–297.

Ye, Y., Grossmann, I. E., and Pinto, J. M. (2017). Mixed-integer nonlinear programming models for optimal designof reliable chemical plants.Computers & Chemical Engineering.

Ye, Y., Grossmann, I. E., Pinto, J. M., & Ramaswamy, S. (2019). Modeling for reliability optimization of system design and maintenance based on Markov chain theory. Computers & Chemical Engineering, 124, 381-404.

Sauro Pierucci, Flavio Manenti, Giulia Bozzano, Davide Manca (Eds.)
Proceedings of the 30th European Symposium on Computer Aided Process Engineering
(ESCAPE30), May 24-27, 2020, Milano, Italy. © 2020 Elsevier B.V. All rights reserved.
http://dx.doi.org/10.1016/B978-0-12-823377-1.50178-6

Synthesis of Sustainable Integrated Process, Water Treatment and Power Generation Networks

Yue Li,[a] Zhihong Yuan,[a*] Rafiqul Gani[b]

[a]Department of Chemical Engineering, Tsinghua University, Beijing10084, China
[b]PSE for SPEED company Ltd, Skyftemosen 6, DK 3450 Allerod, Denmazk
zhihongyuan@mail.tsinghua.edu.cn

Abstract

In this paper, we propose the concept of sustainable synthesis, design and innovation of integrated processes that include water and power generation networks with the overall objective to achieve zero or negative carbon emissions as well as wastes. A superstructure-based framework is developed and leads to the formation of a new consolidated optimization problem, which represents multiple networks at different scales and includes environmental impacts as constraints. Problem was solved step by step using a decomposition-based solution strategy and leads to the design of a totally integrated and sustainable process. The applicability of the framework and solution steps is demonstrated through a realistic conceptual case study under different scenarios to obtain and analyze different sustainable solutions

Keywords: synthesis of processes, power generation, water networks

1. Introduction

Environmental and energy issues have received widespread attention, which has made demand for more environmentally friendly and sustainable production processes. Chemical processes convert selected raw materials to desired chemical products, by-products and waste, while requiring also utility such as water and energy. Usually the process synthesis problem is solved considering the cost of energy and water but without considering their availability limits or their sources. Different sources and generation processes of water and energy (such as electricity) will cause different investment costs, operating costs, carbon emissions and pollutant emissions, which should be optimized along with the production process.

Traditionally chemical processes, power generation processes and water treatment processes are optimized sequentially to find the most profitable production route and the most environmentally friendly or cheapest power generation technology, and the most reasonable water treatment method. This approach does not take into account the interaction of the three networks which cause infeasible solution. Synthesis and design of the production process water network and generation network with specific production targets will lead to a more suitable and comprehensive solution. Inspired by the superstructure-optimization based integrated process and water network design (Handani et al., 2015), in this contribution, we expand the existing framework (Quaglia et al., 2012a) by integrating the process with water treatment and power generation networks. In addition, we also expand the developed generic model (Bertran et al., 2017) to synthesis the integrated process, water treatment and power generation networks. The applicability of proposed multi-network integration is demonstrated by a conceptual example.

2. Concept and Modeling

We propose concepts and modeling methods for integrating process, water treatment and power generation networks to obtain the sustainable solution considering the economic benefit and environmental factor. The systematically description will be shown in this section.

2.1. Concept of integration problem

The process requires the electricity heat and water supplement during production. Usually the optimal design problem is solved by computing the cost of them to maximize the economic benefit. Although some environmentally friendly solutions will also consider carbon emissions and pollutant emissions from the production process, potential carbon emissions and pollutant emissions from the process of energy generation and water treatment are ignored. In order to get the optimized sustainable production route in a more comprehensive and meticulous method. It is necessary to optimize the power generation and water treatment networks while optimizing the production process. As can be seen in Figure 1a, the electricity heat and water, which touch upon different techniques and sources, will be considered as products of power networks and water networks respectively. The waste water can be treated and recycled by water networks. Moreover, the recovery of carbon dioxide and the use of excess energy will also be considered.

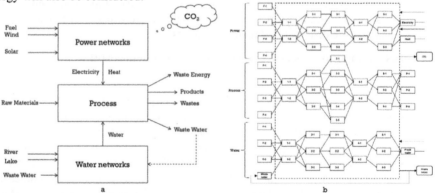

Figure1. Concept of integrated process water treatment and power generation networks
Superstructure of synthesis and design of integrated problem

2.2. Modeling

The systematic framework for processing networks (Quaglia et al., 2012b) and industrial waste water treatment (Quaglia et al., 2014) are extended in this paper. The superstructure-based optimization approach is carried out to simultaneously synthesize and design a chemical process with related power generation and water treatment networks to find optimal process production flowsheet and power generation and water treatment process path.

2.2.1. Superstructure

Figure 1b. illustrates a superstructure of three networks. Each interval of a sub-network represents an alternative technique in different steps. The electricity and heat are presented as two products of power generation networks and supply to the whole process network. The water produced by water treatment networks is used to provide for production and utility consumption.

2.2.2. Generic interval model

The generic model for each interval (Bertran et al. 2017) is adapted to the problem of synthesis and design of integrated process power generation and water treatment networks.

Shown by Figure 2. The flow added to the interval $g_{i,M}^M$ can be divided to chemicals and water. additionally, the consumption of utilities can be divided to the electricity heat and water consumption. For each sub-networks the generic interval model is given in Eqs. 1-12.

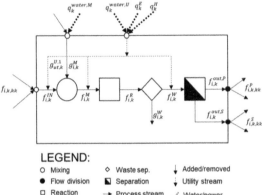

Figure 2. Generic structure of interval

$$g_{i,k}^M = \Sigma_i f_{i,k}^{IN} \mu_{i,ii,k} \tag{1}$$

$$g_{i,k}^M = \Sigma_i f_{i,k}^{IN} \mu_{i,ii,k} \tag{2}$$

$$f_{i,k}^M = f_{i,k}^{IN} + g_{i,k}^M \tag{3}$$

$$f_{i,k}^R = f_{i,k}^M + \Sigma f_{react,k}^M \theta_{react,r,k} Y_{i,r,k} \frac{MW_i}{MW_{react}} \tag{4}$$

$$f_{i,k}^W = f_{i,k}^R (1 - \delta_{i,k}) \tag{5}$$

$$g_{i,k}^W = f_{i,k}^R - f_{i,k}^W \tag{6}$$

$$f_{i,k}^{out,P} = f_{i,k}^W \sigma_{i,k} \tag{7}$$

$$f_{i,k}^{out,S} = f_{i,k}^W - f_{i,k}^{out,P} \tag{8}$$

$$g_{ut,k}^{U,j} = \Sigma_i \beta_{ut,k}^j f_{i,k}^{IN} , \ j = 1,2,3 \tag{9}$$

$$q_k^{water} = q_k^{water,M} + q_k^{water,U} = g_{water,k}^M + \Sigma_j \varphi_{water,ut} g_{ut,k}^{M,j} \tag{10}$$

$$q_k^E = \Sigma_j \varphi_{E,ut} g_{ut,k}^{M,j} \tag{11}$$

$$q_k^H = \Sigma_j \varphi_{H,ut} g_{ut,k}^{M,j} \tag{12}$$

In Eq. (9), parameter $\beta_{ut,k}^j$ can be estimated by energy balance of mixing reaction and separation process considering heat transfer and loss.

2.2.3. Optimization problem

The new framework combining process, power generation water and treatment allows us to find environmentally friendly solutions while guaranteeing the economic benefit. The Objective function and environmental constraints are given in Eqs. 13-16.

Objective function:

$$Z = S^{PROD} - C^{RAW} - C^{C} - C^{T} - \frac{CAPEX}{\tau} \tag{13}$$

Environmental constraints:

$$\sum CO_2(kk) \leq CONS_{CO2} \tag{14}$$

$$\sum Waste_{solid}(kk) \leq CONS_{solid} \tag{15}$$

$$\sum Waste_{water}(kk) \leq CONS_{water} \tag{16}$$

2.3. Solution step.

In order to obtain a solution to a specific problem through the proposed framework, the following four steps are recommended.

Step1: Problem definition. The first step is the definition of the goal of optimization problem including the determination of objective function, environmental constraints and other conditions based on the exact scenario.

Step2: Superstructure representation and data collection. In this step, various alternatives of process, water treatment and power generation are specified to obtain the superstructure in 2.2.1. The process data and physical data of all intervals in each network are collected or estimated.

Step3: model development. The next task is the development of generic model in 2.2.1 using collected process data. Then generate the MI(N)LP model o in optimization software i.e. GAMS.

Step4: Solve MI(N)LP problem. The sustainable solution can be obtained by solving the MI(N)LP model with environmental constraints and objective function designed in different scenarios.

2.4. Solution strategy

We recommend a decomposition-based solution strategy to solve the proposed integration problem to obtain sustainable solution. First solve the process network with assumption of unlimited utilities. Then add constraints of available water and energy. Water treatment network and power generation network need to be solved independently and then combine with the process sequentially to obtain the result.

3. Conceptual Case Study

3.1. Problem definition

The production of xylitol is considered as an example in our work. The current methods of producing xylitol include chemical hydrogenation and biological fermentation (Jain and Mulay 2014). The conceptual case study aims to demonstrate the effectivity of combining process, power generation and water treatment. The object is to check the economic benefit while considering the limitation of carbon dioxide emission and waste water disposal.

3.2. Superstructure and data collection

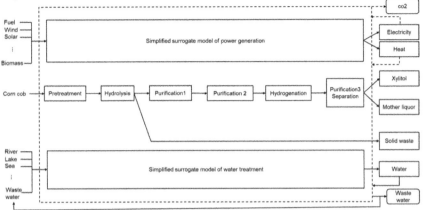

Figure 3. Superstructure of conceptual model

The chemical process converts the xylose from corn cob by Hydrolysis and then convert the xylose to xylitol while requiring a lot of electricity and steam. Different power generation, water supply methods and potential waste water recycle are integrated into this framework based-one simplified surrogate model of power generation and water treatment. The water sources include river, lake, sea, underground water and waste water. Power generation methods include thermal, wind, hydro, solar, nuclear and biomass. Different fuels are considered to generate steam.

3.3. Result and discussion

Market demand for xylitol is fixed at 12,000 t/y. For the first three scenarios, constraints are restricted in different degree. In scenarios 1 and 2, CO_2 emissions are restricted to be less than 390,000 t/y and 480,000 t/y while the waste water disposals are less than 1800,000t/y. In scenario 3 the problem is solved without environmental constraints. In scenario 4, the problem is solved in conventional method without considering the power and water networks. The results are given by Table 1. The radiation pattern of result 1-3 is shown in Figure 4.

Table 1. Xylitol production result in different scenarios

Result	1	2	3	4
Output (t/y)	9,727	12,000	12,000	12,000
Economic benefit ($/y)	8,103,785	11,602,450	14,139,542	9,544,956
Investment($/y)	81,331,530	100,301,888	100,301,888	100,301,888
CO2 emission (t/y)	390,000	479,737	541,084	\
Waste water disposal (t/y)	1800,000	1,800,000	3,662,130	3,662,130
Electricity (kwh)	50,328,788	62,073,333	61,347,100	60,246,710
Water consumption (t/y)	1,804,736	1,805,843	3,667,970	3,667,970
Steam consumption (t/y)	878,330	1,080,430	1,080,430	1,080,430
Electricity source	Wind	Wind	Thermal	\
Steam fuel	Coal	Coal	Coal	\
Water source	River	River	River	\

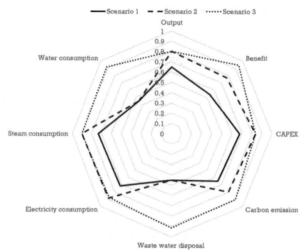

Figure 4. Radiation pattern of scenario 1-3

The scenario 3 has more economic benefit than result 4 since the new framework allows to get power and water at lower cost. By comparing scenarios 1-3, as can be seen in Figure 5, the environmental constraints can significantly influence the results. Strict environmental constraints will lead to environmentally friendly solutions while reducing productivity and economic benefits.

4. Conclusion and Future work

The concept of simultaneous design of process, water network and power generation network was proposed to obtain the sustainable solution. Superstructure-based framework were extended and generic interval model were developed to help construct new optimization problem in a generic approach. Solve the integration problem step by step can lead to sustainable solution with less carbon emission and waste water which has been demonstrated in conceptual case. Furthermore, this concept and method can be used for the synthesis and design of multiple networks to fixed optimal technical route of process, power generation water treatment and carbon recovery. The future work will focus on the design problem of multi-network of various cases and scenarios.

References

Z B. Handani, A. Quaglia, R. Gani, 2015, Synthesis and Design of Integrated Process and Water Networks. Computer Aided Chemical Engineering, 37:875-880.

A. Quaglia, B. Sarup, G. Sin, R. Gani, 2012a, Integrated Business and Engineering Framework for Synthesis and Design of Enterprise-wide Processing Networks, Computers & Chemical Engineering, 38, 213-223.

A. Quaglia, B. Sarup, G. Sin, R. Gani, 2012b, Synthesis and design of processingnetworks: stochastic formulation and solution, Comput. Aided Chem. Eng. 30,467–471.

A. Quaglia, A. Pennati, M. Bogataj, Z. Kravanja, G. Sin, R. Gani, 2014, Industrialprocess water treatment and reuse: a framework for synthesis and design, Ind.Eng. Chem. Res. 53, 5160–5171.

M O. Bertran, R. Frauzem, A S. Sanchez-Arcilla, et al., 2017, A generic methodology for processing route synthesis and design based on superstructure optimization, Computers & Chemical Engineering:S0098135417300303.

H. Jain, S.Mulay, 2014, A review on different modes and methods for yielding a pentose sugar: xylitol, International Journal of Food Sciences and Nutrition, 65(2):135-143.

Sauro Pierucci, Flavio Manenti, Giulia Bozzano, Davide Manca (Eds.)
Proceedings of the 30th European Symposium on Computer Aided Process Engineering
(ESCAPE30), May 24-27, 2020, Milano, Italy. © 2020 Elsevier B.V. All rights reserved.
http://dx.doi.org/10.1016/B978-0-12-823377-1.50179-8

Non-Newtonian Analysis of a Counter-flow Mixing Reactor for Fast Hydrothermal Liquefaction

Khanh-Quang Tran

Department of energy and process engineering Norwegian University of Science and Technology, NO-7491 Trondheim, Norway

Khanh-quang.tran@ntnu.no

Abstract

A CFD (computational fluid dynamics) model has been developed in ANSYNS Fluent for studying the use of the nozzle reactor concept for fast HTL of biomass. A Newtonian system was first assumed to make it possible to utilize data in the literature for calibration, which was then followed by a non-Newtonian assumption to simulate flows containing biomass particles. This paper presents and analyses results from the study.

Keywords: Hydrothermal liquefaction; Fast HTL; Nozzle reactor; Process intensification; Wet biomass.

1. Introduction

Fast hydrothermal liquefaction (HTL) may be defined as fast processing of biomass in hot compressed water (below 374°C, 22.1 MPa) for production of HTL oil or bio-crude. Similar to fast pyrolysis, the process of fast HTL requires heating rates higher than hundreds degrees per minute, aiming at maximized bio-crude yields and minimized coke formation of biomass HTL. Recently, the concept of fast HTL has been validated (Bach, Sillero et al. 2014, Bach, Tran et al. 2016). The possibility to improving the conversion efficiency and product selectivity of HTL by fast heating up to 585°C/min has been successfully demonstrated, using sealed capillary quartz reactors with a volume of approx. 0.5 cm³ per reactor (Bach, Sillero et al. 2014, Bach, Tran et al. 2016). More recently, it has been identified that the concept of nozzle reactor may be suitable for fast HTL of biomass at both laboratory and industrial scales (Tran, Håkansson et al. 2017). A CFD (computational fluid dynamics) study on the nozzle reactor design for fast HTL has been performed (Tran, Håkansson et al. 2017) using ANSYS FLUENT. The results show that the mass flowrate ratio of hot and cold flows plays the most important role in establishing high heating rates in the reactor. Tests for pure water (viscosity = 0.001 Pa.s), the mass flowrate ratio of 60:20 (hot/cold, mil/min) gave very good mixing and thus high heating rate. Effect of the total mass flow on the temperature profile in the reactor was not significant. However, an analysis of the model for fluid flow with elevated viscosities was not in agreement with the experimental validation. The reason of the disagreement is probably due to the Newtonian assumption to make it possible to utilizing the validation data from the literature. Therefore, new attempts to study the reactor for fast HTL using ANSYS Fluent, assuming non-Newtonian fluid flows have been made, which will be presented in this present paper.

2. Reactor and study methods

2.1. Reactor and process

Figure 1 presents schematically the concept of nozzle reactor, which has been succesfully developed for production of nanoparticles from equaeous solution of metal salts (Lester, Blood et al. 2006, Sierra-Pallares, Huddle et al. 2016). The reactor 1 is essentially a pipe-in-pipe concentric setup in which the internal pipe has an open-ended nozzle with a cone attached (optional). The "hot" stream (or flow) of preheated water is fed downwards through the internal pipe, reaching out at the exit end (nozzle) of the pipe. The "cold" stream is fed upwards through the outer pipe. The reactor outlet is situated on top of the outer pipe, leading the reactant mixture to a cooling unit. Because of the impingement of the hot and cold streams, the forced counter-current mixing process is enhanced by the natural convection due to the difference in density between the two steams. As a result, very good mixing and thus high heating rates can be achieved in the reactor.

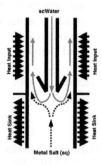

Figure 1: Schematic diagram of the nozzle reactor for hydrothermal synthesis of nanoparticles
(Lester, Blood et al. 2006, Sierra-Pallares, Huddle et al. 2016)

2.2. Computational fluid dynamic approach

2.2.1. Geometry and messing

In this work, a full geometry similar to Figure 1B was created and presented in Figure 2, of which the main dimensions are given in Table 1.

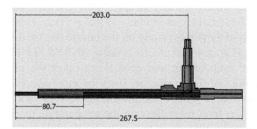

Figure 2. Geometry of the reactor used for CFD modelling

Table 1: Main dimensions of the reactor

Tube	Outer diameter (mm)	Thickness (mm)	Length (mm)
Hot flow inlet	3.175	0.89	186.72
Outer reactor tube	9.53	1.65	157.5
Cold flow inlet	3.175	0.89	20
Outlet flow	6.35	1.65	25

Due to the symmetry, only half of the reactor was meshed, using a hexahedral cell mesh with a maximum cell size of 0.2 mm. For meshing the fluids flowing through the reactor. a Virtual Body Group was added to the geometry of the reactor. For this purpose, the commercial CFD software ANSYS FLUENT, version 18.0 was used. Each analysis consisted of two steps; first a steady state run that established the flow and temperature fields of the entire reactor, and then a subsequent transient analysis to establish the *residence time distribution* (RTD) of the mixing zone. During the transient analyses, the flow and temperature fields were left unchanged at their steady state values; only the evolution of an inert scalar was simulated.

2.2.2. Governing equations and turbulence model

The behaviour of a fluid flow is governed by the fundamental set of Navier-Stokes equations for conservation of mass, momentum and energy. When modelling turbulent fluid flows, a suitable averaging method must be used (Sierra-Pallares, Huddle et al. 2016). For flow and mixing of fluids under supercritical conditions, it is convenient to use density or Favre averaging method, which applies fluctuation to average values instead of actual flow parameter in order to derive a time averaged solution (H.K.Versteeg and W.Malalasekera 2007, Sierra-Pallares, Huddle et al. 2016). The density averaged conservation equations for momentum, mass and energy are represented as

$$\frac{\partial \bar{\rho}}{\partial t} + \frac{\partial (\bar{\rho} \tilde{u}_i)}{\partial x_i} = 0 \tag{1}$$

$$\frac{\partial (\bar{\rho} \tilde{u}_i)}{\partial t} + \frac{\partial}{\partial x_j} (\rho u_i u_j) = -\frac{\partial \tilde{p}}{\partial x_i} + \frac{\partial}{\partial x_j} \left(\tilde{\sigma}_{ij} - \bar{\rho} \widetilde{u_i'' u_j''} \right) + \rho g_i \tag{2}$$

$$\frac{\partial (\bar{\rho} \tilde{e})}{\partial t} + \frac{\partial}{\partial x_j} \left(\bar{\rho} \tilde{u}_j \left[\tilde{e} + \frac{\tilde{p}}{\bar{\rho}} \right] \right) = \frac{\partial}{\partial x_j} \left[\lambda \frac{\partial \bar{T}}{\partial x_j} + \tilde{u}_j \left(\tilde{\sigma}_{ij} - \bar{\rho} \widetilde{u_i'' u_j''} \right) - \bar{\rho} \widetilde{e'' u_j''} \right] \tag{3}$$

$$\frac{\partial (\bar{\rho} \tilde{\phi})}{\partial t} + \frac{\partial}{\partial x_j} \left(\bar{\rho} \tilde{u}_i \tilde{\phi} \right) = \frac{\partial}{\partial x_j} \left[\bar{\rho} \mathcal{D} \frac{\partial \tilde{\phi}}{\partial x_j} - \bar{\rho} \widetilde{\phi'' u_j''} \right] \tag{4}$$

where u_j is the fluid velocity in direction x_j; p is the fluid pressure; ρ is the fluid density; e is the internal energy of the fluid; ϕ is a passive scalar; σ_{ij} is the viscous tress tensor of the fluid; and g_i is gravitational acceleration constant in direction x_i. If the viscosity fluctuation is neglected, the viscous tress tensor σ_{ij} will reduce to Eq. (5) where η is the molecular viscosity of the fluid and δ_{ij} is the unit matrix.

$$\sigma_{ij} = \eta \left[\left(\frac{\partial \tilde{u}_i}{\partial x_j} + \frac{\partial \tilde{u}_j}{\partial x_i} \right) - \frac{2}{3} \delta_{ij} \frac{\partial \tilde{u}_k}{\partial x_k} \right] \tag{5}$$

The set of equations Eq. (1-3) is not closed because the averaging procedure creates new variables for the Reynolds stress tensor $-\bar{\rho} \widetilde{u_i'' u_j''}$. In order to close the equation set, the Reynolds stress tensors is modelled and calculated, adopting the Reynolds-averaged Navier–Stokes (RANS) method and the Realizable k- ε turbulent model, of which further details can be found in the literature (Sierra-Pallares, Huddle et al. 2016) .

3. Results and discussion

In the first instance, the thermodynamic and fluid dynamic setup was defined with a Newtonian assumption. A RTD-based validation was performed, which gave similar results as for the simplified geometry assumption presented earlier (Tran, Håkansson et al. 2017). In addition, the mixing and thus reactor temperature profile, is in good agreement with the literature (flow ratio of 20:10 ml/min) (Sierra-Pallares, Huddle et al. 2016). Then the power law non-Newtonian model was adopted to simulate the cold flow of biomass slurry. Three investigations were performed using the developed non-Newtonian model. The first looked at the effect of the flow ratio on the mixing and thus temperature profile of the reactor. The second analyzed the effect of the viscosity change of the cold flow of biomass slurry. Third studied the effect of the total mass flow.

3.3.1 Effect of the flow ratio

Two simulations were performed and analyzed for the hot flow of the same pressure (25 MPa) and temperature (450°C) and a cold flow of 10% wt lignin slurry solution. The flows analyzed have been 20:10 and 30:10 ml/min. The results are shown in Figure 3.

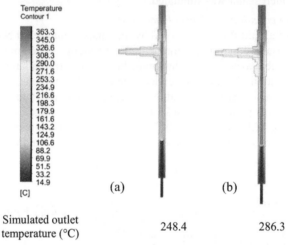

Figure 3. Temperature profile of the 20:10 (a) and 30:10 (b) ml/min for non-Newtonian model

It is clearly shown from the simulation result that the temperature at the outlet of the reactor is strongly dependent on the flow ratio. In addition, the temperature profile obtained from the non-Newtonian model is lower than that from the Newtonian. For example, comparing the 20:10 ml/min contours (Figure 3a and 3b) it can clearly be seen that for non-Newtonian fluid, the temperature of the hot inlet arriving the mixing point has drastically been reduced to an around value of 280°C compared to the 340°C obtained from the Newtonian one. On the other hand, as presented in Figure 4, clear differences in the shape of the mixing between the Newtonian and non-Newtonian simulations were observed. Indeed, the mixing of the fluids occurs in a point nearer to the hot inlet tube outlet in the non-Newtonian model than in the Newtonian simulation. In addition, the heat transfer takes place in a smaller space although the mixture temperature is notably lower.

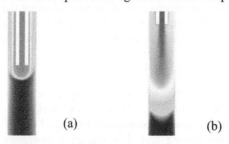

Figure 4: a) Mixing zones for non-Newtonian (a); and b) Newtonian model. (Flow ratios of 30:10 ml/min)

3.3.2 Effect of viscosity of the cold flow

The effect of viscosity of non-Newtonian fluid was used to simulate the effect of lignin concentration and particle size in the cold flow. The investigation was performed for the flow ratio of 30:10 ml/min and the result is presented in Figure 6. It is interesting to see that the temperature profiles obtained from the simulations are pretty similar, with their outlet temperatures of 286.32°C and 288.3°C, respectively. The main difference between them resides in the asymmetry which appears along the reactor in the 12.5%wt case (Figure 5d). Furthermore, the hot mixing zone appearing in the 10%wt is considerably longer than the one for 12.5%wt although being the same flow rates.

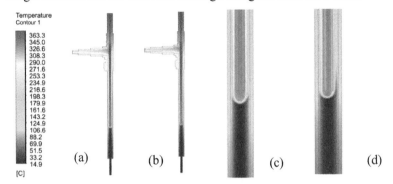

Figure 5: Temperature contour and c) mixing point for 10% wt (a and c), and 12.5%wt (b and d) lignin

3.3.3 Effect the total mass flow rate

For this study, the total mass flow rate were varied within 30:10, 60:20, 90:30 and 120:40 ml/min to insure a constant flow rate ratio of 3:1. In addition, a cold flow containing 10% wt lignin was employed all cases. In Figure 6 the obtained temperature contours for these flows and their outlet temperature are shown. The temperature in the mixing zone increases and this mixing zone moves downwards with increased total mass flow rate.

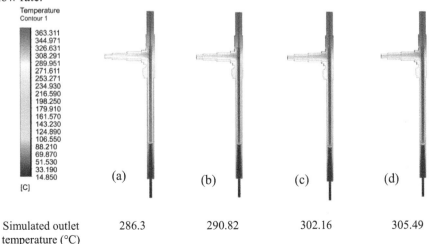

Simulated outlet temperature (°C)	286.3	290.82	302.16	305.49

Figure 6: Temperature profile for 30:10 (a), 60:20 (b), 90:30 (c) and 120:40 (d) ml/min, 10%wt lignin cold flow

4. Conclusions

In this study, a full geometry of the nozzle reactor design was developed and modelled for Newtonian and non-Newtonian fluids. The Newtonian assumption was used for model validation. The non-Newtonian assumption was used for studying the effects of the flow rate ratio, total mass flow rate, and the viscosity of the cold flow on the mixing the thus temperature profile of the reactor. The results indicated that

- Non-Newtonian fluids behave in a different way of Newtonian ones in important terms such as viscosity, temperature or flow.
- An important reduction in the temperatures along the reactor appears when working with non-Newtonian fluid compared to the results obtained with Newtonian one.
- The temperature profiles suffer very little change in value with the change of the viscosity.
- The mixing zone shape suffers a big change compared to the Newtonian fluid.
- Higher content of solid in the cold flow cause a bigger asymmetry in the temperature along the cross sections of the reactor. This fact can be solved using higher hot:cold flow ratios.
- The outlet temperature increases with the increment of the total mass flow rate.

Acknowledgement

The data presented in this paper is extracted from the master thesis of my ex-student, Gastón Mauricio Cocco, whose efforts are acknowledged.

References

Bach, Q.-V., M. V. Sillero, K.-Q. Tran and J. Skjermo (2014). "Fast hydrothermal liquefaction of a Norwegian macro-alga: Screening tests." Algal Research 6(B): 271-276.

Bach, Q. V., K. Q. Tran and K. Q. Lystad (2016). Fast hydrothermal liquefaction of macro-alga: Characterization of products. Chemical Engineering Transactions. 50: 97-102.

H.K.Versteeg and W.Malalasekera (2007). An Introduction to Computational Fluid Dynamics: The Finite Volume Method, Pearson Education Limited.

Lester, E., P. Blood, J. Denyer, D. Giddings, B. Azzopardi and M. Poliakoff (2006). "Reaction engineering: The supercritical water hydrothermal synthesis of nano-particles." The Journal of Supercritical Fluids 37(2): 209-214.

Sierra-Pallares, J., T. Huddle, J. García-Serna, E. Alonso, F. Mato, I. Shvets, O. Luebben, M. J. Cocero and E. Lester (2016). "Understanding bottom-up continuous hydrothermal synthesis of nanoparticles using empirical measurement and computational simulation." Nano Research 9(11): 3377-3387.

Tran, K.-Q., L. Håkansson and T. T. Trinh (2017). "CFD pre-study of Nozzle reactor for fast hydrothermal liquefaction." Energy Procedia 142: 861-866.

Sauro Pierucci, Flavio Manenti, Giulia Bozzano, Davide Manca (Eds.)
Proceedings of the 30th European Symposium on Computer Aided Process Engineering
(ESCAPE30), May 24-27, 2020, Milano, Italy. © 2020 Elsevier B.V. All rights reserved.
http://dx.doi.org/10.1016/B978-0-12-823377-1.50180-4

Techno-economic Analysis of Heat Pumping Technology for Oleochemical Fatty Acid Fractionation

Norul M. Sidek,[a,b]* Mohamad R. Othman[a,b]

[a]*Process Systems Engineering & Safety Research Group, Faculty of Chemical & Process Engineering Technology, Universiti Malaysia Pahang, 26300 Gambang, Pahang, Malaysia.*
[b]*Department of Chemical Engineering, College of Engineering, Universiti Malaysia Pahang, 26300 Gambang, Pahang, Malaysia.*
norulmalakiah.sidek@gmail.com

Abstract

Distillation unit is often known as a major energy consumer in chemical refineries. Recent researches have shown an increased interest in heat pumping technology. So far, previous studies of heat pump integrated column have not dealt with industrial oleochemical separation. The aim of this research paper has therefore been to investigate the implications of using heat pumping technology on oleochemical fractionation. This work takes the form of an industrial case-study of palm kernel oil (PKO) fatty acid fractional distillation. Two different arrangements of mechanical vapour recompression (MVR); namely direct vapour recompression (VRC) and bottom flashing heat pump (BFHP), were introduced to the process and their performances were assessed for technological efficacy as well as cost effectiveness. All simulations were carried out using Aspen Plus process simulator and UNIQUAC was chosen as the most suitable thermodynamic package. Economic analysis in terms of capital expenses (CAPEX) and operational expenses (OPEX) was evaluated. Though both MVR systems have shown relative reduction in energy load, however the CAPEX performance demonstrated in this study was not very appealing due to the additional equipment to satisfy the energy requirement. One anticipated finding was that the OPEX for the VRC showed only 50% from the conventional column (CC). On the contrary, the BFHP was ruled out for its CAPEX and OPEX, which showed twice as much as the CC.

Keywords: Oleochemical, vapour recompression, bottom flashing, fractional distillation.

1. Introduction

In the new global economy, energy consumption has become a central issue in chemical plants. One of the most significant discussions in this alarming issue is the energy utilization in major separation units. Distillation is commonly known as a prominent technology for separation process; however, it suffers from low thermodynamic efficiency which directly contributes to a large energy consumption. In view of this, any method of minimizing this associated energy would be of great advantage. Apparently, there is a large volume of published studies describing the important role of heat integration in energy saving. A number of mature heat-integrated technologies have already made a debut decade ago in chemical refineries. Heat pump assisted distillation has evolved to become one of those promising technologies that is commercialized for industrial practice.

In principle, application of heat pumping system would be worthwhile in an effort to reduce the associated external utility consumption, by recovering heat from column top vapour to aid the evaporation process in the reboiler. The state-of-the-art heat pump system used in many distillation operations worldwide is known as MVR. The typical MVR configuration, VRC, utilizes the overhead vapour as a heat transfer medium entering the compressor and will be compressed to a higher pressure and enters the bottom reboiler to heat the liquid. The other way is by flashing the liquid leaving the bottom reboiler and will be used to cool the overhead vapour, termed as BFHP.

To date, however, research on the subject has been mostly focused on petroleum processes. No previous study has investigated the influence of heat pumping system in energy saving for oleochemical separation thus far. As claimed by McKetta Jr. (1997) in his book, columns with the operation pressure of less than 100 mbar, which is common in oleochemical separation, are not suitable for VRC unless the system uses an auxiliary working fluid as to save the compressor cost. In addition to this, it was reported that most oleochemicals sustain limited familiarity and flexibility (Faessler et al., 2007). In this regard, far too little attention has been paid to heat integration measures in oleochemical separation due to the intricacy of low-pressure operation. This study therefore set out to assess the effect of MVR technology on the oleochemical separation particularly in fatty acid fractionation process. The findings of this study should make an important contribution to the oleochemical sector towards energy-efficient operation. The performance, external utility usage and capital investment were evaluated accordingly once the simulations were successfully established.

2. Process Simulations

2.1. Conventional column

Fat splitting of PKO generates crude fatty acid that can either be purified by distillation, giving a whole-cut purified fatty acid or separated into individual fatty acids by fractional distillation. In fractionation process, crude fatty acid is separated into its narrower cuts; light cut (C8-C10), medium cut (C12-C14) and heavy cut (C16-C18) (Illner and Othman, 2015; Othman and Rangaiah, 2020). Conventionally, the separation of low boiling point fatty acid component is commonly achieved by employing two units of fractionation columns. For the purpose of simplifying the process simulation in this study, only one fractionation column was used to separate the desired component, which in this case is 99% of lauric acid in distillate. Table 1 indicates the PKO fatty acid compositions obtained from an industrial oleochemical refinery.

Table 1: Compositions of PKO fatty acid (Othman and Rangaiah, 2020).

Component	Formula	Mole Fraction
Caproid acid	$C_6H_{12}O_2$	0.00121
Caprylic acid	$C_8H_{16}O_2$	0.03320
Capric acid	$C_{10}H_{20}O_2$	0.03420
Lauric acid	$C_{12}H_{24}O_2$	0.47681
Myristic acid	$C_{14}H_{28}O_2$	0.16296
Palmitic acid	$C_{16}H_{32}O_2$	0.07947
Oleic acid	$C_{18}H_{34}O_2$	0.15713
Linoleic acid	$C_{18}H_{32}O_2$	0.02615
Stearic acid	$C_{18}H_{36}O_2$	0.01891
Triglyceride (methyl-oleate)	$C_{19}H_{36}O_2$	0.00996

The process with a feed flow rate of 9000 kg/h was operated under high vacuum, 50 mbar. It is very important to keep the operating temperature below 250 °C to avoid chemical decomposition of fatty acid. The pressure drops in the column, condenser and reboiler throughout this work were taken to be zero due to too low operating pressure. For the simulation, the shortcut model in Aspen Plus, DSTWU was used to estimate the column performance such as number of stages and reflux ratio, which was later used for rigorous distillation (RADFRAC). 20 stages were needed for this separation process with a reflux ration of 0.75. In all simulations, the suitable model, UNIQUAC was chosen to predict the thermodynamic properties of the system (Sidek and Othman, 2019). The MVR assisted column configurations were also simulated based on the same column conditions and desired product specifications as the CC to promote a fair comparison.

2.2. MVR-assisted column with VRC

Various VRC configurations can be constructed depending on the process conditions. The latest novel VRC configuration was proposed by Cong et al. (2018) for a number of petroleum separation by introducing a middle VRC system. For this study, a typical VRC configuration will be adopted by Kazemi et al. (2016) but with some modification made based on the process conditions. The flow diagram of this scheme is shown in Figure 1. In this heat pump configuration, the low-quality heat of overhead vapour stream was upgraded by raising the temperature such that it was hotter than that in the reboiler. The elevated vapour temperature allowed the utilization of the latent heat for bottom liquid reboiling (Parhi et al., 2019). This was done by introducing the vapour into the compressor (C-101), eliminating the use of the condenser unit. Prior to that, the top vapour stream underwent superheating in order to prevent partial condensation from occurring. Moreover, it was appeared that even by using maximum practical compression of 3.0 as suggested by Felbab et al. (2014) without superheating, the compressor outlet temperature was not sufficiently hot for heat exchange with the bottom liquid. In view of this, the overhead vapour was superheated in the superheater (SH-101) at a temperature increase of 20 °C, while the compression ratio was taken as 3.0 to guarantee maximum heat was supplied to the heat exchanger (HX-101).

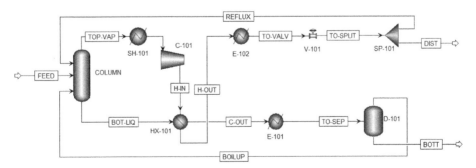

Figure1: Simulation flow diagram of the VRC

The early precaution of not letting the process temperature exceeded 250 °C was complied. The temperature difference in the heat exchanger was kept at a range of 5-8 °C for a cost-effective process. It was somewhat surprising to note that even with the aid of superheating and application of maximum compression ratio, the recovered heat could not provide required heat to evaporate the liquid. As a result, a trim-reboiler (E-101) was needed to supply the low-pressure steam to satisfy the remaining energy requirement.

The heated stream was flashed in the flash drum (D-101), where the vapour stream was routed to the column as boil-up, while the remaining liquid was drawn as a bottom product. On the other hand, the effluent stream from the heat exchanger was air-cooled in the trim-cooler (E-102) and expanded in the throttle valve (V-101) before being split in the splitter (SP-101). Part of the liquid was returned to the column as reflux, while the remaining was discharged as distillate.

2.3. MVR-assisted column with BFHP

This heat pump system is almost similar to the VRC, only in the BFHP, bottom liquid was flashed and used as working fluid in the compressor. In this configuration, the temperature of the bottom column outlet stream is normally reduced in the expansion valve (V-201). In that way, both condensation and evaporation can be fulfilled despite the omission of the reboiler and the condenser. The pressure drop during the expansion was determined such that the temperature difference between the hot inlet and cold inlet temperatures was exactly the same as in the VRC. Part of the reboiler duty was met during heat transfer in the heat exchanger (HX-201) and the remaining part was provided by the trim-reboiler (E-201). For similar reason as the VRC system, the stream was first routed to the superheater (SH-201) to avoid condensation. In Figure 2, it can be seen that the superheated cold outlet stream was recompressed to column operating pressure in the compressor (C-201) and sent to the flash drum (D-201) for vapour-liquid separation. The resulting vapour returned to the column as boil-up. Meanwhile, the liquid was subcooler in the air-cooler (E-202) and pumped out as final bottom product. The hot outlet stream from the heat exchanger was divided into two streams; reflux and distillate streams.

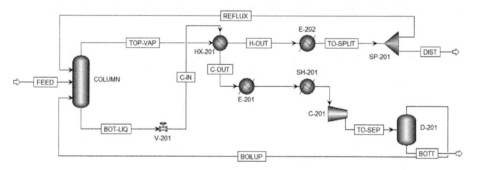

Figure 2. Simulation flow diagram of the BFHP.

3. Techno-economic analysis

3.1. Energy and utility requirement

Based on the results tabulated in Table 2, it was apparent that application of both MVR configurations to the column can reduce energy load despite the addition of the superheater unit in each system. On average, the CC reboiler duty was not entirely replaced by the heat exchangers, instead trim reboilers were employed to satisfy the remaining duty. The BFHP was shown to have a greater demand in energy consumption as only 40% of reboiler duty can be satisfied during heat exchange. This is due to the limitation set in temperature difference between the shell and tube inlet temperatures. As a result, overall heating duty for the BFHP was escalated to almost 20% close to what was needed in the CC. Operation of the BFHP also required even more extreme vacuum condition which is unfavourable, owing to its operation complexity.

On top of that, the MVR-assisted columns needed mechanical work to drive the compressor which accounts for the highest utility expenses. Taken together, it would be uneconomical to adopt the BFHP for this oleochemical separation, given that the mechanical compression work was twice the number reported in the VRC. To further validate this claim, a simple economic analysis will be discussed in the next section. Table 2 also reveals that there is a clear trend of decreasing in cooling utility to half of the number recorded by the CC condenser.

Table 2. Summary of utility requirements.

System	CC	VRC	BFHP
Cold utility requirements (kW)	969.25	423.36	496.16
Hot utility requirements (kW)	1185.83	556.06	965.32
Mechanical work requirements (kW)	-	94.58	192.40

3.2. Economic analysis

The economic performances of MVR-assisted columns were assessed in terms of CAPEX and OPEX. Sizing of individual equipment was primarily obtained from the calculated value in the simulator to determine the cost. These equipment details were then specified in the free capital cost estimation program, CAPCOST to determine the CAPEX for all configurations. Since all equipment was in contact with fatty acid, material of construction used in this study was 316 Stainless Steel for all units. The CAPEX mainly consists of major equipment; column tower, condenser, reboiler, heat exchanger, compressor, heaters and cooler costs. The Chemical Engineering Plant Cost Index (CEPCI) was used for cost adjustment from CAPCOST base year to a current year (2019). It was assumed that the plant was operated approximately 10 years, with 8000 operating hours per year. To calculate the OPEX, utility prices were taken from Parhi et al. (2019), where the electricity tariff for industry was \$0.084/kWh, high-pressure (HP) steam was \$17/t and cooling water \$0.06/t. The cost breakdown is detailed in Table 3.

Table 3. Summary of cost estimation for the CC and MVR configurations.

Configuration	CC	VRC	BFHP
CAPEX (x10^6 \$)			
Column tower	1.240	1.240	1.240
Column condenser	0.188	-	-
Column reboiler	0.475	-	-
Trim-reboiler	-	0.173	0.205
Trim-cooler	-	0.144	0.144
Superheater	-	0.271	0.487
Compressor	-	0.388	1.310
Heat exchanger	-	0.532	0.225
Total	*1.903*	*2.748*	*3.611*
OPEX (x10^6 \$/y)			
Electricity	-	0.064	0.129
High-pressure steam	0.338	0.158	0.275
Cooling water	0.080	-	-
Total	*0.418*	*0.222*	*0.404*

The findings of the current study in reviewing the performance of the MVR system in oleochemical fractionation are not very consistent with the previous researches. Both MVR configurations showed higher CAPEX than the CC. Nonetheless, it was somehow predictable because there were an additional equipment unit employed such as superheater and trim-reboiler to meet the energy requirement. In the typical configuration in most previous studies, liquid reboiler duty was entirely achieved during heat exchange, hence, no trim-boiler was needed and lower CAPEX recorded. Whilst, the estimated CAPEX of the BFHP was the highest amongst the three configurations, which was doubled the cost in the CC. This rather contradictory result may be due to the expensive compressor cost that was installed with high compression ratio to recompress the bottom stream to column operating pressure. On the other hand, it is interesting to note that, no cold utility was calculated for the MVRs. Since the trim cooler used in this study was an air-cooler, the cooling utility cost can be eliminated for both MVR systems. The VRC experienced 50% less utility expenses than the CC, and surprisingly, the higher utility was not coming from the electricity but HP steam. Approximately 1164 kg/h of HP steam was supplied to the superheater and the trim reboiler in the VRC and 2021 kg/h in the BFHP. The similar pattern was observed in the BFHP, only it was twice the amount of the utility used in the CC. Looking at the bigger picture, there is a strong possibility that in 10 years of the VRC operation, plant earnings can be increased by the amount saved on utility consumption. It is undoubtedly that a significant increase in profitability could be achieved in years to come, despite higher CAPEX recorded during the start of the operation.

4. Conclusions

The present study was designed to determine the implication of heat pumping technology application in PKO fatty acid fractionation. The energy usage evaluation suggests that the VRC was capable to operate excellently at lower heat load. Despite the VRC excellent performance in utility reduction, this thermal integration technology, however, relies greatly on the mechanical compression, which entails high costs. Furthermore, the use of the trim-reboiler with HP steam has also affected both CAPEX and OPEX performances. It is expected that the saving in utility consumption could contribute to the increase in future earnings in 10 years of the VRC operation and that it could exceed the CAPEX value. Meanwhile, the results for the BFHP was not very encouraging, not only it was costly, but it also worked under extreme vacuum condition which is not preferable. It is important to keep in mind that these simulations were only for a comparative study and the selected configurations might not be the most optimal design for fatty acid fractionation process. Further study is necessary to design the VRC system specifically for this process that works under vacuum condition.

References

A. Kazemi, A. Mehrabani-Zeinabad and M. Beheshti, 2018, Appl. Energy, 221, 1261-81.
H. Cong, J. P. Murphy, X. Li, H. Li, and X. Gao, 2018, Ind. Eng. Chem. Res., 57, 6317-29.
J. J. McKetta Jr., 1997, Encyclopedia of Chemical Processing and Design, Volume 61, 406-407.
M. Illner and M. R. Othman, 2015, PERINTIS e-Journal, 5, 34-44.
M. R. Othman and G. P. Rangaiah, 2020, J. of Oil Palm Res., In Press.
N. Felbab, B. Patel, M. El-Halwagi, D. Hildebrandt and D. Glasser, 2013, AIChE J., 59, 2977-92.
N. M. Sidek and M. R. Othman, 2019, Mat. Sci. Eng., In Press.
P. Faessler, K. Kolmetz, K. W. Seang and S. H. Lee, 2007, Asia- Pacific J. Chem. Eng., 2, 315-321.
S. S. Parhi, G. P. Rangaiah and A. K. Jana, 2019, Sep. Purif. Technol., 213, 553-570.

Sauro Pierucci, Flavio Manenti, Giulia Bozzano, Davide Manca (Eds.)
Proceedings of the 30th European Symposium on Computer Aided Process Engineering
(ESCAPE30), May 24-27, 2020, Milano, Italy. © 2020 Elsevier B.V. All rights reserved.
http://dx.doi.org/10.1016/B978-0-12-823377-1.50181-6

GHG Emission Reduction Assessment for Desalination Systems through Carbon Capture and Renewable Energy Options

Rachid Klaimi[a,b], Sabla Y. Alnouri[a,]*

The Baha and Walid Bassatne Department of Chemical Engineering and Advanced Energy, American University of Beirut, PO Box 11-0236, Riyad El-Solh, Beirut, Lebanon

Department of Mechanical Engineering, American University of Beirut, PO Box 11-0236, Riyad El-Solh, Beirut, Lebanon
sa233@aub.edu.lb

Abstract

Many existing desalination plants are energy intensive, relying on fossil fuels to provide the energy requirements of the process. In the long run, such desalination operations are unsustainable, and result in excessive carbon dioxide emissions. Since shifting towards renewable energy technologies has been identified as a plausible remedy for carbon dioxide emission reduction in the desalination market, the ability to invest in the most appropriate desalination/renewable energy technologies calls for the need to assess the many different options that do exist. When it comes to switching over to renewable energy options, policy makers are always concerned about the relatively high cost of renewable energy technologies compared to fossil fuels. Hybrid energy systems usually offer a relatively good compromise between conventional and renewable energy technologies, since such energy systems can address carbon footprint reduction to some extent. Moreover, carbon capture can be coupled with hybrid and conventional energy sources to reduce the carbon dioxide emission associated with their operation. To date, there exist no assessment methods that have captured the effects of imposing different carbon reduction targets on the optimal design of desalination systems, and their respective energy sources. Hence, the main objective of the model is to minimize the total desalination network cost, while satisfying a set of conditions and constraints related to water recovery, as well as heat and power production. Most importantly, the associated carbon emission levels may be controlled through renewable energy or a combination of conventional and hybrid energy options, in addition to the possibility of combining those options together with standard carbon capture methods.

Keywords: Desalination, Carbon dioxide emissions, Renewable energy, Hybrid energy systems, Carbon capture

1. Introduction

In light of the increased global water demand, due to population growth and excessive water use in the industrial and domestic sectors, the need to address eminent water shortage problems has become vital. Several studies have looked into potential solutions that could alleviate water scarcity through wastewater treatment and water reuse. By looking into ways that can help design Zero Liquid Dicharge (ZLD) systems, brine wastewater can potentially be utilized to recover treated water for reuse (Mansour and Alnouri 2019). Many other studies tackled water scarcity from a different perspective. For instance, some focused on utilizing industrial symbiosis strategies for this purpose (Somoza-Tornos et al. 2019). However, seawater desalination remains one of the most appealing techniques for alleviating water scarcity, even though most desalination technologies are energy intensive. Desalination systems that rely on the use of conventional energy sources, such as fossil fuels, are often associated with high levels of GHG emissions (Mannan et al. 2018). Therefore, many desalination industries are trying to shift into more renewable energy sources that have recently invaded the markets, in an attempt to reduce emissions and abide by the international regulations (Klaimi et al. 2019). Since renewable technologies are often associated with high costs, hybrid energy systems are gaining more attention due to their ability of meeting required energy demands while easing off some of the environmental limitations that are often faced when using conventional fuel sources only. Moreover, their moderate costs when integrated with desalination technologies also make hybrid systems quite attractive (Khan, Rehman, and Al-Sulaiman 2018). Similarly, carbon capture and storage (CCS) is one of the most common techniques utilized for emission reduction, and has been widely utilized due to its maturity and moderate costs compared to renewable energy (Al-Mohannadi and Linke 2016). The question of whether investing in carbon capture or renewable energy in order to achieve desalination operations still remains a challenge, especially due to the lack of tools that can help assess such situations. Hence, this paper presents a Mixed Integer Nonlinear Problem (MINLP) optimization model that enables a generic assessment of those carbon emission reduction methods, when coupled with desalination systems.

2. Methodology

The proposed model, shown in Figure 1 below, consists of four different sets of technologies: thermal desalination units (set T), membrane (set M), renewable energy (set R) and hybrid systems (set H), in addition to a carbon capture unit.

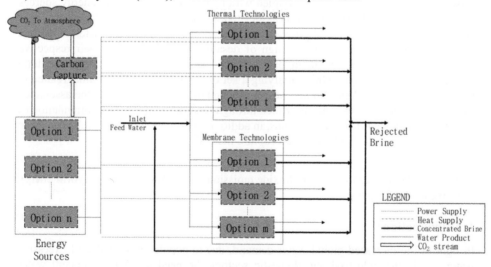

Figure 1: Desalination Network Structure

A seawater feed stream is mainly fed into the system and split between the thermal and membrane technologies. Two streams leave each desalination unit: a water product stream, and a concentrated brine stream. The system is designed such that a portion of the concentrated brine streams can be recycled back and mixed with the original feed stream, as this could potentially enhance the performance of the system. Additionally, the model allows for renewable energy and hybrid systems options to be available for providing the respective desalination units with their heat and power requirements. Unlike renewable energy sources, hybrid systems and conventional fuel energy sources are associated with certain amounts of carbon dioxide emissions. Therefore, the emissions resulting from those systems can be captured using CCS, which must undergo a treatment stage in order to reduce the environmental harm with respect to the imposed net carbon reduction target.

Designing an optimal desalination network integrated with renewable and hybrid energy systems requires a complete assessment of all the available technology options. This assessment is based on the specifications of each technology, which differ between desalination and energy units. For instance, the specifications of desalination units include the capacity limit, water recovery, salt rejection, heat and power requirements, in addition to the feed water characteristics, while those of energy sources include the capacity limit, capital and operational costs, as well as the amount of CO_2 associated with their operation, which is mainly based on the type of utilized fossil fuel. Different constraints can be imposed on those entities, as well as on the overall network. This makes the proposed approach very flexible, since it can be then modified based on the user specifications. Such constraints fall under one of the following categories: i) capacity constraints (the maximum flowrate that a desalination unit can withstand or the maximum amount of energy that can be produced by an energy unit), ii) composition constraints (the inlet and outlet brine concentrations), iii) water production (the required amount of product water), iv) and emission constraints (the maximum allowable carbon emissions).

3. Mathematical Formulation

The proposed optimization model is a MINLP, in which the cost objective function, represented by Eq. (1), is defined subject to various equality and inequality constraints:

$$\text{Minimize } Cost^{therm} + Cost^{mem} + Cost^{energy} + Cost^{carbon\ capture} \tag{1}$$

The objective function is to minimize the total network cost of the desalination system, which includes the capital and operational costs of desalination technologies, renewable and hybrid energy systems, as well as the carbon capture cost. The decision variable in the objective function refers to the flowrate vector which includes the flows into thermal and membrane units, the flows into technologies of the same type, and for the flows of the recycled streams. The objective function is subjected to two types of constraints: equality and inequality constraints. The equality constraints cover the mass and energy balances of different material throughout the system. The mass balance equations include total (Eq. (2)) and component (Eq. (3)) balances for brine and water streams in the system, while the energy balance equations, described by Eq. (4), target the amount of energy produced by the energy sources and integrated with the desalination technologies. In the following equations, F^{in} refers to the inlet feed flowrate, F^P is the flow entering desalination units, R refers to recycled streams, x_c is the concentration of component c,

E_r is the total energy produced by source r, and the subscripts t and m refers to thermal and membrane units.

$$F^P = (F^{in} + R^{therm} + R^{mem}) - B^{purge} \tag{2}$$

$$F^P x_c^P = (F^{in} x_c^{in} + R^{therm} x_c^{B,therm} + R^{mem} x_c^{B,mem}) - B^{purge} x_c^{purge} \tag{3}$$

$$E_r = \sum_{t \in T} E_{r,t} + \sum_{m \in M} E_{r,m} \ \ for \ \forall r \in R \tag{4}$$

On the other hand, the inequality constraints, represented by the capacity of desalination units and energy sources, maximum inlet salinity of desalination units, water production rate, and the net carbon reduction target, are described by Eq. (5-8), respectively, where PW refers to product water flow, χ_{PW} is the water recovery, while F_{CO2}^{total} is the exact CO_2 emission rate, F_{CO2}^{conv} is the CO_2 emissions of the base case and NCRT is the net carbon reduction target.

$$F^{min} \leq F \leq F^{max} \qquad \forall t \in T, \ \forall m \in M \tag{5}$$

$$x_c^{min} \leq x_c \leq x_c^{max} \qquad \forall c \in C, \forall t \in T, \ \forall m \in M \tag{6}$$

$$PW^{total} \geq \chi_{PW} F^{in} \tag{7}$$

$$F_{CO2}^{total} \leq NCRT * F_{CO2}^{conv} \tag{8}$$

4. Case Study Illustration

This case study features the desalination of Mediterranean seawater with TDS content of 38,600 ppm. Various thermal and membrane-based technologies have been considered as options for desalination, while renewable technologies and hybrid energy systems have been considered besides the conventional fuel option for energy production. A list of all the options that were included in this study is provided in Table 1. As for the carbon capture unit, only one technology has been assessed, which involves chemical adsorption using amine solvents due to its high level of maturity and easy application.

Table 1: List of Technology Options

Desalination technologies		Energy Production Technologies	
Thermal	Membrane	Renewable	Hybrid
Multi-Stage Flashing (MSF)	Seawater Reverse Osmosis (SWRO)	Photovoltaic Cells (PV)	PV-Wind
Multi-Effect Distillation (MED)	Brackish Reverse Osmosis (BWRO)	Wind	PV-Natural gas (PV-NG)
Mechanical Vapor Compression (MVC)	Electrodialysis (ED)	Concentrated Solar Power (CSP)	CSP-Natural gas (CSP-NG)
		Geothermal	

As previously mentioned, each of those technologies are associated with their own specifications and constraints, such as capacity limits, water recovery, and salt rejection, in addition to the carbon footprint parameters associated with energy production from natural gas. All these parameters and the technologies associated costs are obtained from (Klaimi et al. 2019). It should be noted that BWRO and ED options were not considered in this specific case, since their maximum inlet TDS is 12,000 ppm which is much lower than seawater TDS. On the other hand, a carbon removal efficiency of 90 % has been set on the carbon capture unit, and an overall water recovery of 50 % has been imposed on the system in all the studied cases. The model has been solved for different Net Carbon Reduction Targets (NCRT) that range from 0 % to 100 %. This Mixed Integer Non-Linear problem has been implemented using "What's Best 16.0" LINDO Global Solver for Microsoft Excel 2016 via a laptop with Intel Core i5 Duo Processor, 8 GB RAM and a 64-bit Operating System. In the first scenario, the system has been solved for 0 % NCRT. The obtained results showed that MVC and SWRO are the optimal technologies for desalination. This is mainly due to the high recovery of these two units and their lower cost compared to the thermal technologies which require both thermal and electrical energy. Only one energy source has been selected in this case which is the conventional fuel (natural gas), since it has the lowest cost among the available options and no carbon reduction target has been imposed on the system. The estimated amount of carbon emission was found to be 20.59 t/d, which is also used as the base case value for carbon reduction. When the NCRT is increased to 20 %, natural gas remains the only selected source of energy. However, the carbon reduction appears by the selection of the carbon capture option, as illustrated in Figure 2, where 4.58 t/d of CO_2 has been considered for capture to end up with a total carbon emission of 16.47 t/d.

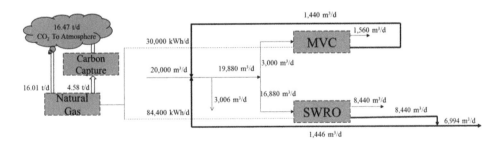

Figure 2: Desalination network for 20 % NCRT

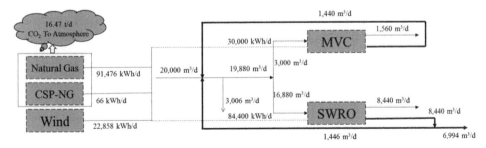

Figure 3: Desalination network for 20 % NCRT with model relaxation

When the NCRT is further increased to 40 %, a combination of wind energy and natural gas has been selected for power supply, in addition to carbon capture of 3.15 t/d of the resulted emission. At 60 % NCRT, the carbon capture option is no longer selected, while wind energy and natural gas remain the optimal energy sources until 80 % where only renewable wind energy has been selected to satisfy the stringent constraint on carbon emission. On the other hand, the water production cost associated with 100 % NCRT is estimated by 21.93 USD/m^3. Regarding the second scenario, the model has been relaxed by allowing the desalination units to be integrated with more than one energy source. This results in a completely different integration network regarding energy sources. The new obtained results (shown in Figure 3) witness the absence of carbon capture in all NCRT studied cases. The trend observed after model relaxation highlights the system's ability of selecting hybrid energy as a third party solutions, besides renewable and conventional energy options, and this helps achieve lower total network costs. Wind, CSP-NG and natural gas were the selected energy sources for NCRT values between 20 % and 80 %, while only wind energy has been selected for at 100 % NCRT.

5. Conclusions

The proposed approach presents an assessment of different carbon reduction strategies for seawater desalination systems. It was found that the selection of the optimal carbon reduction techniques depends on the net carbon reduction target imposed by the user. Carbon capture is highly recommended for reduction targets up to 40 % after which renewable energy, especially wind, gains higher attention. Moreover, hybrid energy systems were found to be a good compromise between renewable and conventional energy for carbon reduction targets that range between 0 % and 80 %.

Acknowledgment

The authors would like to acknowledge the financial support received from the University Research Board (Award# 103187; Project# 23308) and (Award# 103780; Project# 25352) at the American University of Beirut.

References

Al-Mohannadi, Dhabia M, and Patrick Linke. 2016. 'On the systematic carbon integration of industrial parks for climate footprint reduction', *Journal of Cleaner Production*, 112: 4053-64.

Khan, Meer AM, S Rehman, and Fahad A Al-Sulaiman. 2018. 'A hybrid renewable energy system as a potential energy source for water desalination using reverse osmosis: A review', *Renewable and Sustainable Energy Reviews*, 97: 456-77.

Klaimi, Rachid, Sabla Y Alnouri, Mahmoud Al-Hindi, and Fouad Azizi. 2019. 'Optimization techniques for coupling renewable/hybrid energy options with desalination systems for carbon footprint reduction', *Chemical Engineering Research and Design*, 151: 270-90.

Mannan, Mehzabeen, Tareq Al-Ansari, Hamish R Mackey, and Sami G Al-Ghamdi. 2018. 'Quantifying the energy, water and food nexus: A review of the latest developments based on life-cycle assessment', *Journal of Cleaner Production*, 193: 300-14.

Mansour, Fatima, and Sabla Y Alnouri. 2019. 'End-of-Pipe Zero Liquid Discharge Networks for different brine water qualities.' in, *Computer Aided Chemical Engineering* (Elsevier).

Somoza-Tornos, Ana, Manuel Rives-Jiménez, Antonio Espuña, and Moisés Graells. 2019. 'A circular economy approach to the design of a water network targeting the use of regenerated water.' in, *Computer Aided Chemical Engineering* (Elsevier).

Sauro Pierucci, Flavio Manenti, Giulia Bozzano, Davide Manca (Eds.)
Proceedings of the 30th European Symposium on Computer Aided Process Engineering
(ESCAPE30), May 24-27, 2020, Milano, Italy. © 2020 Elsevier B.V. All rights reserved.
http://dx.doi.org/10.1016/B978-0-12-823377-1.50182-8

NMPC based Temperature Control in Fed-batch Reactor to Avoid Thermal Runaway

Alex Kummer, Lajos Nagy, Tamás Varga

Department of process engineering, University of Pannonia, H-8200 Veszprém, Hungary
kummera@fmt.uni-pannon.hu

Abstract

Numerous fatal accidents occurred in the recent past caused by thermal reactor runaway, despite the fact, that the phenomenon of thermal runaway is well-known. However, accidents caused by runaway can be foreseen by using correct model and proper reactor runaway criteria, hence the operators can intervene in time in the system to prevent undesired events. Model Predictive Control (MPC) methodology is proposed to avoid reactor runaway during the optimal operation of fed-batch reactors. Fed-batch reactors are applied to carry out highly exothermic reactions safely, where the reactor and the sequence of process steps in normal operation are designed model-based. However, some of the parameters of reactor system (e.g. heat transfer coefficient) can change slightly over time or operators can make mistakes which can lead to trigger a runaway reaction. MPC can support the safe production by keeping the reactor controllable zone during the whole operation, in which also reactor runaway criteria can be implemented to predict the development of thermal runaway. Since the heat removal is limited the temperature is controlled by the inlet rate of feeding reactant and the cooling capacity is operating almost at maximum. To avoid thermal runaway, the feed rate of reactant is constrained by runaway criterion (namely Modified Dynamic Condition) which increases the safety of the process operation. Modified Dynamic Condition is implemented in NMPC algorithm as a penalty term, and also the criterion is used to define the minimal length of the considered prediction horizon based on process safety time. Moreover, the variable feed rate has an impact on economic of the operation since with decreasing the reactant concentration the feed rate increases to keep the reactor temperature close the optimal. Reactor efficiency is increased while the whole operation stays in controllable zone. The objective is to maximize productivity under the whole region of parameter uncertainty.

Keywords: thermal runaway, safe operation, early indication, process safety time

1. Introduction

Although the phenomenon of thermal reactor runaway is well-known, unfortunately lethal accidents still occurred in recent-past. In 2001 a polymerization reactor exploded because of a reactor runaway [1] and in 2007 an explosion occurred at T2 Laboratories caused death of four people. Thermal runaway results a rapid and significant temperature increase in the reactor which can lead to explosion due to the pressure increase in the reactor. Therefore it is highly important to keep the whole path of reaction under control to avoid the development of runaway. Fortunately, thermal runaway can be predicted by applying runaway criteria. Several runaway criteria exists which classify the reaction operation states as runaway or non-runaway, hence these equations can be applied to predict the development of thermal runaway [2]. Tailored runaway criteria were developed also to get a more specific critical equation [3]. Thermal runaway criteria can be successfully implemented in NMPC to keep the reactor always in the controllable regime, where the impact of parameter uncertainty was also investigated [4], although the prediction horizon has to be long enough to capture the development of runaway.

It is difficult to obtain a perfect model of the plant, hence there always will be some model-plant mismatch. A lot of method can be found in the literature to handle this problem, like taking into account uncertain parameters or applying state observers. These methods lead to a robust controller which satisfies the constraint for all possible realizations of the uncertainty [5]. Parameter uncertainty can be considered by applying the well-known min-max formulation [6], multi-stage methods [7], or tube-based methods [8]. Min-max MPC taking into account the worst-case realization of the parameter uncertainty, although it is conservative and it may results an infeasible optimization problem [9]. The conservativeness of min-max MPC was reduced by taking into account the future feedback information [5]. Multi-stage NMPC realizes the uncertainty by a tree of discrete scenarios, where each scenario has to satisfy the predefined constraints [7].

Our goal is to propose a method which is able to handle potential runaway reactions under parameter uncertainty, hence a Multi-Stage NMPC algorithm with implemented thermal runaway criterion is proposed.

2. Case study

Williams-Otto process has been used for years to test different control and optimization algorithms. We optimize the fed-batch version of this process as it is presented in [10]. In Williams-Otto process three exothermic reactions take place, which are presented in Eq. 1-3 followed by the equation of reaction rates.

$$A + B \rightarrow C \qquad\qquad r_1 = k_{0,1} exp\left(-\frac{E_1}{RT}\right) c_A c_B \qquad (1)$$

$$B + C \rightarrow P + E \qquad\qquad r_2 = k_{0,2} exp\left(-\frac{E_2}{RT}\right) c_B c_C \qquad (2)$$

$$C + P \rightarrow G \qquad\qquad r_3 = k_{0,3} exp\left(-\frac{E_3}{RT}\right) c_C c_P \qquad (3)$$

Two reactants (component A and B) are fed into the process, component A is preloaded and component B is continuously fed into the reactor. The desired product is component P, while two by-products are component E and G. The following differential equations (Eq. 4-8) describe the behaviour of the reactor system:

$$\frac{dc_i}{dt} = \frac{F^{in}}{V_R}\left(c_i^{in} - c_i\right) + \sum_{l=1}^{N_R} v_{il} R_l \ \ i = 1 \ldots N_C \qquad (4)$$

$$\frac{dV_R}{dt} = F^{in} \qquad (5)$$

$$\frac{dT_R}{dt} = \frac{4U}{D_R \sum_{i=1}^{N_C} c_i c p_i}\left(T_j - T_R\right) + \frac{F^{in} \sum_{i=1}^{N_C} c_i^{IN} c p_i}{V_R \sum_{i=1}^{N_C} c_i c p_i}\left(T^{in} - T_R\right) - \frac{\sum_{l=1}^{N_R} \Delta H_{r,l} R_l}{\sum_{i=1}^{N_C} c_i c p_i} \qquad (6)$$

$$\frac{dT_j}{dt} = \frac{4UV_R}{D_R V_j \rho_j cp_j}(T_R - T_j) + \frac{F_j}{V_j}(T_j^{in} - T_j) \qquad (7)$$

The kinetic parameters, component properties and reactor constructional and operating parameters can be found in [10], [11].

3. Formulation of Multi-Stage NMPC

The goal is to maximize the productivity while thermal runaway does not develop, hence the conversion of component A (x_A) and selectivity of component P (S_P) are considered in the objective function next to that runaway states should be avoided (I_k) and reactor temperature cannot exceed Maximum Allowable Temperature (*MAT*). Also the significant changes in the manipulated variables are penalized. We have applied Modified Dynamic Condition (Eq. 8) to operate the semi-batch reactor [2], where the slope of generated and removed heat, generated and removed heat and the decrease of reaction rate due to decrease of reagents concentration are considered to identify runaway states.

$$\qquad (8)$$

Formulation of nominal open-loop optimization problem can be seen in Eq. 9-12.

$$e^+ = max(T_{R,k} - MAT; 0) \qquad (9)$$

$$L = -w_x x_A - w_s S_p + w_u|u_k - u_{k-1}| + w_I I_k + w_T e^+ \qquad (10)$$

$$\min_u \sum_0^{t_{pred}} L(x_k, u_k) \qquad (11)$$

subject to

$$0 \le u_k \le 100\,\% \qquad (12)$$

where u_k is the control input at k-th time step, I_k is the sum of runaway states in the prediction horizon.

In case of Multi-Stage NMPC combination of maximal, minimal and nominal values of uncertain parameters are considered, which usually results a robust behaviour of the controller [5]. Each path of the scenario tree is called a scenario and indicated as i, and it contains all the states x_k^j and control inputs u_k^j that belong to scenario i. The set of all occurring indices (j,k) is denoted by I [12]. Formulation of Multi-Stage NMPC can be seen in Eq. 13.

$$\min_{u^j} \sum_{i=1}^N \frac{1}{N} L_i(x_k^i, u_k^i, d_k^i) \qquad (13)$$

subject to

$$0 \le u_k^j \le 100\,\% \qquad \forall(j,k) \in I \qquad (14)$$

$$u_k^j = u_k^l \text{ if } x_k^{p(j)} = x_k^{p(l)} \quad \forall(j,k),(l,k) \in I \qquad (15)$$

where $x_k^{p(i)}$ is the parent node. Eq. 15 represents the non-anticipativity constraints, which is about to equal all the control inputs at the same node.

The optimization problem was solved by modified progressive hedging algorithm, which is a decomposition algorithm, where non-anticipativity constraints are relaxed by penalizing the difference between the control inputs that should satisfy the non-anticipativity constraints. Its advantage that the scenarios can be solved independently, hence the following (Eq. 16) optimization problem has to be solved. Since the length of robust horizon is one in this case, only the first control inputs (u_0^i) of different scenarios have to satisfy the non-anticipativity constraint.

$$\min_{u^j} L_i(x_k^i, u_k^i, d_k^i) + \lambda^i(u_0^i - \hat{u}_0^i) + \rho^i(u_0^i - \hat{u}_0^i)^2 \qquad (16)$$

subject to

$$0 \leq u_k^j \leq 100\% \quad \forall (j,k) \in I \qquad (17)$$

$$\hat{u}_0^i = \sum_{i=1}^{N} \frac{1}{N} u_0^i \qquad (18)$$

where $\hat{u}_1^i$ is the fictious value towards which the control input converge to satisfy the anticipativity constraints. Parameters λ^i and ρ^i are updated at each iteration to improve the convergence, where the update rule is the following:

$$\lambda^i = \lambda^i + \rho^i(u_0^i - \hat{u}_0^i) \qquad (19)$$
$$\rho^i = min(\beta\rho^i, \rho_{max}) \qquad (20)$$

where β determines the increase of ρ^i. Eq. 16-20 are solved iteratively until $max(u_1^i - \hat{u}_1^i) < \varepsilon$. After several iterations the non-anticipativity constraints are satisfied with a desired tolerance ε.

4. Results of reactor control with full feedback information

This section presents the results of comparison between Nominal NMPC and Multi-Stage NMPC, where the results are shown in Figure 1-2. The reactor temperature is controlled by manipulating the feed rate of reagent, while the cooling proceeds almost at maximum. Open-loop optimization problem has been solved by the classical SQP optimization algorithm, and the algorithm proceeds with a moving horizon. The sampling time was 100 second, length of control horizon was 500 seconds and length of prediction horizon was 2200 seconds.

Weights for equation 10 are summarized in Table 1.

Table 1 Weight factors in Eq. 10

w_x	1
w_s	1
w_u	0.001
w_I	100
w_T	100

As it can be seen in Figure 2, the uncertain parameters decrease the productivity. In our case the kinetic parameters of the first reaction ($k_{0,1}$, E_1) have $\pm 10\%$ uncertainty, hence the control of reactor becomes conservative. This two uncertain parameters result nine scenarios. This is understandable since runaway cannot occur at none of the scenarios, because the implemented MDC criterion penalizes the objective if runaway states occur. Results of Multi-Stage NMPC can be seen in Figure 2, and it does not allow to feed the reagents with high rate, and also there are no runaway states during the whole period of reactor operation, means that the method resulted a safe operation under parameter uncertainty.

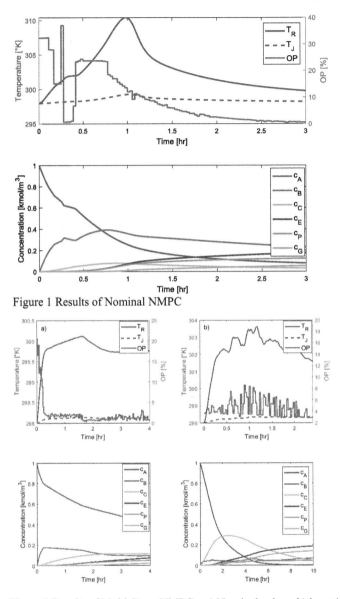

Figure 1 Results of Nominal NMPC

Figure 2 Results of Multi-Stage NMPC – a) Nominal values, b) $k_{0,1}$ +10%, E_1-10% (T_R – Reactor temperature, T_J – Jacket temperature, OP – Output Variable)

5. Conclusions

A nonlinear model predictive control approach has been analyzed in case of a fed-batch reactor which is carrying out a highly exothermic reaction. Modified Dynamic Condition was implemented in NMPC to avoid the development of thermal runaway under parameter uncertainty. The length of the prediction horizon was defined based on the process safety times of the system, which were calculated for the worst cases. Two different algorithms were compared to each other, which are nominal NMPC without any uncertain parameter and Multi-Stage NMPC with parameter uncertainty. The kinetic parameters ($k_{0,1}$, E_1) of the first reaction were chosen as uncertain to analyze the behavior of different control algorithms, whose possible min and max values were ±10%. Uncertain parameters resulted a conservative operation of the reactor, because runaway cannot develop at any of parameter combination. Our future research will be about to decrease the possible region of uncertain parameters during the reactor operation and to apply state estimation methods to estimate the different states.

Acknowledgment

We would like to express our acknowledgement for the financial support of Széchenyi 2020 under the GINOP-2.2.1-15-2017-00059.

References

[1] C.-S. Kao and K.-H. Hu, "Acrylic reactor runaway and explosion accident analysis," *Journal of Loss Prevention in the Process Industries*, vol. 15, no. 3, pp. 213–222, May 2002, doi: 10.1016/S0950-4230(01)00070-5.

[2] A. Kummer and T. Varga, "Completion of thermal runaway criteria: Two new criteria to define runaway limits," *Chemical Engineering Science*, vol. 196, pp. 277–290, Mar. 2019, doi: 10.1016/j.ces.2018.11.008.

[3] A. Kummer, T. Varga, and J. Abonyi, "Genetic programming-based development of thermal runaway criteria," *Computers & Chemical Engineering*, p. 106582, Sep. 2019, doi: 10.1016/j.compchemeng.2019.106582.

[4] A. Kanavalau, R. Masters, W. Kähm, and V. S. Vassiliadis, "Robust thermal stability for batch process intensification with model predictive control," *Computers & Chemical Engineering*, vol. 130, p. 106574, Nov. 2019, doi: 10.1016/j.compchemeng.2019.106574.

[5] S. Thangavel, S. Lucia, R. Paulen, and S. Engell, "Dual robust nonlinear model predictive control: A multi-stage approach," *Journal of Process Control*, vol. 72, pp. 39–51, Dec. 2018, doi: 10.1016/j.jprocont.2018.10.003.

[6] P. Kühl, M. Diehl, A. Milewska, E. Molga, and H. G. Bock, "Robust NMPC for a Benchmark Fed-Batch Reactor with Runaway Conditions," in *Assessment and Future Directions of Nonlinear Model Predictive Control*, vol. 358, R. Findeisen, F. Allgöwer, and L. T. Biegler, Eds. Berlin, Heidelberg: Springer Berlin Heidelberg, 2007, pp. 455–464.

[7] S. Lucia, T. Finkler, and S. Engell, "Multi-stage nonlinear model predictive control applied to a semi-batch polymerization reactor under uncertainty," *Journal of Process Control*, vol. 23, no. 9, pp. 1306–1319, Oct. 2013, doi: 10.1016/j.jprocont.2013.08.008.

[8] D. Q. Mayne, M. M. Seron, and S. V. Raković, "Robust model predictive control of constrained linear systems with bounded disturbances," *Automatica*, vol. 41, no. 2, pp. 219–224, Feb. 2005, doi: 10.1016/j.automatica.2004.08.019.

[9] P. O. M. Scokaert and D. Q. Mayne, "Min-max feedback model predictive control for constrained linear systems," *IEEE Transactions on Automatic Control*, vol. 43, no. 8, pp. 1136–1142, Aug. 1998, doi: 10.1109/9.704989.

[10] F. Rossi, F. Manenti, C. Pirola, and I. Mujtaba, "A robust sustainable optimization & control strategy (RSOCS) for (fed-)batch processes towards the low-cost reduction of utilities consumption," *Journal of Cleaner Production*, vol. 111, pp. 181–192, Jan. 2016, doi: 10.1016/j.jclepro.2015.06.098.

[11] M. Sriram and W. F. Stevens, "An Example of the Application of Nonlinear Programming to Chemical-Process Optimization," *Operations Research*, vol. 21, no. 1, pp. 296–304, Feb. 1973, doi: 10.1287/opre.21.1.296.

[12] Sergio Lucia, *Robust Multi-stage Nonlinear ModelPredictive Control*. 2014.

Sauro Pierucci, Flavio Manenti, Giulia Bozzano, Davide Manca (Eds.)
Proceedings of the 30th European Symposium on Computer Aided Process Engineering
(ESCAPE30), May 24-27, 2020, Milano, Italy. © 2020 Elsevier B.V. All rights reserved.
http://dx.doi.org/10.1016/B978-0-12-823377-1.50183-X

A Framework for Application of Forward Iterative Dynamic Programming to Mixed Integer Control and Sequencing Problems

Michael Mulholland

Chemical Engineering, University of KwaZulu-Natal, Durban 4041, South Africa
mulholland@ukzn.ac.za

Abstract

A stepwise receding horizon predictive controller was arranged to use the Forward Iterative Dynamic Programming (FIDP) method to optimise the forward trajectory on each step. This format allowed for a completely arbitrary predictive model specification. Non-linear and hybrid systems with logical mode-changes and recipe-based decisions could be accommodated because it is only required to solve the model in the forward direction. In this paper the method is demonstrated in two situations, together with the interventions required to accommodate conditional mode sequences.

Keywords: MPC, FIDP, hybrid, batch, scheduling.

1. Introduction

In Model Predictive Control (MPC) one seeks to optimise a future dynamic path. Bellman (1957) made a succinct observation that simplifies this task: If an optimal policy has been established from one state onwards, then any other trajectory arriving at that state would have to continue with that policy in order to be optimal. This Dynamic Programming technique is made far more efficient if it focuses on the "reachable" zones of the state-space, thus reducing the "curse of dimensionality" (Bellman, 1957). In Iterative Dynamic Programming (Luus, 1989) this is done by sending out random complete trajectories from the first point in time, and considering only nearby parts of the *state grid*. A variation of this is Forward Iterative Dynamic Programming (FIDP – Lin and Hwang, 1996) where the random complete trajectories themselves actually constitute the *path grid* of points available at each time. Thus the grid point becomes defined not so much as a state, but by the fact that it is possible to get there.

In the present work, FIDP will be used as the path optimiser, in conjunction with stepwise receding horizon MPC to offer a flexible dynamic control solution (Rusnák et al., 2001). FIDP as a forward calculation easily accommodates dead-time and constraints, and it will be seen later that logical branches, modes, schedules and recipes can be included.

2. Method

The process model is represented as the arbitrary input-output step

$$y_i = f(y_{i-1}, y_{i-2}, \dots, u_i, u_{i-1}, u_{i-2}, \dots) \tag{1}$$

This step has a cost

$$c_i = g(y_i, y_{i-1}, u_i, u_{i-1}) \tag{2}$$

where $\boldsymbol{u}_i$ is the piecewise-constant input vector in the interval which *ends* with the output vector at $\boldsymbol{y}_i$.

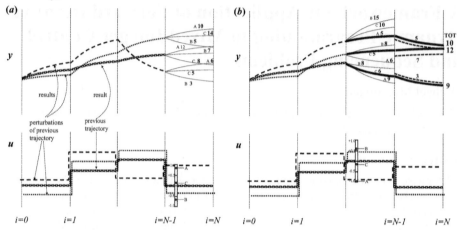

Figure 1. Building lowest cost trajectories using best combined trajectories established sequentially from (a) $i=N-1$, (b) $i=N-2$, etc.

On each time-step, P random forward trajectories of length N are generated by shifting the previous best trajectory one step back, and subjecting it to random input perturbation according to a specified sensitivity. Any trajectories violating input or output bounds are discarded. At each of the P *path grid* points thus established at each time, a further M input perturbations are applied for one time-step (Figure 1). In this way, moving backwards from the last step, the best combined trajectory from each *path grid* point is established through the "nearest" *path grid* point at the next step. The result is P improved trajectories. That with the lowest overall cost is selected, and its first control action implemented on the plant. The reference frame then moves forward one time-step, and actual plant data is gathered to repeat the entire calculation.

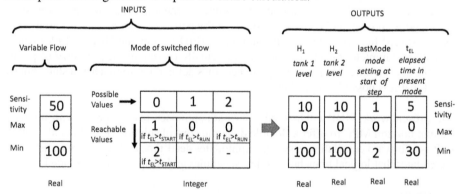

Figure 2. Pump/Tank system: Inputs: one continuous flow and one discrete (switched) flow; Outputs: four (including two tank levels). t_{EL} is the elapsed time so far in a mode.

The proposed framework is best illustrated by previewing the IO table of the simple Pump/Tank system in section 3. Discrete variables are declared in a "possible-value / "reachable-value" table (Figure 2). Here one notes that modes 1 and 2 can only change by passing through a standby mode 0. In the perturbation of trajectories, both the present possible value, and its associated reachable values, are available for random selection, unless other conditions are stipulated.

(a) Viewing possible values as "modes", sometimes additional variables play a part in determining the reachable values, eg. reactor contents must be cooled before discharge.

(b) Bearing (a) in mind, there is an obvious complication in Bellman's "backward stepping" outlined above, where the M one-step perturbations are applied: Arrival points need to lie within the set of reachable values.

The product of the backward-stepping above is effectively a vector-field, with an optimal vector direction determined at each *path grid* point. Rather than simply accepting the best of the N adjusted trajectories, we rather integrate through the vector field from the start to create a properly compliant "best" trajectory as the basis for the next time-step.

3. Applications

3.1. Pump/Tank system

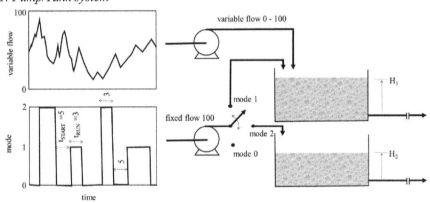

Figure 3. Example: Pump/Tank system: Level control of two tanks using one variable flow and one switched flow with a restart delay of 5, and minimum runtime of 3.

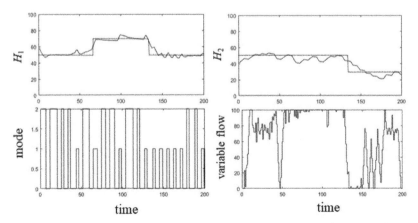

Figure 4. Pump/Tank system: Set-point step responses of the two levels using a 30-point model predictive control horizon.

3.2. Multiple batch reactors sharing utilities

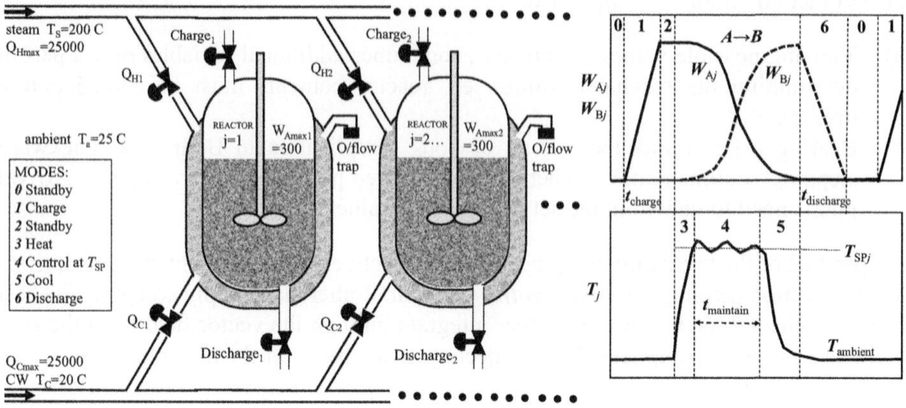

Figure 5. Multiple batch reactors converting A to B using common heating and cooling utilities.

Figure 5 shows a typical situation where multiple batch reactors, potentially having different sizes and different recipes, share common resources such as heating and cooling utilities. Each reactor must progress through a series of "modes". Conditions will determine whether a mode can start or end, and usually only a specified mode can follow. In the FIDP algorithm one wishes to provide a series of *different* trajectories, and then to allow a trajectory to borrow parts of other trajectories to improve itself. Only a few modes involve discretionary lengths, which allow one to generate random shifts (modes 0 and 2 in Figure 5). Furthermore, even at such "break-out" points, preceding and following conditions must be met in the combined trajectory.

A simple exothermic 1st order reaction is simulated as follows for reactor j over interval i
Mass balance:

$$\Delta W_{Aji} = -[k_0 + k_1(T_{ji} - T_a)]W_{Aji-1}\Delta t \tag{3}$$

$$W_{Aji} = W_{Aji-1} + \Delta W_{Aji} \tag{4}$$

$$W_{Bji} = W_{Bji-1} - \Delta W_{Aji} \tag{5}$$

Mutually exclusive heating/cooling selector Q_{Sj} :   0=Cool; 1=Standby; 2=Heat

$$\Delta Q_{Hji} = \begin{cases} (UA)_j (T_S - T_{ji}) & \text{if } Q_{Sj} = 2 \\ 0 & \text{otherwise} \end{cases} \tag{6}$$

$$\Delta Q_{Cji} = \begin{cases} (UA)_j (T_{ji} - T_C) & \text{if } Q_{Sj} = 0 \\ 0 & \text{otherwise} \end{cases} \tag{7}$$

$$\Delta Q_{aji} = (uA)_j (T_{ji} - T_a) \qquad \text{ambient loss} \tag{8}$$

Heat balance:

$$T_{ji} = T_{ji-1} + \left[(-\Delta H_A)(-\Delta W_{Aji}) + (\Delta Q_{Hji} - \Delta Q_{Cji} - \Delta Q_{aji})\Delta t\right]/[Mc_P]_j \tag{9}$$

Total heating/cooling demand and production for n reactors in interval i-1 to i:

$$Q_{Hi} = \sum_{j=1}^{n} \Delta Q_{Hji} \qquad Q_{Ci} = \sum_{j=1}^{n} \Delta Q_{Cji} \qquad P_i = \sum_{j=1}^{n} \Delta W_{Bji} \tag{10}$$

Total trajectory production up to interval i:

$$P_{TOTi} = \sum_{k=1}^{i} P_k \tag{11}$$

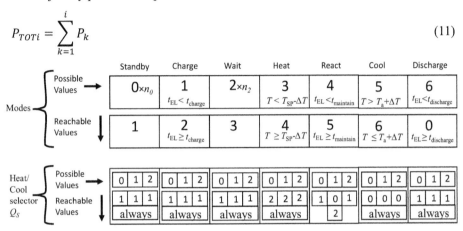

Figure 6. IO table for a single reactor - Inputs: possible (present) and reachable values.

For a single reactor j stepping from interval i-1 to i, the discrete values in the input vector $\mathbf{u}_i$ are randomly selected according to the possible-value/reachable-value tables in Figure 6. Here t_{EL} is the elapsed time so far in a mode, and T_{SP} is the set-point reaction temperature. The conditions shown force the associated choice. The multipliers "$\times n$" repeat the presence of the choice in the random selection vector to make it more likely, thus generating a greater range of standby periods.

A two-reactor example is demonstrated over 200 time-steps with a 100 step horizon. The cost function is formulated to maximise cumulative production and minimise deviations from the set-point temperature whilst in reaction mode (4). The primes below indicate normalisation according to the specified sensitivity.

$$c_i = -100 P_{TOTi} + \left\{ 10^2 (T'_{ji} - T'_{jiSP})^2 + 10 \sum_{k=1}^{i} (T'_{jk} - T'_{jkSP})^2 \right\}_{IF\ MODE=4\ ONLY} \tag{12}$$

In Figure 7, an output constraint of 15000 has been specified on the total steam heating power consumed Q_H at any time. This effectively allows only one instance of mode 3 or mode 4 amongst the reactors. The algorithm correctly manipulates the available standby periods to prevent such a clash, at the same time attempting to reduce these periods to maximise production. Enough break-out scope was provided by an extra $n_0=2$ and $n_2=2$ repeats in Figure 6.

Figure 7 includes at bottom right an example of the P random forward trajectories at an intermediate solution time – in this case for T_2, the temperature of reactor 2. The shifts in these responses provide the scope for the dynamic programming optimisation. As one steps backwards from the horizon, the randomised starts at these *path grid* points provide the opportunity to start the next mode earlier or later.

The particular model under investigation is only distinguished *within* service functions such as those that evaluate equations (1) and (2). An IO table as in Figures 2 and 6 must be provided to the core solution for input choice prior to each step. This is achieved by a prior "dummy" call of (1) which reconfigures the IO table for current *start* conditions. This would be a "forward" match. A flag is set if a "backwards" match is required, and the required *end* condition is specified in this case. If this is not achievable with the given input, an alternative input is sought and returned to the core solution.

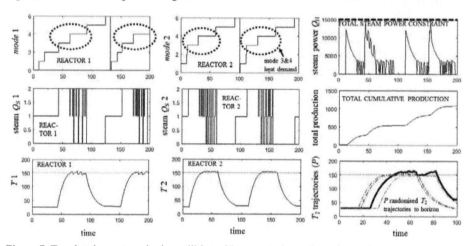

Figure 7. Two batch reactors sharing utilities with a constraint on heat demand.

4. Conclusions

In this framework a core FIDP solution loop is serviced on each time step by a set of functions (Step, Cost, Set-point, IO table) which index particular applications. These functions provide data in a fixed format (eg. Figure 6). Various mixed integer control problems have been dealt with, as well as dead time, integral action, and instantaneous set-point objectives. Sequencing requirements may hamper the dynamic programming, possibly causing some degrading to an evolutionary solution.

The forward modelling of FIDP allows the "mode" of a plant to be manipulated as a control input – a useful feature for flow-rerouting, start-up, recipe changes, etc.

References

R. Bellman, 1957, Dynamic Programming, Dover edition 2003.

J.-S. Lin and C. Hwang, 1996, Optimal control of time-delay systems by forward iterative dynamic programming, Industrial and Engineering Chemical Research, 35 (8) ,2795-2800

R. Luus, 1989, Optimal control by dynamic programming using accessible points and region reduction. Hung. J. Ind. Chem., 17, 523–543.

A. Rusnák, M. Fikar, M.A. Latifi and A. Mészáros, 2001, Receding horizon iterative dynamic programming with discrete time models", Computers and Chemical Engineering, 25 (1), 161-167.

Sauro Pierucci, Flavio Manenti, Giulia Bozzano, Davide Manca (Eds.)
Proceedings of the 30th European Symposium on Computer Aided Process Engineering
(ESCAPE30), May 24-27, 2020, Milano, Italy. © 2020 Elsevier B.V. All rights reserved.
http://dx.doi.org/10.1016/B978-0-12-823377-1.50184-1

Robust Short-term Planning of Combined Heat and Power Plants Participating in the Spot Market

Lise Mallier[a*], Gilles Hétreux[a], Raphaele Théry-Hétreux[a], Philippe Baudet[b]

[a]*Laboratoire de Génie Chmique (LGC), Université de Toulouse, CNRS, INPT, UPS, Toulouse, France*
[b]*Proesis SAS, 42 avenue du Général de Croutte, Toulouse 31100, France*
lise.mallier@toulouse-inp.fr

Abstract

Following the liberalization of the electricity market, many private producers have come into play through trading mechanism to ensure the balance between production and needs. This context is particularly beneficial for utilities plants such as Combined Heat and Power (CHP) plants. In this context, a previous work has shown the economic and environmental benefits of implementing a decision support tool for short-term planning of CHPs using a *Mixed Integer Linear Programming* (MILP) formulation. However, planning is subject to uncertainty about the steam demand that the plant must meet. A methodology is therefore put in place to obtain a robust production plan. The accuracy of this work is demonstrated with an industrial case study and shows significant improvements to obtain feasible plans under steam demand uncertainty.
Keywords: Combined Heat and Power, Robust Planning, Uncertainty, MILP

1. Introduction

Combined Heat and Power (CHP) plants represent an interesting solution to improve the energy efficiency of industrial sites while reducing greenhouse gas emissions. Indeed, it consists in simultaneously producing electricity and hot utilities (steam, hot water) from the same primary energy and within the same installation. In addition, following the liberalisation of the energy market, CHP plants have become both interesting contributors to electricity production and a significant source of profit (Santos and Uturbey, 2018). However, these new challenges have made the management of these facilities noticeably more complex (Figure 1). Indeed, similar to trading offers, the energy market is very time-sensitive (Mitra et al., 2013), forcing production units to be increasingly flexible and responsive. As a result, the management of CHP plants plays a key role in taking advantage of these opportunities. In this context, a good survey on short-term cogeneration planning has been published (Salgado and Pedrero, 2008), showing the value of implementing a planning model. However, scheduling is highly susceptible to unexpected events and uncertain input data such as demand fluctuations. These uncertainties often make the schedule generated under the deterministic assumption suboptimal or even infeasible. Uncertainty consideration, thus, is very important to preserve plant feasibility and viability during operations. Some excellent reviews in scheduling under uncertainty can be found in (Li et Ierapetritou, 2008b) and in (Verderame et al., 2010). Typical techniques used are stochastic scheduling that handle future uncertainty through recourse decision according to different uncertainty scenarios (De Ridder and Claessens, 2014) and robust scheduling that focuses on building the preventive scheduling ensuring that the predictive and realized scheduled do not differ drastically (Zhang et al., 2015).

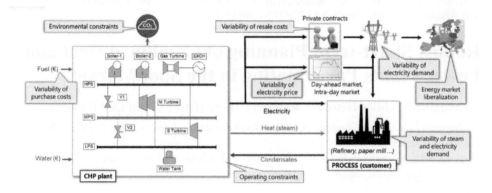

Figure 1: The Context of the Management of a Combined Heat and Power Plant

The work presented in this communication concerns a part of the methodology carried out in a prototype software named *PLANENER* dedicated to the management of the CHP plant. A previous work (Mallier et al., 2019) has introduced a methodology which implements MILP formulation and has shown significant improvements for the site's economic profitability as wells as its environmental impact. However, to ensure that the CHP plant's scheduling remains feasible, a robust counterpart problem has to be solved to deal with the presence of demand uncertainty. The remainder of this paper is organized as follows. Given the problem statement in Section 2, the uncertain scheduling model is presented in Section 3. In Section 4, an industrial case study is presented based on realistic data and results are discussed in Section 5.

2. Problem statement

The main objective of the *PLANENER* project is to propose a decision making tool dedicated to the management of CHP plant able to:
• take into account the real and multiple constraints of production (operational, economic, environmental, etc.) in order to build feasible planning,
• integrate the various opportunities for electricity sales into these plans, by evaluating them at the same time as production constraints,
• evaluate and manage short and medium strategies, as well as near-real-time decisions.
The short-term planning model is a generic scheduling model described in (Hétreux et al., 2011). Given the size of the problem, this model is based on a Mixed Integer Linear Programming (MILP) formulation for its qualities of computational stability and convergence. As shown in (Théry et al., 2012), the scheduling model can be instantiated by using the graphical formalism *ERTN* that allows an unambiguous modeling of production recipes.
Among the model's input parameters, forecast electricity prices and forecast demand (e.g steam demand) are subject to uncertainty. Many techniques have been used to forecast electricity prices such as artificial neural networks (Conejo et al., 2005) and time series model (Dimoulkas and Amelin, 2014). In this communication, the price of electricity sold on the Day-ahead market is assumed to be fixed by this type of forecast model. While the resale price of electricity influences the economic profitability of the utility plant, the demand to be met is a real constraint for the site. In all cases, the demand must be met by the CHP plant, otherwise the operation of the process will be affected. Thus, the forecast demand is not considered as a well-defined value but as an interval with bounded values. For this reason, a small number of variables and additional constraints have been

introduced into the original MILP problem, generating a robust counterpart problem that provides the optimal and feasible solution given the magnitude of the uncertain demand.

3. Robust Short-term planning

The robust planning approach has been adopted and implemented through a sliding horizon (24-hour rescheduling periodicity) decision-making structure divided into two levels (Figure 2) named respectively *forecast level* and *operational level*. These two decision-making levels are necessary in order to take into account the variety of constraints and data dynamics. Indeed, some organizational constraints are defined on specific time horizons. Similarly, some production data, initially defined with uncertainty, are periodically updated and become deterministic data.

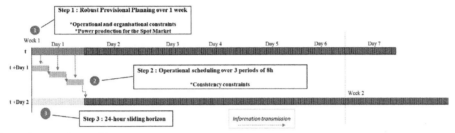

Figure 2: Decision-making process

3.1. Forecast scheduling

A first so-called *forecast scheduling model* M^{forc} establishes a plan for a week by taking into account the uncertainty on the steam demand, in an analytical way via specific capacity constraints. One of the objectives of this plan is to determine the state in which "critical" equipment should be positioned in order to satisfy any need within the uncertainty range. Critical equipment are defined as equipment subject to operational or organisational constraints. For example, the boiler has non-instantaneous shutdown and start-up phases. For this purpose, the minimum and maximum steam production capacities are evaluated for each possible configuration combination of these critical devices by calculating the minimum and maximum flow in the network thus constituted (preliminary calculation carried out only once). At this decision-making level, particular operating constraints (see case study) are taken into account. This first level makes it possible to anticipate the operating status of critical equipment by ensuring that production can satisfy steam demand regardless of its effective value. In addition, the operation of the Day-ahead market, also known as Spot, requires power producers to make a production offer the day before for each hour of the following day. The objective of the forecast plan is to establish a technically and economically viable power offer. This production offer, if accepted by the market, becomes a production order for the power plant. The 24-hour sliding horizon allows the electricity price and steam demand forecasts to be updated daily before sending the production offer to the Day-ahead market.

3.2. Operational scheduling

A second model, known as the *operational scheduling model* M^{oper}, establishes the effective workload plan for the equipment over an 8-hour cycle (shift rotation cycle and period over which the actual utility needs are known and fixed). The decisions made by the forecast plan are the input data for the operational scheduling. Consistency constraints make it possible to define the initial state of the system at each planning level. The degrees of freedom are associated with non-critical equipment: activation, deactivation and load.

4. Case Sudy

The CHP plant shown in Figure 1 is set up as an industrial case. This plant produces steam at three pressure levels and electricity by means of various equipment. Two gas boilers (Boiler-1 and Boiler-2) and one cogeneration train (Gas Turbine coupled to the heat recovery exchanger EXCH) generate High Pressure Steam (HPS) from deaerated water. The desuperheating valve V1 converts HPS into Medium Pressure Steam (MPS) whereas the desuperheating valve V2 converts MPS into Low Pressure Steam (LPS). In addition, the multi-stage steam turbine M-Turbine convert HPS into MPS and LPS, and the steam turbine S-Turbine converts HPS into LPS. Deaerated water is produced in a tank from LPS and demineralized water. The Gas Turbine, M-Turbine and S-Turbine equipment generate electricity, sold on the Spot market. All steam producers use natural gas as fuel. Figure 3 depicts the electricity prices in the Epex Spot forecast for a coming week. The price of gas fuel is set at 280 €/t and the price of demineralised water is set at 8 €/t. Finally, the utility plant must satisfy the steam demand of a production unit. Figure 4 shows the global steam demand, ranging from 10 t/h to 28 t/h, that is forecast for the coming week with an uncertainty of 15%.

Several operating constraints are taken into account. First of all, the number of boiler starts is set at 3 per week. Then, there can be no more than 3 changes in the cogeneration train production regime in 8 hours. These constraints have an impact on *forecast* and *operational* decision-making levels. In particular, the boiler start-up periods established in the *forecast* scheduling must be respected in the *operational* scheduling.

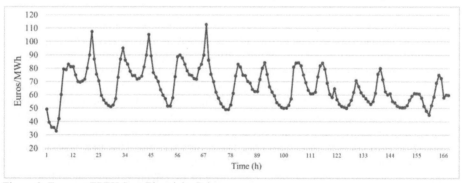

Figure 3: Forecast EPEX Spot Electricity Prices

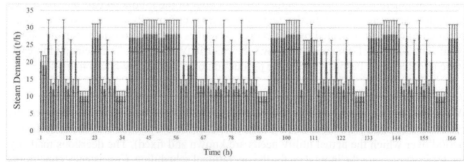

Figure 4: Forecast Steam Demand with an Uncertainty of 15%

5. Results and Discussion

The objective function aims to minimize the operating cost of the CHP plant (i.e. minimize fuel purchase cost and water purchase cost minus the profit resulting from the sale of the electricity produced).

5.1 Forecast schedule

The resolution of the planning model is performed on IntelCore i7 (2.8 GHz, 16 Go RAM). The preventive schedule of the CHP is presented in Figure 5, in the form of a GANTT chart, over 1 week (168 periods of 1 h). Taking into account the steam demand with its uncertainty and the Spot market price, the model $\mathcal{M}^{for}$ determines the optimal power production, as shown in Figure 6, and the periods during which the boilers can be shut down without risk on the satisfaction of the steam demand. The maximum of 3 starts in the week is reached for Boiler-1 and Boiler-2. Without this long-term vision, the shutdown and restart of the boilers cannot be foreseen. Taking into account the operational constraint of the cogeneration train ensures the feasibility of the plan.

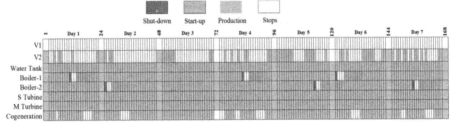

Figure 5: Provisional Schedule over 1 week (275,908 constraints, 146,348 variables with 6552 binary / CPU time = 83.80 s)

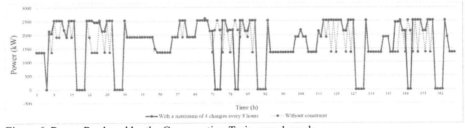

Figure 6: Power Produced by the Cogeneration Train over 1 week

5.2 Operational schedule

At this level of decision, the steam demand is known for sure. Decisions made by the *forecast* level become input data for the *operational* level. Thus, electricity production is dictated by the production supply sent to the Spot market and the load plan of the cogeneration train as well boiler shut-downs and starts are imposed to respect the operational constraints. The degrees of freedom are found in the activation/deactivation of valves and turbines and in the production load of boilers, valves and turbines. The production load is optimized according to the effective steam demand. In addition, the boiler may be in an alternative state called the *Low Boiling* mode. This mode is a conservation mode in which the boiler does not produce steam and consumes a small amount of fuel (5% of its nominal consumption) to be able to switch without transition to a production mode. This mode provides more flexibility in the operation of the plant. Figure 7 shows the operational schedule for the first day of the horizon. The model $\mathcal{M}^{oper}$

is run consecutively for the 3 periods of 8 hours. The operational schedule respects the decisions taken at the forecast level by allowing production to be adjusted to the effective value of steam demand to minimize the plant's operating cost.

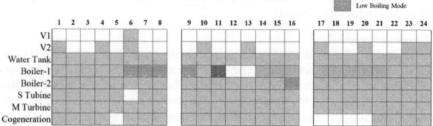

Figure 7 : Operational Schedule for the first day, over 8 hours

6. Conclusions

The methodology implemented makes it possible to establish a robust production plan for a utility plant that interacts with the *Day-ahead* electricity market. The *forecast level* smooths the load of the cogeneration train while regulating the operation of the boilers. The *operational level* then optimizes the production of *CHP* based on actual data and within the framework defined by the higher level. If the offer accepted by the market must be made by the power plant, it is nevertheless possible to value an overproduction of electricity on the market called *Intra-Day*. It would also be interesting to include financial penalties for non-compliance with the *Spot* offer.

References

A.J. Conejo, J. Contreras, R. Espinola, M.A. Plazas, 2005, Forecasting Electricity Prices for a Day-Ahead Pool-Based Electric Energy Market, International Journal of Forecasting, 21 (3), 435–462.

F. De Ridder, B. Claessens, 2014, A Trading Strategy for Industrial CHPs on Multiple Power Markets, International Transactions on Electrical Energy Systems, 24 (5), 677–697.

I. Dimoulkas, M. Amelin, 2014, Constructing Bidding Curves for a CHP Producer in Day-Ahead Electricity Markets, Energycon Conference, 487–494.

G. Hétreux, F. Fabre , J. LeLann, P. Zaraté, 2011, Dynamic Hybrid Simulation of Batch Processes Driven by a Scheduling Module, Computers and Chemical Engineering, 35 (10), 2098-2112.

Z. Li, M. Ierapetritou, 2008, Process Scheduling under Uncertainty: Review and Challenges, Computers & Chemical Engineering, 32 (4), 715–727.

L. Mallier, G. Hétreux, R. Théry, P. Baudet, 2019, Short-term Planning of Combined Heat and Power Plants Participating in the Electricity Day-ahead Market, 22nd Conference on Process Integration, Modelling and Optimisation for Energy Saving and Pollution Reduction

S. Mitra, L. Sun, I.E. Grossmann, 2013, Optimal Scheduling of Industrial Combined Heat and Power Plants under Time-Sensitive Electricity Prices, Energy, 54, 194–211.

F. Salgado, P. Pedrero, 2008, Short-Term Operation Planning on Cogeneration Systems: A Survey, Electric Power Systems Research, 78 (5), 835–848.

M.I. Santos, W. Uturbey, 2018, A Practical Model for Energy Dispatch in Cogeneration Plants, Energy, 151, 144–159.

R. Théry, G. Hétreux, M.H. Agha, A. Hait, J.M. Le Lann, 2011, The Extended Resource Task Network : a Framework for the Combined Scheduling of Batch Processes and CHP Plant, International Journal of Production Research, 50 (3), 623-646.

P. Verderame, J. Elia, J. Li, C. Floudas, 2010, Planning and Scheduling under Uncertainty: A Review Across Multiple Sectors, Industrial Engineering Chemistry Research, 49 (9), 3993–4017

Q. Zhang, M.F. Morari, I.E. Grossmann, A. Sundaramoorthy, J.M. Pinto, 2016, An Adjustable Robust Optimization Approach to Scheduling of Continuous Industrial Processes Providing Interruptible Load, Computers & Chemical Engineering, 86, 106–119.

Sauro Pierucci, Flavio Manenti, Giulia Bozzano, Davide Manca (Eds.)
Proceedings of the 30th European Symposium on Computer Aided Process Engineering
(ESCAPE30), May 24-27, 2020, Milano, Italy. © 2020 Elsevier B.V. All rights reserved.
http://dx.doi.org/10.1016/B978-0-12-823377-1.50185-3

Plantwide Control Structure Selection Methodology based on Economics: a Quadratic Approximation

Christos S. Patilas [a,b], Ioannis K. Kookos [a,b*]

[a]*University of Patras, Department of Chemical Engineering,Patras, Greece*

[b]*Research Infrastructure for Waste Valorisation and Sustainable Management of Resources, Patras, Greece*

i.kookos@chemeng.upatras.gr

Abstract

The back-off methodology has been developed and refined in the last decades and offers a systematic tool for solving the simultaneous design and control problem. The first formulation of the methodology was based on linear process and control models. In previous work an improved formulation was proposed where use is made of a nonlinear process model that ensures improved accuracy but increases the complexity and the computational cost of the final problem. In this work, another formulation is presented which is based on the quadratic approximation of the objective function, resulting in a Mixed Integer Quadratic Programming (MIQP) formulation. This approximation can offer greater accuracy than the linear counterpart with a reasonable increase in the computational complexity. The three formulations are evaluated in a reactor-separator-recycle process.

Keywords: process control, control structure selection, mathematical programming

1. Introduction

In industry, processes are designed to operate at specific conditions dictated by economics, equipment capacity constraints and environmental and safety considerations. However, a wide range of disturbances may cause process operation to deviate from the optimal operating point which can not only cause performance deterioration but also operation infeasibility. These phenomena are treated with corrective actions in the form of control mechanisms. In designing those systems, the objective is to develop control structures that satisfy the constrains under the effect of disturbances with minimum performance loss. This is known as the Control Structure Selection Problem (CSSP) and refers to the synthesis of optimal regulatory control structures by considering both structural and parametric optimization issues.

A systematic method, that is known as the back-off methodology for simultaneous design and control, has been proposed and latter refined by Heath et al. (2000). More recently Psaltis et al. (2013) proposed some implementation improvements that made the application of the methodology possible to plantwide control problems.

The initial formulation of the method was based on linearized economics that ensure quick determination of the optimal solution at the expense of a possible loss in the accuracy due to the nonlinearities. In (Kookos and Perking, 2016) a new formulation is proposed which uses the nonlinear model of the process assuming that all design (structural) decisions have been made. This new formulation ensures improved accuracy

and also offers the opportunity for the simultaneous consideration of process design and control. The nonlinear formulation increases the complexity and the computational cost of the final problem. Therefore, a new formulation based on the quadratic approximation of the objective function (economic penalty) is introduced resulting in a Mixed Integer Quadratic Programming (MIQP). This approximation can be more accurate when compared with the linear counterpart at reasonable increase in computational effort.
A short review of the back-off methodology is first presented followed by the formulation of the quadratic approximation. Finally, all three formulations are evaluated in a case study involving a reactor-separator-recycle process (Luyben and Floudas ,1993).

2. Mathematical Framework and Formulation

Operation of chemical process systems may be modeled by a set of nonlinear differential and algebraic equations and inequality constraints that involve an n_x vector of state variables $\mathbf{x}(t)$, an n_z vector of algebraic variables $\mathbf{z}(t)$, an n_u vector of control variables $\mathbf{u}(t)$, a vector of design variables that consist of continuous ($\mathbf{d}$) as well as integer ($\mathbf{\Delta}$) variables and an n_p vector of disturbances $\mathbf{p}(t)$ (variables that are determined exogenously). Finally, J is the objective function usually used to evaluate the economic performance of the process. The control structure selection problem can be modeled as a Mixed Integer Non-Linear Programming (MINLP) and described by the following set of equations:

$$\min_{\mathbf{x}(t),\mathbf{z}(t),\mathbf{u}(t),\mathbf{p}(t);\mathbf{d},\Delta} J(\mathbf{x}(t),\mathbf{z}(t),\mathbf{u}(t),\mathbf{p}(t);\mathbf{d},\mathbf{\Delta})$$

$$s.t.$$

$$\mathbf{h}(\dot{\mathbf{x}}(t),\mathbf{z}(t),\mathbf{u}(t),\mathbf{p}(t);\mathbf{d},\mathbf{\Delta}) = 0$$

$$\mathbf{g}(\mathbf{x}(t),\mathbf{z}(t),\mathbf{u}(t),\mathbf{p}(t);\mathbf{d},\mathbf{\Delta}) \leq 0$$

(1)

For the ideal case, in which the uncertain parameters are set to their nominal values the above formulation is restricted to steady state. The solution of the steady state problem yields the optimum steady-state operating point which usually lies at the intersection of active constraints. In general, the uncertain parameters deviate from their nominal values and therefore the process operation may shift to the infeasible region.
In order to ensure the feasibility of the operation under the effect of disturbances, the back-off vector $\mathbf{\mu}$ is introduced:

$$\mu_k = \max_t \left| g_k - g_k^N \right|, k = 1, 2, ..., n_g$$

(2)

where, g_k^N is the value of the k-th constraint at the nominal optimal operating point. Each element of the back-off vector is defined as the maximum violation of the corresponding constraint over the time horizon. The magnitude of the back-off vector depends not only on the disturbance characteristics but also on the structure and the parameters of the regulatory control system.
The dynamic behavior of a process under the effect of disturbances, in a region close to a steady state point can be described with adequate accuracy by the linearization of Eq. (1) at the optimal operating point. Furthermore, to avoid the complexity of solving a dynamic problem, the system of differential and algebraic equations can be transformed into the frequency domain. The latter is performed by taking the Laplace transformation of the system and decompose the transformed variables into real (superscript R) and

imaginary (superscript I) parts. The final system of equations is described below in Eq. (3):

$$0 = \mathbf{A}\mathbf{X}^R + \mathbf{B}\mathbf{U}^R + \mathbf{E}\mathbf{P}^R + \omega\mathbf{X}^I$$

$$0 = \mathbf{A}\mathbf{X}^I + \mathbf{B}\mathbf{U}^I + \mathbf{E}\mathbf{P}^I - \omega\mathbf{X}^R$$

$$\mathbf{Y}^R = \mathbf{C}\mathbf{X}^R + \mathbf{D}\mathbf{U}^R + \mathbf{F}\mathbf{P}^R$$

$$\mathbf{Y}^I = \mathbf{C}\mathbf{X}^I + \mathbf{D}\mathbf{U}^I + \mathbf{F}\mathbf{P}^I \qquad (3)$$

$$\mathbf{\Sigma}^R = \mathbf{H}\mathbf{X}^R + \mathbf{P}\mathbf{U}^R + \mathbf{S}\mathbf{P}^R$$

$$\mathbf{\Sigma}^I = \mathbf{H}\mathbf{X}^I + \mathbf{P}\mathbf{U}^I + \mathbf{S}\mathbf{P}^I$$

If we set $P^R =1$ and $P^I =0$, we can obtain the frequency response of the system (i.e. the asymptotic response to sinusoidal variation of the disturbances with frequency ω). However, the system of linear equations is undetermined as $2n_u$ equations are missing. These are the equations that are needed to describe the controller in the frequency domain. To resolve this issue and simultaneously avoid the introduction of the controller design problem, the implementation of perfect control was proposed. Integer variables Ψ_j are introduced to denote the selection ($\Psi_j =0$) or not ($\Psi_j =1$) of potential controlled variable (CV) y_j. In a similar way the integer variables Θ_j are introduced to select ($\Theta_j =1$) or not ($\Theta_j =0$) a potential manipulated variable (MV) u_j in the regulatory control structure and perfect control is implemented through the following linear inequalities. Finally, consideration is also restricted to square control structures. The equations of the controller are presented in Eq. (4).

$$\left. \begin{array}{c} -y_j^U \Psi_j \leq Y_j^R \leq y_j^U \Psi_j \\ -y_j^U \Psi_j \leq Y_j^I \leq y_j^U \Psi_j \end{array} \right\} j = 1,2,\dots,n_y \qquad \left. \begin{array}{c} -u_j^U \Theta_j \leq U_j^R \leq u_j^U \Theta_j \\ -u_j^U \Theta_j \leq U_j^I \leq u_j^U \Theta_j \end{array} \right\} j = 1,2,\dots,n_u$$

$$(4)$$

$$\sum_{j=1}^{n_y} \Psi_j + \sum_{j=1}^{n_u} \Theta_j = n_y$$

Psaltis et al. (2013) have shown that the back-of vector can be determined accurately through a set of linear inequalities that avoid the need for the iterative application of the algorithm used earlier by Heath et al (2000).

$$\mathbf{\Pi}^R \mathbf{\Sigma}^R + \mathbf{\Pi}^I \mathbf{\Sigma}^I \leq \mathbf{\mu} \qquad (5)$$

For the linear formulation equations Eq. (3) - Eq. (5) can be combined with the state space model of the process and can be written in Eq. (6), where $\mathbf{J_x}$ and $\mathbf{J_u}$ are the gradients of the objective function with respect to the state and control vectors accordingly and EP_{lp} is the economic penalty resulting from the occurrence of the disturbances. Additionally, the non-linear formulation is also presented in Eq. (6) and makes use of the linear approximation for the back-off estimation and the initial formulation Eq. (1) for the estimation of the economic penalty.

$$\min_{\delta x, \delta u, \Theta, \Psi, \mu} EP_{lp} = \mathbf{J}_x^T \delta x + \mathbf{J}_u^T \delta u$$

s. t.

$$\mathbf{A}\delta x + \mathbf{B}\delta u = 0$$

$$\mathbf{C}\delta x + \mathbf{D}\delta u = \delta y$$

$$\mathbf{g}_N + \mathbf{H}\delta x + \mathbf{P}\delta u \leq -\mu$$

$$-\delta x^u \leq \delta x \leq \delta x^u$$

$$-\delta u^u \leq \delta u \leq \delta u^u$$

$$\Theta_j, \Psi_j \in \{0,1\}$$

Eqs 3 – 5

$$\min_{x_s, z_s, u_s, d, \Delta, \Theta, \Psi, \mu} EP_{nlp} = J\big|_{\mu \neq 0} (x_s, z_s, u_s, p_N; d, \Delta) - J\big|_{\mu = 0}$$

s. t.

$$\mathbf{h}(x_s, z_s, u_s, p_N; d, \Delta) = 0$$

$$\mathbf{g}(x_s, z_s, u_s, p_N; d, \Delta) \leq -\mu$$

$$\Theta_j, \Psi_j \in \{0,1\} \tag{6}$$

Eqs 3 – 5

The proposed formulation has the same set of equations as the linear and a quadratic approximation of the economic penalty. The objective function of this formulation is stated below in Eq. (7), where $\mathbf{Q}$ is the hessian matrix.

$$EP_{qp} = \mathbf{J}_x^T \delta x + \mathbf{J}_u^T \delta u + \frac{1}{2} \begin{bmatrix} \delta x^T & \delta u^T \end{bmatrix} \mathbf{Q} \begin{bmatrix} \delta x^T \\ \delta u^T \end{bmatrix} \tag{7}$$

3. Case Study

The reactor-separator-recycle process examined in this case study is presented in Figure 1. Fresh feed of 90% A is fed into the reactor, where the first order irreversible reaction A → B takes place. The reactor product is then fed to the distillation column. The main product B is obtained as the bottom product, while unreacted A is recycled back to the reactor.

The design strategy of the process was based on a structural optimization problem for finding the optimal steady state regarding the topology and the operating point (Luyben and Floudas ,1993) and (Viswanathan and Grossmann ,1992).

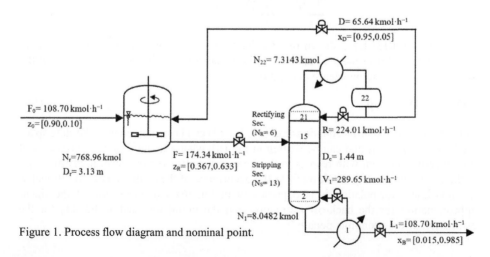

Figure 1. Process flow diagram and nominal point.

Table 1. Results of the CSSP- Nonlinear, Linear and Quadratic for 5% variation in Disturbances

N_o	EP_{nlp}	N_o	EP_{lp}	N_o	EP_{qp}	Manipulated	Controlled
1	0.01 %	1	0.00 %	1	0.00 %	F, L_1, V_1, R, D	N_r, x_B, x_D, N_1, N_{NT}
2	0.14 %	2	0.08 %	2	0.21 %	F, L_1, V_1, R, D	N_r, x_2, x_{21}, N_1, N_{NT}
3	0.32 %	3	0.21 %	3	0.21 %	F, L_1, V_1, R, D	N_r, x_3, x_{21}, N_1, N_{NT}
4	0.56%	5	0.36 %	4	0.37 %	F, L_1, V_1, R, D	N_r, x_4, x_{21}, N_1, N_{NT}
5	0.58 %	4	0.34 %	9	0.56 %	F, L_1, V_1, R, D	N_r, x_2, x_{20}, N_1, N_{NT}
6	0.85 %	9	0.77 %	6	0.77 %	F, L_1, V_1, R, D	N_r, x_2, x_{19}, N_1, N_{NT}
7	0.85 %	8	0.61 %	7	0.77 %	F, L_1, V_1, R, D	N_r, x_4, x_{20}, N_1, N_{NT}
8	0.85 %	7	0.55 %	5	0.56 %	F, L_1, V_1, R, D	N_r, x_5, x_{21}, N_1, N_{NT}
9	1.22 %	-	-	8	0.79 %	F, L_1, V_1, R, D	N_r, x_6, x_{21}, N_1, N_{NT}
10	1.22 %	6	0.46 %	10	1.08 %	F, L_1, V_1, R, D	N_r, x_3, x_{20}, N_1, N_{NT}

The mathematical problem for the optimal design of the process is a MINLP problem which was solved using the SBB solver available in GAMS. The optimal solution is presented in Figure 1.

The state vector consists of the mole fractions of component A and the molar holdups in the reactor and the column. The potential MV are the reactor product flowrate F, the vapor boilup V_1, the bottom's product flowrate L_1, the reflux rate R and the recycle stream flow D. The potential CV are the reactor's holdup N_r and composition x_r, the holdup of the reboiler N_1 and condenser N_{NT} and finally the composition of component A in all trays. It should be noted that for this case study the choice of compositions as CV rather than temperatures will not make any difference because it is well known that both of them are equivalent for binary mixtures. As a result, there are 5 potential MV and 26 CV giving rise to an exploding size of potential control structures. The CSSP was then solved applying the three formulations to determine the 10 most promising structures and to examine if the quadratic performs better when compared to the linear. Table 1 summarizes the results.

All structures make use of all MV resulting in 5x5 control structures. An RGA analysis was performed to design the interconnection between the variables. In all cases, the reactor holdup is controlled by the reactor's outflow, the reboiler's holdup by the bottom's product flow and the condenser's holdup by the reflux rate. Finally, the boilup is connected with a composition in the stripping section and the recycle stream flow (distillate) with a composition in the rectifying section. The best structure was identified by all formulations and makes use of the compositions of the bottom and distillate product streams. Direct control of variables that appear in design specifications is often unrealistic therefore, these were eliminated as CV to examine structures based on the compositions of the internal trays.

Based on the results, the quadratic formulation managed to identify all of the structures produced by the non-linear and rank them more accurately than the linear. Some selected structures were evaluated in closed loop simulations in a rather aggressive disturbance scenario, where the inlet flow F_0 to the reactor was increased by 10 %, then decreased by 20 % and finally returned to the nominal point. The same procedure was followed for the composition z_0. In the closed loop system, PI controllers were implemented and tuned via the ATV method. In Figure 2, the deviation of the composition in the bottom's product is presented. As expected, the most promising structure is CS1 in which the purity specifications are directly controlled. Apart from that, the performance of the other three structures is also smooth with small deviations of order 10^{-3}.

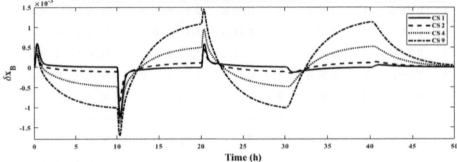

Figure 2. Deviation of bottom's product composition.

Finally, in order to evaluate the economic performance of the structures, the cost of utilities regarding the examined time domain was calculated. More specifically, the examined structures resulted in 2001.4\$, 2001.5\$, 2001.6\$ and 2001.7 \$ accordingly. Considering the order of the resulted economic penalties, it can be said that all structures feature in the same cost. The difference between the cost although insignificant, manages to ascertain the ranking of the structures presented in Table 1. These findings prove that the proposed formulation is successful in identifying promising control structures in a systematic way based on economic performance and not on rules of thumb and heuristics.

Conclusions

This paper presents, the main concepts of the back-off methodology for the CSSP problem. A new formulation is presented and evaluated for the reactor-separator-recycle process. The results are very promising and the new formulation may offer advantages in the study of even more aggressive non-linear processes. The back-off methodology in general, handles efficiently the CSSP and based on the size of the current case the proposed methodology is not size-limited.

Acknowledgement

This work was supported by the project "INVALOR: Research Infrastructure for Waste Valorization and Sustainable Management" (MIS 5002495) which is implemented under the Action "Reinforcement of the Research and Innovation Infrastructure", funded by the Operational Programme "Competitiveness, Entrepreneurship and Innovation" (NSRF 2014-2020) and co-financed by Greece and the European Union (European Regional Development Fund).

References

1. J. Heath,I. Kookos,J. Perkins, 2000, Process control structure selection based on economics, AIChe J., 46, 10, 1998-2016.
2. I. Kookos,J. Perkins, 2016, Control Structure Selection Based on Economics: Generalization of the Back-Off Methodology, AIChE J., 62, 9, 3056-3064
3. M. Luyben, C. Floudas, 1994, Analyzing the interaction of design and control-2. Reactor-Separator-Recucle system, Comp. Chem. Eng, 18, 10, 971-944
4. A. Psaltis,I. Kookos, C. Kravaris, 2013, Plant-wide control structure selection methodology based on economics, Comp. Chem. Eng.,52, 240-248
5. J. Viswanathan, I. Grossmann, 1993, An alternate minlp model for finding the number of trays required for a specified separation objective, Comp. Chem. Eng.,17, 9, 949-955

Sauro Pierucci, Flavio Manenti, Giulia Bozzano, Davide Manca (Eds.)
Proceedings of the 30th European Symposium on Computer Aided Process Engineering
(ESCAPE30), May 24-27, 2020, Milano, Italy. © 2020 Elsevier B.V. All rights reserved.
http://dx.doi.org/10.1016/B978-0-12-823377-1.50186-5

Optimal Design and Planning of Biomass-to-Biofuel Supply Chain Considering Economic Dimension under Strategic and Tactical Levels: a Case Study in Ethiopia

Brook Tesfamichael[a,b,c], Ludovic Montastruc[a,b,*], Stéphane Negny[a,b], Abubeker Yimam[c]

[a.] Université de Toulouse, INP-ENSIACET, 4, allée Emile Monso, F-31432 Toulouse Cedex 04, France
[b.] CNRS, LGC (Laboratoire de Génie Chimique), F-31432 Toulouse Cedex 04, France
[c.] Addis Ababa University, Addis Ababa Institut e of Technology, School of Chemical and Bio Engineering, Addis Ababa, Ethiopia
ludovic.montastruc@ensiacet.fr

Abstract

Biofuel derived from biomass on account of being renewable energy source and having high potential to substitute fossil fuels, have attracted considerable interest in both developed and developing countries like Ethiopia. However, the lack of optimal design and planning of the biomass-to-biofuel projects in countries like Ethiopia results in poor economic attractiveness of the sector. Therefore, this study presents a novel economic optimization model to design and plan biomass-to-biofuel supply chain (BBSC) at strategic and tactical level simultaneously. The problem is formulated as spatially explicit, multi-feedstock, multi-period and multi-echelon mixed integer linear programming model that seeks to maximize the NPV of the entire supply chain. The proposed model covers all the entities along the supply chain including biomass cultivation, feedstock pretreatment, conversion into bioethanol or biodiesel, as well as distribution, transportation and storage of the biomass, products and byproducts. A county-level case study in Ethiopia is provided to demonstrate the applicability of the model. Results show the effectiveness of the model as a quantitative decision-making or planning tool to design different BBSC configurations. Optimal location, technology, and capacity of the preprocessing facility, biorefinery and biofuel distribution centers are determined simultaneously with inventory levels, material flows and transportation capacities between network nodes of the supply chain.

Keywords: Biomass-to-biofuel supply chain (BBSC), economic optimization, strategic and tactical level.

1. Introduction

Biomass-to-biofuel industry has been grown in recent years since it has a tremendous potential to reduce oil imports and greenhouse gas (GHG) emissions, support agricultural and forestry growth, and foster social benefits like job creation. As a result of this, biofuel targets have been set by many developed and developing nations including Ethiopia. Biomass based biofuel production particularly bioethanol production from sugar byproducts - Molasses and Bagasse and biodiesel production from the nonedible oil seed bearing plants - Jatropha curcas and Castor seed - is a key strategic direction outlined in the biofuels strategy of the Government of Ethiopia. The main objective underlying the strategy include substitution of imported gasoline and diesel oil used in the transport sector while at the same time contributing to the local and global greenhouse gasses (GHG) reduction efforts (Gabisa et al., 2018).

To demonstrate the feasibility and validate the economic interest in the production of biofuel from biomass, the development of systematic studies is becoming imperative. Accordingly, many Process Systems Engineering (PSE) approaches focusing on Biomass-to-Biofuel Supply Chain (BBSC) optimization through mathematical programming have been recently developed, considering mostly the economic dimension (Espinoza Pérez et al., 2017a). However, these studies have some drawbacks: a) the strategic level decision has been the center of investigation in most researches (Akhtari et al., 2018; Barbosa-Povoa et al., 2018). However, tactical and operational level studies are also essential to provide comprehensive information and realistic representation to support decisions; b) most of the BBSC studies considered only one type of biofuel product. The simultaneous bioethanol and biodiesel production in one supply chain has not been considered so far; and c) Most of the BBSC researches deal the system complexity in a fragmented and partial manner, either on the upstream biomass supply chain, from the biomass cultivation site to the production plant or on the downstream biofuel supply chain, from the production plant to the end customer (Yu et al., 2013). Moreover, because of not incorporating some important components while planning the BBSC, the project incurs high amount of cost that discourages investors, government and other stakeholders (Espinoza Pérez et al., 2017a). For instance, overlooking a pre-processing operation in the BBSC may bring an increment of transportation cost due to the higher moisture content and large size of the raw biomass.

Henceforth, to overcome the above drawbacks, this study presents a decision-support optimization model that maximizes the net present value (NPV) of the entire BBSC considering: a) both strategic and tactical level planning and decisions; b) BBSC with two-product (bioethanol and biodiesel) processing plants those are located at different sites; and c) comprehensive supply chain which incorporates all relevant components from biomass feedstock supply to biofuel end-users: namely, biomass feedstock supply centers, preprocessing centers, bio-Refineries, biofuel (bioethanol & biodiesel) distribution centers, biofuel and by-product market zones

The proposed approach will be applied for Ethiopia's case to provide decision or planning support tool for the policy makers, investors and other pertinent stakeholders in order to bring the biomass-to-biofuel sector economically sustainable.

2. Problem Statement

The core driver of this study is to deal with the strategic and tactical design and planning of BBSC for the production of bioethanol and biodiesel in Ethiopia over 30-years' time horizon. The problem addressed in this paper is presented schematically on **Figure 1** and the problem is described as follows. The BBSC optimization model proposed in this work considers different types of biomass b that can be procured from a variety of supply sources h. In each candidate location i, there are preprocessing facilities that can be installed for pretreating the biomass with candidate technologies f and capacities c. The technologies are mainly drying and size reduction for bioethanol feedstocks and oil extraction for biodiesel feedstocks. Then the preprocessed feedstock d goes to a biorefinery located at j, where there are g candidate technologies with capacities e that can be installed for the production of biofuel u and generation of byproduct v. There are two possibilities for the biofuel u to reach to the demand zone m from the biorefinery j; either it goes to the distribution center k with capacity a and then to the demand zone m or it directly goes to the demand zone m without going to distribution center k, whereas the byproduct v directly goes to the demand zone n from the biorefinery j.

The deterministic parameters used in the proposed BBSC are the following:
- ➢ Biomass supply location and amount over a fixed time horizon
- ➢ Bioethanol and biodiesel demand location and amount over a fixed time horizon.
- ➢ The procurement cost of biomass and selling price of the biofuels and useful by-products.
- ➢ The candidate locations, capital and operating costs, and maximum capacities of the pre-processing, biorefinery, and biofuel distribution facilities.
- ➢ The transport logistics (distances, availability, costs and modes).
- ➢ Government policies relating to the BBSC, e.g. taxation and subsidies.

Having the above parameters, the key variables of the model that need to be optimized, refer to both strategic and tactical decisions for the entire supply chain. Precisely, the strategic decisions regard the location of biomass procurement sites and location, technology, and capacity of the preprocessing facility and biorefinery as well as location and capacity of biofuel distribution sites, whereas the tactical decisions deal with inventory levels, material flows and transportation capacities between network nodes.

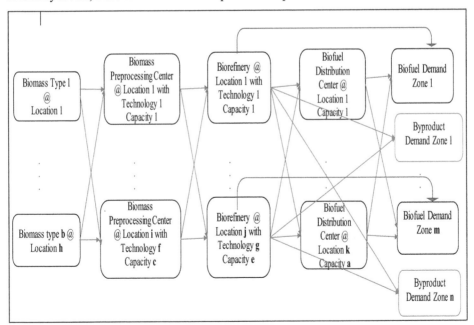

Figure 1: Model Superstructure

3. Model Formulation

In order to address the entire behavior of BBSC, the mathematical modeling framework has been formulated as an MILP problem. The design process is conceived as a single-objective optimization problem targeting at NPV maximization of the entire supply chain. The problem is formulated as a spatially explicit multi-period, multi-feedstock, multi-product and multi-echelon modeling framework. Precisely, the objective function, as illustrated in eq. 1, comprises of cash inflows, cash outflows and initial investment. Revenues obtained by selling, and tax credit for producing the desired products and byproducts are considered as the cash inflows whereas cash outflows comprised of biomass procurement, operational, inventory and transportation costs along the supply chain. The initial investment considers the capital investments for the preprocessing, biorefinery and product storage facilities, and government incentive for biorefinery installation. In this work, the cash inflow and outflow are calculated for a lifetime project of 30 years (y ∈ Y, Y = {1,2,…,30}), based on the planning years optimized over 12 months (t ∈ T, T = {1,2,…,12}).

$$NPV = \left[\sum_{n=1}^{Y} \frac{1}{(1+\partial)^y} \left(CashInflow^y - CashOutflow^y \right) \right] - InitalInvestment$$

(1)

The design process is also subjected to logical constraints that must be satisfied at each of the supply chain nodes; including feedstock availability constraints, mass balances in the preprocessing facility for the feedstock and preprocessed biomass, mass balances in the biorefinery for the preprocessed biomass, biofuel product and byproducts, mass balances in the distribution center for the biofuel, and biofuel and byproduct demand satisfaction. The model also takes into account the biomass seasonality and biomass degradation over time.

4. Case Study

The developed model in this study will be applied to a case study in Ethiopia to support the government and other stakeholders engaged in the country's biomass-to-biofuel projects. In this study, the candidate locations of the biomass collection, pre-processing, biorefinery, and biofuel and byproduct storage and distribution facilities were restricted to the nine regions (Afar, Amhara, Benishangul, Gambella, Harari, Oromia, SNNP, Somali and Tigray) and two city administrations (Addis Ababa and Diredawa) of the country due to the availability of data. The prior feedstocks for biofuel development in Ethiopia are considered in this study; sugar cane molasses, bagasse and corn stover for bioethanol and jatropha and castor bean for biodiesel production. Annual productions of sugar cane molasses and bagasse are acquired from Ethiopian Sugar Corporation since sugar industries are the only place where these two biomass feedstocks are released from. The amount of corn stover produced was estimated using corn grain yield values which are available on Ethiopia Statistical Agency reports. The stover mass to grain mass ratio of 1:1 (i.e., a dry weight harvest index [HI] of 0.5) (Graham et al., 2007) and taking in to consideration if 50 % of the stover in each region is used for bioethanol production. Having the amount of suitable land available in each region of the country for jatropha and castor plantation from Ministry of Agriculture, bibliographic data were used to determine the average amount of seed produced per hectare of suitable land. The pre-processing mechanism considered for the two bioethanol feedstocks; bagasse and corn stover is only drying and size reduction. However, no preprocessing is required for the molasses. On the other hand, technologies considered for the pre-processing facility of the biodiesel feedstocks are steam explosion and acid hydolysis. Biochemical and thermo-chemical conversion processes for bioethanol production (Hamelinck et al., 2005) and homogenous and heterogenous catalysis transesterification for biodiesel production (Saifuddin et al., 2015) are considered as biorefinery technologies in this study. These technologies are chosen for their relative practice in current Ethiopia biofuel industries and availability of detailed techno-economic data. The six capacity levels of the preprocessing facilities considered in this study are 65, 125, 190, 250, 320 and 380 kton of wet biomass per year and the biorefinery capacities are 25, 50, 75, 100, 125 and 150 kton of biofuel per year. Due to the lack of real preprocessing and biorefinery investment and production costs data from commercial plant within Ethiopia, these costs were estimated with bibliographic data, assuming that the components follow the economy of scale, and then corrected with the available information and recent data. The biofuels demand was calculated based on the current government plan to blend bioethanol and biodiesel at a rate of 15 and 5% in the gasoline and diesel respectively. Based on the case study area features, only road transportation mode is assumed for transporting different materials within the supply chain.

5. Result and Discussion

The proposed MILP model was solved using the ILOG CPLEX solver. The model for this case study had 21,242,485 constraints and 315,161 decision variables of which 44,352 were binary variables. An optimal solution was found in 17 hours, after 132,326,057 iterations on an Intel 2.60-GHz processor.

Aiming the maximization of the NPV of the entire BBSC, the model decides the installation of biorefinery with technology of biochemical conversion with acid pretreatment and homogenous catalysis transesterification for the bioethanol and biodiesel production respectively. The optimal solution showed that, from the eleven different allocation options, one of them (Oromia), two of them (Oromia and Amhara) and three of them (Oromia, Amhara and Afar) for the first 10, 11-20, and 21-30 years respectively are feasible locations for bioethanol production. The optimal capacity of both the Oromia and Amhara plants is 125 kton/year, and 50 kton/year for the Afar plant. Meanwhile, two allocations (Addis Ababa and Oromia), four allocations (Addis Ababa, Oromia, SNNP and Tigray), and five allocations (Addis Ababa, Oromia, SNNP, Tigray and Benishangul) are the best alternatives to have biorefinery producing biodiesel for the first 12, 13-23, and 24-30 years respectively. The optimal capacity of both Addis Ababa and Oromia plants is 150 kton/year, and 125, 50 and 25 kton/year for the SNNP, Tigray and Benishangul plants respectively to address the required biodiesel demand.

Regarding the pre-processing facility, the optimal solution showed that, installation of drying and size reduction for the bioethanol feedstocks are required in Oromia, Amhara, Afar, SNNP and Tigray regions for the years 7-30. Solvent extraction is the best option starting from year 1 to pretreat the biodiesel feedstocks and the selected location for the plant are all the regions except Harari. Moreover, the best selected locations for the distribution centers are Addis Ababa, Amhara and Diredawa.

The optimal result also show that, molasses is the only biomass feedstock to fulfill the bioethanol demand of the country for the next 6 years, whereas molasses and bagasse for the years 7-15, and corn stover is also required with the previous two feedstocks for the years 16-30. Regardless of the biodiesel feedstocks, all the demand of the biodiesel for the next 26 years can be fulfilled by using jatropha as a feedstock if the country utilizes only 10% of the highly suitable land for jatropha cultivation. Castor seed is required together with jatropha for the years 27-30 to address the biodiesel demand.

Although the availability and price of biomass, and price of products were assumed to be fixed over the planning period, revenue shows increment over the 30-year period due to increasing demand of the products. Biomass purchase, transport, operating, and storage costs are accounted for about 23.48 %, 17.08 %, 54.94 % and 4.49 % of the total cash outflow respectively for the first 10 years. In the last 10 years, biomass procurement cost decreased by 8.8 %, transportation cost increased by 42.44 %, operating cost decreased by 9 %, and insignificant change on storage cost compared with those first 10 years.

6. Conclusions

In this work, a novel optimization model has been developed as a decision-making tool for the strategic and tactical design and planning of BBSC. A spatially explicit, multi-period MILP modeling framework for optimization of multifeedstock and multiechelon BBSC, has been presented and discussed. To demonstrate the applicability of the model, it is implemented to determine the optimal supply chain, in terms of maximizing NPV, of the abundant residual biomass available in Ethiopia to produce bioethanol and biodiesel. Results showed that the design and planning of economically sustainable biofuel production and utilization can be enhanced significantly through the optimization of all the entities involved in the BBSC. Finally, future extensions of this work will incorporate the integration of other sustainability dimensions: environment and social, to come-up with comprehensive decision-making tool.

References

E.W. Gabisa, S.H. Gheewala, 2018. Potential of bio-energy production in Ethiopia based on available biomass residues. Biomass and Bioenergy 111, 77-87.

A. Espinoza Pérez, M. Camargo, P.C. Narváez, M. Alfaro, 2017a. Key challenges and requirements for sustainable and industrialized biorefinery supply chain design and management: A bibliographic analysis. Renewable and Sustainable Energy Reviews 69, 350-359.

S. Akhtari, T. Sowlatia, V.C. Griess, 2018. Integrated strategic and tactical optimization of forest-based biomass supply chains to consider medium-term supply and demand variations. Computers and Chemical Engineering 113, 11-31.

A.P. Barbosa-Póvoa, C. Silva, A. Carvalho, 2018. Opportunities and challenges in sustainable supply chain: An operations research perspective. European Journal of Operational Research 268, 2, 399-431.

M. Yu, F. Cecelja, S.A. Hosseini, 2013. Design and optimization of biofuel supply chain network in UK. Computer Aided Chemical Engineering 32, 673-678.

R.L. Graham, R. Nelson, J. Sheehan, R.D. Perlack and L.L. Wright, 2007. Current and Potential US Corn Stover Supplies. Agronomy Journal 99, 1-19.

C.N. Hamelinck, G.V. Hooijdonk, A.C. Faaij, 2005. Ethanol from lignocellulosic biomass: Techno-economic performance in short-, middle- and long-term. Biomass Bioenergy 28, 384-410.

N. Saifuddin, A. Samiuddin, P. Kumaran, 2015. A Review on Processing Technology for Biodiesel Production. Trends Applied Sciences 10, 1, 1-37.

Sauro Pierucci, Flavio Manenti, Giulia Bozzano, Davide Manca (Eds.)
Proceedings of the 30th European Symposium on Computer Aided Process Engineering
(ESCAPE30), May 24-27, 2020, Milano, Italy. © 2020 Elsevier B.V. All rights reserved.
http://dx.doi.org/10.1016/B978-0-12-823377-1.50187-7

Modelling a Penicillin Fermentation Process Using Attention-Based Echo State Networks Optimized by Covariance Matrix Adaption Evolutionary Strategy

Kai Liu, Jie Zhang

School of Engineering, Merz Court, Newcastle University, Newcastle upon Tyne NE1 7RU, UK.
jie.zhang@newcastle.ac.uk

Abstract

Echo state network (ESN) has emerged as an effective alternative to conventional recurrent neural networks due to its simple training process and good modelling ability for solving a variety of problems, especially time-series modelling tasks. To improve modelling capability and to decrease the reservoir topology complexity, a new attention mechanism based ESN optimised by covariance matrix adaption evolutionary strategy (CMA-ES) is proposed in this paper. CMA-ES is a stochastic and derivative-free algorithm for solving non-linear optimization problems. Attention mechanism is incorporated to guide ESN to focus on regions of interest relevant to the modelling task. The proposed optimised ESN with attention mechanism is used to model a fed-batch penicillin fermentation process and the results are better than those from the standard ESN and ESN with attention mechanism.

Keywords: Echo State Network, Attention Mechanism, CMA-ES, Fed-batch Bioprocess

1. Introduction

Fed-batch fermentation processes are widely used in the pharmaceutical industry. In fed-batch fermentation processes, the maximization of yield is often regarded as the main objective, but the features of fed-batch fermentation processes including strong nonlinearity, non-steady-state condition, batch-to-batch variations, and strong time-varying condition make the yield hard to be predicted (Ashoori et al., 2009).

Due to the increasing demand on product quality and safety, optimization of fed-batch fermentation processes is becoming very important. One optimization approach is to use first principle models and stochastic optimisation algorithms such as evolutionary algorithm (EA), differential evolution (DE) and particle swarm optimization (PSO) (bin Mohd Zain et al., 2018). Another optimization approach for fed-batch bioprocesses is to use data-driven models such as artificial neural networks. Yu (2012) presented a Bayesian inference based two-stage support vector machine for soft sensor development in batch bioprocesses. Chen et al. (2004) proposed a cascade recurrent neural network combining with modified genetic algorithm for the modelling and optimisation of fed-batch fermentation processes.

In recent years, recurrent neural networks (RNNs) attracted a mass of attention because of its dynamic temporal nonlinear behaviour and processing arbitrary sequences of inputs by its internal memory. RNNs are appropriate for modelling complex dynamic processes such as fed-batch fermentation processes. RNNs include but no limit to long short-term memory networks (LSTM), gated recurrent unit (GRU) and reservoir computing (RC). Comparing to LSTM and GRU, the benefit of RC is lower computational training cost and faster convergence with excellent performance. Due to the randomly generated input scaling matrix, the normal ESNs are not able to distinguish the different property of input elements. The concept of "attention mechanism", which allows models to learn alignments between different modalities, has drawn significant attention in the training of neural networks. Attention mechanisms have been successfully used in speech translation and image caption generation (Luong et al., 2015), but have rarely been used in modelling complex bioprocesses, especially fed-batch fermentation process with a large number controllable and monitoring variables.

In this paper, an input elements scaling method based on the attention mechanism is integrated with ESN which is optimized by covariance matrix adaption evolutionary strategy (CMA-ES). Three global reservoir parameters in ESN are optimized by CMA-ES and they are reservoir size, spectral radius, and leak rate.

2. Methodology

2.1. Echo state networks

An ESN is composed of a reservoir and a linear output layer which maps the reservoir states to the network output. Figure 1 shows the original ESN. The input weights are generated randomly. The internal weights between reservoir neurons can be created with a sparse connection density which means that internal neurons may not be fully connected to each other but connected sparsely. The weights mentioned above will not change during the training process and only the readout output weights need to be learned. The reservoir states of ESN with leak rate are shown in Eq(1) (Lukoševičius and Jaeger, 2009):

$$x(t) = (1 - \alpha) \cdot x(t - 1) + \alpha \cdot f(W^{in} \cdot u(t) + W \cdot x(t - 1) + W^{back} \cdot y(t - 1) \quad (1)$$

where $u(t)$ and $x(t)$ are the inputs and the reservoir states at time t respectively, α is the leak rate, $f()$ is the general activation function, and the weights donated by W^{in}, W^{back}, and W represent the weights for inputs, feedback, and reservoir respectively. Then W needs to be rescaled by a spectral radius (the largest absolute eigenvalue of W, $|\theta_{Max}|$) and then multiplied by a spectral radius factor δ as shown in Eq(2) to keep its echo state property.

$$W \leftarrow \delta W / |\theta_{Max}| \quad (2)$$

The readout matrix is then obtained by solving a linear regression problem:

$$X \cdot W^{out} = Y \quad (3)$$

where X is a matrix of hidden states which are updated at discrete time steps using Eq(1) and Y is the corresponding target outputs.

Ridge regression has been shown to be an efficient method to calculate the readout matrix (Dutoit et al., 2009). Ridge regression is a shrinkage method that consists of adding a penalty term proportional to the Euclidean norm of the readout matrix:

$$W^{out} = arg \min_{w}(\|Xw - Y\|^2 + \gamma\|w\|^2) \quad (4)$$

where $\gamma \geq 0$ is the ridge parameter determined on a hold-out validation set. The solution of readout matrix is given as:

$$W^{out} = (X^T X + \gamma^2 I_N)^{-1} X^T Y \quad (5)$$

where I_N is the identity matrix of size N.

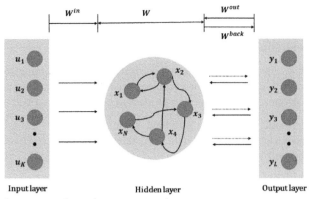

Figure 1. Typical structure of an echo state network

2.2. Covariance matrix adaption evolution strategy

CMA-ES is a well-established evolutionary algorithm for real-valued optimization with many successful applications. The main advantages of CMA-ES lie in its invariance properties, which are achieved by carefully designed variation and selection operators and its efficient adaptation of the mutation distribution. The CMA-ES is invariant against order-preserving transformations of the fitness function value and in particular against rotation and translation of the search space. It has been demonstrated by experiments that the covariance matrix $C^{(g)}$ is similar to the inverse of the Hessian matrix of the problem at the optimum point. CMA-ES is particularly useful on non-smooth and ill-conditioned problems as it estimates a covariance matrix using an iterative procedure.

In CMA-ES, the population of new search offspring $x \in \mathbb{R}n$ is generated by sampling a multivariate normal distribution (Hansen et al., 2003):

$$x_k^{(g+1)} \sim m^{(g)} + \sigma^{(g)} \cdot \aleph(0, C^{(g)}) \ for \ k = 1, \dots, l \qquad (6)$$

where $x_k^{(g+1)}$ denotes the kth offspring at the $(g+1)$th generation; $m^{(g)}$ is the mean value of the search distribution at generation g ; $\aleph(0, C^{(g)})$ is a multivariate normal distribution with zero mean and covariance matrix $C^{(g)}$; and $\sigma^{(g)}$ is the step-size at generation g.

After those l individuals have been created, they are evaluated on the objective function which is the mean squared errors (MSE) of the ESN and sorted according to their objective function values.

2.3. Attention mechanism

Attention mechanism in neural networks was proposed to guide networks to focus on regions of interest relevant for a particular modelling task. This prunes the network search space and avoids computing features from irrelevant input data (Luong et al., 2015). In order to make predictions based upon the relative input data, a variable-length alignment vector a_t, whose size equals the input dimension, is derived by comparing the current target state s_t with input hidden state h_{ut}:

$$a_t = align(s_t, h_{ut}) = sigmoid[score(s_t, h_{ut})] \qquad (7)$$

Here, score is obtained as:

$$score(s_t, h_{ut}) = s_t^T W_a h_{ut} \qquad (8)$$

where W_a is a rescale matrix of s_t and h_{ut}.

The original input matrix is pruned by a_t and updated input data $\widehat{u_t}$ is calculated as:

$$\widehat{u_t} = a_t \odot u_t \qquad (9)$$

where $\odot$ denotes element-wise multiplication.

3. Proposed modelling strategy

This paper proposes using CMA-ES to optimize the structure parameters of ESN with attention mechanism (Atten-ESN) for nonlinear process modelling. Figure 2 shows the flow chart of the proposed algorithm. The procedure can be summarized as follows:

1. Data for model building are divided by into three sets: training data, testing data, and unseen validation data, and then they are normalized to have zero mean and unit variance.

2. Prune the input matrix by global attention mechanism.

3. Establish an ESN with random R, α, and δ in the range based on sufficient internal units as default. The activation function used here in the hidden layer (reservoir) is $f = tanh$ and the input weights and reservoir weights are generated randomly.

4. Train the established ESN with training data using ridge regression.

5. Optimize the Atten-ESN by CMA-ES. The MSE on the testing data is used as objective function. The optimization objective is to upgrade the values of R, α, and δ to minimize the MSE on the testing data.

6. Test the optimized Atten-ESN (O-Atten-ESN) on the unseen validation data.

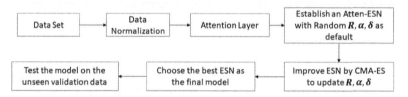

Figure 2. Graphical illustration of the proposed approach

4. Experiments

The benchmark industrial penicillin fermentation simulator, IndPenSim (Goldrick et al., 2015), is used to produce simulated process operation data. The simulator code in Matlab R2013b is available to download at www.industrialpenicillinsimulation.com. Three benches of data generated by IndPensim are used in model development. One batch is used as training data, the second batch is used as testing data, and the third batch is used as the unseen validation data. The penicillin concentration is taken as the target output and 30 controllable and monitoring variables are used as model inputs. The fitness function to minimize is the MSE of the ESN on the training data:

$$MSE = \frac{\sum_{i=1}^{N}(y_i - \hat{y}_i)^2}{N} \tag{10}$$

where y_i and $\hat{y}_i$ are target value and predicted value at sample i respectively, and N is the number of data samples.

5. Results and discussion

In order to investigate the performance of O-Atten-ESN, it is compared with standard ESN, Atten-ESN, and standard LSTM. The comparison between standard ESN and Atten-ESN is to investigate the effect of integrating attention mechanism with ESN. The comparison between Atten-ESN and O-Atten-ESN is to illustrate the effect of optimization using CMA-ES. In all ESNs, the three structural parameters, reservoir size, leak rate, and special radius, are randomly generated in the ranges of [1-1000], [0-1], and [0-1.5] respectively. The initial step size of CMA-ES is 0.1 and the ridge regression parameter is 0.005.

The prediction results on unseen validation batch with different methods are shown in Figure 3 with the MSE of each method shown in the legend. Figure 4 shows the corresponding prediction errors. It can be seen in Figure 3, comparing to the predictions of the standard ESN, predictions of both O-Atten-ESN and Atten-ESN are closer to target values, especially when the slope of the target values is steep. This illustrates that the attention mechanism can take out some irrelevant input signals to reduce their influence. In other words, attention mechanism can increase the model robustness. Figure 4 shows that the errors of O-Atten-ESN are much smaller than those of the other two methods, demonstrating that high dimensional optimized algorithm such as CMA-ES can optimize ESN by searching better structure parameters. Table 1 gives the average MSE values and standard deviations of the three methods which were run 50 times with different random parameters. In summary, the attention mechanism and CMA-ES can improve ESN on predicting penicillin concentration in the fed-batch fermentation process in terms of prediction accuracy and robustness.

Table 1. Average MSE and standard deviation of different ESNs

Methods	Average MSE	Standard deviation
O-Atten-ESN	0.0781	0.0122
Atten-ESN	0.9723	0.1740
Standard ESN	1.6871	0.4116

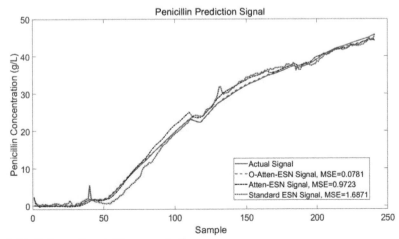

Figure 3. Predictions of penicillin concentration

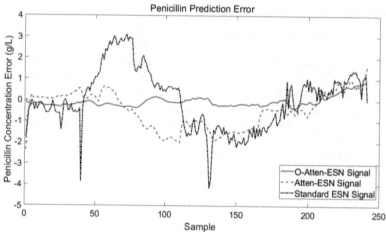

Figure 4. Prediction errors of penicillin concentration

6. Conclusions

An ESN with attention mechanism and optimized by CMA-ES is proposed in this paper to model a fed-batch penicillin fermentation process. Based on the preliminary results, the attention mechanism and CMA-ES can improve standard ESN on modelling complex bioprocesses with enhanced accuracy and reliability. It is expected that the proposed method will be effective for modelling other complex bioprocesses.

References

Ashoori, A., Moshiri, B., Khaki-Sedigh, A., and Bakhtiari, M. R., 2009. Optimal control of a nonlinear fed-batch fermentation process using model predictive approach. Journal of Process Control, 19(7), 1162-1173.

bin Mohd Zain, M. Z., Kanesan, J., Kendall, G., and Chuah, J. H., 2018. Optimization of fed-batch fermentation processes using the Backtracking Search Algorithm. Expert Systems with Applications, 91, 286-297.

Chen, L., Nguang, S. K., Chen, X. D., and Li, X. M., 2004. Modelling and optimization of fed-batch fermentation processes using dynamic neural networks and genetic algorithms. Biochemical Engineering Journal, 22(1), 51-61.

Dutoit, X., Schrauwen, B., Van Campenhout, J., Stroobandt, D., Van Brussel, H., Nuttin, M., 2009. Pruning and regularization in reservoir computing. Neurocomputing, 72(7-9), 1534-1546.

Goldrick, S., Stefan, A., Lovett, D., Montague, G., Lennox, B., 2015. The development of an industrial-scale fed-batch fermentationsimulation. Journal of Biotechnology, 193, 70–82.

Hansen, N., Müller, S. D., Koumoutsakos, P., 2003. Reducing the time complexity of the derandomized evolution strategy with covariance matrix adaptation (CMA-ES). Evolutionary Computation, 11(1), 1-18.

Lukoševičius, M., Jaeger, H., 2009. Reservoir computing approaches to recurrent neural network training. Computer Science Review, 3(3), 127-149.

Luong, M. T., Pham, H., and Manning, C. D., 2015. Effective approaches to attention-based neural machine translation. Conference on Empirical Methods in Natural Language Processing, EMNLP 2015, Lisbon; Portugal, 17 - 21 September 2015, 1412-1421.

Yu J., 2012. A Bayesian inference based two-stage support vector regression framework for soft sensor development in batch bioprocesses. Computers & Chemical Engineering, 41, 134-144.

Sauro Pierucci, Flavio Manenti, Giulia Bozzano, Davide Manca (Eds.)
Proceedings of the 30th European Symposium on Computer Aided Process Engineering
(ESCAPE30), May 24-27, 2020, Milano, Italy. © 2020 Elsevier B.V. All rights reserved.
http://dx.doi.org/10.1016/B978-0-12-823377-1.50188-9

Tailored Time Grids for Nonlinear Scheduling Subject to Time-variable Electricity Prices by Wavelet-based Analysis

Pascal Schäfer,[a] Alexander Mitsos[b,a,c,*]

[a]*Process Systems Engineering (AVT.SVT), RWTH Aachen University, 52074 Aachen, Germany*
[b]*JARA-CSD, 52056 Aachen, Germany*
[c]*Forschungszentrum Jülich, Energy Systems Engineering (IEK-10), 52425 Jülich, Germany*
amitsos@alum.mit.edu

Abstract

Typically, the consideration of nonlinear process models in discrete-time scheduling is limited to short planning horizons and/or coarse discretizations due to a linear scaling of the problem size with the number of considered scheduling intervals. To overcome this limitation, we recently proposed a wavelet-based algorithm focusing on scheduling problems with time-variable electricity prices, which iteratively adapts the time grid (Schäfer et int., Mitsos, doi:10.1016/j.compchemeng.2019.106598). In this work, we extend our approach by presenting a systematic method for the identification of promising initial aggregated time grids based on the analysis of the wavelet representation of the time series of electricity prices. We apply the procedure to a literature example addressing the scheduling of a seawater reverse osmosis (Ghobeity and Mitsos, doi: 10.1016/j.desal.2010.06.041). We demonstrate that substantial reductions in the number of optimization variables in a reduced-space formulation are possible, while furnishing feasible schedules that lead to insignificant deviations below 0.05 % in the objective value compared to the global optimum using the full time grid.

Keywords: Demand side management, Discrete-time scheduling, Reduced-space, Global optimization, Adaptive refinement

1. Introduction

The adjustment of the electricity consumption to time-variable electricity prices is an important measure to increase the competitiveness of industrial consumers (Mitsos et al., 2018). Consequently, sophisticated methodologies for discrete-time scheduling with time-variables prices have been proposed, mostly aiming at formulating mixed-integer linear programs (MILPs) that can be handled efficiently by state-of-the-art solvers (e.g., Ierapetritou et al., 2002; Mitra et al., 2012; Zhang et al., 2015). In contrast, although many processes are governed by strongly nonlinear characteristics, only few authors tried to consider nonlinear models in discrete-time scheduling (e.g., Ghobeity and Mitsos, 2010), as this leads to nonlinear programs (NLPs) with potentially multiple local solutions. Consequently, solving these problems requires global solution approaches that currently prohibit long planning horizons and/or fine discretizations. To overcome this limitation and allow for nonlinear scheduling with relevant horizons and sufficiently fine discretizations, we recently proposed an iterative algorithm combining three key ideas (Schäfer et al., 2019): a reduced-space scheduling formulation, a time series aggregation, and a wavelet-based grid adaptation procedure.

In this work, we extend our approach by a systematic method to identify a promising initial aggregated time grid. In particular, we perform an analysis of the wavelet representation of the time series of electricity prices to derive the initial grid. The proposed procedure is examined and benchmarked against state-of-the-art solution approaches for a case study. Therein, we consider the scheduling of a seawater reverse osmosis (SWRO) formulated as a mixed-integer nonlinear program (MINLP).

2. Case study and solution approaches

2.1. Process model and problem description

We focus on the same case study as Ghobeity and Mitsos (2010), cf. Figure 1. All modeling equations, parameters and operating bounds can be found in their work. The SWRO model comprises eleven variables and ten nonlinear equations. The operation of the SWRO is hence fully determined by specifying one degree of freedom, e.g., the recovery ratio. As in the original reference, we further introduce a disjunction represented by an additional binary variable that allows for shutting down the plant. Discrete-time scheduling of the SWRO consequently corresponds to solving an MINLP with potentially multiple local minima, thus global solution approaches are preferred. We further assume an hourly discretization considering historic time-variable German Day-Ahead spot electricity prices retrieved from EPEX SPOT SE (https://www.epexspot.com/en/). The objective is to achieve lowest electricity costs for fulfilling a given production target, i.e., a fixed cumulated permeate production. Furthermore, the SWRO's operation is constrained by bounds on the key variables: transmembrane pressure, high-pressure pump shaft frequency, recovery ratio and salt concentration in concentrate.

2.2. Solution approaches using the full time grid

When considering the full time grid, i.e., one grid point per hour of the horizon, we apply two different solution approaches for the MINLP. In the first one – referred to as full-space (FS) – all model variables and equations of each scheduling interval are exposed to the optimizer, as it is common practice in the formulation of discrete-time scheduling problems. In this case, model equations simply correspond to equality constraints and operating bounds to box-constraints on selected variables.

In the second approach – referred to as reduced-space (RS) – only a truncated set of

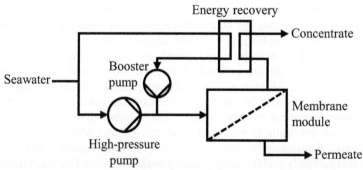

Figure 1: Schematic flowsheet of the considered process configuration for seawater reverse osmosis from Ghobeity and Mitsos (2010).

model variables is exposed to the optimizer; objective and constraints are expressed as functions thereof. This concept has been shown promising for global optimization of process flowsheets (Bongartz and Mitsos, 2017). In the considered case study, we expose two model variables per scheduling interval to the optimizer, although the SWRO's operation would be fully determined by specifying only one, as the model equations cannot be solved analytically. We herein select the high-pressure pump shaft frequencies and the recovery ratios as optimization variables. All other model variables are expressed as explicit functions thereof. One equality constraint per scheduling interval ensures that the selected values of the optimization variables comply with the process model. We remark that, like in the FS formulation, the disjunction introduces an additional binary optimization variable per scheduling interval.

2.3. Solution approaches using an aggregated time grid

Using an RS scheduling formulation allows for the application of our recently proposed time series aggregation scheme (Schäfer et al., 2019), which aims at tailored time grids and thus avoids a global optimization considering the full grid with individual optimization variables in each interval. This is achieved by mapping one optimization variable to multiple intervals with similar electricity prices Thereby, the number of optimization variables in RS is reduced and thus decoupled from the number of considered scheduling intervals, enabling substantial savings in computational time. However, due to the mapping, all scheduling intervals and consequently all constraints are considered further on, ensuring that feasible schedules are furnished. In the computational study below, we make furthermore use of the proposed iterative grid adaptation. Therein, a wavelet transform of the solution from the previous iteration using a coarser grid is conducted and the obtained coefficients are analyzed as proposed by Schlegel et al. (2005), allowing for a systematic adjustment of the mapping procedure by inserting promising new and deleting insignificant grid points.

In this work, we extend our approach by a systematic method to identify promising initial grids for the adaptation algorithm. More precisely, we first perform a wavelet transform of the input time series of electricity prices. Those wavelet coefficients with absolute values above a defined threshold are identified. Then, we use only the set of significant coefficients for the construction of the initial aggregated time grid following the procedure described in our previous work. Note that starting from this initialized grid, the same iterative adaptation algorithm as described above could be applied. However, for illustration purposes, we herein omit this possibility, so that we confine to one single optimization using the initial aggregated grid.

3. Computational results

3.1. Implementation and solver settings

The FS formulation (full time grid) is implemented in GAMS version 26.1.0 (GAMS Development Corp.) and corresponding optimization problems are solved globally using BARON version 18.11.12 (Tawarmalani and Sahinidis, 2005) with standard settings. For RS formulations (full time grid, grid adaptation, and grid initialization), the model is implemented as sequential C++ code and global optimizations are conducted using our in-house open-source software MAiNGO (Bongartz et al., 2018). Inside MAiNGO, CPLEX (IBM Corp.) is used for the lower bounding procedure and KNITRO (Exler and Schittkowski, 2007) for the upper bounding. Apart from that, we apply standard settings. For all optimizations, we set the relative optimality tolerance to

0.005. Furthermore, we apply a time limit of 100,000 s of CPU time. For the grid adaptation algorithm, threshold values of 0.0001 for deletion and 0.7 for insertion are used. Concerning the construction of the initial aggregated grid, we apply a threshold value of 0.03. All threshold values are relative to the Euclidean norm of the considered vector of wavelet coefficients. For the grid adaptation approach, three iterations of the algorithm starting from an equally distributed initial grid (6 grid points) are conducted.

3.2. Day-ahead scheduling

First, we consider a day-ahead scheduling, i.e., 24 intervals of one hour, targeting the exploitation of price spreads between day and night. Table 1 summarizes the results for all solution approaches described in Section 2. Note that in all cases, the best feasible schedule is obtained within negligible time. Reported CPU times thus primarily stem from the lower bounding procedures. Due to the good performance of local solvers in the upper bounding even when considering the full time grid (in both FS and RS), the reported solution in this case is considered as the global optimum and thus used as the benchmark for all solutions with aggregated grids. We emphasize that in contrast to the approaches considering the full grid, the approaches using aggregated grids lead to converged solutions within the defined time limit. In particular, savings in computational time when using the aggregated grids are more than two orders of magnitude. Moreover, we find that substantial reductions in the number of considered grid points are possible, while causing only minor deviations in the objective value. For instance, when applying the initial aggregated grid using only eight grid points, a feasible schedule is furnished with a difference in the objective value of ~0.025 % compared to the global optimum. Likewise, the final schedule after the third iteration of the adaptation algorithm starting from an equally distributed grid leads to only ~0.01 % deviations compared to the global optimum by using ten grid points.

Consequently, the corresponding final schedules obtained when using the aggregated grids look highly similar to the globally optimal schedule, as can be seen in Figure 2 (left). In contrast, the intermediate results of the grid adaptation using 6 and 8 grid points respectively lead to inferior schedules that do not make use of the possibility for a temporary shutdown during peak hours. The reason for this finding lies in a distinct price peak at 21 h, which can only be exploited by assigning individual optimization variables to that hour, which is not possible in the first two iterations of the adaptation, as they are limited to aggregating at least four (first) or two (second) intervals.

Table 1: Summary for solution approaches addressing a day-ahead scheduling (24 intervals). Asterisks indicate converged solutions.

Solution approach	Solver	#Grid points	CPU time	Optimality gap	Objective value
		[-]	[s]	[%]	[%]
RS-grid initialization	MAiNGO	8	273	0.005*	100.025
RS-grid adaptation iteration 1	MAiNGO	6	47	0.005*	100.66
RS-grid adaptation iteration 2	MAiNGO	8	1,027	0.005*	100.65
RS-grid adaptation iteration 3	MAiNGO	10	3,055	0.005*	100.01
FS-full time grid	BARON	24	100,000	0.006	100
RS-full time grid	MAiNGO	24	100,000	0.021	100

Table 2: Summary for solution approaches addressing a week-ahead scheduling (168 intervals). Asterisks indicate converged solutions.

Solution approach	Solver	#Grid points	CPU time	Optimality gap	Objective value
		[-]	[s]	[%]	[%]
RS-grid initialization	MAiNGO	10	22,334	0.005*	100.041
FS-full time grid	BARON	168	100,000	0.077	100

We highlight that we successfully resolve this issue by following the proposed grid initialization procedure. In particular, we thereby a priori identify the most significant parts of the horizon requiring fine discretizations, while relying on coarser discretizations in insignificant parts.

3.3. *Week-ahead scheduling*

We also consider an hourly planning for one week, which allows for further exploiting weekly price patterns, such as lower prices on weekends. For the sake of brevity, we confine ourselves to comparing the proposed procedure for identifying an initial aggregated grid to the FS approach considering the full time grid. A solution summary is given in Table 2. Again, local searches perform exceptionally well, so that the best feasible solution is found in the upper bounding within short time. Thus, the reported solution using the full time grid is again assumed to be the globally optimal schedule.

As in case of day-ahead scheduling, applying the initial aggregated grid from wavelet analysis of the price time series leads to a feasible schedule, while limiting losses in the objective value to <0.05 % compared to the global optimum and schedules look highly similar, cf. Figure 2 (right). Most impressively, this is achieved by using only ten grid points for the scheduling problem, corresponding to a reduction of the temporal dimensionality by 94 %, illustrating the efficacy of the approach for a priori identifying promising tailored aggregated time grids. Moreover, whereas the RS formulation using the aggregated grid results in a converged solution within the time limit, the approach considering the full grid leaves a substantial remaining optimality gap after exceeding the time limit. Comparing Tables 1 and 2 finally illustrates the superior scaling behavior

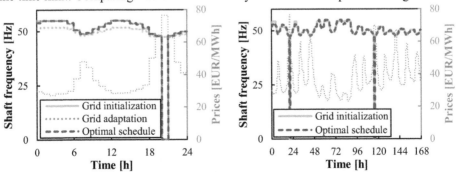

Figure 2: Final production schedules from the different solution approaches for day-ahead (left) and week-ahead (right) scheduling. Orange solid lines: result of a single optimization using an initial aggregated grid following the proposed procedure. Green dotted line: outcome after three iterations of the grid adaptation algorithm when using an equally distributed initial grid (transparent lines correspond to intermediate results). Blue dashed lines: globally optimal production schedule considering the full time grid. Light dotted grey lines: electricity prices.

of solution approaches using aggregated time grids. More precisely, decoupling the number of optimization variables from the number of scheduling intervals avoids the typically exponential scaling with the horizon length when using full time grids.

4. Conclusions

We extend our previously proposed algorithm for adaptive grid refinements in scheduling problems with time-variable electricity prices by a systematic method for the identification of promising initial aggregated time grids. The presented case study is suitable for assessing the efficacy of the approach due to a good performance of local solvers on this problem even for long horizons. Our results show that substantial reductions in the number of grid points and hence in the dimensionality of the scheduling problem are possible, enabling promising speed-ups in the optimization, while leading to only insignificant deviations in the objective value. Future work should focus on the application of the procedure to more challenging problems, where generating favourable feasible points is already difficult if considering the full time grid.

Acknowledgment

The authors gratefully acknowledge the financial support of the Kopernikus project SynErgie by the Federal Ministry of Education and Research (BMBF) and the project supervision by the project management organization Projektträger Jülich.

References

D. Bongartz, A. Mitsos, 2017. Deterministic global optimization of process flowsheets in a reduced space using McCormick relaxations, Journal of Global Optimization 69 (4), 761-796.

D. Bongartz, J. Najman, S. Sass, A. Mitsos, 2018. MAiNGO – McCormick-based Algorithm for mixed-integer Nonlinear Global Optimization. http://permalink.avt.rwth-aachen.de/?id=729717.

O. Exler and K. Schittkowski, 2007. A trust region SQP algorithm for mixed-integer nonlinear programming. Optimization Letters 1 (3), 269-280.

A. Ghobeity, A. Mitsos, 2010. Optimal time-dependent operation of seawater reverse osmosis. Desalination 263 (1), 76-88.

M.G. Ierapetritou, D. Wu, J. Vin, P. Sweeney, M. Chigirinsky, 2002. Cost minimization in an energy-intensive plant using mathematical programming approaches. Industrial & Engineering Chemistry Research. 41 (21), 5262-5277.

S. Mitra, I.E. Grossmann, J.M. Pinto, N. Arora, 2012. Optimal production planning under time-sensitive electricity prices for continuous power-intensive processes. Computers & Chemical Engineering 38, 171-184.

A. Mitsos, N. Asprion, C. A. Floudas, M. Bortz, M. Baldea, D. Bonvin, A. Caspari, P. Schäfer, 2018. Challenges in process optimization for new feedstocks and energy sources. Computers & Chemical Engineering 113, 209-221.

P. Schäfer, A.M. Schweidtmann, P.H.A. Lenz, H.M.C. Markgraf, A. Mitsos. Wavelet-based grid-adaptation for nonlinear scheduling subject to time-variable electricity prices. Computers & Chemical Engineering 132, 106598.

M. Schlegel, K. Stockmann, T. Binder, W. Marquardt, 2005. Dynamic optimization using adaptive control vector parameterization. Computers & Chemical Engineering 29 (8), 1731-1751.

M. Tawarmalani, N.V. Sahinidis, 2005. A polyhedral branch-and-cut approach to global optimization, Mathematical Programming 103 (2), 225-249.

Q. Zhang, I.E. Grossmann, C.F. Heuberger, A. Sundaramoorthy, J.M. Pinto, 2015. Air separation with cryogenic energy storage: Optimal scheduling considering electric energy and reserve markets. AIChE Journal 61 (5), 1547-1558.

Sauro Pierucci, Flavio Manenti, Giulia Bozzano, Davide Manca (Eds.)
Proceedings of the 30th European Symposium on Computer Aided Process Engineering
(ESCAPE30), May 24-27, 2020, Milano, Italy. © 2020 Elsevier B.V. All rights reserved.
http://dx.doi.org/10.1016/B978-0-12-823377-1.50189-0

Troubleshooting an Industrial Batch Process for the Manufacturing of Specialty Chemicals using Data Analytics

Federico Zuecco,[b] Pierantonio Facco,[a] Stefan R. Hoeser,[b] Mattia R. Fogli,[b] Matteo Cicciotti,[b] Fabrizio Bezzo,[a] Massimiliano Barolo[a*]

[a]CAPE-Lab – Computer-Aided Process Engineering Laboratory), Department of Industrial Engneering, University of Padova, via Marzolo 9, 35131 Padova, Italy
[b]BASF Italia S.p.A., via Pila 6/3, 40037 Pontecchio Marconi, Italy
max.barolo@unipd.it

Abstract

The troubleshooting of an industrial, multi-unit, multi-phase batch process for the manufacturing of specialty chemicals is considered in this study. The investigated problem is inconsistency in the final product quality, leading to the need of applying "corrections" to some batches with consequent significant increase of the processing time. Product quality information is scarce and available only for the last unit in the process flow diagram. It is shown that, by coupling the use of multivariate statistical methods to engineering understanding, one can step back in the process flow diagram to identify the unit wherein the problem originates, and to single-out the root-cause of the fault. For the process under investigation, fault isolation led to reduction of the cycle times and increase of productivity.

Keywords: troubleshooting; data analytics; batch processes; multivariate analysis

1. Introduction

Batch processing is common in the manufacturing of specialty chemicals due to its flexibility and ability to process relatively small amounts of materials. Batch processes are typically operated through a sequence of prescribed operations resulting in a recipe. While a recipe can be automated easily, it basically results in open-loop operation of the plant. This is the main reason why product quality control in a batch process is typically more difficult than in a continuous one, an issue that is often tackled by adjusting the recipe in real time through a "correction" (i.e., a recipe modification) if the product quality is found not to be on specification at an assigned manufacturing step. Although a correction can be effective in bringing the product to specification in a given batch, it typically results in an increase of the batch time, hence in productivity decrease. Additionally, if the root-cause of the fault causing the product off-specification is not isolated, the product quality issue can manifest again in subsequent batches.

Multivariate statistical methods have found many applications in batch process monitoring (Nomikos and MacGregor, 1995; Ündey and Cinar, 2002; Garcia-Muñoz et al., 2003; Faggian et al., 2009). However, most of the reported studies are related to fault detection and isolation in single processing units, whereas plantwide analyses are lacking. In this study we show how, even in the absence of real-time quality measurements, a complex industrial batch process can be troubleshooted using multivariate statistical methods, in such a way as to find out the root causes leading to product quality inconsistency across batches.

2. Process, data and methods

2.1. Process description

An industrial batch process for the manufacturing of a specialty chemical to be used for polymer stability enhancement is considered. The reaction scheme involves two main liquid-phase reactions:

$$C + D \rightarrow E + N \tag{1}$$

$$E + D \rightarrow F + N \tag{2}$$

where C and D are the reactants, E an intermediate, F the desired product, and N a by-product. Some secondary reactions also occur, which are responsible for the consumption of both the reactants and the final product. However, they can be disregarded for the purpose of this study.

A simplified block flow diagram of the process is shown in Figure 1. The plant layout involves five main units connected in a series-parallel arrangement. Due to limitations in the vessel sizes, each batch is operated according to a two-step recipe. The first step (called "part A") comprises three sub-steps: *i*) a suspension of reactant C in solvent S is obtained in unit R101; *ii*) the suspension is sent to reactor R201, to which also reactant D (through intermediate tank T201-A) and other species are fed to carry out the synthesis of F in an assigned time; *iii*) the resulting reaction mixture is sent to R202, where a decantation occurs followed by the separation of the aqueous solution from the desired organic phase (which then remains on hold in R202). In the second step of the recipe ("part B"), a second charge of reactants (with the same amount and composition of that of part A) is fed to R201, and the reaction is left to occur for an assigned time; after that, the product is transferred directly to reactor R203; then, the R202 content is also transferred to R203, and the reaction is completed for an assigned time. Finally, a product sample is taken and sent to the lab for quality analysis.

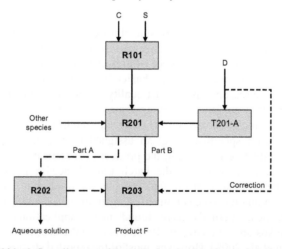

Figure 1. Simplified block flow diagram of the units involved in the analyzed process.

If the product is found to be out of specification, an additional amount of reactant D (namely, a correction) is fed to R203 according to a semi-empirical law based on the impurity levels in the product, and the reaction is left to proceed further. A second quality sample is then taken at a given time, and if the product is still not on specification, a second correction is applied, and the product is sampled again after a prescribed time. At this point, typically additional corrections are not required anymore.

Since the process is recipe-driven and the recipe is automated, there is no apparent reason why some batches do not require a correction, whereas some others may require one or even two corrections. The net result is that the overall batch length is strongly variable and, if two corrections are required, R203 becomes the bottleneck of the entire manufacturing process. Finding the root-cause of the product quality variability is the objective of this study.

2.2. Available data

Data from 116 batches from the same production campaign were extracted from the historians, and divided into three categories: process data, recipe data, and quality data. With respect to the process data, the measurements available on-line from each unit were organized in three-dimensional arrays $\underline{\mathbf{X}}$ [116×J×K_i], where J is the number of measurement sensors available for the unit, and K_i is the total number of observations for batch i (the batches have different lengths). The recipe data for a given unit were arranged in matrix $\mathbf{Z}$ [116×N], where N is the number of parameters through which the recipe can be characterized for that unit. Finally, the quality variables (compositions) related to the first product sample were arranged into a $\mathbf{Y}$ matrix [116×5]. Overall, the analyzed dataset comprised over 3.5 million data entries.

2.3. Mathematical methods

To extract meaningful information from the available data, two multivariate statistical techniques were used: principal component analysis (PCA; Jackson, 1991) and projection to latent structures (PLS; Geladi and Kowalski, 1986).

PCA finds A maximum variability directions (called principal components or PCs) in a bidimensional matrix $\mathbf{X}$ [I×S]. A notable characteristic of the PCs is that they are orthogonal linear combinations of the original data that allow to summarize the data in a reduced-order subspace with no major loss of information. PCA can be used to represent $\mathbf{X}$ as:

$$X = TP^T + E \quad , \tag{3}$$

where $\mathbf{T}$ [I×A] is the scores matrix, $\mathbf{P}$ [S×A] is the loadings matrix, and $\mathbf{E}$ [I×S] is the residuals matrix.

PLS is used to correlate an input matrix $\mathbf{X}$ [I×S] and a response matrix $\mathbf{Y}$ [I×M]. Similarly to PCA, the relationship is based on the projection on a common space of A maximum variability directions (called latent variables or LVs) that are most predictive for the responses according to the model structure composed of Eq. (3) and of:

$$Y = UQ^T + F \tag{4}$$

$$T = XW^* \tag{5}$$

where $\mathbf{Q}$ [M×A] is the loadings matrix, $\mathbf{F}$ [I×M] is the residuals matrix, and $\mathbf{W}^*$ [S×A] is the weights matrix.

In both techniques, the scores matrix $\mathbf{T}$ represents the coordinates of the I observations in the new space of the LVs, which describe how different observations relate to each other. Information about the relation between the original variables is provided by the loadings and weights matrices.

3. Results and discussion

In the following sections, the main steps followed to troubleshoot the process will be discussed.

3.1. Data pre-processing

Data pre-processing is important because it prepares the data in the most meaningful way for the subsequent detailed analysis. In particular, missing process observations were replaced by interpolating the observations that bracket them; some feature variables (e.g., heat removed from a reactor) were calculated from the available measurements and added to the $\underline{X}$ dataset. Trajectories in $\underline{X}$ were synchronized over a fixed number K of samplings using dynamic time warping (Kassidas et al., 1998). This allowed batch-wise unfolding $\underline{X}$ into $\mathbf{X}$, with $S = J \cdot K$.

3.2. Quality data analysis

Analysis of the available quality data ($\mathbf{Y}$ matrix) was used to uncover the inherent multivariate nature of product quality (Duchesne and MacGregor, 2004). The main results of a PCA model that uses 2 PCs (explaining 80% of the overall variance in the quality data) are shown in Figure 2.

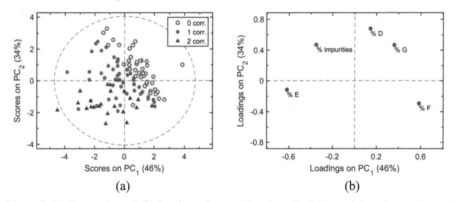

Figure 2. (a) Scores plot and (b) loadings plot resulting from the PCA model on the quality matrix $\mathbf{Y}$. In (a) the dashed ellipse indicates the 99% confidence limit. The percentages on the axis represent the explained variance of the $\mathbf{Y}$ matrix for each PC.

The scores plot (Figure 2*a*) shows the clustering of the on-spec batches (0 corrections) with respect to the off-spec ones (1 or 2 corrections). In particular, from the loadings plot (Figure 2*b*), the off-spec batches are characterized by a greater amount of intermediate species E (% E) and a smaller amount of reactants D and G (% D, % G) in the product. The desired species concentration (% F) and the amount of impurities (% impurities) in the product do not particularly contribute to the batch separation in the scores plot and, therefore, to the batch clustering.

3.3. Single-unit analysis

The subsequent step is to analyze the behavior of each unit separately by comparing the process data available for that unit across all batches carried out in the unit. In fact, even if product quality is assessed only in reactor R203, information about the final product quality may in principle be available even earlier, both in R203 and in upstream units, in the form of time profiles of the process measurements. Therefore, by stepping back through the process equipment (starting from R203), one can track how the fault propagates across the units until it manifests itself as an off-specification product in R203.

For each unit, multi-way PLS discriminant analysis (PLS-DA) was used to classify on-spec and off-spec batches using the time profiles of the available process measurements. To this purpose, a Boolean vector $\mathbf{y}$ identifying the two classes (on-spec batches vs. off-spec ones, as seen in R203) was defined. The PLS-DA models could correctly classify the batches for units R203, R202, and R201; instead, correct batch classification was not possible for R101. This suggested that R201 (and, more specifically, part B in that reactor) is the unit where the batch anomalies originate.

The PLS-DA modeling results for part B of R201 are shown in Figure 3. As can be noticed from the scores plot (Figure 3*a*), the process variable time profiles can indeed cluster most of the batches according to the number of corrections they underwent. Interestingly, the separation between normal batches and a large fraction (about two thirds) of the anomalous batches occurs along the direction of the bisector of the first and third quadrants, and the first quadrant collects anomalous batches only. This suggests that a large fraction of the batches that undergo at least one correction are characterized by a time evolution of the measured process variables that is different from that of the regular batches.

The importance of each variable in defining the direction of maximum variability in the process data can be assessed by analyzing the weights plot for the first LV. Figure 3*b* shows that the contributions of variables no. 6, 7 and 11 dominate over those of the remaining variables. The dominating variables are two mass measurements (coming from two distinct flowrate totalizers) and level in tank T201-A. All these variables refer to the load of reactant D in R201. Since the weights for these variables are negative, it can be concluded that most of the off-spec batches (namely, those located in the first off-spec quadrant) are characterized by a smaller load of reactant D in reactor R201 during part B.

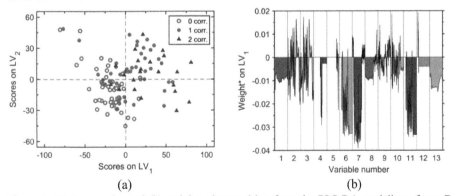

                (a)   (b)

Figure 3. (a) Scores plot and (b) weights plot resulting from the PLS-DA modeling of part B in R201. In (b), the time evolutions of the weights of the first latent variable are reported for each process variable included in the $\underline{\mathbf{X}}$ array.

3.4. Root-cause analysis

The single-unit analysis suggested that most of the batch anomalies are related to a lower load of reactant D to R201. The final step of the troubleshooting exercise is therefore to identify the root-cause of the problem. To this purpose, the process line responsible for the feeding of reactant D was investigated in detail. Three mass flowrate totalizers (FQ-001, FQ-002 and FQ-003) are installed in the line, and each of them measures the amount of reactant D fed to R201. The mass measured by FQ-001 comes from reactant D storage tank; this mass is fed to tank T201-A, which is subsequently fully discharged into R201; the mass fed to R201 is measured by FQ-002 and FQ-003, which are installed at the end of the feeding line. Inspection of the data showed that, during part B of the manufacturing recipe, FQ-001 provided a wrong measurement, as highlighted by the correlation matrix in Table 1. The correlation coefficients between the measurements from FQ-001 and all other sensors are very low, meaning that sensor FQ-001 is not working appropriately.

Table 1. Correlation matrix between the amounts of reactant D measured by the mass totalizers and the level in the intermediate tank T201-A for the part B of the process.

	FQ-001	FQ-002	FQ-003	LI-201A
FQ-001	1.000	0.465	0.474	0.452
FQ-002	0.465	1.000	0.999	0.885
FQ-003	0.474	0.999	1.000	0.885
LI-201A	0.452	0.885	0.885	1.000

A faulty sensor in the feed line to R201 was therefore the reason of product quality inconsistency in most of the batches that later required a correction in R203. Namely, the faulty sensor caused a defect in the reactant D load with respect to the on-specification batches.

4. Conclusions

Although product quality data in a batch process may be scarce, process data are typically abundant and embed information that can be very useful for process troubleshooting. In this study we have shown how a complex, multi-unit, multi-phase batch process can be troubleshooted by coupling multivariate statistical methods to engineering understanding of the process. By stepping back from the unit where quality data are intermittently available to each of the upstream units, the unit where the fault originates can be identified. Then, engineering inspection of the data in that unit and of the relevant plant section layout can provide a reliable indication of the root-cause of the batch anomalies. In the problem under investigation, the root-cause was identified in a faulty sensor, which was responsible for the feeding of the reactant in the main reactor. Fixing this problem significantly reduced the number of batches requiring corrections.

References

C. Duchesne, J. F. MacGregor, 2004, Establishing multivariate specification regions for incoming materials, J. Qual. Technol., 36, 78-94.

A. Faggian, P. Facco, F. Doplicher, F. Bezzo, M. Barolo, 2009, Multivariate statistical real-time monitoring of an industrial fed-batch process for the production of specialty chemicals, Chem. Eng. Res. Des., 87, 325-334.

S. García-Muñoz, T. Kourti, J. F. MacGregor, 2003, Troubleshooting of an industrial batch process using multivariate methods, Ind. Eng. Chem. Res., 42, 3592-3601.

P. Geladi, B. R. Kowalski, 1986, Partial least-squares regression: a tutorial, Anal. Chim. Acta, 185, 1-17.

J. E. Jackson, 1991, A user's guide to principal components, John Wiley & Sons Inc., New York (USA).

A. Kassidas, J. F. MacGregor, P. A. Taylor, 1998, Synchronization of batch trajectories using dynamic time warping, AIChE J., 44, 864-875.

P. Nomikos, J. F. MacGregor, 1995, Multi-way partial least squares in monitoring batch processes, Chemometr. Intell. Lab., 30, 97-108

C. Ündey, A. Cinar, 2002, Statistical monitoring of multistage, multiphase batch processes, IEEE Contr. Syst. Mag., 22, 40-52.

Sauro Pierucci, Flavio Manenti, Giulia Bozzano, Davide Manca (Eds.)
Proceedings of the 30th European Symposium on Computer Aided Process Engineering
(ESCAPE30), May 24-27, 2020, Milano, Italy. © 2020 Elsevier B.V. All rights reserved.
http://dx.doi.org/10.1016/B978-0-12-823377-1.50190-7

On the Role of State Estimation in Real-time Scheduling

Venkatachalam Avadiappan, Christos T. Maravelias*

Department of Chemical and Biological Engineering, University of Wisconsin –Madison, 1415 Engineering Drive, Madison, WI 53706, USA
christos.maravelias@wisc.edu

Abstract

We formally introduce the concept of "state" of a batch in production scheduling, we examine how this state impacts the scheduling process, and propose an approach to estimate it based on real-time plant information. We present an online scheduling algorithm based on a state-space resource task network (RTN) formulation and show why and how the resource-task interaction coefficients (which have always been thought to be constants) should be updated based on the state of the executed batches, using real-time information, to obtain better implemented solutions.

Keywords: State estimation, online scheduling, resource task network

1. Introduction

Scheduling plays a crucial role in many industrial sectors such as pharmaceutical, petrochemical and food industries. Optimization-based scheduling methods can lead to multi-million dollars increase in profits, compared to schedules generated by heuristics. In a dynamic environment, disturbances or new information may render a computed schedule sub-optimal or infeasible, thereby necessitating rescheduling (Gupta and Maravelias, 2016). Therefore, it is important to exploit all the available real-time information from the plant during (re)scheduling. However, while the incorporation of such information through the modeling of process dynamics has been explored, there are no methods available for standalone scheduling approaches. Accordingly, we propose the first systematic methods that account for the state of the system, at real-time, and propose generalize models that exploit such information.

In most scheduling models, a single task has been used to approximate the entire batch recipe. However, in reality, task is composed of a sequence of steps (say, filling of raw material, heating, reaction, quality control and draining of product) with step transitions guided by logic conditions (Rawlings et al., 2019). In this work, we present a discrete-time RTN model in which a task encompasses information regarding the steps involved. We develop an online scheduling algorithm based on the RTN model, and update equations, used for calculating the initial state of the plant based on real-time data. Furthermore, we introduce features that have not been examined before, such as considering delays in batch processing as optimization decisions, to avoid infeasibility.

In section 2, we present a brief overview of the features of the scheduling model. In section 3, we propose the online scheduling algorithm involving the recalculation of the resource-task interaction coefficients coupled with initial state estimation. In section 4, we illustrate the need to consider delays as optimization decisions through a motivating example and in section 5, we apply the proposed methods to a case study.

2. Scheduling Model

2.1. State-space representation

The standard discrete-time state-space models popular in model predictive control (MPC) approaches have the following general form for state-evolution constraints:

$$x(t + 1) = Ax(t) + Bu(t) + B_d d(t) \tag{1}$$

where $x(t)$ indicates the state of the plant, t is the index of time and A, B, B_d are coefficient matrices.

In this work, we pose the scheduling model in state-space form so that the complete status of the plant can be interpreted from the states at any given point of time (Subramanian et al., 2012, and Gupta and Maravelias, 2016). The scheduling decisions or inputs $u(t)$ are whether to start a new task and the amount of material to ship. The state of the plant $x(t)$ includes the progress of the task, the amount of inventory and backlog of materials and the resources engaged/available at that time.

2.2. Resource task network framework

The Resource Task Network (RTN) is a popular framework to represent the different elements of the scheduling problem. It consists of resources $r \in \mathbf{R}$ that include materials, equipment, and utilities and tasks $i \in \mathbf{I}$, which consume and/or release certain resources during its execution.

2.3. Mathematical formulation of state-space RTN model

The state of a batch of task i is indicated by the progress status $k \in \mathbf{K}_i$. The progress status of task i varies from $k = 0$ at the start, to $k = \tau_i$ at the end, where τ_i is its processing time. As opposed to state estimation in MPC approaches, wherein the vector of states is estimated based on the actual inputs and measured outputs, here the state of a batch is solely determined by its progress status k, calculated based on measurements. The main decision variables (inputs) are $N_{it} \in \{0,1\}$, which equals 1, when task i starts at time t. These inputs have a lagged effect on the state of the system, say, the inventory of material produced after τ_i periods. So, these inputs are lifted forward and augmented with states $\bar{N}_{it}^k \in \{0,1\}$, which equals 1, when task i has progress status k at time t. The evolution of the progress status is achieved through equations (2) and (3), where $\hat{N}_{it}^0$ is determined from real-time data as explained later.

$$\bar{N}_{it}^0 = N_{it} + \hat{N}_{it}^0 \quad \forall i, t \tag{2}$$

$$\bar{N}_{i(t+1)}^k = \bar{N}_{it}^{k-1} \quad \forall i, t, k \in \{1, \dots, \tau_i\} \tag{3}$$

Equation (4) expresses the resource balance, wherein the resource level in a given period depends on the level in the previous period, consumption/production resource-task interactions, and the shipment quantity V_{rt}. The consumption/production of resource r by task i at progress status k is represented by μ_{irk}. The bounds on the resource levels are given by constraint (5) and the backorder quantity, U_{rt}, in cases where the demand α_{rt} cannot be met, is determined based on equation (6).

$$S_{rt} = S_{r(t-1)} + \sum_{i \in \mathbf{I}} \sum_{k=0}^{\tau_i} \left(\mu_{irk} \bar{N}_{it}^k \right) - V_{rt} \quad \forall r, t \in \{1, 2, \dots\} \tag{4}$$

$$0 \leq S_{rt} \leq \lambda_r^M \quad \forall r, t \tag{5}$$

$$U_{rt} = U_{r(t-1)} - V_{rt} + \alpha_{rt} \quad \forall r, t \in \{1, 2, \dots\} \tag{6}$$

2.3.1. Update equations

The update equations (7), (8) and (9) are written at $t = 0$ based on real-time data. The initial resource levels S_r^0 and the backorder quantity U_r^0 are determined based on real-time information from the plant. In equation (9), the progress status of currently executed tasks $\widehat{N}_{i(t=0)}^k$ is determined from real-time data as explained in section 3, and assigned to the appropriate task state binary variable $\bar{N}_{it}^k$.

$$S_{rt} = S_r^0 + \sum_{i \in I} \sum_{k=0}^{\tau_i} \left(\mu_{irk} \bar{N}_{it}^k \right) - V_{rt} \quad \forall r, t = 0 \tag{7}$$

$$U_{rt} = U_r^0 - V_{rt} + \alpha_{rt} \quad \forall r, t = 0 \tag{8}$$

$$\bar{N}_{it}^k = \widehat{N}_{it}^k \quad \forall i \in I^C, t = 0, k \in \{1, \dots, \tau_i\} \tag{9}$$

We assume that the measurements are error free and the system is observable (i.e., current state of the system can be determined from measurements/outputs).

2.3.2. Objective function

The objective function as given in (10), is to minimize the total cost composed of the backorder cost and fixed cost of executing tasks.

$$\min \sum_{r \in R^P} \sum_{t \in T} \gamma_r^U U_{rt} + \sum_{i \in I} \sum_{t \in T} \gamma_i^F N_{it} \tag{10}$$

3. Online Scheduling Algorithm

3.1. Motivating example

The system consists of two batch reactors U1 and U2, and two tasks I1 and I2 representing the conversion of raw material M1 into products P1 and P2, respectively. The tasks are composed of various steps, namely, *Feed, React, Filter, Sample,* and *Empty.* In the *Feed* step in I1, raw material M1 is fed to the reactor U1 at a flow rate of 50 kg/min and a total quantity of 600 kg is required for executing I1, so the *Feed* step spans $\left(\left\lceil \frac{600}{50} \right\rceil = \right)$ 12 min. In the *React* step, the raw material is converted to the product. The solid particles in the product mixture are removed using a filter F in the *Filter* step. The product quality is analyzed by an operator O in the *Sample* step and finally, the product is drained from the reactor in the *Empty* step. There is a demand for a batch of task I1 at 40 min, so task I1 starts at time 0 and requires equipment resource U1, material resource M1, filter resource F and operator resource O during its execution (refer to Figure 1 (**A**)). Similarly, task I2 has its own sequence of steps and associated resources, which are not described here. We use a time grid with a discretization (δ) of 5 min in the scheduling model and we reschedule every 5 min.

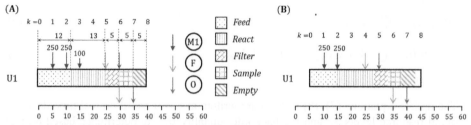

Figure 1. Schedule showing steps and resource interactions (i.e. consumption/release) for task I1. **(A)** Nominal optimal schedule at time 0. **(B)** Schedule obtained while rescheduling after 5 min.

3.2. Re-computation of resource-task interaction coefficients

Given the batch recipe, we know the different resources that are associated with the different steps. There can be a variety of reasons such as delays or resource unavailability, that may lead to steps in the batch not starting at their prescribed times. When a particular step is delayed, the subsequent steps shift forward in time, resulting in an increase in the batch end time. Therefore, the resource-task interaction coefficients need to be recalculated to account for the shift in steps.

A detailed explanation of the algorithm to recalculate the resource-task interaction coefficients is not possible given the limited space, so we illustrate selected modules of the algorithm using the motivating example. A source of delay could be disruptions in raw material flow rates. In the nominal case, 250 kg of M1 is supposed to flow into U1. However, after 5 min, when we reschedule, we realize that only 100 kg has flown in. So, the remaining 500 kg would flow as 250 kg in the two subsequent periods as shown by the arrows and the numbers in Figure 1 **(B)**. The *Feed* step is supposed to end at 15 min as opposed to the nominal end time of 12 min.

After determining the end time of the current step, we determine the start and end times of the subsequent steps as well as the (revised) batch end time. Here, the batch of task I1 ends at 45 min. The discrete renewable resources are consumed at the start of a step and released at its end. The *Filter* step is supposed to start at 28 min and end at 33 min. Since $\delta = 5$ min, the filter resource F is consumed at 25 min and released at 35 min which is different from the nominal resource-task interactions shown in Figure 1 **(A)**. Similarly, the resource-task interactions for the operator resource O also need to be re-computed.

3.3. Initial state estimation

The current state of the batch represented by the status indicator $\hat{N}_{i_k(t=0)}$ is determined based on periods remaining for the batch to end. Note that when we reschedule after 5 min, $t = 0$ in the scheduling model corresponds to the absolute time of 5 min. In the motivating example, in the nominal case, the batch would have progressed to a status of $k = 1$ after 5 min. Since, we determined the revised batch end time to be 45 min, 8 periods still remain for the batch to end and the progress status remains at $k = 0$, owing to disruptions in flow rates.

We introduce a parameter β_{irk} to capture the dependence of resource-task interactions on the current state indicated by the progress status k. For the filter resource F in task I1, consumption is at $k = 4$ (i.e., $\beta_{I1,F,4} = -1$) and release is at $k = 6$ (i.e., $\beta_{I1,F,6} = 1$). Whereas in the nominal case, the *Filter* step was supposed to start at 25 min and end at

30 min. So, the consumption was at $k = 5$ (i.e., $\mu_{11,F,5} = -1$) and release at $k = 6$ (i.e., $\mu_{11,F,6} = 1$). Therefore, we clearly see the distinction between the nominal μ_{irk} and "updated" β_{irk} resource-task interaction coefficients.

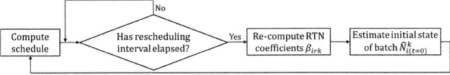

Figure 2. Online scheduling algorithm.

To summarize, in the online scheduling algorithm (refer to Figure 2), we compute a schedule and after the rescheduling interval has elapsed, we re-compute the resource-task interaction coefficients β_{irk}, estimate the initial state $\hat{N}_{i(t=0)}^k$ based on the revised batch end time, and re-solve the scheduling model with the updated state and parameters. Importantly, we have illustrated the necessity and the methodology to update the models in real-time. This is a major departure from all previous standalone scheduling approaches for real-time scheduling, in which models were assumed to remain unchanged.

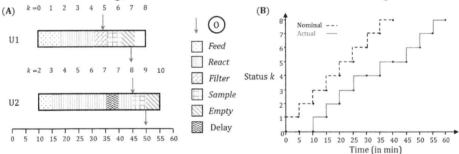

Figure 3. **(A)** Schedule showing delays triggered by optimizer in task I2 to avoid schedule infeasibility. **(B)** Plot showing the comparison between the nominal and actual evolution of progress status of batch of task I1 with time.

4. Delays as Optimization Decisions

To account for delays in other tasks and maintain schedule feasibility, we introduce delays as optimization decisions (provided that pre-emption is allowed at some steps of a task). For example, when steps in different tasks require the same shared resource at a given point in time, one of the steps will have to be delayed. To model delays as decisions, we introduce $E_{it}^k \in \{0,1\}$, which equals 1, if a batch of task i with progress status k at time t is delayed. The progress status evolution (equation (3)) and resource balance (equation (4)) are modified as follows:

$$\bar{N}_{i(t+1)}^k = \bar{N}_{it}^{k-1} - E_{it}^{k-1} + E_{it}^k \quad \forall i, t, k \in \{1, \dots, \tau_i\} \tag{11}$$

$$S_{rt} = S_{r(t-1)} + \sum_{i \in I} \sum_{k=0}^{\tau_i} \left\{ \hat{\mu}_{irkt} \left(\bar{N}_{it}^k - E_{it}^k \right) \right\} - V_{rt} \quad \forall r, t \in \{1, 2, \dots\} \tag{12}$$

where $\hat{\mu}_{irkt}$ is assigned the value of β_{irk} for currently executed batches and μ_{irk} for the batches scheduled in the future.

In the motivating example, after 10 min, we observe that there is an overlap in the *Sample* step in tasks I1 and I2. Since both *Sample* steps require an operator and there is only one operator available, the schedule is infeasible. To maintain feasibility, the start of *Sample* in I2 is delayed as shown in Figure 3(**A**). The differences in progress status evolution for a batch of I1 for the nominal and actual cases are shown in Figure 3(**B**).

5. Case Study

We apply the proposed methods to a case study consisting of 3 reactors, 15 resources of different types (i.e., continuous/discrete and renewable/non-renewable) with demands for various products. Here, the steps in tasks are associated with multiple resources and the limiting resource determines the step duration. In Figure 4, we show the difference between the nominal predicted and actual implemented schedule for the first batch in each reactor.

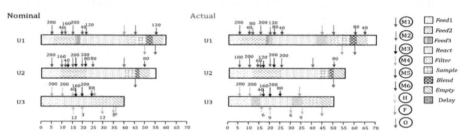

Figure 4. Gantt charts showing the nominal predicted and actual implemented schedule for the case study.

6. Conclusions

Although state-space models for production scheduling are available, the concept of state estimation, unlike in process control, has not been studied in the context of scheduling. In this paper, we introduced progress status as the key state, and discussed, for the first time, how it should be used in real-time. Specifically, we showed that real-time information can be used to calculate the progress status and, importantly, update the resource-task interaction parameters which, in all previous approaches, were thought to be constant. Finally, motivated from the mismatch between the predicted and actual progress status, we introduced delays as optimization decisions, thus allowing the seamless execution of real-time scheduling. The proposed work is a major departure from previous real-time scheduling approaches in which the scheduling model was assumed to remain the same between iterations.

References

Gupta, D. and Maravelias, C.T., 2016, On deterministic online scheduling: Major considerations, paradoxes and remedies, Computers & Chemical Engineering, 94, 312-330.
Rawlings, B.C., Avadiappan, V., Lafortune, S., Maravelias, C.T., and Wassick, J.M., 2019, Incorporating automation logic in online chemical production scheduling, Computers & Chemical Engineering, 128, 201-215.
Subramanian, K., Maravelias, C. T., and Rawlings, J.B., 2012, A state-space model for chemical production scheduling, Computers & Chemical Engineering, 47, 97-110.

Sauro Pierucci, Flavio Manenti, Giulia Bozzano, Davide Manca (Eds.)
Proceedings of the 30th European Symposium on Computer Aided Process Engineering
(ESCAPE30), May 24-27, 2020, Milano, Italy. © 2020 Elsevier B.V. All rights reserved.
http://dx.doi.org/10.1016/B978-0-12-823377-1.50191-9

Augmenting Heat Balance of the Wastewater Treatment Plant Model and Improving Plant Control by Counteracting Temperature Disturbances

Daniel Crîstiu, Melinda Simon-Várhelyi, Alexandra Veronica Luca, Marius Adrian Brehar, Vasile Mircea Cristea[*]

Babeş-Bolyai University, Faculty of Chemistry and Chemical Engineering, 11 Arany János Street, Cluj-Napoca 400028, Romania

mcristea@chem.ubbcluj.ro

Abstract

Municipal wastewater treatment has become one of the most challenging environmental problems due to the volume increase of urban wastewaters and stricter regulations imposed to effluent pollutants concentration. Besides the tough pollutants concentration and flow rate influent disturbances, the influent temperature changes also affect the complex biochemical processes taking place in WWTP bioreactors. As a result, the WWTP dynamic behavior description relying on the mass balance needs to be completed either with temperature correction factors or by comprehensive heat balance equations. The latter approach was considered in the present research, addressing a municipal WWTP using the activated sludge technology in the Anaerobic-Anoxic-Oxic (A^2O) configuration. The heat balance enhanced WWTP model was developed on the basis of the Activated Sludge Model No. 1 (ASM1), coupled with a modified version of the Benchmark Simulation Model no. 1 (BSM1). The wastewater temperature changes were evaluated and a control system structure was proposed in order to counteract the negative effects of the influent temperature associated to other typical influent disturbances. Simulation results performed with the calibrated municipal WWTP model and the proposed control system demonstrate twofold benefits. They may reduce the aeration and pumping energy costs by 12 % and improve the effluent quality by 5 %.

Keywords: wastewater treatment, heat balance, temperature disturbances, control system design

1. Introduction

Explorations based on dynamic mathematical models of the biological wastewater treatment plants (WWTPs) are valuable tools for investigating the process performance. This capability leads to straightforward evaluation of potential improvements produced by the design of different operating and control strategies within a municipal wastewater treatment plant (Makinia, 2010).

The Activated Sludge Model No. 1 made available a coherent framework for describing biological processes in activated sludge systems taking into consideration the mass balances for substrate utilization and microbial growth (Henze et al., 2002). For further improvements in performance predictability, besides the dynamics of the flow and pollutants load, the temperature dynamics could be also taken into consideration. Hence, an accurate heat balance model may be incorporated in the simulator in order to predict the changes of the activated sludge wastewater temperature (Lippi et al., 2009).

Temperature variations affect the efficiency of wastewater treatment plant due to their influence on microbial kinetics and physic-chemical parameters (Fernández-Arévalo et al., 2014). Based on a previous study it was shown that the WWTP process is negatively affected by temperature drops, especially for the nitrogen removal (Brehar et al., 2019). Model based predictions of the WWTP behavior may be considerably influenced by temperature disturbances, although this issue is not always taken into consideration. When performing simulation studies the water temperature is often assumed constant or, at the most, temperature changes are only considered by empirical factors.

The changes in basins wastewater temperature are frequently caused by a combination of various factors. Several literature sources present the development of temperature models. They have been incorporated into integrated models which contain the mass balance and energy balance as well (Arnell et al., 2017). A steady-state model was developed by Novotny and Krenkel (1973) in which four terms of the heat transfer were introduced. They are the short wave (solar) radiation (Q_s), long wave (atmospheric) radiation (Q_{lr}), surface evaporation heat (Q_e) and surface convection heat (Q_c). An extension of this model was presented by Argaman and Adams (1977) by adding mechanical energy input (Q_p), biochemical reaction heat (Q_b) and heat loss through basin walls (Q_{tw}). Talati and Stenstrom (1990), with the support of the existing models, enhanced the accuracy of the temperature predictions and reduced the required site-specific information. Sedory and Stenstrom (1995) developed a dynamic model for estimating the wastewater temperature in aerated basins, in the form shown in Eq. (1):

$$\rho_w \cdot V \cdot c_{pw} \frac{dT_w}{dt} = Q_t + \rho_w \cdot q_w \cdot c_{pw} \cdot (T_i - T_w) \tag{1}$$

where (V) is the basin volume, (q_w) flow rate, (ρ_w) density, (c_{pw}) specific heat and (T_i) water inlet temperature. Net sum of the heat gains and losses (Q_t) is presented in Eq. (2).

$$Q_t = Q_s + Q_p + Q_b - Q_{lr} - Q_e - Q_c - Q_a - Q_{tw} \tag{2}$$

The heat gains produce the increase of the basin temperature (T_w) while heat losses determine its decrease.

2. WWTP model development

The Benchmark Simulation Model No. 1 (BSM1) and the Activated Sludge Model No. 1 (ASM1) are the roots of the dynamic WWTP model developed in this work. Appropriate changes to BSM1 were applied to the model in order to fit it to the investigated municipal WWTP having an Anaerobic-Anoxic-Oxic (A^{2}O) configuration. The dynamic WWTP model consists of a primary settler model based on the equations proposed by Otterpohl and Freund (1992), five ASM1 bioreactor models connected in series and a secondary clarifier model incorporating the double exponential velocity function introduced by Takács et al. (1991).

The developed WWTP model, relying on the mass balance equations, was previously calibrated based on plant size information and measured data collected from the investigated municipal WWTP during the month of May 2016 (Várhelyi et al., 2019).

In this research, additional meteorological and construction data were collected in order to describe the temperature dynamics in the bioreactors. For each of the five bioreactors the heat balance was introduced according to Eq. (1) by considering the net heat gain or loss described by Eq. (2). Matlab software and Simulink graphical extension were used for the model development. The process mass and heat balance equations were coded in C programming language and incorporated in the simulation environment as S functions.

3. Implemented control strategy

The calibrated and heat balance enhanced WWTP simulation model was augmented with two feedback control loops. They are the ammonia concentration control in the last aerated bioreactor (reactor no. 5) and the nitrates concentration control in the anoxic bioreactor (reactor no. 2). The proposed control system design is presented in Figure 1.

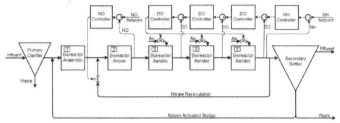

Figure 1. Structure of the proposed control system

The ammonia control loop includes an ammonia controller and three dissolved oxygen controllers arranged in a cascade setup. Proportional-Integral (PI) control law was considered for all four controllers. Based on the difference between the ammonia concentration setpoint value and the actual ammonia concentration value in the last bioreactor, the master ammonia (NH) controller computes the setpoint value for the first dissolved oxygen (DO) slave controller. This setpoint value is compared to the dissolved oxygen concentration in the last bioreactor and the control signal of the first DO controller is sent as setpoint to the second DO controller. The other two DO slave controllers work in a similar way. Consequently, the third DO controller computes the control signal which is distributed equally to the air control valves in order to change the air flow rate entering the three aerobic bioreactors. Ammonia concentration was measured with the AMTAX™ sc ammonia analyzer, based on the colorimetric method. The nitrates and nitrites feedback control loop also uses a PI controller. The controlled variable is the nitrates and nitrites concentration in the anoxic bioreactor, while the manipulated variable is the nitrate recirculation flow rate. The nitrates and nitrites concentration was determined with the patented 2-beam NITRATAX™ clear sc sensor, using the UV absorption method of measurement.

4. Investigated influent temperature disturbances

Influent temperature disturbances can act for a short or a long period of time. The season originating temperature changes result in weeks or months long lasting variations of the wastewater temperature. Rapid changes in influent temperature, occurring during a few hours or days, can be the consequence of sudden weather changes (e.g. storm, rain, snowing, snow melting). The effect of influent temperature disturbances needs to be minimized for preserving the desired WWTP performance. The temperature influences processes in the activated sludge plant. For example, the heterotrophic and autotrophic biomass growth, ammonification rate, dissolved oxygen saturation and mass transfer rates are all temperature dependent. The influent temperature disturbances may be also accompanied by flow rate and influent pollutants concentration disturbances. Different cases were investigated in the present work for the effects of the influent temperature disturbances. Case 1 represents a reference simulation with the WWTP measured influent temperature data collected during the first 22 days of May 2016. Based on the measured influent temperature, different influent temperature profiles were created. The second case incorporates the disturbance of 2 °C influent temperature decrease for the whole 22 days period of time (Case 2). Additionally, changes in the influent flow rate and influent Chemical Oxygen Demand (COD) concentration were considered in Case 3. The investigated cases are presented in Table 1. Simulations were performed for all three considered cases, both with and without the operation of the proposed control system.

Table 1. Investigated cases for effects of influent temperature and typical disturbances

CASE	DESCRIPTION
Case 1	Simulation using the municipal WWTP measured influent temperature data
Case 2	Simulation with influent temperature decreased by 2 °C
Case 3	Simulation with influent temperature decreased by 2 °C, associated to 10% influent flow rate increase and 10% influent COD concentration decrease

5. Results and discussion

5.1. Simulation results for the heat balance extended WWTP model

The previously calibrated model was extended with the heat balance equations and simulation was performed with the influent measured data from the municipal WWTP under study. The solar radiation heat, mechanical power heat and biological reaction heat are the heat gain terms, while the long-wave (atmospheric) radiation heat, surface convection heat, surface evaporation heat, aeration heat and basin wall heat are responsible for the heat losses. Representative simulation results shows for the last bioreactor that the most significant heat component proved to be the solar radiation heat, which corresponds to 32.1 % of the total heat gains and heat losses. The biological reaction heat component represents 29.2 %, while the mechanical power heat component represents 10.2 % of the total heats. All these three components are corresponding to the heat gains. From the heat losses components, the surface evaporation heat is the most significant (15.2 %), while the heat losses through the basin wall are almost negligible. The net heat exchange has a positive value. The distribution of the heat components in the fifth bioreactor is presented in Figure 2.

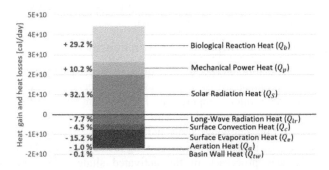

Figure 2. Representative distribution of the heat terms, for the last of the bioreactors

According to the simulation with the extended WWTP model, the Celsius temperature in the last aerobic bioreactor increased by 4 % compared to the inlet wastewater temperature. The average value of the influent temperature is of 15.8 °C, while the temperature predicted in the last aerated bioreactor by the extended WWTP model is of 16.5 °C. The variations of the measured influent wastewater temperature and the predicted temperature in the fifth bioreactor are presented in Figure 3.

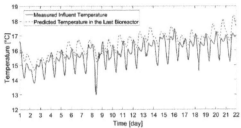

Figure 3. Measured influent and model predicted water temperature in the last reactor

Figure 3 reveals the increase in the wastewater temperature along the WWTP and the buffer effect of the bioreactors for the influent temperature changes.

5.2. Simulation results for the WWTP performance without the proposed control system

For all of the three presented cases, simulations were firstly run with the extended WWTP model but without the proposed control system. The performance indices (aeration energy (AE), pumping energy (PE) and effluent quality (EQ)) were calculated according to Eqs. (3-5).

$$AE = C_{AE} \cdot \frac{SO_{sat}}{T \cdot 1.8 \cdot 1000} \int_0^T \sum_{aerated\ bioreactor} \left[V_{bioreactor} \cdot K_L a_i(t) \right] dt \tag{3}$$

$$PE = C_{PE} \cdot \frac{1}{T} \int_0^T \left[0.004 \cdot Q_{NR}(t) + 0.08 \cdot Q_{RAS}(t) + 0.05 \cdot Q_{waste}(t) \right] dt \tag{4}$$

$$EQ = \frac{1}{T \cdot 1000} \int_0^T \left[PU_{TSS}(t) + PU_{COD}(t) + PU_{BOD}(t) + PU_{TKN}(t) + PU_{NO}(t) \right] Q_{effluent}(t) dt \tag{5}$$

The values of the performance indices obtained by simulation for the municipal WWTP are presented in Table 2, when temperature and the other typical disturbances are acting.

Table 2. Results of the performance indices for the different influent disturbance cases, without the proposed control system

Performance index	Case 1	Case 2	Case 3
AE [kWh/day]	14,886.4	14,775.4	14,781.5
PE [kWh/day]	8,831.7	8,831.7	8,831.7
Total Energy [kWh/day]	23,718.1	23,607.1	23,612.5
EQ [kg P.U./day]	18,412.0	19,681.3	21,387.4
AE+PE+EQ	42,130.1	43,288.4	44,999.9

Table 2 shows that in the presence of disturbances the effluent pollutant concentrations increase. The worst case is Case 3 when the influent temperature decreases, the influent flow rate increases and influent COD concentration decreases, revealing an overall WWTP performance (sum of AE, PE and EQ) deterioration of about 7%.

5.3. Simulation results for the WWTP performance with the proposed control system

The three disturbance investigated cases were tested on the enhanced WWTP model with the proposed control system. The simulation results are shown in Table 3.

Table 3. Results of the performance indices for the different influent disturbance cases and with application of the proposed control system

Performance index	Case 1	Case 2	Case 3
AE [kWh/day]	10,003.4	11,872.7	12,243.2
PE [kWh/day]	8,720.8	8,486.1	8,464.1
Total Energy [kWh/day]	18,724.2	20,358.8	20,707.3
EQ [kg P.U./day]	13,988.6	18,068.5	20,249.0
AE+PE+EQ	32,712.8	38,427.3	40,956.3

Results presented in Table 3 show that by implementing the proposed control system, the performance of the municipal WWTP can be improved by reducing the energy costs and enhancing the effluent quality, in all cases. When comparing the simulation results in the presence and absence of the proposed control system, the overall performance was improved by 9 % for the most challenging Case 3. This is owing to the reduction of operational energy (AE+PE) by 12 % and improvement of the effluent quality by 5 %.

6. Conclusions

The dynamic WWTP calibrated model including the mass balance was enhanced with the heat balance equations. Effluent wastewater temperature changes were investigated in the presence of different influent wastewater temperature, flow rate and COD concentration disturbances. Simulations of the enhanced model showed as most significant heat component for the month of May the solar radiation heat, followed by the biological reaction heat. In the studied month the net heat exchange has a positive value and the mean water temperature is increasing along the WWTP basins by 0.7°C. The negative effect of the influent temperature decrease, coupled with other typical disturbances, can be minimized by implementing the proposed control system. Control simulation results demonstrate an overall performance improvement for the spent energy and for the effluent quality of about 9 %. The proposed control system shows potential benefits for the implementation in the municipal WWTP in order to achieve efficient operation in the presence of temperature disturbances.

References

Y. Argaman, C.E. Adams, 1977, Comprehensive temperature model for aerated biological systems, Progress in Water Research, 9, 397-409

M. Arnell, E. Lundin, U. Jeppsson, 2017, Sustainability Analysis for Wastewater Heat Recovery Literature Review, Lund, Sweden, 1-40

M.A. Brehar, M. Várhelyi, V.M. Cristea, D. Crîstiu, Ș.P. Agachi, 2019, Influent temperature effects on the activated sludge process at a municipal wastewater treatment plant, Studia UBB Chemia, 64, 1, 113-123

T. Fernández-Arévalo, I. Lizarralde, P. Grau, E. Ayesa, 2014, New systematic methodology for incorporating dynamic heat transfer modelling in multi-phase biochemical reactors, Water Research, 60, 141-155

M. Henze, W. Gujer, T. Mino, M. van Loosdrecht, 2002, Activated Sludge Models ASM1, ASM2, ASM2d and ASM3, Padstow, Cornwall, UK, 1-121

S. Lippi, D. Rosso, C. Lubello, R. Canziani, M.K. Stenstrom, 2009, Temperature modelling and prediction for activated sludge systems, Water Science & Technology, 59, 1, 125-131

J. Makinia, 2010, Process temperature model, Mathematical Modelling and Computer Simulation of Activated Sludge Systems, IWA Publishing, London, UK, 98-118

V. Novotny, P.A. Krenkel, 1973, Simplified Mathematical Model of Temperature Changes in Rivers, Journal of the Water Pollution Control Federation, 45, 240-248

R. Otterpohl, M. Freund, 1992, Dynamic Models for Clarifiers of Activated Sludge Plants with Dry and Wet Weather Flows, Water Science and Technology , 26, 5-6, 1391-1400

P.E. Sedory, M.K. Stenstrom, 1995, Dynamic prediction of wastewater aeration basin temperature, Journal of Environmental Engineering, 121, 609-618

I. Takács, G.G. Patry, D. Nolasco, 1991, A Dynamic Model of the Clarification-Thickening Process, Water Research, 25, 20, 1263-1271

S.N. Talati, M.K. Stenstrom, 1990, Aeration-Basin Heat Loss, Journal of Environmental Engineering, 16, 70-86

M. Várhelyi, V.M. Cristea, M. Brehar, E.D. Nemeș, Abhilash Nair, 2019, WWTP Model Calibration Based on Different Optimization Approaches, Environmental Engineering and Management Journal, 18, 8, 1657-1670

Sauro Pierucci, Flavio Manenti, Giulia Bozzano, Davide Manca (Eds.)
Proceedings of the 30th European Symposium on Computer Aided Process Engineering
(ESCAPE30), May 24-27, 2020, Milano, Italy. © 2020 Elsevier B.V. All rights reserved.
http://dx.doi.org/10.1016/B978-0-12-823377-1.50192-0

Optimal Start-Up of Air Separation Processes using Dynamic Optimization with Complementarity Constraints

Adrian Caspari[a], Steffen R. Fahr[a], C. Offermanns[a], Adel Mhamdi[a], Lorenz T. Biegler[d], Alexander Mitsos[b,a, c,]*

[a] *Process Systems Engineering (AVT.SVT), RWTH Aachen University, 52074 Aachen, Germany*

[b] *JARA-CSD, RWTH Aachen University, 52056 Aachen, Germany*
[c] *IEK-10, Forschungszentrum Jülich, 52425 Jülich, Germany*
[d] *Carnegie Mellon University, Department of Chemical Engineering, Pittsburgh, PA 15213, USA*
amitsos@alum.mit.edu

Abstract

Fluctuating electricity prices create an incentive for the flexible operation of electricity intensive processes, such as air separation units (ASUs). Shutting down an ASU during times with peak electricity prices has been claimed economically attractive but requires an efficient and largely automated start-up procedure. Previous works have considered simulations of plant start-ups and dynamic optimization of load scheduling near the nominal operation mode. Discrete events like the appearance of a liquid phase have impeded any rigorous ASU start-up optimization. In this work, we formulate the optimal start-ups as dynamic optimization problems with regularized algebraic complementarity constraints (Caspari et al., 2019b) using a mechanistic dynamic process model in Modelica. Our approach captures physical effects appearing during start-up like the appearance and disappearance of phases. We solve the resulting optimization problems with direct single-shooting using the dynamic optimization framework DyOS. We perform in-silico dynamic offline optimizations of an ASU start-up and consider different process modifications. We consider cold start-up optimizations, where the process medium is initialized at cryogenic conditions just before liquefaction. The results illustrate that the proposed approach can be applied to large-scale processes. The results show further that liquid assist operation reduced the optimal start-up time by about 70 % compared to the start-up without this modification.

Keywords: dynamic optimization, complementarity constraints, air separation, optimal start-up

1. Introduction

The flexible operation of continuous processes in the presence of fluctuating electricity prices enable economic benefits (Daryanian et al., 1989). Since air separation units (ASUs) are large-scale electricity consumers, they are well suited for exploiting electricity price fluctuations (Caspari et al., 2019c). Irrespective of the different perspectives on flexible operation, whether scheduling (Zhang et al., 2015) or control (Huang et al., 2009), the start-up or shut-down of processes have been either assumed to be known or neglected; estimates of the start-up or shut-down times are used in the transitional constraints in scheduling and the control approaches assume the

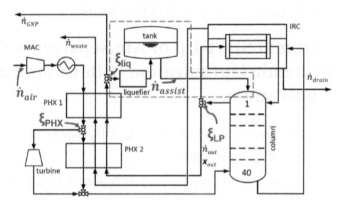

Figure 1 ASU flowsheet. Liquid nitrogen assist operation option indicated by dashed, red frame.

process to be in operation around nominal conditions. However, start-up and shut-down are crucial for the exploitation of the economic potential when the electricity price dynamics and process dynamics are in the same range, like in the case of ASUs (Miller et al., 2008b). While start-ups are currently performed with a fixed recipe under the surveillance of skilled workers, a rigorous optimization-based approach would be desirable leading to faster commissioning, higher energy efficiency, and reduced labour (Vinson, 2006). While simulations of an ASU start-up has been reported in literature, e.g, (Kender et al., 2019; Miller et al., 2008a), the optimization of a start-up process has not yet been considered. The optimization has to deal with discrete events like the appearance and disappearance of phases. The ASU can be described by a nonsmooth differential algebraic equation (DAE) system and the start-up optimization can be formulated as a dynamic optimization problem with complementarity constraints (CCs). Optimization problems of this form have been solved using full discretization leading to a nonlinear program (NLP) with equilibrium constraints, e.g., (Raghunathan et al., 2004). Recently, we proposed an approach for the efficient solution of such problems based on direct shooting (Caspari et al., 2019b). In this work, we apply this approach for the start-up optimization of an ASU. The start-up optimizations allow us to evaluate different process designs regarding their impact on the start-up. We therefore consider liquid assist operation in addition to a basic process design and perform start-up optimizations for both designs. We consider a cold process start-up, i.e., we assume the medium in the process to be already at cryogenic conditions, just before liquefaction. A warm start-up would assume that the medium inside the process is at ambient conditions. The cold start-up occurs when the plant was shut down for no more than several hours up to a few days (Miller et al., 2008a), which covers most of the scenarios occurring during flexible operation of an ASU. This could be the case in an operation scenario where the process is turned-off in the presence of very high electricity prices and turned-on otherwise. We briefly describe the process and its model in Section 2 and summarize the problem formulation and solution approach in Section 3. We show the results in Section 4 and conclude in Section 5.

2. Process and Model

We consider the ASU depicted in Figure 1, which is similar to the process we used in (Caspari et al., 2018).Ambient air (nitrogen, oxygen, argon) enters the process,is compressed to 11 bar, inter-cooled to 298 K and fed to the heat exchanger. There, the air stream is cooled in counter current with the waste and the gaseous nitrogen product (GNP) stream. A part is split-up and expanded to the column feed pressure in a turbine. The remaining part enters zone 2 of the heat exchanger, where it is further cooled and may be liquefied. Both streams are mixed and fed to the column. The condenser pressure is 5.5 bar whereas the reboiler outlet pressure is 1.5 bar. We adapt the liquid assist modification proposed in Miller et al. (2008a) for an ASU with an argon column; the GNP stream is liquefied and stored in a tank and can be fed into the column top stage to accelerate the process start-up. We implement a mechanistic dynamic model that is able to represent the transient process behaviour during the ASU start-up. The model includes CCs for modelling the appearance and disappearance of vapour-liquid equilibria (VLEs), overflow weirs and valves. It uses a relaxed VLE formulation similar to (Raghunathan et al., 2004), which includes CCs of the form $0 \leq y_{i_k}(t) \perp y_{i'_k}(t) \geq 0$. We apply similar formulations with CCs for overflow weirs and vapor outlet streams valves of the column trays. We briefly summarize the model and refer to previous works. We use the unit models from (Caspari et al., 2019b), the column model and the relaxed VLE formulation from (Raghunathan et al., 2004), and the physical property models from Johansson (2015). Thermodynamics: The vapour phase is modelled as an ideal gas and the liquid phase as a nonideal liquid. We apply standard models for the physical properties. We refer to Johansson (2015). Distillation Column: We use the same distillation column model as in (Raghunathan et al., 2004) with 40 trays. The model includes vapour and liquid holdups. Every tray has an overflow weir. The vapour outlet is calculated based on the pressure difference between the trays. Every tray includes 4 CCs: for the liquid outlet, the gas outlet, and two for the relaxed VLE. Consequently, the column model includes 160 CCs. PHX: We use a 1-dimensional distributed model for the heat exchangers. The fluid behaves quasistationary. We consider dynamic energy balances for the wall. Liquefaction can take only place in the PHX2 in the feed air stream, justified by several simulations. The PHX1 has 50 finite elements. We use 1 finite element for the PHX2. The PHX 2 include 2 CCs for the VLE. Compressor/Turbine: The compressor and turbine are modelled with an adiabatic efficiency of 0.8. The turbine includes 2 CCs for the relaxed VLE. Integrated reboiler and condenser: We model the reboiler as an equilibrium tray with a heat supply and the condenser as pseudo-steady-state. Reboiler and condenser are energetically integrated using a heat transfer correlation. The reboiler includes 4 CCs. The condenser includes 2 CCs for the VLE. Liquefier: We model the liquefier with a liquefaction efficiency of 0.8. The resulting process model is a differential index 1 DAE including 270 differential and about 3060 algebraic states. The model includes 170 CCs.

3. Problem Formulation and Solution Approach

The optimal start-up problems are formulated as a dynamic optimization problem with algebraic CCs. We described how to handle these in single shooting in detail in our previous work (Caspari et al., 2019b): We substitute each CCs using a regularized Fischer-Burmeister function of the form $0 = y_{i_k}(t) + y_{i'_k}(t) - \sqrt{y_{i_k}(t)^2 + y_{i'_k}(t)^2 + \varepsilon}, \varepsilon > 0$. The Fischer-Burmeister function is directly used as model equation. Regularization of the Fischer_Burmeister function leads to a smooth DAE, enabling the application of standard integrators and optimizers to solve the optimization problems using direct shooting. We minimize the deviation of the GNP purity $x_{GNP}^{N_2}$, the GNP flowrate n_{GNP}, the liquefier splitfactor ξ_{liq}, and the tank holdup n_{tank} from there desired setpoints by using the following objective function: $\Phi =$

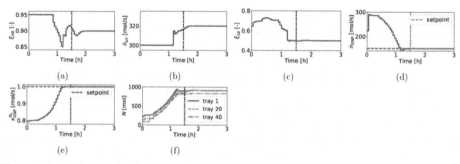

Figure 2: Optimal control and state variable profiles for start-up without liquid assist operation. Start-up range indicated by vertical, dotted lines. (a) PHC split factor to turbine. (b) Feed air flowrate. (c) Column split factor. (d) GNP flow rate. (e) GNP purity. (f) Column tray holdups.

$$\int_0^{t_f} w_{purity}\left(x_{GNP}^{N2}(t) - x_{GNP}^{N2,set}\right)^2 + w_{flow}\left(\dot{n}_{GNP}(t) - n_{GNP}^{set}\right)^2 + w_{liq}\left(\xi_{liq}(t)\right)^2 +$$

$w_{tank}\left(n_{tank}(t) - n_{tank}(t = 0h)\right)^2 dt$, with the weight parameters $w_{purity} = 10^{-3}$, $w_{flow} = 10^{-3}$, $w_{liq} = 10^{-4}$, $w_{tank} = 10^{-10}$, $x_{GNP}^{N2,set} = 0.99995$, $n_{GNP}^{set} = 150$ mol/s. We penalize the liquefier stream, since the liquefication uses electricity and could thus just be used as a bonus reflux for the column; we aim to minimize the liquefier activity in order to keep the electricity demand as low as possible while still allowing its use for the tank refill. We penalize the deviation of the tank holdup from the initial value to avoid unnecessary tank withdrawal. We use the following controls and bounds: $\xi_{PHX}(t) \in [0.85,0.95]$, $\xi_{LP}(t) \in [0.2,0.8]$, $\xi_{liq}(t) \in [0.5,1]$, $\dot{n}_{air}(t) \in [300,340]$ mol/s, $n_{assist}(t) \in [0,30]$ mol/s. The control variables are initialized with the constant profiles $\xi_{PHX}(t) = 0.9$, $\xi_{LP} = 0.5$, $\xi_{liq} = 1$, $\dot{n}_{air} = 320$ mol/s, $n_{assist} = 0$ and are discretized piecewise constant with 60 intervals. We use the path constraints $\varphi_{turbine}(t) \in [0.95,\infty)$ and $x_{tank}^{N2}(t) \in [0.99995,1]$. The turbine vapour fraction $\varphi_{turbine}$ is constrained due to technical limitations of the turbine. The tank purity x_{tank}^{N2} is constrained to the nominal product purity to avoid contamination in the tank. The last two summands of the objective function with the respective weights, the liquefier split factor, and the liquid assist flowrate are used only in the case with liquid assist operation. We assumed the start-up procedure to be finished when the product purity and the product flowrate are at their desired setpoints. We implement the process model in Modelica and use direct single-shooting (Brusch and Schapelle, 1973) to solve the optimization problems with the shooting framework DyOS (Caspari et al., 2019a). The DAE integrator is NIXE (Hannemann et al., 2010) and the NLP solver is SNOPT (Gill et al., 2005). We use integration tolerances of 10^{-6}, NLP tolerances of 10^{-4}.

4. Numerical Results

4.1. Start-Up without Liquid Assist Operation

Figure 2 shows results from the dynamic optimization of the start-up without liquid assist operation. The start-up time is about 1.5 h (Figures. 2d and 2e). At the beginning, the turbine activity is at the maximum (Figure 2a), while the air feed flowrate is at the lower bound (Figure 2b), and the column split factor is increased (Figure 2c) leading to a higher column reflux. This supports the cooling of the medium in the process since the turbine withdraws energy from the process and the reduced feed air flowrate reduces the energy fed to the process through the air feed. We see that the amount of liquid in the column increases

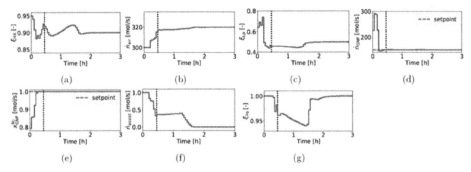

Figure 3: Optimal control and state variable profiles for start-up using liquid assist operation. Start-up range indicated by vertical, dotted lines. (a) PHC split factor to turbine. (b) Feed air flowrate. (c) Column split factor. (d) Liquid assist flowrate. (e) Liquefier splitfactor. (f) GNP flow rate. (g) GNP purity.

starting with the first tray followed by the other trays (Figure 2f). With the optimal control profiles, the product flowrate increases in the beginning before it settles down to the setpoint (Figure 2d). The product purity begins from ambient conditions and increases until it reaches the desired setpoint (Figure 2e).

4.2. Start-Up with Liquid Assist Operation

Figure 3 shows results from the dynamic optimization of the start-up with liquid assist operation. The optimal start-up takes about 24 min (Figures 3d and 3e), which corresponds to a reduction of the optimal start-up time of about 70 % compared to the optimal startup without liquid assist operation. The control variable profiles for the PHX splitfactor (Figure 3a), the feed air flowrate (Figure 3b), and the column splitfactor (Figure 3b) look qualitatively similar to the case without liquid assist operation (Figure 3c). The start-up is clearly supported by the liquid assist operation; The assist stream is at the upper bound in the beginning before it is reduced and set to zero at the end (Figure 3f). Remember that we penalize the liquid assist flowrate. The liquefier is used to refill the tank, in which the holdup is decreased due to the liquid assist stream. The tank refill is induced by the holdup penalization. However, due to the tank purity constraint, the liquefier can only be activated if the GNP purity is suitable and does not pollute the tank. The liquefier is thus activated as soon as the GNP purity is at the desired value (Figures 3g and 3e). The state variable profiles, e.g., for the product flowrate and purity (Figures 3d and 3e) look qualitatively similar as for the case without liquid assist option, though the operating level is obtained faster.

5. Conclusions

We use dynamic optimization with CCs to optimize start-ups of an ASU. The optimizations allow to evaluate process design modifications with respect to the effect on the process start-up time. We therefore perform cold start-up optimizations for ASU designs with and without liquid assist option. The results demonstrate the applicability of the approach to large-scale processes. They show further the effectiveness of liquid assist operation. This modification reduces the optimal process start-up time by about 70 % compared to a start-up without this modification. Further work can consider the start-up of ASUs with additional design modifications, other topologies, a warm process start-up starting from ambient conditions, and the application of the obtained start-up procedure to a real process. Future work can use the approach to obtain start-up and shut-down times as required for transitional constraints in scheduling, and for online control.

Acknowledgement: The authors gratefully acknowledge the financial support of the Kopernikus project SynErgie by the Federal Ministry of Education and Research (BMBF) and the project supervision by the project management organization Projektträger Jülich (PtJ). The authors thank Anna-Maria Ecker, Florian Schliebitz, Gerhard Zapp from the Linde AG for fruitful discussion.

References

R. G. Brusch, R. H. Schapelle, 1973. Solution of highly constrained optimal control problems using nonlinear programing. AIAA Journal 11 (2), 135–136.

A. Caspari, J. M. Faust, P. Schäfer, A. Mhamdi, A. Mitsos, 2018. Economic nonlinear model predictive control for flexible operation of air separation units. IFAC-PapersOnLine 51 (20), 295–300.

A. Caspari, J. M. M. Faust, F. Jung, C. Kappatou, S. Sass, Y. Vaupel, R. Hannesmann-Tamás, A. Mhamdi, A. Mitsos, 2019a. Dyos - a framework for optimization of large-scale differential algebraic equation systems. Computer-Aided Chemical Engineering 46.

A. Caspari, L. Lüken, P. Schäfer, Y. Vaupel, A. Mhamdi, L. T. Biegler, A. Mitsos, 2019b. Dynamic optimization with complementarity constraints: Regularization for direct shooting. Optimization Online.

A. Caspari, C. Offermanns, P. Schäfer, A. Mhamdi, A. Mitsos, 2019c. A flexible air separation process: 2.optimal operation using economic model predictive control. AIChE Journal 65 (11).

B. Daryanian, R. E. Bohn, R. D. Tabors, 1989. Optimal demand-side response to electricity spot prices forstorage-type customers. IEEE Power Eng. Rev. 9 (8), 36–36.

P. E. Gill, W. Murray, M. A. Saunders, 2005. SNOPT: An SQP algorithm for large-scale constrained optimization. SIAM Rev. 47 (1), 99–131.

R. Hannemann, W. Marquardt, U. Naumann, B. Gendler, 2010. Discrete first- and second-order adjoints and automatic differentiation for the sensitivity analysis of dynamic models. Procedia Comput. Sci. 1 (1), 297–305.

R. Huang, V. M. Zavala, L. T. Biegler, 2009. Advanced step nonlinear model predictive control for air separation units. J. Process Control 19 (4), 678–685.

T. Johansson, 2015. Integrated scheduling and control of an air separation unit subject totime-varying electricity prices. Master's Thesis. KTH Royal Institute of Technology, Stockholm, Sweden.

R. Kender, B. Wunderlich, I. Thomas, A. Peschel, S. Rehfeldt, H. Klein, 2019. Pressure-driven dynamic simulation of start up and shutdown procedures of distillation columns in air separation units. Chem. Eng. Res. Des. 147, 98–112.

J. Miller, W. L. Luyben, P. Belanger, S. Blouin, L. Megan, 2008a. Improving agility of cryogenic air separation plants. Ind. Eng. Chem. Res. 47 (2), 394–404.

J. Miller, W. L. Luyben, S. Blouin, 2008b. Economic incentive for intermittent operation of air separation plants with variable power costs. Ind. Eng. Chem. Res. 47 (4), 1132–1139.

A. U. Raghunathan, M. S. Diaz, L. T. Biegler, 2004. An MPEC formulation for dynamic optimization of distillation operations. Comput. Chem. Eng. 28 (10), 2037–2052.

D. R. Vinson, 2006. Air separation control technology. Comput. Chem. Eng. 30 (10-12), 1436–1446.

Q. Zhang, I. E. Grossmann, C. F. Heuberger, A. Sundaramoorthy, J. M. Pinto, 2015. Air separation with cryogenic energy storage: Optimal scheduling considering electric energy and reserve markets. AIChE J. 61 (5), 1547–1558.

Sauro Pierucci, Flavio Manenti, Giulia Bozzano, Davide Manca (Eds.)
Proceedings of the 30th European Symposium on Computer Aided Process Engineering
(ESCAPE30), May 24-27, 2020, Milano, Italy. © 2020 Elsevier B.V. All rights reserved.
http://dx.doi.org/10.1016/B978-0-12-823377-1.50193-2

Scheduling of a Large-scale Industrial Make-and-Pack Process with Finite Intermediate Buffer using Discrete-time and Precedence-based Models

Christian Klanke[a]*, Vassilios Yfantis[a], Francesc Corominas[b], Sebastian Engell[a]

[a]*TU Dortmund University, Faculty of Biochemical and Chemical Engineering,*
Process Dynamics and Operations Group, Emil-Figge-Straße 70,
44227 Dortmund, Germany
[b]*Procter & Gamble, Temselaan 100, 1853 Strombeek-Bever, Belgium*
christian.klanke@tu-dortmund.de

Abstract

We address the short-term scheduling of a two-stage continuous make-and-pack process with finite intermediate buffer and sequence-dependent changeovers from the consumer goods industry. In the current layout of the plant under consideration, the two stages, product formulation and packing, are directly coupled, i.e. the products of the formulation stage go directly to the packing stage. As for different products either one of both stages can be the bottleneck, a gain in productivity can be obtained if the two stages are decoupled by a buffer so that the formulation lines and the packing lines can both run at full capacity. The disadvantage of this setup is an increased complexity of the scheduling problem, so that support for the schedulers must to be provided. We employ a mixed-integer programming problem formulation for this purpose. The problem at hand is characterized by a large number of products in several product families, product specific order quantities and deadlines, product dependent production times, sequence-dependent changeover times, and a finite intermediate buffer. As the problem turned out to be intractable for the planning horizons of interest, a solution approach that employs a discrete-time scheduling model, a precedence-based presorting model and a decomposition strategy that is enhanced by several heuristics was developed.

Keywords: MILP modelling, Industrial scheduling, Heuristic decomposition, Make-and-Pack processes, Shifting bottlenecks, Precedence-based models.

1. Introduction

In the consumer goods industry, satisfying rapidly growing product demands poses a challenge to the decision makers: It needs to be decided whether to invest into new processing lines or to increase the productivity of an existing production plant either by improved operation or by revamping it to ensure market demand satisfaction.

In the make-and-pack plant under consideration, the two stages, formulation and packing, are closely coupled, i.e. the products of each line of the formulation stage flow directly to the corresponding packing line. A limitation of the current layout is the necessity to synchronize the production rates of the two stages within a line. Since the processing rate of the packing lines can be larger or smaller than the processing rate of the formulation lines, depending on the product, the bottleneck of the plant can either be the formulation or the packing stage. In order to reduce the total changeover time and to utilize the higher processing rates in each stage, an option is to decouple the two stages via an intermediate buffer. To establish such a buffer requires a significantly smaller investment than to add additional processing or packing lines. The scheduling of the different products in the layout with such a buffer is even more challenging than the scheduling of the plant with a direct feed of the packing lines from the formulation lines, that was addressed in Elekidis et al. (2019), due to the larger number of degrees of freedom. In both cases, decomposition strategies are necessary to solve the problem for realistic problem sizes in reasonable computation times.

In this paper, we extend a discrete-time formulation for the scheduling problem with an intermediate buffer by a precedence-based model which is used for presorting the jobs which are then scheduled sequentially. The efficiency of the extension is demonstrated for relevant problem instances. The solution quality is measured by the total idle time, total changeover time, and total completion time.

This contribution is composed as follows: In Section 2 the case study is presented in detail. In Section 3 the proposed iterative solution procedure is introduced. Finally, the results for an exemplary case are discussed in Section 4 before final conclusions are drawn in Section 0.

2. Case study

In this section, a possible new layout of the plant under consideration is presented. In the first stage, a formulation process takes place on parallel, identical machines, and the formulated products can be, but do not necessarily have to be, stored in an intermediate buffer. The formulated products are fed to the second stage where they are packed on parallel, non-identical machines. The number of different products in the formulation stage is considerably less than the number of final packed products. Changeovers that require sequence-dependent changeover times occur in both stages of the process. Figure 1 shows a scheme of the plant layout that is considered here.

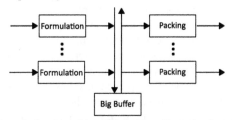

Figure 1: Layout of the make-and-pack production plant.

The buffer can store any product of the first stage, and only the total content of the buffer is limited. Any product can be withdrawn from the buffer at any time. There are two types of packing lines which are dedicated to specific types of products, those packed into large and those packed into small containers. The processing rates of small containers are lower than those of large containers. The assignment of the products to the two sets of packing lines is fixed, due to the lack of flexibility of the equipment. The formulated products feed a significantly larger number of differently packaged products. A single type of formulated product, hereinafter denoted a product family, can be used for a variety of final products. Each product has to be produced prior to a delivery date (deadline), but there are only up to three deadlines within the scheduling horizon. The transfer times between the formulation stage and the buffer and between the buffer and the packing stage are assumed to be small compared to the production times and are therefore neglected. The production rates and the order sizes are fixed and known for each product.

3. Solution approach

The MILP-based solution that we present here is based on the discrete-time mixed-integer linear programming (MILP) model from Yfantis et al. (2019). It is augmented by a precedence-based MILP presorting model. The discrete time MILP model solves the timing and allocation problem iteratively for sets of products. The inventory of each product family in the buffer is tracked at each discrete time point and the total buffer content is constrained. As the planning time horizon usually is three days of non-stop production, the problem instances become large, e.g., weekend schedules with around ninety products are generated. Due to the high number of decision variables that results from the high temporal resolution of the discrete-time model, a tailored decomposition strategy is applied. The decomposition approach is based on splitting the original set of orders into smaller subsets I^k with $|I^k| = N$ which are scheduled in each iteration k. After each iteration, the timing and allocation decisions of the set of orders considered are fixed. For a detailed description of the decomposition algorithm, the reader is referred to Yfantis et al. (2019).

The discrete-time model does not provide explicit sequencing information for the different production lines, therefore the changeover times cannot be optimized directly. As stated by Harjunkoski et al. (2014), considering changeovers in a discrete-time model would significantly increase its size. This is undesirable because of limitations of the computation time and memory. Therefore, in addition to the discrete-time model of the overall problem, an immediate precedence-based model, that bears similarities to the one introduced by Cerda et al. (1997), has been developed. The precedence-based model is solved in each iteration of the decomposed solution process and the allocation and sequencing decisions of certain packing lines are fixed prior to the solution of the discrete-time model. The precedence-based model has a much smaller size compared to the discrete-time model, and therefore larger sets of products and longer prediction horizons can be considered than in the solution of the full model. In order to maintain enough degrees of freedom in the discrete-time model, e.g. to still be able to satisfy the buffer mass balance and buffer capacity constraint, the precedence-based model is only applied to a subset of packing lines $J^{préc} \subset J$ and the formulation stage is not considered in this model. The buffer mass balance is ignored because the discrete-time model takes care of it in the second step. Based on the results of the precedence-based model, a heuristic chooses the final subset of products that is scheduled by the discrete-time model.

The iterative procedure of presorting and choosing appropriate products to be scheduled in the discrete-time model is shown in Figure 3. The set I^k_{prec} denotes the products that are scheduled with the precedence-based model in iteration k. I^k_{prec} is generated iteratively from those orders from the initial set of orders I which are not scheduled yet. For the order decomposition a totally ordered set I_j of orders is created prior to the optimisation. Details on the computation of I_j are described in Yfantis et al. (2019). The order heuristic picks products either from I_j or seq_j in each iteration. The totally ordered set seq_j contains the sequence of orders in line j and is calculated from the solution of the precedence-based model. Deadlines are accounted for in the following manner: For lines $j \notin J_{prec}$ the set I_j is sorted with respect to the deadlines. For lines $j \in J_{prec}$, the heuristic chooses a product with the closest deadline, if not all products in seq_j have the same deadline. Otherwise deadlines pose no issue in the respective iteration and the first product from seq_j is taken. After the timing of the products has been determined by the discrete-time model, the allocation and timing information for each line is fed back to compute co_{ij}^{k-1}, C_{max}^{k-1} and the line-specific completion time C_j^{k-1}.

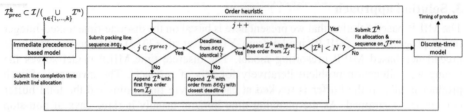

Figure 2: Iterative interaction of the immediate precedence-based model, the discrete-time model, and the order heuristic.

The precedence-based model makes use of binary line-specific immediate precedence variables $X_{ii'j}$, line allocation variables Y_{ij} and first/last-scheduled variables Z_{ij}^f/Z_{ij}^l. The variable $X_{ii'j}$ is active if product i precedes product i' on line i.

In the following the most important equations of the precedence-based model are given:

$$2 \cdot (X_{ii'j} + X_{i'ij}) \leq Y_{ij} + Y_{i'j}, \quad \forall j \in J^{prec}, i \in I_{prec}^k, i' \in I_{prec}^k \setminus \{i\} \tag{1}$$

$$Z_{ij}^f + \sum_{i' \in I_{prec}^k \setminus \{i\}} X_{ii'j} \leq 1, \quad \forall i \in I_{prec}^k, j \in J^{prec} \tag{2}$$

$$Z_{ij}^l + \sum_{i' \in I_{prec}^k \setminus \{i\}} X_{i'ij} \leq 1, \quad \forall i \in I_{prec}^k, j \in J^{prec} \tag{3}$$

$$M \sum_{i \in I_{prec}^k} Z_{ij}^f \geq \sum_{i \in I_{prec}^k} Y_{ij}, \quad \forall j \in J^{prec}, M \sum_{i \in I_{prec}^k} Z_{ij}^l + 2 \geq \sum_{i \in I_{prec}^k} Y_{ij}, \quad \forall j \in J^{prec} \tag{4}$$

$$Z_{ij}^l + Z_{ij}^f \leq 1, \quad \forall j \in J^{prec}, i \in I_{prec}^k \tag{5}$$

$$X_{ii'j} + Z_{i'j}^l + Z_{ij}^f \leq 2, \quad \forall j \in J^{prec}, i \in I_{prec}^k, i' \in I_{prec}^k \setminus \{i\} \tag{6}$$

$$2 \cdot (2 - Z_{ij}^f - Z_{i'j}^l) + \sum_{\hat{i} \in I_{prec}^k \setminus \{i,\tilde{i}\}} X_{\tilde{i}ij} + \sum_{\tilde{i} \in I_{prec}^k \setminus \{i,\tilde{i}\}} X_{\tilde{i}ij} \geq 2,$$
$$\forall i \in I_{prec}^k, i' \in I_{prec}^k \setminus \{i\}, \tilde{i} \in I_{prec}^k \setminus \{i,i'\}, j \in J^{prec} \tag{7}$$

$$\min_{X_{ii'j}, Y_{ij}, Z_{ij}^f, Z_{ij}^l} -C_{max}^{k-1} + C_{max} + \rho \cdot co^{tot} \tag{8}$$

$$co^{tot} := \sum_{j \in J^{prec}} \sum_{i \in I_{prec}^k} co_{ij}^{k-1} Z_{ij}^f + \sum_{l \in L} \sum_{j \in J^{prec} \cap J^l} \sum_{i' \in I_{prec}^k} \sum_{i \in I_{prec}^k \setminus \{i'\}} co_{ii'l} X_{ii'j} \tag{9}$$

$$C_{max} \geq C_{il}, \quad \forall i \in I_{prec}^k, \forall l \in L \tag{10}$$

$$C_{il} \geq \sum_{j \in J^{prec} \cap J^l} (co_{ij}^{k-1} + p_{il}) Z_{ij}^f + \sum_{j \in J^{prec} \cap J^l} C_j^{k-1} Y_{ij}, \quad \forall i \in I_{prec}^k, l \in L \tag{11}$$

$$C_{i'l} \geq C_{il} + co_{ii'l} + p_{il} - M(1 - X_{ii'j}), \quad \forall j \in J^{prec} \cap J^l, i \in I_{prec}^k, l \in L \tag{12}$$

Constraint (1), as given in Elekidis et al., (2019), states that if product i' is followed by product i both allocation variables have to be active. Eqs. (2) and (3) prohibit that products which are the first respectively last on their line can be the successor respectively predecessor of another product. Eqs. (4) make sure that there is a first product on every line with at least one product and a last product on every line with at least three products. This is complemented by Eq. (5) allowing each product to either be the first or the last on a line. If there is just one product on a line, Z_{ij}^f is one, as Z_{ij}^f accounts for the changeover with products from previous iterations in the objective function. Eq. (6) prevents that on a line with two products i and i' all three variables Z_{ij}^f, Z_{ij}^l and $X_{ii'j}$ are active. Finally, constraint (7) enforces two different products i and i' being the first and the last product on a line to be the predecessor and successor of at least one other product. For all other combinations of two products not being the first and the last one, the constraint is relaxed. In addition to the above constraints, simple logic constraints, for example prohibiting that a line can contain more than one first product or that a product is scheduled twice, are imposed.

The objective function Eq. (8) minimizes the makespan and the weighted total changeover time. Eq. (9), which also considers changeover times with previously scheduled products co_{ij}^{k-1}, defines the total changeover time. The objective function is normalized by the parameter C_{max}^{k-1} which is the makespan of the previous iteration to maintain a consistent effect of ρ throughout the iterations. Eq. (10) defines the makespan. Eq. (11) constraints the completion of a product to be at least the previous completion time C_j^{k-1} of the line where product i is allocated plus the processing time p_{il} of this product in the respective stage l. Eq. (12) transforms the precedence relations into the completion time of each product, similar to the completion time constraints in Elekidis et al. (2019).

4. Example

The resulting schedule for an exemplary case is shown in Figure 3. Six formulation lines (Line1L to Line6L) and six packing lines (Line1P to Line6P) are considered. The numbers above the bars indicate the product family of which products are produced respectively consumed by the packing lines. The bars in the formulation lines are not distinguished by different colours, as they do not represent different final products like in the packing lines. Black bars between the product bars indicate changeover times, while dotted lines indicate idle times. The vertical bold dashed grey line represents a deadline at 2019-03-16 08:00 PM. To solve this problem instance $N = 6$ products per iteration and stage were scheduled by the discrete-time model and $N_{prec} = 15$ by the precedence-based model. The time resolution was set to 6 minutes and the penalty parameter ρ was linearly decreased from 20 to 0 to favour a reduced makespan over reduced changeovers and therefore balanced packing lines in later iterations. The buffer was initialised at 50 % of the maximum value. The proposed approach was implemented in Julia 1.1.1 with Gurobi 8.1.0 as the MILP solver on a MS Windows 10 desktop PC (Intel Core i7-3770 CPU @ 3.40 GHz, 32 GB RAM).

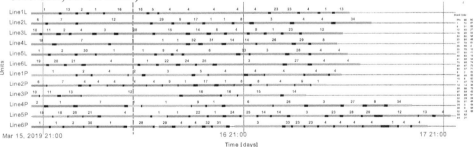

Figure 3: Optimised schedule for the case study.

Due to the demand structure, the last three packing lines, although producing only products that are packed faster, take significantly longer. The algorithm managed to balance the formulation lines well. As can be seen, idle times could not be fully avoided. This is a consequence of significantly different processing rates in the formulation and packing lines which could not be compensated fully by the utilization of the intermediate buffer or from the initially available product families.

In Table 1 the main quality measures for the exemplary case with and without precedence-based presorting are summarized. The precedence-based presorting could improve all criteria listed. While improvements in changeover times are an obvious consequence from the presorting approach, the reduction in idle times results from dynamically choosing the products on non-presorted lines within the iterations. Also, the computation times could be reduced, as the optimizer that solved the discrete-time model is given less degrees of freedom by fixing the allocation and sequencing decisions for the presorted lines.

Table 1: Comparison of relevant quality measures and computation time of the optimized schedule with and without precedence-based presorting.

Presorting?	Makespan [min]	Completion time packing stage [min]	Changeover time total [min]	Idle time total [min]	Computation time [s]
No	3,042	15,204	2,670	186	739
Yes	3,024	14,940	2,628	120	636
Improvements	0.59 %	1.74 %	1.57 %	35.48 %	13.92 %

5. Conclusions

We presented an iterative solution of a challenging real-world two-stage scheduling problem with intermediate buffer based on a discrete-time formulation. The discrete-time model was extended by a precedence-based presorting algorithm that directly minimizes the changeover times. The precedence-based presorting is used to split the set of orders into tractable subproblems. A heuristic coordinates the proposed sequences from the precedence-based model with the eligibility and deadline constraints to obtain the set of orders that are scheduled in each iteration. The extension improves the quality of the schedules while at the same time reducing the computational time.

The main drawback of the proposed strategy is that it employs only a very limited look-ahead horizon. It would be desirable to enlarge the horizon of the precedence-based optimization but for more than 15 products per iteration a rapid growth of the solution times was observed.

Acknowledgements

The project leading to this publication has received funding from the European Union's Horizon 2020 research and innovation programme under grant agreement No 723575 (CoPro, spire2030.eu/copro) in the framework of the SPIRE PPP.

References

J. Cerda, G. Henning, I. Grossmann, 1997, A Mixed-Integer Linear Programming Model for Short-Term Scheduling of Single-Stage Multiproduct Batch Plants with Parallel Lines, Industrial and Engineering Chemistry Research, 36, 5, 1695-1707

A. Elekidis, F. Corominas, M. Georgiadis, 2019, Optimal short-term Scheduling of Industrial Packing Facilities, Computer Aided Chemical Engineering, 46, 1183-1188

I. Harjunkoski, C. Maravelias, P. Bongers, P. Castro, S. Engell, I. Grossmann, J. Hooker, C. Méndez, G. Sand, J. Wassick, 2014, Scope for industrial applications of production scheduling models and solution methods, Computers and Chemical Engineering, 62, 161-193

V. Yfantis, F. Corominas, S. Engell, 2019, Scheduling of a Consumer Goods Production Plant with Intermediate Buffer by Decomposition and Mixed-integer Linear Programming, Proc. IFAC MIM, Berlin 2019, to appear in IFAC-PapersOnLine

Sauro Pierucci, Flavio Manenti, Giulia Bozzano, Davide Manca (Eds.)
Proceedings of the 30th European Symposium on Computer Aided Process Engineering
(ESCAPE30), May 24-27, 2020, Milano, Italy. © 2020 Elsevier B.V. All rights reserved.
http://dx.doi.org/10.1016/B978-0-12-823377-1.50194-4

Optimization of Business Transactional Processes in a Digital Supply Chain

Hector D. Perez,[a] Satyajith Amaran,[b] Esra Erisen,[b] John M. Wassick,[b] Ignacio E. Grossmann[a*]

[a]*Carnegie Mellon University, Pittsburgh 15213, USA*
[b]*The Dow Chemical Company, Midland 48674, USA*
grossmann@cmu.edu

Abstract

A new continuous time multistage scheduling Mixed-Integer Linear Programming (MILP) model is proposed to optimize the business transactional processes in supply chains. The novelty of this approach is in using techniques from the Process Systems Engineering (PSE) and Operations Research (OR) communities to address a side of supply chain optimization (information flow) that has not been targeted previously. This model accounts for the allocation of resources in processing orders at each of the stages of a business transactional process. The objective of the model is to improve customer experience, using on-time-delivery (OTD) as a surrogate metric for this target. An illustrative example, featuring a subset of the business transactional steps in the Order-to-Cash (OTC) process is presented, showing the potential of using mathematical programming to improve supply chain performance. The model enables identifying bottlenecks in the processes and determining where additional resources should be allocated. The model can also be used as a valuable tool to assist customer service representatives in establishing realistic promise-to-delivery dates for their clients.

Keywords: scheduling, MILP, supply chain, optimization, business transactions.

1. Introduction

Supply chains have been traditionally modelled and optimized by the Process Systems Engineering (PSE) (Grossmann, 2012) and Operations Research (OR) (Owen and Daskin, 1998) communities, with the focus being on the optimization of material flow within the supply chain network. Literature has shown the need to expand this vision to also include the financial flows in supply chain optimization. Jahangiri and Cecelja (2014) show how financial models of supply chain can be used to understand the effect of supplier penalty and manufacturer lead time on the company profit. Kees et al. (2019) show the benefits of integrating material and financial flows to improve both the availability of drugs in a hospital supply chain as well as the hospital economic performance. Yi and Reklaitis (2004) show the impact that an integrated material and cash flow model can have on the design of chemical plants. Guillen et al. (2006) show the economic benefits of integrating process operations and financial decisions when optimizing a chemical supply chain. However, there is another type of flow that has been overlooked by the optimization communities: information flow. Supply chains are commonly managed via Enterprise Resource Planning (ERP) systems, which log the data associated with business processes. Previous work in this regard has focussed on the simulation (Villarraga et al., 2017) and design (Niedermann and Schwarz, 2011) of business processes, rather than the optimization of its operations.

The purpose of this paper is to propose a mathematical programming model for optimizing the transactional processes in a supply chain. As an example, the model is applied to the Order-to-Cash (OTC) business process. The OTC process is one of the business processes present in virtually all companies, involving the transactions that occur between the time when an order is placed by a client, to the time when payment is received for the goods delivered. The objective is to minimize the occurrence of late product deliveries and thus reduce the time between when orders are placed, and payment is received for the delivered products. Additional benefits of the model include helping to inform production order due dates as well as promise-to-delivery dates for order fulfilment. The model presented in the paper is analogous to the sequential multistage models used by the PSE community for scheduling multistage batch plants (Mendez et al., 2006), but it differs in several important respects from the traditional multistage scheduling models. Although the model is a new model for modelling multistage processes, the novelty of this project is in using techniques from the PSE and OR communities to address an aspect of supply chain optimization that has been largely overlooked by the optimization communities.

2. Problem Statement

The OTC process is analogous in its structure to a flowshop problem. When a company receives a set of orders, $o \in O$, from its clients, there are a set of tasks, $l \in L$, that need to be performed by agents, $a \in A$, until products are delivered to the clients and payment of invoices is received. Each agent has a queue with positions $p \in P$ to which orders are assigned for processing. The system can be described as a directed graph of queues that map the trajectory of each order within the supply chain. The overall goal is to assign orders to agents and reorder the queue positions to maximize the number of orders delivered on time. Thus, the problem seeks to find an optimal order processing policy, as opposed to the traditional queue management policies of first-in-first-out (FIFO), last-in-first-out (LIFO), smallest-to-largest, or largest-to-smallest (Villarraga et al., 2017).

3. Mathematical Model

The mathematical model for the OTC process is based on the following assumptions,

1.   Order release dates, due dates, and processing times are deterministic. In practice orders are placed dynamically, but in the base model, the system is assumed to be static.
2.   There are no transition times for orders between steps or stages in the OTC process. Unlike chemical plants, which require waiting times for materials to be transferred between units, instantaneous transitions are possible since data (information) are available to all agents in the OTC process via the company's ERP system.
3.   There are no transitions times between orders in an agent's queue. Unlike chemical processing units, which often require transition times for changeovers, business processing units (agents) can process orders back to back due to their non-material nature.

4. Each order can only be processed at most once at each stage. Inefficiencies in the OTC process may lead to orders being processed multiple times by an agent. However, this degree of complexity is not included in the base model.
5. Each order represents one batch of product. In industrial systems, orders can correspond to multiple sub-orders, and sub-orders can correspond to multiple batches, fractions of batches, or even entire production campaigns in some cases. The assumption of one batch per order is made for simplification purposes.
6. No resource constraints are considered aside from human personnel constraints.

The model described in this section uses continuous time via time slots (Mouret et al., 2011) to model the time events, and is analogous to the model presented by Pinto and Grossmann (1995) for scheduling multistage batch plants. Some differences with the latter model are:

- The model allows for the possibility of not all orders being processed on time. When this occurs in a real scenario, the promise-to-delivery dates would be adjusted by the customer service representatives.
- Order transfers between stages are instantaneous due to the use of ERP systems.
- Based on the agent type, processing times may or may not depend on the quantity ordered.
- Time matching of order stages and unit slots is not required. The assignment of units (agents) to stages is defined *a priori* by the structure of the OTC process steps.
- Instead of minimizing the earliness of an order's end time, the proposed formulation targets maximizing the on-time completion of orders.

3.1. Model Constraints

3.1.1. Time Bounds

There is a start time, $t^s_{o,p,a} \in \mathbb{R}^+$, and an end time, $t^f_{o,p,a} \in \mathbb{R}^+$, for each order assigned to a queue position. The start time occurs between the release date, T^r_o, and due date T^d_o of the order (**Eq. 1**). The binary variable $x_{o,p,a}$ denotes when an agent a has order o in queue position p. The time an order leaves a queue is the sum of the start time and the order processing duration and must occur before the due date of the order (**Eq. 2**). $\tau_{o,a}$ is the average processing time of agent a for order o and can depend on the material quantity requested as well as the material type.

3.1.2. Assignment Constraints

Eqs. 3-4 allow each order to be processed at most once at each stage and allow at most one order to occupy each queue position in the queue of each agent.

3.1.3. Precedence Constraints

Eq. 5 ensures that queue positions are used consecutively in each agent's queue. Agent precedence relations are given in **Eq. 6**. **Eq. 7** enforces that if there is an order present in a queue position, then its start time must be after the end time of the order in the queue position immediately ahead of it. T_{max} is the scheduling horizon. **Eq. 8** ensures that if an order is scheduled to be processed at a downstream stage, it can only be processed after the previous stage, has finished processing it.

$$x_{o,p,a} \cdot T_o^r \leq t_{o,p,a}^s \leq x_{o,p,a} \cdot T_o^d \qquad \forall o \in O, p \in P, a \in A \qquad (1)$$

$$t_{o,p,a}^s + \tau_{o,a} \cdot x_{o,p,a} = t_{o,p,a}^f \leq x_{o,p,a} \cdot T_o^d \qquad \forall o \in O, p \in P, a \in A \qquad (2)$$

$$\sum_{a \in A_l} \sum_{p \in P} x_{o,p,a} \leq 1 \qquad \forall o \in O, l \in L \qquad (3)$$

$$\sum_{o \in O} x_{o,p,a} \leq 1 \qquad \forall p \in P, a \in A \qquad (4)$$

$$\sum_{o \in O} x_{o,p_1,a} \geq \sum_{o \in O} x_{o,p_2,a} \qquad \begin{matrix} \forall p_1, p_2 \in P, p_1 + 1 = p_2 \\ \forall a \in A \end{matrix} \qquad (5)$$

$$\sum_{a \in A_{l_1}} \sum_{p \in P} x_{o,p,a} \geq \sum_{a \in A_{l_2}} \sum_{p \in P} x_{o,p,a} \qquad \begin{matrix} \forall l_1, l_2 \in L, l_1 + 1 = l_2 \\ \forall o \in O \end{matrix} \qquad (6)$$

$$\sum_{o \in O} t_{o,p_1,a}^f \leq \sum_{o \in O} t_{o,p_2,a}^s + T_{max} \cdot \left(1 - \sum_{o \in O} x_{o,p_2,a}\right) \qquad \begin{matrix} \forall p_1, p_2 \in P, p_1 + 1 = p_2 \\ \forall a \in A \end{matrix} \qquad (7)$$

$$\sum_{p \in P} \sum_{a \in A_{l_1}} t_{o,p,a}^f \leq \sum_{p \in P} \sum_{a \in A_{l_2}} t_{o,p,a}^s + T_o^d$$

$$\cdot \left(1 - \sum_{p \in P} \sum_{a \in A_{l_2}} x_{o,p,a}\right) \qquad \begin{matrix} \forall l_1, l_2 \in L, l_1 + 1 = l_2 \\ \forall o \in O \end{matrix} \qquad (8)$$

3.2. Objective Function

The On-Time-Delivery (OTD, percentage of orders fulfilled before their due date) metric is a key performance indicator of the OTC process. Since the model is intended for dynamic implementation, the objective function to be maximized is the total number of business transactions (**Eq. 9**), which measures the sum of orders processed by all agents. This is the objective function of choice since it increases the chances of obtaining a high OTD throughout the optimization horizon. Customer segmentation dictates order priority, such that orders from high priority customers have a higher w_o.

$$OTD = \sum_{a \in A} \sum_{p \in P} \sum_{o \in O} w_o \cdot x_{o,p,a} \qquad (9)$$

4. Illustrative Example

The MILP model was applied to a subset of the OTC process with three stages and four agents (see **Figure 1**). The order and system details are given in **Tables 1-2**. The illustrative example was run using JuMP 0.19.2 (Julia 1.2.0) with Gurobi 8.1.0 as the MIP solver using a PC with an Intel i7, 1.9 GHz, 64-bit processor, and 24 GB of RAM.

Solution time was 0.07 s to full optimality. To show the benefits of using the model over traditional scheduling, the model results were compared to those of a human scheduler using the priority-first approach (orders are scheduled based on customer priority). The results given in **Figure 2** show that for this case, the human scheduler only attains a 60% order fulfilment, whereas the model provides a schedule with 100% order fulfilment. Thus, the benefits of using the model to schedule the operations of the OTC process are evident in even small cases with five orders. Although a human scheduler could potentially come up with the same schedule as that of the optimizer after much trial and error, such a task becomes virtually impossible as the number of orders increases.

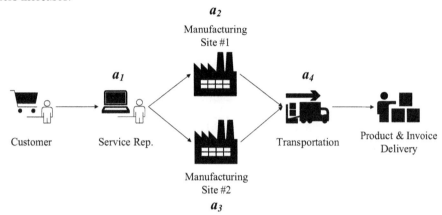

Figure 1. Simplified OTC process flow for illustrative example

Table 1. Order specifications in the illustrative example

Order	1	2	3	4	5
Day Released	0	1	2	2	7
Day Due	10	10	10	12	14
Priority	Medium	High	High	Low	Low

Table 2. OTC agent processing times

Agent	a_1	a_2	a_3	a_4
Processing Time (d)	1	3	3	2

5. Conclusions

A new sequential multi-stage process model is presented to optimize the queues of the agents involved in the OTC business process to improve on-time delivery. An illustrative example is given, which shows that the allocation of resources is key in orders fulfilment. The proposed model can be used to identify bottlenecks in the process and determine which stages need an increase in personnel or a decrease in processing times to improve system performance. Future work in this area includes integrating the business transactional model with manufacturing scheduling models to account for the details involved in the manufacturing and logistic stages of the supply chain. In terms of implementation, a rolling horizon approach can be used for dynamic optimization. Scaling to industrial sized problems, which also contain additional complexities such as rework, and variable processing times will also be addressed in the future.

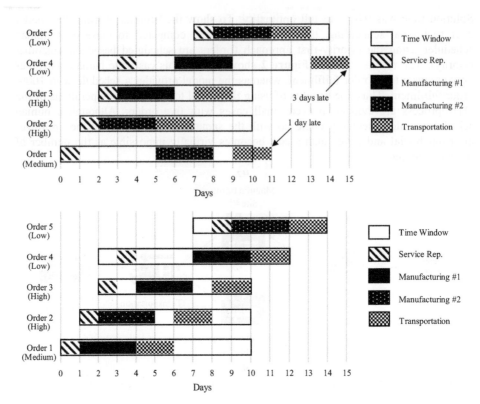

Figure 2. Priority-first human scheduler (top) and model optimized schedule (bottom)

References

I. Grossmann, 2012. Advances in mathematical programming models for enterprise-wide optimization, *Comput. Chem. Eng.*, 47, 2-18.

G. Guillen, M. Badell, A. Espuña, L. Puigjaner, 2006, Simultaneous optimization of process operations and financial decisions to enhance the integrated planning/scheduling of chemical supply chains, *Comput. Chem. Eng.*, 30, 3, 421-436.

M. Jahangiri, F. Cecelja, 2014, Modelling financial flow of the supply chain, IEEE IEEM.

M. Kees, J. Bandoni, M. Moreno, 2019, An optimization model for managing the drug logistics process in a public hospital supply chain integrating physical and economic flows, *Ind. Eng. Chem. Res.*, 58, 9, 3767-3781.

C. Mendez, J. Cerda, I. Grossmann, I. Harjunkoski, M. Fahl, 2006, State-of-the-art review of optimization methods for short-term scheduling of batch processes, *Comput. Chem. Eng.*, 30, 913-946.

S. Mouret, I. Grossmann, P. Pestiaux, 2011, Time representations and mathematical models for process scheduling problems, *Comput. Chem. Eng.*, 35, 6, 1038-1063.

F. Niedermann, H. Schwarz, 2011, Deep Business Optimization: Making Business Process Optimization Theory Work in Practice, *BPMDS 2011, EMMSAD 2011*, Berlin, 88-102.

S. Owen, M. Daskin, 1998, Strategic facility location: A review, *Eur. J. Oper. Res.*, 111, 423-447.

J. Pinto, I. Grossmann, 1995, A Continuous Time Mixed Integer Linear Programming Model for Short Term Scheduling of Multistage Batch Plants, *Ind Eng. Chem. Res.*, 34, 3037-3051.

J. Villarraga, K. Carley, J. Wassick, N. Sahinidis, 2017, Agent-based Modeling and Simulation for an Order-To-Cash Process using NetLogo. Pittsburgh, USA.

G. Yi, G. Reklaitis, 2004, Optimal design of batch- storage network with financial transactions and cash flows, *AIChE J.*, 50, 11.

Sauro Pierucci, Flavio Manenti, Giulia Bozzano, Davide Manca (Eds.)
Proceedings of the 30th European Symposium on Computer Aided Process Engineering
(ESCAPE30), May 24-27, 2020, Milano, Italy. © 2020 Elsevier B.V. All rights reserved.
http://dx.doi.org/10.1016/B978-0-12-823377-1.50195-6

Fault Propagation Path Inference in a Complex Chemical Process Based on Time-delayed Mutual Information Analysis

Cheng Ji, Fangyuan Ma, Xuebing Zhu, Jingde Wang, Wei Sun*

College of Chemical Engineering, Beijing University of Chemical Technology, North Third Ring Road 15, Chaoyang District, Beijing, 100029, China
sunwei@mail.buct.edu.cn

Abstract

Process monitoring plays more and more important role in modern process industry. Early root cause isolation is the most attractive character to process operators. Currently, the signed directed graph (SDG) is a widely used method for fault diagnosis, in which graphs are employed to represent the causality between process variables. In most cases, the SDG model is obtained from expert experience. The challenge of this approach is that it is hard to include all knowledge required in complex chemical process operation, which may not be available to experts and operating professionals, as they can be significantly different with changing control strategies, even to same set of process operation. With the universal application of distributed control system (DCS), operation data have been recorded for a certain long time, which contain comprehensive information regarding the process itself. It can be expected that the logic and time dependence among all variables can be extracted with proper analysis method. Mutual information is a commonly used data-based method for measuring the interaction of two objects. The initiator and responder between a pair of variables can be identified by adding an appropriate time lag. In this paper, the identification of fault propagation path is achieved based on a time-delayed mutual information method. When a fault occurs, the response information among variables will be used to explore the propagation path, which provides a more objective information for fault diagnosis. The methodology is applied to a simulated process and a practical industrial case, an ethylene cracking process. The result illustrates that the proposed data-based method shows a good capability for identifying the fault propagation path.

Keywords: fault diagnosis, mutual information, causal analysis, ethylene cracking process

1. Introduction

Abnormal operating conditions in chemical process industry may lead to economic losses and safety accidents. With the ever-increasing concern on safety and economic benefits, early isolation of fault propagation path is of great significance, but on the other side, the complexity of chemical process as well as the large-scale of chemical equipment make it extremely challenging. Generally, the process fault detection and diagnosis methods can be classified into three categories: the first principle model-based methods, the knowledge-based methods and the data-based methods (Frank, 1990).

The first principle model-based methods can show good performance in some simplified ideal processes, but it is almost impossible to establish for an industrial chemical process due to its high complexity. Knowledge-based methods, such as fault tree analysis and expert system, are generally obtained from causal model established by expert knowledge. As an example tool of expert system, the signed directed graph (SDG) model is widely used for fault diagnosis. However, the challenge of this method is that it is unable to get sufficient knowledge about the process to establish an objective causality model. In contrast, with the wide application of DCS system, the data-based methods have received more and more attention of researchers. Under this category, the contribution plots are widely used for fault diagnosis in industrial processes (Miller, et al., 1998). Generally, the variable with the largest contribution are considered as the root cause of the fault, but sometimes the variable with the largest contribution may be a state variable, which is a result caused by the fault. Vedam and Venkatasubramanian (1999) combined the advantages of the contribution plots and the SDG model, and proposed a model based on the principal component analysis (PCA) and SDG to solve the above problem. However, due to the difference of automatic control strategies applied to a particular system, causal relationship between variables may be inconsistent with previous obtained expert knowledge, which will lead to incorrect fault diagnosis result. The mutual information analysis, as a completely data-based variable correlation identification method, is able to reflect the actual situation of the process. In addition, the mutual information algorithm has an advantage in detecting both linear and nonlinear relationships between variables (Li et al, 2018), making it suitable for fault diagnosis in nonlinear processes, such as chemical processes.

In this work, sufficient historical data is used to obtain the mutual information threshold matrix, the correlation between process variables is identified by comparing the mutual information value in the abnormal state with the threshold, and then the diagnosis of fault propagation path under different control strategies is achieved in a simulated process. An ethylene cracking process as a practical case is studied using the proposed method.

2. Methodology

2.1. Time-delay mutual information(TDMI)

The concept of mutual information is derived from Shannon entropy, which is a measurement of the uncertainty of a random variable proposed by Shannon (Shannon C E, 1948). For two-dimensional random variables X, Y, the independence between them can be measured using the formula as follows:

$$I(X,Y) = -\iint_{xy} p(x,y) \log \frac{p(x,y)}{p(x)p(y)} dydx \tag{1}$$

where $p(x, y)$ is the joint probability of variables X and Y. According to the formula, mutual information is symmetric. In order to establish causal relationships between two variables, TDMI can be applied by adding a time lag to the calculation:

$$I(X,Y,\tau) = -\iint_{xy} p(x+\tau,y) \log \frac{p(x+\tau,y)}{p(x+\tau)p(y)} dydx \tag{2}$$

where $p(x + \tau, y)$ is the joint probability distribution of $X = x + \tau$ and $Y = y$. The time lag parameter τ indicates the time delay when the value of mutual information reaches its peak. A positive τ indicates that the information is transferred from Y to X, which means X is affected by Y, while a negative τ indicates that Y is affected by X.

2.2. Estimation of probability density

The key point or difficulty of the calculation of TDMI lies in the estimation of joint probability. In this work, kernel density estimation model is applied to estimate the probability by considering each sample value of a variable (Silverman, 1986). A kernel function K is centered at every sample point and summed to give an estimation:

$$p(x) = \frac{1}{n} \sum_{i=1}^{n} K(x - x_i) \tag{3}$$

where $K(x)$ is the kernel function, Gaussian function is selected here as the kernel function:

$$K(x - x_i) = \frac{1}{\sqrt{2\pi}d} \exp(-\frac{(x - x_i)^2}{2d^2}) \tag{4}$$

where d is the bandwidth determined by the number of samples N and the standard deviation of the variable X. The estimation of joint probability density distribution can be constructed in a similar way.

2.3. Significant control limit and fault propagation path

According to the definition of mutual information, the value of mutual information has no upper bound. In order to identify the fault propagation path, it is significant to set up a confidence limit. When the system is under normal condition, each variable is in the vicinity of the set value range and can be regarded as independent of each other. The value of mutual information is at a small value other than 0 due to the presence of noise, and a threshold can be determined from the normal operating state. Once a fault occurs, the value of mutual information between two variables exceed this threshold, indicating that they have an interaction relationship, and the direction of the fault propagation path can be obtained from the time lag.

3. Application of the proposed methodology

In this chapter, the proposed methodology is applied to a continuous stirred tank heater (CSTH) simulation process and an ethylene cracking unit.

3.1. Continuous stirred tank heater (CSTH)

The CSTH is a common unit in the chemical process industry. It is built using the first principal models and the real disturbance data (Thornhill, et al., 2008). There are totally six variables as shown in Table 1. In the stirred tank, the cold water and the hot water are mixed together, and the mixture is heated by steam. Finally, the heated mixed water is discharged from the bottom of the heating tank.

Figure 1: The CSTH: control strategy 1   Figure 2: The CSTH: control strategy 2

There are two different control strategies. In Figure 1, the temperature is controlled by steam valve demand. And in Figure 2, the temperature is controlled by the hot water valve demand. Each condition contains 4,500 sample points with a sampling frequency of 1 second and a step fault on the steam flow valve occurs at 3,500th sample.

Table 1: Variables in the CSTH

Variables	Description	Variables	Description
CW	cold water valve demand	LEVEL	level of the tank
HW	hot water valve demand	STEAM	steam valve demand
OW	output water flow rate	TEMP	temperature

3.2. Ethylene cracking furnace

The process of naphtha steam cracking to produce ethylene plays an important role in chemical industry. In pyrolysis furnace, the mixture of naphtha and steam are preheated in convection section and crack in radiation section. The information of major variables is shown in Table 2. The application of the proposed TDMI based fault diagnosis methodology is demonstrated on this process.

Table 2: Variables in ethylene cracking furnace

Variables	Description	Variables	Description
F	Naphtha mass flow rate	P2	Crossover section pressure
COT	Coil outlet temperature	TA	Temperature in furnace A side
P1	Naphtha pressure	TB	Temperature in furnace B side
DS	Diluted steam mass flow rate	QL	Total fuel gas calorific value

3.3. Implement procedure

As mentioned above, the value of mutual information between some pairs of variables will fluctuate with the occurrence of the fault. The fault propagation path model is established based on this principle. As is shown in the figure 3, a PCA model and a significance threshold matrix of mutual information are first established with the historical data in steady state. Once a fault occurs, the value of mutual information between each pair of variables is calculated and compared with the threshold. If the value exceeds the threshold, the corresponding position of the matrix is taken as 1, otherwise 0. The final causal matrix is represented by a SDG and the root cause of the fault is obtained.

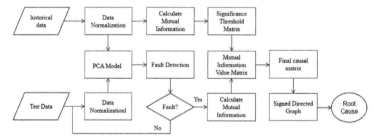

Figure 3: Fault detection and diagnosis procedure

4. Result and discussion

4.1. Results of the CSTH simulation process

For the first condition, the result of the fault detection is shown in Figure 4. It can be seen that the value of T^2 statistic exceeds the 99% control limit at 500th sample, indicating that a fault has been detected. The mutual information value between each pair of variables is shown with the significance thresholds in Table 3.

Variables	CW	OW	LEVEL	HW	TEMP	STEAM
CW		-0.147(0.318)	0.031(0.288)	0.043(0.280)	-0.049(0.252)	-0.193(0.277)
OW			-0.055(0.343)	-0.041(0.248)	-0.099(0.242)	-0.188(0.420)
LEVEL				-0.024(0.247)	0.023(0.366)	0.013(0.355)
HW					0.038(0.242)	-0.001(0.253)
TEMP						0.584(0.231)
STEAM						

Table 3: Mutual information value matrix

It can be seen from the Table 3 that only the mutual information value between the temperature and the steam flow exceeds the threshold. A SDG is depicted in Figure 5 and the time lag is 12 seconds, indicating that the direction of fault propagation is from the steam flow to the temperature. Therefore, it can be concluded that the root cause of the fault is the steam flow, which is verified by operation record.

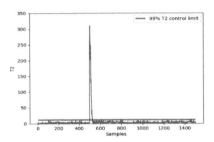

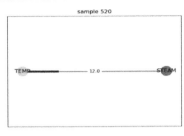

Figure 4: Fault detection result 1   Figure 5: Fault diagnosis result 1

For the second condition, in the similar way, the fault detection result is shown in Figure 4. The mutual information matrix and its threshold are shown in Table 4.

Table 4: Mutual information value matrix

Variables	CW	OW	LEVEL	HW	TEMP	STEAM
CW		-0.284(0.318)	0.302(0.288)	0.260(0.280)	-0.224(0.252)	0.233(0.277)
OW			0.134(0.343)	-0.145(0.248)	-0.136(0.242)	0.138(0.420)
LEVEL				0.302(0.247)	0.245(0.366)	0.195(0.355)
HW					0.329(0.242)	0.366(0.253)
TEMP						0.331(0.231)
STEAM						

According to the fault diagnosis result in Figure 7, it can also be concluded that the steam valve is the root cause of the fault. However, the fault propagation path is different due to the difference in control strategy. In this condition, when the temperature is fluctuated by the fault in the steam valve, the hot water valve is controlled to restore the temperature. Then the level is affected by the fluctuation of the hot water flow and the cold water valve is controlled to restore the level. It can be noted in this case that the interrelationships between variables vary when the same fault occurs under different control strategies.

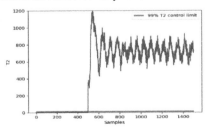

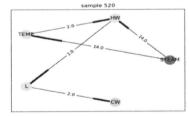

Figure 6: Fault detection result 2   Figure 7: Fault diagnosis result 2

4.2. Results of the ethylene cracking process

In this section, data for a complete production cycle in ethylene cracking process with one-minute interval is selected to test the applicability of the proposed method. As shown in Figure 8, the fault is detected since the 87489th sample. The mutual information between variables is then calculated. The result of part of the variables and the threshold obtained from steady state are shown in Table5, and the fault diagnosis result is shown in Figure 9.

Table 5: Mutual information value matrix

Variables	F	DS	COT	TA	TB	QL
F		-0.103(0.153)	-0.033(0.154)	0.031(0.122)	0.096(0.165)	0.046(0.160)
DS			-0.046(0.192)	-0.051(0.151)	0.050(0.203)	-0.023(0.152)
COT				0.186(0.315)	0.409(0.309)	1.035(0.258)
TA					-0.178(0.327)	-0.173(0.324)
TB						0.506(0.244)
QL						

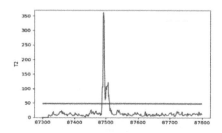
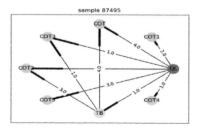

Figure 8: Fault detection result   Figure 9: Fault diagnosis result

The result indicates that temperature in furnace B side rises due to high total fuel gas calorific value. And the high total COT and COT in whole coil 6 caused by high temperature in furnace B side lead to the alarm. Therefore, the root cause of this fault is the fluctuation of fuel gas feed flow. As shown above, with comparing the TDMI value with the threshold, the fault propagation path and the root cause of the fault is recognized.

5. Conclusions

In this work, the interaction between variables is correctly identified by TDMI analysis. By the proposed method, the fault diagnosis in both a simulated CSTH under different control strategies and an ethylene cracking unit has been implemented. Not only the root cause of the fault can be isolated, but also the fault propagation path can be identified, which is consistent with process operation record. The method provides a brand new way to obtain the causal relation between variables for fault propagation path identification solely based on the historical data, which makes the online fault diagnosis more feasible.

References

P. M. Frank, 1990, Fault diagnosis in dynamic systems using analytical and knowledge-based redundancy: A survey and some new results, Automatica, 26(3), 459-474.

P. Miller, R. Swanson and C. Heckler, 1998, Contribution Plots: A missing link in multivariate quality control, Appl. Math. and Comp. Sci., 4(8), 775-792.

H. Vedam, V.Venkatasubramanian, 1999, PCA-SDG based process monitoring and fault diagnosis, Control engineering practice, 7(7), 903-917.

S. Li, Y. Xiao, D. Zhou, D. Cai, 2018, Causal inference in nonlinear systems: Granger causality versus time-delayed mutual information, Physical Review E, 97(5).

C. E. Shannon, 1948, A mathematical theory of communication, Bell Labs Technical Journal, 27(4):379-423.

B. W. Silverman, 1986, Density estimation for statistics and data analysis, London, U.K.: Chapman & Hall.

N. F. Thornhill , S. C. Patwardhan and S. L. Shah, 2008, A continuous stirred tank heater simulation model with applications, Journal of Process Control, 18(3-4):347-360.

Sauro Pierucci, Flavio Manenti, Giulia Bozzano, Davide Manca (Eds.)
Proceedings of the 30th European Symposium on Computer Aided Process Engineering
(ESCAPE30), May 24-27, 2020, Milano, Italy. © 2020 Elsevier B.V. All rights reserved.
http://dx.doi.org/10.1016/B978-0-12-823377-1.50196-8

Dynamic Optimization of an Emulsion Polymerization Process Using an Embedded Monte Carlo Model for Bimodal MWD

Johannes M. M. Faust, Lars Henrichfreise, Adel Mhamdi, Alexander Mitsos*

AVT Process Systems Engineering, RWTH Aachen University, 52056 Aachen, Germany
amitsos@alum.mit.edu

Abstract

The molecular weight distribution (MWD) of polymers affects many end-use properties and is therefore a major production target. The desired MWD can also be multi-modal, which can be achieved by using chain-transfer agents. As these products are specialty chemicals, they are most often produced in semi-batch operation leading to inherent non-linear dynamics. By using dynamic optimization, production time can be reduced while producing the targeted quality. In this work, we consider the model-based dynamic optimization of an emulsion polymerization process to achieve a bimodal MWD while reducing the batch time. The degrees of freedom consist of the isothermal reactor temperature, feed rates of monomer, initiator and chain-transfer agent. We use a combined model consisting of a deterministic kinetic model and a stochastic Monte Carlo polymer architecture model. The kinetic model describes macroscopic variables, such as concentrations. Distinct chains are simulated in a polymer particle using the Monte Carlo model, and many particles are computed in parallel. The time-varying reaction rates used in the Monte Carlo model are computed in the kinetic model. By taking all simulated chains and their respective weights, the MWD can be constructed. A Monte Carlo approach is chosen as it allows to simulate properly the transfer to polymer and branching reactions. To solve the dynamic optimization problem, we select a derivative-free surrogate model based optimizer due to the stochastic nature of the Monte Carlo model. For the Monte Carlo model, gradients are not readily available. The results show a reduction of the batch time between 6.2 and 7.5 % compared to the base recipe while the product quality is satisfied.

Keywords: Dynamic Optimization, molecular weight distribution, derivative-free optimization, Monte Carlo simulation

1. Introduction

Polymers produced via emulsion polymerization have various applications such as paints, adhesives or drug delivery. For each use case, the polymer product should have usually different properties like viscosity, stickiness, etc. An important quality attribute of polymers is the molecular weight distribution (MWD), which can be narrow or broad, unimodal or bimodal. Due to strong competition among manufactures, optimal process operations can save cost and therefore protect operating margins. Especially polymer products are affected heavily by process operations, as they are known to be products-by-process (Asua, 2007). Therefore, optimal process operations must both increase the economic benefit and achieve the same customer demanded quality. Several authors have addressed the problem of optimal control of polymerization processes. Sayer et al. (2001) use iterative dynamic programming to optimize the operations of a semicontinuous emulsion process with fixed batch time to reach a desired MWD in-silico. The MWD is computed via an adaptive collocation technique. Vicente et al. (2001) decompose the MWD into instantaneous MWD distributions over the global conversion, which is possible as only linear polymer chains are considered. They optimize the total process time. Vicente et al. (2002) also use iterative dynamic programming to achieve a desired composition and MWD, which is modeled by adaptive orthogonal collocation. They test the computed optimal feed rates in a lab scale reactor and achieve MWDs fairly close to the desired ones. Saliakas et al. (2007) optimize for minimal batch time and the deviation to the desired MWD is added as quadratic penalty to the objective function. Two models describing the MWD of the homopolymerization are compared, one model with fixed pivots and one using orthogonal collocation on finite elements. Pontes et al. (2011) model the MWD with orthogonal collocation for a continuous steady state operation and optimize operations for an economic objective function, consisting of the cost of raw materials and sale price of product.

All the works mentioned so far use deterministic models to describe the MWD. Despite the vast use of Monte Carlo models for polymerization systems, there is little work on the optimization with such models embedded. Gao et al. (2018) compare three derivative-free optimizers in case studies with a kinetic Monte Carlo process embedded. A free-radical polymerization is modeled which allows to describe microstructural aspects of the copolymer such as the dyad fractions. Ma et al. (2018) employ a steady-state Monte Carlo simulation in a derivative-free optimization environment. The chemical composition distribution is used as a micro-structural quality attribute. Overall the optimization problem consists of seven degrees of freedom. Mohammadi et al. (2018) use the outputs of a Monte Carlo model to train an artificial neuronal network which is optimized using a genetic algorithm to find optimum reaction conditions consisting of the monomer ratio, catalyst composition and chain shutting agent concentration.

In this contribution, a typical industrial setting is considered, where a given recipe should be optimized. The desired MWD is known from a reference batch. Using this recipe as starting point, an optimal process operation scheme is computed achieving the same MWD as quality while reducing the batch time. The contribution is structured as follows. In Section 2, the model and its extensions are briefly described. The dynamic optimization problem is formulated in Section 3 and its solution approach is presented. A case study with a bimodal MWD is dealt with in Section 4 and the contribution is summarized and conclusions are drawn in Section 5.

2. Model description and model extensions

The considered copolymerization is modeled by a hybrid model consisting of a deterministic kinetic model and Monte Carlo model describing the polymer chains described by Chaloupka et al. (2017) and shortly introduced here. The macroscopic variables, like concentrations, are solved using a deterministic kinetic model of the emulsion polymerization. Then, the computed trajectories of reaction rates are used in the Monte Carlo simulation, where each single particle is computed and individual chains are simulated. The Monte Carlo simulation is sped up by considering the propagation reaction separately. The models are implemented in Matlab. As it is assumed that the polymer particles do not influence each other, they can be computed easily in parallel. For this contribution, this model is extended by chain-transfer agent (CTA) and its related reactions. Therefore, bimodal distributions can be simulated and optimized. Chain transfer agents increase the chain transfer reaction rate and lead in general to shorter chains. For a bimodal distribution, the CTA is added in a later stage to produce shorter chains while the long chains have already been generated. The new chain transfer reaction is added to the overall scheme:

$$M_n^\bullet + R - X \rightarrow M_n - X + R^\bullet, \tag{1}$$

where Mn, R-X, the superscript $^\bullet$ define a polymer chain with n monomeric units, the chain transfer agent and a radical, respectively. The parameters for the CTA kinetics are chosen from literature. An isothermal operation is assumed.

In the overall simulation scheme, the kinetic part cannot be parallelized in the same fashion as the Monte Carlo part. However, for different inputs, different ODE integrators compute the solution faster. Matlab offers six different integrators, each with different advantages and disadvantages. There is no additional cost to integrate the kinetic model with all available integrators in parallel and the simulations are stopped after the first result is available. All integrators use the same integration tolerances and the same model. Compared to (Faust et al., 2019), a new binning strategy for the computed chains is applied which increases the exactness of the MWD calculation. Here, the computed polymer chains from all particles are taken and binned into the MWD. Therefore, the computation accuracy increases.

3. Dynamic optimization problem formulation and solution approach

The goal of the dynamic optimization is to find an operating scheme that minimizes the batch time while producing the desired MWD, which is given by the base recipe operation (2). In Faust et al. (2019) the reactor temperature, batch time, monomer and initiator feed are optimized. Here, the CTA feed is added to the degrees of freedom.

$$\min_{\dot{m}_M(t),\dot{m}_I(t),\dot{m}_{CTA}(t),T_R,t_f} t_f \tag{2a}$$

$$\text{s.t. kinetic ODE model} \tag{2b}$$

$$\text{stochastic MWD model} \tag{2c}$$

$$\int_{t_0}^{t_f} \dot{m}(t)_M dt = m_M^{total} \tag{2d}$$

$$T_R^{min} \leq T_R \leq T_R^{max} \tag{2e}$$

$$\epsilon_{MWD}^{max} \geq \sum_{k=1}^{N_k} (MWD(k) - MWD^{ref}(k))^2 \tag{2f}$$

$$X^{ref} \leq X(t_f) \tag{2g}$$

where $\dot{m}_M(t), \dot{m}_I(t), \dot{m}_{CTA}(t), T_R, t_f$ refer to the monomer feed rate, initiator feed rate, CTA feed rate, reactor temperature and total time, respectively. ϵ_{MWD}^{max} denotes the absolute squared deviation to the reference MWD and is constrained in (2f). Constraint (2g) refers to the minimum conversion at the end of the batch.

In this work, the open source solver MaTSumoTo, developed by Müller et al. (2013), is used. A thin-plate spline with a polynomial tail is used as surrogate function. Matlab's fmincon is used as local optimizer of the surrogate function. Two new sample points are generated for each version of the surrogate function. If these two sample points are close to each other or close to already evaluated inputs, the search space is explored by maximizing the distance the evaluated points. As we optimize the surrogate with a local gradient-based optimizer, we can add constraints if we know the underlying function in terms of the degrees of freedom. Of course, the reformulation using penalties would not be necessary, if we have a functional expression of all constraints using the degrees of freedom. One could argue that at least the conversion constraint (2g) could be added as nonlinear constraint as it depends only on the evaluation of the ODE system. However, this would slow down the optimization of the surrogate with such an embedded ODE problem. Therefore, only the ratio feeds are used as linear inequality constraints (3b) to the optimization problem to be solved:

$$\min_{\substack{x_j^M, x_j^I, \hat{m}_I^{total}, x_j^{CTA}, \hat{m}_{CTA}^{total}, \hat{T}_R, \hat{t}_f \\ j \in [2, \dots, N]}} \sum_{k=1}^{N_k} (MWD(k) - MWD^{ref}(k))^2 + w_{time}t_f^2 + w_{conv}(\min(0, X(t_f) - X^{ref}))^2 \quad (3a)$$

$$\text{s.t.} \sum_{j=2}^{N} x_j^p \leq 1 \quad \forall p \in \{M, I, CTA\} \quad (3b)$$

4. Case study with bimodal target MWD

In this case study, a given reference batch recipe is optimized for batch time while achieving the same quality measures, such as the molecular weight distribution and the overall monomer conversion at the end of the batch. The desired bimodal molecular weight distribution is a result of the use of CTA.

The reference process operation takes 12600 seconds. The monomers are fed for the first 9000 seconds, and the CTA is fed from that time point on for one hour. The initiator feed is stopped after 7200 seconds. The problem is discretized using seven piecewise constant control profiles for each controlled feed rate. No CTA is fed during the first two control intervals, as it is known that the CTA will shorten the chains and the long chains will not be generated. Together with the reactor temperature and the total batch time, the problem consists of 20 degrees of freedom for optimization. The number of function evaluations is limited to 1000. In Table 1, an overview of the numerical results is given, both for the reference case and three optimization runs. As the model is stochastic and the optimization of the surrogate is started from random points, the optimization is started three times to check the consistency of the result. In total, 100 particles are simulated in parallel with the Monte Carlo model.

Compared to the reference, the batch time is reduced between 6.2 and 7.4% for the three runs by the optimization. The trajectories for different key states and inputs are shown in Figure 1. The reactor temperature is more or less unchanged compared to the reference, which is an indication that the quality is affected strongly by the reactor temperature. The reactor temperature difference between the runs is less than 0.2 K. In a pure batch time minimization with an inequality constraint on the overall conversion only, it is expected that the reactor is operated at the maximum allowed temperature. The overall conversions for the three runs differ in the first interval, but are relatively similar from that point on. The monomer feed for the optimized cases is higher than in the reference case leading to a faster reaction rate. Qualitatively, the optimized CTA feed very similar to the reference, only the total amount is increased.

Table 1 Numeric values of reference and optimization runs

	Conversion[-]	Time[s]	Objective value	Time saving[%]
Reference	0.984	12600	1.68	-
Run 1	0.983	11777	1.47	6.5
Run 2	0.983	11815	1.47	6.2
Run 3	0.982	11662	1.47	7.4

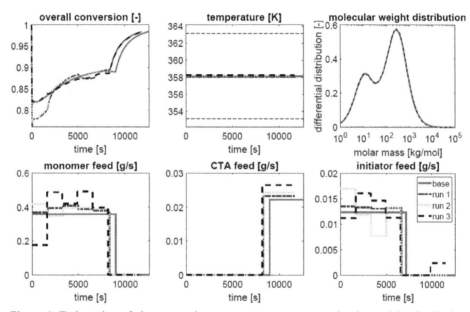

Figure 1 Trajectories of the conversion, reactor temperature, molecular weight distribution, monomer, initiator and chain transfer agent feed for the reference case and the three optimization runs.

The initiator in the base recipe is stopped after 57% of the batch time. This behavior is still observed for the best solutions found, while the total initiator amount is larger.

5. Summary and Conclusion

We presented an approach to optimize the process operation of a semi-batch reactor while achieving desired product specifications. The molecular weight distribution defines the product quality and is bimodal due to the use of chain transfer agent being added during the end of the batch. As the underlying model has embedded Monte Carlo simulations, a gradient-free optimization solver is used. A surrogate model is built from objective function evaluations, which consists of the objective and penalty terms for the nonlinear constraints where no algebraic function of degrees of freedom is known. Using random starting points, the surrogate model is optimized locally to generate new sample points and which are used to update the surrogate function. For the case study considered, the batch time is reduced between 6.2 and 7.2 % while achieving the same polymer properties. The optimization problem formulation is flexible and does allow for integrated product and process development. It can be tested whether for a given new molecular weight distribution, a process producing this quality can be found.

Acknowledgement

The financial support of the RECOBA project (funding from European Framework Horizon 2020, No. 636820) and the support of the KoPPonA 2.0 project of the German Federal Ministry for Economic Affairs and Energy (BMWi) under grant number 03EN2004L and the project supervision by the project management organization Projektträger Jülich (PtJ) is gratefully acknowledged.

References

Asua, J. M., 2007. Polymer Reaction Engineering. Blackwell Pub, Oxford, UK and Ames, Iowa, USA.

Chaloupka, T., Zubov, A., Kosek, J., 2017. Real-time hybrid monte carlo method for modelling of 4 monomer semi-batch emulsion copolymerization. In: 27th European Symposium on Computer Aided Process Engineering. Vol. 40 of Computer Aided Chemical Engineering. Elsevier, pp. 259–264.

Faust, J. M. M., Chaloupka, T., Kosek, J., Mhamdi, A., Mitsos, A., 2019. Dynamic optimization of an emulsion copolymerization process for product quality using a deterministic kinetic model with embedded monte carlo simulations. Computers & Chemical Engineering 130, 106566.

Gao, H., Waechter, A., Konstantinov, I. A., Arturo, S. G., Broadbelt, L. J., 2018. Application and comparison of derivative-free optimization algorithms to control and optimize free radical polymerization simulated using the kinetic Monte Carlo method. Computers & Chemical Engineering 108, 268–275.

Ma, Y., Chen, X., Biegler, L. T., 2018. Monte-Carlo-simulation-based optimization for copolymerization processes with embedded chemical composition distribution. Computers & Chemical Engineering 109, 261–275.

Müller, J., Shoemaker, C. A., Piché, R., 2013. SO-MI: A surrogate model algorithm for computationally expensive nonlinear mixed-integer black-box global optimization problems. Computers & Operations Research 40 (5), 1383–1400.

Mohammadi, Y., Saeb, M. R., Penlidis, A., Jabbari, E., Zinck, P., Stadler, F. J., Matyjaszewski, K., 2018. Intelligent Monte Carlo: A new paradigm for inverse polymerization engineering. Macromolecular Theory and Simulations 6, 1700106.

Pontes, K. V., Embiruçu, M., Maciel, R., Hartwich, A., Marquardt, W., 2011. Optimal process operation for the production of linear polyethylene resins with tailored molecular weight distribution. AIChE Journal 57 (8), 2149–2163.

Saliakas, V., Chatzidoukas, C., Krallis, A., Meimaroglou, D., Kiparissides, C., 2007. Dynamic optimization of molecular weight distribution using orthogonal collocation on finite elements and fixed pivot methods: An experimental and theoretical investigation. Macromolecular Reaction Engineering 1 (1), 119–136.

Sayer, C., Arzamendi, G., Asua, J., Lima, E., Pinto, J., 2001. Dynamic optimization of semicontinuous emulsion copolymerization reactions: composition and molecular weight distribution. Computers & Chemical Engineering 25 (4-6), 839–849.

Vicente, M., Leiza, J. R., Asua, J. M., 2001. Simultaneous control of copolymer composition and MWD in emulsion copolymerization. AIChE Journal 47 (7), 1594–1606.

Vicente, M., Sayer, C., Leiza, J. R., Arzamendi, G., Lima, E., Pinto, J., Asua, J. M., 2002. Dynamic optimiza- tion of non-linear emulsion copolymerization systems Open-loop control of composition and molecular weight distribution. Chemical Engineering Journal 85 (2-3), 339–349.

Sauro Pierucci, Flavio Manenti, Giulia Bozzano, Davide Manca (Eds.)
Proceedings of the 30th European Symposium on Computer Aided Process Engineering
(ESCAPE30), May 24-27, 2020, Milano, Italy. © 2020 Elsevier B.V. All rights reserved.
http://dx.doi.org/10.1016/B978-0-12-823377-1.50197-X

A Hybrid Model Predictive Control Strategy using Neural Network Based Soft Sensors for Particle Processes

Rasmus Fjordbak Nielsen, Krist V. Gernaey, Seyed Soheil Mansouri*

Process and Systems Engineering Centre, Department of Chemical and Biochemical Engineering, Technical University of Denmark, Kongens Lyngby, 2800, Denmark
seso@kt.dtu.dk

Abstract

Particle processes, such as crystallization, flocculation and emulsification constitute a large fraction of the industrial processes for removal of insolubles, product isolation, purification and polishing. The outcome of these processes typically needs to comply with a given set of quality attributes related to particle size, shape and/or yield. With recent technological advances in commercially available on-line/at-line particle analysis sensors, it is now possible to directly measure the particle attributes in real-time. This allows for developing new direct control strategies. In this work, a model predictive control (MPC) strategy is presented based on a hybrid machine-learning assisted particle model. The hybrid model uses mechanistic models for mass and population balances and machine learning for predicting the process kinetics. In the presented approach, the hybrid model is trained in real-time, during process operation. Combined with MPC, this allows for continuous refinement of the process model. Thereby, the calculated control actions are provided robustly. This approach can be employed with limited prior process knowledge, and allows for directly specifying the target product properties to the controller. The presented control strategy is demonstrated on a theoretical case of crystallization to show the potential of the presented methodology.

Keywords: Hybrid model, Machine learning, Soft-sensor, On-line particle analysis, Model predictive control (MPC)

1. Introduction

Particle processes, including crystallization, fermentation and flocculation play an important role in many chemical and biochemical industries. However, due to their complexity, these processes also pose a number of challenges when it comes to monitoring and process control. The outputs of many of these processes are required to comply with a number of quality attributes related to particle size, shape and/or yield. However, due to a historical lack of on-line sensor data on these attributes, the processes have historically been controlled using heuristics and based on indirect process variables. At the same time, the kinetics behind these processes are highly non-linear and multivariable, which results in process variations in industry, and in the end also significant product losses.

In the last two decades, a number of on-line and at-line particle analysis sensors have become commercially available, opening up for the development of new control strategies for particle processes. This includes flow-cell system based dynamic particle analysis (QicPic, ParticleTech), in-line dynamic particle analysis (PVM from Mettler Toledo) and laser based techniques such as Focused Beam Reflectance Measurement (FBRM). Especially FBRM has been examined in new control strategies, especially within control of crystallization processes. FBRM allows for obtaining a relative count of particles in a given liquid suspension, and a chord-length size distribution. The chord-length size distribution gives an estimate of the mean particle size distribution, along one axis, and thus not a direct measure of the particle dimensions.

Both model-based and model-free control approaches have been suggested using these new monitoring tools (Nagy et al. (2013)). Amongst the model-free control approaches, direct nucleation control (DNC) has shown acceptable results for several crystallization cases, using only little prior process knowledge, by controlling the FBRM count of crystals to a given set-point. However, this approach only gives an indirect control over the particle size properties, as it is the count that is controlled. Model-based control approaches have also been suggested, where the process kinetics have been assumed to follow a number of mathematically simple kinetic expressions, where a number of parameters are estimated based on experimental data. Eren et al. (2019) have also shown how these approaches can be combined.

Nielsen et al. (2019a, 2019b) have suggested a systematic hybrid modelling framework that uses a machine learning assisted approach for estimating the process kinetics instead of using fixed kinetic expressions. The remaining part of the model, including mass and population balances are retained, ensuring physical constraints not to be violated. This allows for increased flexibility towards capturing complex dynamics and relations between measured process variables, which have an impact on the process kinetics.

In the present work, a model based control strategy is presented, using a hybrid model suggested by Nielsen et al. (2019a). It is shown how the hybrid model can be trained continuously during process operation, and thus incorporating the latest obtained process sensor data. The real-time updated process model is used in parallel for calculating the optimal control, by solving a shrinking horizon model predictive control problem. By combining the continuous training and model predictive control, the hybrid model will continuously be refined, thus also refining the process control.

2. Hybrid model

The hybrid model used in this work is created based on the hybrid model framework by Nielsen et al. (2019a), consisting of a machine learning model f, in this work, a deep feed-forward neural network, and a mechanistic population balance model g, as illustrated in Figure 1. The hybrid model is flexible towards incorporating multiple process sensors, physical or soft, that may have an impact on the process kinetics. Here, $\bar{x}$, is the measured process variable(s), $\bar{z}$, is the controlled process variable(s) and N is particle population discretized by one or more particle properties. The output of the machine learning model is one or more kinetic rates, related to general particle phenomena. This includes nucleation rate, α, bin-specific growth, β, bin-specific shrinkage, γ, bin-specific agglomeration, ε, and bin-specific breakage κ, and the corresponding daughter particle distribution, θ.

The machine learning model is trained indirectly using time-series measurement pairs of particle size distributions from two time-stamps, N_0 and $N(t+\Delta t)$. By implementing the hybrid model in a math library that allows for rapid calculation of derivatives, using methods such as Automatic Differentiation (AD), one can train the model in real-time and continuously update the machine learning weights to the latest measurements.

Note here that case specific models needs to be specified for the measured variables, $\bar{x}$, to allow for long-term predictions of the particle properties. These are specified based on prior process knowledge, or simply set to be constant.

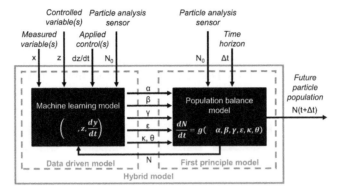

Figure 1: Hybrid model structure

Nielsen et al. (2019a) have previously successfully applied this hybrid modelling framework on two experimental cases of crystallization, including lab-scale food crystallization and industrial scale pharmaceutical crystallization.

3. Model predictive control

In this work, a model predictive control (MPC) is applied to the hybrid model structure presented in the previous section. As many of the mentioned particle processes are carried out in batch operation in industry, it is intended to demonstrate the application using a shrinking horizon MPC. For every new measurement of the particle distribution N, the following optimization problem is solved:

$$\min_{d\bar{z}/dt} \sum_{i=1}^{M} \omega_i \cdot (p_i(N^{end}) - r_i) \tag{1}$$

Here, M is the number of controlled particle properties, denoted p, that are either directly related to the predicted particle distribution N, or any derivative thereof. r_i is here the corresponding controller set point. Each of the controlled variables is furthermore weighted by a factor $\bar{\omega}$, reflecting the relative importance of the controlled variables.

The hybrid model is used to predict the final particle distribution, N^{end}, given the calculated control slopes, $d\bar{z}/dt$. The hybrid model is solved, $\Delta t = t^{batch} - t^{current}$, into the future where t^{batch} is the batch duration. Note that the presented approach requires a fixed batch duration wherein that target particle properties should be obtained.

A differential evolution algorithm (DE/rand/1/bin), implemented in the Tensorflow framework (Abadi et al. (2015)), is used in this work to solve the MPC optimization problem. The reason for using a differential evolution algorithm is to reduce the risk of converging to local minima. This carries a risk when using heavily parametric machine learning models.

As the case for any MPC, the computational time for solving the MPC optimization problem should be less than the sampling rate. The kinetics for many of the particle processes mentioned previously are relatively slow and only require sampling rates of approximately 0.5 min^{-1} – 0.2 min^{-1}. The choice of particle analysis sensor may limit this sampling rate.

4. Parallel training and MPC

A continuous learning approach is suggested (see Figure 2) to run together with the model predictive control algorithm. This allows for the MPC not only to use the current process measurements, but also to use the data to refine the process model and to refine the future calculated process control actions. Due to the computational time of both model training and solving the MPC problem, it is suggested to run these processes in parallel. The number of training iterations (epochs) is fixed to 2 per cycle.

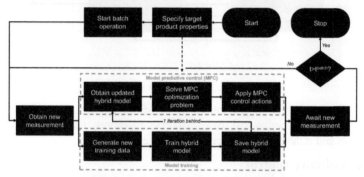

Figure 2: Parallelized model training and model predictive control

Note that the MPC optimization problem will be using the hybrid model from the last training iteration to reduce the time from current state to calculated MPC control actions. This structure allows distributed computing in cases where the hybrid model may be computationally expensive to evaluate and train concurrently.

5. Application example

The continuous learning and model predictive control strategy is demonstrated through a theoretical crystallization case. This is to showcase the feasibility of the presented approach. The given example is a temperature-controlled crystallization of α-lactose. An in-silico crystallizer is utilized, which is based on the crystallization model by Wong et al. (2012). An overview of the in-silico experimental setup can be seen in Figure 3.

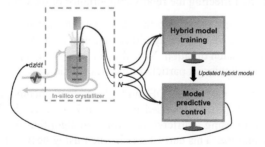

Figure 3: In-silico experimental setup for demonstrating the feasibility of the suggested control strategy

The in-silico crystallizer constitutes a real crystallizer, where a number of sensors are fitted. This includes a temperature sensor, solute concentration sensor and a particle analysis sensor (emulating image analysis of 1 μL sample). To make this feasibility study as realistic as possible, Gaussian noise is added to the sensor readings corresponding to realistic measurement uncertainties of these sensors. Furthermore, the maximum sampling rate is set to 0.2 min^{-1}, corresponding to a measurement every 5 minutes.

In the hybrid model, the evolution in temperature is modelled assuming ideal temperature control, and the concentration of the solute is modelled using a simple mass balance, knowing the approximate density of lactose crystals ρ and given a bin characteristic size L_i, as shown in Equation (2).

$$\frac{dC}{dt} = \rho \cdot \sum_{i=1}^{m} \frac{dN_i}{dt} \cdot L_i^3 \qquad (2)$$

The control performance is now examined for two controlled variables; final temperature (1) and the mean crystal size (2).

The batch duration is here fixed to be 2.5 hours. The initial batch conditions are the same for each batch, but with random uniformly distributed disturbances in both seed mass and mean seed size, to illustrate the controller performance. Furthermore, the hybrid model is initialized without any prior training, which means that the first control iterations are expected to be erroneous.

To evaluate on the presented control strategy, the case is compared to a simple benchmark control with a linear cooling profile. The details of initial conditions, disturbances, control targets and objective function weights can be found in Table 1 and Table 2, respectively. Note that the target mean particle size of 41 μm corresponds to the final particle size of the benchmark control without any process disturbances.

Table 1: Initial conditions and disturbances for feasibility study

T_0 [°C]	C_0 [g/mL]	Seed mass fraction [%]	Seed mean size [μm]	Disturbance seed mass fraction [%]	Disturbance seed mean size [μm]
50	0.337	0.5	10	[-0.2; 0.2]	[-5; 5]

Table 2: Control targets and objective function weights

Final temperature control		Final mean particle size control	
ω_1 [°C^{-1}]	r_1 [°C]	ω_2 [μm^{-1}]	r_2 [μm]
1/10	10	10/41	41

The controller performance over 10 batch operations is presented in Figure 4 on the following page, where the hybrid model is initialized from the first batch without any prior training. The employed MPC achieves stable control of the final temperature within +/- 0.01 °C for all batches. For the final mean particle size, the MPC performs equally good compared to the reference control in the first two batches. After this, it can be seen that the hybrid model has been trained to an extent that results in the MPC outperform the reference control. This is especially evident in batch 9.

One should be aware that overfitting of the hybrid model may occur after a number of batches. Thus, the model prediction accuracy will decrease, which has a negative effect on the model predictive control performance. Steps to mitigate this must be taken to stabilize the presented approach. This is subject to future investigations.

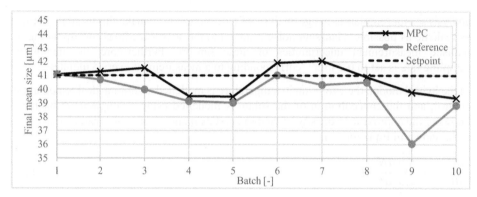

Figure 4: Controller performance of MPC vs reference control

6. Conclusions

A new hybrid model based control strategy has been presented, that allows for direct specification of the ideal particle product properties, by measuring the particle properties on-line. The approach is flexible towards use of multiple process sensors, and requires little prior process knowledge. The control strategy has been illustrated on a theoretical food crystallization. The case study shows that it is possible to obtain an accurate control with only little process data. However, overfitting of the hybrid model must actively be mitigated to obtain a more stable training and control approach.

Acknowledgments

This work partly received financial support from the Greater Copenhagen Food Innovation project (CPH-Food), Novozymes, from EU's regional fund (BIOPRO-SMV project) and from Innovation Fund Denmark through the BIOPRO2 strategic research center (Grant number 4105-00020B).

References

R. F. Nielsen, K. V. Gernaey, S. S. Mansouri, 2019a. Hybrid machine learning assisted modelling framework for particle processes, submitted to Computers & Chemical Engineering.

R. F. Nielsen, N. K. Arjomand, L. C. Freiesleben, K. V. Gernaey, S. S. Mansouri, 2019b. Novel strategies for predictive particle monitoring and control using advanced image analysis, Computer Aided Chemical Engineering, 46, 1435-1440.

Z. K. Nagy, G. Fevotte, H. Kramer, L. L. Simon, 2013. Recent advances in the monitoring, modelling and control of crystallization systems, Chemical Engineering Research and Design Volume, 91, 1903-1922.

A. Eren, B. Szilágyi, J. Quon, M. Furuta, C. Papageorgiou, Z. Nagy. 2019, Development of a Model-Based Quality-by-Control Framework for Crystallization Design, Computer Aided Chemical Engineering, 46, 319-324.

M. Abadi, A. Agarwal, P. Barham, E. Brevdo, Z. Chen, C. Citro, G. Corrado, A. Davis, J. Dean, M. Devin, S. Ghemawat, I. Goodfellow, A. Harp, G. Irving, M. Isard, R. Jozefowicz, Y. Jia, L. Kaiser, M. Kudlur, J. Levenberg, D. Mané, M. Schuster, R. Monga, S. Moore, D. Murray, C. Olah, J. Shlens, B. Steiner, I. Sutskever, K. Talwar, P. Tucker, V. Vanhoucke, V. Vasudevan, F. Viégas, O. Vinyals, P. Warden, M. Wattenberg, M. Wicke, Y. Yu, X. Zheng. TensorFlow: Large-scale machine learning on heterogeneous systems, 2015. Software available from tensorflow.org.

S. Wong, R. Bund, R. Connelly, R. Hartel. 2012. Designing a lactose crystallization process based on dynamic metastable limit. Crystallization Growth Design, 111, 642–654.

Sauro Pierucci, Flavio Manenti, Giulia Bozzano, Davide Manca (Eds.)
Proceedings of the 30th European Symposium on Computer Aided Process Engineering
(ESCAPE30), May 24-27, 2020, Milano, Italy. © 2020 Elsevier B.V. All rights reserved.
http://dx.doi.org/10.1016/B978-0-12-823377-1.50198-1

Water Distribution Network Optimization Considering Uncertainties in the Nodes Demands

R. Salcedo-Díaz[a*], R. Ruiz-Femenia[a], J. A. Caballero[a], M. A. S. S. Ravagnani[a,b]

[a]*Chemical Process Engineering Institute, University of Alicante, Spain*
[b]*Chemical Engineering Department, State University of Maringá, Brazil*
raquel.salcedo@ua.es

Abstract

The design of Water Distribution Networks (WDN) can be formulated as an optimization problem for the minimization of the total network cost, which depends on the pipe diameters and the pumping power required. The variability in water demand at nodes can be modelled as a set of finite scenarios generated from a multivariate normal distribution assuming correlations between the selected pair nodes of the network. A disjunctive stochastic Mixed Integer Nonlinear Programming (MINLP) model is proposed for the optimal synthesis of WDN considering correlated uncertainties in nodal demands. Strategies for avoiding nonconvex nonlinearities in the equations are applied to avoid unnecessary complexities. We analyse the effect of different correlation matrices to gather insight into how the model faces uncertainty. A case study was used to test the model and the optimization techniques proposed. Results show that under uncertainty the stochastic solution of the WDN improves the deterministic one (i.e. the design obtained for nominal values of nodes demand), evincing that neglecting uncertainty in the optimization process may lead to suboptimal or, even worse, infeasible design of WDNs.

Keywords: Water distribution networks, nodes demand uncertainty, stochastic optimization.

1. Introduction

Water Distribution Networks (WDN) are important systems in urban centers and in industrial facilities. The design of WDN can be formulated as an optimization problem, involving, generally, the minimization of the total network cost, which depends on the pipe diameters and flow directions known a priori (Caballero & Ravagnani, 2019).

In some WDN, there exist variations in the nodal water demands, which could exert a huge influence on the optimal network. In such cases, it is reasonable to account for such uncertainty in the design phase of the WDN. Following this approach, it is guaranteed that the WDN designed under uncertainty is able to cope once the unknow water nodal demands are unveiled, otherwise a design of the WDN assuming nominal values could offer an economically inadequate behaviour. The design under uncertainty one of the key area of Process Systems Engineering, and consequently has been applied to different cases studies (Carrero-Parreño et al., 2019; Ruiz-Femenia et al., 2013). Some authors have considered nodal water demand uncertainty (uncorrelated) in the WDN design, and have used genetic algorithms to find the optimal solution (Branisavljević et al., 2009). Other approach is to handle uncertainty (uncorrelated) through fuzzy logic (Geranmehr et al., 2019). Furthermore, the variability of the water demand (and head) has been represented using log-normal probability distribution uncorrelated functions (Marquez Calvo et al., 2018), but to best our knowledge water demand uncertainty implemented by a set of correlated scenarios with desired marginal distributions for each uncertain parameter has not been considered in WDN optimization (for an exhaustive list of works in WDN optimization see Mala-Jetmarova et al, 2018).

2. Problem statement

In this work we consider the design of a generic WDN that includes a set of water demand nodes with a set of pipes connecting them (i.e. edges) with fixed flow directions. Given are a set of nodes, described by their elevation and by the expected values and variance of the water flow demand; a set of pipes characterized by their initial and final nodes, their length and whose diameters must be assigned from a set of commercial diameters (with its corresponding price per unit of length); minimum and maximum velocities allowable; and a set of pumps than can provide head at each pipe.

The goal is to determine the configuration of the WDN that minimizes the Total Annualized Cost (TAC) under nodal water demand uncertainty, which is modeled by random variables with the special feature of being correlated. Decisions to be made are of two types: structural and operational. The former includes the diameter and capital cost of each selected pipe, whereas the operational decisions are effective pressure (i.e. total pressure at each node), the velocity, volumetric flow rate and pressure drop at each pipe, and the pump head and its operational cost for each pump.

3. Representation of the uncertainty

We model the water demand uncertainty by a set of correlated scenarios, generated by Monte Carlo sampling and with the key feature that each random variable follows the desired marginal distribution (we assume lognormal distribution for the water demand at each node). To enable this flexibility in the scenario modelling, we implement a two-step transformation algorithm (Reyes-Labarta et al., 2014). Given are the expected value and the variance for each nodal water demand, and the correlation matrix. These three inputs define the covariance matrix, whose diagonal elements contain the variances for each variable, while the off-diagonal elements the covariance between variables. First, we apply a standard multivariate normal probability distribution function for each pair of the uncertain parameters to obtain a correlated sampling (Onishi et al., 2017), where each random variable follows a normal marginal distribution (Figure 1a). Then, we apply a transformation to each random variable using the normal cumulative distribution function with the corresponding expected mean and standard deviation to obtain a correlated distribution with uniform marginal distributions on the interval (0,1). And finally, we apply the inverse cumulative distribution of the lognormal distribution (i.e., the desired marginal distribution) to each random variable (Figure 1b).

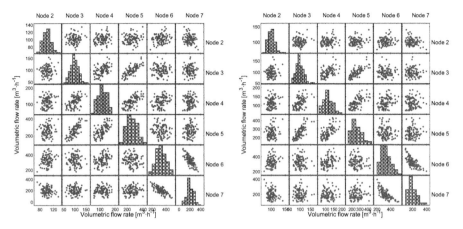

Figure 1. Correlated scenarios between every pairs of nodes for the water demand: a) normal marginal distribution; b) lognormal marginal distributions.

4. Stochastic mathematical model

The approach proposed in this work relies on stochastic programming, in particular a two-stage stochastic model. In our case, stage-1 decisions, which are taken before the uncertainty is resolved, are given by the design variables, like establishing a new plant or warehouse. In contrast, stage-2 decisions, which are made after the uncertainty is revealed, model operational variables (mainly production levels and transportation flows) that can be adjusted according to the uncertainty resolution. We assume that the uncertain parameters are described by a set of explicit scenarios with given probability of occurrence. Such scenarios together with their associated probabilities must be provided as input data to the model. In our case, these scenarios are generated from probability distributions using sampling methods.

4.1. Objective function
The WDN design is assessed by the Total Annualized Cost (TAC), which includes the annualized pipe capital cost and the pump operation cost. For each scenario s, a TAC value is computed, and to collect the performance of the WDN in face of uncertain in a single metric, we minimize the expected value of the TAC, which is compute as follows:

$$E[\text{TAC}] = \sum_p prob_s TAC_s \tag{1}$$

where $prob_s$ is the given probability of occurrence of scenario s.

4.2. Constraints
A logic equation is included in the model to assign a diameter for each pipe:

$$\sum_k y_{i,j,k} = 1, \forall i, j \in R_{i,j} \tag{2}$$

where $R_{i,j}$ define all the pipes by their starting node i and ending node j.

In addition, the minimization of the expected value is subject these set of equality and inequality constraints that must be satisfy in each scenario: mass balance at each node; flowrate velocity relation (linearized) at each pipe; mechanical energy balance at each pipe; and the Hazen-Williams at each pipe, that in its linearized form is as follows:. The expression for the last constraint is as follows:

$$\ln\_pressureDrop_{i,j,s}=\log(10.674)+1.852\ln\_flowRate_{i,j,s}+\log(LENGTH_{i,j})$$
$$-\sum_{k}(1.852\log(RUGOSITY\_COEFFICIENT_{i,j,k})y_{i,j,k}) \qquad (3)$$
$$-\sum_{k}(4.871\log(DIAMETER_{i,j,k})y_{i,j,k})$$

where we use the variable logarithmic transformations of the variables, named $\ln\_pressureDrop_{i,j,s}$ and $\ln\_flowRate_{i,j,s}$, instead of their current variables. Also, remark that Eq. (3) arises from a convex hull reformulation of the initial disjunctive model in order to activate only the contribution corresponding to the selected diameter k.

5. Case Study

The case study is a WDN with seven nodes and eight pipes forming two loops. Figure 2 shows its topology, the node elevations and the direction of the flow. We generate the correlated scenarios with the expected values and variances for water demand shown in Table 2. Node 1 represents the initial water reservoir which flow rate is the summation of water demands in nodes 2 to 7. The correlation matrix elements between two nodes ρ different from 0: $\rho_{2,3}=0.6$, $\rho_{2,4}=0.8$, $\rho_{3,4}=0.7$, $\rho_{3,5}=0.4$ and $\rho_{5,6}=-0.8$.

Table 1. Water demand expected values in nodes.

Water demand (m³/h)	Node 2	Node 3	Node 4	Node 5	Node 6	Node 7
Expected value of the	100	100	120	270	330	200
Standard deviation	9.6	18.3	32.0	72.1	74.6	69.2

All pipes have 1000 m length and the velocities are bounded between 0.3 m/s and 3 m/s. Pipe diameters are selected from a set of available commercial ones (Table 2). Hazen–Williams dimensionless roughness coefficient C is 130 for all pipes. The use of pumps is considered in case it is necessary to satisfy the nodes demand in any of the scenarios generated. The pumping operational cost is calculated using an electricity cost of 0.24 $/kWh.

Table 2. Set of available pipe diameters and costs.

Diameter (m)	0.0254	0.0508	0.0762	0.1016	0.1524	0.2032	0.254
	0.3048	0.3556	0.4064	0.4572	0.508	0.5588	0.6096
Cost ($/m)	2	5	8	11	16	23	32
	50	60	90	130	170	300	550

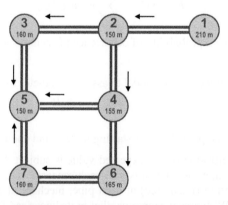

Figure 2. Topology of the WDN studied.

6. Results and discussion

The stochastic Mixed Integer Nonlinear Programming (MINLP) problem is solved in GAMS using BARON (version 18.11.12). To confirm the suitability of accounting for the uncertainty in the WDN, the problem has been solved again against all the scenarios but fixing the network topology (i.e. binary variables) according to the solution obtained from a deterministic problem, where there is no uncertainty in the nodal water demand (i.e., a unique scenario with water demand equal to the expected value). In addition, the problem has been solved for the case that nodal demands are uncorrelated and correlated according to the above-mentioned correlations coefficients.

Figure 3 shows this comparison in terms of the TAC ($/y). In both cases the expected TAC for stochastic designs is smaller than the expected TAC for the deterministic ones, which refers to the solution for all scenarios fixing the WDN topology (pipe diameters). Therefore, in some scenarios the system is forced to make use of pumps to satisfy the respective demands of some nodes, thus increasing the cost of the WDN. Another issue with the deterministic solution is that could lead to infeasible solutions as in some scenarios the velocity in pipes must be greater than the imposed upper bound (3 m/s) in order to satisfy nodal demands.

Regarding data correlation, both stochastic and deterministic designs yield lower expected TAC when the uncertain parameters are correlated (
Figure 3). Moreover, when distances between nodes are not too large (1000 m), it is expected a certain correlation between nodes demands. Figure 4 shows the optimal topology (pipe diameters) for the stochastic and deterministic WDN designs with correlated scenarios.

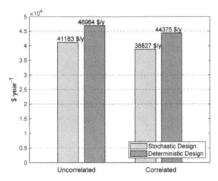

Figure 3. Comparison of the WDN expected total annualized cost between the stochastic and deterministic designs, and for uncorrelated and correlated and nodes demands.

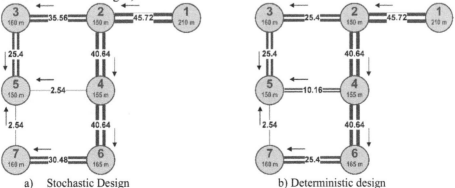

a) Stochastic Design   b) Deterministic design

Figure 4. WDN topology for the stochastic and deterministic designs with scenario correlation (pipe diameters in cm).

7. Conclusions

A stochastic MINLP optimization model has been developed for the optimal design of water distribution networks under nodal water demand uncertainty. The model has been applied to a case study with 7 nodes seeking to minimize the expected total annualized cost, which includes the pipe capital cost and the pumping operational cost. The solution of the stochastic problem is compared with that obtained fixing the pipe diameters according to the solution of the problem that assumes no variability in water demand at nodes. The results show that the stochastic design reduces the expected TAC by more than 12 % with respect to the deterministic one. This is mainly due to the need of using pumps to satisfy the nodes demand in some scenarios in the deterministic design. Additionally, the deterministic design could become infeasible due to the excessive water velocity in pipes needed to satisfy the water demand in some scenarios. These facts demonstrate that neglecting uncertainty in the optimization process may lead to suboptimal or, even worse, infeasible design of WDNs.

Acknowledgements

The authors acknowledge financial support to the Spanish «Ministerio de Economía, Industria y Competitividad» under project CTQ2016-77968-C3-2-P (AEI/FEDER, UE).

References

Branisavljević, N., Prodanović, D., & Ivetić, M. (2009). Uncertainty reduction in water distribution network modelling using system inflow data. Urban Water Journal, 6, 69-79.

Caballero, J. A., & Ravagnani, M. A. S. S. (2019). Water distribution networks optimization considering unknown flow directions and pipe diameters. Computers & Chemical Engineering, 127, 41-48.

Carrero-Parreño, A., Quirante, N., Ruiz-Femenia, R., Reyes-Labarta, J. A., Salcedo-Díaz, R., Grossmann, I. E., & Caballero, J. A. (2019). Economic and environmental strategic water management in the shale gas industry: Application of cooperative game theory. AIChE Journal, 65, e16725.

Geranmehr, M., Asghari, K., & Chamani, M. R. (2019). Uncertainty analysis of water distribution networks using type-2 fuzzy sets and parallel genetic algorithm. Urban Water Journal, 16, 193-204.

Mala-Jetmarova, H., Sultanova, N., & Savic, D. (2018). Lost in optimisation of water distribution systems? A literature review of system design. Water (Switzerland), 10.

Marquez Calvo, O. O., Quintiliani, C., Alfonso, L., Di Cristo, C., Leopardi, A., Solomatine, D., & de Marinis, G. (2018). Robust optimization of valve management to improve water quality in WDNs under demand uncertainty. Urban Water Journal, 15, 943-952.

Onishi, V. C., Ruiz-Femenia, R., Salcedo-Díaz, R., Carrero-Parreño, A., Reyes-Labarta, J. A., & Caballero., J. A. (2017). Optimal Shale Gas Flowback Water Desalination under Correlated Data Uncertainty. Computer Aided Chemical Engineering, 40, 943 - 948.

Reyes-Labarta, J. A., Salcedo-Díaz, R., Ruiz-Femenia, R., Guillén-Gosálbez, G., & Caballero, J. A. (2014). Handling of uncertainty in life cycle inventory by correlated multivariate lognormal distributions: Application to the design of supply chain networks. Computer Aided Chemical Engineering, 33, 1075-1080.

Ruiz-Femenia, R., Guillén-Gosálbez, G., Jiménez, L., & Caballero, J. A. (2013). Multi-objective optimization of environmentally conscious chemical supply chains under demand uncertainty. Chemical Engineering Science, 95, 1-11.

Sauro Pierucci, Flavio Manenti, Giulia Bozzano, Davide Manca (Eds.)
Proceedings of the 30th European Symposium on Computer Aided Process Engineering
(ESCAPE30), May 24-27, 2020, Milano, Italy. © 2020 Elsevier B.V. All rights reserved.
http://dx.doi.org/10.1016/B978-0-12-823377-1.50199-3

Enabling Dynamic Real-Time Optimization under Uncertainty using Data-Driven Chance Constraints

Joris Weigert, Christian Hoffmann, Erik Esche, Jens-Uwe Repke

Technische Universität Berlin, Process Dynamics and Operations Group, Straße des 17. Juni 135, 10623 Berlin, Germany
joris.weigert@tu-berlin.de

Abstract

Dynamic real-time optimization has been suggested in the past to ensure feasible and economic trajectories. These approaches typically neglect uncertainty, which may lead to constraint violation. However, the introduction of uncertainty significantly increases computational demand and thus makes these approaches non-applicable to real-time applications. In this contribution, we present a framework for chance-constrained (CC) optimization with online capability for dynamic real-time optimization (D-RTO) under uncertainty in which fast recurrent neural networks replace the rigorous dynamic process models. To demonstrate the performance and the online applicability of the presented framework, it is applied on a dynamic model of a simplified Williams-Otto process.

Keywords: Dynamic Real-time Optimization, Optimization under Uncertainty, Chance-constrained Optimization, Data-driven Models, Recurrent Neural Networks

1. Introduction

The application of dynamic real-time optimization (D-RTO) instead of a two layer approach based on steady-state real time optimization combined with model predictive control has been suggested for process operation tasks in the past. This suggestion is motivated by the need to describe the nonlinear dynamic system behaviour of complex processes (Biegler, 2009).

Process models describing real systems always contain a certain amount of uncertainty (Sahinidis, 2004), even though it is scarcely ever quantified. Uncertainty can originate, e.g., from little known or uncertain physical properties, from uncertainty in thermodynamic models, from neglected phenomena, or from over-simplification. This fact may lead to safety relevant constraint violations or unstable operation resulting from determnninistic optimization.

A possible approach to include uncertainty in optimization problems is the application of chance-constrained (CC) optimization (Charnes and Cooper, 1962). Nevertheless, existing frameworks cannot be used for online application given that the computational effort is still a major challenge (Esche et al., 2016).

In a previous contribution we presented a framework for CC optimization with online capability for steady-state systems, in wich fast data-driven models are used instead of rigorous models (Weigert et al., 2019). In this work, we extend the existing framework to dynamic systems.

In the next section, we give a general definition of dynamic chance-contrained optimization. In section 3 and 4 we present the developed framework in detail. Finally, we apply this framework to a case study of a simplified Williams-Otto process, in which the activation energies are assumed uncertain.

2. Dynamic Chance-Constrained Optimization

One appoach for solving optimization problems under uncertainty is chance-constrained optimization (Charnes and Cooper, 1962). Here, the uncertainty information is incorporated into the optimization problem by ensuring that inequality constraints are fulfilled by a desired minimum probability level α. For the present case, the dynamic optimization problem can be formulated as

$$
\begin{aligned}
\min_{u(t)} \quad & E[\phi(x(t), y(t), u(t), \xi, t)] \\
s.t. \quad & \dot{x} = f(x(t), y(t), u(t), \xi, t) \quad , \dim x = \dim f \\
& 0 = g(x(t), y(t), u(t), \xi, t) \quad , \dim y = \dim g \\
& Pr\{h_i(x(t), y(t), u(t), \xi, t) \geq 0\} \geq \alpha \\
& 0 \leq h_j(x(t), y(t), u(t), E[\xi], t) \\
& u^{LB} \leq u(t) \leq u^{UB}
\end{aligned}
\tag{1}
$$

where the expected value of ϕ represents the objective function, x are the differential variables corresponding to f, y the variables corresponding to the algebraic system g and u the decision variables of the optimization problem. The variables ξ and t describe the uncertain parameters and time, respectively. The fourth term in Eq. (1) introduces a lower bound on the probability of the fulfilment Pr of the inequality constraint h_i into the optimization problem. h_j represent the inequality constraints that are not enforced with a user-defined probability, but are evaluated at the expected value of the uncertain parameters.

To solve optimization problems as given by Eq. (1), a sequential optimization approach with an additional layer for the probability computation is used conventionally. The basic idea of this additional layer is to map inequality constraints $h_i(x, y, u, \xi, t) \geq 0$ into the uncertain parameter space. Then, the probability is calculated by integrating over the multivariate probability distribution of the uncertain parameters in the feasible region of the uncertain parameter space (Esche et al, 2016). For this purpose, multiple additional simulations and numerical integrations are carried out at every iteration step of the optimization. Especially for high dimensional parameter spaces, this leads to rapidly increasing computational effort, which is the reason why existing frameworks for CC optimization are not suitable for online application.

3. Dynamic Data-Driven Optimization under Uncertainty

Within the proposed approach, two classes of data-driven models for usage in chance-constrained optimization problems are set up. The in- and output dependencies of both model types are shown in Figure 1. A more detailed description of the recursive neural network structure shown in Figure 1 will be given below (see section 4.3.).

The data-driven process model is generated to describe a dynamic input-output relationship of variables based on a rigorous dynamic process model. It describes the relationship between the decision variables u and the predefined output variables z_i at a certain time step k. The output variables z_i in general include the expected values of the objective function $E[\phi(t)]$ and the inequality constraints $E[h(t)]$, but additional variables of the rigorous model can also be added as outputs.

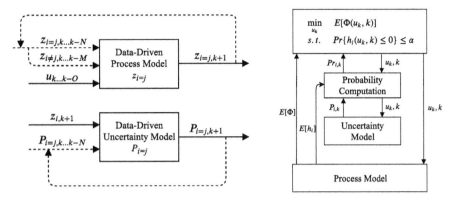

Figure 1: In- and output specifications of the data-driven process and the uncertainty model (solid lines). Additionally, the input specifications of the utilized recurrent neural networks are shown (dashed lines)

Figure 2: Dynamic data-driven chance-contrained optimization framework

The uncertainty model (UM) is generated to describe uncertainty included in the rigorous dynamic process model. It relates decision variables u and probability distribution parameters P_i of the predefined output variables z_i at a certain time k. Depending on which probability distribution model is chosen for the uncertainty description, the number of parameters in P_i can vary. In the moment a normal, a beta or a gamma distribution can be selected. In case the output uncertainty is, e.g., assumed to be normally distributed, $P_{i,k}$ contains the variance of z_i at the time point k.

By combining the expected value of $h_{i,k}$ with the paramters from $P_{i,k}$ the cumulative density function (CDF) of h_i at time step k can be approximated to calculate the probability of the inequality constraint fulfilment $Pr_{i,k}$ directly.

By applying the data-driven process and uncertainty model to a CC optimization problem, the general dynamic optimization problem from Eq. (1) can be simplified to

$$
\begin{aligned}
\min_{u_k} \quad & E[\phi(u_k, k)] \\
s.t. \quad & Pr\{h_i(u_k, k) \leq 0\} \leq \alpha \\
& u^{LB} \leq u_k \leq u^{UB}
\end{aligned}
\tag{2}
$$

Here, the equation system of f and g, the corresponding variables x and y, and the uncertain parameters ξ from Eq. (1) are replaced by the data-driven process and uncertainty models. Additionally, time t is now described as discrete points k. The discretization step size is predefined in the artificial data generation procedure (see section 4.1.).

In Figure 2 the optimization workflow of the dynamic data-driven CC optimization is shown. At each iteration step the optimization layer calls the process model and the requested objective function is returned. Additionally, the expected values of the inequality contraints are returned to the probability computation layer. Here, the probability $Pr_{i,k}$ is calculated by evaluating the CDF based on $E[h_i]$, and the probability distribution parameters $P_{i,k}$. In contrast to traditional CC optimization, only explicit data-driven models and cumulative densitiy functions have to be evaluated during the optimization calculations, which leads to a significant decrase of computation time with a minimum factor of 7^{n_ξ}, where n_ξ describes the number of uncertain parameters.

4. Modeling Workflow

The presented modeling workflow is carried out in a framework implemented entirely in Python. Different rigorous process models, formulated and solved in different programming languages, can be connected to the framework. The utilized recurrent neural networks are trained and tested in the machine learning toolbox Scikit-learn (Pedregosa et al., 2011) and the probability distribution analysis and fitting capabilities are used from the Python toolbox Scipy.stats. A simplified flowchart of the presented modeling workflow is shown in Figure 3.

4.1. Artificial Data Generation

In a first step, artificial data for training and testing of the data-driven models needs to be created based on a dynamic rigorous process model. For this purpose, three different sampling methods are used. For the predefined uncertain parameters ξ samples are generated by sampling from a pseudo-random normal distribution. The time dependent

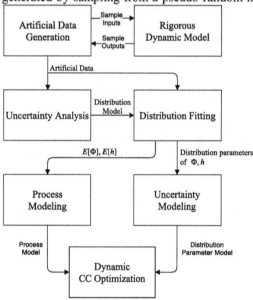

decision variables u are sampled from an amplitude pseudo random binary sequence (APRBS). This method ensures high information content in training data for identification of input-output relationships within the recurrent neural networks (Nelles, 2001). Additionally, a well-distributed sampling method (e.g., Hammersley sequence sampling (HSS)) can be used on the initial conditions of the output variables (h, ϕ), which increases the valid space of the output variables in the data-driven models. Based on the created samples, dynamic simulations with time dependent decision variable changes (APRBS) are carried out at every sample point in the parameter and initial condition space and the resulting dynamic simulation

Figure 3: Simplified flowchart of the developed modeling workflow, which is applied offline.

results are stored at predefined equidistant time points. This step size defines the discretiziation step size between the discrete time points k in the data-driven models (see Figure 1).

4.2. Uncertainty Analysis and Distribution Fitting

The obtained dynamic simulation results are clustered with respect to the uncertain parameter sampling. For every output variable a qualified probability distribution model is found and fitted at each time point accordingly. Based on these distributions, the expected values of h and ϕ at ever time point, and the respective distribution parameters are handed over to the subsequent modeling steps

4.3. Recurrent Neural Networks

To create independent data sets for training and testing of the data-driven models, the aforemetioned steps need to be carried out twice with two independent sets of APRPS samples for the decision variables. The in- and output specifications of the recurrent neural networks are shown in Fig. 1. For each output, a single process and a single uncertainty model is generated. Each process model uses O past values of the decision variables, N past values of the associated output variable and M past values of the remaining output variables to predict the output at the next time step. Each uncertainty model uses the past N values of the corresponding probability parameters and the current values of the output variables to predict the parameter at the next time step.

5. Case Study

To demonstrate the performance and the applicability in D-RTO under uncertainty, the presented framework is applied on a dynamic model of a Williams-Otto process (Hoffmann et al., 2019). This process consists of a continously-stirred tank reactor, a decanter, and a distillation column. Part of the bottom product of the column is recycled into the reactor. The activation energies of the three reactions are assumed to be uncertain with a standard deviation of 1% of the specified value.

The following optimization problem has been specified for the case study

$$\min_{T_j, \alpha_{recycle}} \quad -\sum_{k=1}^{120} E\left[w_{product}(T_j, \alpha_{recycle}, k)\right]$$

$$s.t. \quad Pr\left\{T_{reactor}(T_j, \alpha_{recycle}, k) \le 172°C\right\} \tag{3}$$

$$56°C \le T_j \le 64°C$$

$$0.52 \le \alpha_{recycle} \le 0.63$$

where $w_{product}$ is the mass fraction of the product in the reactor, $T_{reactor}$ and T_j are the temperatures in the reactor and its cooling jacket, and $\alpha_{recycle}$ is the ratio of recycled bottom product.

Based on the decision variable bounds, artificial training and testing data sets are generated. A simulation time of 10,000 seconds with a step size of 1 second, 500 APRBS changes and 500 samples in the parameter space are used. The process and uncertainty models are based on the specifications shown in Fig. 1 with = 3, $M = 1$, and $O = 3$. The uncertainty in the data is found to be normally distributed. The resulting recurrent neural networks have a normalized mean squared error of around $1 \cdot 10^{-4}$ regarding the testing data, which is accurate enough to predict the 10,000 seconds of testing data with a mean deviation of around 1%.

The Optimization is carried out in Scipy.optimize using the method SLSQP for a time horizon of 120 seconds with a

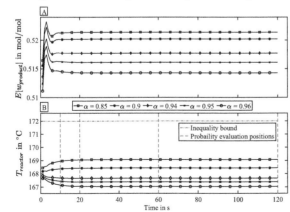

Figure 4: Results of the CC optimization at different probability levels. (A) objective function, (B) inequality contraint

tep size of 1 second. The decision variables are set to be constant over the whole horizon and the probability constraint is evaluated at 10, 20, 60, and 120 seconds. In Fig. 4, the resulting objective variable (A) and the chance-constrained variable (B) are shown for different probability levels α. It is apparent that an increasing probability level for the fulfilment of the temperature constraint leads to a lower product mole fraction in the reactor. This is the expected behavior given that a high probability level is supposed to shift the optimum to a more conservative solution.

The computation for an entire CC optimization run with the developed framework takes about 1 second (9 iterations), which is definitely fast enough for real-time application.

6. Conclusion and Outlook

A framework for generating dynamic data-driven process and uncertainty models for enabling dynamic real-time optimization under uncertainty is presented. The framework generates recurrent neural networks based on a dynamic rigorous process model and uses these data-driven models to compute the objective function and the probability contraints in a CC optimization framework.

To demonstrate the performance and the applicability in D-RTO under uncertainty, the presented framework is applied on a dynamic model of a simplified Williams-Otto process. It can be shown that the computation time for the CC optimization is suitable for application in online environments.

In future work, we will focus on developing techniques to update the data-driven models based on online measaurements from the real process.

Additionally, the framework will be tested extensively with a variety of different process models and a precise comparison with other CC optimization techniques regarding the computational effort will be performed.

References

Biegler, L. T., 2009. Technology advances for dynamic real-time optimization. In Computer Aided Chemical Engineering (Vol. 27, pp. 1-6). Elsevier.

Charnes, A., Cooper, W., 1962. Chance constraints and normal deviates. Journal of the American Statistical Association, 57(297), 134-148.

E. Esche, D. Müller, S. Werk, I. E. Grossmann, G. Wozny, 2016. Solution of chance-constrained mixed-integer non- linear programming problems. In: Z. Kravanja, M. Bogataj (Eds.), Proceedings of the 26th European Symposium on Computer Aided Process Engineering - ESCAPE 26. No. 38. Elsevier, pp. 91–94.

Hoffmann, C., Esche, E., Repke, J.-U., 2019. Integration of Design and Control Based on Large-Scale Nlp Formulations and An Optimal Economic NMPCs. In: Proceedings of the 9th International Conference on Foundations of Computer-Aided Process Design, vol. 47. Elsevier, pp. 125–130.

Nelles, O., 2001. Nonlinear system identification: From classical approaches to neural networks and fuzzy models. Springer, Berlin, 785 S.

Pedregosa, F., Varoquaux, G., Gramfort, A., Michel, V., Thirion, B., Grisel, O., Blondel, M., Prettenhofer, P., Dubourg, V., Vanderplas, J., 2011. Scikit-learn: Machine learning in Python. Journal of machine learning research, *12(Oct)*, 2825-2830.

Sahinidis, N.V., 2004. Optimization under uncertainty: state-of-the-art and opportunities. Computers & Chemical Engineering 28 (6-7), 971–983. 10.1016/j.compchemeng.2003.09.017.

Weigert, J., Esche, E., Hoffmann, C., Repke, J.-U., 2019. Generation of Data-Driven Models for Chance-Constrained Optimization, Proceedings of the 9th International Conference on Foundations of Computer-Aided Process Design, Elsevier, 311-316.

Sauro Pierucci, Flavio Manenti, Giulia Bozzano, Davide Manca (Eds.)
Proceedings of the 30th European Symposium on Computer Aided Process Engineering
(ESCAPE30), May 24-27, 2020, Milano, Italy. © 2020 Elsevier B.V. All rights reserved.
http://dx.doi.org/10.1016/B978-0-12-823377-1.50200-7

Flexibility Analysis of High-dimensional Systems via Cylindrical Algebraic Decomposition

Chenglin Zheng,[a] Fei Zhao,[a] Lingyu Zhu,[b] Xi Chen[a*]

[a]*State Key Laboratory of Inductrial Control Technology, College of Control Science and Engineering, Zhejiang University, Hangzhou, Zhejiang, 310027, China*
[b]*College of Chemical Engineering, Zhejiang University of Technology, Hangzhou, Zhejiang, 310014, China*
xi_chen@zju.edu.cn

Abstract

In process design, flexibility analysis is an important technique for evaluating the operability of a chemical process. The cylindrical algebraic decomposition (CAD) method has been proposed for flexibility analysis to derive analytical expressions of a feasible region. Due to the heavy computational burden caused by symbolic computation, this method can only handle small-scale problems currently. To overcome this limitation, a novel method is proposed for high-dimensional systems in this work. As the inequality constraints for flexibility analysis are usually limited in most cases, a surrogate model is first built to correlate the inequality constraints based on an initial sample set. Then, the flexibility region is obtained with explicit expressions via the CAD method. Next, the sampling validation is conducted on the boundary. For any violation, a refinement will be activated by taking an iterative process of data sampling, surrogate modelling, and region deriving, until the correctness condition is satisfied. The case study shows the proposed method can effectively describe the flexibility region for high-dimensional systems.

Keywords: Flexibility analysis, surrogate model, cylindrical algebraic decomposition.

1. Introduction

All chemical plants are subject to the uncertainties and variations during their design and operation. Given this fact, it is clearly important to conduct flexibility analysis of a system in the presence of the uncertainties. The main purpose of the flexibility analysis is to determine and describe the feasible region for a feasible and safe operation. The existing methods for describing flexibility region can mainly be divided into four categories: (1). formulating the flexibility analysis model into a global or parametric optimization problem (Bansal et al. 2002); (2). constructing boundary iteratively by simple approximation method (Goyal and Ierapetritou, 2003); (3). generating polygonal representation by appropriate sampling points (Banerjee and Ierapetritou, 2005); (4). establishing response surface of flexibility functions via the surrogate models (Wang and Ierapetritou, 2017). The aforementioned methods mainly rely on numerical calculation methods to estimate the outer envelope of a flexibility region. They cannot provide analytical descriptions for flexibility regions. Recently, a novel method based on quantifier elimination was proposed by Zhao and Chen (2018). The cylindrical algebraic decomposition (CAD) method (Collins, 1975) was utilized for analytically representing the flexibility region, which is suitable for both convex and nonconvex systems. However, due to the heavy computational burden caused by symbolic computation, the CAD method is more applicable to small-scale problems. Regarding high-dimensional systems, how to apply the CAD method to analytically depict the flexibility region is still an open challenge. In this work, a novel method integrating the surrogate modeling technique and the CAD method is proposed to analytically depict the flexibility region for high-dimensional systems. In many cases, most of the constraints in a high-dimensional system are equalities. Thus, the number of the inequalities for the flexibility analysis is usually limited. A surrogate model is first built to approximate the inequality constraints, where only uncertain parameters and control variables are involved. Then, the CAD method is applied to the surrogate system to derive the flexibility region with explicit expressions. Next, the boundary check is conducted. Once a sampling point on the boundary violates constraints, additional points will be gathered and the process will be repeated, until the correctness condition is satisfied.

2. Cylindrical algebraic decomposition

A given design system can be described by the following set of constraints.

$$F = \begin{cases} h(\boldsymbol{\theta}, z, x) = 0 \\ g(\boldsymbol{\theta}, z, x) \leq 0 \end{cases} \tag{1}$$

where h is the vector of equations (e.g., mass or energy balance equation); g is the vector of inequalities (e.g., physical operating limit); x, $\boldsymbol{\theta}$, and z represent vectors of the state variables, the uncertain parameters and the control variables, respectively.

The CAD method is a symbolic computation method, which can depict the flexibility region with explicit expressions. It regards the flexibility analysis problem as an existential quantifier formula shown in Eq. (2).

$$\exists (\boldsymbol{\theta}, z, x) \begin{bmatrix} h(\boldsymbol{\theta}, z, x) = 0 \wedge \\ g(\boldsymbol{\theta}, z, x) \leq 0 \end{bmatrix} \tag{2}$$

Based on the quantifier elimination, the CAD method can eliminate the quantifier in Eq. (2) and generate an equivalent quantifier-free formula, which is the solution space of Eq. (2). There are two phases, namely the projection phase and lifting phase, in the CAD method. In the projection phase, through calculating discriminates and resultants on each dimension, variables are eliminated one by one with the predefined elimination order. In the lifting phase, through repeatedly sampling points within the cells, checking the signs and substituting the sampled points, the valid cells can be lifted, which constitute the feasible region of Eq. (2).

3. Flexibility region based on surrogate model and CAD

Instead of conducting the elimination, the surrogate-based method is utilized to approximate the inequality constraints g with explicit expressions. First, the initial sampling set (θ^{ini}, z^{ini}) can be obtained within the design space of uncertain parameters and control variables. The corresponding state variables x^{ini} can be deduced by running the simulation. Based on the initial sample set, the inequality constraints can be represented as the function of uncertain parameters and control variables; Then, the surrogate system can be used to approximately describe the flexibility region.

$$F^s = g^s(\boldsymbol{\theta}, z) \leq 0 \tag{3}$$

Noted that the surrogate system F^s only involves inequalities; thus, the computational burden for the CAD method will be alleviated due to the model reduction. Subsequently, the CAD method is applied to the surrogate system F^s. The projection order is specified as $\theta \prec z$, where the uncertain parameters are $\theta = [\theta_1, \ldots, \theta_m]$ and control variables are $z = [z_1, \ldots, z_n]$. Through the CAD method, the solution space of θ and z can be split into a union set of finite k disjoint flexibility subspaces.

$$\varphi'(\theta, z) = \varphi'_1(\theta, z) \vee \varphi'_2(\theta, z) \vee \ldots \vee \varphi'_k(\theta, z) \tag{4}$$

where the kth subspace is

$$\varphi'_k(\theta, z) = \begin{vmatrix} p_{k,1} \le \theta_1 \le q_{k,1} \wedge \\ p_{k,2}(\theta_1) \le \theta_2 \le q_{k,2}(\theta_1) \wedge \\ \ldots \\ p_{k,m}(\theta_1, \ldots, \theta_{m-1}) \le \theta_{m-1} \le q_{k,m}(\theta_1, \ldots, \theta_{m-1}) \wedge \\ p_{k,m}(\theta_1, \ldots, \theta_{m-1}, \theta_m) \le z_1 \le q_{k,m+1}(\theta_1, \ldots, \theta_{m-1}, \theta_m) \wedge \\ \ldots \\ p_{k,m+n}(\theta_1, \ldots, \theta_m, z_1, \ldots, z_{n-1}) \le z_n \le q_{k,m+n}(\theta_1, \ldots, \theta_m, z_1, \ldots, z_{n-1}) \end{vmatrix} \tag{5}$$

where p_k and q_k are continuous algebraic functions, $-\infty$ or $+\infty$. Thus, the flexibility region $\varphi'(\theta, z)$ can be depicted by the logical combination of the semi-algebraic system $\varphi'_k(\theta, z)$, which has the explicit expression. However, the accuracy of surrogate model depends on the number and location of samples in the design space. One must acknowledge that the surrogate model might result in an inaccurate description of flexibility region. A refined procedure should be executed to iteratively check and update the flexibility region until it satisfies the correctness condition in Eq. (6).

$$\forall(\theta^{val}, z^{val}) \; [g(\theta, z, x)] \le 0 \tag{6}$$

where (θ^{val}, z^{val}) are validation samples on the boundary of flexibility region. The correctness condition requires all the validation samples on the boundary should satisfy the inequalities g in Eq. (1). The refined procedure involves two parts: the boundary check, and the update of surrogate modeling and CAD solution.

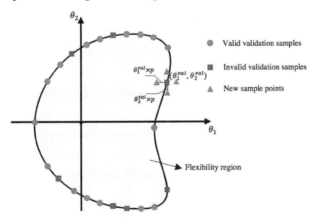

Figure 1. Geometric illustration of validation samples and new points for the proposed method.

3.1. Boundary check

Since the analytical expressions of the flexibility region have been obtained in Eqs. (4)-(5), validation points (θ^{val}, z^{val}) can be sampled on the boundary through uniform sampling. For ease of understanding, an illustration for these validation samples on the boundary is provided in Figure. 1. It is a case with two uncertain parameters θ_1 and θ_2. When a validation sample on the boundary satisfies the inequalities g in Eq. (1), denote it as the valid sample marked by a circle; otherwise, denote it as the invalid sample marked by a square. The existence of the invalid samples indicates that the inaccurate surrogate model results in an incorrect derivation of the flexibility region around those sample points.

3.2. Iterative process of the surrogate modelling and CAD updating

Once the flexibility region does not hold the condition in Eq. (6), i.e., there exist invalid samples on the boundary, a refinement will be activated by taking an iterative process of surrogate modeling and CAD updating. First, new points (θ^{new}, z^{new}) are sampled around invalid validation samples. Regarding the two-dimensional case as illustrated in Figure 1, four points located on the upper, lower, left and right sides of the invalid validation points are sampled as new points. Then, add validation samples and new points into the initial sample set. Based on the updated sample set, the updated surrogate model can be built. Subsequently, though applying the CAD method to the updated surrogate system, the new flexibility region can be depicted. After the iterative process of constructing a surrogate model based on the current sample set, applying the CAD method for the current surrogate system and doing the sampling validation on the boundary are converged, the final flexibility region can be obtained for high-dimensional systems.

4. Results and discussion

Flexibility analysis problem of a vacuum distillation is studied in this paper. The distillation process can be described by a rigorous tray-by-tray MESH model which includes a total of 917 variables. The uncertain parameter lies in the flowrate of the feed stream, F, which is bounded within 1000 kg/h $\leq F \leq$ 3000 kg/h. The control variable is the operating pressure P of vacuum distillation. The bounds of P are 3.7 kPa $\leq P \leq$ 39.7 kPa. In addition, it also involves several inequalities for capacity or quality restrictions: $y_B \leq 850$, $T_{oil} \leq 265$ and $0.5 \leq \sigma \leq 2$, where y_B is the residue in the bottoms (ppm), T_{oil} is the inlet temperature of thermal oil (°C), and σ is the flooding factor of the column.

$$F^s = \begin{cases} g_1: 1000 \leq F \leq 3000, \\ g_2: 3.7 \leq P \leq 39.7, \\ g_3: y_B = -188.639 + 0.604F - 11.437P - 2.749 \times 10^{-4} F^2 + 1.992P^2 \\ -0.025FP + 1.340 \times 10^{-7} F^3 - 0.094P^3 - 1.258F^2P + 0.002P^2F \leq 850, \\ g_4: T_{oil} = 220.134 + 0.002F + 3.248P + 1.797 \times 10^{-8} F^2 - 0.088P^2 + 4.122 \times 10^{-5} FP \\ +1.278 \times 10^{-11} F^3 + 0.001P^3 - 6.083 \times 10^{-9} F^2P + 2.018 \times 10^{-7} P^2F \leq 265, \\ g_5: 0.5 \leq \{\sigma = 1.884 + 1.149 \times 10^{-5} F - 0.188P + 1.552 \times 10^{-8} F^2 + 0.011P^2 + 7.044 \\ \times 10^{-7} FP - 5.421 \times 10^{-12} F^3 - 2.070 \times 10^{-4} P^3 + 9.103 \times 10^{-10} F^2P - 2.123 \times 10^{-7} P^2F\} \leq 2 \end{cases}$$ (7)

The proposed method carries out the sampling in the space of uncertain parameter and control variable first. The number of samples in the initial sample set is 75. Based on the initial sample set, inequality constraints can be represented as a function of the uncertain parameter and control variable using the cubic polynomials. The surrogate system can be represented in Eq. (7). The computational time of the surrogate system is 9.18 s. Then, the projection order is defined as $F<P$. Applying the CAD method to the surrogate system F^s, the flexibility region can be described by $\{(F,P)\in R^2\,|\,\varphi'\}$. The computational time of the CAD method is 0.117 s.

$$\varphi' = \begin{vmatrix} 1: \begin{vmatrix} 1000 \le F \le 2204.81 \wedge \\ 3.7 \le P \le Root[f_1(F,\#1)\&,1] \end{vmatrix} \vee \\ 2: \begin{bmatrix} 2204.81 \le F \le 2896.91 \wedge \\ Root[f_2(F,\#1)\&,1] \le P \le Root[f_1(F,\#1)\&,1] \end{bmatrix} \end{vmatrix} \tag{8}$$

where $f(F,\#1)$ is a pure function with a parameter F.

$$f_1(F,\#1) = -3.51\times10^{10} + 1.21\times10^{8}F + 1406.43F^2 + F^3 + (2.54\times10^{11} + 3.23\times10^{6}F - 476.14F^2)\#1$$
$$+ (-6.90\times10^{9} + 15799.3F)\#1^2 + 1.01\times10^{8}\#1^3$$

$$f_2(F,\#1) = 7.75\times10^{9} - 4.51\times10^{6}F + 2051.22F^2 - F^3 + (8.53\times10^{7} + 1.84\times10^{5}F + 93.83F^2)\#1$$
$$+ (-1.49\times10^{7} - 13084.8.3F)\#1^2 + 700648\#1^3$$

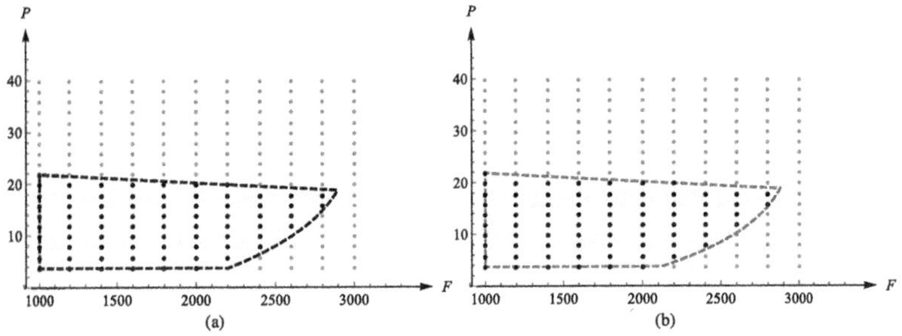

Figure 2. (a) Flexibility region φ'; (b) Final Flexibility region φ'_{final} for the vacuum distillation.

φ' shows that the flexibility region consists of two 2D cells. The complete flexibility region is depicted in Figure 2(a). However, since it is inevitable that the surrogate model will exist fitting error, the iterative process of the boundary check, surrogate modelling and CAD updating, is executed to refine the flexibility region. After 17 iterative processes, the final flexibility region φ'_{final} can be obtained, as shown in Figure 2(b).

$$\varphi'_{final} = \begin{vmatrix} 1: \begin{vmatrix} 1000 \le F \le 2121.2 \wedge \\ 3.7 \le P \le Root[f_1'(F,\#1)\&,1] \end{vmatrix} \vee \\ 2: \begin{bmatrix} 2121.2 \le F \le 2880.96 \wedge \\ Root[f_2'(F,\#1)\&,1] \le P \le Root[f_1'(F,\#1)\&,1] \end{bmatrix} \end{vmatrix} \tag{9}$$

where $f'(F,\#1)$ is a pure function with a parameter F. The difference between φ'_{final} and φ' is on the depiction for the right boundary, which is illustrated in Figure 3(b). It should be noted that after the iterative refined process, the right boundary of flexibility region φ'_{final} is a little bit tighter than φ' since the validation samples on the right boundary of φ' is invalid. Thus, in order to obtain the flexibility region satisfying the correctness condition, the right boundary should be retracted.

$$f_1'(F,\#1) = -4.58 \times 10^{12} + 1.58 \times 10^8 F + 1132.88 F^2 + F^3 + (3.34 \times 10^{11} + 4.30 \times 10^6 F - 507.06 F^2)\#1$$
$$+ (-9.29 \times 10^9 + 13728.9 F)\#1^2 + 1.40 \times 10^8 \#1^3$$

$$f_2'(F,\#1) = 6.37 \times 10^9 - 4.73 \times 10^6 F + 2222.49 F^2 - F^3 + (1.92 \times 10^8 + 1.97 \times 10^5 F + 102.56 F^2)\#1$$
$$+ (-2.75 \times 10^7 - 15177.6 F)\#1^2 + 1.14 \times 10^6 \#1^3$$

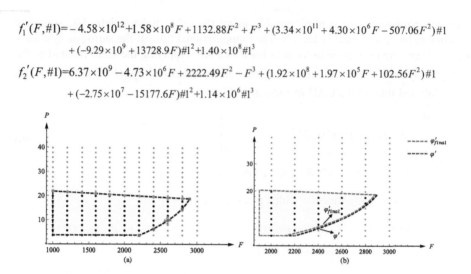

Figure 2. (a) Validation samples and new points; (b) The difference illustration of φ'_{final} and φ' .

5. Conclusions

In this study, a novel method is proposed to analytically describe the flexibility region for high-dimensional systems. First, based on the idea of model reduction, a surrogate model is built to approximate the inequality constraints and reduce the equalities. Then, the CAD method is utilized to depict the flexibility region with explicit expressions. Last, an iteratively refined procedure including the boundary check and the process of surrogate modelling and CAD updating is activated until the correctness condition is satisfied. The proposed method integrates the advantage of the surrogate model which is less computationally expensive and the CAD method which can describe the flexibility region analytically.

Acknowledgements

We gratefully acknowledge the financial support of the National Natural Science Foundation of China (No.61973268), the National Key Research and Development Program of China (No. 2017YFE0106700), and China Scholarship Council.

References

V. Bansal, J. D. Perkins, E. N. Pistikopoulos, 2002, Flexibility analysis and design using a parametric programming framework, AIChE Journal, 48, 2851-2868.

V. Goyal, M. G. Ierapetritou, 2003, Framework for evaluating the feasibility operability of nonconvex processes, AIChE Journal, 49, 1233-1240.

I. Banerjee, M. G. Ierapetritou, 2005, Feasibility evaluation of nonconvex systems using shape reconstruction techniques, Industrial & Engineering Chemistry Research, 44, 3638-3647.

Z. Wang, M. G. Ierapetritou, 2017, A novel feasibility analysis method for black-box processes using a radial basis function adaptive sampling approach, AIChE Journal, 63, 532-550.

F. Zhao, X. Chen, 2018, Analytical and triangular solutions to operational flexibility analysis using quantifier elimination, AIChE Journal, 64, 3894-3911.

G. E. Collins, 1975, Quantifier elimination for real closed fields by cylindrical algebraic decomposition, Lecture Notes in Computer Science, 33, 134-183.

Sauro Pierucci, Flavio Manenti, Giulia Bozzano, Davide Manca (Eds.)
Proceedings of the 30th European Symposium on Computer Aided Process Engineering
(ESCAPE30), May 24-27, 2020, Milano, Italy. © 2020 Elsevier B.V. All rights reserved.
http://dx.doi.org/10.1016/B978-0-12-823377-1.50201-9

Online Optimal Cleaning Scheduling and Control of Heat Exchanger Networks under Fouling with Large Disturbances

Federico Lozano Santamaria, Sandro Macchietto

Department of Chemical Engineering, Imperial College London South Kensington Campus, London SW7 2AZ, UK

Abstract

Fouling in refining applications reduces the energy recovery in the pre heat train, increasing the overall cost of the operation. To mitigate fouling, cleanings of the exchangers are scheduled, and the flow distribution in the network modified. Usually, these two decisions are considered independently, and the dynamic behavior and disturbances affecting the network are ignored. Without considering process variability, fouling mitigation alternatives will become suboptimal or infeasible over time. This work builds on our previous research where an online NMPC-MHE multiloop approach was developed for fouling mitigation and tested under nominal model mismatch. Here, the performance of the framework for simultaneous optimal online flow control and cleaning scheduling is demonstrated for large and realistic disturbances found in refining operations (+/- 50% inlet temperatures and flow changes, and processing different types of crudes). A realistic case is used to demonstrate the advantages of the framework, and results show its effectiveness to react to disturbances over various time scales while minimizing the total operating cost.

Keywords: integrated scheduling and control, NMPC, MHE, heat exchanger network, crude oil fouling, large disturbances.

1. Introduction

Fouling reduces the efficiency of energy recovery and has a large impact on refining applications. It increases the energy consumption, carbon emissions, and operating cost of the refinery. Mitigation alternatives are necessary for a reliable operation. The most important mitigation actions to reduce the deposition rate or recover heat transfer efficiency are: changing the flow distribution (e.g. flow splits between parallel branches) and periodic cleaning of the units. Modelling and mathematical programming have been used to solve independently for the optimal flow distribution (de Silva et al. 2015) or optimal cleaning schedule (Georgiadis et al. 2000). If formulated as an MINLP, the main limiting factor is the complexity and combinatorial nature of the optimal cleaning scheduling problem. Simplifications are usually made to solve it, using linear fouling models, linearization of the heat exchanger models (Lavaja and Bagajewicz 2004), or heuristic algorithms (Ishiyama et al. 2009). A simultaneous solution of the flow control and cleaning scheduling problems exploits the interactions and synergies between all decision levels, with large economic benefits (Lozano Santamaria and Macchietto 2018). However, in refining operations, the type of crude processed, inlet flow rates and streams temperature change frequently. These disturbances impact significantly the operation and performance of HEN, but are usually ignored. Furthermore, a single solution to the problem at some nominal conditions may rapidly become suboptimal or infeasible given the large uncertainty and variability of the operation. In our previous research (Lozano Santamaria and Macchietto 2019a) we solved online the optimal cleaning scheduling and flow control problem of HEN using a NMPC-MHE (Nonlinear model predictive control – Moving horizon estimator) approach with multiple loops. It was shown that the method worked well with relative small noise (coefficient of variance of 5% - 8% in the inlet flow rates and 12% - 30% in the deposition rates). Here, we expand on that work, addressing the much more extreme disturbances which are usually observed in refining operations (+/- 50% change or greater in inlet flows). It is demonstrated that the proposed online fouling mitigation approach, that updates the prediction models and optimally reacts to the disturbances, is able to minimize operating cost and satisfy all constraints even in these more demanding and realistic situations.

2. Multi loop online integration of cleaning scheduling and control

The online integration of cleaning scheduling and control (Figure 1) is based on two feedback loops: the flow control problem which has a time scale of hours/days, and the cleaning scheduling problem which has a time scale of months/years. Each loop is composed by i) a MHE that estimates fouling model parameters and current HEN conditions by minimizing the error between measurements and predictions over a past estimation horizon (PEH), and ii) a NMPC controller that, using the model and conditions estimated, defines optimal future actions (flow distribution and/or cleaning scheduling) by minimizing the total operating cost over a (long) future prediction horizon (FPH). The measurements inputs to all MHE problems are flow rates, temperature, and pressure drops. As in standard NMPC, only actions in the first step are implemented, the rest are discarded, and the problem is solved again at the next sampling instance.

At the core of each MHE and NMPC problem there is a formulation and solution of an optimization problem: an MINLP (for the scheduling layer including binary decisions for the cleanings) or an NLP (for the control layer, where cleanings are known and fixed).

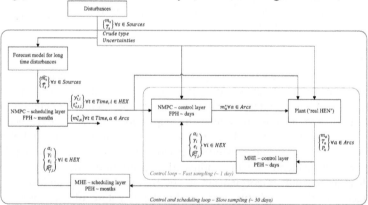

Figure 1. Schematic representation of the multi loop control scheme for the optimal cleaning scheduling and control in mitigating fouling.

The problem formulation (Lozano Santamaria and Macchietto 2018) includes: an axially lumped radially distributed model for shell and tube heat exchangers (P-NTU model) that accounts for radial temperature profiles in the tubes, the Ebert-Panchal model to characterize crude oil deposition (Ebert and Panchal 1995), a continuous time representation with variable length for the periods, tube side pressure drop correlations, and operational constraints (e.g. firing limit, pressure drop limits). The MINLP for the simultaneous flow control and cleaning scheduling optimization is reformulated as a NLP using complementarity constraints and solved using an iterative ϵ regularization approach (Lozano Santamaria and Macchietto, 2019b). The control layer is updated frequently (~daily) to respond rapidly to changes, while the scheduling layer is updated less frequently (~ weekly or monthly). The disturbances considered are: changes in flow rates and temperatures of all inlet streams to the network, and changes in the type of crude processed. The latter are modelled by modifying the deposition constant in the fouling rate model. All these disturbances have a significant impact on the performance of the network, on the fouling rates of each exchanger, and thus on the optimal operation of the system. In the control layer, the current realization of the disturbances (last measured value at each update) is used as a constant forecast within the FPH in the NMPC problem. In the scheduling layer a moving average of each disturbance realization over the most recent month is used to forecast it over the FPH. These two different forecasting strategies are necessary because of the differences in time scales and frequency updates of each layer.

3. Refinery case study

Figure 2 shows the preheat train of a real refinery used as case study. It has 5 exchangers, of which 4 are double shell, arranged in two parallel branches. The flow control degree of freedom is the split fraction between the branches. Historical data collected daily from actual operations over 4 years were used as process inputs and to characterize their variability.

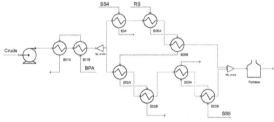

Figure 2. Heat exchanger network used for the case study.

A model for the actual operation of this plant was validated previously (Lozano Santamaria and Macchietto 2019b). Here, in order to "carry out" alternative operations, the 'plant' in the online scheme is defined artificially using the same predictive model as that of the optimization problems. To mimic changes in crude slates (no records were available), fouling parameters were changed in a pseudo random manner. The deposition constant of each exchanger of the plant model was modified, based on a normal probability distribution characteristic of the process variability. Because all exchanger processed the same crude, the deposition constants are positively correlated (i.e. heavier crudes increase the fouling rate in all exchangers). Two types of large disturbances were imposed representing large deviations from normal operation: a) changes in the type of crude (modelled as a change in the deposition constant of the Ebert-Panchal model), and b) changes in the inlet streams flow rates. These disturbances are modelled as step changes with +/- 50%, and +/- 30% with respect to their average value, respectively. Note that the nominal variability of these variables is characterized by a coefficient of variance of 21% for (a) and of 7% for (b), hence the disturbances represent a large departure from the operating point of the system. Figure 3 shows the disturbances imposed for three of the exchangers over 1 year. Flow rates exhibit a natural variability with significant step change deviations from normal operation. The parameters used in the multiloop scheme are: a sampling frequency of 1 day for the plant and the control layer, and 15 days for the scheduling layer; a future prediction horizon (FPH) of 10 days for control and 90 days for scheduling; a past estimation horizon (PEH) of 20 days for control, and 60 for scheduling.

a)   b)

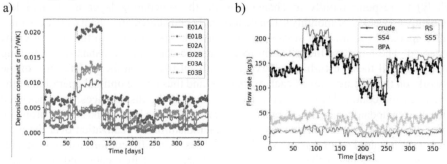

Figure 3. Large disturbances considered for the case study. a) deposition constants, b) inlet flow rates.

4. Results and analysis

The integrated cleaning scheduling and control problem is solved repeatedly online for 1 year of operation, with the actual refinery inputs to the network and the large disturbances as above. The optimal closed loop solution is compared to the actual mitigation strategies used in the refinery (records of cleanings and flow control). Figure 4 shows the closed loop cleaning schedule obtained at the end of the year, with the periods of step change disturbances highlighted (red area for a positive disturbance, blue area for a negative one), and the number of cleanings per exchanger on the right. For scenario a) (deposition changes), the number of cleanings is higher during the period of high fouling (+50% in deposition constants) than during periods of low fouling (-50% in deposition constants) or periods of nominal operating conditions. For scenario b) (flowrate changes), a higher number of cleanings is observed during the periods of high flow rates than during those of low flow rate. The time between cleanings (e.g. for E01) decreases when the inlet flow rate decreases. The online schemes reacts well to the higher/lower fouling caused respectively by higher/lower deposit rates and lower/higher flowrates (high flows increase shear stress, partially removing deposits or reducing the fouling rate in some exchangers).

a)   b)

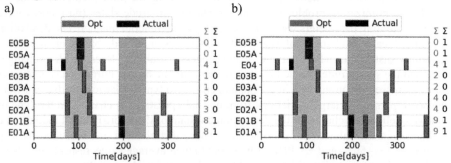

Figure 4. Closed loop cleaning scheduling considering large disturbances. a) Disturbance in the deposition constant, and b) disturbance in the inlet flow rates

Figure 5 shows the closed loop response of the split ratio to E02 branch (a) and fouling resistance in exchanger E03A/B (b) following large disturbances in the inlet flow rates (scenario b). The effect of the natural variability is observed as small oscillations of the fouling resistance, while a larger departure from nominal behavior is introduced by the large disturbances. High crude flow rates (red area) increase the shear stress in the exchangers of branch E03A/B and the deposit is partially removed. The optimal flow distribution plays a key role in reducing deposition in some units, thus enabling to avoid or delay cleaning. This is not observed in the mitigation strategy previously used, where the benefits of the reacting to disturbances and integrating decisions are not observed. All these interactions and trade-offs are here considered implicitly at each update in the online methodology, at the two decision levels of control and scheduling.

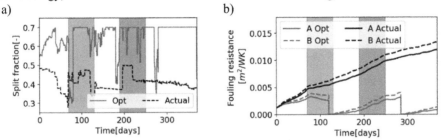

Figure 5. Closed loop response of split ratio profile a) and fouling resistance in exchanger E03A/B b) following large disturbances in the inlet flow rates (scenario b).

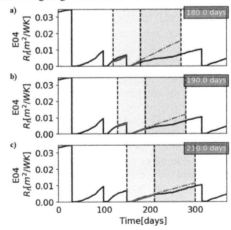

Figure 6. Fouling resistance of E04 in the PEH (light blue band) and the FPH (grey band) for three consecutive solutions of the scheduling layer, scenario (a). The top right corner of each figure indicates the current time (solution of MHE and NMPC).

Figure 6 shows the solution of the scheduling layer problems (MHE and NMPC) at three consecutives updates of scenario (a) around the second major step from nominal operation to low deposition rate. It shows the actual fouling resistance in E04 during the closed loop operation (black, continuous line), the values estimated by the MHE (blue, dotted line), and the predicted values by the NMPC solution (red, dashed line). This shows that large disturbances affect the prediction capabilities of the model, and that without any modification or update of the model, the predictions are erroneous and lead to suboptimal of infeasible operating modes. This figure also illustrates the excellent predictive capabilities achieved using the online framework, how the model adapts to large disturbances and how it improves the prediction at each update. Initially (Fig. 6a), the

MHE problem includes most of the points of the nominal operation, so the NMPC solution overestimates the effects of fouling during low deposition operation. Then (Fig. 6b), more recent information about the disturbances is available to the MHE problem and the NMPC prediction improves. Finally (Fig. 6c), with a larger data set from the current operation the prediction matches the actual realization observed in the plant. The adaptive solution of the scheduling layer problems allows improving the prediction capabilities and accuracy of the model faster in the presence of large disturbances. Overall, for scenario a) this approach reduces total operating cost from $ 12.3 MM (actual operation) to $ 11.4 MM, representing savings of $ 0.9 MM (7.3%) during one year of operation. If no cleanings are performed and the flow split is fixed at 50%, the total cost of the operation for this scenario is $ 13.0 MM, highlighting the need of mitigation strategies.

5. Conclusions

The online approach presented simultaneously and optimally defines the flow distribution and cleaning schedules of HEN under fouling. Its two feedback control loops accurately capture process variability over various time scales and react appropriately to it. It deals efficiently with both the nominal variability of the process and the large operational changes characteristic of actual refinery operation. Operational feasibility is maintained, and the total operating cost is minimized regardless of disturbances. Results for a realistic case study show the importance of considering disturbances, and how varying operating conditions – inlet flow rates and fouling rates – affect the optimal flow distribution and cleaning schedules. Future work will investigate other disturbances, the feedback loop specification, and the overall closed loop stability of the integrated solution.

References

Ebert, Richmond, and IL Panchal. 1995. "Analysis of Exxon Crude-Oil-Slip Stream Coking Data." In . United States. http://www.osti.gov/scitech/servlets/purl/453433.

Georgiadis, Michael C, Lazaros G Papageorgiou, and Sandro Macchietto. 2000. "Optimal Cleaning Policies in Heat Exchanger Networks under Rapid Fouling." *Industrial & Engineering Chemistry Research* 39 (2): 441–54. https://doi.org/10.1021/ie990166c.

Ishiyama, E M, W R Paterson, and D I Wilson. 2009. "Platform for Techno-Economic Analysis of Fouling Mitigation Options in Refinery Preheat Trains." *Energy & Fuels* 23 (3): 1323–37. https://doi.org/10.1021/ef8005614.

Lavaja, Javier H, and Miguel J Bagajewicz. 2004. "On a New MILP Model for the Planning of Heat-Exchanger Network Cleaning." *Industrial & Engineering Chemistry Research* 43 (14): 3924–38. https://doi.org/10.1021/ie034178g.

Lozano Santamaria, Federico, and Sandro Macchietto. 2018. "Integration of Optimal Cleaning Scheduling and Control of Heat Exchanger Networks Undergoing Fouling: Model and Formulation." *Industrial & Engineering Chemistry Research* 57 (38): 12842–60. https://doi.org/10.1021/acs.iecr.8b01701.

Lozano Santamaria, Federico, and Sandro Macchietto. 2019a. "Online Integration of Optimal Cleaning Scheduling and Control of Heat Exchanger Networks under Fouling." *Industrial & Engineering Chemistry Research*, November, acs.iecr.9b04531. https://doi.org/10.1021/acs.iecr.9b04531.

Santamaria, Federico Lozano, and Sandro Macchietto. 2019b. "Integration of Optimal Cleaning Scheduling and Control of Heat Exchanger Networks under Fouling: MPCC Solution." *Computers & Chemical Engineering* 126 (July): 128–46. https://doi.org/10.1016/J.COMPCHEMENG.2019.04.012.

Silva, R. L. de, L.H. Costa, and Eduardo M Queiroz. 2015. "Stream Flow Rate Optimization for Fouling Mitigation in the Presence of Thermohydraulic Channeling." In *Proceedings of International Conference on Heat Exchanger Fouling and Cleaning*, edited by M.R Malayeri, H Muller-Steinhagen, and A.P Walkinson, 384–91.

Sauro Pierucci, Flavio Manenti, Giulia Bozzano, Davide Manca (Eds.)
Proceedings of the 30th European Symposium on Computer Aided Process Engineering
(ESCAPE30), May 24-27, 2020, Milano, Italy. © 2020 Elsevier B.V. All rights reserved.
http://dx.doi.org/10.1016/B978-0-12-823377-1.50202-0

Integrated Planning of Industrial Gas Supply Chains

Yena Lee[a], Alba Carrero-Parreño[a], Lazaros G. Papageorgiou[a,*],
Sivaraman Ramaswamy[b], Jose M. Pinto[b]

[a] *Centre for Process Systems Engineering, Department of Chemical Engineering, UCL
(University College London), Torrington Place, London WC1E 7JE, UK*

[b] *Linde plc., 10 Riverview Drive, Danbury CT 06810, United States*

l.papageorgiou@ucl.ac.uk

Abstract

In this work, we propose a Mixed Integer Linear Programming (MILP) model for optimal
planning of industrial gas supply chain, which integrates supply contracts, production
scheduling, truck and rail-car scheduling, as well as inventory management under the
Vendor Managed Inventory (VMI) paradigm. The objective used here is minimisation of
the total operating cost consisting of purchasing of raw material, production, and
transportation costs by trucks/rail-cars so as to satisfy customer demands over a given
time horizon. The key decisions for production sites include production schedule and
purchase schedule of raw material, while the distribution decisions involve customer to
plant/depot allocation, quantity transported through rail network, truck delivery amounts,
and times. In addition, a relaxation approach is proposed to solve the problem efficiently.
An industrial case study is evaluated to illustrate the applicability of the integrated
optimisation framework.

Keywords: Integrated supply chain planning, discount contract model, rail-car and truck
scheduling, relaxation approach

1. Introduction

The optimisation of supply chain planning for the industrial gas business is a challenge
when the supply chain structure integrates multiple decisions such as: supply contracts,
inventory management, production and distribution scheduling, etc. As the level of detail
increases, it becomes more difficult to optimally solve the model due to its complexity.
However, optimal decisions considering a coordinated industrial gas supply chain have
significant benefits (Marchetti et al., 2014). In their research, potential cost savings were
identified with coordination between production and distribution in industrial gas supply
chain. Nevertheless, expensive computational cost is required when dealing with large
size examples. Recently, some efforts have been made to tackle this limitation. You et al.
(2011) developed a mixed integer linear programming model which considers distribution
and inventory decisions of industrial gas supply chain planning simultaneously. They also
proposed two different approaches to solve the large-scale instances. The first one is
based on a two-level decomposition method and the second one is based on a continuous
approximation method. Additionally, Zamarripa et al. (2016) proposed a rolling horizon
decomposition approach for full space optimisation problem which coordinate
production-distribution decisions, and Zhang et al. (2017) proposed an MILP model and
an iterative heuristic approach for the multiscale production routing problem which
integrates production, distribution, and inventory decisions.

In this work, we investigate a problem of optimal integrated production and distribution planning that reliably produces CO_2 from a number of plants (and sourced from external third-party suppliers) and distributes high quality CO_2 product to a network of depots and customers. The problem is formulated as a mixed integer linear programming (MILP)model which can simultaneously deal with purchase contracts, inventory management, production, and truck/rail-car scheduling. Furthermore, we present a relaxation approach to handle the computational complexity of a large-scale industrial problem.

2. Problem Definition

This study considers an existing CO_2 supply chain network (schematized in Figure 1) located in the U.S. which comprises of external CO_2 suppliers, production plants, depots, third-party suppliers, and customers. The crude CO_2 is purchased from external suppliers by discount contracts and transformed into high purity CO_2 in the plants. This pure CO_2 can also be sourced from third-party suppliers. The distribution between different locations to satisfy the customers' demand is guaranteed via rail-cars or trucks. The rail-cars can distribute the CO_2 product from plants/third-parties to depots using existing rail infrastructure, and the trucks from the plants, depots and/or third parties to the customers. The customers' demand is controlled by the Vendor Managed Inventory (VMI) paradigm. Under this policy, each customer inventory level is monitored to deliver the product when it reaches close to the minimum level.

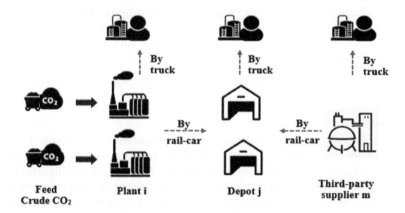

Figure 1. Network structure for the CO_2 supply chain planning problem

The problem can be stated as follows:

Given (a) for each plant: its location, maximum production capacities, and corresponding production and crude CO_2 purchasing costs; (b) for each depot: its location; (c) for each third-party supplier: its location, maximum purchasing amount, and purchasing costs; (d) for customers: their locations, and daily consumption rates; (e) for inventories: initial levels, minimum levels, and maximum levels; (f) for trucks and rail-cars: its loading capacities, maximum quantities, and transfer unit costs;

Determine (a) Production schedule; (b) Purchasing schedule of crude CO_2 and CO_2 product from external suppliers and third party suppliers, respectively; (c) Allocation of plant/depot/third party to customer; (d) Rail-car schedule;

So as to minimise the overall cost of integrated CO_2 supply chain planning by satisfying customer demands over a given time horizon.

3. Mathematical Framework

The overall problem is formulated as a Mixed Integer Linear Programming (MILP) model which integrates supply contracts, truck and rail-car scheduling, as well as inventory management under the Vendor Managed Inventory (VMI) paradigm. A brief outline of some of the model constraints is next given.

$$min. \ TC^{total} \tag{1}$$

$$TC^{total} = TC^{raw} + TC^{prod} + TC^{st} + TC^{os} + TC^{rail} + TC^{truck} \tag{2}$$

Eq. (1) is the objective function and considers the minimization of total cost which consists of crude CO_2 cost, production cost, plant start-up cost, product CO_2 purchasing cost, and transportation cost via rail-car and truck.

$$TC^{raw} = \sum_{in} C_{in}^{raw} F_{in} \tag{3}$$

$$\sum_n F_{in} = \sum_t R_{it} \qquad\qquad \forall \, i \tag{4}$$

$$(\lambda_{in} - \lambda_{i,n-1})y_{i,n+1} \leq F_{in} \leq (\lambda_{in} - \lambda_{i,n-1})y_{in} \quad \forall \, i, n = \{1,2, \dots N-1\} \tag{5}$$

$$F_{in} \leq My_{in} \qquad\qquad \forall \, i, n = N \tag{6}$$

$$y_{in} \geq y_{i,n+1} \qquad\qquad \forall \, i, n = \{1,2, \dots N-1\} \tag{7}$$

Eq. (3)-(7) represent a discount contract model for crude CO_2. The proposed discount contract model follows the model published by Park et al. (2006). In their formulation, the purchasing cost is decided by a binary variable depending on both cost region n and time period t. However, as in our problem the discount is applied to the total cumulative purchasing amount, it is reformulated considering a non-time-dependent binary variable. Eq. (3) calculates the total cost for crude CO_2 which depends on the purchased amount in the cost region n (F_{in}), and the corresponding cost for plant i (C_{in}^{raw}). Eq. (4) indicates that the total purchased amount in each cost region is equal to the sum of the purchased amount in each time period t. Eq. (5) determines the amount corresponding on each cost region; i.e. y_{in} is equal to 1 when the total purchased amount $\sum_t R_{it}$ is in the cost region n. Here, λ_{in} is the breakpoint of cost region n, where the price is reduced when the total cumulative purchasing amount during a time horizon excess the breakpoint. Eq. (6) restricts the amount in the last lost region ($n=N$); i.e. F_{iN} has to be lower than the M value.

Finally, Eq. (7) is a logical relationship which avoid the selection of intermediate cost regions.

$$TC^{truck} = \sum_{s \in \{I,J,M\}} \sum_{k} \sum_{l \in l_{Truck}} \sum_{t} C^{truck} D_{sk} Q_{sklt} \tag{8}$$

$$\sum_{l \in l_{Truck}} \sum_{k} \alpha_{sk} Q_{sklt} \leq NT_s^{max} Cap^{truck} \qquad \forall t, s \in \{I,J,M\} \tag{9}$$

Eq. (8)-(9) state the relaxed formulation for the truck scheduling problem to estimate the trucking cost and allocate plants/depots/third-parties to customers without considering the detailed scheduling. By using this formulation, the discrete variables associated with the detailed truck scheduling are relaxed; therefore, the computational efficiency is improved when dealing with a large number of customers, plants and time horizon. Eq. (8) calculates the transfer cost by trucks departing from plants i, depots j, and third-parties m. The truck cost is based on the unit transfer cost (C^{truck}), travelling distance (D_{sk}), and loading amount (Q_{sklt}). Constraint (9) limits the total product amount transferred by trucks. Because trucks can make multiple trips per time period t, not only the loading capacity but also the number of the multiple trips should be considered to limit the total amount transferred during a time period t. However, the complexity of the model increases if integer variables are introduced to consider the number of the multiple trips. Here, the duration of the round-trip between the locations (α_{sk}), which is formed as a fraction of a time period, is introduced to approximate the total transferred amount by the multiple trips instead of introducing the integer variables. By using the fraction of travelling time (α_{sk}), all the integer variables can be relaxed into continuous variables (Q_{sklt}). Finally, the total amount transferred by trucks during a time period t is restricted by the loading capacity (Cap^{truck}), and the number of trucks available at each plant, depot, and third-party (NT_s^{max}).

4. Case Study and Results

The proposed model is applied for a large-scale industrial supply chain planning problem given by Linde which includes 700+ customers, total 30+ of plants, depots, transshipments, third-parties, and one month discretised into 30 days. To compare the efficiency and validity of the relaxation approach, the case study is solved with the proposed MILP model (M^R), which includes the approach and the integrated one (M), which involves the discrete variables to indicate the multiple trips made by trucks. Both models are implemented into GAMS software and solved using Gurobi 8.1.0 on Intel 3.60 GHz, 16.0 GB RAM computer.

Table 1. Optimal solution and computational performance

Model	M	M^R
Equations	252,364	140,869
Continuous variables	138,253	138,253
Discrete variables	653,156	5,411
Optimality gap [%]	5	1
CPU time [s]	144,371	145
Total cost [M$]	5.73	5.25

Table 1 describes the problem size, optimal solution and computational performance of the rigorous and relax model. It can be observed that the case study cannot be solved with the rigorous formulation in an acceptable computational time since the large number of discrete variables. It requires 40 h to reach an optimal solution with 5 % of optimality gap. Conversely, the CPU time significantly decreases solving the relaxed formulation as the number of discrete decisions is reduced to 5,411. This enables the model to handle the large-scale problem by reducing computational time dramatically. Additionally, to validate the optimal solution, the gaps of the optimal costs generated by model M and model M^R are presented in Table 2. The table shows that these gaps are within 5 % except for the start-up and third-party cost, but they only account for 1 % and 2 % of the total cost, respectively as it can be shown in the total cost breakdown of Figure 2.

Table 2. Gaps between optimal solution from the model M and model M^R

Cost breakdown	TC^{raw}	TC^{prod}	TC^{st}	TC^{os}	TC^{rail}	TC^{truck}
Gap [%]	1	0	14	0	5	2

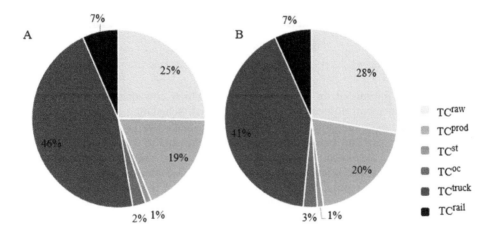

Figure 2. Total cost breakdown of (A) the model M and (B) the model M^R

In the figure, each breakdown cost of total cost obtained from each model account for almost the same percentage which means that the relaxed approach proposed can predict optimal costs without significant degradation of solution quality.

Figure 3 and Figure 4 illustrate part of the production and rail-car scheduling results gained from model M^R. In the production scheduling result, each value in the colored cells shows the production amount during a time period *t*. In the rail-car scheduling result, the solid cells represent one-way trip, whereas the vertical striped cells represent returning trip. The figures reveal that the proposed model is capable of providing detailed solutions for the production scheduling problem and rail-car scheduling problem without considering detailed truck scheduling.

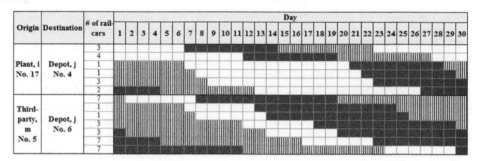

Figure 3. Gantt chart for rail-car schedule

Plant, i	Day																													
	1	2	3	4	5	6	7	8	9	10	11	12	13	14	15	16	17	18	19	20	21	22	23	24	25	26	27	28	29	30
No. 1	325	247	228	228	228	228	228	228	228	228	228	228	228	228	228	228	228	228	228	228	228	228	228	228	325	228				
No. 2	50	50	50	50	50	50	50	50	50	50	50	50	50	50	50	50	50	50	50	50	50	50	50	50	50	50	50	50	50	50
No. 3	430	372	301	420	430	362	301	301	301	351	301	376	308	301	301	301	368	338	301	311	301	301	301	301	301	403				
No. 4			161	161	161	161	161	161	161	190	230	230	230	230	230	230	161	230	161	161	161									
No. 5	400	284	400												318	400	280	400	305	280	280	280	280							
No. 6						209	170	188	154	154	168	220	220	154	154	154	154	154	154	164	154	154	154	154	154	154				
No. 7	263	263	263	263	263	263	263	263	263	263	263	263	263	263	263	263	263	263	263	263	263	263								
No. 8						350	350	350	350	350	350	350	350	305	350	350	350	350	350	350	350	350	245	350	350	350				

Figure 4. Production schedule

5. Conclusions

This work has introduced an MILP formulation which considers supply contracts, inventory management, production, rail-car and truck scheduling simultaneously. To handle the complexity of the integrated problem, a relaxation approach is applied in the truck scheduling problem where discrete variables associated with the detailed truck scheduling are relaxed to continuous variables. The proposed strategy successfully solve a real large-scale industrial gas supply chain planning case study given by Linde. The results prove that the proposed approach has the capability of finding an optimal solution without significant degradation of quality, as well as high computational efficiency.

References

P. A. Marchetti, V. Gupta, I. E. Grossmann, L. Cook, P.-M. Valton, T. Singh, T. Li, J. André, 2014. Simultaneous production and distribution of industrial gas supply-chains. Computers & Chemical Engineering 69, 39–58.

M. Park, S. Park, F. D. Mele, I. E. Grossmann, 2006. Modeling of purchase and sales contracts in supply chain optimization. Industrial & Engineering Chemistry Research 45 (14), 5013–5026.

F. You, J. M. Pinto, E. Capón, I. E. Grossmann, N. Arora, L. Megan, 2011. Optimal distribution-inventory planning of industrial gases. i. fast computational strategies for large-scale problems. Industrial & Engineering Chemistry Research 50 (5), 2910–2927.

M. Zamarripa, P. A. Marchetti, I. E. Grossmann, T. Singh, I. Lotero, A. Gopalakrishnan, B. Besancon, J. André, 2016. Rolling horizon approach for production–distribution coordination of industrial gases supply chains. Industrial & Engineering Chemistry Research 55 (9), 2646–2660.

Q. Zhang, A. Sundaramoorthy, I. E. Grossmann, J. M. Pinto, 2017. Multiscale production routing in multicommodity supply chains with complex production facilities. Computers & Operations Research 79, 207–222.

Sauro Pierucci, Flavio Manenti, Giulia Bozzano, Davide Manca (Eds.)
Proceedings of the 30th European Symposium on Computer Aided Process Engineering
(ESCAPE30), May 24-27, 2020, Milano, Italy. © 2020 Elsevier B.V. All rights reserved.
http://dx.doi.org/10.1016/B978-0-12-823377-1.50203-2

Advanced Process Control of an Industrial Depropanizer Column using Data-based Inferential Sensors

Martin Mojto[a], Karol Ľubuský[b], Miroslav Fikar[a] and Radoslav Paulen[a]

[a]*Faculty of Chemical and Food Technology, Slovak University of Technology in Bratislava, Bratislava, Slovakia*
[b]*Slovnaft, a.s., Bratislava, Slovakia*
martin.mojto@stuba.sk

Abstract

Inferential sensors are used in industry to infer the values of the imprecisely and infrequently measured (or completely unmeasured) variables from measured variables (e.g., pressures, temperatures). This work deals with the design of inferential sensors suitable for an advanced process control of a depropanizer column of the Slovnaft refinery in Bratislava, Slovakia. We design linear inferential models of top and bottom product compositions. Model calibration is performed using historical production data. We study the effectiveness of several data-based methods (PCA, PLS, LASSO) for the design of inferential sensors. Our results show that the methods, which promote model sparsity are more suitable. Validation using a rigorous mathematical model shows that the designed inferential sensors are sufficient for the advanced process control of the column.

Keywords: Inferential Sensors, Data-based Models, Process Control.

1. Introduction

Majority of advanced controllers in industry is based on linear input-output models (Qin and Badgwell, 2003). This is usually sufficient because of the existence of corrective feedback actions, i.e., receding-horizon principle. In many cases, the input-output models do not include main process characteristics, e.g., product quality, since they are often expensive or impossible to measure. The process performance can thus be improved by designing soft-sensors (also called inferentials), which can infer the values of the unmeasured variables from other measured variables (e.g., pressures, temperatures) and improve the overall process management (Weber and Brosilow, 1972; Joseph and Brosilow, 1978; Joseph, 1999).

The inferential sensor stands for a model designed to predict hard-to-measure variable according to other easily measured variables. In chemical industry, hard-to-measure variables are typically concentrations of products, since online concentration sensors are expensive or too slow for effective monitoring and control. Several works were devoted to state estimation and control of (chemical) process using inferentials (Mejdell and Skogestad, 1991, 1993; Zhang, 2001; Kano et al., 2003; Parvizi Moghadam et al., 2019). The approaches are ranging from simple enhancement of monitoring and control—by heuristically combining several variables to compensate the sensor-noise or external disturbance (e.g., pressure-corrected temperature control)—to the use of

Acknowledgements: This research received funding from the Slovak Research and Development Agency under the project APVV 15-0007 and from the Scientific Grant Agency of the Slovak Republic under the grant 1/0004/17.

Table 1: Composition of feed stream of the depropanizer column.

C3 fraction	C4 fraction			C5 fraction
Propane	n-Butane	Trans-2-Butene	1-Butene	Isopentane
Propylene	Isobutane	Cis-2-Butene	Isobutene	

sophisticated data-mining techniques, which select the optimal structure of the inferential sensor using available measured outputs and their historical records (Morari and Stephanopoulos, 1980).

This work deals with the design of inferential sensors for advanced process control (APC) of a depropanizer column of the Slovnaft refinery situated in Bratislava, Slovakia. We design linear inferential models of top and bottom product composition in order to provide a simple and appropriate structure of the soft-sensors for the APC of the plant. Model calibration is carried out using historical production data. We use various data-based modeling techniques, including principal component analysis (PCA), partial least-squares (PLS), and Least Absolute Shrinkage and Selection Operator (LASSO). We compare the accuracy and the effectiveness of the designed inferential sensors using the validation dataset from historical plant data and also using a rigourous mathematical model of a depropanizer column via gPROMS ModelBuilder. We also assess the appropriateness of the use of a linear soft-sensor for the control of the product quality.

2. Problem Description

The studied depropanizer column (see scheme in Fig. 1) contains 40 trays, operates in above-the-atmospheric pressure, and its feed composition is shown in Tab. 1. The column serves to separate feed mixture to C3-fraction-rich distillate product and to C4/C5-fraction-rich bottom product. The available operational degrees of freedom are feed flowrate F, bottom product flowrate B, distillate flowrate D, reflux flowrate R, heat duty in the reboiler Q_B, and heat duty in the condenser Q_D. Several of these variables are available as historical data. These are marked correspondingly in Fig. 1. The plant measurements, also available from historical data, are pressure at the top of the column p_D, pressure at the bottom of the column p_B, and temperatures of distillate T_D, at the 10th tray T_{10}, at the 37th tray T_{37} and at the bottom T_B.

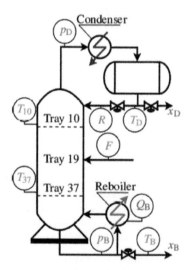

Figure 1: A schematic diagram of the depropanizer column.

It is evident that the use of thermodynamic properties model to monitor top/bottom stream compositions is prohibitive in this case, even under any appropriate ideality assumptions. This is because there are too many degrees of freedom for a seven-component mixture that cannot be inferred from plant data. According to previous paragraph, there are eleven possible input variables to select for the design of an inferential sensor. Current inferentials (denoted as ref), used in the refinery for monitoring/control of concentrations of C4/C5 fraction in the distillate (x_D) and of C3 fraction in the bottom stream (x_B), are designed according to King (2011) in the following form:

$$x_D = a_1 p_D + a_2 T_{10} + a_3 \frac{R}{F}, \qquad x_B = a_1 p_B + a_2 T_{37} + a_3 \frac{Q_B}{F}. \qquad (1)$$

Our goal will be to identify models of inferential sensors in the following form

$$x = (a_1, a_2, \ldots, a_{n_p}) \left(F, R, Q_B, p_D, p_B, T_D, T_B, T_{10}, T_{37}, \frac{R}{F}, \frac{Q_B}{F} \right)^T = a^T m, \tag{2}$$

where m is the vector of available input variables for the inferential sensor and $a \in \mathbb{R}^{n_p}$ is the vector of parameters of the inferential sensor.

3. Identification of Inferential Models

Given n data points, we use various statistical methods in order to design the inferential sensors.

- The basic method is Ordinary Least-Squares (OLS) regression. This method estimates the parameters of an inferential sensor according to

$$\min_a \sum_{i=1}^n (x_i - a^T m_i)^2, \tag{3}$$

  which minimizes sum of squared errors between measured compositions and compositions estimated from inferential sensors.

- Principal Component Analysis (PCA) (Pearson, 1901) is a method of identifying a $\tilde{n}_p$-dimensional subspace ($\tilde{n}_p \leq n_p$) of orthogonal coordinates that exhibit a maximum variation in a given dataset. The principal components are identified by SVD decomposition of the covariance matrix of the input dataset MM^T, $M := (m_1, m_2, \ldots, m_n)$, taking the eigenvectors (for subset definition) and the associated eigenvalues (for measure of variance). The (PCA) regression is then done over the selected subspace using (3).

- Partial Least Squares (PLS) regression (Wold et al., 1984) is similar to PCA (Dunn et al., 1989) with the difference that it takes a cross-covariance matrix between inputs and outputs MX^T, $X := (x_1, x_2, \ldots, x_n)$.

- Least Absolute Shrinkage and Selection Operator (LASSO) (Santosa and Symes, 1986) is a method that simultaneously identifies the structure of the model and model parameters by

$$\min_a \sum_{i=1}^n (x_i - a^T m_i)^2 + \lambda \|a\|_1, \tag{4}$$

  where λ is a weight between model accuracy and model over-parameterization.

Note that among the presented methods, the PCA method comprises a certain distinct feature. As it does not require any output data, it can potentially be applied on much larger datasets in our general problem setup. This comes since the industrial data are usually available with much finer time granularity for the online sensors rather than for infrequent and expensive measurements.

4. Design of Inferential Sensors using Industrial Data

The design of inferential sensors is performed according to the data from more than two years of production (13.12.2016–21.2.2019) of the depropanizer column. The distillate composition is measured once per month and therefore only 28 measurements is available for the given period. Bottom inferential sensor is design according to 176 measurements as the concentration of this product is measured approximately once per week. The input data provided by online sensors are measured every 30 minutes, which gives an input dataset of 38,360 measurements.

A gross error detection and its subsequent reduction was performed on the given dataset by performing an SVD decomposition of the covariance matrix MM^T and by retaining only those data

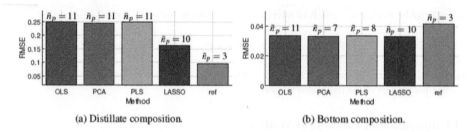

(a) Distillate composition. (b) Bottom composition.

Figure 2: Accuracy of the designed inferential sensors according to the industrial validation data. The number of model input variables ($\tilde{n}_p$) is shown on top of each bar.

points that are inside the $\pm 3\sigma$ confidence ellipsoid given by the covariance matrix. The excluded points consist mostly of plant start-up, shutdown and upsets data.

When applying the methods mentioned in Section 3, we use 50% of the data for training and 50% of the data for validation. We use the implementations of the design methods available within MATLAB. We are interested in simplest possible structures, which is interesting for APC applications. For this reason, when using PCA and PLS to identify the model structure, we select only those input variables whose principal components explain 90% of variance in the data. We use root mean square error (RMSE) to assess the accuracy of the designed inferential sensors.

We designed inferential sensors according to the OLS, PCA, PLS and LASSO. We repeated the design 1,000 times, each time randomly distributing the available data among the training and validation datasets. Presented results stand for mean values obtained. The results are shown in Fig. 2 in terms of accuracy of the sensors on the validation dataset for distillate and for bottom composition. Accuracy of the model is influenced by the ability of the method to escape from model over-parameterization. We show the number of variables that the model uses on the top of the bar that represents model accuracy.

Overall, we notice that the nature of the problem of designing the inferential sensors differs between distillate and bottom sensor. While the best distillate sensor uses only few (three) input variables, the most accurate bottom soft-sensors retain 7–11 out of eleven available input variables (all the temperatures and pressures). This is attributed to the small dataset available for the tuning of the distillate sensor and is subject of further analysis.

When comparing the different methods, we can find that OLS is not able to reduce the number of parameters/inputs of the inferential model in both cases. PCA and PLS perform similarly, although the promotion of model sparsity improves with the number of available data (bottom sensor). LASSO achieves slightly better results than OLS in both cases by being able to sparsify the model slightly, even if the dataset is small. The performance of the current on-site inferential sensor (ref) is very good in case of distillate composition inferential. However, there seems to be a room for improvement (around 20%) of the inferential sensor for bottom composition.

5. Analysis of Inferential Sensors using Synthetic Data

In order to confirm our findings from the previous chapter and to analyse the further possible enhancements of inferential sensors, we designed the mathematical model of depropanizer column in gPROMS ModelBuilder. The model is built according to the parameters from the technical documentation of the depropanizer in the Slovnaft refinery and validated in the simulations with several step changes. We use 200 different (steady state) measurements for the design of inferential sensors. Compared to the historical data from the refinery, this is much larger dataset with many more different operating points (steady-states). The simulated measurements are corrupted with normally distributed random noise of similar magnitudes as present in the industrial data.

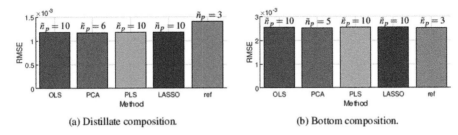

(a) Distillate composition.   (b) Bottom composition.

Figure 3: Accuracy of the designed inferential sensors according to synthetic validation data. The number of model input variables ($\tilde{n}_p$) is shown on top of each bar.

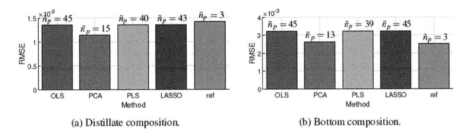

(a) Distillate composition.   (b) Bottom composition.

Figure 4: Accuracy of the designed inferential sensors according to synthetic validation data for 49 possible input variables. The number of model input variables ($\tilde{n}_p$) is shown on top of each bar.

First, we use the information from the same sensors as in the previous section to mimic the case of studied column instrumentation. The results are shown in Fig. 3. We can mostly see that they confirm our previous conclusions. As the noise present in the data corresponds to the assumptions of the least-squares regression and variance analysis, all the methods exhibit an improved performance. Even the OLS method is able to sparsify the model to the extent of PLS and LASSO method. PCA can go even further without compromising the model quality. The slight improvement of the PCA-based distillate sensor w.r.t. ref is caused by adding variables R and F into the sensor structure.

Next, we consider data from more online sensors, 49 instead of 11. The input dataset is enriched by all the tray temperatures (T_{1-40}). In this case, we can conclude that bottom sensor cannot be much improved using new instrumentation. The optimal distillate inferential sensor seems to be 21 % more accurate that the current ref model but it is also much more complicated, one would need at least nine new sensors for the model by PCA. Lastly, we also see that the LASSO method does not cope well with situations when much dimension-reduction is needed.

At last, we tested the inferential control in the scenario, where the plant model is controlled by PI controllers using the following CV-MV pairs: p_D-Q_C, h_B-B, h_C-D, x_D-R, and x_D-Q_B. The results from the simulation of control using PCA-based inferential sensors are shown in Fig. 5. The prediction and steady-state error is indicated by evaluating the true plant response. We observe 90–95 % accuracy of the control, which is correspondence with the results from prediction accuracy analysis. The designed sensors are thus appropriate for control (APC) purposes.

6. Conclusions

We studied the design of linear inferential sensors for the top and bottom product composition of an industrial depropanizer column. We studied the accuracy and the effectiveness of several advanced data-based methods (PCA, PLS, LASSO). We used historical plant data for model calibration.

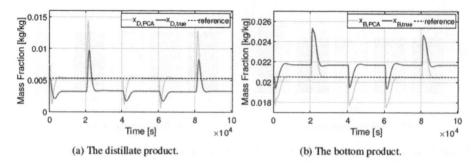

(a) The distillate product.　　　(b) The bottom product.

Figure 5: The comparison of product concentrations from the simulation of depropanizer column with implemented PCA inferential sensors.

Further we used a rigorous process model to confirm our findings and to analyze appropriateness of inferential control of the depropanizer column and its potential further improvements. The results show that the designed inferential sensors are sufficient for the advanced process control of the column. The methods that separate model-structure identification and the model regression are found more suitable.

References

W. Dunn, D. Scott, W. Glen, 1989. Principal components analysis and partial least squares regression. Tetrahedron Computer Methodology 2 (6), 349 – 376.

B. Joseph, June 1999. A tutorial on inferential control and its applications. In: Proceedings of the 1999 American Control Conference. Vol. 5. pp. 3106–3118.

B. Joseph, C. B. Brosilow, 1978. Inferential control of processes: Part i. steady state analysis and design. AIChE Journal 24 (3), 485–492.

M. Kano, N. Showchaiya, S. Hasebe, I. Hashimoto, 2003. Inferential control of distillation compositions: selection of model and control configuration. Control Engineering Practice 11 (8), 927 – 933.

M. King, 2011. Process Control: A Practical Approach. John Wiley & Sons Ltd., iSBN: 978-0-470-97587-9.

T. Mejdell, S. Skogestad, 1991. Composition estimator in a pilot-plant distillation column using multiple temperatures. Industrial & Engineering Chemistry Research 30 (12), 2555–2564.

T. Mejdell, S. Skogestad, 1993. Output estimation using multiple secondary measurements: High-purity distillation. AIChE Journal 39 (10), 1641–1653.

M. Morari, G. Stephanopoulos, 1980. Studies in the synthesis of control structures for chemical processes: Part iii: Optimal selection of secondary measurements within the framework of state estimation in the presence of persistent unknown disturbances. AIChE Journal 26 (2), 247–260.

R. Parvizi Moghadam, J. Sadeghi, F. Shahraki, 2019. Optimization of time-variable-parameter model for data-based soft sensor of industrial debutanizer. Optimal Control Applications and MethodsIn Press.

K. Pearson, 1901. Liii. on lines and planes of closest fit to systems of points in space. The London, Edinburgh, and Dublin Philosophical Magazine and Journal of Science 2 (11), 559–572.

S. J. Qin, T. A. Badgwell, 2003. A survey of industrial model predictive control technology. Control Engineering Practice 11 (7), 733 – 764.

F. Santosa, W. W. Symes, 1986. Linear inversion of band-limited reflection seismograms. SIAM Journal on Scientific and Statistical Computing 7 (4), 1307–1330.

R. Weber, C. Brosilow, 1972. The use of secondary measurements to improve control. AIChE Journal 18 (3), 614–623.

S. Wold, A. Ruhe, H. Wold, W. J. Dunn, III, 1984. The collinearity problem in linear regression. the partial least squares (PLS) approach to generalized inverses. SIAM Journal on Scientific and Statistical Computing 5 (3), 735–743.

J. Zhang, 2001. Inferential feedback control of distillation composition based on PCR and PLS models. In: Proceedings of the 2001 American Control Conference. Vol. 2. pp. 1196–1201.

Sauro Pierucci, Flavio Manenti, Giulia Bozzano, Davide Manca (Eds.)
Proceedings of the 30th European Symposium on Computer Aided Process Engineering
(ESCAPE30), May 24-27, 2020, Milano, Italy. © 2020 Elsevier B.V. All rights reserved.
http://dx.doi.org/10.1016/B978-0-12-823377-1.50204-4

MPC for Process Heat Supply Systems: Considering Load Prediction Uncertainty Caused by Human Operators

Florian Fuhrmann[*],Alexander Schirrer, Martin Kozek

Technische Universität Wien, Institute of Mechanics and Mechatronics,

Getreidemarkt 9/BA, 1060 Vienna, Austria
florian.fuhrmann@tuwien.ac.at

Abstract

The aim of this work is to define guidelines for model predictive control dealing with uncertain pulse-like disturbances caused by human operators. Measurement data of an industrial use case is utilized to carry out a simulation study to investigate the influence of control parameters on the robustness and efficiency of the controller. Special focus is laid on an efficient way to introduce suitable slack constraint formulations into the mixed-integer model predictive controller formulation to cope with uncertain peak loads. Methods to calibrate such a control structure with industrial operational data are given.

Keywords: Model predictive control, industrial application, uncertain load prediction;

1. Introduction and Motivation

Decarbonisation of power production induces an increasing share of renewable energy sources with fluctuating availability. Varying power availability has led to varying electricity prices, which can be utilized by consumers to reduce energy costs, by energy demand management (EDM). This is especially interesting for industry plants which accounted for 41.9% of the worldwide electricity demand in 2017 (International Energy Agency, 2019). The economic potential of EDM for industrial plants is shown in several studies, but is still rarely applied in industry (Ding and Hong, 2013; Schäfer *et al.*, 2018). According to McKane et al., 2008 this is, among other reasons, caused by the risk of affecting production safety. Efficient EDM and production safety can be realized simultaneously by utilizing model predictive controllers (MPC) in the energy supply systems. Crucial for the performance of an MPC is an accurate prediction of the disturbances, in this case the energy demand. In partially automated manufacturing plants, human operators are often responsible for the starting time of single process steps and thereby heavily influence the schedule of the energy load. This is of particular importance for energy-intensive batch processes where pulsed energy loads occur. Uncertain starting times of such batch processes lead to significant prediction errors, which can cause bottlenecks in the energy supply. Insufficient energy supply, in turn, affects the production safety and thereby has to be prevented under all circumstances. Typical examples of energy-intensive batch processes are heat treatments in which products undergo temperature trajectories in order to reach required quality attributes.

This work is motivated by an industrial use-case where human operators are responsible for preparatory works of heat treatment steps and thereby affect the starting times of these steps. In a previous work of the authors (Fuhrmann *et al.*, 2019) a load prediction method for pulsed heat loads was developed and tested on the very same industrial use case. The estimated predictions therein are accurate in disturbance and their temporal profile, but rely on known starting times. In the present work, the influence of stochastic starting times of pulsed energy loads on the performance of a model predictive controller (MPC) is investigated. The main contributions of this paper are:

1. Modelling an industrial use case based on measurement data.
2. Executing a simulation study in which the performance of a mixed-integer MPC in the heat supply system is tested with:
   a. Varying controller settings for the slack variable and the prediction horizon N_p
   b. Varying random time shifts of the pulsed heat loads.
3. Deducing guidelines and hints to effectively adjust the MPC parameters for the case of time-varying pulse-like disturbances.

2. Problem Set-Up

The structure and characteristics of the considered industrial use case are illustrated in Figure 1 and Figure 2. The essential components are a heat source (HS), a thermal energy storage (TES), and N batch-like heat consumers (BC) with temperatures $T_{BC,n}$ ($n=1,2,..,N$) which demand pulsed heat loads. The sum of the heat loads $\dot{Q}_{BC,sum}$, is the disturbance affecting the heat stored in the TES Q_{TES}, which is controlled utilizing the heat supply unit's heat flow, $\dot{Q}_{HS}$ as manipulated variable. Typical BC are heat treatment steps in the manufacturing industry that are used to alter the physical or chemical properties of a material (e.g. annealing, tempering, pasteurization). Heat treatments start with a heating phase, were the treated material is brought from the initial temperature to a desired temperature level. The heating phases typically induce short pulse-like heat loads to accomplish fast temperature transients that are necessary for product quality. Delayed or incomplete heating phases, caused by insufficient heat supply, may affect product quality and thereby incur additional costs. One central heat source provides the heat. Thermal liquid and heat exchangers transport it to the BC. The maximum of $\dot{Q}_{BC,sum}$ is typically many times higher than the maximum heat production rate $\dot{Q}_{HS}$ Therefore, a TES is installed to buffer the transient heating process. In this setting, predictive control provides multiple economic benefits: 1. bottlenecks in the heat supply can be detected and prevented before the production process is affected, 2. the energy consumption can be shaped according to the objectives of EDM (e.g. reduce energy costs), 3. the usage of the HS can be evened out, which reduces wear, 4. better exploitation of TES and HS enables a smaller design of these components, lowering investment costs. A precise load prediction is crucial for the performance of a predictive controller. In Fuhrmann et al, 2019, a prediction method for pulse-like heat loads is presented and applied to the very same industrial use-case considered in the present publication. The prediction method shows good results but it is based on an assumption, which does not hold in many manufacturing plants: The starting time point t_0 of the heat treatments is known. In reality, the starting times are often defined by human operators and thereby have to be considered a stochastic quantity. Human operators usually try to follow a given schedule, but preparation steps may introduce delays, for example due to loading tasks or quality checks. In the present work, the influence of a stochastic starting time t_0 on the performance of a model predictive

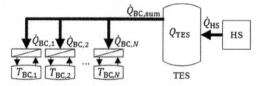

Fig. 1 Industrial use-case consisting of a heat source (HS), a thermal energy storage (TES) and N batch consumers (BC).

controller (MPC) is investigated. The influence of the controller settings for the slack variable and the prediction horizon N_p on robustness and efficiency of the MPC are tested and characterized in a simulation study. To incorporate the influence of human operators, the actual starting times of HT t_0 are altered by random time-shifts Δt_0. As conclusions of the simulation study, guidelines and hints to adjust the MPC parameters so that the control task can cope with the uncertainties efficiently are devised.

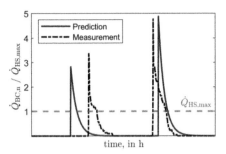

Fig. 2 Typical pulse-like heat loads of BC compared to the maximum heat production.

3. Methodology

The main control goals of the industrial use case are:

- Minimize the number of heat treatments affected by insufficient energy supply
- Minimize the total heat consumption

To decide whether a heat treatment is affected by insufficient energy supply, a critical state of charge $Q_{TES,crit}$ is defined. Heat treatments where $Q_{TES,crit}$ is exceeded at any time instant between starting time t_0 and the end time t_{end} of the heat treatment, such that

$$Q_{TES}(t) < Q_{TES,crit} \ \forall t \in \left[t_0, t_{end}\right] \tag{1}$$

is true, is considered as affected. Heat losses correspond to the temperature T_{TES} in the storage. By minimizing Q_{TES} and thereby T_{TES}, losses can be reduced. To quantify losses without knowledge of T_{TES}, the deviation Q_{dev} from the minimal allowed state of charge

$$Q_{dev} = \sum_{t_i=0}^{t_i=t_{max}} Q_{TES}(t_i) - Q_{TES,crit}(t_i) \tag{2}$$

is used where t_{max} is the duration of the used measurement-data. Equations 1 and 2 show a conflict of objectives, as Q_{TES} shall be as close to, but never fall below $Q_{TES,crit}$. Model predictive controllers (MPC) allow to weight different control goals and offer a convenient way to introduce constraints. The system is modelled as discrete linear state-space model. Defining the storage as simple integrator, $x = Q_{TES}$ as state, $u = \dot{Q}_{HS}$ as input $z = \dot{Q}_{BC,sum}$ as disturbance and T_s as sampling time, the system model is given by

$$Q_{TES}(t_i + 1) = Q_{TES}(t_i) + T_s \dot{Q}_{HS}(t_i) + T_s \dot{Q}_{BC,sum}(t_i) \tag{3}$$

The storage state must lie between bounds $x \in [x_{min}, x_{max}]$. The heat is supplied by a heat pump. The control input $\dot{Q}_{HS}$ can be either zero or between operational limits, such that

$$\dot{Q}_{HS} = \begin{cases} 0 \\ \dot{Q}_{HS,min} \le \dot{Q}_{HS} \le \dot{Q}_{HS,max} \end{cases} \tag{4}$$

holds.

To avoid a violation of the critical minimal storage level $Q_{\text{TES,crit}}$ the slack cost C_{Slack} penalizes an undershoot of $r = Q_{\text{Slack}} = Q_{\text{TES,crit}} + Q_{\text{Buffer}}$, where Q_{Buffer} is a safety margin (Figure 3). The resulting MPC formulation yields a mixed-integer quadratic programming problem, with δ_k as discrete variable describing whether the HP is on ($\delta_k = 1$) or off ($\delta_k = 1$) at step k. The optimization problem is defined as

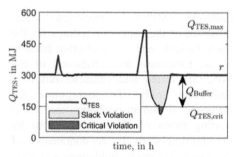

Fig. 3 Critical level of Q_{TES} and safety margin.

$$J_i = \frac{1}{2} \sum_{k=i}^{i+N_p-1} [(Q_{\text{TES},k+1} - r)^T C_R (Q_{\text{TES},k+1} - r) + (\dot{Q}_{\text{HS},k} - \dot{Q}_{\text{HS},k-1})^T C_{dU} (\dot{Q}_{\text{HS},k} - \dot{Q}_{\text{HS},k-1}) +$$

$$\dot{Q}_{\text{HS},k}^T C_U \dot{Q}_{\text{HS},k} + s_k C_{\text{Slack}} + \text{abs}(\delta_{k-1} - \delta_k) C_{\text{on}}]$$

$$s.t.$$

$$Q_{\text{Slack}} - s_k \leq Q_{\text{TES},k+1} \leq Q_{\text{TES,max}} \tag{5}$$

$$\delta_k \cdot u_{\min} \leq u_k \leq u_{\max} \cdot \delta_k$$

$$s_k \geq 0$$

$$\delta_k \in \{0,1\}$$

$$k \in [i,...,i+N_p-1]$$

where N_P is the prediction horizon, C_R, C_{dU}, C_U, C_{Slack} and C_{on} are weight factors and s_k are slack variables. A basic MPC, formulated in the Matlab toolbox YALMIP (Lofberg, 2019), was utilized and modified for this paper. Gurobi is used as solver (Gurobi, 2018).

Load Manipulation

To imprint the stochastic time shift, on the heat load, the starting time t_0 of each heat treatment was altered using random time shifts:

$$t_{0,\text{shifted}}^i = t_0^i + T_s \cdot \text{ceil}\left(\Box N_{\text{Shift,max}} \cdot U(-1,1)\right) \tag{6}$$

where $U(-1,1)$ is a uniform distribution in interval $[-1, 1]$. Eleven deviated predictions with maximum time shifts $\Delta t_{0,\text{max}}$ from 0 to 60 minutes were generated.

Simulation Study

The aim of the simulation study was to investigate the influence of the slack variable limit Q_{Buffer}, slack costs C_{slack}, and prediction horizon N_p on robustness and efficiency of the MPC, considering a varying accuracy of disturbance prediction. For this purpose, data of one week with 26 heat treatments is taken from the industrial measurement data and the basic parameters of the MPC were defined. Then simulations were made with different settings for Q_{Slack}, C_{Slack} and N_p. Table 1 shows the boundaries these parameters were varied in, the values of the basic parameters, and the constraints of Q_{TES} and $\dot{Q}_{\text{HS}}$.

Table 1 MPC Parameter.

N_p	$\{5,10,...,60\}$
C_{Slack}	$\{10^0,10^1,...,10^{10}\}$
Q_{Buffer}	$\{5,10,20,...,50,$ $75,100,150,200\}$
C_R	10^{-1}
C_U	2.5
C_{dU}	10^{-1}
C_{on}	10^1
$Q_{\text{TES,max}}$	504 MJ
$\dot{Q}_{\text{HS,max}}$	0.206 MW

The simulations were repeated for 13 different cases:

- Perfect information (PI): the applied load is equal to the load prediction
- No information (NI): the applied load does not correlate with the load prediction
- The eleven differently manipulated loads are applied and the predicted load used as load prediction.

4. Results & Discussion

The performance of the different controller settings is quantified by two quality attributes:

1. The number of heat treatments n_{aff} affected by insufficient heat supply.
2. Heat losses Q_{dev} quantified as deviation from the optimal state of charge.

As expected, a conflict of objectives is visible in the results. In Figure 4, pareto fronts for different $\Delta t_{0,max}$ are visible. Q_{Buffer} is the decisive control parameter to adjust the trade-off between Q_{dev} and n_{aff}. The diamond markers and the square markers show the results for constant values of Q_{Buffer} with different load prediction quality. For imprecise load predictions with high $\Delta t_{0,max}$, production losses occur more often (n_{aff} increases) while Q_{loss} shows only a slight increase. Furthermore, for high Q_{Buffer} a strong increase of Q_{dev} is detectable but little change on the production safety. To calculate the optimal trade-off between Q_{dev} and n_{aff}, the cost of production losses and the energy costs have to be compared. Figure 5 is a heatmap where the number of affected heat treatments for different values of Q_{Buffer} are displayed for all 13 different load prediction cases. Even with the applied heat load as load prediction, (PI) four heat treatments are affected by insufficient energy supply. This shows that the heat storage installed in the industrial use case is too small to guarantee production safety for all possible production plans. Still these production losses could be avoided utilizing an MPC, as the bottlenecks in energy supply would be detectable before they occur. A human machine interface could be installed to warn the operator, who then would have the opportunity to reschedule the heat treatments. Figure 5 further shows that even with perfect information (PI) a minimal Q_{Buffer} is needed to guarantee an acceptable production safety.

To deduce guidelines for the correct choice of Q_{Buffer} two variables proved appropriate: the average duration $t_{load>supply}$ of periods where the heat load $\dot{Q}_{BC,sum}$ is bigger than the maximum heat supply

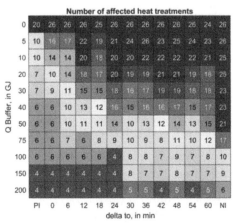

Fig. 5 Number of heat treatments with insufficient energy supply for different values of Q_{Buffer} and different load predictions: perfect information (PI) no information (NI) and predictions with varying maximum deviation of starting time points $\Delta t_{0,max}$.

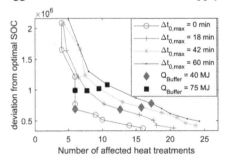

Fig. 4 Deviation from the optimal state of charge versus number of heat treatments with insufficient energy supply for varying $\Delta t_{0,max}$ and Q_{Buffer}.

$\dot{Q}_{HS,max}$ and the average heat amount $Q_{load>supply}$ which is delivered in these periods. For the simulation data $Q_{load>supply,avg} = 22.94$ MJ which is a good choice as minimal Q_{Buffer} for processes with known starting time t_0. Further, $t_{load>supply,avg} = 12{,}5$ min holds. Simulation results for varying slack weight C_{Slack} show that it needs to be a minimum of three magnitudes higher than the other weights to ensure production safety. The simulation results for varying prediction horizon N_P show that the optimal prediction horizon is dependent on the storage size $Q_{TES,max}$ and the maximum heat production $\dot{Q}_{HS,max}$. The heat source needs maximum $t_{load,max} = Q_{TES,max}/\dot{Q}_{HS,max}$ to charge the TES. Therefore, $N_{P,max} = t_{load,max}/T_s$ is sufficient for any occurring heat loads.

5. Conclusions

The following guidelines and hints to effectively adjust the MPC parameters for the case of time-varying pulse-like disturbances can be deduced from the results above:

1. Soft constraints with a slack variable are a proper method to avoid production losses caused by critical low state of charge $Q_{TES,crit}$. Guidelines for tuning are:

    a) Define Q_{slack} as:

$$Q_{slack} = Q_{TES,crit} + Q_{Buffer} = Q_{TES,crit} + Q_{load>supply,avg}\left(1 + \frac{\Box t_{0,max}}{t_{load>supply,avg}}\right) \tag{7}$$

    b) Define slack costs C_{slack} as:

$$C_{slack} \geq C_{slack,min} = 10^3 \max\left(C_R, C_{dU}, C_U, C_{ON}\right) \tag{8}$$

2. Define prediction horizon N_P as:

$$N_P \leq N_{P,max} = t_{load,max}/T_s \tag{9}$$

Acknowledgment

This work was supported by the project 'EDCSproof', which is part of the energy model region NEFI - New Energy for Industry and is funded by the Austrian Climate and Energy Fund (FFG, No.868837).

References

Ding, Y. and Hong, S. H. (2013) 'A model of demand response energy management system in industrial facilities', *2013 IEEE International Conference on Smart Grid Communications, SmartGridComm 2013*. IEEE, pp. 241–246. doi: 10.1109/SmartGridComm.2013.6687964.

Fuhrmann, F. *et al.* (2019) 'Prediction of pulsed heat loads in manufacturing plants', Puplication under review.

Gurobi, O. (2018) 'Gurobi Optimizer Reference Manual, Version 5.0', *www.Gurobi.Com*.

International Energy Agency (2019) *Electricity Statistics*. Available at: https://www.iea.org/statistics/electricity/ (Accessed: 25 October 2019).

Lofberg, J. (2019) *YALMIP standard MPC*. Available at: https://yalmip.github.io/example/standardmpc/ (Accessed: 6 November 2019).

McKane, A. T. *et al.* (2008) 'Opportunities, Barriers and Actions for Industrial Demand Response in California Environmental Energy Technologies Division'. Available at: https://industrialapplications.lbl.gov/sites/default/files/lbnl-1335e.pdf.

Schäfer, P. *et al.* (2018) *Nonlinear Dynamic Optimization for Improved Load-Shifting Agility of Cryogenic Air Separation Plants, Computer Aided Chemical Engineering*. Elsevier Masson SAS. doi: 10.1016/B978-0-444-64241-7.50086-0.

Sauro Pierucci, Flavio Manenti, Giulia Bozzano, Davide Manca (Eds.)
Proceedings of the 30th European Symposium on Computer Aided Process Engineering
(ESCAPE30), May 24-27, 2020, Milano, Italy. © 2020 Elsevier B.V. All rights reserved.
http://dx.doi.org/10.1016/B978-0-12-823377-1.50205-6

Swarm Optimisation for Shipping Fleet Scheduling, Routing and Delivery in Sustainable Liquified Natural Gas (LNG) Supply Chain Models

Sara Al-Haidous[a], Rajesh Govindan[b], Tareq Al-Ansari[a,b]

[a] Division of Sustainable Development, College of Science and Engineering, Hamad Bin Khalifa University, Qatar Foundation. Doha, Qatar.
[b] Division of Engineering Management and Decision Sciences, College of Science and Engineering, Hamad Bin Khalifa University, Qatar Foundation. Doha, Qatar.

talansari@hbku.edu.qa

Abstract

Natural gas is a relatively clean fuel when compared to other hydrocarbon fuels, such as oil and coal. It can be liquified into what is known as liquefied natural gas (LNG) with the potential for cost-effective transportation thereby allowing it to be adopted as a major energy source in many parts of the world. Whilst there exists an increasing global demand for LNG of up to 20 % annually, supply chains lack objective approaches that enable decision-making for planning and delivery, and encourage the global mobilisation of LNG reserves in an economically and environmentally sustainable manner. The objective of this study is to develop a multi-objective mathematical model for shipping fleet scheduling, routing and delivery for sustainable LNG supply chains. The model incorporates flexibility in delivery times; inventory management and berth availability constraints; and fuel consumption and carbon emissions. The model formulation is based on a real-case LNG supply chain in the state of Qatar, which represents the business-as-usual scenario, with polynomial number of variables and constraints corresponding to 248 cargoes spread across 90 days. The problem formulation is subsequently solved using the Binary Particle Swarm Optimisation (BPSO) algorithm. The solutions for scheduling, routing and delivery over the representative planning horizon obtained thus far demonstrate that the average total costs and emissions associated with a single cargo is approximately 1.6 million USD and 38 million kg CO_2/day respectively.

Keywords: LNG Supply Chain, LNG Shipping, Particle Swarm Optimisation, Natural gas

1. Introduction

Natural gas, is an important fuel bridging environmentally benign hydrogen and a renewable energy-based economy (Shively, and Ferrare, 2011). It can be liquified into what is known as liquefied natural gas (LNG), thus enabling more efficient transport through specialised carrier vessels over large distances and time horizons. Depending on its composition, natural gas is generally liquified at approximately -162 °C and atmospheric pressure. This liquefied state enables the natural gas to be shrunk to about 600 times its original volume. Currently, the state of Qatar has the largest chartered fleet of LNG vessels globally, including a new generation of state-of-the-art vessels enabling Qatari LNG to reach global markets in a safe, efficient, and reliable manner. Qatar provides 33 % of global LNG supply (IGU, 2014), representing 63 % of the government revenues. In addition, Qatar's customer portfolio is spread throughout the world in Asia, Europe, and America. Evidently, the optimal and sustainable delivery of hydrocarbon products to customers play is an important part of Qatar's economy.

Maritime transportation problems have unique practical and theoretical perspectives. Practical perspectives consider economies of scale making the case for the cheapest per unit transportation across all transport modes, fitting well with heavy industrial activities. From a theoretical perspective, however, maritime transportation is complex, and as such are difficult to solve within in a reasonable time frame. As with many energy supply chains, the transport of LNG is rather challenging. The producer is obligated to deliver a certain amount of LNG to re-gasification terminals each year because of a set of long-term contracts. These contracts have a duration of several years that specify the quantity and time for deliveries. They also state how the deliveries should be spread throughout the year; either evenly spread or if there are seasonal variations. Based on the mutually agreed information, the LNG producer needs to develop the annual delivery plan (ADP) accordingly. Variations in ADP may impact LNG inventories, and can occur due to fluctuations of production as a result of planned or unplanned shutdown, seasonality and slowdowns at the end of the planning horizon. Transport of LNG is particularly important as the associated costs represent 30 % of the total LNG supply chain (Cornot-Gandolphe *et al.*, 2003). The LNG fleet is usually heterogeneous, with specific tank capacities and cruising speeds as scheduled and operated by the LNG producer. The duration of a voyage may also depend on the time of year, as sailing conditions may vary between summer and winter seasons. At the beginning of the planning horizon, there are several factors that affect the availability of vessels in the fleet. Whilst some vessels could serve other customers, others may be unavailable due to certain pre-planned activities, such as maintenance. It is technically possible for a vessel to sail between the liquefaction and a re-gasification terminals with partially filled-up tanks. In addition, there are several components that affect the transportation costs. Fixed costs are related to charter rates and cannot be changed during the time horizon. Variable costs relate to canal fees, load and discharge operation and fuel consumption for serving a scheduled voyage based on the vessel type and the duration of the voyage. Furthermore, cruising speeds affect the fuel consumption and exhaust gas emissions. Moreover, a vessel will also require re-fueling after each voyage.

The scheduling, routing and delivery problem for LNG supply could be more difficult to solve when further complexities are incorporated into the system, *e.g.* the consideration of sustainable development in terms of integrated environmental and economic objectives. The International Maritime Organization (IMO) aims to achieve a reduction of CO_2 emissions from shipping operations by 50% by 2050 (IMO, 2019). Incidentally, there is little published work pertaining to the overall planning of sustainable LNG supply chains. As such, developing sustainable LNG supply chains presents a large research opportunity as various quantitative models can be utilised to model and analyse such supply chains (Al Haidous. S. and Al Ansari, T, 2019). As such, (Al Haidous. S. and Al Ansari, T, 2019) introduces a model that integrated approaches to manage energy supply chains to deliver cargo at minimal cost and environmental impact, and to ensure that supply chains can overcome vulnerabilities withstanding potential disruptions to the supply chain. The LNG inventory routing problem is a unique case in what is known as the maritime inventory routing problem (MIRP), which considers variable production, contractual obligations, and berth constraints at production and liquefaction terminals (Christiansen *et al.*, 2004). Other studies have focused on single objectives. From an economic perspective, Mutlu *et al.* (2016) developed a model to minimise total operational costs considering production, inventory, and delivery routing decisions at the lowest possible cost for LNG. Meanwhile, from an environmental perspective, Fagerholt *et al.* (2010) developed a model to reduce fuel emissions by optimising speed on the shipping routes. As such, it has been identified that, from the perspective of sustainable planning of the LNG supply chain, the trade-offs involved in costs and environmental impacts have not been fully investigated, particularly in the case of supply chains served by large-sized heterogeneous delivery fleet. Evidently, there is a need to develop methods that integrate multiple dimensions of sustainability within a complex LNG supply chain. The aim of this study is thus to address the critical factors in the planning of a sustainable LNG supply chain management. It considers sustainability objectives within an integrated multi-objective optimisation-based methodology accounting for factors, including shipping fleet scheduling, flexibility in delivery times, inventory management, berth availability, fuel consumption and associated carbon emissions.

2. System Definition and Model Formulation

Developing models for LNG supply chain problems require defining the long-term contracts delivery dates and the assignment of the different type of the vessels to the cargoes, whilst accommodating several constraints including partial delivery, berth, and liquefaction terminal inventory and carbon emissions to achieve the objective by supporting innovative solutions that achieve greater efficiency, flexibility, and optimisation of resources whilst meeting customer needs. As such, the methodology adopted in this study includes a multi-objective mixed integer programming model for the problem to minimise both the total cost and environmental impact, treating them as competing objective functions. The notation that shall be used throughout the paper are introduced below, followed by the proposed model formulation for optimisation:

Sets:
- T: set of days that cover planning horizon; $\{1,...,T\}$.
- V: set of vessels indexed by v.
- C: set of cargoes indexed by c_{in}.
- V^i: set of vessels that can visit port i.
- P^v: set of ports that vessel v can visit.

Parameters:
- I^{min}/I^{max}: minimal and maximal inventory levels of the storage tank at the liquefaction terminal.
- P_t: daily production rate.
- B: number of available berths.
- q_{vit}: loaded or unloaded quantity from vessel v on day t.
- $[T_{in}^e, T_{in}^a]$: time window during which should be delivered cargo c_{in}.

- d_{voj}: Travel time of vessel v from port i to j.
- E: CO$_2$ emissions (ton/day)

Nodes:
- (i, j): any port including customer ports and loading port.
- o: source node.

Decision Variables:
- x_{vijt}: Binary variable, which is equal to 1 if the vessel v arrives at port j from port i on day t, and 0 otherwise.
- I_t: Inventory level of liquefaction terminal's storage tank on day t, $t \in T$

The formulation reads as follows.

$$Min \sum_{v \in V} \sum_{i \in p^v} \sum_{j \in p^{vi}} \sum_{t \in T} C_{vij} x_{vijt}$$

$$Min \sum_{v \in V} \sum_{i \in p^v} \sum_{j \in p^{vi}} \sum_{t \in T} E \, d_{ij} x_{vijt} \tag{1}$$

Subject to:

Initialization and termination constraints

$$x_{voo0} = 1 \qquad\qquad v \in V \tag{2}$$

$$\sum_{t \in T_o} \sum_{j \in p^{vo} \setminus \{0\}} x_{vojt} = 1 \qquad\qquad v \in V \tag{3}$$

$$x_{vojt} = 0 \qquad\qquad v \in V, j \in P^v \setminus \{0\}, t < d_{voj} \tag{4}$$

$$x_{vijt} = 0 \qquad\qquad v \in V, i \in P^v \setminus \{0\}, j \in P^v, t \tag{5}$$
$$< d_{voi} + d_{vij}$$

Flow constraints

$$\sum_{k \in P_o^{vi}} x_{vkit} - \sum_{j \in p^{vi}} x_{vij(t+T_{vij})} = 0 \qquad v \in V, i \in P^v, t \in T_o \tag{6}$$

$$\sum_{i \in P^v} \sum_{j \in p^{vi}} x_{vijt} = 1 \qquad\qquad v \in V, t \in T \tag{7}$$

Inventory management constraints

$$I_t = I_{t-1} + P_t - \sum_{v \in V} q_{vlt} x_{vijt} \qquad t \in T \tag{8}$$

$$I^{min} \le I_t \le I^{max} \qquad\qquad t \in T \tag{9}$$

Berth constraint

$$\sum_{v \in V} x_{vijt} \leq B \qquad\qquad t \in \text{T} \qquad\qquad (10)$$

Vessel speed constraints

$$t_j - t_i - d_{vij} \geq 0 \qquad\qquad v \in \text{V}, i \in P^v \qquad\qquad (11)$$

$$\text{T}^e_{in} \leq t_i \leq \text{T}^a_{in} \qquad\qquad i \in P^v \qquad\qquad (12)$$

$$x_{vijt} \in \{0,1\} \qquad\qquad v \in \text{V}, t \in T \qquad\qquad (13)$$

The objective is to minimise the overall operating costs and fuel consumption for the planning horizon of 90 days. Constraints (2-5) are initialisation constraints to ensure that all vessels originate from the origin port *o* and prevent any vessel going to two different ports during the same time intervals. Constraint (6) Controls the flow of each vessel during the planning horizon. In this constraint if a vessel arrived at port *i* at time *t* then it should go to another port *j* that is accessible from port *i* at time $t + \text{T}_{vij}$. Where constraint (7) ensures that each cargo should be served only by one vessel. Constraints (8-9) are inventory balance and limits constraints for the liquefaction terminal. Berth capacity constraint at the loading port presented by constraint (10). Constraint (11) ensures that the ship does not start services prior to arrival at the node. Constraint (12) represents the time window limits, and finally constraint (13) demonstrates the binary nature of the decision variable. The average solution is determined from the Pareto front, representing the best trade-off obtained for the cost and environmental impact.

3. Computational experiments

The test instances are based on real data provided by an LNG producer. In this instance, three months for the planning horizon are considered for 248 cargoes using 6 berths, 70 vessels with different sizes and fuel consumption for each type of the vessel. The Binary Particle Swarm Optimisation (BPSO) algorithm was used to perform a heuristic search in the high-dimensional binary solution space for feasible solutions that solves the model formulation described above. The algorithm was implemented in a manner that it would work on balancing between the minimisation of the multi-objective functions and the number of constraints satisfied (Yazdi *et al.*, 2019). As such, the implementation splits up the high-dimensional binary solution into multiple swarms and solve them locally using BPSO to determine local Pareto sets, before combining them to determine the global Pareto set. When compared to earlier studies that have looked at similar problems using single objective functions using MILP solvers that guarantee optimality as studied by Mutlu *et al.* (2016), the current implementation was able to provide a convergence of the Pareto set under one hour. However, the main limitation of the study is the lack of objective assessment of the quality of the solutions obtained, when compared to the optimal solutions obtained using exact methods with industry-standard solvers such as CPLEX. Table 1 provides illustrative numbers for the total cost and environmental impact for an average point on the preliminary Pareto front results obtained in this study.

Table 1. Results for Total costs and emissions for planning horizon, corresponding to an average solution from the Pareto front.

No. of cargoes	Time horizon (days)	No. of berths	No. of vessels	Total Costs ($)	Total CO2 emissions (kg/day)
248	90	6	70	0.4 Billion	38 Million

4. Conclusion

The volume of maritime transportation of LNG is expected to continue to grow in the coming years due to the accelerating supply and demand for natural gas. The expanding opportunities in this business require decision support systems that fit the specific problem characteristic. The main contribution of this paper is to introduce sustainability within the LNG supply chain model by considering economic and environmental dimensions using BPSO to solve the problem optimally. The results have been tested on real instance to ensure model validity and reliability. The model developed in this paper can be further developed by considering multi discharges on the same route, ship to ship transfer operation and alternative routing between Asia and Europe. Going forward, development of integrated sustainable LNG supply chain models should be further enhanced to capture all sustainability dimensions at higher resolutions.

References

B. Shively, and J. Ferrare, (2011), Understanding today's natural gas business. Enerdynamics.

IGU, 2014, Natural gas, the energy for today and the furure, Available on: https://www.igu.org/sites/default/files/node-document

S. Cornot-Gandolphe, O. Appert, R. Dickel, M.-F. Chabrelie, and A. Rojey, (2003), The challenges of further cost reductions for new supply options (pipeline, LNG, GTL). 5, 1-17.

IMO, 2019, Low carbon shipping and air pollution control, Available on: http://www.imo.org/en/MediaCentre/HotTopics/GHG/Pages/default.aspx

S. Al-Haidous, and T. Al-Ansari, (2019), Sustainable Liquefied Natural Gas Supply Chain Management: A Review of Quantitative Models, Sustainability, 12(1), 243.

M. Christiansen, K. Fagerholt, and D. Ronen, (2004), Ship Routing and Scheduling: Status and Perspectives. Transportation Science, 38(1), 1–18.

F. Mutlu, M. K. Msakni, H. Yildiz, E. Sönmez, and S. Pokharel, (2016). A comprehensive annual delivery program for upstream liquefied natural gas supply chain. European Journal of Operational Research, 250(1), 120–130. https://doi.org/10.1016/j.ejor.2015.10.031

K. Fagerholt, G. Laporte, and I. Norstad, 2010, Reducing fuel emissions by optimizing speed on shipping routes, Journal of the Operational Research Society, 61, 523-529.

A. Karbassi Yazdi, M. A. Kaviani, A. Emrouznejad, and H. Sahebi, H., (2019). A binary particle swarm optimization algorithm for ship routing and scheduling of liquefied natural gas transportation. Transportation Letters, 1-10. https://doi:10.1080/19427867.2019.1581485

Sauro Pierucci, Flavio Manenti, Giulia Bozzano, Davide Manca (Eds.)
Proceedings of the 30th European Symposium on Computer Aided Process Engineering
(ESCAPE30), May 24-27, 2020, Milano, Italy. © 2020 Elsevier B.V. All rights reserved.
http://dx.doi.org/10.1016/B978-0-12-823377-1.50206-8

Online Decoupled Data-Driven Estimation of Nonlinear Kinetic Parameters

Wilfredo Angulo, Dany De Cecchis, Santiago D. Salas*

Escuela Superior Politécnica del Litoral, ESPOL, Facultad de Ciencias Naturales y Matemáticas, Campus Gustavo Galindo Km 30.5 Vía Perimetral, P.O. BOX 09-01-5863, Guayaquil, Ecuador.

sdsalas@espol.edu.ec

Abstract

A data-driven parameter estimation strategy is assessed and tested for the estimation of nonlinear parameters in a classic continuous stir tank reactor (CSTR). A decoupled version of the retrospective cost model refinement (RCMR) algorithm serves as the estimation structure. The proposed method studies the simultaneous estimation of three kinetic parameters within a CSTR considering one available measurement. The decoupled RCMR algorithm is adapted and implemented as an efficient estimation structure for the proposed problem, and contrasted with its original structure.

Keywords: Continuous stirred tank reactor, decoupled RCMR, nonlinear parameter estimation, data-driven estimation.

1. Introduction

The chemical engineer requires to count with a reliable set of physicochemical, transport and kinetic parameters for the design and simulation of industrial reactors. The information related to the kinetics is required for the implementation of well-specialized laboratory or pilot scale experiments. For the proper adjustment of kinetic parameters, it is necessary to formulate and resolve an optimization problem, which minimizes the error between the variables measured experimentally and those calculated from the fundamental model. Due to the growth of computing power, nonlinear optimization methods have become an alternative for parameter estimation. Among these methods, gradient-based ones such as the Levenberg Marquardt (L-M) algorithm has demonstrated a good local performance (*A. Neumaier*, 2004). Other methods that include stochastic optimization require significantly higher computations, but have a relatively easy implementation. Eftaxias et al. (2002) tested separately the performance of L-M and Simulate Annealing to estimate the kinetic parameters that describe a catalytic oxidation. The stochastic method was competitive when compared with the L-M algorithm.

However, the use of such optimization methods in real-time is computationally expensive. Real-time estimation techniques are commonly based on the implementation of the extended Kalman filter, geometric observer or their variations which adapt to the problem under study (*Salas et al.*, 2017, 2018). Nonetheless, these methods have the limitation of requiring an adjoint model, or explicit knowledge of the dependence of the parameters. Hence, the mathematical model for the chemical kinetics must be computable and known by the estimation algorithm. In contrast, the retrospective cost model refinement (RCMR) algorithm overcomes these notable disadvantages. This algorithm has been applied in the estimation of parameters with nonlinear dependence considering single or multiple estimation, linear or nonlinear gray-box models, and first-principle models for polymerization systems using real experimental data (*Goel and Bernstein*, 2018; *Salas et al*, 2019). Advantageous characteristics of this strategy are that it does not require the incorporation of the model to the estimation structure nor evinces to be CPU intensive. After applying a recursive computation based on the retrospective cost function, the coefficients of the estimator are updated for later calculating the estimated parameters. Salas, Angulo and De Cecchis (2020) proposed a decoupled version of this method (denoted by dRCMR) which improves the speed of convergence and stability for some cases in the estimation of strongly non-linear parameters.

The main contribution of this work is the implementation of the dRCMR algorithm for the online data-driven estimation of nonlinear kinetic parameters in a classic isothermal CSTR system, and to compare the obtained results when using the RCMR. This study analyses the dynamic behavior of the CSTR, and it can be approached by means of phenomenological-based semi-physical models coupled with expressions that represent the kinetics of the reaction (or reactions), with a strongly non-linear dependence among its parameters.

2. Background

2.1. Mathematical model of an isothermal CSTR

In this work, a classical isothermal CSTR is under consideration. It composes by a system of n chemical reactions, and m chemical species, with second order kinetics, that can be expressed in the form:

$$\sum_{j=1}^{m} v_{ij} A_j = 0; \quad i = 1, \dots, n, \tag{1}$$

where A_j denotes the j-th chemical species and v_{ij} is its stoichiometric coefficient in the i-th reaction. The component A_j is defined as the j-th reactant of the reaction i if $v_{ij} < 0$, and as the product of the reaction i if $v_{ij} > 0$. The information contained in the reaction mechanism (1) can be summarised as a matrix $C \in \mathbb{R}^{n \times m}$ where the elements are the stoichiometric coefficients of reactants and products. The reaction rate in each mechanism is a nonlinear function of the temperature T, and the vector of the concentrations of the reacting species x^r. For (1), it is defined a vector $r(x^r, T) \in \mathbb{R}^n$ which contains the reaction rates, and it is a separable function with respect to its arguments, i.e.,

$$r(x^r, T) = \Theta(x^r) G(\mu(T)), \tag{2}$$

where the vector $G(\mu(T)) \in \mathbb{R}^n$ is in general a nonlinear function of the specific speed vector (kinetic parameters) $\mu(T) \in \mathbb{R}^n$, which is composed of bounded positive functions of the temperature while $\Theta(x^r) \in \mathbb{R}^{n \times n}$ is a diagonal matrix which elements are functions of the vector x^r. This vector is defined as $x^r = (x_1^r, \dots, x_n^r)$, with

$$x_i^r = \mathcal{P}_i^r x; \quad i = 1, \dots, n, \tag{3}$$

and $\mathcal{P}_i^r$ as the operator that projects the concentration vector $x \in \mathbb{R}^m$ of the reactants in the i-th reaction into the vector x_i^r, such that

$$r(x^r, T) = \begin{pmatrix} \phi_1(x_1^r) & \cdots & 0 \\ \vdots & \ddots & \vdots \\ 0 & \cdots & \phi_n(x_n^r) \end{pmatrix} \begin{bmatrix} g_1(\mu(T)) \\ \vdots \\ g_n(\mu(T)) \end{bmatrix}, \tag{4}$$

Then, the matrix $\Theta(x^r)$ is related to the vector x, which components are the m concentrations of chemical species involved in the reaction network (reactants and products), by the projection operator $\mathcal{P}_i^r$. The functions $\phi_i(x_i^r)$, for $i = 1, \dots, n$, are nonlinear functions respecting the concentration of the reactants involved in the i-th reaction, i.e., $\phi_i(x_i^r) = \prod_{j \in J_r} \psi_{ij}(x_j)$, $i = 1, \dots, n$, where, in the presence of an elementary reaction, $\psi_{ij}(x_j) = x_j^{v_{ij}}$, with $v_{ij} \in \mathbb{N}$, represents the mass action law, and J_r is the set of indices associated with the reactants.

The mathematical model of an isothermal CSTR reactor describes the relationships between the state variables given by the vector $x \in \mathbb{R}^m$, the operation variables, and the kinetic parameters given in the vector $G(\mu(T))$. This model is in general very complex. However, in this study some assumptions are introduced in the attempt to reduce its complexity. In particular, it is assumed that the reactant inside the tank is perfectly mixed, the volume of the reactant is constant during the reactions, and the inlet flow rate is equal to the outlet flow rate. Then, using the dynamic material balances inside the reactor, the mathematical model of the system reactions-CSTR is the initial value problem:

$$\begin{cases} \dot{x}(t) = d\left(x^{in} - x(t)\right) + C^T r(x^r(t)), & \forall t \in (0, +\infty), \\ x(0) = x^0, \end{cases} \tag{5}$$

where $\dot{x}$ denotes the derivative of x with respect to the time t, $d \in \mathbb{R}_+$ is the dilution rate, which is the ratio between the feed stream flowrate and the volume of the reactor, $x^{in} \in \mathbb{R}^m$ is the vector of non-negative reactor feed concentrations, and $x^0 \in \mathbb{R}^m$ is the vector of non-negative initial concentrations. In this model, $r(x^r)$ does not depend on the temperature because the system is assumed to be isothermal. The vector $\mu = (\mu_1, \dots, \mu_n)$ is, in fact, the vector of parameters estimated by the dRCMR.

2.2. Decoupled RCMR

The dRCMR is a variation of the RCMR; hence, the latter is introduced first to then describe the decoupled strategy.

The first step to use the RCMR for estimating the vector of kinetic parameters μ consists on discretizing the mathematical model in (5) by means of a suitable numerical method, e.g., a fourth-order Runge-Kutta or a *stiff*-method among others. The purpose of this first step is to obtain a dynamic system in the form of:

$$\begin{aligned} x_{k+1} &= f(x_k, u_k, \mu) + w_k; \quad k \in \mathbb{N}, \\ y_k &= h(x_k, u_k, \mu). \end{aligned} \tag{6}$$

where $u \in \mathbb{R}^{l_u}$ is the input vector, $\mu \in \mathbb{R}^{l_\mu}$ is the unknown parameters vector, $y \in \mathbb{R}^{l_y}$ is the measurements vector, and $w \in \mathbb{R}^{l_y}$ is the output error of the system. Here, f and h are known maps that depend non-linearly on the states x, inputs u and parameters μ. Thereafter, at every step $k \in \mathbb{N}$, the RCMR calculates an estimated vector $\hat{\mu}$ based on an ARMA (Auto Regressive Moving Average) model. Specifically, the estimation problem consists of determining a vector $\theta \in \mathbb{R}^{l_\theta}$, at each $k \in \mathbb{N}$, such that,

$$\hat{\mu}_k = \Phi_k \theta_k; \quad k \in \mathbb{N}, \tag{7}$$

where $\Phi \in \mathbb{R}^{l_\mu \times l_\theta}$ is the regressor matrix, and $\theta \in \mathbb{R}^{l_\theta}$ is an alternative representation of the adaptive integrator in the ARMA model. Here, $l_\theta = l_\mu^2 n_c + l_\mu l_y (n_c + 1)$, where the notation n_c refers to both the number of autoregressive terms and the moving-average terms. The vector $\theta \in \mathbb{R}^{l_\theta}$ is approximated by a vector $\hat{\theta}_k \in \mathbb{R}^{l_\theta}$, which is determined by minimizing in every step $k \in \mathbb{N}$ the retrospective cost function defined as

$$J_k(\widehat{\boldsymbol{\theta}}_k) = \sum_{m=0}^{k-1} \lambda^{k-m} \widehat{\boldsymbol{z}}_m^T R_z \widehat{\boldsymbol{z}}_m + \lambda^k \widehat{\boldsymbol{\theta}}_k^T R_\theta \widehat{\boldsymbol{\theta}}_k, \tag{8}$$

where $0 < \lambda \leq 1$ is the forgetting factor, $R_z \in \mathbb{R}^{l_y \times l_y}$ and $R_\theta \in \mathbb{R}^{l_\theta \times l_\theta}$ are positive definite matrices. The vector $\widehat{\boldsymbol{z}} \in \mathbb{R}^{l_y}$ in (8) is the retrospective performance variable defined as

$$\widehat{\boldsymbol{z}}_k = (\widehat{\boldsymbol{y}}_k - \boldsymbol{y}_k) + N \widetilde{\boldsymbol{\Phi}}_k \widehat{\boldsymbol{\theta}}_k - N \widetilde{\boldsymbol{U}}_k \widehat{\boldsymbol{\theta}}_k, \tag{9}$$

where $\widehat{\boldsymbol{y}} \in \mathbb{R}^{l_y}$ is the estimated output vector corresponding to the dynamic system (6). When the output error $\boldsymbol{w}$ is neglected, $N = [N_1, \cdots N_{n_f}]$, with $N_i \in \mathbb{R}^{l_y \times l_\mu}$, are the coefficients associated to a finite impulse response (FIR) filter of order n_f, and the matrices $\widetilde{\boldsymbol{\Phi}}_k \in \mathbb{R}^{l_\mu n_f \times l_\theta}$ and $\widetilde{\boldsymbol{U}}_k \in \mathbb{R}^{l_\mu n_f}$ are, respectively,

$$\widetilde{\boldsymbol{\Phi}}_k = \begin{bmatrix} \Phi_{k-1} \\ \vdots \\ \Phi_{k-n_f} \end{bmatrix}; \quad \widetilde{\boldsymbol{U}}_k = \begin{bmatrix} \mu_{k-1} \\ \vdots \\ \mu_{k-n_f} \end{bmatrix}. \tag{10}$$

The dRCMR algorithm consists of using l_μ instances of a modified version of the RCMR to estimate every parameter of the system, as illustrated in Figure 1. The nonlinear parameter estimation structure compares two outputs, the one generated by the physical system and the one generated by the estimation model. Each parameter estimation box is an instance of the modified RCMR, which is set for estimation purposes with only two parameters, i.e., $l_\mu = 2$, and calculates one parameter as an element of the system parameters. The other parameter within the instance is kept constant, and its value can be tuned proportionally between the other parameters of the system.

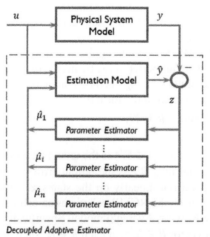

Figure 1: Nonlinear kinetic parameter estimation framework.

3. Results

For the numerical test, the model is a technological case taken from Kense et al. (2012). There are three chemical reactions, $n = 3$, involving five chemical spices, $m = 5$, and $\boldsymbol{G}(\boldsymbol{\mu}) = (10^{\mu_1}, 10^{\mu_2}, 10^{\mu_3})$. The parameter vector to be estimated is $\boldsymbol{\mu} = (\mu_1, \mu_2, \mu_3)$, and its exact value is $(-3.301, -1.301, -1.699)$.

Figure 2 portrays the results for the RCMR only, which is the structure proposed by Goel & Bernstein (2019). It is implemented with $n_c = 1$, considering a sampling time of 0.1 s. The initial values of the state vector and parameters is zero. For 20,000 iterations the estimated parameters remain trapped at a similar value.

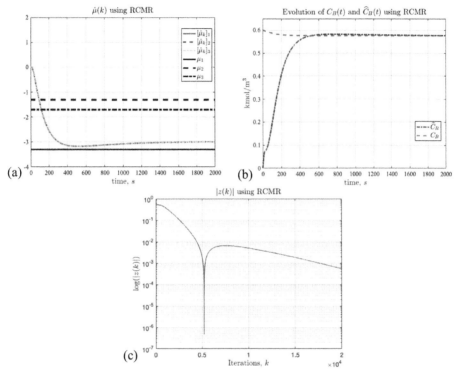

Figure 2: RCMR results when estimating three kinetic parameters and C_B as measurement: (a) the evolution of the kinetic parameters; (b) measured variable evolution; (c) Evolution of $|z(k)|$ at each iteration.

Figure 3 portrays the results for the dRCMR, $n_c = 1$ remains considering a sampling time of 0.1 s. The initial values of the state vector and parameters is zero. When using the decoupled version, the estimated parameters vector converges to its theoretical value after 800 iterations. The proposed approach shows a stable convergence.

4. Discussion and Conclusions

In this contribution, a decoupled data-driven methodology based on the RCMR algorithm was introduced for estimating nonlinear kinetic parameters. The proposed dRCMR attains good parameter estimates while the original RCMR remains trapped in unrepresentative values.

For estimating kinetic parameters in CSTRs, typically an optimization formulation is required for its subsequent kinetic parameter estimation. Nonetheless, dynamic methods such as the dRCMR open the possibility to immediately estimate kinetic parameters of nonlinear systems while or right after running experiments. Additionally, the proposed methodology could be applied in other pieces of equipment including heat exchangers. Yet, the use of a first-principles model might be mandatory for understanding the physical meaning of the estimated parameters. Grey-box models might be useful for certain applications although they lack of a fully descriptive structure.

Future steps in the subject include to test the performance of the algorithm with multiple parameters and observations in polymerization systems.

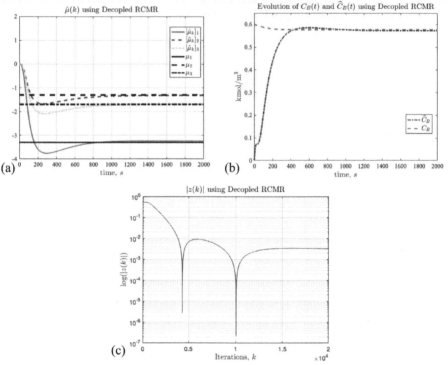

Figure 3: dRCMR results when estimating three kinetic parameters and C_B as measurement: (a) the evolution of the kinetic parameters; (b) measured variable evolution; (c) Evolution of $|z(k)|$ at each iteration.

References

Neumaier A. 2004. Complete Search in Continuous Global Optimization and Constraint Satisfaction. in Acta Numerica (A. Iserles, ed.), Cambridge University Press, Cambridge.

Eftaxias A., Font J., Fortuny A., Fabregat A., Stüber F. 2002. Nonlinear kinetic parameter estimation using simulated annealing. Computers and Chemical Engineering, (26), 1725-1733.

Goel A., & Bernstein D. S. 2018. Data-Driven Parameter Estimation for Models with Nonlinear Parameter Dependence. In 2018 IEEE Conference on Decision and Control (CDC) (pp. 1470-1475). IEEE.

Kanse N. G., Dhanke P. B., & Thombare A. 2012. Modeling and Simulation Study of the CSTR for Complex Rection by Using Polymath. Research Journal of Chemical Sciences, 2(4) 79-85.

Salas S. D., Angulo W. , & De Cecchis D. 2020. A Decoupled Data-Driven Strategy for Estimating Parameters with Nonlinear Dependence. In ICIT 2020 (accepted). IEEE.

Salas S. D., Brandão A. L., Soares J. B., & Romagnoli J. A. 2019. Data-Driven Estimation of Significant Kinetic Parameters Applied to the Synthesis of Polyolefins. *Processes*, 7(5), 309.

Salas S. D., Chebeir J., Tronci S., Baratti R., & Romagnoli J. A. 2018. Real-Time Nonlinear State Estimation in Polymerization Reactors for Smart Manufacturing. In *Computer Aided Chemical Engineering* (Vol. 43, pp. 1207-1212). Elsevier.

Salas S. D., Ghadipasha N., Zhu W., Romagnoli J. A., Mcafee T., & Reed W. F. 2017. Online DEKF for State Estimation in Semi-Batch Free-Radical Polymerization Reactors. In *Computer Aided Chemical Engineering* (Vol. 40, pp. 1465-1470). Elsevier.

Sauro Pierucci, Flavio Manenti, Giulia Bozzano, Davide Manca (Eds.)
Proceedings of the 30th European Symposium on Computer Aided Process Engineering
(ESCAPE30), May 24-27, 2020, Milano, Italy. © 2020 Elsevier B.V. All rights reserved.
http://dx.doi.org/10.1016/B978-0-12-823377-1.50207-X

Linear Combination of Gradients as Optimal Controlled Variables

Dinesh Krishnamoorthy and Sigurd Skogestad

Department of Chemical Engineering, Norwegian University of Science and Technology, Trondheim 7491, Norway
dinesh.krishnamoorthy@ntnu.no

Abstract

In this paper, we show that optimal economic operation can be achieved using feedback control, by controlling the right variables that translate economic objectives into control objectives. We formulate a generic framework for selecting the controlled variables based on the Karsh-Kuhn-Tucker (KKT) conditions, that can be used to select the optimal controlled variables for different operating conditions. The proposed generalized framework is given as a linear combination of cost gradients. Furthermore, we also show that, the proposed linear gradient combination framework can be used to select the economically optimal controlled variables for parallel operating units. The proposed linear gradient combination framework can be used with any gradient estimation scheme. A benchmark Williams-Otto reactor example is used to demonstrate the effectiveness of the proposed CV selection framework.

Keywords: Measurement-based optimization,self-optimizing control, gradient

1. Introduction

One of the challenges that impede practical implementation of traditional real-time optimization is the need to solve numerical optimization problems online. In order to avoid the need to solve numerical optimization problems, there is an increasing interest in a class of methods for real-time optimization, known as "feedback-optimizing control" or "direct-input adaptation". Here the objective is to indirectly move the optimization into the control layer, thereby converting the optimization problem into a feedback control problem.

The idea of achieving optimal operation using feedback control predates 1980s, where Morari et al. (1980) proposed a "feedback optimizing control" structure that translates the economic objectives into process control objectives. This idea was further studied in detail by Skogestad (2000), where the objective was to find a simple feedback control strategy,with near optimal cost subject to constraints.

When converting the optimization problem into a feedback control problem, one of the most important question that arises is *"What to control?"*. In other words, one has to find appropriate controlled variables that translates the economic objectives into control objectives. Addressing this problem, Skogestad (2000) advocates that it is important to control the constraints tightly that are optimally active. This is known as active constraint control and results in zero loss. In fact, the feedback optimizing control structure presented by Morari et al. (1980) also resulted in active constraint control. If there are any unconstrained degrees of freedom, Skogestad (2000) advocates that one should find self-optimizing variables, which when kept at a constant setpoint, leads to acceptable loss.

The simplest and the earliest methods to find a self-optimizing CV was using a brute-force method that evaluates the performance loss of different possible candidate CVs (Skogestad, 2000). Since then there has been several developments in methods to select the optimal measurements or linear measurement combinations $\mathbf{c} = \mathbf{Hy}$ as self-optimizing CVs, where $\mathbf{H}$ is known as the optimal selection matrix. Some notable approaches of finding the optimal selection matrix $\mathbf{H}$ include the nullspace method (Alstad and Skogestad, 2007) and the exact local method (Alstad et al., 2009), which are based on linearized models around some nominal operating point.

The main drawback of using a linear measurement combination is that the loss increases as the optimal point moves away from the point of linearization. Using linear measurement combination also involves selecting a subset of all the available measurements that one wants to include in the measurement combination $\mathbf{c} = \mathbf{Hy}$, which may require additional offline analysis and/or process insight.

In this paper, we consider the linear combination of cost gradients as self-optimizing variables instead of linear measurement combination. By using a linear *gradient* combination, we show that one can achieve zero loss even when disturbances occur. To this end, we propose a generalized framework for selecting the self-optimizing variables based on the Karush-Kuhn-Tucker (KKT) conditions that can be used for different operating scenarios.

2. Selection of controlled variables

Consider the steady-state economic optimization problem

$$\min_{\mathbf{u}} \quad J(\mathbf{u}, \mathbf{d})$$

$$\text{s.t. } \mathbf{g}(\mathbf{u}, \mathbf{d}) \leq 0 \tag{1}$$

where $\mathbf{u} \in \mathbb{R}^{n_u}$ denotes the vector of manipulated variables (MV) and $\mathbf{d} \in \mathbb{R}^{n_d}$ denotes the vector of disturbances, $J : \mathbb{R}^{n_u} \times \mathbb{R}^{n_d} \to \mathbb{R}$ is the scalar cost function and $\mathbf{g} : \mathbb{R}^{n_u} \times \mathbb{R}^{n_d} \to \mathbb{R}^{n_g}$ denotes the vector of constraints. The Lagrangian of the optimization problem is given by

$$\mathcal{L}(\mathbf{u}, \mathbf{d}) = J(\mathbf{u}, \mathbf{d}) + \lambda^{\mathsf{T}} \mathbf{g}(\mathbf{u}, \mathbf{d}) \tag{2}$$

where $\lambda \in \mathbb{R}^{n_g}$ is the vector of Lagrangian multipliers for the constraints. The Karush-Kuhn-Tucker conditions for optimality states that the first order necessary conditions are satisfied when

$$\nabla_{\mathbf{u}} \mathcal{L}(\mathbf{u}, \mathbf{d}) = \nabla_{\mathbf{u}} J(\mathbf{u}, \mathbf{d}) + \lambda^{\mathsf{T}} \nabla_{\mathbf{u}} \mathbf{g}(\mathbf{u}, \mathbf{d}) = 0 \tag{3a}$$

$$\mathbf{g}(\mathbf{u}, \mathbf{d}) \leq 0 \tag{3b}$$

$$\lambda^{\mathsf{T}} \mathbf{g}(\mathbf{u}, \mathbf{d}) = 0 \tag{3c}$$

$$\lambda \geq 0 \tag{3d}$$

Depending on the disturbances realization, different constraints may be active. By active constraints, we mean a set of constraints $\mathbf{g}_{\mathrm{A}} \subseteq \mathbf{g}$ that are optimally at its limiting value. Let $n_a \leq n_g$ denote the number of active constraints $\mathbf{g}_{\mathrm{A}}(\mathbf{u}, \mathbf{d})$. The complementary slackness condition (3c) states that, for the active inequality constraints $\mathbf{g}_A(\mathbf{u}, \mathbf{d}) = 0$, the corresponding Lagrange multipliers are positive $\lambda_A > 0$ and for the constraint $\mathbf{g}_{\mathbb{I}}(\mathbf{u}, \mathbf{d}) < 0$ that are not active, the corresponding Lagrange multipliers are zero, $\lambda_{\mathbb{I}} = 0$.

The Lagrangian (2) can be re-written as

$$\mathscr{L}(\mathbf{u}, \mathbf{d}) = J(\mathbf{u}, \mathbf{d}) + \begin{bmatrix} \lambda_A & \lambda_{\mathbb{I}} \end{bmatrix}^{\mathsf{T}} \begin{bmatrix} \mathbf{g}_A(\mathbf{u}, \mathbf{d}) \\ \mathbf{g}_{\mathbb{I}}(\mathbf{u}, \mathbf{d}) \end{bmatrix} \Rightarrow J(\mathbf{u}, \mathbf{d}) + \lambda_A^{\mathsf{T}} \mathbf{g}_A(\mathbf{u}, \mathbf{d}) \tag{4}$$

For a system with n_g constraints, we can have at most 2^{n_g} active constraint regions. To convert the optimization problem into a feedback control problem, we need to find optimal controlled variables for each active constraint region.

Active constraint control: As mentioned in Skogestad (2000), if there are any active constraints, we control the active constraints tightly. For each active constraint, we choose an associated CV, usually the constraint itself, i.e. CV = $\mathbf{g}_A$ which is controlled to its limit. If the number of active constraints is the same as the number of MVs, then active constraint control is sufficient to achieve optimal operation.

Unconstrained degrees of freedom: After controlling the active constraints, we need to find CVs for any remaining $(n_u - n_a)$ unconstrained degrees of freedom. In this case, from (3) and (4), the necessary conditions of optimality is given by

$$\nabla_{\mathbf{u}}\mathscr{L}(\mathbf{u}, \mathbf{d}) = \nabla_{\mathbf{u}}J(\mathbf{u}, \mathbf{d}) + \lambda_A^{T} \nabla_{\mathbf{u}}\mathbf{g}_A(\mathbf{u}, \mathbf{d}) = 0 \tag{5}$$

$$\Rightarrow \nabla_{\mathbf{u}}J(\mathbf{u}, \mathbf{d}) = -\lambda_A^{T} \nabla_{\mathbf{u}}\mathbf{g}_A(\mathbf{u}, \mathbf{d}) \tag{6}$$

Since λ_A is unknown in (6), we can eliminate it by looking into the nullspace of the active constraint gradients $\nabla_{\mathbf{u}}\mathbf{g}_A(\mathbf{u}, \mathbf{d})$. (Jäschke and Skogestad, 2012). $\mathbf{N}$ is defined as the nullspace of $\nabla_{\mathbf{u}}\mathbf{g}_A(\mathbf{u}, \mathbf{d})$ if $\mathbf{N}^{\mathsf{T}}\nabla_{\mathbf{u}}\mathbf{g}_A(\mathbf{u}, \mathbf{d}) = 0$.

Theorem 1 (Linear combination of gradients as self-optimizing variables). *Given a steady-state optimization problem (1) with $n_a < n_u$ active constraints $\mathbf{g}_A(\mathbf{u}, \mathbf{d})$. Let $\mathbf{N} \in \mathbb{R}^{n_u \times (n_u - n_a)}$ be the nullspace of the active constraint gradients $\nabla_{\mathbf{u}}\mathbf{g}_A(\mathbf{u}, \mathbf{d})$, such that $\mathbf{N}^{\mathsf{T}}\nabla_{\mathbf{u}}\mathbf{g}_A(\mathbf{u}, \mathbf{d}) = 0$. Then the necessary conditions of optimality can be achieved by controlling the linear combination of the gradients*

$$\mathbf{c} = \mathbf{N}^{\mathsf{T}}\nabla_{\mathbf{u}}J(\mathbf{u}, \mathbf{d}) \tag{7}$$

to a constant setpoint of zero.

Proof. Pre-multiplying (6) by $\mathbf{N}^{\mathsf{T}}$ gives

$$\mathbf{N}^{\mathsf{T}}\nabla_{\mathbf{u}}J(\mathbf{u}, \mathbf{d}) = -\mathbf{N}^{\mathsf{T}}\nabla_{\mathbf{u}}\mathbf{g}_A(\mathbf{u}, \mathbf{d})^{\mathsf{T}}\lambda_A \tag{8}$$

Since $\mathbf{N}^{\mathsf{T}}\nabla_{\mathbf{u}}\mathbf{g}_A(\mathbf{u}, \mathbf{d})^{\mathsf{T}} = 0$, $\Rightarrow \mathbf{N}^{\mathsf{T}}\nabla_{\mathbf{u}}J(\mathbf{u}, \mathbf{d}) = 0$ □

Therefore, controlling $\mathbf{c} = \mathbf{N}^{\mathsf{T}}\nabla_{\mathbf{u}}J(\mathbf{u}, \mathbf{d}) \in \mathbb{R}^{(n_u - n_a)}$ to a constant setpoint of zero satisfies the necessary condition of optimality (Krishnamoorthy and Skogestad, 2019). Since $n_a < n_u$, Linear independent constraint qualification (LICQ) is satisfied (i.e. $\nabla_{\mathbf{u}}\mathbf{g}_A(\mathbf{u}, \mathbf{d})$ has full row rank) and $\mathbf{N}$ is well defined. If $n_a = 0$ (fully unconstrained case), $\mathbf{N} = I_{n_u \times n_u}$, which means that the n_u self-optimizing CVs are simply the cost gradients $\mathbf{c} =$

$\nabla_{\mathbf{u}} J(\mathbf{u}, \mathbf{d})$. Therefore, for any active constraint region, $(n_u - n_a)$ CVs can be chosen as $\mathbf{c} = \mathbf{N}^\mathsf{T} \nabla_{\mathbf{u}} J(\mathbf{u}, \mathbf{d})$ which by construction is of size $(n_u - n_a)$.

The proposed framework also enables us to select the CVs without having to develop reduced models for each active constraint region. One the CVs are chosen from each active constraint region, one can switch between the different active constraint regions using simple logic blocks such as selectors or split-range, as demonstrated by Krishnamoorthy and Skogestad (2019) and Reyes-Lúa et al. (2018). Although the gradients are ideal self-optimizing CVs, they are not readily available measurements. One has to estimate the gradients using the measurements. There are several model-based and model-free gradient estimation algorithms, which are briefly summarized by Srinivasan et al. (2011).

3. Illustrative example: Williams-Otto reactor

Consider the benchmark Williams-Otto reactor example, where the raw materials A and B are converted to useful products P and E through a series of reactions

$$A + B \rightarrow C \qquad\qquad k_1 = 1.6599 \times 10^6 e^{-6666.7/T_r}$$

$$B + C \rightarrow P + E \qquad\qquad k_2 = 7.2177 \times 10^8 e^{-8333.3/T_r}$$

$$C + P \rightarrow G \qquad\qquad k_3 = 2.6745 \times 10^{12} e^{-11111/T_r}$$

The feed stream F_A with pure A component is a disturbance to the process and the manipulated variables are the feed stream F_B with pure B component and the reactor temperature T_r. The objective is to maximize the production of valuable products P and E, subject to some purity constraints on G and A in the product stream,

$$\min_{T_r, F_B} -1043.38 x_P (F_A + F_B) - 20.92 x_E (F_A + F_B) + 79.23 F_A + 118.34 F_B \qquad (9)$$

$$\text{s.t.} \quad x_G \leq 0.08, \qquad x_A \leq 0.12$$

Since we have two constraints, we can have at most $2^2 = 4$ active constraint regions, namely, 1) x_A and x_G active, 2) only x_G active, 3) only x_A active, and 4) unconstrained. However, the max limit on x_G is so low that x_G will always be active. Therefore, we can eliminate regions 3 and 4, and we only need to choose CVs for regions 1 and 2. In region 1, we simply control the concentration of x_A to its limit of $0.12 kg/kg$ and x_G to its limit of $0.08 kg/kg$. In region 2, we control x_G to its limit of $0.08 kg/kg$, and control the linear gradient combination $c := 0.9959 \nabla_{F_B} J + 0.0906 \nabla_{T_r} J$ to a constant setpoint of zero.

Region 1 ($F_A = 1.8275 kg/s$): - When the disturbance is $F_A = 1.8275 kg/s$, we are operating in region 1, with both the constraints active. This is the simplest case, where optimal operation is achieved using active constraint control.

Region 2 ($F_A = 1.3 kg/s$): - When the disturbance is $F_A = 1.3 kg/s$, we are operating in region 2, with only x_G constraint active. We use the reactor temperature T_r to control this constraint tightly and use F_B to control the linear gradient combination $c := 0.9959 \nabla_{F_B} J + 0.0906 \nabla_{T_r} J$. In this case, we use a model-based gradient estimation method proposed by Krishnamoorthy et al. (2019). The simulation results are shown in Fig. 2, where it can be seen that the proposed CVs are able to drive the process ot its true optimum.

Switching between x_A and c can automatically be achieved using a selector block. Additional results such as, comparison of the proposed approach with the linear measurement

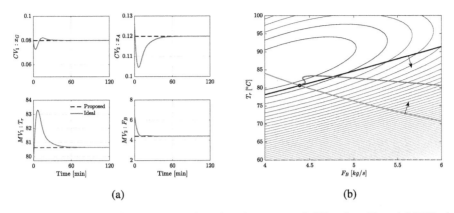

Figure 1: Region 1: Simulation results using the proposed CVs when $F_A = 1.8275 kg/s$.

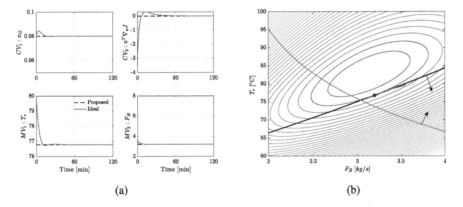

Figure 2: Region 2: Simulation results using the proposed CVs when $F_A = 1.3 kg/s$.

combination and brute force method, including automatic CV-CV switching between x_A and c using a selector block can be found in the first author's PhD thesis (Krishnamoorthy, 2019, Appendix D).

4. Optimal operation of parallel operating units

In this section, we show how the proposed linear gradient combination framework can be used to choose the CVs for optimal operation of parallel operating units. Often in practice, when a plant capacity expands, this is done by simply adding new units in parallel to the existing units. The parallel units often share common resources such as feed, hot water etc. The different units may have different capacities, different equipment condition and different efficiencies.

Consider the optimal operation of p parallel units each with a cost function $\ell_i(u_i)$ and a given total feed U^{max}. The optimization problem is given as

$$\min_{u_i} J = \sum_{i=1}^{p} \ell_i(u_i) \quad \text{s.t.} \quad \sum_{i=1}^{p} u_i - U^{max} = 0 \tag{10}$$

In this case, $\nabla_{\mathbf{u}}\mathbf{g}_A = \mathbf{1}^p$ and $\mathbf{N} \in \mathbb{R}^{(p-1)\times p}$ is chosen such that $\sum_{j=1}^{p} \eta_{i,j}\nabla_{\mathbf{u}_j}J$ and $\sum_{j=1}^{p} \eta_{i,j} = 0 \quad \forall i = 1, \ldots, p-1$ where $\eta_{i,j}$ is the i and j^{th} element in $\mathbf{N}$. This implies $\nabla_{\mathbf{u}_i}\ell_i = \nabla_{\mathbf{u}_j}\ell_j$ for all $i \neq j$. That is the optimal operation of parallel units occur when the marginal cost is the same for all the units, which was also proved by Downs and Skogestad (2011) and commonly used in practice.

To illustrate this, consider a process with $p = 3$ parallel units. Using the nullspace of $\nabla_{\mathbf{u}}\mathbf{g}_A = [1, 1, 1]^T$, we get

$$c_1 : -0.5774\nabla_{\mathbf{u}_1}J + 0.7887\nabla_{\mathbf{u}_2}J - 0.2113\nabla_{\mathbf{u}_3}J = 0$$
$$c_2 : -0.5774\nabla_{\mathbf{u}_1}J - 0.2113\nabla_{\mathbf{u}_3}J + 0.7887\nabla_{\mathbf{u}_3}J = 0$$

Adding $c_1 + c_2$ yields $-\nabla_{\mathbf{u}_2}J + \nabla_{\mathbf{u}_3}J = 0$. Substituting this in c_1 gives $-0.5774\nabla_{\mathbf{u}_1}J + 0.5774\nabla_{\mathbf{u}_2}J = 0$, which results in $\nabla_{\mathbf{u}_1}J = \nabla_{\mathbf{u}_2}J = \nabla_{\mathbf{u}_3}J$. Although this is not a new result and is a well known concept, this re-iterates the general applicability of the proposed linear gradient combination framework.

5. Conclusion

In this paper, we proposed a generalized framework for selecting *what to control* in order to achieve optimal economic operation. An optimization problem can be converted into a feedback control problem by controlling:

- Active constraints $\mathbf{g}_A \to 0$

- Linear gradient combination $\mathbf{c} = \mathbf{N}^T\nabla_{\mathbf{u}}J \to 0$ (with $\mathbf{N}^T\nabla_{\mathbf{u}}\mathbf{g}_A = 0$)

References

V. Alstad, S. Skogestad, 2007. Null space method for selecting optimal measurement combinations as controlled variables. Industrial & engineering chemistry research 46 (3), 846–853.

V. Alstad, S. Skogestad, E. S. Hori, 2009. Optimal measurement combinations as controlled variables. Journal of Process Control 19 (1), 138–148.

J. J. Downs, S. Skogestad, 2011. An industrial and academic perspective on plantwide control. Annual Reviews in Control 35 (1), 99–110.

J. Jäschke, S. Skogestad, 2012. Optimal controlled variables for polynomial systems. Journal of Process Control 22 (1), 167–179.

D. Krishnamoorthy, 2019. Novel approaches to online process optimization under uncertainty. Ph.D. thesis, Norwegian University of Science and Technology.

D. Krishnamoorthy, E. Jahanshahi, S. Skogestad, 2019. A feedback real time optimization strategy using a novel steady-state gradient estimate and transient measurements. Industrial and Engineering Chemistry Research 58, 207–216.

D. Krishnamoorthy, S. Skogestad, 2019. Online process optimization with active constraint set changes using simple control structures. Industrial & Engineering Chemistry Research.

M. Morari, Y. Arkun, G. Stephanopoulos, 1980. Studies in the synthesis of control structures for chemical processes: Part i: Formulation of the problem. process decomposition and the classification of the control tasks. analysis of the optimizing control structures. AIChE Journal 26 (2), 220–232.

A. Reyes-Lúa, C. Zotică, T. Das, D. Krishnamoorthy, S. Skogestad, 2018. Changing between active constraint regions for optimal operation: Classical advanced control versus model predictive control. In: Computer Aided Chemical Engineering. Vol. 43. Elsevier, pp. 1015–1020.

S. Skogestad, 2000. Plantwide control: the search for the self-optimizing control structure. Journal of process control 10 (5), 487–507.

B. Srinivasan, G. François, D. Bonvin, 2011. Comparison of gradient estimation methods for real-time optimization. In: 21st European Symposium on Computer Aided Process Engineering-ESCAPE 21. No. EPFL-CONF-155235. Elsevier, pp. 607–611.

Sauro Pierucci, Flavio Manenti, Giulia Bozzano, Davide Manca (Eds.)
Proceedings of the 30th European Symposium on Computer Aided Process Engineering
(ESCAPE30), May 24-27, 2020, Milano, Italy. © 2020 Elsevier B.V. All rights reserved.
http://dx.doi.org/10.1016/B978-0-12-823377-1.50208-1

Optimisation of Petroleum Production Well Placement under Geological Uncertainty

Emmanuel I. Epelle, Dimitrios I. Gerogiorgis

Institute for Materials and Processes (IMP), School of Engineering, University of Edinburgh, The Kings Buildings, Edinburgh, EH9 3FB, United Kingdom
D.Gerogiorgis@ed.ac.uk

Abstract

Large investments are required for the positioning and drilling of oil and gas wells, implying that decisions related to these activities may be significantly aided by sound and proven mathematical-oriented methods. The use of intuitive engineering judgement alone cannot guarantee sustainable profitability over long periods, especially under geological (reservoir model) uncertainty. To capture significant uncertainty sources in the subsurface geology of the reservoir considered in this study, geostatistical model realisations are obtained using available information (permeabilities and porosities). We use specialised algorithms of the MATLAB Reservoir Simulation Toolbox (MRST, interfaced with PETREL™) in order to determine optimal petroleum production well locations and production rates and thus maximise the field oil recovery. The developed computational workflow has been applied to a realistic case study, for which robust optimality is demonstrated using the worst-case realisation for determining optimal well locations.

Keywords: Production optimisation; optimal well placement; geological uncertainty.

1. Introduction

Well placement optimisation at the early planning stages of field development is necessary to achieve the best possible economic benefits. Reservoir simulations that quantify fluid flow behaviour with respect to well positions can be used to describe subsurface flow phenomena over a long time horizon. However, these simulations can be computationally expensive and this limits the number of iterations that can be performed in the search for an optimal operation strategy. The application of mathematical optimisation to well placement problems usually includes gradient-based methods, mixed integer programming, genetic algorithms and particle swarm optimisation (Bangerth et al., 2006; Onwunalu and Durlofsky, 2010). The complexity of this problem is aggravated by geological uncertainty, which can be accounted for by incorporating multiple geological realisations in the optimisation formulation. The use of the entire superset and a subset of equiprobable geological realisations for well placement optimisation has been carried out by Yeten et al. (2003) and Wang et al. (2012), with intense computational efforts. However, the application of flow diagnostics adopted in this work for well placement optimisation, utilises an adjoint code for gradient evaluations (Møyner et al., 2015), thus enabling faster and accurate computations compared to previous studies. The objective of the present study is to offer a systematic exploration of different operational strategies (with flow visualisations) for optimal oil recovery, demonstrated on a realistic field using the functionalities of the MATLAB Reservoir Simulation Toolbox (MRST).

2. Methodology

Static modelling: The first step in this stage involves the mapping of horizons and faults from the available seismic data in PETREL™ (Figs. 1a and 1b). This is followed by the creation of surface maps that mark the reservoir's boundary (Fig. 1c). Well log interpretations are carried out next to identify the productive geological zones based on the reservoir's lithology, porosity and fluid resistivity (Fig. 1d). The result of this interpretation is the final static model as shown in Fig. 1e, which is upscaled for dynamic simulation purposes (Fig. 1f). The field contains 5 injection wells and 3 production wells.

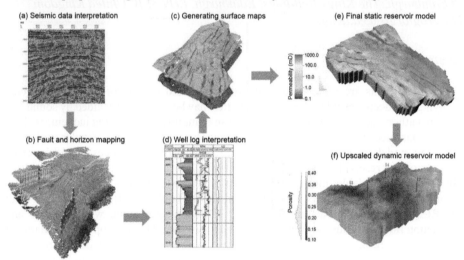

Figure 1: Static and dynamic reservoir model development procedure.

Incorporating uncertainty: Geological uncertainty exists because it is difficult to know the exact properties of every section of the realistic reservoir (Rahim and Li, 2015). Using the sequential Gaussian simulation functionality of PETREL™, 50 realisations of the reservoir's permeability (horizontal and vertical) are generated. The grid structure and the fluid and rock properties of each realisation are imported into MATLAB (where optimisation tasks are performed using the MRST toolbox). The Lorenz coefficient (L_c) is the main

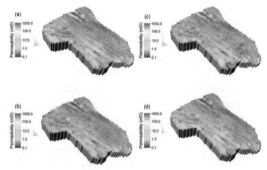

Figure 2: 4 out of 50 geological realisations.

ranking metric applied and the worst realisation is that with the highest L_c.

Dynamic modelling and optimisation formulation: Optimisation tasks are carried out over the worst case scenario after ranking the geological realisations, thus ensuring robust feasibility of the obtained solution (worst-case optimisation). The mathematical formulation of the reservoir model, objective function, operational constraints and adopted solution strategy (Møyner et al., 2015) are shown in Table 1. The dynamic reservoir model (Eqs. 1–3) describes the flow field in the reservoir and the time-of-flight (TOF, the time required for a fluid particle to travel along a streamline from its starting point to the current position). The pressure is denoted as p, the TOF as τ, the Darcy velocity as $\vec{v}$, the reservoir's storage capacity as ϕ, the permeability tensor as $\mathbf{K}$, and the fluid mobility as λ_f. Flow in the reservoir can be driven by wells, n_{bh}, which are controlled by the bottomhole pressure (BHP), but also by other wells, n_r, which are rate controlled. Both well types, n_w, have perforations, n_{pf}, through which fluid flows from the reservoir into the wellbore. All wells are modelled using the Peaceman well model (Eq. 4) in which the well perforation fluxes are denoted by q_{pf}. The index of the well to which perforation number j belongs is denoted as $N_w(j)$. Moreover, k is the well index and W^j_{pf} is the Peaceman well index. Furthermore, a set of manipulations (controls), in the form of closure relations, are specified for each well type (Eqs. 5–6); $\mathbf{u}$ is the control vector.

Table 1: Modelling and optimisation framework for well placement optimisation.

Reservoir Model		
	$NPV(T) = \int_{t=0}^{T} \sum_{c=o,w} (r_c q_c + r_{ci} q_{ci})(1+d)^{-1} dt$	(8)
$\mathcal{P}(q,\vec{v}) = \nabla \times \vec{v} - q = 0$ (1)	$u \leftarrow u - P\left(\alpha \dfrac{dG_\lambda}{du}\right)^T$	(9)
$\mathcal{V}(p,\vec{v}) = \vec{v} + \mathbf{K}\lambda_f \nabla p = 0$ (2)	*Solution Strategy*	
$\mathcal{T}(\tau,\vec{v}) = \vec{v} \times \nabla \tau - \phi = 0$ (3)	$\begin{bmatrix} 0 & \partial_v \mathcal{P} & \partial_q \mathcal{P} & 0 \\ \partial_p \mathcal{V} & \partial_v \mathcal{V} & 0 & 0 \\ \partial_p \mathcal{Q} & 0 & \partial_q \mathcal{Q} & \partial_{p_{bh}} \mathcal{Q} \\ 0 & 0 & \partial_q \mathcal{C} & \partial_{p_{bh}} \mathcal{C} \end{bmatrix} \begin{bmatrix} \mathbf{p} \\ \mathbf{v} \\ \mathbf{q} \\ \mathbf{p_{bh}} \end{bmatrix} = \begin{bmatrix} 0 \\ 0 \\ 0 \\ 0 \end{bmatrix}$ (10)	
$\mathcal{Q}^j(q_{pf}, q_{pf}, p) = q^j_{pf} - W^j_{pf}\lambda_f\left[p^{N_w(j)}_{bh} - p\right]$ $= 0; j = 1,\dots,n_{pf}$ (4)	*Adjoint Formulation*	
$\mathcal{C}_{bh} = u^k_{bh} - p^k_{bh} = 0; k = 1,\dots,n_{bh}$ (5)	$G_\lambda = G[x(u), u] + \lambda^T g[x(u), u]$	(11)
$\mathcal{C}_r = u^k_r - \displaystyle\sum_{j \in N_{pf}(k)} q^j_{pf} = 0; k = n_{bh}+1,\dots,n_{bh}$ (6)	$\dfrac{dG_\lambda}{du} = \dfrac{\partial G}{\partial u} + \left(\dfrac{\partial G}{\partial x} + \lambda^T \dfrac{\partial g}{\partial x}\right)\dfrac{\partial x}{\partial u} + \lambda^T \dfrac{\partial g}{\partial u} + g^T \dfrac{\partial \lambda}{\partial u}$	(12)
Objective Function & Constraints	$\left(\dfrac{\partial g}{\partial x}\right)^T \lambda = \mathbf{J}^T \lambda = -\left(\dfrac{\partial G}{\partial x}\right)^T$	(13)
$L_{c,o} = 2\displaystyle\int_0^1 [F(\phi) - \phi] S_o d\phi$ (7)	$\dfrac{dG_\lambda}{du} = \dfrac{\partial G}{\partial u} + \lambda^T \dfrac{\partial g}{\partial u}$	(14)

Besides the well placement optimisation, rate control optimisation is subsequently performed on the optimally located wells. The first objective function (Eq. 7) is applied to the well placement optimisation task; the objective function is based on the Lorenz coefficient (Eq. 7), which is written in terms of the flow capacity, F, and the storage capacity, ϕ. This coefficient measures how the oil displacement efficiency for a given well pattern differs from that of an ideal (piston-like) displacement pattern in the reservoir. Thus, this coefficient is a measure of the optimality of the water flooding operation and hence the oil recovery in the reservoir. However, a simplified Net Present Value (*NPV*) expression (without installation cost of wells and other factors) is utilised as the objective function of the rate control procedure (Eq. 8). T represents the length of the time horizon, q_c and q_{ci} are the field production and injection rates of components c (oil and water) respectively. The revenues and costs of production and injection of components c are r_c and r_{ci} respectively and d is the discount rate. Furthermore, we note that $\mathcal{C}, \mathcal{T}, \mathcal{V}, \mathcal{Q}$ and $\mathcal{P}$ represent the discretised system in terms of variables, $q_{pf}, p_{bh}, p, v, \tau$.

To perform optimisation computations, the primary variables (pressure, rates and TOF) in Eqs. 1–3 are solved for, and the objective function gradients are computed for a set of controls. The solution strategy (two-point flux approximation for spatial discretisation – Eq. 10) minimises computational workload and makes it adaptable to different linear algebraic solvers. The adjoint equations comprises the Lagrange function for the problem (Eq. 11), its derivatives (Eq. 12) and simplifications (Eqs. 13–14) that yield an objective function which depends on the state variables, $\mathbf{x}$ and not on the control variables $\mathbf{u}$. $\mathbf{x}^T$ is a vector of the solution quantities $\mathbf{p}^T$, $\mathbf{v}^T$, τ^T, $\mathbf{q}^T$ and $\mathbf{p}_{bh}{}^T$. $G[\mathbf{x}(\mathbf{u})]$ represents the objective function and $\mathbf{g}[\mathbf{x}(\mathbf{u}),\mathbf{u}] = 0$ represents a set a constraints; λ is the Lagrange multiplier, $\mathbf{J}$ is the Jacobian, and superscript T denotes the vector/matrix transpose, as applicable above.

Optimal well controls: A steepest-descent algorithm is implemented for finding optimal controls (Eq. 9). This utilises the supplied *NPV* objective function, the well rate bounds (maximum and minimum) and voidage replacement; α represents the step size and P is a projection to the constraints. While evaluating the objective, the value of α is adjusted and the algorithm stops when the improvement in the objective function between two successive iterations is less than the specified tolerance (in this case, equal to: 5×10^{-4}).

Well placement algorithm: The algorithm begins by adding pseudowells with a zero-rate in the region around each injector and computes the gradients of the added wells (based on the Lorenz coefficient). The original well is then replaced by the pseudowell with the largest gradient. The process is repeated until all wells remain stationary.

3. Simulation and optimisation results

In carrying out the optimisation procedure it is assumed that the production wells have been drilled whereas the injection wells are yet to be drilled. Thus, the aim of the optimisation task to determine the optimal injection well positions that yields the best possible oil displacement in the reservoir. In our case study, the reservoir model contains 2,726 cells with an initial pressure of 500 bar; two phases are present (oil and water). Densities and viscosities of both phases are 859 kg m^{-3}, 1014 kg m^{-3}, 2 cP and 0.5 cP respectively; the relative permeability exponents of both phases were set as 2. All 5 injection wells and 3 production wells are assumed to have vertical geometries. The initial injector placement was done such as to maintain good hydraulic connectivity between the injection and production wells given the faulted nature of the reservoir – this is based on reservoir engineering judgement (Fig. 3a). However, on applying the well placement algorithm, optimal injector locations that guarantee improved oil sweep are obtained. This can be observed in the oil saturation plots for both placement patterns (unexplored regions of the reservoir - the yellow patches in Fig. 3a are absent in Fig. 3b). The well paths taken by the algorithm during the search for optimal injector well position are shown in Fig. 3c.

The Lorenz coefficient (a measure of reservoir heterogeneity and the efficiency of oil displacement) is also shown for the two placement scenarios. A smaller value of this parameter represents a better displacement scenario; this is the case with the optimised well positions as shown in Fig. 3b compared to Fig. 3a. F/ϕ denotes the ratio of the reservoir's flow capacity to its storage capacity (Fig. 4a). For a perfect/idealised oil displacement in the reservoir, the F/ϕ ratio = 1. It is observed that the optimised well placement yields an F/ϕ curve closer to an idealised displacement scenario compared to initial well positions. In order to further validate the optimality of the new well configurations determined by the algorithm, we run multiphase flow simulations for a production timeframe of 5 years and obtain the oil recovery over this period. It is shown in Fig. 4b that the oil recovery of the optimised well placement far supersedes that of the initial well placement (twice the recovery of the initial placement at the end of the production forecast – Fig. 4b). This indicates that intuitive-based well placements will hardly yield similar performance and oil recovery (field profitability) to that obtained by sound mathematical techniques. The well placement algorithm thus capitalises on the underlying permeability distribution for optimal determination of injection well locations.

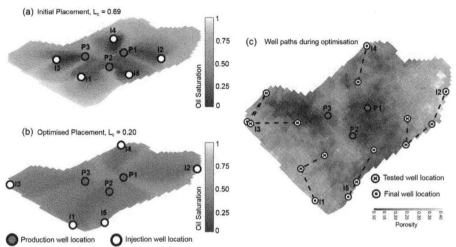

Figure 3: Oil saturation distribution before and after well placement optimisation.

The optimal control configurations (injection and production rates for respective wells) based on the new well placements are thus illustrated in Fig. 4c and 4d, respectively.

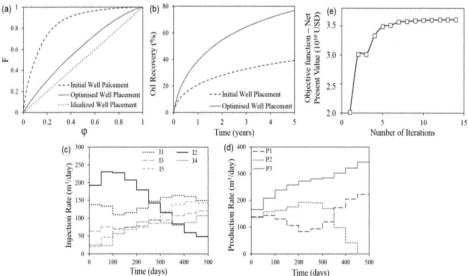

Figure 4: (a) Oil displacement efficiency F/ϕ diagram, (b) percentage oil recovery, optimal manipulations for injection (c) and production (d) wells in the field considered, (e) NPV evolution.

The application of the rate optimisation algorithm, which is based on the *NPV* indicates that injection well I2 with a steady decreasing injection rate at each timestep should be allocated the highest injection rate at the start of production. Next in magnitude is I1 with a relatively lower injection rate. I4 has the lowest injection rate compared to other injection wells and may be considered the least performing. Since operators have control over the injection rates at the surface, it can be said that the rate optimisation algorithm also inherently solves a rate allocation problem. The production rate responses from the different wells indicates that P3 is the most productive well and significantly contributes to the overall field *NPV*. The evolution of the *NPV* objective function is shown in Fig. 4e. It is observed that within the first 5 iterations, the algorithm is able to find a near optimal solution. Compared to a methodology that requires numerous direct calls to a high-fidelity simulator or an approximation of the simulator's output (Epelle and Gerogiorgis, 2019a; b), the implemented algorithm attains optimality in fewer iterations (within 2 min of run time). Although the presented case study is somewhat small (in terms of the number of wells), such rapid computational performance is also expected when the problem size increases. Beyond the computational time required for the rate control optimisation step, we present the time required for the entire workflow (Fig. 5). Most of the time is spent on static model development and preliminary dynamic simulations to ascertain performance.

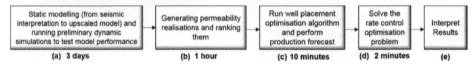

Figure 5: Time requirement for each step of the computational workflow.

4. Conclusion

This study presents an injection well placement and rate control problem of a realistic oil field under geological uncertainty. A worst-case scenario optimisation is performed based on 50 geological realisations obtained from static reservoir modelling, via Sequential Gaussian Simulation. By implementing a well placement optimisation algorithm, oil recovery in the field is boosted to twice the value obtained via intuition-based methods (for a 5-year forecast period). Furthermore, the robust computational methodology for rapid determination of gradients enables rate control (using *NPV* is the objective function) and well placement optimisation (using the Lorenz coefficient as the objective function). These tasks are performed in a matter of minutes, thus demonstrating the applicability of the implemented approach towards real-time decision support in reservoir management.

References

W. Bangerth, H. Klie, M.F. Wheeler, P.L. Stoffa and M.K. Sen, 2006. On optimization algorithms for the reservoir oil well placement problem. *Comput. Geosci.*, 10, 3, 303–319.

E.I. Epelle and D.I. Gerogiorgis, 2019a. A multiperiod optimisation approach to enhance oil field productivity during secondary petroleum production. *Comput. Aided Chem. Eng.,* 46, 1651–1656.

E.I. Epelle and D.I. Gerogiorgis, 2019b. Optimal rate allocation for production and injection wells in an oil and gas field for enhanced profitability. *AIChE J.*, 65, 6 (DOI: 10.1002/aic.16592).

O. Møyner, S. Krogstad and K.A. Lie, 2015. The application of flow diagnostics for reservoir management. *SPE J.*, *20*(02), 306–323.

J.E. Onwunalu and L.J. Durlofsky, 2010. Application of a particle swarm optimization algorithm for determining optimum well location and type. *Comput. Geosci.*, 14, 1, 183–198.

S. Rahim and Z. Li, 2015. Reservoir geological uncertainty reduction: an optimization-based method using multiple static measures. *Math. Geosci.*, 47, 4, 373–396.

H. Wang, D. Echeverría-Ciaurri, L.J. Durlofsky and A. Cominelli, 2012. Optimal well placement under uncertainty using a retrospective optimization framework. *SPE J.*, 17, 1, 112–121.

B. Yeten, L.J. Durlofsky and K. Aziz, 2003. Optimization of nonconventional well type, location, and trajectory. *SPE J.*, 8, 3, 200–210.

Sauro Pierucci, Flavio Manenti, Giulia Bozzano, Davide Manca (Eds.)
Proceedings of the 30th European Symposium on Computer Aided Process Engineering
(ESCAPE30), May 24-27, 2020, Milano, Italy. © 2020 Elsevier B.V. All rights reserved.
http://dx.doi.org/10.1016/B978-0-12-823377-1.50209-3

Oil Production Optimisation using Piecewise Linear Approximations (MILP): Computational Performance Comparison vs. MINLP Formulation

Emmanuel I. Epelle, Dimitrios I. Gerogiorgis

Institute for Materials and Processes (IMP), School of Engineering, University of Edinburgh, The Kings Buildings, Edinburgh, EH9 3FB, United Kingdom
D.Gerogiorgis@ed.ac.uk

Abstract

Typical daily operations of oil and gas production systems are characterised by numerous decisions that must be carefully made if field profitability is to be sustained. These systems are usually nonlinear, nonconvex and involve binary decision variables; hence, the application of mathematical optimisation often results in an MINLP formulation. Piecewise linearisation techniques based on Special Ordered Sets of type 2 (SOS2) constraints have been used to approximate the nonlinear functions of the optimisation problem for complexity reduction. However, a computational analysis of these MILP-based formulations in comparison to their MINLP equivalents in oil production systems is scarce in literature. In this study, the benefits of MILP reformulation are applied to a synthetic but realistic case. In comparing both formulations, we evaluate solution sensitivity to the number of breakpoints, solution time, accuracy, and ease of automation.

Keywords: Mixed-integer optimisation; piecewise linear approximation; oil production.

1. Introduction

The application of mathematical optimisation for the recovery improvement of hydrocarbon reserves is vital for a field's sustainability (Gunnerud and Foss, 2010; Epelle and Gerogiorgis, 2019a). Novel algorithmic advancements have enabled engineers model, simulate and optimise complex nonlinear phenomena characterising the production activities in the petroleum industry (Codas et al., 2012). This results in Mixed Integer Nonlinear Programs (MINLP) which can be difficult to solve. A simplification approach involves reformulating the MINLP to a Mixed Integer Linear Program (MILP) via piecewise linear approximations (Silva and Camponogara, 2014; Kronqvist et al, 2018). Nonlinearities in the formulation are mainly attributable to the multiphase flow rate relationships in the wells, pipelines and valves (Epelle and Gerogiorgis, 2019b). These complex relationships are usually not explicitly known and are dependent on several operational parameters estimated via high fidelity simulators. Piecewise linear models have the advantage of establishing linear relationships directly from the simulator sample points; a property that reduces problem complexity. This study explores this benefit and compares the computational performance of the MILP with the corresponding MINLP. The novel analysis presented herein also enables quality assessment of the optimisation formulation on the overall oil production. Furthermore, another novel element of this study is the combination of operationally distinct well behaviours with complex flow physics and bi-level flow routings within the optimisation formulation.

2. Methodology

The surface network model is first constructed in a steady state multiphase flow simulator (PIPESIM®). As shown in Fig. 1, the model consists of the wells, chokes, flowlines, manifolds, pipelines and separators, which are all connected. Robust multiphase flow correlations are adopted to capture complex flow physics in the respective network components. Some of these phenomena include: water coning behaviour in well (W1), non-vertical/deviated well trajectories (W2 and W4), and downhole pressure assistance to maintain production by means of Progressive Cavity Pumps (PCPs) and Electrical Submersible Pumps (ESPs), as seen in Fig. 1 (denoted as W3 and W4, respectively).

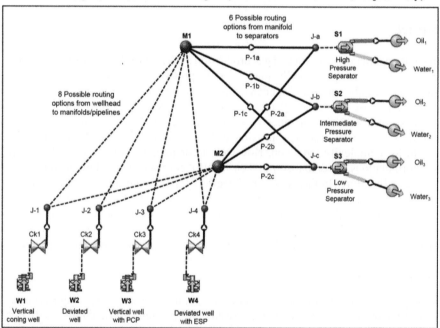

Figure 1: Surface production network and routing superstructure for optimisation.

Although water coning (a change in well inflow that occurs when the water-oil interface changes to a bell shape in the reservoir) is a transient process, the steady state simulator is capable of modelling this process using data tables (implemented herein) that describe oil production rate as a function of the water cut. Several design considerations are also made during the selection of the PCP and ESP for optimal oil delivery from the wells. The surface network design procedure was followed by the generation of large data tables. This involved performing several simulations at different well and pipeline conditions, which correspond to different wellhead pressures (300 – 380 psia) and liquid production rates. Using these data, algebraic (polynomial) proxy models are developed for each network component. These proxy models are then utilised together with an objective function (Eq. 1) to optimise the oil production rate. This methodology takes advantage of the decomposable nature of the production network, in that separate equations can be written for each component, which constitute the optimisation constraints. The complexity of the optimisation problem herein also stems from the presence of discrete routing variables at different levels: the well to manifold level and the pipeline to separator level. The nonlinear pressure-rate responses of the wells and pipelines coupled with these routing decisions inevitably result in an MINLP model, described in Table 1.

Table 1: Mathematical formulations (MINLP and MILP) for oil production optimisation.

Objective function

$$\text{Max } (NPV) = ROP - CWP \tag{1}$$

$$ROP = r_o \times \sum_{w=1}^{Nprod} q_o \tag{2}$$

$$CWP = r_{wt} \times \sum_{w=1}^{Nprod} q_w \tag{3}$$

Constraints of the MINLP formulation

$$P_{w,min}^{wh} \leq P_w^{wh} \leq P_{w,max}^{wh} \quad \forall w \tag{4}$$

$$q_{i,w,NF} = f(P_w^{wh}) \; \forall i, \forall w \tag{5}$$

$$q_{i,w,ESP} = f(P_w^{wh}, f_{i,w,ESP}) \quad \forall i, \forall w \tag{6}$$

$$q_{i,w,PCP} = f(P_w^{wh}, \Omega_{i,w,PCP}) \; \forall i, \forall w \tag{7}$$

$$\Delta P_p = f(q_{p,o}, q_{p,wt}) \quad \forall p \tag{8}$$

$$x_{w,p} P^m \leq P_w^{wh} \quad \forall w, \forall p \tag{9}$$

$$z_{p,s} P^s \leq P^m \quad \forall p, \forall s \tag{10}$$

$$Q_{i,p} = \sum_w (x_{w,p} \times q_{i,w}) \; \forall i, \forall p \tag{11}$$

$$LC^s = \sum_p (z_{p,s} \times Q_{i,p}) \; \forall i, \forall s \tag{12}$$

$$\sum_p x_{w,p} = 1 \tag{13}$$

$$\sum_s z_{p,s} = 1 \tag{14}$$

$$P^s = P^m - \Delta P \tag{15}$$

$$\sum_p q_p \leq LC^s \tag{16}$$

Piecewise linearization in 2 dimensions

$$P_w^{wh} = \sum_{j \in J} \sum_{k \in K} \lambda_{j,k} P_{(w)j}^{wh} \tag{17}$$

$$f_{w,ESP} = \sum_{j \in J} \sum_{k \in K} \lambda_{j,k} f_{(w,ESP)k} \tag{18}$$

$$q_{w,ESP} = \sum_{j \in J} \sum_{k \in K} \lambda_{j,k} q_{(w,ESP)j,k} \tag{19}$$

$$\sum_{j \in J} \sum_{k \in K} \lambda_{j,k} = 1 \tag{20}$$

$$\delta_j = \sum_{k \in K} \lambda_{j,k} \quad \forall j \tag{21}$$

$$\delta_k = \sum_{j \in J} \lambda_{j,k} \quad \forall k \tag{22}$$

$$\lambda_{j,k}, \delta_j, \delta_k \geq 0 \tag{23}$$

$$\delta_j \text{ and } \delta_k \text{ are SOS2} \tag{24}$$

Piecewise linearization in 1 dimension

$$P_w^{wh} = \sum_{j \in J} \lambda_j P_{(w)j}^{wh} \tag{25}$$

$$q_w = \sum_{j \in J} \lambda_j q_{(w)j} \tag{26}$$

$$\sum_{j \in J} \lambda_j = 1 \tag{27}$$

$$\lambda_j \text{ is SOS2} \tag{28}$$

Linearizing bilinear terms of type ($C_1 \cdot C_2$ and $B \cdot C$)

$$C_1 \cdot C_2 = \xi_1^2 - \xi_2^2 \tag{29}$$

$$L_1 \leq C_1 \leq U_1; \quad L_2 \leq C_2 \leq U_2 \tag{30}$$

$$\xi_1 = 0.5(C_1 + C_2); \quad 0.5(L_1 + L_2) \leq \xi_1 \leq 0.5(U_1 + U_2) \tag{31}$$

$$\xi_1 = 0.5(C_1 - C_2); \quad 0.5(L_1 - U_2) \leq \xi_2 \leq 0.5(U_1 - L_2) \tag{32}$$

$$\tau = B \cdot C; \quad 0 \leq C \leq U \tag{33}$$

$$\tau \leq U \cdot B \tag{34}$$

$$\tau \geq C - U(1 - B) \tag{35}$$

$$\tau \geq 0; \quad \tau \leq C \tag{36}$$

Proxy model structure

$$q_{o,ESP} = \alpha_0 + \alpha_1 P_{wh} + \alpha_2 f_{ESP} + \alpha_3 P_{wh}^2 + \alpha_4 f_{ESP}^2 + \alpha_5 P_{wh} f_{ESP} \tag{37}$$

This MINLP formulation is linearised in 3 ways to generate MILPs; the computational performance of these 4 formulations (including the MINLP) are compared. The first MILP formulation (MILP-3) applies standard algebraic transformation and Special Ordered Sets of type 2 (SOS2) to linearise nonlinear terms (quadratic and bilinear terms – products of 2 continuous variables and products of a continuous and binary variable) in the MINLP formulation using 3 breakpoints. The second MILP formulation (MILP-5) uses 5 breakpoints instead; the third (MILP-LKT) directly utilises the look-up data tables for linear interpolation in 1 and 2 dimensions. Table 1 presents the detailed formulations for the MINLP and MILP, respectively. The aim is to maximise the objection function (in terms of the Net Present Value – *NPV*, Eq. 1); where the Revenue from Oil Production (ROP) and Cost of Water Production (CWP) are given by Eqs. 2 and 3 respectively; r_o is the oil price (USD/STB), r_{wt} denotes the water production unit cost (USD/STB) and N_{prod} is the number of wells. Eq. 4 ensures that the wellhead pressure (P^{wh}) is tightly bounded. The proxy models for Naturally Flowing (NF) well, ESP well, PCP well and pipelines are given by Eqs. 4–7 respectively; q represents the flowrate, f_{ESP} the ESP frequency, Ω, the PCP impeller rotation speed and ΔP_p, the pipeline pressure drop. Indices o, wt, i, w, p, wh, m, s denote oil phase, water phase, all phases, wells, pipelines, wellheads, manifolds, and separators, respectively. P_m and P_s are manifold and separator pressure, respectively.

Binary variables $x_{w,p}$ assigned to each well, ensure that the produced fluids from a well are routed by the choke (Eq. 9) to one of the pipelines. Similarly, $z_{p,s}$ in Eq. 10 ensures that the pipelines are routed to the separator. The mass balance constraint between wells and pipelines is represented by Eq. 11; Eq. 12 ensures material balance between the pipelines and the separators (which operate at a fixed pressure). The selection of only 1 binary variable is enforced using Eqs. 13–14. The constraint defined by Eq. 15 ensures the target separator pressure is met, while the liquid capacity constraints of the separators are represented by Eqs. 16. The procedure for linearising functions in 2D and 1D are shown in Eqs. 17–28 respectively; where j and k represent the breakpoints associated with the different variables. Bilinear terms which occur in the MINLP formulation as shown in the typical proxy model structure (Eq. 37) are linearised using Eqs. 29–36. In these equations, C represents, a continuous variable, and B a binary variable; L and U denote the lower and upper bounds of a continuous variable. ξ and τ are additional variables introduced in the linearisation procedure. BONMIN (v.1.8.6) and CPLEX (v.12.8.0.0) have been employed in order to solve the MINLP and MILP formulations, respectively.

3. Optimisation results

The proposed formulations were programmed in MATLAB® R2016a (using OptiToolbox v2.28) and solved with BONMIN and CPLEX on an Intel Core i7-6700 processor at 3.40 GHz running on a 64 bit Windows workstation with 16GB of RAM. The MILP-LKT formulation consists of 25 polytopes (squares) for the well performance function (5 breakpoints for the ESP frequency/rotational speed and 5 breakpoints for the wellhead pressure). For the pipelines, 144 polytopes (squares) were adopted (12 breakpoints for the oil and water phases respectively). This resulted in a total of 8,740 variables; this is significantly larger than the number of variables required in the other formulations (as shown in Table 2). Despite this considerably large number of variables, the MILP model is solved in a shorter time, compared to the MINLP formulation which has 36 variables. This increase in problem size (number of constraints and variables) that ensues with an increasing number of data points is a major drawback of the SOS formulation; hence, it is only suitable for low-dimensional problems. With the MINLP, the increase in number of data points would hardly affect the approximations of the simulator output. In this regard, the MINLP formulation can be regarded as more robust and scalable compared to the MILP reformulation. The convergence of proposed formulations to different optimal solutions (Table 1) is an indication of the non-convexity of the optimisation problem. Nevertheless, high-quality, reliable solutions have been obtained from all formulations as demonstrated in the relative gap obtained (Table 2). The MINLP formulation has provided the best solution in terms of the NPV. Our computational analysis has also shown that the improvement in resolution quality affects the solution quality of both formulations. With 5 breakpoints (MILP-5), the NPV obtained is closer to that of MINLP compared to the lower resolution formulation, consisting of 3 breakpoints (MILP-3).

Table 2: Computational performance of optimisation formulations

Optimisation formulation	MINLP	MILP-3 (SOS2)	MILP-5 (SOS2)	MILP-LKT (SOS2)
Solver used	BONMIN	CPLEX	CPLEX	CPLEX
Number of constraints	34	184	184	340
Number of variables	36	134	170	8702
Relative gap (%)	0.00	0.00	0.00	0.00
Solution time (s)	0.536	0.111	0.152	0.287
Number of nodes	0	229	253	292
NPV (USD)	989,228	979,934	986,832	979,261
Total oil production rate (STB/day)	15,219	15,076	15,182	15,066
Total water production rate (STB/day)	3,803	3,767	3,794	3,766

The MILP-LKT formulation has provided the lowest NPV (1% lower than the MINLP). This may be attributed to the fact the solutions are always approximated by linear segments (in the SOS formulation – with inherently limited extrapolation capabilities when flowing conditions change), which are generated between nonlinear data points. Water coning behaviour is a broadly known source of nonlinearity in the wellbore model. Another important observation from results is that the high-pressure separator with lower capacity (S1) is the least preferred option for routing fluids from manifolds (Fig. 2).

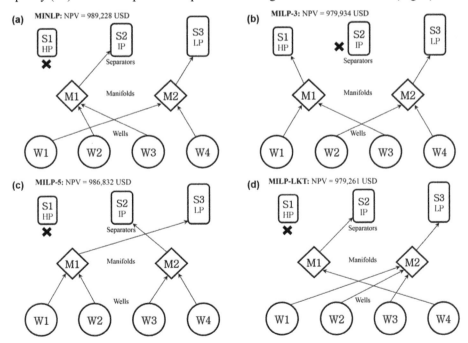

Figure 2: Optimal discrete routing structure for all optimisation formulations considered.

The pipeline diameter and length, and the high pressure drop that ensues, makes it difficult for fluids to be delivered to S1 which operates at 45 psia, compared to S2 and S3 at 35 psia and 25 psia respectively. The algorithm has shown good utilisation of separator capacities for routing the fluids. As shown in Table 2, the MILP formulations converge faster than the MINLP. Furthermore, the time required for proxy model development if incorporated will further make the MINLP slower compared to the MILP (which directly uses the table data points). It can also be observed that the differences between the oil and water production rates of the respective formulations are minimal. Despite this, very different optimal routing structures are obtained. This indicates that the algorithmic treatment of discrete variables is complicated, especially when they exist at different levels. However, the low number of nodes utilised for finding the optimal solution in all formulations reflects the efficiency of the CPLEX solver (which uses the Branch and Bound algorithm). On applying the CBC solver (based on the Branch and Cut algorithm) to our problem, the number of nodes reduces by an order of magnitude, although with a higher relative gap and a longer computational time. While a detailed comparison of solver performances is beyond the scope of this study, such analysis may be conducted to further evaluate the performances of these formulations especially for bigger-sized problems. Although the computational time requirement is expected to increase with larger production networks, the fast solution times obtained herein should be attributed to the nature of our optimisation formulation, rather than just problem size. On performing a network optimisation task (on Fig. 1) using PIPESIM's v2019.3® optimisation module, we observed the required runtime is over 30 s, resulting in a 10% lower NPV obtained: this attests to the superior performance of our proposed and implemented formulation.

4. Conclusion

This study proposes MINLP and MILP formulations for optimising production from a synthetic oil field consisting of 3 separators, 2 manifolds and 4 wells with complex downhole/multiphase flow physics. The nonlinear models were developed using regression analysis that resulted in algebraic polynomial models; whereas piecewise linear models were developed from production points sampled from a look-up table. A computational analysis performed on the formulations showed superior performance of the MILP formulation in terms of the runtime despite the significantly increased number of variables involved in comparison to the MINLP. Improved resolution of the MILP formulation from 3 to 5 breakpoints resulted in a better NPV. However, compared to other formulations, the MINLP yielded the highest NPV. Despite the similarity in the production rates, different optimal routing strategies are obtained for each formulation.

References

A. Codas, S. Campos, E. Camponogara, V. Gunnerud and S. Sunjerga, 2012. Integrated production optimization of oil fields with pressure and routing constraints: The Urucu field. *Comput. Chem. Eng.*, 46, 178–189.

E.I. Epelle and D.I. Gerogiorgis, 2019a. Optimal Rate Allocation for Production and Injection Wells in an Oil and Gas Field for Enhanced Profitability. *AIChE J.*, 65, 1, (DOI: 10.1002/aic.16592).

E.I. Epelle and D.I. Gerogiorgis, 2019b. Mixed-Integer Nonlinear Programming (MINLP) for production optimisation of naturally flowing and artificial lift wells with routing constraints. *Chem. Res Des.*, 152, 134–148.

V. Gunnerud and B. Foss, 2010. Oil production optimization—A piecewise linear model, solved with two decomposition strategies. *Comput. Chem. Eng.*, 34, 11, 1803–1812.

J. Kronqvist, D.E. Bernal, A. Lundell, and I.E. Grossmann, 2018. A review and comparison of solvers for convex MINLP. *Optimization Eng.*, 1–59.

T.L. Silva, and E. Camponogara, 2014. A computational analysis of multidimensional piecewise-linear models with applications to oil production optimization. *Eur. J. Op. Res.*, 232, 3, 630–642.

Sauro Pierucci, Flavio Manenti, Giulia Bozzano, Davide Manca (Eds.)
Proceedings of the 30th European Symposium on Computer Aided Process Engineering
(ESCAPE30), May 24-27, 2020, Milano, Italy. © 2020 Elsevier B.V. All rights reserved.
http://dx.doi.org/10.1016/B978-0-12-823377-1.50210-X

A Fuzzy Control Approach for an Industrial Refrigeration System

Robert Menzhausen[a], Manuel Merino[b], Bogdan Dorneanu[a,c], José José Manrique Silupú[b], William Ipanaqué Alama[b], Harvey Arellano-Garcia[a,c,*]

[a]LS Prozess- und Anlagentechnik, Brandenburgische Tecnische Universität Cottbus-Senftenberg, Cottbus, D-03046, Germany
[b]Departamento de Ingeneria Mecánico Eléctrica, Universidad de Piura, Piura, Peru
[c]Department of Chemical Process Engineering, University of Surrey, Guildford, GU2 7XH, United Kingdom
arellano@b-tu.de

Abstract

This contribution presents the development of a model for the refrigeration plant used for mangos, which is able to simulate both the chamber and the fruit temperatures. The model is developed from energy balances for each section of the refrigeration system and the fruits, and is the basis for the setup of a fuzzy controller, capable of regulating continuously the compressor's frequency to achieve the desired temperature. The model is able to accurately predict the chamber temperature profiles, but is more sensitive when simulating the fruit temperature. The fuzzy controller is able to achieve the set-point more accurately and in a shorter time than the on/off control, achieving a decrease in energy consumption as well.

Keywords: modelling, refrigeration system, fuzzy control.

1. Introduction

Tropical fruits are important products on the global market. The change to a healthier nutrition, the development of new products and great availability let to a rise in their consumption during the last decade (Provido, 2016). For example, the worldwide production of mangos rose by about 4.5% between 2007 and 2016 (Provido, 2016).
Piura is a region in the north of Peru, with a very diverse economy. Agriculture is the second biggest sector in the region, with main products such as mangos (8%), bananas (6%) and grapes (12%). Due to their perishable nature, fruits are stored in cooling chambers until they reach the distribution stations. To achieve rapid and efficient decrease in fruit's temperature, refrigeration systems are employed, using vapor compression refrigeration plants. They consist of four main components: the compressor, the condenser, the expansion valve and the evaporator. Within the system a refrigerant is circulating. Though designed to satisfy maximum load, these plants usually work at part-load for much of their life, generally regulated by on/off cycles of the compressor (Aprea, et al., 2004). The fast growth of fruit exports lead to an increase demand of reliable and efficient refrigeration systems.
A big disadvantage of cooling systems is that they count as the biggest consumers of electricity today (IIR, 2015). This implies a high cost in operating cold storage or controlled atmosphere storage systems, which becomes a pressing problem for developing countries (Aprea, et al., 2004).

Research into these challenges enabled development in the area of cooling systems in the past years, especially in the field of energy efficiency (Basediya, et al., 2013). Among these achievements is the use of variable speed compressors, which allow the use of new and more beneficial control approaches, such as fuzzy or PID controllers, where the applied frequency takes values between a minimum and maximum (Saleh & Aly, 2015). The following sections will present the development of a model for a refrigeration plant used for mangos, starting from first principles, as well as of a control system to enable the operation of the plant, to improve the fruit conservation and reduce the energy consumption. The resulting models are tested experimentally on a refrigeration plant located on the campus of the University of Piura (Peru).

2. Mathematical model of the refrigeration system

Starting from energy balances for each section of the refrigeration system and the fruits, a simple model is developed to simulate the temperature in the cooling chamber and for approximating the fruits' temperature.

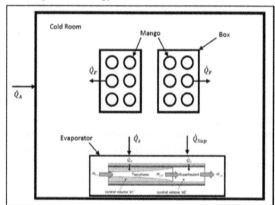

2.1. Refrigeration chamber temperature

The cooling chamber temperature is determined by balancing the heat flows inside the room. Fig.1 shows the individual heat sources and sinks around the cooling chamber.

Figure 1. Heat flows inside the cooling chamber

The energy balance for the refrigeration chamber is expressed as:

$$\frac{dQ_{CR}}{dt} = \dot{Q}_{F,total} + \dot{Q}_A - \dot{Q}_S - \dot{Q}_{Sup} \tag{1}$$

With Q_{CR} the energy stored in the cooling chamber [J]; $\dot{Q}_{F,total}$ the total heat flow of the fruits [J/s]; $\dot{Q}_A$ the heat flow equivalent from the ambient [J/s]; $\dot{Q}_S$ the heat flow of the saturation section [J/s]; $\dot{Q}_{Sup}$ the heat flow of the superheated section [J/s].

Writing the terms in Eq.1 in terms of the temperatures, the following equations are obtained:

$$\frac{dQ_{CR}}{dT_{CR}} = V_{CR} \cdot \rho_{A,CR} \cdot c_{p,A,CR} \tag{2}$$

$$\dot{Q}_{F,total} = \alpha_F \cdot A_{F,total} \cdot (T_F - T_{CR}) \tag{3}$$

$$\dot{Q}_A = \dot{V}_A \cdot \rho_A \cdot c_{p,A} \cdot (T_A - T_{CR}) \tag{4}$$

$$\dot{Q}_S = U_S \cdot A_S \cdot (T_S - T_{CR}) \tag{5}$$

$$\dot{Q}_{Sup} = U_{Sup} \cdot A_{Sup} \cdot (T_{Sup} - T_{CR}) \tag{6}$$

Where V_{CR} is the volume of the cooling chamber [m³]; $\rho_{A,CR}$ the air density in the cooling chamber [kg/ m³]; $c_{p,A,CR}$ the air specific heat capacity in the chamber [J/(kgK)]; T_{CR} the cooling chamber temperature [K]; α_F the overall fruit heat transfer coefficient [J/(m²K)]; $A_{F,total}$ the total heat transfer area of the fruits [m²]; T_F the fruit temperature [K]; $\dot{V}_A$ the ambient air volume flow [m³/s]; ρ_A the ambient air density [kg/ m³]; $c_{p,A}$ the ambient air specific heat capacity [J/(kgK)]; T_A the ambient air temperature [K]; U_S the overall heat transfer coefficient of the saturation section [W/(kgK)]; A_S the heat transfer area of the saturation section [m²]; T_S the saturation section temperature [K]; U_{Sup} the overall heat transfer coefficient of the superheated section [W/(kgK)]; A_{Sup} the heat transfer area in the superheated section [m²]; T_{Sup} the superheated section temperature [K].

Replacing the heat flows in Eq.1 results in the following equation for the cooling chamber temperature:

$$\frac{dT_{CR}}{dt} = \alpha_F \cdot \frac{A_{F,total} \cdot (T_F - T_{CR}) + U_S \cdot A_S \cdot (T_S - T_{CR}) + U_{Sup} \cdot A_{Sup} \cdot (T_{Sup} - T_{CR}) + \dot{V}_A \cdot \rho_A \cdot c_{p,A} \cdot (T_A - T_{CR})}{V_{CR} \cdot \rho_{A,CR} \cdot c_{p,A,CR}} \quad (7)$$

As fruits are heterogeneous, with different shapes, sizes and weight, their heat transfer area was determined using an averaged fruit diameter, and assuming spherical shape.

2.2. Fruit temperature
The energy balance for the fruits stored inside the cooling chamber follows:
$$\frac{dQ_F}{dt} = \dot{Q}_{F,total} \quad (8)$$

With Q_F the energy stored inside the fruits [J].

Eq.8 can be rewritten in terms of the fruit temperature as:
$$\frac{dT_F}{dt} = \frac{\alpha_F \cdot A_F \cdot (T_F - T_{CR})}{m_F \cdot c_{p,F}} \quad (9)$$

Where m_F is the fruit mass [kg]; $c_{p,F}$ the fruit specific heat capacity [J/(kgK)].

2.3. Model parameters
The values of the refrigeration chamber and heat transfer areas of the saturation and the superheated sections were measured. For the average values of the mango diameter and weight, 20 mangos were measures and the average was calculated. Other values such as the mango heat transfer coefficient, or the saturated and superheated section heat transfer coefficients were assumed. The values used are presented in Table 1.

Table 1. Model parameters

Parameter	Value	Parameter	Value
Chamber volume, V_{CR}	34.24	Heat transfer area superheated section, A_{Sup}	0.27
Chamber air density, $\rho_{A,CR}$	1.2	Ambient air density, ρ_A	1.2
Chamber air heat capacity, $c_{p,A,CR}$	1.4	Ambient air heat capacity, $c_{p,A}$	1.4
Overall heat transfer coefficient saturation section, U_S	0.1	Fruit heat transfer coefficient, α_F	0.0005
Heat transfer area saturation section, A_S	0.27	Fruit average mass (one mango), m_F	0.3
Overall heat transfer coefficient superheated section, U_{Sup}	0.1	Fruit average diameter (one mango), D_F	0.1

3. Control of the refrigeration cycle

The aim of the refrigeration cycle is to ensure a pre-set temperature in the cooling chamber. The most common and simple method to control refrigeration system is the on/off controller (Saleh & Aly, 2015), which works with a fixed speed compressor.

The controller transmits a fixed frequency to the compressor if the temperature is higher than the set-point, or the compressor is turned off if the temperature is lower than the pre-set temperature. An on/off controller is easy to design and use, and it is not expensive to implement (Mosayebi, 2011). The disadvantages of these controllers are that they consume a lot of energy, they have low accuracy due to oscillating overshooting and undershooting temperature and they reduce the compressor life by attrition of the continuous on/off mode operation. Variable speed compressors are becoming more popular, as they have the ability to improve the energy efficiency and allow the use of more complex control systems that provide more accuracy.

3.1. Fuzzy control

The main idea of fuzzy control is to use human knowledge for creating the controller by describing the state of system with fuzzy variables, using words and gradings such as very hot, hot, warm, medium, cold, very cold, freezing to describe the temperature. These variables are connected by IF-clauses defining actions. For example, if the room temperature is cold, the heater will be running a little bit. Fuzzy controllers are structured in four blocks: the fuzzification, which receives the input variables and transforms the information into fuzzy variables the inference mechanism is able to interpret; the rule-base, which contains defined rules as IF-clauses; the inference mechanism, which checks which rules are complied and passes the output variable to the defuzzification; the defuzzification, which transforms the output to process values.

The fuzzy controller for the refrigeration plant (Fig.2) has the frequency applied to the compressor as its output variable, $u(t)$. As its inputs it takes the error, $e(t)$, defined as the difference between the desired temperature and the actual cooling chamber temperature, and the derivative of the error with the time, $\partial e / \partial t$. This is done to improve the control accuracy.

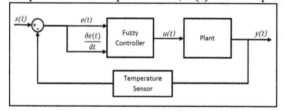

Figure 2. Block diagram of the control system

The rule-base connecting the membership functions are shown in Table 2, with values between the available functions of 25 and 70 Hz. Experimental investigations showed that the separation into small sections improve the control accuracy.

Table 2. Rule base for the fuzzy controller

Frequency $u(t)$		$\frac{\partial e(t)}{\partial t}$		
		positive	zero	Negative
	big	70	70	70
	small	55	60	65
$e(t)$	tiny	45	50	55
	zero	35	40	45
	minus	25	25	25

The next step in developing the control system is to establish membership functions for the input variables. Triangular membership functions are considered, shown in Fig.3a, with values developed by experimental investigation. Trapezoidal functions are considered for the beginning and the end of the intervals, as in these cases a fast approach is desired. In case of the output variable (the compressor frequency), ten membership functions (Fig.3b) are defined over small sections, to improve the control accuracy. The range of the membership functions was chosen to be high, leading to a crossing with each other. This overlap results in a smooth gradient from the highest to the lowest frequency, and benefits the control.

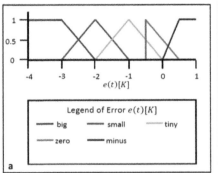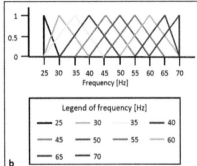

Figure 3. Membership functions of the a) input variable (error); b) output variable (frequency)

4. Results

The models developed in the previous sections have been tested experimentally in a refrigeration plant located on the campus of the University of Piura (Peru). It is divided into two rooms covered with a simple corrugated sheet roof, for protection against environmental impact. The walls and the top of the refrigeration room are insulated to reduce the heat flow from the ambient. The control room is located next to the refrigeration chamber. And contains a computer used to run and control the refrigeration system. The fruits are stored in boxes and stacked on palettes, located right under the evaporator. The arrangement of the temperature sensors is fixed during the experiments, in the top and the bottom boxes of a stack.

4.1. Control of the refrigeration system

The model developed in the previous sections is used to validated a set of experiments performed in the refrigeration plant. The first experiments are done implementing an on-off controller and using 230 kg mangos, assuming a set-point of 9 ^{0}C. The results for the cooling chamber temperature (Fig.4) show that the model is able to predict very well the experimental data, and the set-point is reached after 2,700 seconds. An energy consumption of 18.97 kWh is recorded in this case.

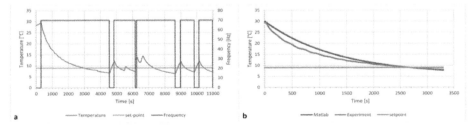

Figure 4. a) Experimental results for on/off control with 230 kg mango; b) Model vs. experimental results for on/off control and 230 kg mango

Furthermore, further experiments were performed to investigate the performance of the fuzzy control on the refrigeration plant. The initial temperature was set to 25 ^{0}C and the refrigeration process was started to achieve a set-point of 9 ^{0}C. When the equilibrium for the chamber temperature is achieved for about 10 minutes, a disturbance is introduced by opening the door for 4 minutes. Then the door is closed again, and the procedure repeated once equilibrium is reached. At this point, the set-point was changed to 8 ^{0}C. For the fuzzy control experiments, a total mass of 200 kg of mangos is considered.

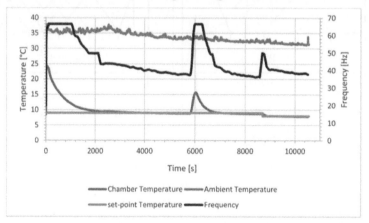

Figure 5. Results for fuzzy control of the refrigeration plant with 200 kg mango

The experiment (Fig.5) was run between 3:41 and 6:38 PM. The results show that the controller is able to achieve both set-point temperatures quite well even after the disturbance was introduced. The experiment consumed 10.92 kWh.

5. Conclusions

A simplified model to determine the temperature of the cooling chamber and the fruit in a refrigeration plant is presented. The model starts from energy balances for the different components of the plant, and is able to predict the temperatures with a good accuracy. Furthermore, the model is used in the development of a fuzzy controller of the refrigeration system. This controller is then implemented in the plant, being able to achieve a good performance and a reduced energy consumption compared to PID controllers. Future work will consider more accurate representation of the heat transfer coefficients to improve the temperature predictions, as well as other types of control approaches, such as model predictive control.

References

Aprea, et al., 2004, International Journal of Refrigeration 27, pp. 639-648

Basediya, et al., 2013, J Food Sci Technol 50 (3), pp. 429-442

IIR, 2015, The role of refrigeration in the global economy, pp. 1-16

Mosayebi, 2011, On/off control, Australia: AQUARIUS Technologies PTY Ltd.

Provido, 2016, Business Mirror, https://businessmirror.com.ph/2016/09/06/global-demand-for-tropical-fruits-increasing-international-network-says

Saleh & Aly, 2015, International Journal of Control, Automation and Systems 4 (1), pp. 14-25

Sauro Pierucci, Flavio Manenti, Giulia Bozzano, Davide Manca (Eds.)
Proceedings of the 30th European Symposium on Computer Aided Process Engineering
(ESCAPE30), May 24-27, 2020, Milano, Italy. © 2020 Elsevier B.V. All rights reserved.
http://dx.doi.org/10.1016/B978-0-12-823377-1.50211-1

Online Process Monitoring in SMB Processes

Stefanie Gerlich,* Yannik-Noel Misz, Sebastian Engell

Process Dynamics and Operations Group, Department of Biochemical and Chemical Engineering, TU Dormund University, Emil-Figge-Str. 70, 44227 Dortmud, Germany
stefanie.gerlich@tu-dortmund.de

Abstract

Conventionally, preparative chromatographic separation processes are operated in batch mode. For more efficient separation, the simulated moving bed (SMB) process has been introduced. Due to its hybrid dynamics, optimal operation of the SMB process is challenging. For increased process efficiency, model-based optimizing control schemes can be applied. These schemes require online information about the states and the parameters of the plant. The online process monitoring strategy presented here is based on the transport dispersive model of the SMB process and simultaneously estimates the states and the parameters of the individual columns by exploiting the switching nature of the SMB process. The scheme can be activated before the process reaches its cyclic steady state (CSS). The strategy is demonstrated for the separation of two amino acids.

Keywords: state estimation, parameter estimation, SMB process, chromatography

1. Introduction

 In the production of fine chemicals, pharmaceuticals and biotechnological products chromatography is an important separation technique due to its high selectivity, low operating temperatures and ability to handle of aqueous solutions (Schmidt-Traub et al., 2012). Preparative chromatographic processes are usually operated in batch mode. In order to use the stationary phase more efficiently, the continuously operated simulated moving bed (SMB) process can be used (Rajendran et al., 2009). This multi-column chromatographic process simulates a counter-current flow of the stationary and mobile phase by periodically switching the inlet and outlet ports between the individual columns (Schmidt-Traub et al., 2012). It is schematically depicted in Figure 1.

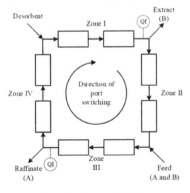

Figure 1: Schematic representation of a 4-zone SMB process with 2 columns per zone.

Due to the hybrid dynamics of the SMB process that lead to discontinuities and sharp fronts in the state trajectories, the optimal operation of the SMB process is challenging.

To improve performance, model-based optimizing control schemes can be used, which adjust the manipulated variables of the process such that the operating point moves towards an optimal operation. Such schemes have been demonstrated successfully at real SMB plants (Toumi and Engell, 2004, Küpper and Engell, 2007). These schemes require online information about the states and the parameters of the plant. In Toumi and Engell (2004) the states were computed by forward simulation of a plant model with identical columns. Küpper and Engell (2009) employed a moving horizon estimator for state and parameter estimation assuming identical columns. The estimation of individual column parameters can help to optimize the operation and online monitoring of individual column parameters is important to detect degrading columns.

The main problem in the estimation of individual column parameters is that only scarce measurement information is available in SMB processes. Küpper and Engell (2006) developed an Extended Kalman Filter-based scheme for estimating parameters of each column individually using concentrations measurements at the two outlet ports and at one fixed location between the columns. An optimization-based scheme for estimating individual column parameters one by one was presented in Lemoine-Nava and Engell (2014). This scheme only relies on concentration measurements in the extract and raffinate streams.

In this contribution, we apply the latter scheme to the online estimation of states and parameters of each individual column for a separation of amino acids. Compared to previous work which was based on the general rate model (GRM) for describing the dynamic behavior of each individual column, the transport dispersive model (TDM) and the weighted essentially non-oscillatory (WENO) scheme for its numerical solution are employed. The TDM contains less parameters compared to the GRM resulting in a decreased experimental effort for determining them. The GRM contains the particle diffusion as a parameter which cannot be identified accurately from experiments indicating that the GRM is over-parameterized (Toumi and Engell, 2004). The TDM is applicable for low molecular weights of the solutes(Schmidt-Traub et al., 2012) which applies here. The two amino acids are tryptophan and phenylalanine. Concentration measurements are only available at the extract port and at the raffinate port (see Figure 1). We demonstrate that the state and parameter estimation can already be activated during the start-up phase of the process before a cyclic steady state (CSS) is reached.

The remainder of the paper is structured as follows: First, the employed first principle model, the TDM, is briefly explained. Second, the state and parameter estimation scheme that is considered here is described. Afterwards, the scheme is applied to the continuous separation of two amino acids, phenylalanine and tryptophan. We conclude the paper with a summary, a discussion of outcomes and future research.

2. Modeling of the SMB process

Here the SMB process is modeled by directly considering its switched dynamics. Models describing the dynamics of the individual columns in the system are connected through mass and component balances at the inlet and outlet ports:

$$0 = -Q_I + Q_{IV} + Q_{Des} \tag{1}$$
$$0 = -Q_{II} + Q_I - Q_{Ex} \tag{2}$$
$$0 = -Q_{III} + Q_{II} + Q_{Fe} \tag{3}$$
$$0 = -Q_{IV} + Q_{III} - Q_{Raf} \tag{4}$$
$$0 = -c_{i,in,I}Q_I + c_{i,out,IV}Q_{IV} \tag{5}$$
$$0 = -c_{i,in,III}Q_{III} + c_{i,out,II}Q_{II} + c_{i,Fe}Q_{Fe} \tag{6}$$

Where Q represents the flow rate in the respective zone or at the respective port. c_i refers to the concentration of component i.

For dynamic modeling of the individual chromatography columns, the TDM is chosen and the adsorption behavior is described by a multi-component Langmuir isotherm. The respective model equations can be found in Schmidt-Traub et al. (2012). The model consist of a set of two partial differential equations (PDEs) per component present in the system. The PDEs here are spatially discretized using a finite volume approach combined with the WENO scheme (von Lieres and Andersson, 2010). The method is suitable for handling systems with steep concentration gradients as they appear in chromatography columns.

3. State and Parameter Estimation Scheme for the SMB process

A scheme for estimating the states and the parameters of each column individually was proposed by (Lemoine-Nava and Engell, 2014) and is illustrated in Figure 2. The scheme consists of two main parts, a state estimation and a parameter estimation routine.

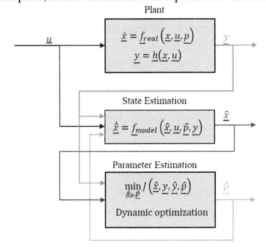

Figure 2: Structural overview of the state and parameter estimation scheme

In the state estimation routine, the process is simulated based on the current process inputs and the parameters from the parameter estimation routine. Additionally, measured concentrations at the extract and raffinate port are fed to the process model as inlet concentrations for the column behind the measurement location.

For the parameter estimation routine, a least-squares optimization problem is solved periodically that aims at minimizing the deviations between measured and simulated concentrations. It estimates the model parameters separately for each column. During one full cycle of the SMB process, two virtual batch experiments can be identified for each individual column of which each has a length of two periods. For the first experiment, the respective column is located next to the extract port and measurements are collected at the column inlet during period k. For the next period k+1, measurements are then collected at the column outlet. This procedure is repeated for the periods when the respective column is connected to the raffinate node, generating the second experiment.

Thus, individual optimization problems for parameter estimation are set up for each column exploiting the switching nature of the SMB process. The formulation of the optimization problem is given in Lemoine-Nava and Engell (2014). Each period, the parameter estimation is started for one column leading to updating the parameters once per cycle. The first parameter estimation is activated after six periods of operation as this marks the time when enough measurement information is available for the first column. Regarding the implementation, the symbolic math framework CasADi is employed that provides derivatives using automatic differentiation (Andersson et al., 2019). For the process simulation in the state estimation routine, the integrator CVODES from the Sundials suite is used.

The underlying dynamic optimization problem is solved using direct collocation, in which both, inputs and states are fully discretized in the time domain. The time domain is discretized using orthogonal collocation on finite elements (OCFE). The resulting non-linear program (NLP) is solved with the interior point solver IPOPT.

The parallel execution of state and parameter estimation is realized using Matlab's Parallel Computing toolbox. After each complete period, the parameter estimation for the column with the extract port at its outlet is started on a parallel worker as a background Matlab process without a user interface. In total four parallel workers are available. To prevent jobs from forming long queues on the workers, a parameter estimation is only started, if the result of the previous estimation step for the same column is available. The results from all finished optimizations are transferred to the state estimation model after each period.

4. Case Study: Continuous Amino Acid Separation using the SMB process

The continuous separation of two amino acids, phenylalanine and tryptophane, on an eight column SMB pilot plant with 2 columns per zone is studied in this contribution. For this case study, the estimated parameters are the parameters H_{Phe} and H_{Trp} in the multicomponent Langmuir isotherm as these have sensitivity strong influence on the outlet concentration profile of a column. Their initial estimates as well as all other model parameters that are needed for modeling are presented in Table 1. Unless otherwise indicated, it is assumed that all 8 columns in the system are described by the same set of parameters although slight deviations occur from column to column in real plants.

Table 1: Model parameters (Phe = phenylalanine, Trp = tryptophane)

Parameter	Description	Value
d_c	Column diameter	8 mm
L_c	Column length	125 mm
r_p	Solid phase particel radius	7.5 μm
ε	Void fraction	0.80
ε_p	Solid phase porosity	0.26
ρ	Liquid phase density	1 g/mL
η	Liquid phase viscosity	1 mPa s
$k_{eff,phe}$	Mass transfer coefficient (Phe)	28.38 μm/s
$k_{eff,trp}$	Mass transfer coefficient (Trp)	156.80 μm/s
b_{Phe}	Isotherm parameter (Phe)	0.0682 L/g
b_{Trp}	Isotherm parameter (Trp)	0.2697 L/g
$H_{i0,Phe}$	Initial estimate for the Henry coefficient (Phe)	8.1858
$H_{i0,Trp}$	Initial estimate for the Henry coefficient (Trp)	36.2682

As $H_{Phe} > H_{Trp}$, tryptophan represents the stronger adsorbing component and thus it is retrieved at the extract port, while the less retained component phenylalanine is withdrawn at the raffinate port. The solvent is a methanol/water mixture with 5 vol.-% of methanol and a phosphate buffer. The feed contains 0.2 g/L of phenylalanine and tryptophane each and ports are shifted every three minutes giving a period length of

$\tau = 3$ min. The process is operated with $Q_I = 13.32$ g/L, $Q_{Des} = 9.75$ g/L, $Q_{Ex} = 6.82$ g/L, and $Q_{Fe} = 4.72$ g/L.

5. Results and discussion

The performance of the state and parameter scheme described in section 3 is tested for two different scenarios that are relevant for applications at real plants. All results shown are simulation results.

5.1. Tracking offsets in all parameters

In a real plant, differences in the parameters of all columns have to be expected. Here, it is assumed that the initial estimates of the parameters H_{Phe} and H_{Trp} for each column deviate up to ±30 % from their true values. The resulting accuracy of the state estimation, measured by the sum of the squared errors between the estimated and the true states, is depicted in Figure 3. Here, the true states of the plant are available as the measurement data is obtained from a process simulation with the true parameter values.

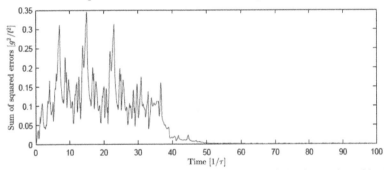

Figure 3: Sum of squared errors in the state estimation over 100 periods of operation with adaptation of the individual Henry parameters of the columns when all initial Henry parameter estimates deviate up to ±30 % from their true values. The initial error of the state estimation is zero as the plant is initially empty, meaning that all concentrations are zero. The peaks in the state estimation error that can be observed over the first 35 periods are caused by the deviations in the initial parameter estimates from column to column leading to larger or smaller deviations in the state trajectories if components are traversing through the respective column. After period 48, the state error is negligible, as the parameter estimates for each individual column have converged to their true values.

5.2. Plant-model mismatch in the void fractions of the columns

Here a mismatch of ±5 % between the true column void fraction and the column void fraction used in the estimation model is assumed, leading to different flow velocities inside the columns. The void fractions are not estimated, only the Henry coefficients as in the simulation in the previous section. The initial estimates for H_{Phe} and H_{Trp} are at their true values. The accuracy of the state estimation is depicted in Figure 4. Again, the initial error is zero as all concentrations in the process are initially zero. During the first 30 periods of operation, the error increases and exhibits many peaks resulting from the deviations in the void fraction from column to column. Around period 30, the state and parameter estimation has converged. In order to compensate for the plant-model mismatch in the column void fraction, the estimated values of H_{Phe} and H_{Trp} converged to values that are different from their true values. Due to the high sensitivity of the outlet concentration profile to H_{Phe} and H_{Trp}, effects from other model parameters can be lumped into H_{Phe} and H_{Trp}, if the deviations are not too large. It is remarkable that the state estimation is almost perfect after convergence of the parameters.

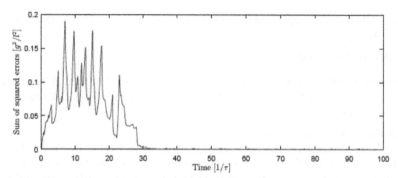

Figure 4: Sum of squared errors in the state estimation over 100 periods of operation in the presence of plant-model mismatch in the column void fractions with adaptation of the Henry coefficients

6. Conclusion and Future Works

In this work, a state and parameter estimation scheme for individual columns has been presented that is based on the work by Lemoine-Nava and Engell (2014). Modifications to original scheme include the use of the simpler TDM model that is sufficient for most practical applications with the WENO scheme for the numerical solution, and the activation of the estimation scheme before the CSS is reached. It is shown that the state and parameter estimation scheme is capable of successfully estimating the process states if all isotherm parameters have different but constant values or if plant-model mismatch in the column porosities is present. This is the basis for combining the estimation scheme with a model-based optimizing control scheme to ensure optimal SMB process operation for not exactly known or slowly varying column parameters.

References

J. Andersson, J. Gillis, G. Horn, J. Rawlings, M. Diehl, 2019, CasADi: a software framework for nonlinear optimization and optimal control, Mathematical Programming Computation, 11, 1, 1-36

A. Küpper, S. Engell, 2006, Parameter and state estimation in chromatographic SMB processes with individual columns and nonlinear adsorption isotherms, IFAC Proceedings Volumes, 39, 2, 611-616

A. Küpper, S. Engell, 2007, Optimizing Control of the Hashimoto SMB Process: Experimental Application, IFAC Proceedings Volumes, 40,5, 149-154

A. Küpper, M. Diehl, J. Schröder, H. Bock, S. Engell, 2009, Efficient moving horizon state and parameter estimation for SMB processes, Journal of Process Control, 19, 5, 785-802

R. Lemoine-Nava, S. Engell, 2014, Individual Column State and Parameter Estimation in the Simulated Moving Bed Process: an Optimization-based Method, IFAC Proceedings Volumes, 47, 3, 9376-9381

E. von Lieres, J. Andersson, 2010, A fast and accurate solver for the general rate model of column liquid chromatography, Computers & Chemical Engineering, 34, 8, 1180-1191

A. Rajendran, G. Paredes, M. Mazzotti, 2009, Simulated moving bed chromatography for the separation of enantiomers, Journal of Chromatography A, 1216, 4, 709-738

H. Schmidt-Traub, M. Schulte, A. Seidel-Morgenstern, 2012, Preparative Chromatography, Wiley-VCH, Weinheim, Germany

A. Toumi, S. Engell, 2004, Optimization-based control of a reactive simulated moving bed process for glucose isomerization, Chemical Engineering Science, 59, 18, 3777-3792

Sauro Pierucci, Flavio Manenti, Giulia Bozzano, Davide Manca (Eds.)
Proceedings of the 30th European Symposium on Computer Aided Process Engineering
(ESCAPE30), May 24-27, 2020, Milano, Italy. © 2020 Elsevier B.V. All rights reserved.
http://dx.doi.org/10.1016/B978-0-12-823377-1.50212-3

Conceptual Design of Novel Processes for 4-Hydroxybutyl Acrylate Production

Mihai Daniel Moraru[a,b,*], Elena Zaharia[b], Costin Sorin Bildea[b]

[a]*Department of Technology, Engineering and Projects, Hexion, Seattleweg 17, 3195 ND Pernis, The Netherlands*
[b]*Department of Chemical and Biochemical Engineering, University Politehnica of Bucharest, Str. Gh. Polizu 1-7, 011061 Bucharest, Romania*
mihai.moraru@hexion.com

Abstract

This paper is the first to present novel solid-based catalytic processes for the production of 4-hydroxybutyl acrylate (HBA): three conventional reaction-separation-recycle (RSR) systems, and one reactive distillation-based (RD) process. Each of them tackles the selectivity and difficult separations in various ways, achieving a final HBA product within the required specification. While the RD process is less capital and energy intensive, each process has its trade-offs that are worth further optimization, followed by a rigorous comparison on economic basis.

Keywords: Aspen, esterification, hydrolysis, reactive-distillation, side-reactor

1. Introduction

4-Hydroxybutyl Acrylate (HBA) is used to obtain homopolymers and copolymers with end-use in a variety of products. HBA is also used in chemical syntheses, because it readily undergoes addition reactions with a wide variety of organic and inorganic compounds (BASF, 2016). The patent literature (Tanaka et al., 2017, and the references therein) describes that HBA is produced by esterification of acrylic acid (AA) and 1,4-butanediol (BD), with formation of water as byproduct, using acidic catalysts as sulfonic acid, para-toluene sulfonic acid or dibutyltin oxide.

A relatively recent journal article (Yang et al., 2007a) shows that this esterification reaction can be performed using an ion-exchange resin as solid catalyst, overcoming the well-known issues of the liquid catalysts (e.g. side reactions, difficult product recovery, corrosion, and other environmental problems during the disposal of waste).

This work presents the conceptual design of several process alternatives for HBA production, using solid catalysis. The reaction scheme consists of two consecutive reactions: (1) formation of the desired HBA in the reaction between AA and BD, and (2) formation of the undesired 1,4-butanediol diacrylate (BDA) from HBA and AA; water is formed in both reactions.

$$AA + BD \rightleftarrows HBA + H_2O \tag{1}$$

$$AA + HBA \rightleftarrows BDA + H_2O \tag{2}$$

We develop three reaction–separation–recycle (RSR) and one reactive distillation (RD) processes. Each process has a capacity of roughly 20 kt/y of 99.4 %mass HBA. The

RSR processes use fixed-bed reactors and common distillation equipment for separation of product and recycle of reactants; the very difficult HBA/BD separation is achieved by pressure-swing distillation. The RD process uses a standard column (i.e., the fresh reactants are fed at the top and bottom of a catalytic section located in the middle of the column). The bottom product stream contains both HBA and BDA (the heaviest components). Therefore, an additional column is required to perform the HBA/BDA split. Finally, BDA is hydrolyzed in a side-reactor and recycled to the RD column.

2. Thermodynamics and Reaction Kinetics

The chemical system in this study has 5 components, namely, H_2O, AA, BD, HBA and BDA. The pure component physical properties for H_2O, AA and BD are available in the Aspen databanks. The properties of HBA and BDA are estimated using group contribution methods by the Property Constant Estimation System (PCES) in Aspen. For HBA, the parameters of the Antoine vapor pressure equation are regressed from experimental data (4 data points, BASF brochures). The UNIQUAC model is selected to model the phase equilibria, using one set of binary interaction parameters. The H_2O/AA and H_2O/BD interaction parameters are available in Aspen; for all the remaining binary systems, they are estimated with the UNIFAC method. The vapor pressure of all components and the azeotropes at 0.05 and 0.8 bar are presented in Figure 1, left. In a mixture in which all components are present, H_2O and AA are easily separated due to their low boiling points and not forming azeotropes; H_2O does form a heterogeneous azeotrope with BDA, however it does not play an essential role in the separation processes described here. From the mixture of the remaining components (i.e., BD, HBA and BDA), it may seem that BDA can be easily separated because it has the highest boiling point throughout the whole range of pressure (say, above 0.003 bar). However, the BDA/BD and BD/HBA azeotropes are important for the separation of this mixture. In addition, BD and HBA have close vapour pressure, which makes the BD/HBA split to be very challenging. This difficult separation was observed in the experiments reported by Yang et al. (2007b), where they state that, after the reaction, it is very difficult to obtain a high purity of HBA by general separation techniques such as distillation and extraction. Consider Figure 3, top-left diagram: from a mixture having the composition in region I (point F), BD can be removed by distillation as a bottom product, but neither HBA nor BDA can be separated; if the composition is in region II, HBA and BDA can be separated, in a two-column sequence, but not BD (or one should accept sending back to the reactor a large recycle stream containing large amounts of HBA, using one distillation column less). Independent of the choice, the separation of this mixture remains challenging.

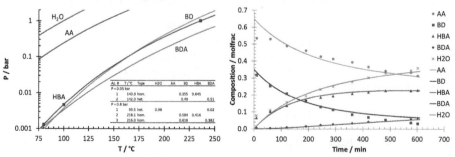

Figure 1. Left: Vapor pressure and azeotropes (by *Distillation Synthesis* tool in Aspen Plus); Right: Comparison between experimental and regressed composition during reaction at 100 °C.

The course of reaction catalyzed by Amberlyst 15 can be described by the kinetic model given by equations (3)-(5) proposed by Yang et al. (2017a); the pre-exponential factors were determined by regression using the data reported in the same reference. The comparison between experimental and regressed data at 100 °C is presented in Figure 1, right; a good agreement is observed.

$$r_1 / \left[kmol/kg_{cat} \cdot s \right] = 91.49 \exp \left(-\frac{58300}{8.314 \cdot T} \right) \left(C_{AA} C_{BD} - (1/K_{eq,1}) C_{HBA} C_{H_2O} \right) \tag{3}$$

$$r_2 / \left[kmol/kg_{cat} \cdot s \right] = 181625 \exp \left(-\frac{86700}{8.314 \cdot T} \right) \left(C_{AA} C_{HBA} - (1/K_{eq,2}) C_{BDA} C_{H_2O} \right) \tag{4}$$

$$K_{eq,1} = \exp \left(1457.6/T - 2.0212 \right); \ K_{eq,2} = \exp \left(810.4/T - 0.4614 \right) \tag{5}$$

3. Process Concepts and Design

3.1. Reaction–Separation–Recycle (RSR)

Three RSR process concepts are developed, starting with their basic process structure as presented in Figure 2; while all processes share many similarities, there are also key differences between these process concepts. Consider first the **RSR-A** concept: The fresh ($F_{AA,0}$, $F_{BD,0}$) and recycled reactants ($F_{AA,RCY}$, $F_{BD,RCY}$) are mixed and fed to a fixed-bed tubular reactor (PFR) operated adiabatically, with an inlet temperature of 100 °C and an inlet molar ratio BD/AA of 3. The reactor is modeled using the kinetic model (3)–(5). From the separation section (SEP), H_2O, HBA and BDA are removed from the system, while AA and BD are recovered and recycled to the reaction section as two separate streams. This structure with two recycles is possible since AA can be easily separated from the mixture, while BD can be separated by pressure–swing distillation as it will be described later. In the RSR-A, the selectivity to HBA is about 97.8 %mole, therefore a loss of reactants. **RSR-B** achieves 100% selectivity recycling the BDA back to PFR; hence, this process has 100 % selectivity to HBA. A particularity of this concept, important for designing the separation section, is that the reactions are performed at high concentrations of BDA (the composition of key streams around the reactor is shown in Figure 2).

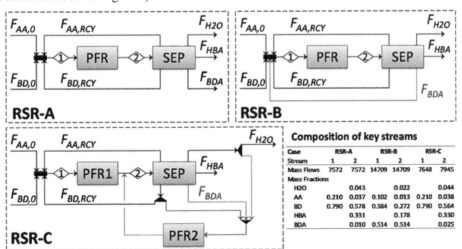

Figure 2. Structure of three RSR process concepts and composition of key streams.

Another alternative is to convert BDA back to AA, HBA and BD in a hydrolysis reactor; this is shown in **RSR-C**, where BDA is mixed with part of the H_2O and part of the BD streams and reacted in a second reactor (PFR2).

While developing the RSR concepts using the rigorous reactor modeling and black-box separation, a rough sensitivity analysis (not presented here) showed that, in the RSR-A and RSR-C processes, 2,500 kg of catalyst are sufficient for complete reactants conversion, while RSR-B requires 10,000 kg; hence, a four-times larger reactor; PFR2 of RSR-C, requires roughly 1,500 kg of catalyst. As expected, trade-offs exist and are worth future exploration: utilization of reactants versus larger recycle and larger reactor (RSR-A/RSR-B); utilization of reactants versus a second reactor (RSR-A/RSR-C).

The structure of each separation system is developed starting with the composition of stream 2 (see table in Figure 2) and making use of thermodynamic insights. Consider first the RSR-A process. The low-boiling H_2O and AA are removed first, by simple distillation. The remaining components are separated in a series of three distillation columns. The first two columns operated at different pressures overcome the minimum boiling homogeneous azeotrope BD-HBA by pressure-swing, as explained by the ternary diagrams (Figure 3, top) and the block scheme of the system (Figure 3, bottom). At 0.05 bar (top-left diagram), the concentration of the feed (F) entering the distillation column C-3 (bottom-left) falls in region I. Thus, BD is obtained as bottoms stream (B) and recycled to the reaction section, while the distillate (T*, containing all three components) is near the distillation boundary connecting the two binary azeotropes. At 0.8 bar, the locations of the binary azeotropes and distillation boundary change and the composition of the C-3 distillate (T*), which is the same as C-4 feed (F*), falls in region II (top-right diagram). Having crossed the distillation boundary, it is possible to obtain a bottoms stream (B) containing HBA and BDA, and a distillate (T) close to the distillation boundary. The former can be easily separated. The later falls back in region I at lower pressure, and can be recycled as feed to C-3.

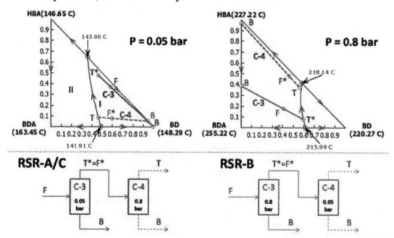

Figure 3. Top: Ternary diagrams showing the singular points (boiling and azeotropes) for the ternary system BD/HBA/BDA at two pressures, and mass balance for columns C-3 and C-4 that form the Pressure–Swing distillation system. Bottom: Columns sequence for each RSR processes.

With respect to RSR-B, sending back the BDA stream to the reactor brings a major change in the mass balance. As BDA is not allowed to leave the process, its overall generation rate (reaction-outlet vs. reaction-inlet) must be zero. For this reason, the

BDA concentration in the reactor is high, hence a composition of the stream leaving the reactor which is significantly different compared to RSR-A and RSR-C (see table in Figure 2). Given this change, the separation system is different. After H_2O and AA removal, the feed (F) to C-3 falls in region II of the ternary diagram at 0.8 bar (Figure 3, top-right diagram). Now, it is possible to obtain the binary mixture HBA/BDA, free of BD, as bottoms of C-3 (B in Figure 3, bottom-right diagram); this mixture can be easily split in a next distillation column. Changing the pressure to 0.05 bar, the concentration of the C-3 distillate (T*) crosses the distillation boundary. Thus, the feed of C-4 (F*) falls in region I. Here, BD is obtained as bottoms product (high purity is not required) being recycled to the reactor, while the C-4 distillate is sent back as feed to C-3.

The RSR-C process follows the same sequence as RSR-A, the difference being that the BDA is mixed with part of the H_2O and BD, and hydrolysed in a second reactor (PFR2) back to AA, HBA and BD. The outlet stream, containing all components, is returned to the separation section. The complete process flow diagram of RSR-C process, together with a mass balance and key sizing and operating parameters, is shown in Figure 4.

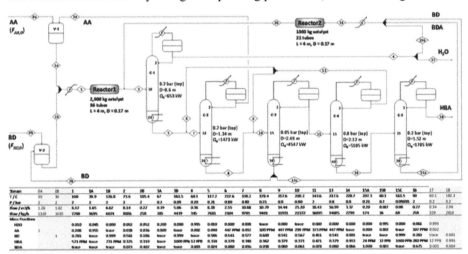

Figure 4. Process flow diagram and mass balance (selected streams) of the RSR-C process.

3.2. Reactive Distillation (RD)

HBA can be conveniently produced also in a RD-based process. The process flow diagram is showed in Figure 5, together with a mass balance, operating conditions and main equipment sizes. The RD column has a standard configuration with the catalytic bed in the middle and standard addition of the fresh feeds: the light reactant as vapor at the bottom of the catalytic bed, the heavy reactant as liquid at its top. The heavier HBA and BDA exit the column with the bottoms, and are further split in the ideal separation block SEP; the HBA/BDA split is easy, and a column as C-5 of RSR-C can be used. The key to obtain HBA at the required specification is avoiding the contamination of the RD bottoms with reactants; otherwise, during the HBA/BDA separation, these low-boiling components will end up in the lighter product, HBA. At the top of RD, high-purity H_2O (99.99 %mass) is obtained. BDA is mixed with part of the H_2O stream and fresh BD, and hydrolyzed back to AA, HBA and BD. The reactor outlet stream is fed to the RD below the catalytic bed, providing in this way the necessary separation of the heavier HBA and BDA from the lighter reactants AA and BD, and side-product H_2O.

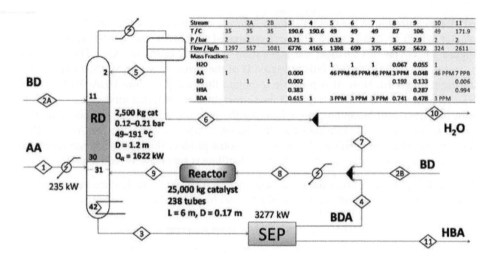

Figure 5. Process flow diagram and mass balance (selected streams) of the RD process.

4. Conclusions

Production of HBA at industrial scale using Amberlyst 15 as solid catalyst is feasible. Due to the nature of the chemical system and reaction conditions, the chemistry is not 100 % selective towards HBA, important amounts of BDA being formed. In the RSR-C process, the per-pass HBA selectivity in the esterification reactor is 98 %mol. Conveniently, a second reactor is used to hydrolyze BDA back to AA, HBA and BD, achieving in this way an HBA overall process selectivity of 100 %. The difficult split of the BD/HBA/BDA mixture is achieved by pressure-swing distillation. This process is capital and energy intensive: 2 reactors, 4000 kg catalyst, 5 distillation columns and about 13.5 MW heating. In the RD process, the reaction conditions in the catalytic column favor even more the BDA production, the per-pass HBA selectivity being only 48 %mol. As in the previous process, the BDA is hydrolyzed back, achieving overall an HBA process selectivity of 100 %. The RD process overcomes the BD/HBA/BDA separation difficulty by reacting BD completely in the column, and therefore achieving the required HBA specification in a subsequent distillation column for HBA/BDA split. This process requires 1 reactor, 27500 kg of catalyst, 2 columns, and about 4.9 MW heating. Hence, triggered by their trade-offs, these processes should be optimized and rigorously compared on economic basis.

References

BASF, 2016, Petrochemicals specialty monomers, Technical information, TI/CP 1331 e.

BASF, Specialty monomers, Technical data, E-CPI/M 1610 booklet.

Y. Tanaka, K. Okamura, K. Ito, 2017, Process for preparing 4-hydroxybutyl acrylate, Patent No. US009670129B2.

J. I. Yang, S. H. Cho, H. J. Kim, H. Joo, H. Jung, K. Y. Lee, 2007a, Production of 4~ hydroxybutyl acrylate and its reaction kinetics over Amberlyst 15 catalyst, Can. J. Chem. Eng., 85, 83-91.

J. I. Yang, S. H. Cho, J. Park, K. Y. Lee, 2007b, Esterification of acrylic acid with 1,4-butanediol in a batch distillation column reactor over Amberlyst 15 catalyst, Can. J. Chem. Eng., 85, 883-888.

Sauro Pierucci, Flavio Manenti, Giulia Bozzano, Davide Manca (Eds.)
Proceedings of the 30th European Symposium on Computer Aided Process Engineering
(ESCAPE30), May 24-27, 2020, Milano, Italy. © 2020 Elsevier B.V. All rights reserved.
http://dx.doi.org/10.1016/B978-0-12-823377-1.50213-5

Physically Consistent Machine Learning Models Using Artificial Data for MISO Systems and Model Predictive Control

Jia-Lin Kang[a], Shi-Shang Jang[b*], Fan-Kai Sun[b], Po-Hsun Chang[b]

a Department of Chemical and Material Engineering, National Yunlin University of Science and Technology, Yunlin, 64002, Taiwan
b Department of Chemical Engineering, National Tsing Hua University, Hsinchu, 30013, Taiwan
ssjang@mx.nthu.edu.tw

Abstract

This work presents a novel artificial data assisted machine learning modelling approach to guarantee the correct physical gain signs between manipulated variables (MV)/controlled variable (CV) in a multi-input-single-output (MISO) model predictive control system (MPC). These industrial systems, such as polymerization reacting systems, are basically controlled based on the operators' experiences due the lack of the trustworthy models. The purpose of this work is to provide an implementable machine learning model for MPC purposed by the aid of artificial data. This approach is shown valid through a numerical problem, real plant test data and plant test.

Keywords: Machine Learning Models, Artificial data, Gain sign consistency, Model predictive Control

1. Introduction

Multi-Input-Single –Output (MISO) systems exist in many problems for example, grade transition and quality control problems in chemical engineering. In many cases, due to the lack of reliable physical model, these operations strongly depend on the experiences of the field operators. These cases result unstable qualities, loss of raw materials and products. In many cases, the on-line quality data can be directly or indirectly detected such as intrinsic viscosity, melting index,… etc.. In case of non-direct measurement, online soft senor is an active research topic and the plant applications (Zhang et al., 2016). Model predict control (MPC) hence becomes a possible solution to these problems. Basically, MPC approaches implement data-driven linear/nonlinear models. In nonlinear cases, machine learning dynamic models are highly active research topics among chemical engineering researchers (Wu et al., 2019). Machine learning models are most likely derived based on historical plant data. However, historical data do not guarantee to cover complete dynamical territories of many MISO systems. These models can be trained well and tested well without any physical consistency due to the existences of many local minima. With a trustworthy model, MPC approaches can be easily implemented to solve the above problems. Back-propagation-neural-network (BNPP) has been mature for many decades (Aglodiya, 2017). It is conceptually easy to understand and implement, but it might cause a large number of inputs and complicated structure if one implements them as a dynamic model with long time lags. Recurrent neural network hence becomes a rather wide spread approach among chemical engineering researchers because of its dynamic and deep learning natures. On the other hand, XGBoost is a most popular machine learning approach in case of large amount of training data. In this paper, the above three different approach are used to show the generality of this artificial data approach. In the area of machine learning approaches, there have been other approaches that have claimed able to solve physical consistent problem of these data-driven models, such as sequence-to-sequence approaches (Hsiao et al.) or model transfer learning (Cho et al., 2014). However, these approaches are either trained with tricky arrangements of network arrangements or with a rather complicated physical model. This work is to propose an easy reasoned approach without changing the general structure of original machine learning models with very limited domain knowledge. This paper is to pursue a physically consistent MISO machine learning model using an artificial data approach. The artificial data matched to the physical properties are created and added to the plant data into the training set. These artificial data should be derived to ensure the gain signs of the output and inputs corrected but the accuracy of the model is not sacrificed. Note that types of these artificial data should depend on different types of machine learning models. In this work, most common implemented models such as artificial neural network (ANN), recurrent neural network (RNN) as well as XGBoost models will be studied. The models should be accurate enough for the implementation of MPC. This modelling approach as well as MPC will be demonstrated using a numerical benchmark problem. A real industrial example is presented to show the applicability and efficiency of this novel approach. Plant test results are also included.

2. Artificial Data Approach for MISO machine learning models

Consider Multi-Input-Single-Output (MISO) system, with a set of manipulated inputs, $U = \{U_1, U_2, \dots, U_N\}$, a set of measurable outside-determined inputs or disturbance inputs, $D = \{D_1, D_2, \dots, D_M\}$, and a single out output variable Y. Let us denote a set of historical operating data:

$$S_H = \left\{ \begin{matrix} (u_{11}, u_{21}, \dots, u_{N1}, d_{11}, d_{21}, \dots, d_{M1}, y_1), \dots, \\ (u_{1S}, u_{2S}, \dots, u_{NS}, d_{1S}, d_{2S}, \dots, d_{MS}, y_S) \end{matrix} \right\} = \{R_1, R_2, \dots, R_S\} \quad (1)$$

where lower case of U, D and Y represent the numerical data of the inputs and outputs, S is the size of the historical data set and the second sub-index indicates the time sequence of the historical data, while R_i represents each event at time i. It is our purpose to obtain a machine learning model G such that each sequence $\{R_{k-K}, R_{k-K+1}, \dots, R_k\}$ with:

$$y_{k+1} = G(R_{k-K}, R_{k-K+1}, \dots, R_k) \quad (2)$$

Assume that the domain knowledge or plant operators knowledge lead to the gains for each inputs are known, i.e. the signs of $\frac{\partial Y}{\partial U_1}, \frac{\partial Y}{\partial U_2}, \dots, \frac{\partial Y}{\partial U_N}, \frac{\partial Y}{\partial D_1}, \dots, \frac{\partial Y}{\partial D_M}$ can be obtained. The problem on the field is that the machine learning model G such that the prediction of y_{k+1} using (2) are correct inside the historical data set S_H with wrong input signs. This would lead to physically unrealizable control actions and even regulatory operations. In this work, we propose to create the following artificial data set:

$$S_A = S_{AH} \cup S_{AI} = \{R_1, R_2, \dots, R_{AH}\} \cup \{R_1, R_2, \dots, R_{AA}\} \quad (3)$$

Note that each element of S_{AH} is termed half artificial data such that $R_i = (u_{1i}, u_{2i}, \dots, u_{Ni}, d_{1i}, d_{2i}, \dots, d_{Mi}, y_i)$ with its next elements $R_{i+1} = R_i$. With these S_{AH} set, the artificial steady state of the system will hence exist in the training set. Then N+M elements of S_{AI} are created corresponding to each element of S_{AH} in a fashion shown in Figure 1. Note that the increments B and C in Figure 1 are tuning factors as proposed below. These data sets are added to guarantee the correct gain sign existed in the model. The following is the proposed artificial data approach:

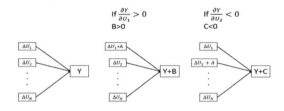

Figure 1. The increment set of the artificial data set

(1) Define the following original loss function:

$$L_0 = \frac{1}{S}\sum_{i=1}^{S}(y_i - \hat{y_i})^2 \qquad (4)$$

where y_i is the plant data while $\hat{y_i}$ is the model prediction of the data in the prediction set.

(2) Perform the following training

Step 1: Create S_{AH} and S_{AI} by assuming that the increment of each variable from artificial steady state $U_i = U_i + \alpha$ yields $Y = Y + \beta$. Note that β can be positive or negative depending on the known gain sign.

Step 2: Train the ANN, RNN and XGBoost model by adding the artificial data set to the original data set.

Step 3: Fine tune the increment β based on the value of loss function (4), and go back to step 2 until the optimal of L_0 is obtained.

It can be well understood that there exists no general rule for the size of the artificial data as well as the tuning factor β. We propose that for the particular industrial case N=4, M=2 with total data set of 13000 time series data (10 minutes/sampling and three months duration), the appropriate size of artificial data $S_{AH} \cup S_{AI}$ should be around 2600 (i.e. 20% of original data set). Besides, as the first trial of β, we implemented 4α and α should be a small value.

3. Model Predictive Control of MISO Systems

Given the machine learning model (2), the following model predictive control is implemented:

$$\min J = \alpha \sum_{n-1}^{H}(y_{SP}(t+n) - \hat{y}(t+n))^2 + \beta \sum_{n=1}^{H}\sum_{i=1}^{M}(u_i(t+n))^2 \qquad (5)$$
$$s.t. \hat{y}(t+k+1) = \quad G(R_{t+k-K}, R_{t+k-K+1}, \dots, R_{t+k}), \quad k = 0, \dots, H$$
$$u_{i,min} < u_i(t+n) < u_{i,max}, i = 1, \dots, M$$

where H is the horizon of the forward prediction, α and β are the penalties of the set point trajectory and the control actions, respectively. Note that in this particular case, only control action lower and upper bounds are implemented. Of course, in many cases, some output properties should also be bounded if they are either measurable or predictable. However, this work is aiming at solving a popular industrial case. Equation (5) can be easily extended to more general situations.

4. The Numerical Example

4.1. The numerical problem

In order to demonstrate the validity of the above approach, the following numerical example was implemented to demonstrate the proposed artificial data method:

$$f_1 = sigmoid(u_1), f_2 = \tanh(u_2), f_3 = -0.2 * u_3, f_4 = \sin(u_4) -1 < u_i(i = 1,2,3,4) < 1 \qquad (6)$$

$$y_{t+1} = \tanh(f_1 + f_2 + f_3 + f_4 - \sin(f_2 * f_3) + f_2 * f_1) + y_t$$

We randomly generated 10000 data sets, and three machine learning models ANN, RNN and XGBoost are trained using 9000 data sets. The remained 1000 data sets were implemented as testing sets

4.2. Traditional Training Approaches

One of 1000 fittings including ANN, RNN and XGBoost of the testing set is shown in Figure 2. Most machine learning models result satisfied fittings as Figure 2 however, none of 1000 gives correct gain sign and MPC to change the set point from 0. 5 to 0.65 is failed as shown in Figure 3.

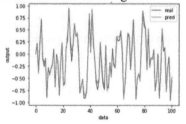

Figure 2. Comparison of the machine learning predictions without artificial data and testing set

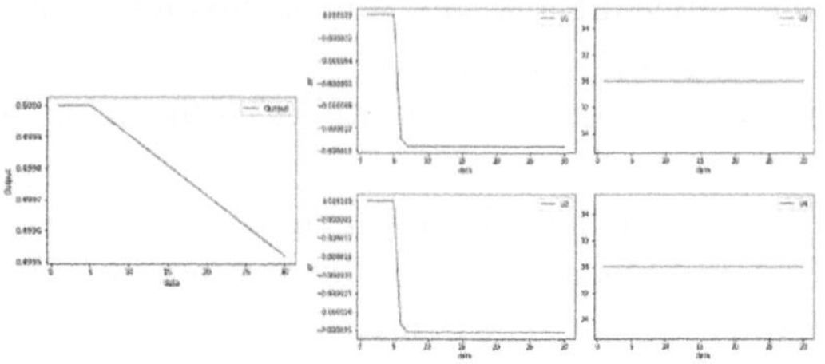

Figure 3. MPC of the numerical example using the machine-learning model without artificial data.

4.3. Traditional Training Approaches

We implemented 2000 artificial data set as described in the previous section, and retrained the model using three different machine learning models. Figure 4 compares the predictions of the testing set. Table 1 shows the fitting results of the testing set in terms of RMSW and R^2. The gain signs are all correct as shown in Figure 5. The MPC control gives correct control results with correct gain signs as shown in Figure 6.

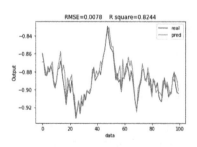

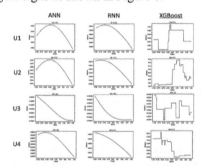

Figure 4. Comparison of the proposed machine learning predictions and testing set.

Figure 5. Gain signs of model with artificial data and Model predictive control of the numerical example

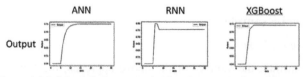

Figure 6. Model predictive control using the proposed model.

Table 1. RMSE and R^2 of the numerical testing set

	RMS	R
ANN	0.026	0.898
RNN	0.037	0.824
XGBoost	0.0074	0.9858

5. The Polymerization Reactor

5.1. *The Proposed Approach*

The models derived using artificial data can also fit the testing set as shown in Figure 7. All three models can fit the testing set well, and Table 2 gives the RMSE and R^2 of three models.

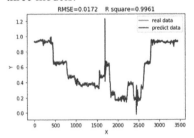

Figure 7. The comparison of plant data and model predictions (the proposed approach) of the testing set

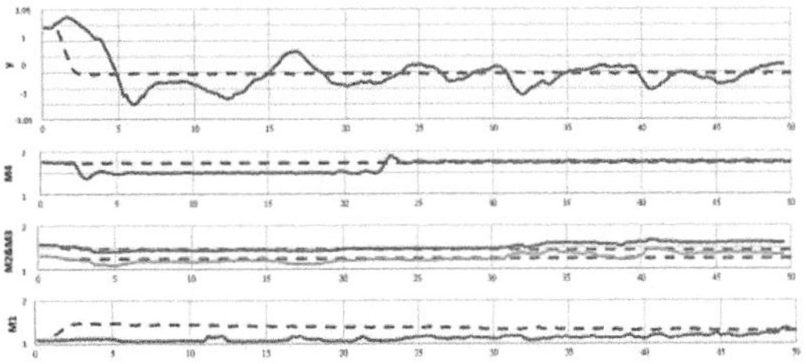

Figure 8 Comparisons of the solution of MPC to the historical set point change operations using the proposed machine learning model

Table 2 RMSE and R^2 of the reactor testing set

	RMSE	R square
ANN	0.0180	0.9875
RNN	0.0172	0.9961
XGBoost	0.0093	0.9990

Figure 8 demonstrates the validity of the proposed modelling approach. In this simulation, the plant and model are all the same machine learning model. Note that in Figure 8, the MPC controller took very different actions compared to the field operators. Interestingly, M4 was discarded by the MPC as a manipulated variable, and it is clearly correct if one observes the field operators adjusted it initially but set it back to the original value as shown in Figure 10.

5.2. *Plant Test*

Plant test was performed 8 hour duration. In Figure 9, during the time zone before the dash line, the plant was controlled by the field operators. The plant was rather stable compared to their historical data. The plant hence was taken over by ANN-MPC after the dash line, the control actions taken by MPC were quite different from the field operators. It is quite interesting if the readers observe the patterns of M1, M2 and M3 are all different from the manual approaches with much smaller oscillations even the disturbances of the plant (D1 and D2) were bigger than the period in manual period.

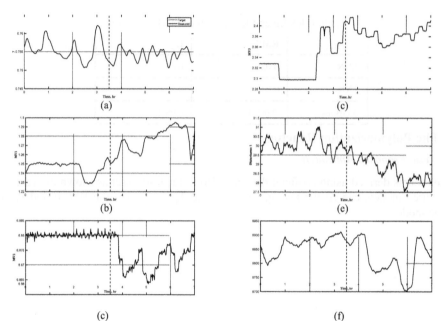

Figure 9. Plant test of the proposed approach. (a) the quality variable, (b) M1, (c) M2, (d) M3, (e) D1, (f)D2 v.s. time

6. Conclusions

A novel artificial data machine learning approach is proposed for MISO control system. The proposed approach demonstrates ability to converge to correct gain sign solutions in these multi-solution cases by adding artificial data sets. The approach also shows versatile in terms different training algorithms such as ANN, RNN and XGBoost. Numerical example and real plant examples are performed to show the validity of the proposed approach. The simulations and plant tests all show that the models derived from this approach is valid in MPC applications, while the machine learning without special treating may fail in these MISO systems.

References

Aglodiya, A. (2017). Application of Artificial Neural Network (ANN) in Chemical Engineering: A Review. *IJARIIE, 3*(2), 5322-5328.

Cho, K., Van Merriënboer, B., Gulcehre, C., Bahdanau, D., Bougares, F., Schwenk, H., & Bengio, Y. (2014). Learning phrase representations using RNN encoder-decoder for statistical machine translation. *arXiv preprint arXiv:1406.1078.*

Hsiao, Y.-D., Chou, C.-H., Wu, H.-b., Kang, J.-l., Wong, D. S. H., Yao, Y., . . . Ou, J. D.-Y. PHYSICALLY CONSISTENT DATA-DRIVEN SOFT-SENSOR DEVELOPMENT.

Wu, Z., Tran, A., Rincon, D., & Christofides, P. D. (2019). Machine learning- based predictive control of nonlinear processes. Part I: Theory. *AIChE Journal, 65*(11).

Zhang, M., Liu, X., & Zhang, Z. (2016). A soft sensor for industrial melt index prediction based on evolutionary extreme learning machine. *Chinese journal of chemical engineering, 24*(8), 1013-1019.

Sauro Pierucci, Flavio Manenti, Giulia Bozzano, Davide Manca (Eds.)
Proceedings of the 30th European Symposium on Computer Aided Process Engineering
(ESCAPE30), May 24-27, 2020, Milano, Italy. © 2020 Elsevier B.V. All rights reserved.
http://dx.doi.org/10.1016/B978-0-12-823377-1.50214-7

CO₂ Reduction by Advanced Process Control in Gasification Processes

Moein Mighani,[a] Karsten Covella,[a] Evrim Örs,[a] Jean-Francois Rauch,[b] Hans-Peter Mönch,[c] Martin Gräbner[a,*]

[a] *AIR LIQUIDE Forschung und Entwicklung GmbH, Frankfurt Innovation Campus, Gwinnerstrasse 27-33, Frankfurt am Main 60388, Germany*

[b] *AIR LIQUIDE Large Industries, 57 avenue Carnot BP 313, Champigny-Sur-Marne 94503, France*

[c] *AIR LIQUIDE Global Management Services GmbH, Olof-Palme-Strasse 35, Frankfurt am Main 60439, Germany*

Martin.Graebner@Airliquide.Com

Abstract

Improvement in energy efficiency and operation of production units plays a key role in reducing carbon intensity of production processes. Entrained-flow gasification is a prevalent technology for converting coal to syngas. However, due to highly nonlinear interactions between process variables and inherent fluctuations, the operation and control of these gasifiers are difficult. This results in often suboptimal gasifier operation and therefore presents significant opportunity for optimization. In this work an advanced process control strategy for improving the operation and control of entrained-flow gasification is developed. This solution involves different components including online coal properties measurement and analysis, real time optimization engine and model predictive control. Finally, it is shown how implementation of this advanced process optimization and control solution improves the production stability and efficiency presenting opportunities for reduction of CO_2 per unit production.

Keywords: Advanced Process Control, CO_2 Emission Reduction, Gasification, Model Predictive Control

1. Introduction

A significant portion of global greenhouse gases and subsequently CO_2 emissions arise from energy conversion and process emissions in the industry. Accelerated worldwide demand of energy and substantial materials including steel, plastic, paper, etc., is accompanied by an increase in emissions. Therefore, effective measures are needed to mitigate CO_2 emissions from industrial activities. Among the existing measures, increasing the energy efficiency of processes via maximizing the production efficiency and reducing the CO_2 intensity per unit production is considered as one the most significant strategies (Allwood et al., 2010).

Partial oxidation is one of the most important processes for hydrogen production from any carbonaceous feedstock. Coal is identified as one of the most abundant carbon sources which can be converted to synthesis gas (syngas) using gasification processes. Among different existing coal gasification technologies, entrained-flow (ETF) gasification is currently the most widely employed choice. It is due to its ability to process a wide variety of coal types and its high syngas yield (Gräbner, 2015). However, the presence of highly nonlinear interactions among relevant process parameters coupled with long dynamic response times make the operation and control of a gasifier complex and challenging. Moreover, fluctuations in the quality of the coal feedstock affecting the operational parameters and efficiency of the gasification (Emami Taba et al., 2012) are not measured in real time and become available much later as laboratory results. These normally lead to suboptimal control and operation of the gasifier. This effect can be traced in noticeable fluctuations of monitored variables such as gasifier reactor wall temperature, CH_4 and CO_2 concentrations in the produced syngas (Gräbner, 2015). Therefore, reducing such fluctuations via implementing an optimized control methodology presents a remarkable opportunity for improving the efficiency of the operation. Consequently, this results in reduction in CO_2 emissions previously caused by suboptimal operation of gasifier (Gräbner, 2015).

In the industrial processes, advanced process optimization and control strategies involve hierarchy of different layers. These layers from a top to bottom sequence can include product scheduling and supply chain, real time optimization (RTO) engine, model predictive control (MPC) and finally, regulatory controllers interacting with process measurements. The RTO layer in general is equipped with high fidelity process models. The function of RTO engine is to calculate the optimum operational window and set points of controlled variable sets in given specific steady-state process conditions (Marchetti et al., 2011). MPC is a process control methodology involving the process knowledge through different process models in order to improve the process controllability and performance. During the recent years MPC has become an attractive and accepted method along the industry due to its ability to handle both process nonlinearities and constraints in multivariate systems (Morari and Lee, 1999).

The current work explains how the fluctuations in ETF gasification are identified and used to build up an advanced process control (APC) strategy benefiting from RTO and MPC to improve the production efficiency of the gasifier. Tools like Python™ and Matlab® were employed for operational data segmentation and signal processing. Moreover, an in-house developed and verified ETF gasification model was used as RTO engine while the Platform for Advanced Control and Estimation (PACE) (Amrit et al., 2015) was the main core of MPC development and implementation. Finally, this work can serve as a practical example to demonstrate how improving the efficiency of gasification processes can lead to CO_2 emission reductions.

2. Computational Methodology

2.1. Advanced Process Control for ETF Gasification

Operation and control of ETF gasification is a challenging task due to highly nonlinear interactions between the process variables and presence of fluctuations caused by changes in coal properties. In order to improve the operation and performance of this process, an APC strategy comprising different components with specific tasks has been developed. The primary component of this solution is a coal online analyzer measuring, calculating and recording the properties of coal feed such as ash content, lower heating value (LHV) and other parameters of relevance (Gräbner et al., 2019). The output information of this online measurement device together with information recorded from process measurements like gasifier pressure, shell steam production rate, carrier gas flow rate, etc., are fed into the RTO engine. Based on this information, the RTO engine calculates the operation window for process control variable sets. This operation window includes allowable high and low limits of controlled variables (operation constraints) as well as optimal steady state set points. This RTO engine is based on a thermodynamic first principle model and was developed and verified in-house (Örs and Gräbner, 2019). The model assumes equilibrium and applies a carbon conversion rate to account for the fuel reactivity and residence time in the ETF gasifier. Details are described elsewhere (Sasi et al., 2018). The last piece of this strategy is MPC. This key player performs the task of stable operation of the gasifier and mitigation of fluctuations while driving the operation towards the optimal set points. A schematic view of this solution can be seen in Figure 1.

2.2. Model Predictive Control

The main idea of MPC is to incorporate the process knowledge in the process control via employing different types of process models. Platform for Advanced Control and Estimation was used for all the development and simulations in the MPC part. The primary step in MPC development is to define the control variable sets and their

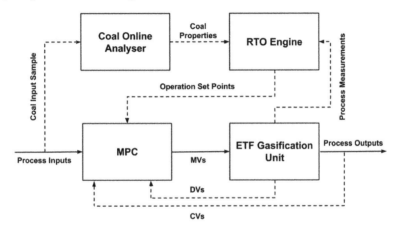

Figure 1. APC Solution Scheme

relationship. Controlled variables (CVs), manipulated variables (MVs), and disturbance variables (DVs) are among possible control variable sets can be defined in PACE. Table 1 represents the employed process parameters and their role in the process control variable set.

Table 1. Control variable set

CVs	O₂/Total Coal (wt/wt), Effective Syngas Production (Nm³/h), CH₄ Slip in Syngas (p.p.m), CO₂ in Syngas (vol. %), Gasifier Wall Temperature (°C)
MVs	Coal Flow Line 1 (kg/h), Coal Flow Line 2 (kg/h), Coal Flow Line 3 (kg/h), O₂ Flow (Nm³/h)
DVs	Feeding tank ΔP (kPa), Shell Steam Density (kg/m³)

After assigning the control variables, the next step is to define the dynamic models and correlations defining the relationships between these variables. Primarily, the relationship between each MV and CV or DV and CV is modeled in single input single output (SISO) mode benefiting from first or second order parametric transfer function models. Then, the developed models are embedded in a control matrix known as dynamic matrix control for calculating the dynamic behavior of the system in multi input multi output (MIMO) mode.

This step is known as dynamic system identification. In the current work, the identification of dynamic models was carried out in closed loop manner exploiting operational data. In the closed loop system identification it has to be made sure that the data lies within acceptable process conditions and is of enough mathematical excitation for effective model identification. Finding the suitable operational data for system identification which is called data segmentation was carried out in Python™ over more than a year of historical data from the operation. This was done by applying different process filters like acceptable gasifier load and stable steam injection (always kept constant; not used as control parameter due to significant temperature moderating effect of conveying CO_2) together with mathematical filters to ensure the suitability of the data set. During the identification period the accuracy of identified models was evaluated using the following formula:

$$1 - \frac{\text{var}(y_i - y_{pred})}{\text{var}(y_i)} \tag{1}$$

Where, y_i is the real data and $y_{pred.}$ is the model output. This accuracy metric explains how good the model performs in explaining the dynamic behavior of the output response. Practically, the models with accuracy of over 0.5 are suitable to be used in control matrix.

After developing the control matrix and corresponding dynamic models, the controller parameters need to be set and fine-tuned. In this stage, parameters related to CVs such as constraints and set points are received from RTO engine based on feeding coal properties. The other constraints related to MVs like maximum and minimum movements and rate of changes are normally set according to process operation manuals and safety prerequisites. Afterwards, the aggressivity and robustness of the controller have to be determined based on the expected control actions. PACE employs a nonlinear solver with infinite horizon formulation which permits the use of nonlinear models (Amrit et al., 2015). The final step is to simulate various process control scenarios in order to evaluate the performance of the designed controller. All the explained steps can be reiterated several times to result in a desired and effective designed MPC application.

3. Results and Discussion

All the developed models are whether first order or second order continuous transfer functions. Employing the formula (1) as the accuracy metric, all the models scored higher than 0.5 and proved to be suitable for MPC usage. Figure 2 illustrates an example of a CV response simulated via identified dynamic model using one MV and one DV as inputs.

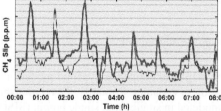

Figure 2.a. Dynamic model response for CH4 Slip in Syngas (p.p.m). Black solid line is real data. Red line is model output.

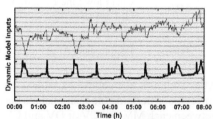

Figure 2.b. Inputs for CH4 Slip Model. Black line is feeding tank ΔP (kPa). Blue line is O2 / Total Coal (wt/wt).

After successful dynamic system identification and development of desired MPC application, a production scenario was simulated to show the benefits of developed APC solution. For doing this, a 42 hours simulation was carried out and the outcomes were compared to real operational data recorded in DCS. The results of this simulation can be seen in Figure 3.a-d (red lines are simulated APC responses while blue lines are real DCS data).

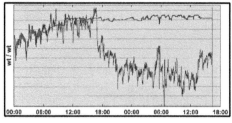

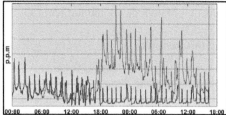

Figure 3.a. O₂ / Total Coal (wt/wt)   Figure 3.b. CH4 Slip in Syngas (p.p.m)

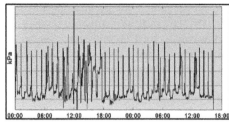

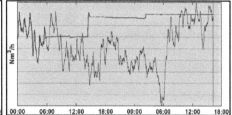

Figure 3.c. Feeding Tank ΔP (kPa)   Figure 3.d. Effective Syngas (Nm³/h)

In the first 6 hours of simulation the APC is off and the shown data is solely real operational data taken from DCS. After around 6 hours, the APC solution is turned on with the primary focus of stabilizing the operation with regard to O_2/Total Coal, CH_4 slip in syngas and effective syngas production. After 10 hours of stable operation, when the stability is ensured, the optimization objective which is the maximization of produced effective syngas is applied (Figure 3.d). During the overall simulation, signals for DVs were taken from real operational data and were fed as feed forward signals (Figure 3.c). As it can be seen in Figure 3.a, after turning the APC on, the fluctuations in O_2/Total Coal have been mitigated by around 80 % which corresponds to tighter and smoother control actions over available MVs related to oxygen and coal input flows.

Real operational data in Figures 3.a, 3.b and 3.d after the first 18 hours of operation reflect suboptimal operation and control actions. The effect of deviation from optimal O_2 / Total Coal set point (seen in Figure 3.a) can be traced in higher amount of CH_4 slip in syngas production for a long period (Figure 3.b) which corresponds to low temperature operation of gasifier leading to inefficiency and reduced conversion. Such deviations from optimal operational window coupled with high bandwidth of unmitigated fluctuations have resulted in highly oscillating and reduced amounts of effective produced syngas which can be seen in Figure 3.d. On the other hand, by looking at same figures for operation with APC on during the same time period, a stable and smooth operation of O_2 / Total Coal around optimum calculated set point is observed while continuously mitigating the effects of fluctuations (Figure 3.a). As it is seen in Figure 3.b, this can lead to lowered and tightly controlled amounts of CH_4 slip in syngas translating to hot gasifier operation and high conversions. Finally, the result of this optimal control and operation can be observed in Figure 3.d, where the amount of effective syngas production is kept at a constant and stable maximum of output while ensuring both operation safety and efficiency.

Ultimately, it was calculated that the developed APC solution delivers on average more than 1 % savings on O_2 input per unit effective syngas production ($Nm^3 O_2$ / Nm^3 effective syngas) as well as up to 3 % savings in total coal input per unit effective syngas production (kg coal / Nm^3 effective syngas). These savings present a significant opportunity for reduction of both direct and indirect CO_2 emissions related to the gasification process.

4. Conclusions

The growing global demand for energy and substantial matters has made the industry to take measures for mitigating the CO_2 emissions corresponding to industrial activities. Here in this work, an APC solution was developed and tested for ETF coal gasification to optimize the operation control and production efficiency targeting the abatement in associated CO_2 emissions. The resulted savings in oxygen input per unit effective syngas production and total coal input per unit effective syngas production suggest considerable savings in direct and indirect CO_2 emission caused by the gasification process. At the end, application of advanced process control and optimization for CO_2 emissions reduction utilizing various objective functions in gasification processes shows a significant potential for further investigations.

References

J. M. Allwood, J. Cullen, R. Milford, 2010, Options for Achieving a 50 % Cut in Industrial Carbon Emissions by 2050, Environmental Science & Technology, Volume 44, 1888-1894.

R. Amrit, W. Canney, P. Carrette, R. Linn, A. Martinez, A. Singh, T. Skrovanek, J. Valiquette, J. Williamson, J. Zhou, B. J. Cott, 2015, Platform for Advanced Control and Estimation (PACE): Shell's and Yokogawa's Next Generation Advanced Process Control Technology, IFAC-PapersOnLine, Volume 48, 1-5.

L. Emami Taba, M. F. Irfan, W. A. M. W. Daud, M. H. Chakrabartial, 2012, The Effect of Temperature on Various Parameters in Coal, Biomass and CO-Gasification: a Review, Renewable and Sustainable Energy Reviews, Volume 16.

M. Gräbner, 2015, Industrial Coal Gasification Technologies Covering Baseline and High-Ash Coal, Wiley.

M. Gräbner, M. Mighani, K. Covella, E. Örs. 2019, CO_2 Reduction by Implementing Online Fuel Analysis in Gasification Processes, International Conference on Coal Science & Technology, Krakow, Poland.

A. Marchetti, P. Luppi, M. Basualdo, 2011, Real-Time Optimization via Modifier Adaptation Integrated with Model Predictive Control, IFAC Proceedings Volumes, Volume 44, 9856-9861.

M. Morari, J. H. Lee, 1999, Model Predictive Control: Past, Present and Future, Computers & Chemical Engineering, Volume 23, 667-682.

E. Örs, M. Gräbner, 2019, FuALadvisor 1 - A Model-Based Fuel Procurement Tool for Gasification, International Conference on Coal Science & Technology, Krakow, Poland.

T. Sasi, M. Mighani, E. Örs, R. Tawani, M. Gräbner, 2018, Prediction of ash fusion behavior from coal ash composition for entrained-flow gasification, Fuel Processing Technology, Volume 176, Pages 64-75.

Sauro Pierucci, Flavio Manenti, Giulia Bozzano, Davide Manca (Eds.)
Proceedings of the 30th European Symposium on Computer Aided Process Engineering
(ESCAPE30), May 24-27, 2020, Milano, Italy. © 2020 Elsevier B.V. All rights reserved.
http://dx.doi.org/10.1016/B978-0-12-823377-1.50215-9

A Deep Learning Approach on Surrogate Model Optimization of a Cryogenic NGL Recovery Unit Operation

Wenbo Zhu, Jorge Chebeir, Zachary Webb, Jose Romagnoli

Department of Chemical Engineering, Louisiana State University, Baton Rouge, Louisiana, 70803, United States

jose@lsu.edu

Abstract

Natural gas liquids (NGL) are utilized in nearly all sectors of the economy such as feedstock for petrochemical plants and blended for vehicles fuel. In this work, the operation of a cryogenic expansion unit for the extraction of NGL is optimized through the implementation of data-driven techniques. The proposed approach is based on an optimization framework that integrates dynamic process simulations with two deep learning based surrogate models. The first model utilizes a recurrent neural network (RNN) based surrogate model to disclose the dynamics involved in the process. The second regression model is built to generate profit predictions of the process. The integration of these models allows the determination of the process operating conditions that maximize the hourly profit. Results from two case studies show the capabilities of the proposed optimization framework to find optimal operating conditions and improve the process profits.

Keywords: Cryogenic expansion unit, Deep learning, Dynamic process simulation, Surrogate model

1. Introduction

Natural gas is a naturally occurring hydrocarbon mostly constituted by methane. The relevance of this energy commodity resides in its abundance, relatively easy transportation and clean burning in comparison to other fossil fuels. As natural gas flows out of the ground, it may also contain reduced amounts of other hydrocarbons such as ethane, propane, butanes and natural gasoline. These heavier hydrocarbon liquids are commonly referred to as NGL. The extraction of NGL components from the raw gas is not only required for hydrocarbon dew point control in a natural gas stream, but also represents a source of revenue, as NGL normally have significantly greater value as separate marketable products than as part of the natural gas.

The extraction of heavier hydrocarbon liquids constitutes a mature and well-known process with a broad literature covering its particular features. The different variants of this process are normally based on external refrigeration, turbo-expansion, Joule-Thompson expansion, and absorption. In the natural gas industry, one of the most common recovery schemes is the industry-standard single stage (ISS). This process replaces the utilization of a Joule-Thompson valve by a turbo-expander in order to enhance the feed gas cooling (Campbell and Wilkinson, 1981). A major drawback of this configuration is the relatively low NGL recovery achieved and the problematic issue of the carbon dioxide freezing (Lynch et al., 2002). These limitations have led to more advanced process schemes, such as the gas sub-cooled process (GSP), cold residue reflux

(CRR) process, and recycle split vapor (RSV) process among others. These processes are based on the implementation of a cold recycle by bypassing a portion of the gas fed to the turbo-expander. The NGL recovery, energy consumption, and economic benefits of each process scheme are not only affected by the efficiency of the process, but also by the operating conditions, including the outlet chiller temperature, column pressure, turboexpander by-pass flow, etc. Surrogate models offer the capability of simplifying large-scale complex process models to perform the optimization. Significant works have been done on applying surrogate models in process optimization. Nevertheless, most of these methods build the predictive models using the correlations among different variables (spatial correlations), while the serial correlations that represents the correlations at different time steps are rarely taken into consideration. Nevertheless, process dynamics commonly exists in chemical systems, which suggests that serial features should also be included into the construction of surrogate models. Recent development of deep learning techniques, particularly recurrent neural network (RNN) have displayed promising performance in sequential data analysis. Compared with traditional methods such as Kriging models, and quadratic best-fit models, the RNN approach can provide additional insights into the time-correlation information (process dynamics). In this work, a simulated-based optimization framework is proposed to determine the optimal operating conditions of an NGL cryogenic unit. A simulation model is developed to emulate the dynamics involved in the operation of a CRR unit utilizing a commercial process simulator. Since the detailed expression of the process model is not available directly in algebraic form, the simulation is treated as an input-output black box. In order to optimize such simulated process, an optimization algorithm based on the utilization of surrogate models is proposed in this work. An RNN-based surrogate model is used to learn the discrete process dynamic behaviors from eight control loops in the NGL process. Based on the system status, e.g. set points (SPs) and present values (PVs), a second regression model is constructed to predict the expected profit at each time step incorporating the current market price of feeds and products. After that, a differential evolution (DE) algorithm is applied to find the optimal operating conditions based on the proposed discrete surrogate model.

2. Dynamic Process Simulation and Control

The CRR process scheme was first introduced in the original design of GSP by Campbell et al. (1981) to improve the ethane recovery efficiency. The model to emulate the real CRR configuration is constructed in the process simulator Aspen HYSYS®. The default values of set-points in the different control loops, operating conditions, and design parameters in the process are based on previous literature, and realistic industrial conditions, which can be referred in Chebeir et al. (2019).

A dynamic simulation of the CRR process scheme is developed for the implementation of the different control strategies. A critical step for the generation of a realistic simulation model is the definition of the equipment design involved in the system. Following the criteria of previous works (Chebeir et al., 2019; Luyben, 2013), the demethanizer column is built with a total number of 30 stages plus a reboiler. The reboiler (E-104) of the column (regular heater and separator reboiler in process simulator) has a diameter of 1.193 m and a length of 1.789 m. The diameter of the column is 1.72 m with a tray space of 0.5 m. In the case of the heat exchangers, the UA for E-100, E-102 and E-103 are $2.038 \cdot 10^5$ kJ/·°Ch, $1.961 \cdot 10^5$ kJ/·°Ch and $1.576 \cdot 10^5$ kJ/·°Ch, respectively. The chiller (E-101) has a volume of 0.10 m^3 and a duty of $1.275 \cdot 10^7$ kJ/h. The flash separator, TK-100, have a diameter of 1 m and a height of 2.5 m. The expansion and compression sections of the turboexpander TE-100, recompressor K-101 and cryogenic compressor K-102 (CRR process) have an adiabatic efficiency of 75%. Joule-Thompson valves (JTV-100 and JTV-101) are also included in the process scheme in order to generate a sudden expansion of the fluids (pressure decrease) to enter into the demethanizer column at the stage pressure. The control structure implemented in the CRR configuration scheme is summarized as follows:

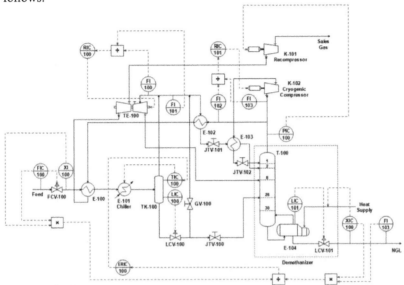

Figure 1. Control structure of the CRR process configuration.

3. Surrogate Modeling and Optimization

In this section, the implementation of the surrogate model that predicts process profit will be discussed. In order to maximize the CRR process profit by the manipulation of the operating conditions, the problem is separated into two main parts namely the CRR system side and the market side.Since the simulation is treated as a black-box, a dynamic surrogate model is implemented to represent the complex dynamics involved in the process. In this sense, a special type of RNN called long short-term memory (LSTM) neural network (Hochreiter and Schmidhuber, 1997) is opted to represent the process simulation in a discrete term. This means that the model would compute the process response at a fixed time interval, instead of representing the dynamics in a continuous-time form. The time interval utilized in this work is 43 seconds, considering the Python-Simulator connection delay and the inherent dynamics of the CRR process. After modelling the CRR process dynamics, the market side information is incorporated into the framework to generate the entire surrogate model of the system. A regression model is built to map the expected profit at each time step from market price of natural gas and NGL, as well as the process operating conditions. Once the surrogate model is completely defined, the optimizer is implemented to guide the operating conditions.

3.1. Data Preparation

Before implementing the surrogate model, data at different operating conditions has to be collected. The initial data was collected randomly from perturbations generated in the eight SP values inside the process and the market prices of sales gas and NGL. The corresponding responses on all eight control loops are recorded through their PVs readings until reaching a new steady state which takes roughly about 6300 seconds in the simulation. The surrogate model is designed to predict process responses at fixed discrete time intervals, where the time interval in the discrete system is 43 second and total time step is set 150.

3.2. Surrogate Model

In this work, a LSTM-based regression model is opted to learn the time sequential dynamics in the CRR process. The basic idea here is that the PVs at next time step are predicted using the SP and PV in previous time steps. Besides the basic LSTM layout, recent developed techniques namely, bidirectional RNN structure (Schuster and Paliwal, 1997) and attention mechanism (Rocktaschel et al., 2015) are also incorporated in the regression model. After incorporating the different elements mentioned above, a schematic representation of the surrogate model is depicted by Figure 2.

Once the dynamic surrogate model is accurate enough to mimic the process dynamics, then a feed-forward neural network is trained separately to predict profit using current market prices of natural gas and NGL, as well as the SP and PV values that represent the current status of the system.

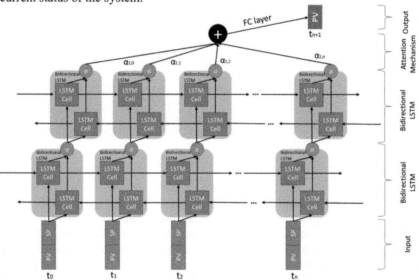

Figure 2. The LSTM based surrogate model

3.3. Optimization Framework

Considering the above information of the surrogate model, the entire surrogate model can be written as:

$$PV_{n+1} = f_d\left(PV_{n-L}\cdots PV_n, SP\right) \tag{1}$$

$$Profit_{n+1} = g_P\left(PV_{n+1}, SP, d_p\right) \tag{2}$$

where d_p is the disturbance from the market price, n is the discrete time index, f_d is the dynamic surrogate model, and g_p is the profit regression model. Hence, the optimization model can be written as:

$$\arg\max \sum_{i=t_1}^{t_n} Profit \tag{3}$$

s.t. $SP_1 \dots SP_j \in \left[SP_j^L, SP_j^H \right]$

where the constraints are the ranges of each SP. The objective of the optimizer is to find proper SPs that can maximize profit profile in a following time period (6300 seconds), in order to bring the process into a new steady state operation. The optimizer used in this work is differential evolution (Storn and Price, 1997), which is a metaheuristic optimization method that find optimal solution from iterative trials.

4. Result and Discussion

4.1. Surrogate Model Results

To initiate the training of the dynamic surrogate model, 330 batches (with 150-time steps in each batch) from different operating conditions were collected by choosing random SPs within their corresponding ranges. Hence, a total of 42,570 training samples are provided in the model training. A validation set was generated separately with alternative time step length to avoid the model overfitting during the training. After that, the error maximization sampling is opted to further improve the model accuracy. The model accuracy is then evaluated by testing data consisting of 40 batches of different operating conditions (5,160 samples), which is summarized in Table 1. The results from a simple two-layer LSTM model without bidirectional layer or attention mechanism are also included to verify the effectiveness of these additional elements. The bidirectional layer and attention mechanism narrow down the averaged relative error from 10.53% to 0.93% compared with the simple LSTM model.

Table 1. Relative error comparison

	Two-layer LSTM	Proposed architecture
Relative Error (%)	10.53	0.93
Std of Error (%)	±2.95	±0.76

4.2. Optimization Results

Two case studies are performed to validate the proposed optimization framework. In Case Study I, the prices are set high for the different products to mimic a profitable scenario. In Case Study II, a feed gas with a high cost is set to create a scenario of losses. The corresponding prices for the different case studies are listed in Table 2, and the optimized results for both scenarios are summarized in Table 3. The optimized SP values for both cases studies were verified through the simulation, which is illustrated in Figure 3. In Case Study I, the optimized operating condition improves the hourly profit by $50.92 in average, while in Case Study II, the optimized operating conditions reduce the hourly loss by $120.17 in average.

Table 2. Market price setting (unit in USD/MMBtu) for two scenarios

	Raw Material	Methane	Ethane	Propane	Butanes	Pentanes
Case I	3.6	3.6	4.5	7.0	7.8	9.7
Case II	4.1	3.1	4.6	7.5	7.8	8.8

Table 3. Optimized SP values for two scenarios

	FIC-100	RIC-100	LIC-100	LIC-101	RIC-101	PIC-100	XIC-100	ERIC-100
Case I	5112	0.621	43.97	51.44	0.451	1101.1	0.009	0.738
Case II	4697	0.624	36.51	46.39	0.453	1076.9	0.009	0.738

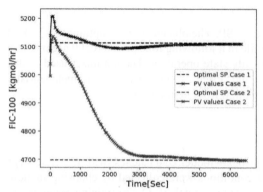

Figure 3. Illustration of the optimized SP values and their corresponding responses for FIC-100 control loop.

5. Conclusion

In this work, an optimization framework based on the use of surrogate models is implemented for optimizing the operating conditions of a CRR unit. Two sub-models are utilized to build the correlation between the profit and the operating conditions of the process. The dynamic surrogate model is established using deep learning techniques, namely a bidirectional LSTM with attention mechanism, which gives accurate predictions of the dynamic behavior. After that, another regression model (a neural network) is opted to incorporate market prices with system status for profit prediction. Utilizing the entire surrogate model, the optimal operating conditions are determined by a differential evolution optimizer that maximizes the profit corresponding to market price.

Reference

J. Chebeir, S. Salas, J. Romagnoli, 2019, Operability assessment on alternative natural gas liquids recovery schemes, Journal of Natural Gas Science and Engineering 71, 102974

J. Lynch, C. Cairo, H. Hudson, J. Wilkinson, 2002, Unique design challenges in the aux sable NGL recovery plant, presented at the 81st Annual Convention of the Gas Processors Association, Dallas, T.

M. Schuster, K. K. Paliwal, 1997, Bidirectional recurrent neural networks, IEEE Transactions on Signal Processing 45 (11) 2673-2681

R. Campbell, J. Wilkinson, 1981, Hydrocarbon gas processing (U.S. Patent 4 278 457).

R. Storn, K. Price, 1997, Differential evolution-a simple and efficient heuristic for global optimization over continuous spaces, Journal of global optimization 11 (4) 341-359

S. Hochreiter, J. Schmidhuber, 1997, Long short-term memory, Neural computation 9 (8) 1735-1780

T. Rocktaschel, E. Grefenstette, K. M. Hermann, T. Kocisky, P. Blunsom, 2015, Reasoning about entailment with neural attention, arXiv preprint arXiv:1509.06664 (2015)

W. Luyben, 2013, NGL demethanizer control, Industrial and Engineering Chemistry Research 52 (33) 11626-11638.

Sauro Pierucci, Flavio Manenti, Giulia Bozzano, Davide Manca (Eds.)
Proceedings of the 30th European Symposium on Computer Aided Process Engineering
(ESCAPE30), May 24-27, 2020, Milano, Italy. © 2020 Elsevier B.V. All rights reserved.
http://dx.doi.org/10.1016/B978-0-12-823377-1.50216-0

Control Strategies for Natural Gas Liquids Recovery Plants

Stefania Tronci[b]*, Jorge A. Chebeir[a], Marta Mandis[b], Roberto Baratti[b],
José A. Romagnoli[a]

[a]Department of Chemical Engineering, Louisiana State University,Baton Rouge, LA
70809, United States of America
[b]Dip. di Ingegneria Meccanica, Chimica e dei Materiali, Università degli Studi di
Cagliari, Cagliari 09123 Italy
stefania.tronci@dimcm.unica.it

Abstract

Nowadays the improvements on the extraction methods of natural gas has increased the availability of natural gas liquids (NGL), which represent a valuable source of energy and industrial feedstock. Several process schemes have been developed in the past for an economical, safe and efficient recovery of these components including the conventional, cold residue recycle (CRR), and gas subcooled process (GSP), each comprising a range of competing advantages. In the present work, the control problem of the NGL extraction in a CRR process scheme is addressed aiming to achieve a recovery of at least 84% of ethane while maintaining low the level of methane impurity in the bottom of the demethanizer. Considering the high cost of composition analyzers, different temperature control structures are assessed. The temperature direct control and cascade control are proposed to improve the rejection of the disturbances. The operability of these NGL recovery technologies is evaluated under typical disturbances.

Keywords: natural gas liquids recovery, multivariable control, controllability, dynamic process simulation, pressure-compensated temperature.

1. Introduction

The technological advancement of recent years on fracking methods for the extraction of natural gas has brought to the access to huge volumes of gas trapped in shale formations. This has led to an increase in the quantities of natural gas available and a consequent decrease in its selling price, fallen drastically to less than 30% of their previous highs (Luyben et al., 2013). Natural gas liquids (NGL) are a valuable commodity consisting of the hydrocarbon fractions of ethane, propane, butane and heavier hydrocarbons contained in natural gas. These compounds have a higher selling price than the raw gas, justifying the construction and implementation of separation plants for their recovery. For this reason, different process configurations have been developed and analyzed for the separation of NGL from the raw natural gas. The conventional NGL recovery process has been modified to improve the separation and reduce the operating costs through the energy integration of flows. Among the new configurations proposed, Cold Residue Recycling Process (CRR) and Gas Subcooled Process (GSP) are the best known and most used in gas treatment plants (Kherbeck and Chebbi, 2015). The first separation equipment used is a high-pressure cryogenic distillation column for the separation of methane (the most important fraction in the raw gas), which is called demethanizer. In the literature, several works covering different NGL recovery processes have been presented by

Manning and Thompson (1991), Kidnay and Parrish (2011), Chebbi et al. (2010), and Park et al. (2015).

The control of concentrations achieved through the separation process under typical disturbances such as changes in flow rate or input compositions, has been investigated in contributions by Luyben et al. (2013) and Chebeir et al. (2019). The latter represents the starting point of this work. The dynamic response of the CRR process scheme is analyzed in terms of achieving the control objectives and reducing process upsets under typical disturbances, considering two alternative control strategies. In particular, a ratio flow rate controller in cascade with temperature controller in the demethanizer column, to reduce the methane concentration in the column bottom flow, and a pressure compensator in the separator to improve ethane recovery were considered. The purpose of this article is to formulate and implement a control strategy for the NGL process avoiding the use of costly concentration analyzers.

2. Background

2.1 Flowsheet

The dynamic simulation of CRR process was developed in the process simulator Aspen HYSYS® and based on realistic operating conditions optimized under nominal operation (Chebeir et al., 2019). The raw gas was fed to the separation units with a molar flow rate of 4980 kmol/h and a composition with a low content of liquids (Table 1), with the following inlet conditions: pressure equal to 5818 kPa and temperature equal to 35 °C.

Table 1: Feed composition (Chebbi et al., 2010)

Components	Mol fractions
Nitrogen	0.01
Methane	0.93
Ethane	0.03
Propane	0.015
Butanes	0.009
Pentanes	0.003
Hexanes	0.003
%C_{2+}	6

The main component of the separation unit was the demethanizer column, with 30 stages and three feed streams introduced at Stages 2, 8 and 26. Another important unit was the separator, positioned upstream of the demethanizer. Variations in inlet flow rate induced a change in its pressure and then, at constant temperature, changes in outflow composition that was fed to the column. In this context, the specifications required by the CRR configuration were 84% ethane recovery and 1% mol methane composition at the base of the demethanizer column.

2.1 Temperature sensor placement

As a first step, the optimal sensor temperature location to control the column temperature profile and consequently the concentration has been carried out. To this aim, an analysis of the temperature and composition gradients inside the column was performed. The temperature and the composition profiles are flat in the main part of the column. This means that separation takes place in the last few stages of the stripping section and in the top of the column. Through the analysis of the temperature gradient with per-component contribution diagram (Porru et al., 2013), it was found that the most appropriate location for the sensor is on tray 28.

3. System Dynamics and Control structure

Different control strategies were compared with two main objectives: to maintain a methane composition of 1% mol in the bottom product stream, to maintain the recovery of ethane at 84 %. In this contribution, the control structure proposed by Chebeir et al. (2019) was modified to consider the possibility of attaining the composition and recovery goals without the utilization of composition analyzers.

3.1 Ethane Recovery

First, the possibility of removing the ethane recovery controller, which manipulated the set point of the separator's temperature controller, was studied. A constant recovery of ethane was maintained by compensating the pressure changes in the separator. This has been achieved by modifying the separator temperature control. The process variable was adapted based on the pressure changes. The pressure-compensated temperature (PCT) was determined by the relation reported below, which is derived from Antoine's Equation: (Brambilla, 2014):

$$PCT = T^m - C \ln \frac{P}{P^{rif}}$$

Here, T^m and P were respectively the measured separator temperature and pressure; P^{rif} was the nominal separator pressure; C was the compensation coefficient determined by obtaining temperature values for pressure variations at constant composition in the Aspen HYSYS® simulation.

3.2 Methane bottom impurity

The responses obtained through the action of two different control structures to maintain the methane concentration at the bottom of the demethanizer were compared. The first structure was a direct control of the temperature on the 28th stage by means of reboiler duty. The second structure was a cascade control, where the temperature on the 28th stage was controlled by means of a temperature primary controller that gave the set point to a ratio controller that maintained constant the ratio between the boilup and the bottom stream, manipulating the reboiler duty. The boilup flow rate measurement, not available in practice, was estimated by knowledge of the measures of bottom flow rate and reboiler duty. The estimation was computed assuming that the boilup was only composed by ethane and considering that only a fraction (correlated to the variation of the duty by means of a regression, estimated under different operating conditions) of the reboiler duty was used to generate the vapor fed back to the column. This was the result of using part of the reboiler duty to bring the mixture to saturation conditions when methane gas solute was present. The control loops were tuned independently once the process transfer function matrix has been evaluated. The tuning was conducted through the step test model identification and using the IMC approximate model rules for PI controllers (Rivera et al., 1986). The tuning parameters for the different structures are reported in Table 2.

Table 2: *Control structures tuning parameters*

Controllers	Kc	τi
Direct	1.33	15.2
Primary Cascade loop	4.04	13.8
Secondary Cascade loop	1.53	0.287

4. Results

4.1 Ethane Recovery

The dynamic response of the ethane recovery in the CRR separation process was investigated considering step changes in the feed flow rate. An increase of 10% and a decrease of the same percentage on the nominal value of 4980 kmol/h were considered. The flow rate changes induced pressure variations in the separator, and the temperature was maintained constant by a temperature controller. In this work, it has been attempted to limit the impact of these pressure variations on the ethane recovery, with a target value of 0.84, through the control of the temperature compensated in pressure on the separator. The results obtained in terms of the ethane recovery objective, performed without concentration control, for a decreasing of 10% in the inlet feed stream are showed in Figure 1. This variation produces a decrease in the separator pressure of 3.87 bar, with a maximum initial variation of 5.71 bar with the temperature controller and a decrease in the pressure separator of 4.26 bar, with a maximum initial variation of 6.35 bar with the pressure compensated temperature controller.

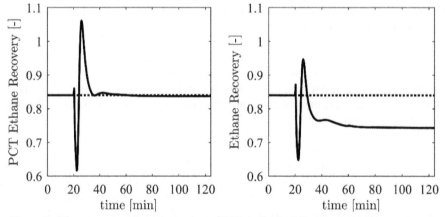

Figure 1: Ethane recovery for a decreasing of 10% in the feed flow rate with the separator pressure compensated temperature control (on the left panel) and with the separator temperature control (on the right panel)

As depicted by Figure 1 (right panel), the process is not able to maintain the recovery target when the ethane recovery control is removed from the configuration. The new steady state reached a value of 0.7437 with an offset of 0.0963. However, with the modification proposed on the separator temperature controller, even without an ethane concentration analyzer and an ethane composition controller, it is possible to bring the ethane recovery to the value 0.8372 with an offset of 0.0028, near to the target value of 0.84. The recovery stays off specification for about 20 minutes from the initial variation. Analog results are obtained with the increasing of 10% in the feed flow rate, that are reported in Table 3.

Table 3: Ethane recovery results for an increasing of 10% in the feed flow rate

	Final DP	Max DP	New steady states value	Offset
PCT control	4.18 bar	7.97 bar	0.838	0.0020
T control	3.66 bar	7.21 bar	0.898	0.0582

4.2 Methane bottom impurity level

The dynamic response of the methane concentration in the demethanizer bottom was investigated by step changes in the feed flow rate. For an increase/decrease of 10% on the nominal value of 4980 kmol/h, the response obtained through the action of the cascade and temperature direct controllers were compared. The results obtained for of 10% decrease in the inlet feed stream for methane concentration, 28th tray temperature and reboiler duty, are depicted by Figure 2.

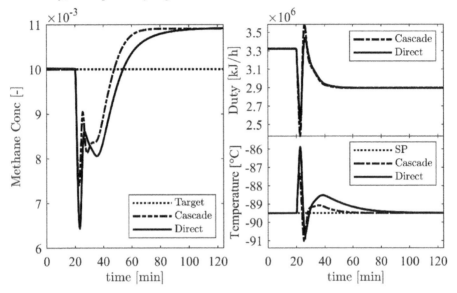

Figure 2: Dynamic response obtained by cascade and temperature direct controls for a decreasing of 10% in the feed flow rate: methane concentration profile (left panel); reboiler duty profile (top right panel); 28th Tray temperature profile (bottom right panel)

Observing the concentration profile in Figure 2 (left panel), obtained by the cascade temperature control, it is possible to appreciate a lower initial deviation and a higher speed of convergence to the new steady state value when compared to the direct temperature control. None of the two configurations can bring back the methane impurity to the target value of 1% mol. In both approaches, the methane concentration achieves a new value of 0.0109 at different times: the temperature direct control after around 65 min with a final off-set of 0.0009; the approximate cascade after around 43 min, with an off-set of 0.0009. In the right-hand side panels of Figure 2, the temperature profiles on the 28th tray are displayed in the bottom. In this case, it can also be concluded that the cascade control structure has a faster response (it reaches the set point value of 89.5°C around 35 minutes earlier) and a lower initial variation. This behaviour could be explained by considering that the column internal flow rates have faster dynamics than the temperature ones and consequently, the ratio controller action is more aggressive (see top right panel of Figure 2). After an initial time, the response of the manipulated actions in these controllers are comparable. Similar results are obtained with an increase of 10% in the feed flow rate (reported in Table 4).

Table 4: Methane bottom impurity level results for an increasing of 10% in the feed flow rate

Controller	New steady states value	Offset	Response time
Direct	0.0094	0.0006	76 min
Cascade	0.0094	0.0006	52 min

5. Conclusions

Several control strategies were compared with the main objective of achieving the methane composition of 1% mol, while maintaining ethane recovery at 84% in the demethanizer bottom in presence of changes in the inlet flow rate. It was shown that even without ethane recovery controller, it was possible to achieve the same recovery when using pressure compensated temperature in the separator as controlled variable. Comparing the impurity control of methane concentration with cascade control and direct temperature control for step changes in the inlet flow rate, we concluded that the cascade configuration had the best control performance. This controller had the fastest response and maximum convergence speed for controlling the temperature and composition of the methane in the bottom product stream.

References

A. Brambilla, 2014. *Distillation Control and Optimization*. McGraw-Hill Education.

A. J. Kidnay, W. R. Parrish, D.G., McCartney, 2011. *Fundamentals of natural gas processing*. Second ed., CRC press. Boca Raton, FL.

D. E. Rivera, M. Morari, S. Skogestad, 1986. *Internal Model Control 4. PID Controller Design*. I&C Process Design Development, 25,252.

F. S. Manning, R. E. Thompson, 1991.*Oilfield Processing: Natural Gas*; PennWell Publishing Co. Tulsa, USA.

J. Chebeir, S. D. Salas, J. A. Romagnoli, 2019. *Operability assessment on alternative natural gas liquids recovery schemes*. Journal of Natural Gas Science and Engineering Volume 71, 102974.

J.H. Park, M.S. Khan, R. Andika, M. Getu, A. Bahadori, M. Lee, 2015. *Techno-economic evaluation of a novel NGL recovery scheme with nine patented schemes for offshore applications*. J Nat Gas Sci Eng. 27, 2-17.

L. Kherbeck, R. Chebbi, 2015. *Optimizing ethane recovery in turboexpander processes*. Ind Eng Chem Res. 21, 292-297.

M. Porru, J. Alvarez, R. Baratti, 2013. *Composition Estimator Design for Industrial Multicomponent Distillation Column*. Chemical engineering transactions vol. 32.

R. Chebbi, N. S. Al-Amoodi, N. A. Jabbar, G. A. Husseini, & K. A. Al Mazroui, 2010. *Optimum ethane recovery in conventional turboexpander process*. Chemical engineering research and design, 88(5-6), 779-787N.

W.L. Luyben, 2013. *NGL demethanizer control*. Ind Eng Chem Res. 52(33), 11626-11638.

Sauro Pierucci, Flavio Manenti, Giulia Bozzano, Davide Manca (Eds.)
Proceedings of the 30th European Symposium on Computer Aided Process Engineering
(ESCAPE30), May 24-27, 2020, Milano, Italy. © 2020 Elsevier B.V. All rights reserved.
http://dx.doi.org/10.1016/B978-0-12-823377-1.50217-2

Global Optimization of Refinery – petrochemical Operations via Process Clustering Decomposition

Ariel Uribe-Rodriguez[a,b], Pedro M. Castro[c], Benoît Chachuat[,b,]*, Gonzalo Guillén-Gozálbez[d]

[a] Colombian Petroleum Institute, ECOPETROL, Colombia
[b] Centre for Process Systems Engineering, Department of Chemical Engineering, Imperial College London, United Kingdom
[c] Centro de Matemática Aplicações Fundamentias e Investigação Operacional, Faculdade de Ciências, Universidade de Lisboa, Portugal
[d] Institute for Chemical and Bioengineering, Department of Chemistry and Applied Biosciences, ETH Zürich, Switzerland
b.chachuat@imperial.ac.uk

Abstract

We consider the short-term planning of an integrated refinery and petrochemical complex using a mixed-integer nonlinear optimization. The process network is represented by input-output relationships based on bilinear and trilinear expressions to estimate yields and stream properties, fuels blending indices and cost functions. Binary variables select the operating modes for the process units. Our global optimization algorithm decomposes the network into small clusters according to their functionality. For the constraints inside a given cluster, we formulate a mixed-integer linear relaxation based on piecewise McCormick envelopes. The partitions for the variables are updated dynamically and their domain is reduced applying optimality-based bound tightening. For the constraints outside the cluster, we use the standard McCormick envelopes. Our approach is demonstrated on an industrial-size case study representing a typical planning scenario in Colombia. Results show that it outperforms the state-of-the-art commercial solvers ANTIGONE and BARON not only in terms of optimality gap (8 vs. 58 and 48%, respectively) but also the quality of the solution itself.

Keywords: planning, refinery-petrochemical, process-clustering, global optimization.

1. Introduction

The integration of refinery and petrochemical operations exploits the synergy between various processes, optimizing utility requirements, reducing operating costs and ensuring the fulfilment of environmental regulations, all together increasing the profitably margin of a wide range of products, from fuels to petrochemicals. Recently, deterministic global optimization and Lagrangean decomposition have been applied to short-term planning of integrated refining and petrochemical operations. These problems were formulated as large-scale nonconvex mixed-integer nonlinear programs (MINLP). Along these lines, Li et al. (2016) reported a profit improvement of 30%–65%, and Zhao et al. (2017) between 14%–53%, compared to optimizing sequentially the refinery and then the ethylene plant.

Herein, we propose a deterministic global optimization algorithm for such large-scale MINLP based on a two-stage procedure, alternating the solution of a mixed-integer linear program (MILP) relaxation and a nonlinear program (NLP) restriction of the original MINLP. Our approach decomposes the process network into small clusters (i.e. crude oil unloading, refining operations and fuels blending), which are then explored sequentially. The bilinear terms present into the constraints of the active cluster are relaxed with piecewise McCormick envelopes (Bergamini, Aguirre, and Grossmann 2005), after reducing the domain of their variables through optimality-based bound tightening (Puranik and Sahinidis, 2017). Outside the active cluster, McCormick envelopes (McCormick, 1976) relax the bilinear terms.

2. Elements for global optimization

The short-term planning problem can be cast as the following nonconvex MINLP, where x represents a $n -$ dimensional vector of non-negative continuous variables for flowrates and stream properties, constrained between given lower x^L and upper x^U bounds; y is a $r -$ dimensional vector of binary variables to determine operating conditions. The functions $f_q \colon \mathbb{R}^n \times \mathbb{R}^r \to \mathbb{R}$, with $q = 0, \dots, Q$, comprising the objective functions and the constraints, are quadratic in x and linear in y: $f_q(x, y) := \sum_{(i,j) \in BL_q} a_{ijq} x_i x_j + B_q x + C_q y + d_q$; BL_q is an (i, j)-index set defining the bilinear terms $x_i x_j$ present in quadratic function f_q; parameters a_{ijq} and d_q are scalars, whereas B_q and C_q are row vectors:

$$\max f_0(x, y) \qquad\qquad\qquad\qquad\qquad\qquad\qquad\qquad \text{(P)}$$
$$\text{s.t.}$$
$$f_q(x, y) \leq 0, \forall q \in \{1, \dots, Q\}$$
$$x \in [x^L, x^U] \subseteq \mathbb{R}_+^n, y \in \{0,1\}^r$$

In order to solve problem P, our deterministic global optimization algorithm solves a series of upper and lower bounding problems, named respectively PR and PF.

2.1. Process clustering

Following the workflow, the physical system is first clustered into process sections dealing with crude unloading and blending, crude distillation, refining processes, petrochemical processes and fuel blending. For example, crude allocation and blending determine the crude distillation unit's feed streams (flowrate and quality) and hence their operation. Crude fractionation then determines the performance of petrochemical and refining processes, which generate all intermediate streams needed for fuel blending.

2.2. Lower bounding

The NLP restriction PF is a version of P with fixed binary variables $\hat{y}$, obtained from solving PR.

$$z^{PF} := \max f_0(x, \hat{y}) \qquad\qquad\qquad\qquad\qquad\qquad\qquad \text{(PF)}$$
$$\text{s.t.} f_q(x, \hat{y}) \leq 0, \forall q \in \{1, \dots, Q\}$$
$$x \in [x^L, x^U] \subseteq \mathbb{R}_+^n$$

If feasible, solution z^{PF} provides a lower bound on the optimal value of P.

2.3. Upper bounding

The MILP relaxation is obtained by substituting bilinear terms $x_i x_j$ in P with new variables w_{ij}, thus linearizing $f_q(x,y)$ into $f_q^R(x,y,w)$. It also includes either standard (SME) or piecewise McCormick (PWME) envelopes, relating w_{ij} to the x_i and x_j variables and their bounds:

$$z^R := \max f_0^R(x,y,w) \qquad \text{(PR)}$$
$$\text{s.t.} f_q^R(x,y,w) \leq 0, \forall q \in \{1, \dots, Q\}$$
$$x \in [x^L, x^U] \subseteq \mathbb{R}_+^n, y \in \{0,1\}^r$$

PWME is tighter but since it uses binary variables to partition the domain of one of the variables (e.g. x_j) in every $x_i x_j$ term, it may lead to an intractable MILP even with a moderate number of partitions N_j. We compromise by partitioning x_j only if j belongs to the current cluster ($j \in CL$). Otherwise, we use SME. Since, PR is a relaxation of P, PR will be feasible whenever P is feasible and its optimal value z^R of PR will provide a finite upper bound UB on that of P.

2.4. Bounds contraction

The PR relaxation is improved by solving optimality-based bound tightening problems (OBBT). The bounds on a variable x_h appearing in a bilinear term of cluster CL can be tightened by solving two optimization problems.

$$x_h^L / x_h^U := \min/\max x_h \qquad \text{(OBBT)}$$
$$\text{s.t.} f_0^R(x,y,w) \geq LB$$
$$f_q^R(x,y,w) \leq 0, \forall q \in \{1, \dots, Q\}$$
$$x \in [x^L, x^U] \subseteq \mathbb{R}_+^n, y \in \{0,1\}^r$$

As PR, OBBT linearizes the bilinear terms and relaxes the problem using the SME and PWME relaxations. The number of partitions N_j is set to 2 for all partitioned variables inside cluster CL so as to keep the problem tractable.

2.5. Dynamic partitions updating

The maximum normalized deviation $\lambda_j \in [0,1]$ between the exact value of the bilinear term $x_i x_j$ and its relaxation w_{ij} drives the partitions update:

$$\delta_j = \begin{cases} \Delta \text{ if } \lambda_j > \tau \\ 0 \text{ Otherwise} \end{cases} \qquad (1)$$
$$N_j^* = \min(N_j + \delta_j, N^{max})$$

For each $j \in CL$. We use the threshold τ to determine the increasing in the number of partitions δ_j. Thus, the number of partitions N_j^* is updated by Δ until reaching its maximum number N^{max}.

2.6. Global optimization algorithm

The models described in sections 2.1 to 2.4 and the dynamic partition scheme showed in section 2.5 are combined into the following global optimization algorithm based on process cluster-decomposition. The model size for PR increases dynamically as a function of CL and N_j (see steps 5.1 and 5.7). Consequently, the runtime for solving PR increases across the iterations until reaching the $MaxRunTimePR$ or ε^{PR}. The algorithm outputs are the lower LB and upper UB bounds on the global objective value of P, as well as a feasible short-plan corresponding to LB.

1. Initialize $MaxRunTime, MaxRunTimePR, MaxNumIter, \varepsilon, \varepsilon^{PR}, N, N^{max}$.

2. Set $UB = -\infty, LB = +\infty, Iter = 0$.

3. Solve problem P and update $LB \leftarrow z$.

4. Solve relaxed problem PR (using the McCormick relaxation for all bilinear terms since there are no active clusters at this point) and update $UB \leftarrow z^R$.

5. For each cluster k do:

5.1. Set active cluster(s) $CL = \bigcup_{l=1}^{k} CL^l$.

5.2. Define $N_j = N$ for every partitioned variable x_j belonging to cluster CL^l. If $l \geq 2$ set the number of partitions in clusters $CL^1, \dots CL^{l-1}$ to their final values N_j^* determined in previous iterations.

5.3. Generate a population with up to PFS feasible solutions of PR and select the best solution, z^R among them. If $z^R < UB$, update $UB \leftarrow z^R$

5.4. Fix binary variables in P ($y \leftarrow \hat{y}$). Solve up to PFS instances of problem PF where the binary variable $\hat{y}$ are set to the feasible solutions of PR, and select the best feasible solution z^{PF}. If $z^{PF} > LB$, update $LB \leftarrow z^{PF}$.

5.5. If the cluster relative optimality gap $\varepsilon_{CL} = (UB - LB)/UB$ does not decrease continue to step 5.8.

5.6. Tighten the variable bounds by solving the OBBT problems.

5.7. Update N_j via Eq. (1). The optimal number of partitions N_j^* for the current cluster is propagated, so it is used as initial number of partitions for the next cluster. Return to step 5.3.

5.8. Do $Iter \leftarrow Iter + 1$. If $MaxRunTime$ is reached, or $Iter > MaxNumIter$, or $\varepsilon_{CL} \leq \varepsilon$, stop. Otherwise, increase cluster index k and loop.

3. Case Study

The industrial complex under study is composed of a medium conversion refinery for manufacturing several grades of gasoline, diesel and fuel oil, and a set of petrochemical processes for providing BTX, polyethylene, propylene, waxes and specialty solvents (see Figure 1). These commodities mostly supply the Colombian market, while a small part is exported. The total refining capacity is 240 kbbl/day. We assume a domestic petroleum production equal to 297 kbbl/day, involving 17 types of crude oil distributed over 8 geographical regions. The refinery can also import 7 types of crude, with up to 15 kbbl/day per crude. The logistic system comprises four river fleet routes and a system of nine pipelines. It deliveries crude oil from the production wells and import ports to the industrial complex as well as commodities from/to the industrial facility to/from the markets. The process network is composed of 60 industrial plants which are represented by about 155 models aggregated into six clusters defined using engineering insight: logistic and crude allocation (8 models), crude distillation units (13), vacuum and debutanizer columns (11), refining (53), petrochemical (48) and fuels blending (22). In total, 88 intermediate refined streams are routed to produce up to 22 different fuels grades (see Table 1) with a given quality specifications as indicated in Table 2. The network has four recycles: (i) LCO recycling from FCC for the fulfillment of diesel HDT feedstock; (ii) in the separation of BTX mix; (iii)-(iv) in the solvent extraction to produce waxes.

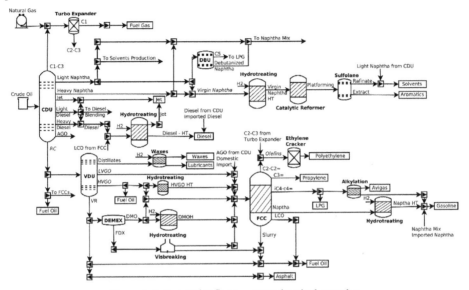

Figure 1. Integrated refinery - petrochemical complex

Table 1. Intermediate refined streams for fuels blending.

Fuel	LPG	Gasoline	Medium distillate	Fuel Oil	Asphalt
Streams to blend	24	23	25	10	6
Products grade	3	7	6	4	2

Table 2. Fuels quality specifications.

Fuel/Quality	Specific gravity	Sulphur content	Cetane number	RON	RVP	Viscosity
LPG	x					
Gasoline	x	x		x	x	
Medium distillate	x	x	x			
Fuel Oil	x	x				X
Asphalt	x	x				X

Figure 2 compares the clustering approach with the two most widely used commercial global optimization solvers, showing the progress of the profit (*LB*) and best-possible solution (*UB*) with the computational time. Both ANTIGONE and BARON are able to quickly identify a feasible solution, but no bound improvements are observed up to the maximum runtime (10 CPU hours). On the other hand, our approach starts with the same profit as ANTIGONE, but with a tighter *UB*, corresponding to $\epsilon = 42$ %. After processing Cluster I, our approach can reduce the optimality gap to 8%. This is accomplished through the OBBT step, which reduces the domain of the decision variables in CL^I by 23% on average, and by increasing the number of partitions for the variables in this sub-system. More importantly, the profit increases sharply from 2.634 to 2.928 MM$/day. During Clusters II and III, ϵ remains unchanged, while the profit increases to 2.964 MM$/day, after going through Cluster IV. This value is 11 % and 10% greater than the figures reported by ANTIGONE and BARON, respectively.

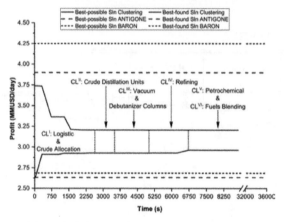

Figure 2. Solvers performance for the case study.

4. Conclusions

This paper has presented a novel cluster-based decomposition approach for the short-term planning of an integrated refinery-petrochemical facility. The problem is formulated as a large-scale MINLP, with the binary variables selecting the optimal operating mode of conversion processes. Nonconvexities also arise from the correlations used to predict yields and stream properties, cost functions, intermediate pooling and fuels blending constraints. The topology complexity of the real-life case study addressed in this work, logistic considerations for the reception and delivery of commodities as well as the complexity of the crude basket selection and product allocation tasks, altogether made it challenging to find high-quality solutions within a reasonable optimality gap. While all algorithms were able to identify feasible solutions, our approach outperformed BARON and ANTIGONE, in terms of profit, optimality gap and computational runtime.

Acknowledgments

The authors would like to acknowledge the financial support from the Colombian Science Council (COLCIENCIAS) and the Colombian Petroleum Company (Ecopetrol S.A.).

References

Bergamini, M. L., Aguirre, P. and Grossmann, I.E. 2005. "Logic-Based Outer Approximation for Globally Optimal Synthesis of Process Networks." *Computers and Chemical Engineering* 29 (9): 1914–33.

Li, J., Xin X., Boukouvala F., Floudas, C.A., Zhao, B., Du, G., Su, X. and Liu, H. 2016. "Data-Driven Mathematical Modeling and Global Optimization Framework for Entire Petrochemical Planning Operations." *AIChE Journal* 62 (9): 3020–40.

McCormick, G. P. 1976. "Computability of Global Solutions to Factorable Nonconvex Programs: Part I - Convex Underestimating Problems." *Mathematical Programming* 10 (1): 147–75.

Puranik, Y. and Sahinidis N.V. 2017. "Domain Reduction Techniques for Global NLP and MINLP Optimization." *Constraints* 22 (3): 338–76.

Sauro Pierucci, Flavio Manenti, Giulia Bozzano, Davide Manca (Eds.)
Proceedings of the 30th European Symposium on Computer Aided Process Engineering
(ESCAPE30), May 24-27, 2020, Milano, Italy. © 2020 Elsevier B.V. All rights reserved.
http://dx.doi.org/10.1016/B978-0-12-823377-1.50218-4

A Robust Nonlinear Estimator for a Yeast Fermentation Biochemical Reactor

Silvia Lisci, Massimiliano Grosso[*], Stefania Tronci

Dipartimento di Ingegneria Meccanica, Chimica e dei Materiali, Università degli Studi di Cagliari, Cagliari I-09123, Italy

massimiliano.grosso@dimcm.unica.it

Abstract

Nonlinear state estimation is an active research area, particularly to address monitoring and control problems in continuous processes. Recently, literature evidenced that bioproduction of chemicals and pharmaceuticals, which usually employs batch manufacturing, can have significant product quality and financial benefits when using continuous mode. In this paper, the geometric approach is used to address the estimation problem of a bioreactor for ethanol production. The work is based on a detailed model reported in the literature, hereafter considered as the virtual plant. The main objective is to compare different estimation solutions depending on the available measurements and the characteristics of the considered sensors.

Keywords: soft-sensing, bioprocessing, nonlinear observer

1. Introduction

Continuous processes are generally quite common in chemical industries, but biomanufacturing, like pharmaceutical industry, still prefers batch processes (Croughan et al., 2015). However, because of the necessity to be more competitive, also biotechnology processes are starting to consider the use of continuous operation (Galvanauskas et al., 2019). The main issue when dealing with continuous process is that an adequate monitoring and control system is required, because possible deviations need to be detected in time and counteracted, leading to a robust production with constant performance (Tronci et al., 2011; Baratti et al., 2018). Product quality indexes of bioprocesses such as biomass, substrate, product or by-product, dissolved oxygen concentrations need to be measured in order to ensure that requirements are met. Unfortunately, those variables are often difficult to measure in real-time, resulting from the complex nature of biological systems (Spigno and Tronci, 2015) and a lack of adequate measuring device (Holzberg et al., 2018). It is worth noting that several disturbances can affect the system and that the states' dynamics are in general governed by complex and nonlinear processes. This means that the application of a continuous mode cannot be considered if a proper monitoring and control system is not applied and this cannot be satisfied if proper sensors are not available.

A nonlinear estimator can be a possible approach to deal with a lack of in-line measurements. The combination of a process model and a measurement processor allows the reconstruction of all the states of the process if the considered system is observable at the given conditions. In this paper, the geometric approach is used to address the estimation problem of a bioreactor for the production of ethanol. The work is based on the model proposed by Nagy (2007), which is considered as the virtual plant. The main objective is to compare different estimation solutions depending on the available measurements and the characteristics of the sensors.

2. Process model

The biochemical process considered in the present paper is a fermentation reactor for ethanol production. The model has been carefully developed by Nagy (2007) and subsequently extended by other authors (Lawrýnczuk, 2008; Imtiaz et al., 2013).

The reactor is modeled as a continuous stirred tank (CSTR) with a constant feed rate. The device contains three different components (Eqs. 1-3): the biomass (C_x), namely a yeast suspension fed to the system and continuously removed from it; the substrate (C_s), which is the glucose solution that feeds the microorganisms; the product (i.e. the ethanol, C_P) that is removed from the reactor together with other components. Dissolved oxygen is also present in the reactor (C_{O2}) and it is consumed during the fermentation (Eq. 4). A low dilution rate (F_e/V) is necessary in order to have a quasi-stationary state for biomass and the consequence is the quite slow dynamics of the process. The heat balances in the reactor and in the jacket are also considered (Eqs. 4-5), describing the dynamics of the reactor temperature (T_r) and the coolant temperature (T_{ag}). For sake of brevity, only the mass and energy balances describing the process are reported in the present paper (Eqs.1-6). More details and the values of the parameters can be found in Nagy (2007).

$$\frac{dC_X}{dt} = \mu_X\, C_X\, \frac{C_S}{K_{S1}+C_S}\, e^{-K_{P1}C_P} - \frac{F_e}{V}C_X \tag{1}$$

$$\frac{dC_P}{dt} = \mu_P C_X\, \frac{C_S}{K_{S1}+C_S}\, e^{-K_{P1}\,C_P} - \frac{F_e}{V}\,C_P \tag{2}$$

$$\frac{dC_S}{dt} = -\frac{1}{R_{SX}}\mu_X C_X\, \frac{C_S}{K_S+C_S}e^{-K_P C_P} - \frac{1}{R_{SP}}\mu_P C_X\, \frac{C_S}{K_{S1}+C_S}\, e^{-K_{P1}C_P} + \frac{F_i}{V}C_{S,in} - \frac{F_e}{V}C_S \tag{3}$$

$$\frac{dT_r}{dt} = \left(\frac{F_i}{V}\right)(T_{in}+273) - \left(\frac{F_e}{V}\right)(T_r+273) + \frac{r_{O_2}\,\Delta H_r}{32\,\rho_r\,C_{heat,r}} - \frac{K_T A_T\,(T_r-T_{ag})}{V\,\rho_r\,C_{heat,r}} \tag{4}$$

$$\frac{dT_{ag}}{dt} = \left(\frac{F_{ag}}{V_j}\right)(T_{in,ag} - T_{ag}) + \frac{K_T A_T(T_r-T_{ag})}{V_j\rho_{ag}C_{heat,ag}} \tag{5}$$

$$\frac{dC_{O_2}}{dt} = k_l a\left(C_{O_2}^* - C_{O_2}\right) - r_{O_2} \tag{6}$$

3. State estimation

Consider a non-linear dynamic system that can be represented as follows:

$$\frac{dx}{dt} = f\big(x, u(t)\big) \tag{7}$$

$$y = h(x, u) \tag{8}$$

where $x \in \mathbb{R}^n$ is the vector of states, which is indicated as x_0 at the initial instant t_0, $u \in \mathbb{R}^q$ is the input vector, $y \in \mathbb{R}^m$ is the output vector, while f is the vector field of n dimension and h is the non-linear vector of m dimension that relates outputs to inputs. As reported in Salas et al. (2019), it is possible to consider a non-linear map ϕ, whose components are the measured outputs and some of their directional derivatives, as reported in Eqs. (9-10)

$$\Phi(x, u) = [\Phi_1, \dots, \dots, \Phi_i, \dots, \dots, \Phi_m]^T \tag{9}$$

$$\Phi_i = \left(h_i(x), L_f^1 h_i(x), \dots, \dots, L_f^{\kappa_i - 1} h_i(x)\right) \tag{10}$$

where $L_f^j h_i(x)$ are the recursive j^{th} Lie derivatives of the time-varying scalar field $h_i(x)$ along the vector field time-variant $f(x, u(t))$, and κ_i is the observability index of the ith output. If the sum of the m observability indices κ_i is equal to the dimension of the state vector and the map $\Phi(x, u)$ is invertible with respect to x, it is possible to relate the measured outputs to the states and to reconstruct the system dynamics. This issue can be assessed by evaluating the rank of the matrix $\partial_x \Phi(x, u)$ for given trajectories, meaning that the system is observable if

$$rank(\partial_x \Phi(x, u)) = n \tag{11}$$

It is important to underline that robust observability can be detected by evaluating the condition number of the observability matrix and its minimum singular value. Such metrics are important tools for choosing the best estimator structure (López and Alvarez, 2004; Salas et al., 2019).

3.1 Geometric observer

If the observability condition is fulfilled then the unmeasured states can be reconstructed at any time, through information obtained from measurements and their derivatives. The estimator used in this work is in the form developed by López and Alvarez (2004)

$$\frac{d\hat{x}}{dt} = \hat{f}(\hat{x}, u(t)) + \Phi_x^{-1} K (y - h(\hat{x})) \tag{12}$$

$$y = h(\hat{x}) \tag{13}$$

where Φ_x^{-1} is the inverse of the Jacobian Φ_x of the map calculated with respect to system states, K is the observer gain matrix, the components of which are tuning parameters and their values are calculated using the procedure suggested in Alvarez and Fernández (2009).

4. Problem statement

The main purpose of the present investigation is to assess if soft sensors have the potential to solve problems related to the monitoring of bioprocesses with the available transducers. The selected algorithm is the geometric observer, because it includes a robust local convergence and a systematic construction-tuning procedure, making it applicable in nonlinear problems (López and Alvarez, 2004; Alvarez and Fernández 2009). Because a real plant is not available for the present investigation, the study is based on the simulation of the bioprocess. In order to mimic a real situation, two sources of errors are present. The first is an additive white noise which behaves like a uniformly distributed random number in the interval (0,1) and that corrupts the available measurements. The second source is responsible for a model mismatch, which implies that the model used in the estimator is different from the model used to simulate the 'virtual plant'. In particular, it is assumed that the kinetic parameters used in the estimator algorithm are different from the ones reported in Nagy (2007). Model mismatch and measurement noise make the estimation problem more demanding and more representative of an industrial plant.

4.1. Estimator structure

In order to select the best estimator configuration, different tests were carried out considering alternative structures, according to the combinations of observability indexes and innovated states, starting from the full order estimator. For the purpose of the study, it is important to specify that all tests have been carried out by making step variations on three inputs of the model. More specifically, the temperature of the feed entering the bioreactor (T_{in}) was changed after 100 h of simulation, the concentration of substrate inlet ($C_{s,in}$) after 150 h and finally the coolant inlet temperature ($T_{in,ag}$) after 250 h (cf. Table 1).

Table 1 - Model parameters submitted to step-change

$T_{in}\ [°C]$	25	30
$C_{s,in}\ [g/l]$	60	75
$T_{in,ag}\ [°C]$	15	10

The first case analed is that of a hypothetical ideal situation in which five measurements are available (C_x, C_s, C_{O2}, T_r, T_{ag}), while the product (C_P) is not measured. Temperature measurements and oxygen sensors are usually present in the real plants, while biological related measurements are seldom available (Randek and Mandenius, 2018). The choice of considering substrate and biomass as measured variables has been accomplished by considering the literature on sensors for biomanufacturing (Holzberg et al., 2018). In more detail, robustness, stability, and costs have been considered. The first scenario considering five measured outputs is the less demanding because almost all variables can be monitored on-line.

The second case considers only 4 measured outputs and, for this purpose, only one of the components' measurements is considered. For guaranteeing the observability property, the substrate concentration is used, while the biomass concentration is not a measured output. This situation is more demanding because less information on the states is accessible. Because the condition to be fulfilled is that the sum of the observability indexes associated with each measurement is equal to n, the second case will require the evaluation of one more Lie derivative in order to compensate the lack of the measured output.

5. Results

The dynamic of the estimator in both the cases described above is here reported. When considering five measured outputs, observability property is satisfied with two configurations (Eqs. 14a-b).

$$\Phi_1 = [C_x, L_f C_x, C_s, C_{O_2}, T_r, T_{ag}], \Phi_2 = [C_x, C_s, L_f C_s, C_{O_2}, T_r, T_{ag}] \tag{14a-b}$$

The best structure between (14a) and (14b) can be selected by considering the minimum singular value and condition number of the Jacobian matrix for the two maps. The mean values of the selected indexes calculated along a reference trajectory are reported in Table 2, and they indicate that the second configuration should be the better choice in terms of robustness (lower condition number) and the relationship between measured outputs and states (highest minimum singular value).

Table 2 - Minimum singular values and condition number with five measurements.

	Φ_1	Φ_2
κ	133.29	28.9358
σ	0.0076	0.069

The choice based on Table 2 has been confirmed by the dynamic simulations, where it is evident that the second configuration allows a better reconstruction of the product composition, which is the only unmeasured state (Figure 1). Indeed, the nonlinear estimator (dotted line) is able to reduce the mismatch between the model without correction (dashed line), indicated as open-loop model, and virtual plant (continuous line). The response is highly corrupted by noise, because of the amplification of the measurement error due to the high gain values used to reduce the offset in the ethanol composition estimation.

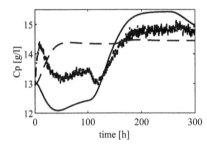 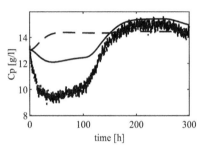

Figure 1. Comparison of the ethanol dynamic behavior between virtual plant (continuous line), open-loop model (dashed line) and estimator (dotted line) for structure with map Φ_1 (left panel)and Φ (right panel).

The same procedure can be used to select the best configuration when only four measured outputs are available. The observability property is satisfied for the following structures (Eqs. 15a-b):

$$\Phi_3 = [C_s, L_f C_s, C_{O_2}, L_f C_{O_2}, T_r, T_{ag}], \quad \Phi_4 = [C_s, L_f C_s, C_{O_2}, T_r, L_f T_r, T_{ag}] \qquad (15a\text{-}b)$$

The means of the minimum singular value and condition number along the reference trajectory are reported in Table 3.

Table 3 - Minimum singular values and condition number with four measurements.

	Φ_3	Φ_4
κ	1814.8	54.29
σ	0.0842	0.0332

The reconstructed dynamic behavior for the two unmeasured states is reported in Figure 2. Results show that the offset is slightly lower with the map Φ_3, confirming the higher value for σ. This indicates that the directional derivative of substrate concentration with respect to oxygen concentration gives more information on the product dynamics.

6. Conclusions

This work was focused on the development of a soft-sensor for estimating the states of a bioprocess. Results show that the states of the bioreactor can be efficiently reconstructed using four measurements and that observability was fulfilled if the substrate concentration was measured. The procedure discussed in this paper can be used to select which is the sensor that can give more information on the whole system if a choice is required for reducing costs related to monitoring and control of the process.

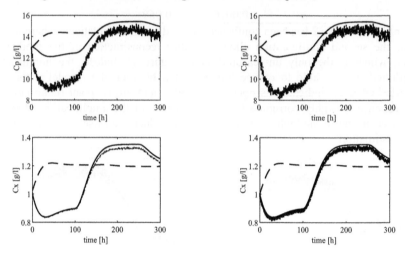

Figure 2. Comparison of the ethanol and biomass dynamic behavior between virtual plant (continuous line), open-loop model (dashed line) and estimator (dotted line) for structure with map Φ_3 (left panel) and Φ_4 (right panel).

References

J. Alvarez, C. Fernández, 2009, Geometric estimation of nonlinear process systems, J. Process Control, 19, 247-260.

R. Baratti, S. Tronci, A. Schaum, J. Alvarez, 2018, Open and closed-loop stochastic dynamics of a class of nonlinear chemical processes with multiplicative noise. Journal of Process Control, 66, 108-121.

M.S. Croughan, K.B. Konstantinov, C. Cooney, 2015, The future of industrial bioprocessing: batch or continuous? Biotechnol Bioeng, 112, 648-651.

V. Galvanauskas, R. Simutis, D. Levišauskas, R. Urniežius, 2019, Practical Solutions for Specific Growth Rate Control Systems in Industrial Bioreactors, Processes, 7(10), 693.

T.R. Holzberg, Timothy R., V. Watson, S. Brown, A. Andar, X. Ge, Y. Kostov, L. Tolosa, G. Rao, 2018, Sensors for biomanufacturing process development: facilitating the shift from batch to continuous manufacturing, Current opinion in chemical engineering, 22, 115-127.

U. Imtiaz, A. Assadzadeh, S.S. Jamuar, J.N. Sahu, 2013, Bioreactor temperature profile controller using inverse neural network (INN) for production of ethanol. Journal of Process Control, 23(5), 731-742.

M. Ławryńczuk, 2008, Modelling and nonlinear predictive control of a yeast fermentation biochemical reactor using neural networks. Chemical Engineering Journal, 145(2), 290-307.

T. López, J Alvarez, 2004, On the effect of the estimation structure in the functioning of a nonlinear copolymer reactor estimator, J. Process Control, 14, 99-109.

Z.K. Nagy, 2007, Model based control of a yeast fermentation bioreactor using optimally designed artificial neural networks, Chemical engineering journal, 127(1-3), 95-109.

S. D., Salas, J.A. Romagnoli, S. Tronci, R. Baratti, 2019, A geometric observer design for a semi-batch free-radical polymerization system. Computers & Chemical Engineering, 126, 391-402.

J. Randek, C.F. Mandenius, 2018, On-line soft sensing in upstream bioprocessing. Critical reviews in biotechnology, 38(1),106-121.

G. Spigno, S. Tronci, 2015, Development of hybrid models for a vapor-phase fungi bioreactor, Mathematical Problems in Engineering, Article ID 801213, 11 pages.

S. Tronci, M. Grosso, J. Alvarez, R. Baratti, 2011, On the global nonlinear stochastic dynamical behavior of a class of exothermic CSTRs, Journal of Process Control, 21(9), 1250-1264.

Sauro Pierucci, Flavio Manenti, Giulia Bozzano, Davide Manca (Eds.)
Proceedings of the 30th European Symposium on Computer Aided Process Engineering
(ESCAPE30), May 24-27, 2020, Milano, Italy. © 2020 Elsevier B.V. All rights reserved.
http://dx.doi.org/10.1016/B978-0-12-823377-1.50219-6

Big Data Generation for Time Dependent Processes: The Tennessee Eastman Process for Generating Large Quantities of Process Data

Emil B. Andersen[a], Isuru A. Udugama[a], Krist V. Gernaey[a], Christoph Bayer[b,*],
Murat Kulahci[c,d]

[a]Technical University of Denmark, Department of Chemical and Biochemical
Engineering, Process and Systems Engineering Center (PROSYS), Building 229, 2800
Kongens Lyngby, Denmark
[b]TH Nürnberg, Department of Process Engineering, Wassertorstraße 10, 90489
Nürnberg, Germany
[c]Technical University of Denmark, DTU Compute, Richard Petersens Plads 324, 2800
Kongens Lyngby, Denmark
[d]Luleå University of Technology, 97817 Luleå, Sweden
christoph.bayer@th-nuernberg.de

Abstract

The concept of applying data-driven process monitoring and control techniques on industrial chemical processes is well established. With concepts such as Industry 4.0, Big Data and the Internet of Things receiving attention in industrial chemical production, there is a renewed focus on data-driven process monitoring and control in chemical production applications. However, there are significant barriers that must be overcome in obtaining sufficiently large and reliable plant and process data from industrial chemical processes for the development of data-driven process monitoring and control concepts, specifically in obtaining plant and process data that are required to develop and test data driven process monitoring and control tools without investing significant efforts in acquiring, treating and interpreting the data. In this manuscript a big data generation tool is presented that is based on the Tennessee Eastman Process (TEP) simulation benchmark, which has been specifically designed to generate massive amounts of process data without spending significant effort in setting up. The tool can be configured to carry out a large number of data generation runs both using a graphical user interface (GUI) and through a .CSV file. The output from the tool is a file containing process data for all runs as well as process faults (deviations) that have been activated. This tool enables users to generate massive amounts of data for testing applicability of big data concepts in the realm of process control for continuously operating time dependent processes. The tool is available for all researchers and other parties who are interested.

Keywords: Data generation, Statistical process control, Data-driven control

1. Introduction

With an ever increasing demand for the generation of large amounts of process data that is required for enabling concepts such as Industry 4.0, Big Data and the Internet of Things there is a need for finding efficient ways to generate large amounts of plant and process data. However, researchers who work in the area of data analytics often face significant barriers in obtaining sufficiently large and reliable plant and process data sets from industrial chemical processes for the development of data-driven process monitoring and control concepts. The main barriers can be summarized as follows:

1. Restrictions on the use of industrial plant and process data by corporations due to confidentiality and intellectual property rights issues. Many researchers find it difficult to obtain realistic plant and process data as they are unable to identify industrial partners willing to share data. In other situations researchers may have access to plant and process data, but will be barred from publishing such data sets or required to publish a partially redacted or altered data set (Udugama et al., 2018).

2. Insufficient quality of available process data due to data compression practices which dates back to the era of limited data storage capacity. Similarly, the general lack of regard for past plant data results in key changes to plant and process not being clearly logged with the plant data.

3. The operational doctrine of a production plant is to ensure on-specification production and safe plant operation at all times. Therefore, the plant operators generally prefer to keep their actions to a minimum and to maintain steady state operations. As a result, a large amount of process data logs may contain little to no process movement, which in turn will not reveal key process features.

4. Many chemical engineering processes have nuances and practical limitations which must be considered, particularly if findings made are to be used for control and corrective purposes. This requires the interlinking of key phenomena, which need to be controlled, with process variables that indeed can be manipulated in practice. Hence, to have an adequate presence of domain knowledge and understanding is a key requirement as this is not a trivial exercise (Gajjar et al., 2018).

One method that has been employed to remedy this lack of process data is the use of process simulations that have a proven track record in being applicable in many process control applications in chemical processes (Udugama et al., 2017a, 2017b). Even though the use of dynamic flowsheet simulators to generate vast amounts of process data is a valid approach, it requires in-depth domain knowledge understanding for the simulation set-up as well a tedious process to set up multiple processes runs required for big data-based approaches. By contrast, industrial benchmark simulations like the Tennessee Eastman Process (TEP) are widely regarded particularly in the area of process control as a realistic and a challenging problem since it was released in the early 1990s (Downs and Vogel, 1993; Udugama et al., 2020). However, it is important to note that this process simulation benchmark was not created for the purpose of generating large amounts of process data. In this manuscript a tool is presented to specifically tackle the requirement of generating large amounts of process data, employing the TEP benchmark process as the simulation engine, while mitigating the above-mentioned barriers.

2. TEP simulation

The Tennessee Eastman Process consists of a reactor, a product condenser, a separator and a stripping column with the objective of reacting feed streams into products. In simple terms, the TEP takes four feed streams (streams 1-4) and partially converts the contents in the reactor into products, including the valuable compounds G and H. The resulting stream is cooled down and partially condensed using the product condenser. The resulting liquid stream, which predominantly contains the products of interest (compounds G and H), is then introduced to a stripping column, where dissolved gaseous compounds and middle-boiling compounds can be removed to meet the required product specifications. Modelled on an actual industrial process, the TEP is valuable as a simulation tool due to its complexity and realistic nature. The model contains 28 predefined fault scenarios that can be applied to the process.

3. Converting the TEP simulation into a data generation tool

The original TEP simulation introduced by Downs and Vogel in the 90's was written in the software language FORTRAN (Downs and Vogel, 1993). In the early 2000's, this original FORTRAN file was augmented with the capabilities of MATLAB Simulink by Ricker (Bathelt et al., 2015) where the control variables (Inputs) to the FORTRAN file can be manipulated via MATLAB while process variables (outputs) are sent back to MATLAB. While this implementation makes the use of the original FORTRAN code much more convenient, the following shortcomings render this implementation in its current form impractical for the purpose of massive data generation.

- The model terminates soon after start up due to lack of control on safety critical variables.
- The data output is generated for a single run and is not available in an easy to export process format such as .CSV or .SQL.
- The data structure requires the user to explicitly track the state of the 28 process disturbances that can influence the operations and record other critical process parameters.
- Prior experience with Simulink and MATLAB is necessary.
- A detailed understanding of the TEP is necessary.

The focus of the TEP tool presented here is on facilitating the fast and simple generation of reliable fault scenario data sets, which can be used by data scientists in fault detection, process monitoring and ultimately process control. From a data generation point of view, the TEP code itself contains a random element (seed) to it which means that no two TEP runs would produce the exact same data set, while still retaining the fundamental characteristics. Hence, the TEP is geared towards the generation of a large number of non-repeating data sets. Moreover, the TEP code and the subsequent TEP big data tool have been developed so that all relevant information related to the process is clearly recorded in the data set, as opposed to most industrial data sets.

3.1. Process control

TEP is an open loop unstable process, and as discussed in the previous section, the simulation reaches shutdown limits and terminates soon after start-up. This does not provide useful results, and for this reason a layer of process control has been implemented. The five safety variables that must remain in a strict interval have each been equipped with a PID controller. It is important to keep in mind the effect that closed loops may have on process dynamics when evaluating the data generated by the tool. The variables used in PID controllers are given in Table 1. The user may implement their own control scheme in the Simulink file that contains the process model.

Table 1 - Process control

Controlled variable	Manipulated variable
Reactor pressure (XMEAS 7)	Purge valve (XMV 6)
Reactor level (XMEAS 8)	Condenser cooling water flow (XMV 11)
Reactor temperature (XMEAS 9)	Reactor cooling water flow (XMV 10)
Product separator level (XMEAS 12)	Separator pot liquid flow (XMV 7)
Stripper base level (XMEAS 15)	Stripper liquid product flow (XMV 8)

3.2. User input

The user may enter the following information in the GUI to tailor the simulations to their needs.

- Runs - How many times should the same setup be simulated?
- Duration – How many hours of operation should be simulated?
- Disturbance – Which fault scenarios should be applied?
- Start time – At what time during the simulation should the fault scenario start?
- End time – At what time during the simulation should the fault scenario stop?
- Seed – What should be the random generator seed for the first simulation?

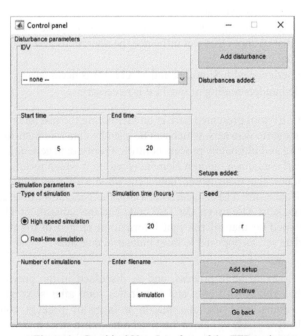

Figure 1 - Graphical User Interface of the TEP tool

The ability to enter the random generator seed allows for reproducibility of results. Alternatively, the user may let the program generate a random number as a seed for the simulation. When simulating multiple runs of the same setup, the seed will increase by one for each simulation to produce distinct data sets.

Inputting the information to the program can be done through loading a .CSV file based on a template, or through the user-friendly interface.

3.3. Output of GUI

The default setting of the GUI is to run the desired simulations as quickly as possible. This generates a set of .CSV files and a .TXT file. Each .CSV file contains the simulation result for a single run of the process and the .TXT file contains a summary of the simulations that have been run. This ensures that the user can keep track of which .CSV contains the results for a given simulation setup and allows for easy reproduction of the data. The simulation produces 81 time-dependent variables. There are 12 input variables, 41 output variables and 28 disturbance variables that indicate whether or not a disturbance scenario is active. The columns in the .CSV files are named to avoid confusion about what a given column of data represents. As an alternative to a quick simulation, the user may run a single simulation in 'real-time'. This will give the user an operator view of the process with displays of the input variables and safety variables. Figure 2 shows the structure of the result files and Figure 3 shows the real time simulation view.

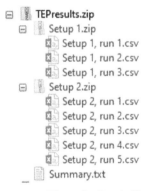

Figure 2 - Result files

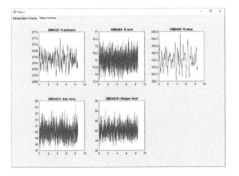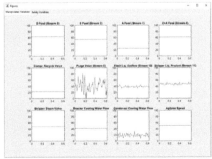

Figure 3 - Real time simulation view

4. Conclusions

In this work a big data tool is presented that can generate a large amount of realistic process data using the well-established Tennessee Eastman process simulation as the data generation engine. The tool addresses the need in the data science and process control community for large amounts of realistic process data to formulate new data-driven solutions for process control and fault detection. The tool is designed such that data can be generated with minimum interaction with MATLAB programming where the input to the tool can be carried out using either a csv-file and/or an easy to use graphical user interface while the output from the tool is also in the form of a csv-file. This allows an interested user to request, generate and process the desired data with minimum interaction with MATLAB. It is expected that the tool will lead to better understanding of process characteristics by data scientists and result in the development of fit-for-purpose data driven process monitoring and diagnosis concepts.

References

Bathelt, A., Ricker, N.L., Jelali, M., 2015. Revision of the Tennessee Eastman Process Model. IFAC-PapersOnLine 48, 309–314.

Downs, J.J., Vogel, E.F., 1993. A plant-wide industrial process control problem. Comput. Chem. Eng. 17, 245–255.

Gajjar, S., Kulahci, M., Palazoglu, A., 2018. Real-time fault detection and diagnosis using sparse principal component analysis. J. Process Control 67, 112–128.

Udugama, I.A., Gernaey, K. V., Taube, M.A., Bayer, C., 2020. A novel use for an old problem: The Tennessee Eastman challenge process as an activating teaching tool. Educ. Chem. Eng. 30, 20–31.

Udugama, I.A., Taube, M.A., Mansouri, S.S., Kirkpatrick, R., Gernaey, K. V., Yu, W., Young, B.R., 2018. A Systematic Methodology for Comprehensive Economic Assessment of Process Control Structures. Ind. Eng. Chem. Res. 57, 13116–13130.

Udugama, I.A., Wolfenstetter, F., Kirkpatrick, R., Yu, W., Young, B.R., 2017a. A comparison of a novel robust decentralised control strategy and MPC for industrial high purity, high recovery, multicomponent distillation. ISA Trans. 69, 222–233.

Udugama, I.A., Zander, C., Mansouri, S.S., Kirkpatrick, R., Yu, W., Young, B.R., 2017b. A novel back-up control structure to manage non-routine steam upsets in industrial methanol distillation columns. Comput. Aided Chem. Eng. 40, 1597–1602.

Sauro Pierucci, Flavio Manenti, Giulia Bozzano, Davide Manca (Eds.)
Proceedings of the 30th European Symposium on Computer Aided Process Engineering
(ESCAPE30), May 24-27, 2020, Milano, Italy. © 2020 Elsevier B.V. All rights reserved.
http://dx.doi.org/10.1016/B978-0-12-823377-1.50220-2

Floating Pressure Control of Vapor Recompression Distillation in Propane-propylene Separation

Jan Marvin Frias,[a] San-Jang Wang,[b,*] David Shan-Hill Wong,[a]

Cheng-Huang Chou,[a] Shi-Shang Jang,[a] En-Ko Lee[b]

[a]*Department of Chemical Engineering, National Tsing Hua University Hsinchu 30013, Taiwan*
[b]*Center for Energy and Environmental Research, Natioinal Tsing Hua University Hsinchu 30013, Taiwan*
wangsj@mx.nthu.edu.tw

Abstract

The separation of propylene from propane is an energy-intensive distillation process. Vapor recompression is commonly used for the separation of propylene and propane. Most studies of vapor recompression were carried out at a given pressure. It is well known that the lower the pressure, the higher the volatility difference and less energy is required to perform the separation. In a traditional column, energy of the distillation can be minimized by operating at the lowest pressure possible. The limit is usually determined by the maximum cooling capacity in the condenser, which is in turn determined by the temperature of the cooling water. Such a practice is known as floating pressure control. In a vapor-recompression column, the condenser and reboiler were replaced by a heat exchanger. Auxiliary condenser and reboiler may or may not be present. The operating constraint is determined by the anti-surge control of the compressor. Furthermore, it is necessary to ensure that the compressed vapor which acts as steam in the reboiler is not substantially subcooled to avoid the vibration of the heat exchanger.

In this study, the implementation of floating pressure control for a vapor-recompression propane-propylene column with an auxiliary condenser is studied using ASPEN Plus dynamics. A control scheme that includes basic inventory control and quality control was proposed. To keep the operation within safe region of the compressor surge curve, the split of the compressed vapor going to the bottom as heating medium and passing through the auxiliary condenser is adjusted. It is shown that the column can be operated under product purity requirements of top and bottom when column pressure is reduced by 1 kg/cm2.

Keywords: vapor recompression, floating pressure control, energy optimization

1. Introduction

Global demand of propylene has been increasing from recent years to present. This makes the industry more viable for technology improvements and energy minimization strategies to make the profits more promising. Propylene is an essential raw material in the production of its various derivatives requiring high purity polymer-grade propylene. In the refinery, it usually comes along propane which is very close to its boiling point making it a very energy-consuming separation process. There is a growing need to improve efficiencies of propylene production due to enlarging gap between supply and demand making it more attractive for businesses to invest in this industry.

Distillation is an energy consuming separation process in chemical process industries. Vapor recompression is one of the energy efficient technologies employed to harness all the heat circulating in a distillation system. For systems where boiling point difference of separated components is small, energy saving obtained is more improved because at decreased system pressure, relative volatility is enhanced. This makes separation process more convenient and economical. However, reduction of column pressure is constrained by the cooling capacity of the condenser, thus it shall be optimized. In this study, the column pressure effect for a vapor-recompression propane-propylene column with an auxiliary condenser is studied by implementing floating pressure control using ASPEN Plus dynamics to minimize energy consumption. Compressor performance curve and anti-surge curve are also involved in the design and control of this column.

2. Review of Related Literatures

2.1. Vapor recompression distillation

A major advantage of vapor-recompression system is that the column can be operated with minimized pressure condition due to independence from cooling or heating media conditions since process fluids heat and cool each other at the same time. With changing feed rates and column overhead pressure, we shall study here how to achieve lowest energy consumption while keeping operation as close to anti-surge curve. According to Ma et al. (2019), the optimal pressure needs to be determined by balancing cost and control. They claim in this study that pressure had different effects on the dynamic controllability of different systems.

Annakou and Mizsey (1995) used two schemes to investigate propylene-propane splitter assisted by a heat pump: single and double compressor schemes. They found that with the double compressor, column pressure is independent of threshold temperature of condenser. They claim both processes are 37% cheaper when compared to conventional column. The literature did not discuss the anti-surge operation of the compressor with every pressure change which we now include in our study. Keeping the operation as near as possible to anti-surge curve will optimize inventory and help minimize energy consumption. Optimum valve conditions are also employed in this study.

2.2 Floating pressure control

In vapor recompression distillation, condenser maximum cooling capacity is the common constraint dictated by the cooling water conditions. In previous studies, most distillation columns are in fixed pressure operation. However, floating pressure control is advantageous in many processes according to Hoffman et al. (2006). Since analyzers are now substituting temperature-based controls, fixed pressure operation argument is also becoming less. One of the major advantages of floating pressure control is the capability of operation at minimum column pressure within system constraints. We know that at low pressure, volatility is improved which entails reduction of heat input and energy to achieve separation. Moreover, if we can operate at the lowest possible pressure, there will be increased reboiler capacity and reboiler fouling can be prevented.

According to Mauricio-Iglesias et.al. (2014), information available in the open literature on pressure control design is scarce and sometimes contradictory. Most distillation systems are at fixed pressure to minimize the compensation of temperature control preventing column flood and weep, optimization of column capacity and operation stability. On the other hand, dynamic pressure control is very advantageous in terms of energy reduction.

2.3 Research Motivation

Floating pressure control has never been employed in vapor recompression distillation. To get minimum energy consumption, it is desired to operate at lowest pressure possible. This FPC shall integrate all quality, inventory and pressure controls such that pressure is optimized, energy is minimized, and purity requirements are satisfied. Along with this is inclusion of performance curve to compressor during simulation which had never been done in recent studies. This paper shall present a control study.

3. Methods of Study

3.1 Process flow diagram

Process flow diagram of this study is shown in Figure 1. Two columns represent just one very high column with 214 stages in the actual scenario. The Aspen Plus steady state file is exported to Aspen Plus Dynamics as a pressure-driven simulation after all required parameters are specified. Conventional PI controllers are used for all controllers except the liquid level controllers which are proportional controllers.

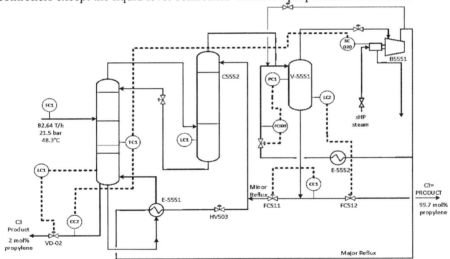

Figure 1. Process flow diagram.

In this study, we employed two kinds of control: inventory control (PC_1, FC_1, LC_1, and LC_2) and quality control (CC_1 and CC_2). Remaining degree of freedom shall be the HV503 valve opening which affects both reflux rate and compressor energy consumption. The features of the loops are outlined as follows: (1) The feed rate is flow-controlled via FC1 (reverse-acting); (2) The pressure in the column is controlled (direct-acting) through FC509 valve at the trim condenser outlet via PC1; (3) The bottom composition control CC2 is cascaded to TC1 column temperature control, output of which dictates the shaft speed of compressor B5551; (4) The top composition is controlled (reverse-acting) through FC511 valve of the minor reflux stream via CC1; (5) Level of column is controlled (direct-acting) through bottom product valve VD-02 via LC1; (6) Level of vessel is controlled (direct-acting) through top product valve FC512 via LC2.

4. Results and Discussion

In this section, we will examine the effects of reducing pressure to compressor power, speed, top and bottom purity, suction flow, pressure ratio, operating point in the anti-surge curve, operating point in the dew point curve of the condenser-reboiler hot stream exit, and the column top and bottom pressure and temperature profiles. Aspen dynamic simulation is used to produce results. Reflux flow rate has a huge effect on both product purity and compressor energy consumption. In this section, it is desired to observe the effects of HV503 reflux valve opening to steam economy. Results show that a certain reflux valve opening will give an operation at which the steam consumption per ton feed is minimized.

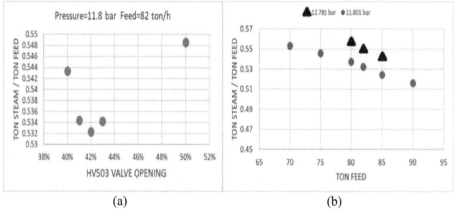

(a)   (b)

Figure 2. (a) Optimum energy consumption as function of HV503 valve opening, (b) Optimum energy consumption at different feed mass-column pressure case.

Figure 2a shows that at a certain feed mass rate and column top pressure, the optimum HV503 opening is 42 %. To verify results, we checked different cases of ton feed rates and pressure and find minimum steam consumption at each case. Moreover, we tried to check the behavior for both high pressure (12.781 bar) and low pressure (11.801 bar). At a specific pressure, if feed rate is changed to 80, 82.6, 85, and 87 tons per hour, there exists an optimum HV504 opening % (which is around 42 to 43 %). The optimum ton steam/ton feed results in every case are shown above. This figure shows that with different feed flow rates and column top pressure fixed, we can obtain a trend line of optimum energy consumption for both high pressure and low pressure. Therefore, our floating pressure control shall operate the reflux valve HV503 at this optimum opening.

We can see from Figure 4a that transition from high to low pressure is in the safe region of the anti-surge curve. Also, HV503 adjustment gears the operating point to the left slightly nearer the anti-surge curve making it more ideal for operation. This proves that the reflux valve opening should be in optimum position to minimize energy consumption while operating as close as possible to anti-surge line. The compressed overhead vapor entering the reboiler-condenser should not be substantially subcooled so that it can be ensured that the heat exchanger will not suffer vibration. This monitor can be traced by observing the operation against the dew point curve of the fluid as shown in Figure 4b. Proposed strategy did not cause pulling away of the operating point from the dew point curve so this process is operated within a safe operation for the heat exchanger.

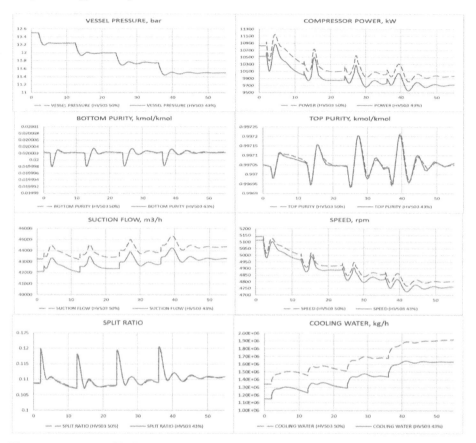

Figure 3. System profile for HV503 opening of 50 % (broken lines) and 43 % (solid lines)

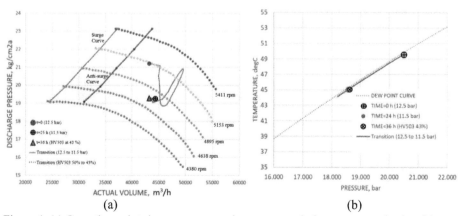

(a)   (b)

Figure 4. (a) Operating points in compressor anti-surge curve during pressure reduction (b)
Operating points in reboiler-condenser dew point curve during pressure reduction

5. Conclusion

In this study, we provided a steady state simulation of propane-propylene splitter system employing vapor recompression distillation. With a feed mass rate of 82.64 ton/h composed of propane and propylene, it is desired to obtain a top distillate product of at least 99.7 mol % propylene and a bottoms product of at most 2 mol % propylene. All equipment are sized using Aspen plus software. Performance curve of the compressor is employed. The converged steady state simulation is translated to dynamic simulation in a pressure-driven mode. The control system includes inventory control and quality control. The remaining degree of freedom, which is the HV503 opening, is examined. It is found that there must be a desirable opening at which optimum conditions will be achieved such as minimized energy consumption and nearness of operation to compressor anti-surge curve and heat exchanger dew point curve.

In the future work, it is intended to make a control study considering preceding results of how floating pressure control can be employed in a vapor recompression distillation process. This includes determination of the pressure limit constrained by the cooling capacity of the trim condenser. The automatic control system shall encompass all inventory and quality control. Observation of operation behavior in the compressor performance curve shall be implemented. To our knowledge, this is the first time a control study like this will be done in literature.

A double compressor scheme given by Annakou and Mizsey (1995) may allow the compressor worked at even smaller pressure. Its performance will be compared with our study's results in the future.

References

O. Annakou, P. Mizsey, 1995, Rigorous investigation of heat pump assisted distillation, Heat Recovery Systems and CHP, 15, 241-247.

A. Choudhari, J. Divey, 2012, Distillation optimization by vapor recompression, Chemical Engineering, 119(3), 43-47.

C.C.E. Christopher, A. Dutta, S. Farooq, I.A. Karimi, 2017, Process synthesis and optimization of propylene/propane separation using vapor recompression and self-heat recuperation, Industrial and Engineering Chemistry Research, 56(49), 14557-14564.

H.L. Hoffman, D.E. Lupfer, L.A. Kane, B.A. Jensen, B.G. Liptak, 2006, Control and Optimization of Unit Operations, Distillation: Basic Controls, Taylor and Francis.

S.S. Jogwar, P. Daoutidis, 2009, Vapor recompression distillation: Multi-scale dynamics and control, American Control Conference, IEEE, 647-652.

Y. Ma, Y. Luo, X. Yuan, 2019, Towards the really optimal design of distillation systems: Simultaneous pressure optimization of distillation systems based on rigorous models, Computers and Chemical Egnineering, 126, 54-67.

M. Mauricio-Iglesias, T. Bisgaard, H. Kristensen, K.V. Gernaey, J. Abildskov, J.K. Huusom, 2014, Pressure control in distillation columns: a model-based analysis, Industrial and Engineering Chemistry Research, 53(38), 14776-14787.

W.L. Luyben, 2013, Distillation design and control using Aspen simulation, John Wiley and Sons.

Sauro Pierucci, Flavio Manenti, Giulia Bozzano, Davide Manca (Eds.)
Proceedings of the 30th European Symposium on Computer Aided Process Engineering
(ESCAPE30), May 24-27, 2020, Milano, Italy. © 2020 Elsevier B.V. All rights reserved.
http://dx.doi.org/10.1016/B978-0-12-823377-1.50221-4

Modern Process Monitoring and Optimization Methods Integrating a Process Simulator into a Distributed Control System

Corinna Busse,[a] Ewa Bozek,[a] Bernd-Markus Pfeiffer,[a] Sreekumar Maroor,[b] Mathias Oppelt[a]

[a] *Siemens AG, Werner-von-Siemens- Str. 60, Erlangen 91052, Germany*
[b] *PSE – A Siemens business, 26-28 Hammersmith Grove, London W6 7HA, UK*
corinna.busse@siemens.com

Abstract

On the one hand, process simulation has become an inherent part of design, engineering and operation of chemical production plants. On the other hand, process industry is moving to highly automated plants, with a distributed control system (DCS) at the core of these facilities. Considering both trends the integration of a process model into a DCS is the consecutive next step, which enables the online use of process models during plant operation. The details of technical integration as well as specific use cases such as soft-sensors and real-time optimization will be presented in this contribution. As introduction, a brief review of applications of simulation along the life-cycle of a process plant is given, leading to a vision for a digital twin concept.

Keywords: digital twin, dynamic process modelling, soft sensor, real-time optimization

1. Introduction

As part of progressing digitalization in process industry, the term "digital twin" is an increasingly popular expression. Although various definitions of this term exist, a common understanding is that a digital twin is a digital counterpart of a physical object. (Kritzinger, et al., 2018) state that within the existing definitions, the expressions such as digital model, digital shadow and digital twin are often used synonymously, although the level of data integration differs for these terms. The authors suggest a classification into three subcategories depending on the level of data integration: a digital model does not use any form of automated data exchange, whereas a digital shadow incorporates an automated data exchange from the physical to the digital world and a digital twin offers a bidirectional automated data flow between real and virtual environment.

Furthermore, there exist various types of digital twins addressing different aspects of a chemical production plant e.g. assets, the product itself, the automation system or the overall production. (Pfeiffer, et al., 2019) described a concept for a digital twin of a process plant as a consistent framework which evolves along the plant life-cycle and contains a representation of the product, assets and the performance of process and product. The new perspectives in this framework is opened by the idea to integrate the individual models and simulation tools to a holistic, semantically integrated system, integrated across different hierarchy levels of the plant, and integrated along all phases of plant life-cycle.

Within this contribution a key part of this overall framework is addressed: the digital process twin, which combines a high-fidelity predictive process model with plant data to generate high-value information enabling online decision support for the operators via the distributed control system (DCS) of the plant. Since process modeling is a core aspect of this contribution, a brief review of its application in the plant life-cycle is given first. Subsequently incorporation of process models into a DCS is presented using the example of an ethylene cracking furnace.

2. Process modeling in the life-cycle of a process plant

Within the life-cycle of a chemical production plant, modeling has become an invaluable tool (Oppelt, 2016). A variety of applications for process models exists, while the modeling rigor depends on the designated purpose of the model.

2.1. Design phase

For continuous processes, the development of a steady-state process model during the design phase has become a standard task and is mandatory for hand-over to engineering phase. These steady-state models are used for conceptual process and equipment design (e.g. column equipment), the generation of a heat and mass balance and detailed simulation e.g. including reaction kinetics. A workflow for developing and validating a high-fidelity predictive model of a catalytic reactor in the design phase is given by (Spatenka, et al., 2019). The authors demonstrate how this model can be used to explore many aspects of the decision space for both design and operation, leading to a more comprehensive workflow than experimentation alone.

2.2. Engineering and commissioning phase

The developed steady-state model can also be used for the development of the overall control scheme and to determine optimal set-points. Transferring this model into a dynamic simulation enables open-loop and closed-loop step tests as well as controller tuning. Furthermore, operability analysis like scenario simulation including start-up and shutdown, or early detection of operational challenges is possible with a dynamic process model.

Simulation can also be used for the validation and testing of an automation system, which is a demanding task, usually executed under very tight schedules. Therefore, the use of simulations to check-out the automation system earlier in the engineering phase can be very beneficial (Oppelt, et al., 2014). Another application of simulation are operator training systems. Based on a detailed process model created in the design and extended in the engineering phase, plant operators can be trained for their job, even before the real plant is up and running.

2.3. Operation phase

During plant operation the application of models can be distinguished between off- and online use. Offline applications can include operational optimization, troubleshooting and debottlenecking. As stated by (Spatenka, et al., 2019) significant additional benefit can be achieved if the model is used to provide day-to-day economic performance improvements online, executing within or in conjunction with the plant automation system. These online applications range from plant monitoring and forecasting to open-loop decision support and closed-loop control (Pantelides & Renfro, 2013).

2.4. Challenges for the application of process modeling along the plant life-cycle

The status quo for most chemical companies and EPCs is that all modeling activities typically start from scratch and the re-use of process models is not yet established (Oppelt, 2016). The only fully-established modeling activity occurs in the initial design phase of a new production facility. Challenges for the uniform application of process models along the whole life-cycle are for instance the higher engineering effort to create a dynamic process model, the divergent development of the real-world process plant from the initial design due to revamps, and changing plant performance due to long-term degradation processes (e.g. catalyst deactivation, fouling, coke formation).

A conceptual workflow to overcome some of these challenges is described by (Labisch, et al., 2019). Here the initial steady-state process model is connected to a data-based plant design tool, where the P&IDs are developed and transferred back to a process simulator to create a dynamic process model. This model can be used in closed-loop form for conceptual control design and as open-loop version for online applications during operation. This concept of a digital twin would ensure consistency between the simulation and planning tool and would reduce the effort to create a process model, since model development would not start from scratch anymore. The challenge of long-term degradation processes effecting the predictive capability of an offline process model can be overcome by the transformation of a digital process model into a digital process twin, which will be explained in the next section using the example of steam cracking furnace in an ethylene plant.

3. Use case: Ethylene production through steam cracking

3.1. Challenges during operation

Thermal cracking of hydrocarbons is still the major process to produce the key intermediate product ethylene in the petrochemicals value chain. Due to the large-scale production capacity of this process, small improvements in efficiency can already yield significant annual savings. The steam cracking furnace is the heart of the ethylene production process and its optimal operation is key to maximizing profitability. Coke buildup within the furnace coils leads to higher pressure drop and lower residence time, thereby affecting the conversion and product yields. It also increases the tube metal temperature and reduces the heat transfer efficiency resulting in higher energy costs. Once the state of coking reaches to a certain limit, the furnace needs to be taken offline for decoking.

Feedstock availability and prices change with time and it hence it is necessary to operate the steam cracking furnaces in the ethylene plant at optimal conversions to maximize profitability and to ensure operation within the plant constraints. Hence reliable information of conversion, product yields and state of coking is key to ensuring optimal operation of the steam cracking furnace. However, measuring conversion and product yields accurately and reliably using gas analyzers is often a challenge due to the process conditions at the point of measurement. Analyzers used to measure composition at the outlet of the furnace are subject to fouling and tend to fail often, making frequent maintenance and calibration necessary. Information on current state of coking and coking rates are useful for better planning of de-coke schedules. However, these are not directly measurable and thus need to be indirectly inferred from the operating data from the furnace.

Due to the economic relevance and the complexity of the aforementioned challenges, academia (Savu, et al., 2010) as well as industry (Goethem, et al., 2001) have addressed this issue over the past. In this contribution a solution is presented which demonstrates and evaluates the combination of a rigorous process model of a steam cracking furnace with the distributed control system.

3.2. Modern process monitoring and optimization methods to overcome these challenges

As discussed by (Pantelides & Renfro, 2013) the online use of first-principle models offers a broad range of possibilities to support operators regarding day-to-day decisions.

The realized infrastructure for combining a rigorous process model with the plant automation is given in Figure 1.

The core element of this infrastructure is a process master model, which is coupled to regularly-updated plant data to enable real-time calibration of the model. Based on this digital model, several model-based applications like e.g. soft-sensing, run length prediction and real-time optimization can be realized.

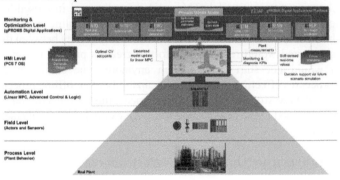

Figure 1: Realized infrastructure to combine a rigorous process model (process master model) with the plant automation system to enable several model-based online applications.

3.2.1. Process master model

As discussed by (Pantelides & Renfro, 2013) one major challenge for the online deployment of process models is to find the best trade-off between modeling rigor and life-cycle sustainability of the online solution. Due to complexity increasing with model rigor, the maintenance of the online solution becomes also more difficult. Therefore, a model which is "fit-for-purpose" should be developed or adjusted from previously developed models. Another requirement for the model is that it is robust and fast solving. The first-principle model used in this contribution was previously described by (Spatenka, et al., 2017). It includes a mass and energy balance as well as kinetics of cracking and coking. A grey-box (or hybrid) modeling approach, which combines rigorous and data-driven model, for this application is currently evaluated by *PSE* within the CoPro project (Nauta, 2019).

The model was developed within the gPROMS ProcessBuilder environment, which offers custom modeling capabilities as well as powerful optimization technology, using an equation-oriented approach. The steam cracking furnace is the core unit of the ethylene production process and is therefore discussed here in more detail. The hydrocarbon feedstock (e.g. ethane) and steam are fed to the convection section of the steam cracking furnace where they are first pre-heated before entering the radiant coils where thermal cracking of the hydrocarbon takes place. The heat input necessary for the cracking is provided by burning fuel gas in the firebox of the furnace. The cracked gas from the radiant coil is subsequently quenched in transfer line exchanges (TLEs) to prevent undesired side reactions.

The olefins model libraries in gPROMS ProcessBuilder allow detailed representation of steam cracking furnaces and support all standard radiant coil configurations. They also provide a framework and workflow for incorporating proprietary knowledge such as custom coil configurations, cracking and coking kinetic models etc. The libraries include cracking kinetic models adopted from literature as well as coking kinetic models to represent the coke build up in the coils. The parameters associated with the cracking and coking kinetic models can be tuned to laboratory or plant data.

3.2.2. Long term monitoring

Plant data (historical and current) is used in conjunction with the described model to track coke build-up in the furnace. The online calibration of this model is a core element of the demonstrated architecture, since it is a crucial input for all other online applications. The current coking state of the furnace is determined by periodically tuning the model using plant data from start of the run until the current time.

3.2.3. Soft sensor

As described in section 3.1, obtaining accurate and reliable measurements of KPIs such as conversion and product yields through direct measurement challenging. The soft sensor application makes use of the up-to-date coke profile and coking kinetics information from the long-term monitoring activity above and provides accurate and real-time estimates of KPIs such as conversion, product yields, coking rates etc. This application runs 24/7 on plant computers and it can be closely coupled to the plant automation systems. The soft sensed KPIs can be displayed as "normal" process variable in the operator station (OS). Therefore, the soft-sensor variables can be directly used as controlled variables for process automation, providing key new information that can be used to implement for improved conversion control.

3.3. Run length prediction

Optimal de-coke planning and scheduling is key to maintain furnace availability and to maximize production. The up-to-date coking information from the long-term monitoring activity above can be used to determine the remaining length of run for each individual furnace in the plant, depending on one or more specified operation scenarios. This information helps in deciding consequences of different operational choices on run length and it can help in better planning and scheduling of decoke operation.

This "what-if" simulation of future operation can be started and adjusted directly from the OS of the DCS, which is offering a common user interface for the operators and therefore could increase acceptance. The results of the simulation are displayed in the OS as well and plant operation can directly be adjusted based on the simulation study.

3.4. Linear model generation for model predictive control (MPC)

Since the conversion and yield is affected by several factors (feed composition, hydrocarbon-to-steam ratio, cracking temperature and furnace residence time) the implementation of a model predictive controller (MPC) is promising to improve operation. The rigorous model can once again be used to derive a linear model which is needed for the MPC. The realization is explained in more detail by (Pfeiffer, et al., 2019).

3.5. Real-time optimization (RTO)

Optimizing the economic performance of a process plant is one of the ultimate goals for operation. The up-to-date plant model together with the current market situation (e.g. feedstock availability, product demand, prices) can be used to determine optimal setpoints for key operational decision variables such as allocation of fresh feed and recycles to the furnaces, and operating conditions for each furnace to maximize economic performance.

The optimization can be started from the operator stations of the DCS and the operator can decide whether the optimized process variables are acceptable. The transition from one steady-state to the other is done by the sub-ordinated control structures by writing the setpoint combinations to the MPC.

3.6. System architecture

The system architecture to realize the described online applications based on a rigorous process model is as follows: real-time input variables for the model-based applications e.g. flow rates, compositions, temperatures, stem positions etc. are transferred via OPC-UA from the DCS or historian (OPC-UA server) to the application (OPC-UA client). The calculated outputs from the different applications such as soft sensed KPIs, optimal conversion set points for each furnace etc. are sent back to the DCS via OPC-UA. Through the DCS these process variables are used for monitoring and control.

4. Conclusion

The incorporation of a process model into a plant automation system offers a broad range of opportunities for decision support of operators. Using the steam cracker of an ethylene production as example, several online applications of the process model are demonstrated, such as soft sensing, run length prediction and real-time optimization. The integration of first-principles models into the DCS offers several advantages like improved acceptance of operators for advanced solutions and use of calculated process variables as "normal" controlled variables for feedback control, interlocks, recipe control or alarming. Please note that the purpose of these online applications is to support the operator and not to replace him or her. The typical focus is optimization, not moving towards autonomous plant operation. Sustainable implementation of such online solutions can be supported by an integrated engineering approach to keep manual maintenance activities as infrequent as possible.

References

Goethem, M., Kleinendorst, F., Leeuwen, C. & Velzen, N., 2001. Equation-based SPYRO (R) model and solver for the simulation of the steam cracking process. *Computers & Chemical Engineering,* 5, Band 25, pp. 905-911.

Hall, S. & Matzopoulos, M., 2018. *Using digital process twin technology to drive Operational Excellence,* s.l.: s.n.

Kritzinger, W. et al., 2018. Digital Twin in manufacturing: A categorical literature review and classification. *IFAC-PapersOnLine,* 1, Band 51, pp. 1016-1022.

Labisch, D. et al., 2019. Evolution eines Digital Twin am Beispiel einer Ethylen-Anlage - Konzept und Umsetzung. *atp magazin,* 6, Band 2019, pp. 70-85.

Nauta, M., 2019. *D1.1 Efficient construction of efficient models,* s.l.: s.n.

Oppelt, M., 2016. *Towards an integrated use of simulation within the life-cycle of a process plant,* s.l.: s.n.

Oppelt, M. et al., 2014. *Automatische Generierung von Simulationsmodellen für die virtuelle Inbetriebnahme auf Basis von Planungsdaten. Vorstellung eines generischen Konzepts und einer prototypischen Implementierung..* s.l., s.n.

Pantelides, C. & Renfro, J., 2013. The online use of first-principles models in process operations: Review, current status and future needs. *Computers & Chemical Engineering,* 4, Band 51, p. 136–148.

Pfeiffer, B.-M., Oppelt, M. & Leingang, C., 2019. *Evolution of a Digital Twin for a Steam Cracker.* s.l., s.n., pp. 467-474.

Savu, A. V., Lazea, G. & Agachi, P.-Ș., 2010. Optimization and advanced control for thermal cracking processes. *Computers & Chemical Engineering.*

SIMATIC PCS 7, V., 2018. *PCS 7 Unit Template "Stirred tank reactor with Kalman filter" using the example of the Chemical Industry,* s.l.: s.n.

Spatenka, S. et al., 2017. Model-Based Real-Time Monitoring of Ethylene Cracking Furnaces. *2017 Spring Meeting and 13th Global Congress on Process Safety.*

Spatenka, S., Matzopoulos, M., Urban, Z. & Cano, A., 2019. From Laboratory to Industrial Operation: Model-Based Digital Design and Optimization of Fixed-Bed Catalytic Reactors. *Industrial & Engineering Chemistry Research,* 6.Band 58.

Sundaram, K. & Froment, G. F., 1977. Modeling of thermal cracking kinetics—I. *Chemical Engineering Science,* 12, Band 32, p. 609–617.

Sauro Pierucci, Flavio Manenti, Giulia Bozzano, Davide Manca (Eds.)
Proceedings of the 30th European Symposium on Computer Aided Process Engineering
(ESCAPE30), May 24-27, 2020, Milano, Italy. © 2020 Elsevier B.V. All rights reserved.
http://dx.doi.org/10.1016/B978-0-12-823377-1.50222-6

A European Optimisation Tool for Carbon Capture and Storage, Accounting for Delays in Public Procurement

Federico d'Amore, Leonardo Lovisotto, Fabrizio Bezzo

CAPE-Lab – Computer-Aided Process Engineering Laboratory, Department of Industrial Engineering, University of Padova, via Marzolo 9, 35131 Padova PD (Italy).
fabrizio.bezzo@unipd.it

Abstract

The global anthropogenic generation of greenhouse gasses experienced an exponential increase compared to pre-industrial levels and, among these, CO_2 is the most abundant, with an emission that rose globally from 2 Gt/year in 1850 to over 35 Gt/year in 2010. Carbon capture and storage has been highlighted among the most promising options to decarbonise the energy sector, especially considering the European context which heavily relies on fossil fuels. When dealing with the strategic design and planning of an international carbon capture and storage infrastructure, the necessity of taking into account the differential behaviour among the European countries in terms of public procurement and assignation delays emerges as a key requirement for attaining an effective implementation of the network. This contribution proposes a mixed integer linear programming modelling framework for the economic optimisation of a multinational European carbon capture and storage supply chain, including the effects of countrywide delays in public procurement. Assignation lags are implemented as an additional cost for the installation of the network. Results show that only minor modifications in the supply chain design should be taken into account with respect to an equivalent non-delayed scenario, with a consequent just moderate increase in transport costs (+3 %). Moreover, it is shown that capture and sequestration stages are barely not affected by the introduction of assignation lags among countries.

Keywords: carbon capture and storage, mixed integer linear programming, supply chain optimisation, delay in public procurement.

1. Introduction

In the last 50 years, CO_2 constituted nearly the 80 % of overall anthropogenic greenhouse gases (GHGs) emissions thus, global actions are needed to tackle the increase of carbon concentration in the atmosphere (IPCC, 2018). Carbon capture and storage (CCS) has emerged among the most promising options, considering its capability at directly decarbonising the energy generation and industry without necessitating a complete rethinking of these sectors (IPCC, 2005). However, in order to attain major environmental benefits, CCS has to be done at scale and across many borders (Bui et al., 2018). To this purpose, mixed integer linear programming (MILP) has often been employed as an effective modelling approach for the optimisation of large-scale networks (Heuberger et al., 2018). For instance, Han and Lee (2012) optimised a CCS supply chain (SC) for North Korea under uncertainty in market prices, Hasan et al. (2015) developed a tool for the optimal design of a CCS system in the United States, while d'Amore and Bezzo (2017) minimised the costs of a European CCS network, also considering social acceptance and risk perception (d'Amore and Bezzo, 2020).

However, one aspect, which typically is not considered in the optimisation of CCS supply chain, is the impact of delays in the public procurement on the overall costs. Public procurement is governments' most commonly employed methodology to assign the construction of an infrastructure to a private company (EC, 2011). The European Commission (EC) keeps track of all the assigned procurements by including them in the Tenders Electronic Daily (TED) dataset and measures the efficiency in procurement timing and cost over the years through different indicators. Among these indicators, the national assignation lag is the most commonly employed to quantify the procurement performance of each European country (EC, 2018). As a matter of facts, a positive assignation lag generates a procurement delay, defined as the overall time for the assignation procedure, which varies in Europe form a minimum of 90 days in Poland to a maximum of 278 days in Greece (EC, 2011). Considering a large-scale international CCS SC, discrepancies in assignation lags may generate differential procurement delays among the European countries.

This contribution proposes a MILP modelling framework for the economic optimisation of a time-dependent, spatially-explicit, multi-echelon European CCS SC, including the effects of delays in public procurement across different countries. In particular, delays in projects assignations are here formulated as an additional cost for the construction of the infrastructure. Only sequestration basins and pipeline networks will be affected by the additional cost, whereas capture facilities will not be included in the delayed-affected formulation, as these are assumed to be placed in existing industrial area, and their project is likely to be only marginally affected by public procurement delays.

2. Material and methods

A multi-echelon, spatially-explicit, time-dependent, MILP model for the economic optimisation of a European CCS SC is presented, with the aim of providing a financial tool that evaluates the additional cost due to delays in countrywide public procurement. In particular, the model provides an optimal European CCS infrastructure (in terms of selection, positioning, and operation of capture nodes, transport routes and sequestration sinks), whilst considering the differential behaviour and characteristics among European countries in terms of infrastructural assignation lags.

The spatial framework is geographically described through a grid of 134 squared cells g, whose size ranges from 123 km to 224 km. This discretisation includes the European continent, few regions of North Africa and some offshore regions in the North Sea, where offshore sequestration basins are located and may be exploited (along with onshore storage options). Data and location of emission sources of CO_2 are obtained from the Emission Database for Global Atmospheric Research (EDGAR) published by Joint Research Centre (JRC, 2016). In particular, only large stationary emission sources (i.e., emitting more than 10^6 t of CO_2/year, corresponding to 37 % of overall European CO_2 emissions) are considered, and include coal- and gas-fired power plants. These emissions can be captured according to a set of technologies k including post-combustion from either coal or gas power plants, oxy-fuel combustion applied to coal power plants, and pre-combustion capture applied to gas power plants. CO_2 flowrates can be transported from region g to region g' by mean of either onshore or offshore pipelines l, towards sequestration in geological basins. The techno-economic characterisation (i.e., costs, efficiencies, feasibility) of capture and transport options is given in d'Amore and Bezzo (2017), while data on the type, location and capacity of the most promising formations for CO_2 storage (i.e., deep saline aquifers, hydrocarbon and coal fields) is obtained from the EU GeoCapacity Project (2009).

The delay in the assignation of projects is here interpreted as an additional cost for the construction of the CCS system. Accordingly, the total cost of the European CCS SC is here revised with respect to d'Amore and Bezzo (2017) in order to include the additional cost generated by a delayed investment, which penalises the installation of the SC nodes and arcs in regions with high assignation lags. In particular, assignation lags generating procurement delays D_g [days] in region g within country c are evaluated from the countrywide lags producing delays D_c [days] according to data provided by the EC (EC, 2011).

Overall, given: the size and location of European large stationary sources of CO_2, the techno-economic characteristics of capture and transport options, the feasible transport links, the capacity and location of geological basins suitable for sequestration, the total European carbon reduction target to be pursued, and the countrywide characteristics in terms of procurement lag; the model is capable at providing: the optimal scale and location of the infrastructural nodes (capture and sequestration) and arcs (transport) according to the additional costs due to national delays.

3. Mathematical formulation

The objective is the minimisation of total cost TC [€] to install and operate the network, given by the sum of capture (TCC [€]), transport (TTC [€]) and sequestration (TSC [€]) costs, including the effect of delays in public procurement:

$$TC = TCC + TTC + TSC \tag{1}$$

On the one hand, the cost for capture TCC of Eq. (1) is calculated from the unitary capture cost UCC_k [€/t] and the captured amount $C_{k,g,t}$ [t] through technology k:

$$TCC = \sum_{k,g,t} (UCC_k \cdot C_{k,g,t}) \tag{2}$$

where costs and flowrates calculations are described in d'Amore and Bezzo (2017) according to the equations reported in the capture problem model. On the other hand, the cost of transport TTC and sequestration TSC of Eq. (1) are evaluated through the transport problem model and the sequestration problem model, respectively. In particular, TTC and TSC include the additional costs due to delays in public procurement. The transport cost TTC is given by two contributions, i.e. the inter-connection cost TTC_t^{inter} [€] and the intra-connection cost TTC_t^{intra} [€]:

$$TTC = \sum_t (TTC_t^{inter} + TTC_t^{intra}) \tag{3}$$

The term TTC_t^{inter} of Eq. (3) accounts for yearly pipelining cost between region g and g' according to the transport size Q_p [t/year] and length $LD_{g,g'}$ [km] as described in d'Amore and Bezzo (2017):

$$TTC_t^{inter} = \sum_{p,g,l,g'} \left[\lambda_{p,g,l,g',t} \cdot UTC_{p,l} \cdot Q_p \cdot LD_{g,g'} \cdot \tau_g \cdot \left(1 + \overline{AC}_{g,g'}\right) \right] \quad \forall t \tag{4}$$

where $UTC_{p,l}$ [€/t/km] (i.e., unitary transport cost) and τ_g (i.e., regional tourtuosity factor) are taken from d'Amore and Bezzo (2017), while $\lambda_{p,g,l,g',t}$ is a binary planning variable representing whether an infrastructure of size p is installed and operated between regions g and g' through a transport mean l at time period t, or not. Besides, $\overline{AC}_{g,g'}$ of Eq. (4) represents the average additional cost due to procurement delays between region g and g'. The term TTC_t^{intra} of Eq. (3) describes the yearly short-distance transport cost within region g according to the flowrate of CO_2 captured $C_{k,g,t}$ [t] through technology k in region g at time period t and the size LD_g [km] of cell g:

$$TTC_t^{intra} = \sum_{k,g} \left[C_{k,g,t} \cdot \overline{UTC} \cdot LD_g \cdot \tau_g \cdot \left(1 + AC_g\right)\right] \qquad \forall t \qquad (5)$$

where $\overline{UTC}$ [€/t/km] (i.e., average unitary transport cost) is taken from d'Amore and Bezzo (2017), while AC_g represents the additional cost due to a procurement delay occurring in region g. The sequestration cost TSC of Eq. (1) is proportional to the number of injection wells $N_{g,t}$ that need to be installed and operated in region g at time period t:

$$TSC_t = \sum_g \left[N_{g,t} \cdot USC_g \cdot \left(1 + AC_g\right)\right] \qquad \forall t \qquad (6)$$

where USC_g [€/well] is the unitary sequestration cost (d'Amore and Bezzo, 2017). The additional cost AC_g assigned to the construction of either a pipeline through Eqs. (4,5) or sequestration basin through Eq. (6) depends on the annual interest rate IR and the public procurement delay D_g for the assignation of a project of region g:

$$AC_g = IR \cdot D_g \qquad \forall g \qquad (7)$$

In particular, IR is set equal to 10 % in analogy with the typical values employed for industrial projects in the oil and gas sector (Lise et al., 2008), whereas D_g is retrieved from data provided by the EC (EC, 2011) (Table 1).

Table 1. Time delay for public procurement D_c [days] in country c (EC, 2011). Regional delays D_g [days] have the same value in cells g belonging to country c.

C	D_c	c	D_c	c	D_c
Poland	90	Norway	123	Belgium	166
Hungary	92	Netherlands	130	Ireland	170
Latvia	93	Average	133	Bulgaria	171
Romania	104	France	133	Italy	174
Lithuania	112	Spain	134	Portugal	184
Slovakia	119	Czech Rep.	135	United Kin.	193
Sweden	120	Denmark	139	Greece	278
Germany	121	Austria	145		
Estonia	122	Finland	160		

4. Results and discussion

The model was implemented in GAMS software and optimised through CPLEX solver on a 2.60 GHz (32 GB RAM) computer in less than 1 hour. Two scenarios have been investigated: Scenario 0 optimised the CCS SC in absence of delay in public procurement and constitutes a reference case to compare the results from Scenario A, in which conversely assignation lags were taken into account as described before.

Table 2. Scenarios 0-A. Total cost *TC* [G€, €/t], capture cost *TCC* [G€, €/t], transport cost *TTC* [G €, €/t], and sequestration cost *TSC* [G€, €/t]. Specific values refer to a t of geologically sequestered CO2.

Scen.	TC		TCC		TTC		TSC	
	[G€]	[€/t]	[G€]	[€/t]	[G€]	[€/t]	[G€]	[€/t]
0	462.8	38.19	433.1	35.75	26.2	2.16	3.4	0.28
A	463.8	38.27	433.4	35.76	27.0	2.23	3.4	0.28

The economic results depict an almost identical situation between the optimised scenarios (Table 2). That for transport *TTC* is the only cost component to be affected by delays in public procurement, since it raises from 26.2 G€ (i.e., 2.16 €/t) in Scenario 0 to 27.0 G€ (i.e., 2.23 €/t) in Scenario A, with an increase of +3.05 %. Besides, capture cost *TCC* (at most slightly higher than 433.1 G€, i.e. 35.8 €/t) and sequestration cost *TSC* (almost steadily equal to 3.4 G€, i.e. 0.28 €/t) are barely not affected by assignation lags. Furthermore, a sensitivity analysis on *IR* was performed in order to test the model response to the chosen level of interest rate attributed to the additional cost of procurement delay. As a result, even when imposing *IR* = 20 %, *TTC* exhibits a moderate increase until 28.1 G€ (i.e., 2.32 €/t, corresponding to +7.25 % with respect to Scenario 0), whereas the growth of *TSC* is still as marginal as it is in Scenario A (+0.37 % with respect to Scenario 0).

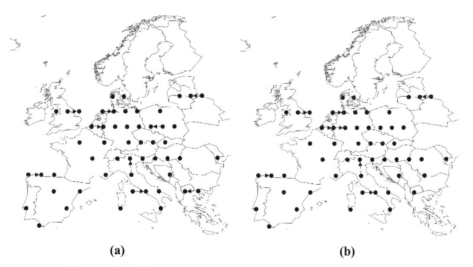

(a)   (b)

Figure 1. Final SC configuration for Scenario 0 (a) and Scenario A (b).

The slight costs differences between Scenario 0 and Scenario A are a consequence of the minor design modifications in the resulting SC configurations. Differently from Scenario 0 (Figure 1a), Scenario A (Figure 1b) limits (e.g., in the case of Bulgaria) or totally avoids (e.g., in the case of Greece) the installation of transport and sequestration infrastructures in those countries characterised by particularly large assignation lags. Apart from this, the main driver for the installation and operation of the CCS network is still constituted by capture costs, which are here assumed to neglect the effects of public procurement given the installation of this SC stage onto already existing power plants. Accordingly, the model solution exploits almost the same capture nodes in both Scenario 0 and Scenario A thus, the final configurations are almost identical.

5. Conclusions

This contribution presented a mixed integer linear programming modelling framework for the strategic optimisation of a European carbon capture and storage supply chain, considering the effects of delays in public procurement among European countries. In particular, countrywide assignation lags were interpreted as an additional expenditure for the installation of the transport and sequestration infrastructures. As a result, only minor design modifications were found between the delayed and non-delayed supply chains, which reflected in a just slight increase in transport costs in the case of the network optimised while taking into account the effects of public procurement. Countrywide delays in public procurement should not constitute an obstacle towards the installation of a European carbon capture and storage network.

On the flip side, the effects of delays in public procurement may affect further aspects beyond the mere increase in investment costs, e.g. difficulties for companies in properly scheduling and planning building works, a growth in uncertainty in the effectiveness of implementation of the overall system, difficulties among stakeholders in terms of transnational cooperation. These issues were not discussed in this contribution and might represent future perspectives to improve the formulation presented in this work.

References

M. Bui, C.S. Adjiman, A. Bardow, E.J. Anthony, A. Boston, et al., 2018, Carbon capture and storage (CCS): The way forward, Energy Environ. Sci., 11, 1062-1176.

F. d'Amore, F. Bezzo, 2017, Economic optimisation of European supply chains for CO_2 capture, transport and sequestration, Int. J. Greenh. Gas Control, 65, 99-116.

F. d'Amore, L. Lovisotto, F. Bezzo, 2020, Introducing social acceptance into the design of CCS supply chains: a case study at a European level, J. Clean. Prod, https://doi.org/10.1016/j.jclepro.2019.119337

EC, 2011, Public procurement in Europe Cost and effectiveness Annex: Detailed methodology and data.

EC, 2018, Single Market Scoreboard, Public Procurement.

EU GeoCapacity Project, 2009, Assessing European Capacity for Geological Storage of Carbon Dioxide.

J.H. Han, I.B. Lee, 2012, Multiperiod Stochastic Optimization Model for Carbon Capture and Storage Infrastructure under Uncertainty in CO_2 Emissions, Product Prices, and Operating Costs, Ind. Eng. Chem. Res., 51, 11445-11457.

M.M.F. Hasan, E.L. First, F. Boukouvala, C.A. Floudas, 2015, A multi-scale framework for CO_2 capture, utilization, and sequestration: CCUS and CCU, Comput. Chem. Eng., 81, 2-21.

C.F. Heuberger, I. Staffell, N. Shah, N. Mac Dowell, 2018, Impact of myopic decision-making and disruptive events in power systems planning. Nat. Energy, 3, 634-640.

IPCC, 2005, IPCC Special Report on Carbon Dioxide Capture and Storage. Prepared by Working Group III of the Intergovernmental Panel on Climate Change.

IPCC, 2018, Global warming of 1.5°C. An IPCC special report on the impacts of global warming of 1.5°C above pre-industrial levels and related global greenhouse gas emission pathways, in the context of strengthening the global response to the threat of climate change.

JRC, 2016, Emission Database for Global Atmospheric Research (EDGAR).

W. Lise, B.F. Hobbs, F. van Oostvoorn, 2008, Natural gas corridors between the EU and its main suppliers: Simulation results with the dynamic GASTALE model, Energy Policy, 36, 1890-1906.

Sauro Pierucci, Flavio Manenti, Giulia Bozzano, Davide Manca (Eds.)
Proceedings of the 30th European Symposium on Computer Aided Process Engineering
(ESCAPE30), May 24-27, 2020, Milano, Italy. © 2020 Elsevier B.V. All rights reserved.
http://dx.doi.org/10.1016/B978-0-12-823377-1.50223-8

Wind and Thermal Generation Portfolio: Optimal strategies in Energy-only Pool Markets under Wind Production Uncertainty

Evangelos G. Tsimopoulos, Michael C. Georgiadis[*]

Aristotle University of Thessaloniki, Department of Chemical Engineering, 54124 Thessaloniki, Greece

mgeorg@auth.gr

Abstract

This work considers a power producer with dominant position in electricity market. A bi-level model is constructed to derive optimal offering strategies for this producer. The bi-level model is reformed into a mathematical programming with equilibrium constraints (MPEC) model which is then recast into a mixed integer linear program using strong duality theorem and Karush-Kuhn-Tacker first order optimality conditions. The proposed algorithm results in optimal scheduled thermal and wind energy production as well as reserve deployments for the strategic producer. It also provides endogenous formation of local marginal prices and optimal offers under network constraints and wind generation uncertainty.

Keywords: generation portfolio, MPEC, withholding strategies, LMPs, wind uncertainty.

1. Introduction

This work investigates the capacity withholding strategies for an electricity producer whose generation portfolio consists of thermal and wind power production to avoid profit losses due to high penetration of renewable resources. The assumption is made that this producer (strategic) can exercise market power and can therefore impact the prices in the market (price maker). The producer competes with other non-strategic producers (price takers) in a jointly cleared energy and balancing market. The market is cleared by the independent system operator (ISO) one day in advance and on an hourly basis providing local marginal prices (LMP's) and energy quantities which are bought and sold.

2. Problem Statement

In the above context, a bi-level complementarity model is designed following the Stackelberg hypothesis of the single leader-follower game. The upper level establishes the expected profits optimization of the relevant strategic producer (leader). Conversely, the lower level is representative of the market clearing procedure conducted by the ISO (follower). The aim of the ISO is to determine the dispatch amount of production and consumption maximizing the social welfare, the difference between the total consumption utility bids, and the total production cost offers, or equivalently to minimize the total social cost. The lower-level of the model is constructed in the form of a linearized direct current (DC) network as two-stage stochastic programming. The first stage enables the day-ahead (DA) market and leads to optimization of the anticipated dispatch (DA scheduled energy production) while the DA market clearing prices are received as dual variables. The second stage is representative of the balancing or real-time (RT) market in which the stochastic nature of wind generation is considered through the realization of all the plausible wind power production scenarios (Tsimopoulos and Georgiadis, 2018). The clearing of the balancing market results in balancing dispatch (reserve deployments) and RT market prices.

For the following formulation the indices i and j indicate the conventional units, and the wind farms respectively while the index d indicates the demands of the system. Additionally, the indices b and f refer to power blocks offered by the conventional units i and the wind farms j, the index k refers to power blocks consumed by load d and the index ω refers to wind power production scenarios. The sets I^s and J^s define units and wind farms owned by the strategic producer while the sets I^o and J^o define units and wind farms owed by non-strategic producers. The set I_n^s, I_n^o, J_n^s, J_n^o and D_n map generation units, wind farms and loads onto the system and the set Θ_n defines the connection of the bus n with the other buses of the network. The parameters c_{ib}, c_{jf}^{DA} and u_{dk} represent the marginal cost of offered power blocks of generation units and wind farms, and the marginal utility of load blocks. In addition, the parameters c_i^{up}, c_i^{down} and $c_{j\omega}^{RT}$ indicate the cost of offered regulations and wind power realization at balancing stage. In addition, the parameter B_{nm} denotes the susceptance of the line n-m. The *here* and *now* decision variables P_{ib}^{DA} and W_{jf}^{DA} represent the scheduled production of conventional units and wind farms respectively and the δ_n^o represents the voltage angle at DA stage. The *wait and see* variables $r_{i\omega}^{up}$ and $r_{i\omega}^{down}$ refer to upward and downward reserves offered by units i, the $W_{j\omega}^{sp}$ indicates the wind power production spillage of wind farm j under scenario ω, the $L_{d\omega}^{sh}$ indicates the load shedding of demand d under scenario ω and the $\delta_{n\omega}$ indicates the voltage angle at RT stage. Finally, O_{ib}^{DA} and O_{jf}^{DA} define the price offer of generation block b and f of strategic unit i and wind farm j in DA market while O_i^{up}, O_i^{down} and O_j^{RT} define the price offer of upward, downward reserves and surplus or shortfall of strategic unit i and wind farm j respectively in RT market.

2.1 Bi-level Formulation

Upper level problem

$$
\begin{aligned}
\max \quad & \sum_{(i\in I_n^S)b} \lambda_n^{DA} P_{ib}^{DA} - \sum_{(i\in I^S)b} c_{ib} P_{ib}^{DA} + \sum_{(j\in J_n^S)f} \lambda_n^{DA} W_{jf}^{DA} \\
& + \sum_{(i\in I_n^S)\omega} \lambda_{n\omega}^{RT} r_{i\omega}^{up} - \sum_{(i\in I^S)\omega} \pi_\omega c_i^{up} r_{i\omega}^{up} - \sum_{(i\in I_n^S)\omega} \lambda_{n\omega}^{RT} r_{i\omega}^{down} \\
& + \sum_{(i\in I^S)\omega} \pi_\omega c_i^{down} r_{i\omega}^{down} + \sum_{(j\in J_n^S)\omega} \lambda_{n\omega}^{RT} \left(W_{j\omega}^{RT} - \sum_f W_{jf}^{DA} - W_{j\omega}^{sp} \right)
\end{aligned}
\tag{1}
$$

Lower level problem

$$
\min \quad \sum_{(i\in I^S)b} O_{ib}^{DA} P_{ib}^{DA} + \sum_{(i\in I^S)\omega} \pi_\omega O_i^{up} r_{i\omega}^{up} - \sum_{(i\in I^S)\omega} \pi_\omega O_i^{down} r_{i\omega}^{down}
$$

$$+ \sum_{(j \in J^S)f} O_{jf}^{DA} W_{jf}^{DA} + \sum_{(j \in J^S)\omega} \pi_\omega O_j^{RT} \left(W_{j\omega}^{RT} - \sum_f W_{jf}^{DA} - W_{j\omega}^{sp} \right)$$

$$+ \sum_{(i \in I^O)b} c_{ib} P_{ib}^{DA} + \sum_{(i \in I^O)\omega} \pi_\omega c_i^{up} r_{i\omega}^{up} - \sum_{(i \in I^O)\omega} \pi_\omega c_i^{down} r_{i\omega}^{down}$$

$$+ \sum_{(j \in J^O)f} c_{jf}^{DA} W_{jf}^{DA} + \sum_{(j \in J^O)\omega} \pi_\omega c_{j\omega}^{RT} \left(W_{j\omega}^{RT} - \sum_f W_{jf}^{DA} - W_{j\omega}^{sp} \right)$$

$$- \sum_{dk} u_{dk} L_{dk}^{DA} + \sum_{d\omega} \pi_\omega vLOL_d L_{d\omega}^{sh} \qquad (2)$$

s.t.
$$- \sum_{(i \in I_n)b} P_{ib}^{DA} - \sum_{(j \in J_n)f} W_{jf}^{DA}$$

$$+ \sum_{(d \in D_n)k} L_{dk}^{DA} + \sum_{m \in \Theta_n} B_{nm}(\delta_n^o - \delta_m^o) = 0 \quad : (\lambda_n^{DA}) \quad \forall n \qquad (3)$$

$$- \sum_{(i \in I_n)} r_{i\omega}^{up} + \sum_{i \in I_n} r_{i\omega}^{down} - \sum_{d \in D_n} L_{d\omega}^{sh}$$

$$- \sum_{(j \in J_n)} W_{j\omega}^{RT} + \sum_{(j \in J_n)f} W_{jf}^{DA} + \sum_{j \in J_n} W_{j\omega}^{sp}$$

$$+ \sum_{m \in \Theta_n} B_{nm}(\delta_{n\omega} - \delta_n^o + \delta_m^o - \delta_{m\omega}) = 0 \quad : (\lambda_{n\omega}^{RT}) \quad \forall n, \forall \omega \qquad (4)$$

$$\sum_b P_{ib}^{DA} + r_{i\omega}^{up} \leq \sum_b P_{ib}^{MAX} \quad : (\mu_{i\omega}^{max}) \quad \forall i, \forall \omega \qquad (5)$$

$$r_{i\omega}^{down} - \sum_b P_{ib}^{DA} \leq 0 \quad : (\mu_{i\omega}^{min}) \quad \forall i, \forall \omega \qquad (6)$$

$$0 \leq W_{j\omega}^{sp} \leq W_{j\omega}^{RT} \quad : (\kappa_{j\omega}^{min}, \kappa_{j\omega}^{max}) \quad \forall j, \forall \omega \qquad (7)$$

$$0 \leq L_{d\omega}^{sh} \leq \sum_k L_{dk}^{DA} \quad : (v_{d\omega}^{min}, v_{d\omega}^{max}) \quad \forall d, \forall \omega \qquad (8)$$

Objective function (1) optimizes the expected profit of the strategic producer, and it is defined by the revenues from the DA and RT market minus the actual incurred cost. The market prices λ_n^{DA} and $\lambda_{n\omega}^{RT}$ are created endogenously and received as dual variables from the lower level problem. Objective function (2) optimizes the expected cost of the power system operation conducted by ISO. It consists of the scheduled production cost and the scenario dependent reserve deployment, spilling wind power and shedding load cost in real time operation. Constraint (3) enforces the energy balance at each node and the transmission capacity limits between them at DA. Thus, the total power flowing into bus n, which is the algebraic sum of generation and load at the bus, should be equal to the power flowing away from the bus. Constraint (4) counterbalances the imbalance occurred in RT due to the uncertain wind production arranging the reserve deployment and the load curtailments. Constraint (5) ensures that scheduled energy and upward reserve cannot exceed unit capacity. Constraint (6) ensures that downward reserve cannot exceed scheduled production. Actually, these two constraints express the strong coupling between scheduled energy and reserves (Morales et al. 2012). Constraints (7) and (8) indicate that the wind energy spillage cannot exceed the scenario dependent actual wind energy production $W_{j\omega}^{RT}$ and the involuntary load curtailment cannot exceed the actual load consumption. Each constraint is followed by its relevant dual variable in parenthesis. Finally, other constraints enforce unit generation limits, transmission capacity limits between two buses, upper and lower bounds of voltage angle at each bus.

2.2 MPEC formulation and linearization

Considering the continuity and the convexity of the lower level problem, the latter is characterized convex therefore it can be replaced by its Karush - Kuhn - Tacker (KKT) first order optimality conditions. Thus, the bi-level model is reduced to a single MPEC model. However, the MPEC is still non-linear due to non-linear KKT complementarity constraints and objective function (1). The former are replaced by linear disjunctive constraints (Fortuny-Amat and McCarl, 1981) while the latter is linearized by applying the strong duality theorem to the lower level problem in combination with some of the KKT equality constraints (Tsimopoulos and Georgiadis, 2018). Hence, the MPEC is reformed in an equivalent MILP solvable by commercial solvers such as GAMS/CPLEX.

3. Illustrative example

The proposed clearing market formulation is applied in a six-node system sketched in Figure 1. The conventional units i1, i2, i3, i4 and the wind farm j1 belong to the strategic producer and the i5, i6, i7,i8 and j2 belong to non-strategic producers. The technical data of the units is taken from Ruiz and Conejo (2009). Two wind farms j1 and j2, located at bus n2 and n5, have installed capacity of 100 MW and 70 MW, and their scheduled power production is offered in one block with zero marginal cost.

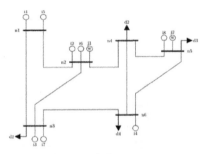

Figure 1. six-bus system

Wind farms' uncertain power production is realized through three scenarios, ω1 (high production) with 100 MWh and 70 MWh, ω2 (medium production) with 50 MWh and 35 MWh, and ω3 (low production) with 20 MWh and 15 MWh while occurrence probability of each scenario is 0.2, 0.5 and 0.3 respectively. A total demand of 1 GWh is allocated according to Figure 1. Demand d1 accounts for 19 % and demands d2, d3 and d4 account for 27 % of the total demand each. Additionally, data about demand bids (energy and utility marginal cost) for each period of time comes from Ruiz and Conejo (2009). Finally, the value of the involuntary load reduction is 200 euro/MWh for all demands and all the connecting lines have a transmission capacity of 500 MW with susceptance equal to 9.412 per unit.

4. Results

4.1. Uncongested network

Based on the above information the proposed MILP model is applied to the system and solved using GAMS/CPLEX. Under cost offer (black) the expected DA price is constant and low at the floor of 11.26 €/MWh throughout the 24-hour period. However, when the producer exercises market power (red) the price moves away from the competitive equilibrium and fluctuates between 16.130 and 19.200 €/MWh (Figure 2). Similarly, the expected real-time prices move upwards when the producer exercises market power in all wind scenarios. Especially, in low wind scenario when the producer offers strategically the RT prices rocket at the level of 37 €/MWh (Figure 3). Note that, the LMP's

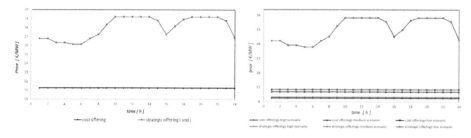

Figure 2. DA clearing prices [€/MWh]   Figure 3. RT clearing prices [€/MWh]

are the same in all buses at each time period, as there is enough line capacity to keep the system uncongested in all wind scenarios. Having a closer look at time period *t12* in Table 1, when the producer offers strategically the scheduled production decreases in all units *i*, giving space for more scheduled wind energy. However, now the production is paid at

Table 1. Energy [MWh] and price outcomes [€/MWh] at time period t12

units i	DA_{ib} b	λ_n^{DA}	r_ω^{up}			r_ω^{down}			$\frac{\lambda_{n\omega}^{RT}}{\pi_\omega}$		
			high	medium	low	high	medium	low	high	medium	low
i1	132.2 [108.8]		.	.	.	15.0 [0.0]	.	.			
i2	.		.	.	.	.	.	.			
i3	155.0 [124.0]		.	.	0.0 [10.0]	.	.	.			
i4	157,6 [118.2]	11.260 [19.200]	.	0.0 [15.0]	15.0 [40.0]	40.0 [40.0]	.	.	9.280 [9.570]	11.470 [12.230]	12.230 [37.237]
wind j	W_{jf}^{DA} f										
j1	15.0 [60.0]										

a higher price. Considering the reserves, in low wind scenario where now the energy shortage is bigger the upward reserve supply increases compared to cost offering and it is paid almost at triple price. On the other hand, in high wind scenario, although the producer is charged at a higher price the downward reserve supply is lower. The proposed model results in an increase in the total expected profit from 23,286 € to 91,950 € even though the scheduled power production of strategic conventional units *i* decreases.

4.2. Offer building process

Considering unit *i1*, it can be seen in Table 2 that under cost offer the unit is fully dispatched as all the energy blocks are accepted by ISO. However, under strategic offer the first two blocks are fully accepted, the third is partially accepted and the fourth is not accepted at all. To create an upward offer curve; the first two blocks are offered at their marginal cost. The third block is offered at a price slightly lower than the clearing price.

Table 2. Day-ahead offer building process for unit i1 at time period t12

			cost offers		strategic offers				
block	c_{ib}	MAX_{ib}	DA_{ib}	λ_n^{DA}	DA_{ib}	λ_n^{DA}	O_{ib}^{DA*}		
b1	9.92	54.25	54.25		54.25		9.92		
b2	10.25	38.75	38.75	11.26	38.75	19.20	10.25		
b3	10.68	31.00	31.00		15.80		19.20 - ε	→	Financial withholding
b4	11.26	31.00	31.00		.		19.20	→	Physical withholding

Actually, this offer defines the DA market price. With this offer the producer exercises financial withholding, raising the offer of block 3 from 10.680 to slightly below 19.200

€/MWh. Now the last block is offered at a price 19.200 €/MWh or higher. In this way the producer guarantees block's rejection, exercising physical withholding (production curtailment).

4.3. Congested line 3-6

Under cost optimization the maximum power flow in line 3-6 is 208 MW. If the capacity is reduced to 220 MW, the system remains uncongested. However, under strategic offer the producer changes the mixture of production rendering the line congested. As a result, LMP's appear at certain time periods, as shown in Figure 4, and the total expected profits compared to those of uncongested system increase at the level of 92,759 €.

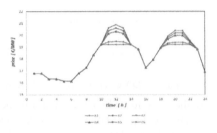

Figure 4. DA LMP's [€/MWh]

4.4. Wind power production increment

The wind power capacity increases from 10% to 14% of the total installed capacity. More specifically, the power production of the wind farms $j1$ and $j2$ is now 150 MW and 100 MW respectively in high wind scenario 1, 75 MW and 50 MW in medium wind scenario 2, and 30 MW and 20 MW in low wind scenario 3. In this case the strategic units i and the wind warm $j1$ incur losses under cost offer as the price

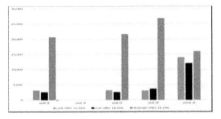

Figure 5. Units' expected profits [€]

formation is lower. Only the units $i4$ shows increased profits because now it is more involved in supply of upward reserves due the higher volatility of wind generation. However, when the producer exercises market power by means of capacity withholdings the expected profits of all units i and $j1$ raise as depicted in Figure 5.

5. Conclusions

This work proposes a bi-level complementarity model to derive capacity withholding strategies for power producer participating in a pool-based market. A representative case study is used to illustrate the applicability of model and how the producer can increase its expected profits considering wind generation uncertainty and line capacity limitations.

References

E.G. Tsimopoulos and M.C. Georgiadis, 2018. Strategic offers in day-ahead market co-optimizing energy and reserve under high penetration of wind power production: An MPEC approach. AIChE Journal.

J. M. Morales, A. J. Conejo, K. Liu and J. Zhong, (2012), Pricing electricity in pools with wind producers. IEEE Transactions on Power Systems, 27(3), 1366-1376.

J. Fortuny-Amat and B. McCarl, (1981). A representation and economic interpretation of a two-level programming problem. Journal of the operational Research Society, 32(9), 783-792.

C. Ruiz and A. J. Conejo, (2009), Pool strategy of a producer with endogenous formation of locational marginal prices, IEEE Transactions on Power Systems, 24(4), 1855-1866.

Sauro Pierucci, Flavio Manenti, Giulia Bozzano, Davide Manca (Eds.)
Proceedings of the 30th European Symposium on Computer Aided Process Engineering
(ESCAPE30), May 24-27, 2020, Milano, Italy. © 2020 Elsevier B.V. All rights reserved.
http://dx.doi.org/10.1016/B978-0-12-823377-1.50224-X

Supply chain optimization for the production of biofuels and bioproducts from lignocellulosic biomass in Mexico

Yulissa M. Espinoza-Vázquez, [a] Fernando Israel Gómez-Castro [a,*], José María Ponce-Ortega [b]

[a] *Departamento de Ingeniería Química, División de Ciencias Naturales y Exactas, Campus Guanajuato, Universidad de Guanajuato, Noria Alta S/N, Col. Noria Alta, Guanajuato, Guanajuato, 36050, México.*
[b] *División de Estudios de Posgrado, Facultad de Ingeniería Química, Universidad Michoacana de San Nicolás de Hidalgo, Francisco J. Múgica S/N, Morelia, Michoacán. 58060, México.*

fgomez@ugto.mx

Abstract

Lignocellulosic biomass is a raw material to produce biofuels and bioproducts. Thus, the proper use of such materials may help to development of a bio-based industry, additionally giving a second use to such waste material. Mexico is a country with a high agricultural production, implying a high production of agricultural residues. Since there are many possibilities for making use of the residues, the question arising is: which are the best products to be obtained from the lignocellulosic biomass available in the country? To answer this question, in this work a mathematical model for the supply chain of the production of biofuels/bioproducts is proposed. The mathematical model is formulated using generalized disjunctive programming (GDP) and relaxed through the convex hull approach. The resulting MILP is solved using the software GAMS, aiming to maximize the profit.

Keywords: lignocellulosic biomass, supply chain, disjunctive programming.

1. Introduction

The production of renewable fuels has taken growing importance on the last years, due to the concerns around the availability of petroleum and the environmental impact due to the use of its derivatives. According to British Petroleum, if the present demand of petroleum remains constant, the reservoirs will be enough for other 50.2 years (British Petroleum, 2018). Among the renewable fuels, those derived from sugar-rich materials, as bioethanol and biobutanol, can be used to partially replace gasoline in engines. Nevertheless, the industrial-scale production of such fuels must take place using non-edible raw materials, as lignocellulosic residues. Particularly, Mexico is a country with a high agricultural production, with corn, sorghum, and wheat as main products. Such crops generate lignocellulosic residues, with a reported production of 75.73 million ton in 2006 (Saval, 2012). Those residues contain cellulose, hemicellulose and lignin, and, as aforementioned, can be used as raw materials to produce biofuels as bioethanol, biobutanol, among others. On the other hand, such residues have also potential to produce high value-added bioproducts, as lactic acid, furfural, levulinic acid, among others, which are the basis for the generation of several derivatives. The production of biofuels may not be profitable by itself, and the success of a biofuel production facility may strongly depend on the politics of each country, in terms of the subsidies offered by the governments. Thus, the use of lignocellulosic materials to produce both, biofuels and bioproducts, may enhance the economy of the biofuel industry. Nevertheless, among the different biofuels and bioproducts which can be obtained from lignocellulosic biomass, a given combination of products must have the highest profitability, making use of as much residues as possible and satisfying the demand for fuels and for a given bioproduct. Maximizing the profit will also depend on the location of the raw material, the production facilities and the markets. To determine the best supply chain for the production of biofuels/bioproducts from lignocellulosic residues, a mathematical model is proposed, considering the distribution of the raw materials, the potential locations for the facilities, the unitary cost for the production of each potential product, and the potential markets for the products. The mathematical model is formulated using generalized disjunctive programming (GDP) and relaxed using the convex hull approach, obtaining a MILP equivalent. The model is then codified in the software GAMS and optimized.

2. Case Study

As a first step, the availability of agricultural residues in Mexico is determined for four main crops: corn, sorghum, wheat and barley. Data for the distribution of such crops in all the country, and their contribution to the production of lignocellulosic residues, has been collected from the Service of Agrifood and Fisheries Information (SIAP, 2018). It has been determined that Mexico has a mean production of 1,394.8 kt/y of corn residues, 264.6 kt/y of sorghum residues, 93.0 kt/y of wheat residues and 40.4 kt/y of barley residues, distributed along the national territory. These raw materials are proposed to be used for the production of bioethanol and/or biobutanol, as biofuel alternatives, and levulinic acid and furfural as high-value added products. As a simplification, a single municipality has been selected as representative for each of the 32 states in Mexico. The selected municipality is the one with the highest production of residues in the spring/summer season. The effect of the change in the production of lignocellulosic materials in the autumn/winter season will be studied in a future work. For the potential location of the facilities, the states with the highest industrial infrastructure have been selected. Finally, the production of each potential product is constrained by its national demand. For bioethanol, mean national demand is 1,748,525.8 m^3/y, assuming covering 10% of the gasoline demand. For biobutanol, demand is set as 2,797,641.2 m^3/y, assuming covering 16% of the gasoline demand. For levulinic acid, demand is 1,667.9 m^3/y; while for furfural is 11.6 m^3/y.

3. Mathematical Model

The mathematical model represents the selection of the four raw materials (i) from the 32 states in Mexico (j). The raw materials from the different states are transported to one of the five states with highest industrial infrastructure (k), where the facilities can be located. On each facility, four products (m) can be obtained: bioethanol, biobutanol, levulinic acid and furfural. Finally, the products can be distributed to ten markets (n), selected among the 32 states because they are the locations with higher demand for gasoline. Figure 1 shows the superstructure for the supply chain. The mathematical model involves the transportation costs for the biomass from the source to the facilities, in terms of the distance between locations, and the transportations costs from the facilities to the markets.

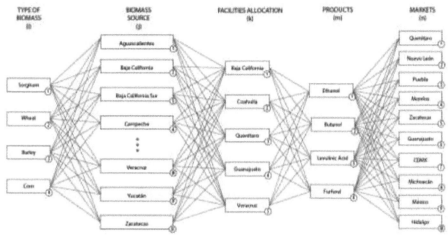

Figure 1. Superstructure for the supply chain of biofuels and bioproducts.

In the proposed model, it is assumed that the production for each product does not exceed the demand:

$$\sum_k MP(m,k) \le \sum_n DP(m,n) \tag{1}$$

Where $MP(m,k)$ is the mass production of the product m in the facility k, and $DP(m,n)$ is the demand for product m in the market n. Additionally, $MPAT(i,j,k)$, the quantity of raw material i from the source j entering to the plant k, cannot be higher than the availability of such raw material in the source j, $MPA(i,j)$:

$$\sum_k MPAT(i,j,k) \le MPA(i,j) \tag{2}$$

Transportation cost $CP(j,k)$ for biomass from a source j to the facility k is given by:

$$CP(j,k) = \sum_i MPAT(i,j,k) * D1(i,j,k) * UPST \tag{3}$$

Where $D1(i,j,k)$ is the distance from the source j of the biomass i to the facility k, and UPST is the transportation cost for solid biomass, which is taken as 0.00508 USD/km·ton. Similarly, the cost for the transportation of the product m obtained in the facility k to the market n, $CD(k,m,n)$ is given by:

$$CD(k,m,n) = MPTM(k,m,n) * D2(k,n) * UPLT \tag{4}$$

Where $MPTM(k,m,n)$ is the quantity of product m obtained in the facility k which is transported to the market n, $D2(k,n)$ is the distance from the facility k to the market n, and UPLT is the unitary transportation cost for the liquid products, which is taken as 0.00671 USD/km·ton.

For the cost of the facilities, the unitary cost of raw material is assumed a 280 USD/t. The unitary cost for the production of bioethanol and the yield have been computed from the results reported by Sassner et al. (2008). For the production of biobutanol, the information given by Alavijeh and Karimi (2019) has been used. For levulinic acid and furfural, the data reported by Gozan et al., (2017) and Cai et al. (2013), respectively, have been taken. The cost of the land has also been included. The selection of the location of the facility and the obtained product(s) on each facility has been modelled through disjunctions, as the following:

$$
\begin{bmatrix}
\begin{bmatrix}
Y(k) \\
TCP(k) = \left\{ \left[\sum_m \left[\frac{MP(m,k)}{\rho(m)} \times 0.66 \times 0.4048 \right] \right] \right\} \\
+ \left[\sum_i \sum_j MPAT(i,j,k) \times (280 + PC(m)) \right]
\end{bmatrix} \\
\begin{bmatrix}
S(m,k) \\
MP(m,k) = \sum_i \sum_j MPAT(i,j,k) \times Yield_m
\end{bmatrix} \vee \begin{bmatrix} \neg S(m,k) \\ MP(m,k) = 0 \end{bmatrix} \\
\vee \begin{bmatrix}
\neg Y(k) \\
MP(m,k) = 0 \\
MPAT(i,j,k) = 0 \\
TCP(k) = 0
\end{bmatrix}
\end{bmatrix}
\tag{5}
$$

where Y(k) is a logical variable associated with the construction of the plant in the location k, and S(m,k) is a logical variable associated with the production of a given product m in the plant k. TCP(k) is the total cost of the production, PC(m) is the cost for processing the raw material to obtain the product m, and SP(m) is the selling price for the product m. The value of 0.66 represents an estimation of the land surface, in m², required per liter of product. This value is estimated using the data reported for the refinery "Francisco I. Madero" in Ciudad Madero, Tamaulipas, Mexico (El Informador, 2019). The cost of the land required to build the facilities is taken as 0.4048 USD/m². The disjunctions have been relaxed through the convex hull approach (Lee and Grossmann, 2000). Additionally, the following implication is established to ensure that the products will be obtained only if the facility is built:

$$
Y(k) \Leftrightarrow S(BE,k) \vee S(BB,k) \vee S(LA,k) \vee S(F,k)
\tag{6}
$$

Where BE represents bioethanol, BB is the biobutanol, LA stands for lactic acid and F is the furfural. The objective function implies the maximization of the profit, given by:

$$
Profit = \sum_m \sum_k [MP(m,k) \times SP(m)] - \sum_k TCP(k) - \sum_j \sum_k CP(j,k) - \sum_n \sum_k CD(k,n)
\tag{7}
$$

The relaxed disjunctions, together with the constraints which are not dependent of the disjunctions, are codified in the software GAMS. The resulting MINLP problem consists of 448 equalities and 134 inequalities. The model has been optimized with the solver DICOPT, in a Dell WorkStation with a Inter Core i5-9300H CPU, 4.00 GB of RAM.

4. Results

According to the obtained results, a single plant must be installed in Querétaro. Table 1 shows the distribution of raw materials to the facility. It can be seen that, for this scenario, wheat and corn are the only raw materials used for the generation of biofuels and bioproducts.

Table 1. Distribution of raw materials (t/yr).

Facility location/Raw material	Sorghum	Wheat	Corn	Barley
Querétaro	--	Querétaro (10)	Querétaro (19)	--

Table 2 shows the products obtained on the plant. It can be seen that the facility produces mainly furfural.

Table 2. Products obtained on the facility (t/yr).

Facility location/Product	Bioethanol	Biobutanol	Levulinic acid	Furfural
Querétaro	2	3	6	13

All the obtained products are used to satisfy the local demand of the city of Queretaro. In this case, only the furfural demand is completely satisfied, with the production of small quantities of the other products. Since the objective function implies the maximization of the profit, the solution implies satisfying the demand of the product with the highest yield, being also the second product with the highest selling prize. With this solution, the profit is 65,289 USD/yr. Further constraints must be added to ensure a better use of the great production potential in the country.

5. Conclusions

A supply chain model is proposed for the production of two biofuels, namely bioethanol and biobutanol, and two bioproducts, levulinic acid and furfural, using the available biomass in Mexico. The supply chain has been optimization in terms of the annual profit. As expected, most of the biofuels and bioproducts are obtained from corn residues. On the other hand, the model predicts the need of a facility in the center on Mexico, only satisfying the demand of furfural. The model can be enhanced to look for a better use of the biomass to satisfy the demand of fuels and chemicals.

References

M.K. Alavijeh, K. Karimi, 2019, Biobutanol production from corn stover in the US, Industrial Crops and Products, 129, 641-653.

British Petroleum, 2018, BP Statistical Review of World Energy, at https://www.bp.com/content/dam/bp/en/corporate/pdf/energy-economics/statistical-review/bp-stats-review-2018-full-report.pdf. Last visited August 19, 2019.

C.M. Cai, T. Zhang, R. Kumar, C.E. Wyman, 2013, Integrated furfural production as a renewable fuel and chemical platform from lignocellulosic biomass, Journal of Chemical Technology and Biotechnology, 89, 1, 2-10.

El Informador, 2019, Serán siete las refinerías de México en 2022, at https://www.informador.mx/Seran-siete-las-refinerias-de-Mexico-en-2022-t201905090003.html. Last visited January 24, 2020.

M. Gozan, B. Ryan, Y. Krisnandi, 2017, Techno-economic assessment of levulinic acid plant from *Sorghum Bicolor* in Indonesia, IOP Conference Series: Materials Science and Engineering, 345, 012012.

S. Lee, I.E. Grossmann, 2000, New algorithms for nonlinear generalized disjunctive programming, Computers and Chemical Engineering, 24, 9, 2125-2141.

P. Sassner, M. Galbe, G. Zacchi, 2008, Techno-economic evaluation of bioethanol production from three different lignocellulosic materials, Biomass and Bioenergy, 32, 5, 422-430.

S. Saval, 2012, Aprovechamiento de residuos agroindustriales: pasado, presente y futuro, BioTecnología, 16, 2, 14-16 (Spanish).

Service of Agrifood and Fisheries Information (SIAP), 2018, Anuario Estadístico de la Producción Agrícola, at https://nube.siap.gob.mx/cierreagricola/ (Spanish). Last visited October 29, 2019.

Sauro Pierucci, Flavio Manenti, Giulia Bozzano, Davide Manca (Eds.)
Proceedings of the 30th European Symposium on Computer Aided Process Engineering
(ESCAPE30), May 24-27, 2020, Milano, Italy. © 2020 Elsevier B.V. All rights reserved.
http://dx.doi.org/10.1016/B978-0-12-823377-1.50225-1

Total Site Synthesis: Selection of Processes to Save Energy and Boost Cogeneration

Konstantinos A. Pyrgakis, Antonis C. Kokossis

*School of Chemical Engineering, National Technical University of Athens, Iroon
Polytechneiou 9, GR-15780, Greece*
akokossis@mail.ntua.gr

Abstract

The design of biorefineries is challenged by new chemistries that need to be evaluated
and properly integrated across industrial sites. Process and energy integration are
necessary to maximize performance and sustainability margins. In a previous work, the
authors addressed the combinatorial nature of the biorefinery synthesis and integration
problem (Pyrgakis and Kokossis, 2019) introducing systems and an optimization model
(MILP) to systematically screen and integrate value chain paths highlighting energy
promising and high profitable biorefinery solutions. This work presents an updated
version of the previous model to simultaneously address cogeneration and utility levels
optimization. The previous version is also combined with cogeneration models to select
processes that benefit energy savings and electricity production, as necessary co-product
to offset price volatilities of upcoming biochemicals. New strategies are proposed to
improve accuracy of Turbine Hardware Model (THM), in light of variable processes and
utility levels, and revise regression parameters of turbine modules and predictions
of input specific heat load. The optimization model (MILP) was used to examine 20
candidate chemistries and revealed biorefinery solutions with high energy savings
(10.5%), shaft work production (25.6 MW) and profitability margins (9.3 M€/yr).

Keywords: Total Site integration, Turbine Hardware Model, Cogeneration, Utility
levels optimization, Biorefineries.

1. Introduction

Chemical engineering is challenged by new bio-based chemistries that need to be tested
in the contexts of building Industrial Biotechnology and Circular economy. Common,
but still questionable, solutions are solely focusing on bio-ethanol and bio-fuels that
hold few evidences for sustainable production. Value chains provide new options
towards numerous biochemicals (commodities and specialties) to examine and integrate
across biorefinery sites. It is still challenging to screen and optimize value chain options
in the scope of recovering sources and securing sustainable production (Kokossis et al.,
2015). Process and energy integration technologies are essential to propose engineering
solutions against high production costs and uncertainties of upcoming markets.

Process integration is commonly provided by means of superstructure optimization to
synthesize chemical paths with common input-output chemicals scoping for complete
biorefining routes form raw materials (biomass) to intermediate and end-bioproducts.
Energy integration is called to improve and evaluate the performance of candidate
process portfolios (Pyrgakis and Kokossis, 2017) by means of (i) direct heat source-to-
sink integration, (ii) indirect process-to-process integration via steam and (iii)

cogeneration optimization. Though not visible through value chains, electricity still counts as a valuable co-product to offset price volatilities of upcoming biochemicals.

In (i), integration is provided by well-known heat cascade technologies. The analysis in (ii) is challenged by the use of graphical tools and multi-stage computational analyses that examine given, rather than variable, process portfolios. The previous work of Pyrgakis and Kokossis (2019) faced these challenges by proposing a new heat cascade concept and an enhanced transshipment model to systematize the analysis in (ii) and simultaneously address (i) and (ii) in light of unknown/variable value chain processes. This paper presents an updated version of previous work to simultaneously address (i), (ii) and (iii) along with utility levels optimization. The enhanced transshipment model is extended with cogeneration technologies and strategies to improve accuracy of turbine models. The biorefineries design is formulated as an MILP problem to select value chain processes that maximize energy performance, cogeneration and profitability.

2. The Cross-Interval Transshipment (CIT) model

Direct integration refers to heat exchange of hot-cold streams belonging to each process, while indirect applies among streams of different processes selected for the industrial site by valorizing available process heat for generation steam utilities. Indirect integration is commonly conducted by means of Site Sources & Sinks Profiles (SSSP) that one should prepare by combining the Grand Composite Curves (GCC) of individual processes. The conventional graphical approach apparently applies for fixed processes by first applying direct integration on GCCs and, then, indirect (process-to-process) integration based on SSSPs. However, the biorefineries design faces with candidate value chain processes (not fixed options) to be properly selected and integrated to optimize performance. A previous work of authors (Pyrgakis and Kokossis, 2019) systematized the graphical procedure through an enhanced heat transshipment model (Figure 1.a) that simultaneously implements direct and indirect integration considering processes (and their hot/cold streams) as additional degrees of freedom in integration.

In Figure 1.a, heat flows (solid lines) around nodes 1, 2 and 3 still count for direct integration along the proposals of Papoulias and Grossmann (1983). Nodes 4 and 5 have been added by Pyrgakis and Kokossis (2019) to simultaneously describe indirect heat exchange of hot-cold streams. Indirect integration exploits excess heat to generate steam, which is introduced to the utilities of the whole plant. Node 4 applies as a pseudo-cold utility level to extract available heat from intervals. The extracted heat load is translated into steam, which travels to lower-temperature intervals providing heat along with fresh utilities through node 5. The proposed CIT transshipment describes the energy balances along the Total Site Cascade (TSC) of Figure 1.b, which is configured by the temperature intervals of all candidate processes that are possible to get integrated across the under-construction biorefinery site. The updated version of CIT further involves options to use fresh and generated steam for shaft work production.

Figure 1.b explains the operation of TSC for a two-process site. Hot-cold streams of Process A are directly integrated along the intervals of TSC, while excess heat from Process A generates steam of level 1. The transshipment addresses energy trade-offs concerning the use of steam either to save fresh steam (indirect integration of Processes A-B) or to generate shaft work by expanding steam to lower steam level 2. The CIT is combined with a turbine model and a strategy to simultaneously optimize utility levels.

3. Integration and cogeneration strategies

Steam utility levels act as energy gates for process-to-process integration by gathering/supplying heat from/to intervals of TSC (Figure 1.b). They also define the

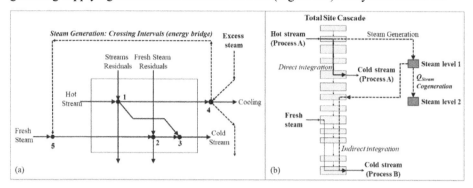

Figure 1: Cross-Interval Transshipment (a) and Total Site Cascade (b)

expansion zones (the span between levels) of turbines operations. Steam savings are estimated by connecting nodes 4 and 5 (Figure 1.a), while steam residuals exiting node 4 correspond to turbines steam loads; nodes 4 and 5 apply for each utility level. This work considers a set of candidate utility levels (Figure 2.a), between the upper and lower temperatures of TSC, to select with a scope to maximize benefits from steam savings and cogeneration. The Turbine Hardware Model (THM) of Mavromatis and Kokossis (1998) is used to describe complex turbines through an equivalent cascade of simple turbines (one inlet and outlet), as shown in Figure 2.b. The THM applies for simple turbines providing a linear approximation of power output (E^{max}) as a function of steam load (M^{max}) facing non-linearities between isentropic efficiency (n_{is}^{max}) and steam load, as shown through Eq.(1).

$$n_{is}^{max} = \frac{\overline{\Delta H}_{real}}{\overline{\Delta H}_{is}} = \frac{E^{max}}{\overline{\Delta H}_{is} \cdot M^{max}} \tag{1}$$

where $\overline{\Delta H}_{is} = \frac{\Delta T^{SAT}}{1854 - 1931 \cdot q_{in}}$ is the isentropic enthalpy change, q_{in} the specific heat load, ΔT^{SAT} the saturation temperature difference and $M^{max} = \frac{Q}{q_{in}}$, where Q corresponds to the steam residuals of node 4 of the transshipment model (Figure 1.a).

The THM is based on the transformation of turbine efficiency data vs power output of Peterson and Mann (1985) into piecewise linear expressions (see Figure 2.c), as: $\overline{\Delta H}_{is} \cdot M^{max} = \frac{E^{max}}{n_{is}} = A + B \cdot E^{max}$, where A, B are regression parameters. Finally, the THM takes the form of:

$$E^{max} = \frac{1}{B}(\overline{\Delta H}_{is} \cdot M^{max} - A) \tag{2}$$

Existing literature strategies use linear expressions for the estimation of A, B as a function of inlet saturation temperature T_{in}^{SAT} (Mavromatis and Kokossis, 1998), or ΔT^{SAT} (Varbanov et al., 2004), or inlet pressure P_{in} (Medina et al., 2010). Also, q_{in} is generally assumed approximately constant at 0.557 MWh/tn (VHP-90 bar, 500 °C) to preserve linearity of THM. However, the existing strategies are not enough to combine

Eq.(2) with the transshipment of Figure 1.a and utility levels optimization. The accuracy of THM is not enough to model turbines operating at extreme conditions (e.g. small ΔT^{SAT} and M^{max} and large T_{in}^{SAT}). For example, let a turbine expanding 5 tn/hr of VHP steam from 90 to 80 bar. The regression parameters (A, B) of Mavromatis and Kokossis

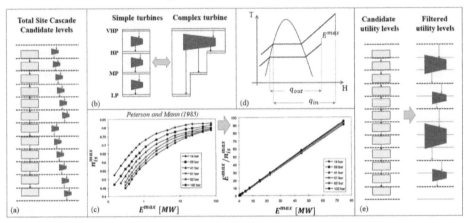

Figure 2: Candidate utility levels (a), Simple turbines cascade (b), Turbine efficiency data (c), T-H diagram (d), Candidate and filtered utility levels (e).

(1998) and Medina et al. (2010) resulted in negative power outputs, while the model of Varbanov et al. (2004) results in the same power output regardless P_{in} or T_{in}^{SAT} variations. The following strategies are proposed to increase accuracy of the THM and the prediction of q_{in}, as well as to prepare a linear optimization model to address the combinatorial nature of process synthesis, integration and shaft work cogeneration.

3.1. Revision of THM regression parameters

The data of Figure 2.c are revisited and regressed preparing a new approach for the estimation of regression parameters A and B as a function of T_{in}^{SAT}, ΔT^{SAT} and q_{in}, as follows: $A = a_1 \cdot \Delta T^{SAT}$ and $B = a_2 + a_3 \cdot T_{in}^{SAT} + a_4 \cdot \Delta T^{SAT} + a_5 \cdot q_{in}$, where a_1=0.0011, a_2=1.0079, a_3=0.00114, a_4=0.00054, a_5=0.001, when E^{max}<3.26 MW; a_1=0.0039, a_2=1.0878, a_3=0.00049, a_4=0.00017, a_5=0.0012, when E^{max}>3.26 MW. The revised parameters return E^{max}=0.037 MW for the above example (90→80 bar).

3.2. A formulation for the prediction of input specific heat load

The input specific heat loads of a turbines cascade are estimated by: $q_{out} = q_{in} + c_p \cdot \Delta T^{SAT} - \frac{E^{max}}{M^{max}}$, where q_{out} of a turbine corresponds to q_{in} of the next one, based on the T-H diagram of Figure 2.d. The common practice of using constant q_{in} for each expansion zone would aggregate multiple errors at the design of the equivalent complex turbine. This work revisits the above expression providing conservative predictions for q_{in}, ahead of optimization.

The term $\frac{E^{max}}{M^{max}}$ of the above expression is replaced by $n_{is}^{max} \cdot \overline{\Delta H_{is}}$, based on Eq.(1). A conservative approximation of q_{in} is obtained, if the turbine operates at maximum feasible performance. Drawing on Eq.(1) and Eq.(2), that performance is considered by term $\frac{1}{B}$, which counts for ΔT^{SAT}, T_{in}^{SAT} and q_{in} variations (see Section 3.1). Given a set of utility levels, q_{in} at each level n is approximated, as: $q_{in}^{n+1} = q_{in}^n + c_p \cdot \Delta T^{SAT^n} - \frac{1}{B} \cdot \frac{\Delta T^{SAT^n}}{1854 - 1931 \cdot q_{in}^n}$, where q_{in}^1 refer to the known steam level (VHP) supplied by the boiler house.

3.3. THM variations

When turbines design is constructed as an optimization problem, additional non-linearities are introduced due to A, B variations with power output; e.g. over/under 3.26 MW (see Section 3.1). The non-linearities are regularly faced by using same values for parameters a_1-a_5 regardless the power output estimations. These inaccuracies are faced by considering changes in parameters a_1-a_5 and by introducing linear logical constraints to switch over different THM formulations, each adjusted with the appropriate parameters, according to power output variations over/under 3.26 MW.

3.4. Turbines cascade optimization

The method assumes a set of candidate utility levels to optimize as shown on the left of Figure 2.e. The use of THM over the multiple narrow expansion zones would aggregate multiple errors at the approximation of power output of the equivalent complex turbine. Inaccuracies are minimized by filtering selected levels against discarded, building a parallel, yet dynamic, cascade of expansion zones, where THM is applied, as shown on the right of Figure 2.e. Processes are treated as degrees of freedom to configure the intervals of TSC, while candidate utility levels are tested to optimize steam savings and cogeneration. The biorefinery is not given at early design stages; steam savings and cogeneration are benefited by the selection of value chain processes and utility levels.

4. Mathematical formulation

The domain is formulated by continuous variables for the capacities of value chain process, the heat flows of the CIT model and the turbines power output. Binary variables are used for the selection of processes and utility levels, to switch among alternative THM formulations and to build the expansion zones, where THM is applied. The optimization model includes mass balances along the value chain, energy balances of CIT and logic constraints to select and filter utilities and address changes of turbine parameters (a_1-a_5). The objective function is formulated by the utilities cost and the profits from cogeneration to maximize energy performance; otherwise, economic data of candidate processes and products are also included to maximize profitability.

5. Case study

The optimization approach was used to address a value chain of 20 candidate chemistries (Figure 3.a) considering both objectives to optimize the use of energy or profitability. In the first case, the integration of xylitol, itaconic acid and poly-urethanes production processes results in 9.3% steam cost savings (due to process-to-process integration), while cogeneration rises to 25.6 MW. In the second case, xylitol, PVC and poly-urethanes production maximized annual profitability to 9.3 M€; steam cost savings rise to 10.5%, while 20.3 MW of electricity are generated. Figure 3.b shows the optimized utility levels and the power output resulted in each case. The selection of narrow expansion zones at lower temperature steam levels justifies the revision of cogeneration modeling strategies; otherwise, the accuracy of existing literature models would not be enough to predict shaft work at those levels, as discussed in Section 3.

6. Conclusions

A modified heat transshipment model is combined with THM to maximize steam savings and cogeneration of shaft work in light of unknown processes. New strategies

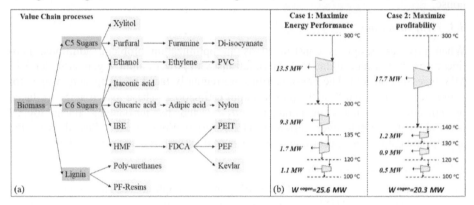

Figure 3: Candidate value chain processes (a), Optimal utility levels and turbines (b).

are proposed to improve accuracy and face limitations at the implementation of THM. The analysis resulted in new formulations to predict THM regression parameters, and approximate q_{in} instead of being considered as constant. The model builds the optimal expansion zones, where THM is accurately applied, also in light of variable utility levels. The model was applied to investigate 20 candidate value chain processes highlighting the most promising bio-based chemistries in terms of energy savings (10.5%), cogeneration potential (25.6 MW) and sustainability margins (9.3 M€/yr).

References

A. Kokossis, M. Tsakalova, K. Pyrgakis, 2015, Design of Integrated Biorefineries, Comp & Chem Eng, 81, 40–56

S.P. Mavromatis, A.C. Kokossis, 1998, Conceptual Optimisation of Utility Networks for Operational Variations-I. Targets and Level Optimisation, Chem Eng Sci, 53, 8, 1585–1608

J.M. Medina-Flores, M. Picon-Nunez, 2010, Modelling the Power Production of Single and Multiple Extraction Steam Turbines, Chemical Engineering Science, 65, 2811–2820

S.A. Papoulias, I.E. Grossmann, 1983 A Structural Optimization Approach in Process Synthesis-I Utility Systems, Comp & Chem Eng, 7, 6, 695–706

J.F. Peterson, W.L. Mann, 1985, Steam-System Design: How it Evolves, *Chem Eng*, 92, 21,62–74

K.A. Pyrgakis, A.C. Kokossis, 2017, Total Site Integration as a Process Synthesis and Scheduling Tool in Multiple-feedstock Biorefineries, CACE, 40, 1825–1830

K.A. Pyrgakis, A. Kokossis, 2019, A Total Site Synthesis Approach for the Selection, Integration and Planning of Multiple-Feedstock Biorefineries, Comp & Chem Eng, 122, 326–355

P.S. Varbanov, S. Doyle, R. Smith, 2004, Modelling and Optimization of Utility Systems, Chemical Engineering Research and Design, 82, A5, 561–578

Sauro Pierucci, Flavio Manenti, Giulia Bozzano, Davide Manca (Eds.)
Proceedings of the 30ᵗʰ European Symposium on Computer Aided Process Engineering
(ESCAPE30), May 24-27, 2020, Milano, Italy. © 2020 Elsevier B.V. All rights reserved.
http://dx.doi.org/10.1016/B978-0-12-823377-1.50226-3

An Extended Approach for the Integration of Heat Pumps into HENS Multi-Period MILP Superstructure Formulation for Industrial Applications

Leopold Prendl [a], René Hofmann [a,b*]

[a]*Technische Universität Wien, Institute for Energy Systems and Thermodynamics, Getreidemarkt 9/BA, 1060 Vienna, Austria*
[b]*AIT Austrian Institute of Technology GmbH, Center for Energy, Sustainable Thermal Energy Systems, Giefinggasse 2, 1210 Vienna, Austria*
rene.hofmann@tuwien.ac.at

Abstract

This paper deals with the extension of the linearized superstructure formulation for heat exchange network synthesis (HENS) proposed by Beck and Hofmann (2018a). The energy consumption of heat pumps as a function of the temperature lift and the thermal energy flow is approximated by a convex linearization. This allows for a linear extension of the cost function that takes the size and the energy consumption of heat pumps into account. As given problem an existing process and a predetermined heat pump characteristic is assumed. A test case consisting of two hot and two cold process streams has been constructed to investigate the proposed optimization method. The test case has been optimized with and without the extended approach for comparable results. The HEN resulting from the newly developed approach has 16.1 % lower total annual costs (TAC) and a 48.1 % lower external energy demand than the network resulting from the HENS without storages or heat pumps. This improvements come with the drawback of a more complex HEN with 15 installations compared to the simple HEN with 7 installations.

Keywords: Mathematical Programming, Linearization, Heat Recovery, Heat Pump, HENS

1. Introduction

The recovery of thermal energy is becoming more and more important, taking into account the overall objective of the reduction of primary energy consumption and thus reduction of greenhouse gas emissions. One way towards achieving this goal is the enhancement of energy exchange and conversion networks. Heat exchange network synthesis (HENS) was broadly investigated and approached with many different approaches over the last decades as recapitulated by Escobar and Trierweiler (2013). The integration of heat pumps into non continuous processes has also been the subject to a number of scientific publications as, for example, by Stampfli et al. (2019). Nonetheless, the integration of heat pumps into HENS for the economic optimization of batch processes with multiple time steps was not being thoroughly investigated. An existing paper from Becker and Maréchal (2012) uses the heat cascade formulation as approach. In contrast to this, a superstructure formulation was used as starting point for this work.

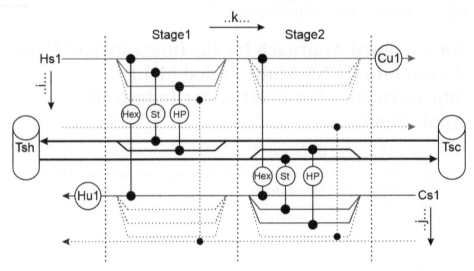

Figure 1: Extended Superstructure with possible Stream-Stream Hex (Hex), Stream-Storage Hex (St), Heat Pumps (HP), Hot/Cold Streams (Hs/Cs), Hot/Cold Storage Temperatures (Tsh/Tsc), Hot/Cold Utilities (Hu/Cu), Stage Subscript (k) and Hot/Cold Stream Subscripts (i/j).

2. Extended Mathematical Model

The superstructure is based on the formulation by Beck and Hofmann (2018a), which is a linearization of the superstructure proposed by Yee and Grossmann (1990). The objective function as shown in Eq. (1) uses the same nomenclature and constraints as Beck and Hofmann (2018a). The extension considers a two tank liquid thermal storage, heat exchangers between the streams and the storage and heat pumps between the streams and the storage. The possible connections for every stream in every stage are exemplarily represented in Figure 1. The two tank storage is modelled according to Beck and Hofmann (2018b). The multiple time periods during the cyclic process are realized by using the time slice model for cutting the process into different time slices in which the process parameters are constant. Isothermal mixing after every stream split is assumed. If heat exchangers occur at the same spot in different time periods p, the largest heat exchanger area A is taken into account for the calculation. In the other time steps the isothermal mixing is assured by bypasses. Furthermore, as a simplification to keep the problem linear, the heat transfer coefficients are assumed to be constant.

$$
\min \; \mathrm{TAC} = \sum_i \sum_j \sum_k c_f Z_{ijk} + \sum_i c_f Zcu_i + \sum_j c_f Zhu_j + \sum_i \sum_j \sum_k cA_{ijk}{}^{\beta}
$$

$$
+ \sum_i cAcu_i{}^{\beta} + \sum_j cAhu_j{}^{\beta} + \sum_i \sum_p c_{cu} qcu_{ip} \tau_p + \sum_j \sum_p c_{hu} qhu_{jp} \tau_p
$$

$$
+ C_{fixst} + C_{varst} Size_{st} + \sum_i \sum_j \sum_k c_f Zst_{ijk} + \sum_i \sum_j \sum_k cAst_{ijk}{}^{\beta}
$$

$$
+ \sum_i \sum_j \sum_k c_{hp} Zhp_{ijk} + \sum_i \sum_j \sum_k cAhp_{ijk}{}^{\beta} + \sum_i \sum_j \sum_k \sum_p c_{Pel} Pel_{ijkp} \tau_p
$$

(1)

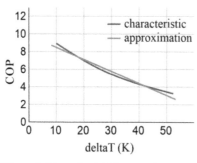

Figure 2: Linearized COP over deltaT

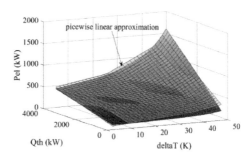

Figure 3: Linear Approximation of P_{el}

3. Linearization

For the integration of heat pumps into the MILP superstructure several linearizations are necessary. In the following chapter the chosen approach is explained in detail.
The coefficient of performance (COP) of heat pumps is defined in Eq. (2) as the ratio of useful heat supplied by the heat pump (Q_{th}) to the required work (P_{el}).

$$COP = \frac{Q_{th}}{P_{el}} \tag{2}$$

In this work it is assumed that the heat pump characteristic curve of the COP over the temperature lift of the heat pump (deltaT) is known. For the linearization this characteristic curve is approximated by a polynomial of first order. In Figure 2 an example for a characteristic curve with its associated linear approximation is shown. From Eq. (2) it is visible that P_{el} can be calculated as the ratio of Q_{th} to COP. This nonlinear relation is linearized with an approach inspired by the linearization of the heat exchange area by Beck and Hofmann (2018a). The nonconvex, nonlinear feasible solution space is split into three regions. Each of these regions is then approximated by a linear equation which is fitted with least squares methods. This piecewise linear approximation is shown in Figure 3 with the underlying solution space. The linear approximations are used as constraints for P_{el} with the help of big-M formulations. In these constraints Γ is a sufficient large number to activate or deactivate Eq. (3) dependent on whether a Heat Pump exists on this position or not.

$$P_{el} \geq P_{el,approx} - (1 - Zhp_{ijk})\Gamma \tag{3}$$

The heat exchanger area between the streams and heat pumps is approximated with the same procedure as for the heat exchangers between the streams. As measure to keep the objective function linear, the heat pump approach temperature, which is the minimum temperature difference between stream or storage and heat pump operation temperature, gets set to a fixed value. Due to the preset storage temperatures it is possible to linearize the reduced heat exchange area between storage and heat pump as function of the heat flow Q_{hpst} as shown in Eq. (4) because the denominator remains constant.

$$A_{hpst}{}^\beta = \left(\frac{Q_{hpst}}{U \, LMTD_{hpst}} \right)^\beta \longrightarrow A_{hpst}{}^\beta \approx c_{A1} + c_{A2}Q_{hpst} \tag{4}$$

4. Test Case

Table 1: Stream data and cost coefficients

Stream	Tin (°C)	Tout (°C)	CP (kW/K) period 1	CP (kW/K) period 2	CP (kW/K) period 3	h (kW/m²K)
H1	120	40	18	50	9	0.5
H2	90	30	22	22	1	0.5
C1	20	100	20	10	10	0.5
C2	50	90	50	40	70	0.5
UT h	150	150	-	-	-	1
UT c	5	10	-	-	-	1

exchanger cost = $4000+500[A(m^2)]^\beta$ €y^{-1}, storage cost = $7000+0.15[kg]$ €y^{-1}, hot utility cost = 0.07 €kW^{-1}h^{-1}, cold utility cost = 0.007 €kW^{-1}h^{-1}, cost exponent $\beta = 0.83$, electrical power costs = 0.06 €kW^{-1}h^{-1}, dTmin = 5 °C, Heat Pump cost = 11000 €y^{-1}

As test case an example which consists of two hot and two cold process streams was investigated. The assumed cyclic process has a duration of three hours and is split into three periods of one hour each. It is assumed that the process is operated annually for 8600 h. The superstructure model was set up with two stages. The cost coefficients and stream data used are given in Table 1. A two tank storage which operates at 70 °C and 100 °C with thermo-oil as storage medium with an specific heat capacity of $cp_{oil} = 2$ kJkg^{-1}K^{-1} and an heat transfer coefficient of $h_{oil} = 0.5$ kWm^{-2}K^{-1} was chosen. The assumed heat pump has a power consumption range from 400 kW to 2000 kW and a given approach temperature of $T_{hpaproach} = 5$ K. The linearized COP characteristic is given as COP = $10 - 0.15$ K^{-1} deltaT and the heat transfer coefficient as $h_{hp} = 5$ kWm^{-2}K^{-1}. A lower boundary of the COP of COPmin = 1 was set as constraint. As solver for the MILP Gurobi 8.1.0 was used.

The plausibility of the optimization was tested with the variation of different cost coefficients. With increasing costs for electrical power or decreasing costs for utilities, the size and number of heat pumps gets reduced until no more heat pumps get chosen for the system. Similarly increasing costs for storage material lead to smaller storage sizes and finally the exclusion of solutions containing storages. This behavior matches the results expected from the structure of the used cost function.

5. Results

The test case was optimized in two different configurations. In the first configuration the HEN was optimized without heat pumps or storages in order to be able to obtain comparable results. In the second configuration the test case was optimized with the extended approach including a storage and heat pumps.

5.1. Configuration 1: Test case without heat pumps and storage

For this setup, the solver found a solution after 0.02 s with total annual costs of TAC = 1,120,500 €y^{-1}. The obtained heat exchange network which is shown in Figure 4 consists of three stream – stream heat exchangers and four utility heat exchangers. The obtained heat flows for the different time periods are given in Table 2. The high amount of needed cold utility in period 2 and needed hot utility in period 3 shows potential for temporal energy shifting. The total utility energy demand adds up to 20.869 GWh y^{-1}.

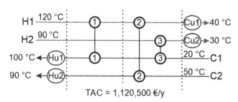

Figure 4: Hen obtained without Heat Pump

Table 2: Heat Flows without Heat Pump (kW)

	p1	p2	p3
1	294.3	150.00	720.00
2	875.70	1600.00	-
3	1300.00	650.00	-
Hu1	5.72	-	80
Hu2	1124.3	-	2800.00
Cu1	270.00	2250.00	-
Cu2	20.00	670.00	60.00

5.2. Configuration 2: Test case with integrated heat pumps and storage

For the extended case a solution was found after 54.12 s with total annual costs of TAC = 940,260 €y^{-1}. The extended heat exchange network which is shown in Figure 6 consists of five stream – stream heat exchangers, two stream – storage heat exchangers, four utility heat exchangers, two heat pumps and a storage tank with 192334 kg of thermo-oil which has a storage capacity of 3.206 MWh. The obtained heat flows and the electrical power demands for the different time periods are given in Table 3. The total utility energy demand is 6.074 GWh y^{-1} and the electrical energy demand for the heat pumps is 4.755 GWh y^{-1}. This adds up to a total external energy demand of 10.829 GWh y^{-1}. The charging state of the storage over the cycle time is given in Figure 5. The storage has a variable storage charge at the beginning of the cycle which has to be reached again at the end of the cycle. This is ensured by suitable boundary conditions.

5.3. Comparison:

The TAC of the extend network are 16.1 % lower compared to the simple network and the total external energy demand of the obtained extended structure is only 51.9 % of the total energy demand of configuration 1. From Table 2 and Table 3 it is visible that the utilities are significantly smaller for configuration 2 and that a big part of the energy is supplied by the heat pumps instead. Although configuration 2 has lower TAC and energy demand it has to be noticed that it is much more complex with 15 installations and a storage compared to the simple configuration 1 with 7 installations.

6. Conclusion

An extension for the integration of heat pumps into HENS for multi-period MILP superstructures by linearizing the energy consumption of heat pumps has been developed. A test case consisting of two hot and two cold process streams with varying mass flows for different time steps has been constructed to demonstrate the proposed method. This test case was optimized with and without the possibility of including a storage and heat pumps to compare the gained results. The obtained extended HEN has 16.1 % lower TAC and 48.1 % lower external energy demand compared to the conventional HEN which comes with the drawback of a higher complexity of the network. The test case was chosen rather small because the target was to check if the optimization results are plausible which is hardly possible for bigger problems. From the results of the optimization without storage and heat pumps it can be concluded that a storage device that shifts energy between the time periods is able to reduce the TAC if the costs of the storage, the heat pumps and the electrical energy are low enough compared to the utility costs. This is consistent with the results of the second configuration. When comparing results it has to be taken into account that the results of these optimizations are strongly dependent on the

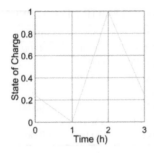

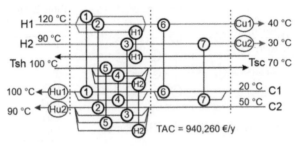

Figure 5: Storage Charging
State over Cycle Time

Figure 6: Hen obtained with Heat Pumps and Storage

Table 3: Heat Flows and P_{el} results with Heat Pump (kW)

	p1	p2	p3		p1	p2	p3
1	549.38	456.93	216.24	Hu1	100.00	-	50.00
2	577.21	630.00	368.76	Hu2	250.00	200.00	-
3	770.00	770.00	-	Cu1	47.84	622.29	-
4	373.64	-	398.76	Cu2	238.59	550.00	60.00
5	402.79	-	262.44	Hp1	-	1947.70	-
6	265.58	343.07	135.00	Hp2	-	-	2168.80
7	311.41	-	-	Pel Hp1	-	1257.80	-
				Pel Hp2	-	-	400.90

chosen coefficients. Small changes of cost coefficients or physical parameters can result in very different network solutions because of the nature of mixed integer programming.

Acknowledgment

The idea of this paper was initiated by the endowment professorship of the Technical University of Vienna (TUW), Institute for Energy Systems and Thermodynamics – Industrial Energy Systems, and the Austrian Institute of Technology (AIT) – Center for Energy – Energy in Industries. This work was funded by the cooperation doctoral school Smart Industrial Concept (SIC!). The authors want to express their great acknowledgment.

References

Beck, A., Hofmann, R. (2018a). A Novel Approach for Linearization of a MINLP Stage-Wise Superstructure Formulation. *Computers & Chemical Engineering, 112,* 17–26.

Beck, A., Hofmann, R. (2018b). Extensions for Multi-Period MINLP Superstructure Formulation for Integration of Thermal Energy Storages in Industrial Processes. *Computer Aided Process Engineering, 43,* 1335–1340.

Becker, H., Maréchal, F. (2012). Targeting industrial heat pump integration in multi-period problems. *Computer Aided Chemical Engineering, 31,* 415–419.

Escobar, M., Trierweiler, J. O. (2013). Optimal heat exchanger network synthesis: A case study comparison. *Applied Thermal Engineering, 51,* 801–826.

Stampfli, J. A., Atkins, M. J., Olsen, D. G., Walmsley, M. R.W., Wellig, B. (2019). Practical heat pump and storage integration into non-continuous processes: A hybrid approach utilizing insight based and nonlinear programming techniques. *Energy, 182,* 236–253.

Yee, T. F., Grossmann, I. E. (1990). Simultaneous optimization models for heat integration—II. Heat exchanger network synthesis. *Computers & Chemical Engineering, 14,* 1165–1184.

Sauro Pierucci, Flavio Manenti, Giulia Bozzano, Davide Manca (Eds.)
Proceedings of the 30th European Symposium on Computer Aided Process Engineering
(ESCAPE30), May 24-27, 2020, Milano, Italy. © 2020 Elsevier B.V. All rights reserved.
http://dx.doi.org/10.1016/B978-0-12-823377-1.50227-5

Enabling Renewable Base Load Generation via Chemical Energy Storage

Antonio Sánchez[a], Mariano Martín[a], Qi Zhang[b,*]

[a]*Departamento de Ingenieria Quimica, Universidad de Salamanca, Salamanca, Spain*
[b]*Departament of Chemical Engineering and Material Science, University of Minnesota, Minneapolis, USA*
qizh@umn.edu

Abstract

Energy storage plays a key role in the modern power system. Recently, the use of chemicals for energy storage, especially in long-term applications, has attracted significant attention. In this work, the potential benefit of using different chemicals – namely methane, methanol, dimethyl ether (DME), and ammonia – as energy carriers is evaluated. For a region of Spain, the optimal locations of plants to supply a portion of the local base-load power demand are determined as well as the transportation modes used to deliver the chemicals to the different demand locations. Moreover, a scheduling optimization is carried out to analyse the system's dynamic performance.

Keywords: energy storage, chemical storage, renewable energy

1. Introduction

Power generation is currently responsible for about 40% of the world's total CO_2 emissions. The main means to reduce the emissions will be the use of renewable energy sources for power generation. The penetration of renewables into the power grid has increased significantly in the last few decades. According to recent predictions (BloombergNEF, 2019), the share of renewables in 2050 will be about 62%, with 48% of solar and wind generation. At this point, energy storage is the main bottleneck for the effective deployment of the intermittent renewable energy sources.

A large number of alternatives to store power have been proposed with different levels of development. Diverse electrical, mechanical, thermal, chemical or electrochemical technologies are being evaluated. Pumped hydro storage (PHS) is the most commonly used technology today, contributing to about 95% of the total storage capacity installed (Christensen et al., 2013). Batteries have been used in a wide spectrum of devices and their integration at the power grid level is being investigated. The use of chemicals is one of the most promising alternatives to store energy in a wide range of capacities and for long time horizons. Besides power generation, these chemicals can also be used as fuels for the transportation sector and as feedstock for the chemical industry. A suitable combination of all the alternatives could be the solution to meet all the requirements for a particular storage application (Gur, 2018).

Different chemicals have been studied for energy storage applications. One of those chemicals that has received considerable attention is hydrogen. However, the use of hydrogen faces two main challenges: the low volumetric energy density and the cost for storage and transportation. To overcome these issues, the synthesis of a wide range of hydrogen derivate chemicals has been proposed. Methane has the advantage that the infrastructure for its storage, transport and supply is already in place. The use of liquid chemicals is also attractive due to the easy storage and transportation and higher energy density. Such liquid chemicals include methanol, dimethyl ether (DME), and ammonia. In the case of ammonia, no carbon sources are involved in its synthesis or utilization.

The objective of this work is to evaluate the storage of solar/wind power in the form of chemicals to provide a source for stable production of electricity out of them on demand. In Spain, due to more restrictive legislation regarding nitrogen and carbon dioxide emissions, coal-based power plants are expected to be decommissioned within the next few years. Hence, there is an urgent need to enable renewable power generation for meeting base load. In this work, we consider two levels of decision making: design at the supply chain level and operation at the scheduling level. At the supply chain level, the production and storage facilities and the transportation network are determined. Then, the impact of the intermittent wind and solar availability on the process performance is analyzed at the scheduling level. The remainder of this paper is organized as follows. In Section 2, the problem to be solved is presented. Section 3 includes the mathematical formulation of the problem. Section 4 presents results from the case study. Finally, some concluding remarks are provided in Section 5.

2. Problem Description

The power-to-chemicals alternative for energy storage is evaluated in this work. The synthesis of four chemicals is considered: methane, methanol, DME, and ammonia. The first three are produced using hydrogen and carbon dioxide. Ammonia does not require a carbon source for its synthesis; instead, nitrogen is needed. Hydrogen is produced using electrolysis of water. Carbon dioxide can be obtained from carbon capture, and different technologies to separate air (distillation, adsorption and membranes) are considered to produce nitrogen. Methane, methanol and DME are produced by CO_2 hydrogenation, and ammonia through the well-stablished Haber-Bosch process. As power collection units, wind turbines and solar PV panels are considered. In Figure 1, a schematic with the different processes and resources involved in this work is presented.

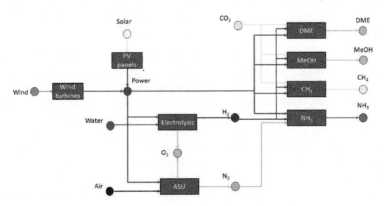

Figure 1: Simplified flowsheet for the proposed superstructure

The supply chain analysis is carried out for Leon, a province of Spain. This region is divided into 29 different sub-regions (see Figure 2). The city/town with the highest population is selected as the representative point for each region. Three different transportation modes are evaluated: truck, rail and pipeline. Truck and rail can be selected for transporting all chemicals, but pipeline is only available for methane. Truck connections are available for transportation between each sub-region and its neighbouring sub-regions. The available rail and pipeline connections are shown in Figure 2.

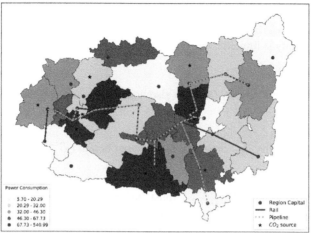

Figure 2: Rail and pipeline connections in a map where the color of the different region represent the power consumption intensity. The CO_2 sources are also presented.

The synthesis of the carbon-based chemical products (methane, methanol and DME) is mainly limited by the availability of CO_2. Figure 2 also shows the sub-regions where there are carbon dioxide sources. It is assumed that water and air are available with no restrictions.

The objective is to determine the optimal plant and transportation network to meet a portion of the base-load power demand, which we assume to be 10% of the total power demand, in each sub-region. After this supply chain analysis, the operation of the installed plants is evaluated. The goal in this second analysis is to determine the required oversize capacity to meet the power demand with the hourly fluctuations in solar and wind availability.

3. Problem Formulation

The multiperiod supply chain optimization is conducted for a time horizon of a year and a monthly time discretization. The problem is formulated as an MILP (Guillén-Gosálbez & Grossmann, 2008). The main equations are presented in the following.

The mass balance for each resource j at each location k in each time period t is formulated as follows:

$$Q_{jkt} = B_{jkt} - S_{jkt} + \sum_{i} \rho_{ij} P_{ikt} + \sum_{k' \in \overline{K}_{jk'k}} W_{jk'kt} - \sum_{k' \in \overline{\overline{K}}_{jkk'}} W_{jkk't} \qquad \forall j,k,t \qquad (1)$$

where Q_{jkt} is the storage level for resource j at location k at time t, B_{jkt} is the amount of resource j consumed by the system and $W_{jkk't}$ is the amount transported from location k to k'. The production level, P_{ikt}, for each process i is limited by its capacity, C_{ik}:

$$P_{ikt} = \eta_{ikt} C_{ik} \quad \forall i \in \{1,2\}, k, t \qquad (2)$$

$$P_{ikt} \le \eta_{ikt} C_{ik} \quad \forall i \in \{3,10\}, k, t$$

The inventory level, Q_{jkt} is limited by the storage capacity ($\overline{C}_{jk}$):

$$Q_{jkt}^{total} \le \overline{C}_{jk} \quad \forall j, k, t$$

$$Q_{jkt}^{total} = Q_{jkt-1}^{total} + Q_{jkt} \cdot 3600 \cdot 24 \cdot 30 \quad \forall j, k, t \tag{3}$$

The process capacity is limited by a maximum value (C_i^{max}):

$$C_{ik} \le C_i^{max} x_{ik} \quad \forall i, k \tag{4}$$

The maximum storage capacity ($\overline{C}_{jk}$) is also bounded by an upper bound ($\overline{C}_j^{max}$):

$$\overline{C}_{jk} \le \overline{C}_j^{max} x_{jk} \quad \forall j, k \tag{5}$$

The resource availability, B_{jkt} is limited by an upper bound (B_{jkt}^{max}):

$$B_{jkt} \le B_{jkt}^{max} \quad \forall j, k, t \tag{6}$$

The power consumption ($D_{power,k,t}$) must be met by the combination of different chemical productions. The heating value, H_j, is used to compute the energy available in each chemical (S_{jkt}):

$$\sum_{j \in J} S_{jkt} H_j \ge D_{power,k,t} \quad \forall k, t$$

$$S_{jkt} = 0 \quad \forall j \in \overline{\overline{J}}, k, t \tag{7}$$

There are three kinds of transportation modes to transfer the chemicals between locations:

$$W_{jkk't} = \sum_{m \in M_{jkk'm}} T_{jkk'mt} \quad \forall j, k, k', t \tag{8}$$

The transported amount, $T_{jkk'mt}$ is limited by an upper bound ($T_{jkk'm}^{max}$) as a function of the transportation mode:

$$T_{jkk'mt} \le T_{jkk'm}^{max} \quad \forall j, k, k', t \tag{9}$$

The production in each plant and time period (P_{ikt}) is limited by a lower and an upper bound:

$$P_i^{min} y_{ikt} \le P_{ikt} \le P_i^{max} y_{ikt} \quad \forall i, k, t \tag{10}$$

The capital costs (CC) are calculated using a linear approximation. The objective value is the operating cost (OP) of the entire grid, including the cost of the processes, the cost of storage of the different chemicals and the transportation cost.

$$OP = \sum_k \left(\sum_t \sum_i J_{ikt} + \sum_i \sigma_i CC_{ik}^p \right) + \sum_k \sum_j \left(\frac{CC_{jk}^{st}}{lifetime} \right) + \sum_j \sum_k \sum_{k'} \sum_m \sum_t T_{jkk'mt} C_{jm}^{transp} Dist_{kk'} \tag{11}$$

In this equation, J_{ikt} includes the operating cost of the different processes not related to the capital cost, C_{jm}^{transp} is the cost of the different modes of transport and $Dist_{kk'}$ is the distance between the different locations.

After the supply chain analysis, for each of the facilities set up in the region, a scheduling problem is solved to determine the operation of the facility and to determine the oversize in the production capacity and storage with respect to the supply chain results when the wind and solar availabilities are considered on an hourly basis. The scheduling model is adapted from Zhang et al. (2019).

4. Results

The supply chain results are presented in Figure 3. Two plants are set up to meet the power demand of the entire region (blue stars on the map). These two facilities have solar PV panels as energy collection units. Wind turbines are not selected. Only two of the chemicals are produced: methane and methanol. The total capital cost for the production and storage of the system is \$393 MM where about 99% corresponds to the investment in the production processes. About 50% is due to the investment in the PV panels, 45% is due to the capital cost of the electrolyzers and 5% due to methane and methanol production units. To transport the methane and methanol produced to the different sub-regions, truck, rail and pipeline are selected. The pipeline is the main option to transport the methane. The storage of chemicals is built up next to the production facilities. Only methanol is stored. The total operating cost of the network is equal to \$45 MM/year. As depicted in Figure 3, the transportation links change depending on the month of the year.

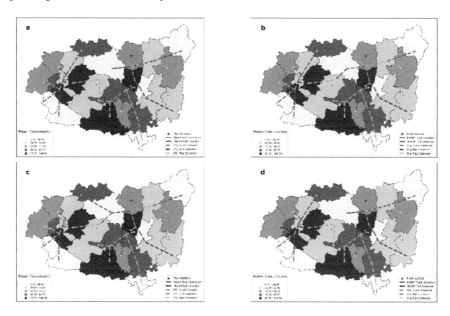

Figure 3: Plant locations and transportation modes for different months: a) January b) June c) September d) December

Considering fluctuations in the solar irradiance and wind speed profiles, the production schedules for the two plants are optimized on an hourly basis for the entire year. To meet the demand calculated in the supply chain stage, it is necessary to increase the capacity of the plant by about 35%. During the day, a fraction of the power produced in the PV panels has to be sold to the local power grid due to the limited capacity in the electrolyzer and other chemical units. Hydrogen storage is also allowed in the scheduling optimization. Figure 4 shows the production schedule for one of the plants over the course of a week. Methane production is kept constant while methanol production fluctuates according to the solar availability. As previously mentioned, methanol is used to storage energy. The production of methanol takes place mainly during the summer where solar energy is more abundant. Methanol is consumed during the winter to meet a fraction of the power demand. In Figure 3, it is also shown that the methanol transportation takes place only during the winter months (January and December).

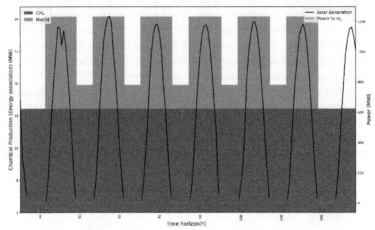

Figure 4: Scheduling results for a representative week in June

5. Conclusions

In this work, an MILP framework has been developed to optimize power-to-chemicals supply chains and the scheduling of the production plants to supply based load power generation. A real-world case study considering a specific region in Spain has been conducted. The results show that methane and methanol production are selected to meet the power demand. The scheduling problem determines the operation of the facility on an hourly basis. Methanol is stored during the summer when more power is generated, and used in the winter when the solar-based power generation is lower. Future work involves the process design and integration of the transformation of these chemicals into electricity.

Acknowledgements: The authors acknowledge the FPU, Spain grant (FPU16/06212) from MECD to AS, and JCYL for S026G18.

References

BloombergNEF, 2019. New Energy Outlook 2019. https://about.bnef.com/new-energy-outlook/
J.M. Christensen, P.V. Hendriksen, J.D. Grunwaldt, A.D. Jensen, 2013, Chemical energy storage. In H. Hvidtfeldt Larsen, L. Sønderberg Petersen (Eds.), DTU International Energy Report 2013: Energy storage options for future sustainable energy systems, 47-52, Technical University of Denmark.
T.M. Gur, 2018, Review of electrical energy storage technologies, materials and systems: challenges and prospects for large-scale grid storage, Energy & Environmental Science, 11, 2696-2767.
G. Guillén-Gosálbez, I.E. Grossmann, 2018, Optimal design and planning of sustainable chemical supply chains under uncertainty, AIChE Journal, 55, 1, 99-121.
Q. Zhang, M. Martín, I.E. Grossmann, 2019, Integrated design and operation of renewables-based fuels and power production networks, Computers & Chemical Engineering, 122, 80-92.

Sauro Pierucci, Flavio Manenti, Giulia Bozzano, Davide Manca (Eds.)
Proceedings of the 30th European Symposium on Computer Aided Process Engineering
(ESCAPE30), May 24-27, 2020, Milano, Italy. © 2020 Elsevier B.V. All rights reserved.
http://dx.doi.org/10.1016/B978-0-12-823377-1.50228-7

On the Benefit of Modular and Mobile Production Units in Biomass Waste-to-energy Supply Chains

Andrew Allman[a], Che Lee[a], Mariano Martín[b], Qi Zhang[a,*]

[a]*Department of Chemical Engineering and Materials Science, University of Minnesota, Twin Cities, 421 Washington Ave SE, Minneapolis, MN, USA 55455*
[b]*Universidad de Salamanca, Departamento de Ingeniería Química. Pza. Caídos 1-5, 37008 Salamanca, España.*
qizh@umn.edu

Abstract

Upgrading biomass waste to energy is a promising technology which enhances the economic values of crop residues such as wheat straw and corn stover, which are typically present in excess in highly agricultural regions such as the United States Midwest. In this work, gasification of biomass to turn a gas turbine is considered as a technology for upgrading biomass waste to energy. We propose to use modular and mobile production units to limit the transportation cost of moving biomass to energy production facilities in a distributed supply chain. We present a generic optimization framework for determining the optimal location and relocation of gasifier and turbine modules over time. To demonstrate the efficacy of our framework, we apply it to a case study where biomass residue in Minnesota is converted to energy. The results show the economic benefits of considering mobility of modules in processing biomass waste, which is produced at different times in different parts of the state.

Keywords: modular manufacturing, distributed manufacturing, biomass waste-to-energy, circular economy, process intensification

1. Introduction

Crop residues, or inedible parts of plants such as stalks, leaves, husks, and straw, account for more than 50% of the biomass present in common agricultural plants such as corn and wheat (Smil 1999). Some of this biomass is necessary for farming: much of it is burned in the fields to replenish the soil with nutrients or left in fields to prevent soil erosion, while some other biomass can be processed into animal feed or bedding. Even still, about 40% of this waste can be sustainably extracted from farms without sacrificing these needs (Batidzirai et al 2016). While exact statistics on the amount of crop residue produced annually are not maintained, it is estimated that by 2030, 155 million tons of biomass waste will be produced in the United States, with more than half coming from the four Midwestern states of Iowa, Illinois, Minnesota, and Nebraska (UCS 2014). The fact that such an abundant resource is readily available without need to change current land use patterns offers immense opportunity for sustainable manufacturing; however, many technical and logistical challenges need to be addressed to make processing biomass waste to more valuable commodities economically feasible.

Biomass is a naturally occurring hydrocarbon resource which has been proposed as a replacement for fossil fuels in energy production. As energy represents an essential resource in modern society, the upgrading of biomass waste to energy offers the potential to convert a low value resource into one of high value. Many different technologies can be used for this conversion, including gasification to turn a gas turbine, gasification with further upgrading to methane or methanol, fermentation to ethanol, or anaerobic digestion to biogas (Iakovou et al. 2010). Recent research has shown that processing agricultural waste to energy can address food-energy-water-waste nexus concerns (Garcia et al. 2019). Other work has analyzed the tradeoff of economies of scale versus efficient resource management in biomass gasification networks (Zetterholm et al. 2018). Ultimately, the low density of biomass can make transportation costs high, providing a key logistical challenge in developing biomass waste-to-energy supply chains. Distributed manufacturing, whereby manufacturing facilities are built at a small scale and located close to supply and demand sites, offers a promising approach to address the aforementioned logistical challenge. Recent research has shown the benefits in using distributed manufacturing to address the challenge of using crop production as an industrial supply, as in the production of biofuels (Marvin et al. 2013), or demand, as in the production of ammonia (Palys et al. 2019). Modular production units, which can be constructed off-site, and then shipped to and assembled at a production site into a working facility, act as an enabling technology for distributed manufacturing (Baldea et al. 2017). Individual unit modules can be relocated between different production sites over time; however, to the best of our knowledge, no previous work exists which analyzes the economic benefits of doing so in a practical waste-to-energy case study. In this work, we present an optimization framework for determining the optimal location and relocation of modular production facilities in a distributed biomass waste-to-energy supply chain, and apply the framework to the case study of biomass waste-to-energy production in Minnesota. The remainder of the paper is structured as follows: in Section 2, a broad problem statement is defined and the mathematical framework is presented. Next, Section 3 introduces the data used for the particular case study considered. Section 4 presents the results of this case study and showcases the benefit of modular mobility. Finally, we provide concluding remarks and areas of future research in Section 5.

2. Problem Statement and Formulation

The objective of this problem is to determine the location and relocation of biomass gasifier and gas turbine modules, as well as the transportation of biomass from farm to energy production site, minimizing a sum of capital and operating costs such that a given amount of biomass waste is processed from each farm over multiple time periods. The mathematical framework for solving this problem is presented in this section, with definitions for the symbols used provided in Table 1.

The objective function of this optimization problem is to minimize a sum of fixed and variable operating costs, capital costs, and module relocation costs:

$$\zeta = \sum_{t \in \mathcal{T}} \left(\sum_{j \in \mathcal{J}} \sum_{m \in \mathcal{M}} \left(g_{jmt} z_{jmt} + \sum_{j' \in \bar{\mathcal{J}}_j} h_{jj'mt} w_{jj'mt} \right) + \sum_{j \in \mathcal{J}} \sum_{l \in \mathcal{L}} \left(\sum_{i \in \mathcal{I}} c_{ijlt} d_{it} x_{ijlt} + f_{jlt} y_{jlt} \right) \right). \tag{1}$$

The problem is constrained such that all of a given biomass waste supply must be processed. As x is a fractional supply, this equation takes the form:

$$\sum_{j \in \mathcal{J}} \sum_{l \in \mathcal{L}} x_{ijlt} = 1 \quad \forall i \in \mathcal{I}, t \in \mathcal{T}. \tag{2}$$

It is important to keep track of the number of modules installed at each energy production site during each time period. This is done according to the following unit conservation

Table 1. Nomenclature for problem formulation.

Symbol	Description
Sets	
I	Set of farms supplying biomass waste
J	Set of candidate energy production sites
$\bar{J}_j$	Set of sites to which modules can be moved from site j, $\bar{J}_j \subseteq J \setminus \{j\}$
$\hat{J}_j$	Set of sites from which modules can be moved to site j, $\hat{J}_j \subseteq J \setminus \{j\}$
L	Set of facility configurations
M	Set of modules
$\bar{M}_l$	Set of modules required for configuration l, $\bar{M}_l \subseteq M$
T	Set of time periods
Parameters	
b_{jl}	Minimum fractional operating capacity of configuration l at production site j
c_{ijlt}	Relative operating cost of processing biomass from farm i at site j in configuration l at time t, \$/t
d_{it}	Total biomass waste supply from farm i in time period t, t
f_{jlt}	Fixed operating cost of producing in configuration l at site j in time t, \$
g_{jm}	Capital cost of installing module m at site j in time t, \$
$h_{jj'mt}$	Cost of relocating module m from site j to site j' in time t, \$
n_{lm}	Number of units of module m operating in configuration l
u_{jl}	Processing capacity of configuration l at production site j, t
v_{jm}^0	Initial number of units of module m present at production site j
v_{jmt}^{max}	Maximum number of units of module m allowed at production site j during time period t
Decision Variables	
$v_{jmt} \in \mathbb{N}$	Number of units of module m present at production site j during time period t
$w_{jj'mt} \in \mathbb{N}$	Number of units of module m moved from site j to site j' during time period t
$0 \leq x_{ijlt} \leq 1$	Fraction of biomass from farm i processed by energy production site j operating in configuration l during time period t
$y_{jlt} \in \{0,1\}$	Binary variable, 1 if production site j operates in configuration l during time period t
$z_{jmt} \in \mathbb{N}$	Number of units of module m built at production site j during time period t

equation, which states that this value will equal the number of modules present at the start, plus the number of modules built, plus the number of modules relocated from other locations, minus the number of modules relocated to other locations:

$$v_{jmt} = v_{jm}^0 + \sum_{t'=1}^{t} \left(z_{jmt'} - \sum_{j' \in \bar{J}_j} w_{jj'mt'} + \sum_{j' \in \hat{J}_j} w_{j'jmt'} \right) \quad \forall j \in J, m \in M, t \in T. \tag{3}$$

A configuration is defined as a fixed number of modules that are actively used to process biomass waste during a specific time period. A production site is only able to operate in a specific configuration if the requisite modules for that configuration are installed, and the total number of modules installed cannot exceed a predefined maximum:

$$n_{lm}y_{jlt} \leq v_{jmt} \leq v_{jmt}^{max} \quad \forall j \in J, l \in L, m \in \bar{M}_l, t \in T. \tag{4}$$

Each facility can only process as much biomass waste as the capacity of its operating configuration allows. Additionally, some configurations may have a minimum capacity at which they can operate:

$$b_{jl}u_{jl}y_{jlt} \leq \sum_{i \in I} d_{it}x_{ijlt} \leq u_{jl}y_{jlt} \quad \forall j \in J, l \in L, t \in T. \tag{5}$$

Furthermore, each facility can only operate in a single configuration at a time:

$$\sum_{l \in L} y_{jlt} \leq 1 \quad \forall j \in J, t \in T. \tag{6}$$

The optimization problem to be solved is to minimize the total cost ζ, defined by Eq. (1), subject to Eqs. (2)-(6). The formulation is a mixed-integer linear program that can be readily solved by an off-the-shelf solver such as CPLEX.

3. Case Study Data

In this work, the framework presented in the previous section to determine the optimal supply chain for processing 1% of total biomass waste produced in Minnesota, or 2.5% of available biomass waste, equal to 562,000 tons of biomass per year. While this percentage seems small, we note that it is unlikely that a single entity would be able to process all available biomass, and more likely that individual farms will supply to different entities or different technologies; thus, processing this fraction of demand is reasonable for a base case. Biomass waste is assumed to be proportional to the amount of corn, wheat, and soy harvested, for which annual data is available at a county scale (USDA 2019). As such, each of Minnesota's 87 counties is considered as a farm supply site for the purpose of this study, with demands derived from 2017 harvesting data. We further consider that different crops are harvested at different times using data provided by the USDA (USDA 2019), considering four time periods which give the biomass produced in August, September, October, and November, respectively. This data is displayed in Figure 1. In each time period, a supply center of mass (SCM) is calculated, which is a supply-weighted average of farm supply locations, given by coordinates ℓ_i:

$$\text{SCM}_t = \frac{\sum_{i \in I} d_{it} \ell_i}{\sum_{i \in I} d_{it}} \qquad (7)$$

The supply center of mass for each month is denoted by a star in Figure 1. Its movement from northwest to south central Minnesota suggests that mobile modules are likely to be economically beneficial for this case study.

To determine candidate production sites, we separate the state of Minnesota into 9 regions and choose the largest city in each region. These locations are also shown in Figure 1. Each candidate site can install a set of gasifier and gas turbine modules, both of which are needed to process biomass waste to electricity. For both module types, units that can process either 2 kg/s or 30 kg/s biomass can be installed. The smaller units can be easily relocated through the supply chain as needed, and are also assumed to be able to operate completely flexibly at any capacity below their maximum. Meanwhile the larger units are assumed to be too large to move or operate flexibly; they can operate at a minimum of 75% of their rated capacity. Because of the 1 month-long time periods considered, we constrain the problem to only allow for building new units in August, the first time period; however, module mobility is allowed at any time. Capital costs for the modules are taken from correlations presented by Larson et al. (2005), while operating costs are taken from Martín and Grossmann (2018). Transportation costs for biomass and relocation costs for modules are determined using driving distances using the Google Maps distance matrix API, and assuming a truck capacity of 10 m^3, fuel economy of 6 mpg, and fuel cost of $3/gal, and negligible module reinstallation costs.

4. Results

The case study for processing Minnesota's biomass waste is solved using CPLEX 12.8 in Julia 0.6.4 using the JuMP v0.18.5 package (Dunning et al. 2017). Computations were performed on a 3.2 GHz Intel Core i7-9700 processor. To determine the practical economic effects of module mobility, the optimization is performed twice, once when small modules are allowed to move, and once where no mobility is allowed (i.e. w is fixed to zero). The optimization problem consists of 70,689 variables (1476 integer), and 77,616 constraints. The mobile supply chain is solved to optimality in 1091 s, while the immobile supply chain is solved to optimality in 455 s.

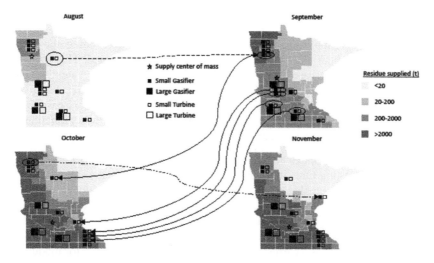

Figure 1. Supply of biomass residue over 4-month period in Minnesota, with optimal facility location and relocation in mobile module case.

The optimal location and relocation of gasifier and turbine modules for the mobile module case is shown in Figure 1. In the mobile supply chain case, the optimal solution builds 3 large gasifier and turbine modules, and 10 small modules. Interestingly, in the immobile supply chain case, the optimal solution builds more small modules, choosing to build 19 small modules and only 2 large modules. We hypothesize that this is because flexibility is essential to optimally responding to the spatiotemporal changes in supply. In the immobile case, the only flexibility that is present is the ability of small modules to operate at any capacity, which is important with supply moving from northwest to southeast over the year. When mobility is allowed, this implements an extra degree of flexibility, nonintuitively also enabling the introduction of additional units which are not flexible, as each small unit provides greater ability for the supply chain to agilely respond to changes. This effect is clear when considering the operating configurations of the mobile system: in August and September, the larger modules are not used since the supply of biomass residue is not yet high enough; as such, smaller modules are also located and operated in the southwestern production sites. In October and November, the larger modules are turned on which enables moving the smaller modules to other locations in the supply chain. In the immobile supply chain, this movement is not allowed but there is not enough supply to run the larger units in the early months. Thus, 5 small modules are installed at the west central production site instead of a large module.

The optimal annualized supply chain cost for the mobile case is determined to be $87.8 MM/y, equivalent to an electricity cost of 10.4 ¢/kWh power produced (assuming 35% efficiency in the energy conversion process). Both results are on the same order of magnitude with those reported in similar biomass-waste to energy works (Garcia et al. 2019, Zetterholm et al. 2018). When units are not mobile, the optimal annualized cost is $89.0 MM/y, equivalent to an electricity cost of 10.6 ¢/kWh, or a 1.4% increase in cost from the mobile case. Surprisingly, this reduction mainly comes from a reduction in capital costs, which are 5.4% lower in the mobile supply chain case, whereas operation and transportation costs are roughly equal. This again results from the added flexibility of mobility also enabling the construction of larger, immobile units in the locations where supply is highest.

5. Conclusions

In this paper, a supply chain optimization framework determining the location and relocation of modular and mobile production units was presented. This framework was then applied to the case study of a biomass waste-to-energy supply chain using gasification and a gas turbine in the state of Minnesota. The results of this work showcased the economic benefits of module mobility in a practical case study. Here, annualized supply chain costs were reduced by 1.4%, driven by a reduction in capital costs when mobile units were considered.

In the future, we aim to extend this work by considering the effects of uncertainty in crop yields and harvesting time, in a multi-year, multi-stage stochastic supply chain planning problem. We anticipate that module mobility will be even more valuable for providing an agile supply chain response to such uncertainty. We also plan to consider additional technologies, such as mobile driers and compactors present at individual farms to increase the density of transported biomass waste. Finally, we intend to consider how different public policies, such as a carbon tax, can also act as a driving force for module mobility.

Acknowledgements

The authors gratefully acknowledge financial support from the University of Minnesota.

References

Baldea, M., Edgar, T.F., Stanley, B.L., Kiss, A.A., 2017. Modular manufacturing processes: Status, challenges, and opportunities. AIChE Journal 63, 4262–4272.

Batidzirai, B., Valk, M., Wicke, B., Junginger, M., Daoiglou, V., Euler, W., Faaij, A.P.C., 2016. Current and future technical, economic, and environmental feasibility of maize and wheat residues supply for biomass energy application: Illustrated for South Africa. Biomass and Bioenergy 92, 106-129.

Dunning, I., Huchette, J., Lubin, M., 2017. JuMP: A modeling language for mathematical optimization. SIAM Review 59, 295–320.

Iakovou, E., Karagiannidis, A., Vlachos, D., Toka, A., Malamakis, A., 2010. Waste biomass-to-energy supply chain management: A critical synthesis. Waste Management 30, 1860-1870.

Larson, E.D., Jin, H., Celik, F.E., 2005. Gasification-based fueld and electricity production from biomass, without and with carbon capture and storage. URL: https://acee.princeton.edu/wp-content/uploads/2016/10/LarsonJinCelik-Biofuels-October-2005.pdf

Martin, M., Grossman, I.E., 2018. Optimal integration of renewable based processes for fuels and power production: Spain case study. Applied Energy 213, 595-610.

Marvin, W.A., Schmidt, L.D., Benjaafar, S., Tiffany, D.G., Daoutidis, P., 2012. Economic optimization of a lignocellulosic biomass-to-ethanol supply chain. Chemical Engineering Science 67, 68–79.

Palys, M.J., Allman, A., Daoutidis, P., 2019. Exploring the benefits of modular renewable-powered ammonia produciton. Industrial and Engineering Chemistry Research 58, 5898-5908.

Smil, V., 1999. Crop residues: Agriculture's largest harvest: Crop residues incorporate more than half of the world's agricultural phytomass. BioScience 49, 299-308.

UCS, 2014. Turning agricultural residues and manure into bioenergy. URL: https://www.canr.msu.edu/uploads/files/Agricultural-Residue-Ranking.pdf

USDA, 2019. National Agricultural Statistics Service. URL: https://www.nass.usda.gov/Statistics_by_State/Minnesota/Publications/County_Estimates/index.php

Zetterholm, J., Pettersson, K., Leduc, S., Mesfun, S., Lundgren, J., Wetterlund, E., 2018. Resource efficiency or economy of scale: Biorefinery supply chain configurations for co-gasification of black liquor and pyrolysis liquids. Applied Energy 230, 912-924.

Printed and bound by CPI Group (UK) Ltd, Croydon, CR0 4YY

03/10/2024

01040326-0009